Evaluation Guide for Merrill Geometry

Merrill Geometry provides a comprehensive course in high school geometry.

Merrill Geometry was high school teacher developed and written. This text provides every opportunity for student success.

To further strengthen the presentation of the text material, many special features have been included. To examine selected examples of the features of *Merrill Geometry,* please turn to the following pages.

(pp. 36, 418) **Student Annotations** help students to identify important concepts as they study.

(pp. 81, 121) **Highlighting** in color helps identify important concepts.

(pp. 61–65, 204) **Review and Test** Material provided in the *Vocabulary, Chapter Summary, Chapter Review, Chapter Test,* and *Cumulative Review* enables students to review and evaluate their progress.

(pp. 500–516) The **BASIC Appendix** at the back of the text provides a short course in BASIC programming.

Special features appear periodically to provide interesting and useful extra topics.

(pp. 151, 399) **Careers:** depict a variety of people in different careers using mathematics.

(pp. 175, 422) **Algebra Reviews:** help students to maintain and use algebraic concepts.

(pp. 165, 386) **Topics in Geometry:** provide information concerning different approaches to geometry.

(pp. 17, 85) **Calculators:** instruct students in using a calculator.

(pp. 128, 339) **Computers:** provide information concerning both the historical background of computers and current uses of computers.

(pp. 48, 50, 504) **Annotations** in the Teacher's Annotated Edition give an objective for each lesson, teaching suggestions, answers to problems, and suggested daily assignments.

(pp. 517–534) **Diagnostic Skills Review:** provides a comprehensive review of algebraic skills.

(pp. 536–547) **Postulates and Theorems:** provide students with a listing of the postulates and theorems used in the text.

Teacher's Annotated Edition

Merrill Geometry

Foster · Cummins · Yunker

Charles E. Merrill Publishing Co.
A Bell & Howell Company
Columbus, Ohio

Toronto · London · Sydney

CONTENTS

Preface T3
Student Features T4
Teacher Features T6
Special Features T8
Additional Features T9
Assignment Guide T10
Teacher's Notes T12
Independent Chapter Tests T26
Answers to Independent Tests T41
Teacher's Answer Key T50

Permission is granted to teachers of *Merrill Geometry* to reproduce and use the tests in this Teacher's Guide entirely or in part.

ISBN 0-675-05219-X

Published by
CHARLES E. MERRILL PUBLISHING CO.
A Bell & Howell Company
Columbus, Ohio 43216

Printed in the United States of America

PREFACE

Merrill Geometry was developed by experienced high school teachers for the classroom. Its goals are to develop student proficiency with geometric skills and to expand understanding of geometric concepts. This text promotes success, improves logical reasoning, and provides a complete course in high school geometry. To achieve these goals the following strategies are used.

Build a Solid Foundation. Geometric concepts are introduced intuitively by drawing upon students' past experience with geometry in real life. Students learn to organize their ideas and gradually are led to the concept of geometric proof. Once the needed background is built, students can progress successfully.

Utilize Sound Pedagogy. *Merrill Geometry* covers in logical sequence all topics generally presented at this level. Each concept presented is then used within that lesson and in later lessons. Concepts are introduced as they are needed.

Facilitate Learning. An appropriate reading level and a concise format make the text easy for students to read and use. Furthermore, many appealing photographs, illustrations, charts, graphs, and tables help students visualize the ideas presented.

Use Relevant, Real-Life Applications. Applications provide motivation by showing the practical value of concepts and the ways geometry prepares students for the future.

Merrill Geometry offers a variety of useful aids for the student studying geometry.

Student Annotations	Help students to identify important concepts as they study.
Selected Answers	Allow students to check their progress as they work. These answers are provided in the back of the book.
Vocabulary Lists	Provide students with a list of important mathematical terms.
Chapter Summaries	Provide students with a listing of major concepts presented within each chapter.
Chapter Reviews	Permit students to review each chapter by working sample problems from each lesson.
Chapter Tests	Enable students to check their progress.
Cumulative Reviews	Help students to maintain and reinforce geometric concepts.
Postulates and Theorems List	Provides students with a listing of the postulates and theorems used in the text.

The following special features, which appear periodically throughout the text, provide interesting and useful extra topics.

Careers	Depict a variety of people using mathematics in different careers. These features present career alternatives that students may pursue.
Topics in Geometry	Provide information concerning different approaches to geometry such as topology and elliptic geometry.
Algebra Reviews	Help students to maintain and use algebraic concepts.
Calculators	Instruct students in using a calculator.
Computers	Provide information concerning both the historical background of computers and current uses of computers.
Excursions in Geometry	Promote student interest by providing interesting side trips. Topics are varied and include glimpses into the development and uses of geometry as well as puzzles, games, and history.
BASIC	Instructs students in writing programs using the BASIC computer language. This feature, provided in the Appendix, can be taught as a unit or interspersed throughout the year.

Students will find the practical, straightforward approach of *Merrill Geometry* both interesting and easy to understand. Teachers will find that the careful sequencing of topics and thorough mathematical treatment of essential ideas provide an effective course in high school geometry.

STUDENT FEATURES

1. The *text* is divided into *14 chapters*. Each *chapter* contains from *5–8* easily managed *lessons*.

2. *Tintblocks* highlight important concepts and ideas.

3. *Lessons* are logically organized, with color and graphics used to enhance the readability of the material.

4. *Examples* illustrate the lesson's objectives and provide students models for working the exercises.

5. *Student annotations* provide explanations and steps for problem solving.

7–4 Tests for Parallelograms 1

Hazel Thompson is cutting glass pieces in the shape of parallelograms. She must know how to be sure her cutting pattern is a parallelogram.

There are several tests for a parallelogram. Hazel is most likely to use the following.

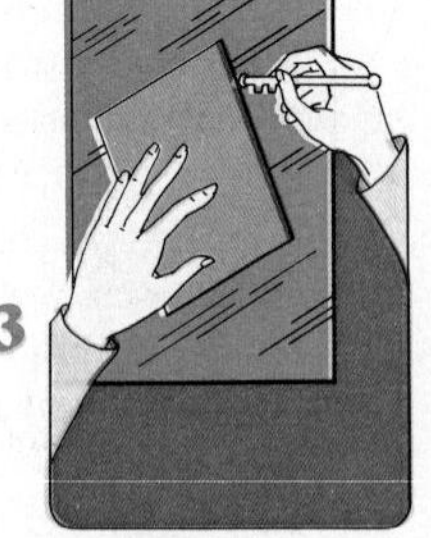

3

2

If both pairs of opposite sides of a quadrilateral are congruent, then the quadrilateral is a parallelogram. *Theorem 7–7*

example

1 **Prove Theorem 7–7.**

Given: $\overline{AB} \cong \overline{CD}$
$\overline{AD} \cong \overline{CB}$

Prove: Quadrilateral *ABCD* is a parallelogram.

4

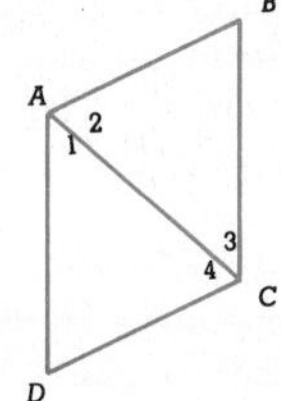

Proof:

STATEMENTS	REASONS
1. $\overline{AB} \cong \overline{CD}$, $\overline{AD} \cong \overline{CB}$	1. Given
2. $\overline{AC} \cong \overline{AC}$	2. Theorem 2–2: Congruence of line segments is reflexive.
3. $\triangle ABC \cong \triangle CDA$	3. Postulate 4–1: SSS
4. $\angle 2 \cong \angle 4$, $\angle 1 \cong \angle 3$	4. Definition of Congruent Triangles *CPCTC*
5. $\overline{AB} \parallel \overline{DC}$, $\overline{AD} \parallel \overline{BC}$	5. Theorem 6–5: In a plane, if two lines are cut by a transversal so that a pair of alternate interior angles are congruent, then the lines are parallel.
6. Quadrilateral *ABCD* is a parallelogram.	6. Definition of Parallelogram

5

220 *Polygons*

exercises

6 **Exploratory** **Determine whether or *not* each of the following tests could be used to prove that a quadrilateral is a parallelogram. State *yes* or *no*.**

1. Both pairs of opposite sides are parallel.
2. Both pairs of opposite sides are congruent.
3. The quadrilateral is regular.
4. Pairs of consecutive sides are congruent.
5. Pairs of consecutive angles are congruent.
6. Both pairs of opposite angles are congruent.

For each of the following given set of conditions, determine whether or *not* the quadrilateral must be a parallelogram. State *yes* or *no*. Then, explain.

7. $\overline{RQ} \cong \overline{SP}$, $\angle 2 \cong \angle 6$
8. $\angle 2 \cong \angle 3$, $\overline{QR} \cong \overline{PS}$
9. $QT = 5$, $RT = 9$, $PT = 5$, $ST = 5$
10. $m\angle 1 = 60$, $m\angle 2 = 70$, $m\angle 5 = 60$, $m\angle 6 = 70$
11. $m\angle PQR = 71$, $m\angle QPS = 109$, $\angle PQR \cong \angle RSP$
12. $QR = 8$, $PQ = 8$, $RS = 4$, $SP = 4$

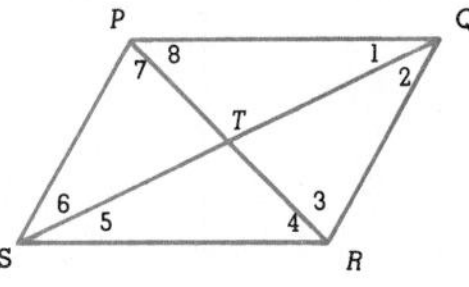

Exercises 7–12

13. E is the midpoint of $\overline{BD}$. E is the midpoint of $\overline{AC}$.
14. $\overline{AB} \cong \overline{BC}$, $\overline{CD} \cong \overline{AD}$
15. $\triangle ABC \cong \triangle CDA$
16. $\triangle ABE \cong \triangle CDE$

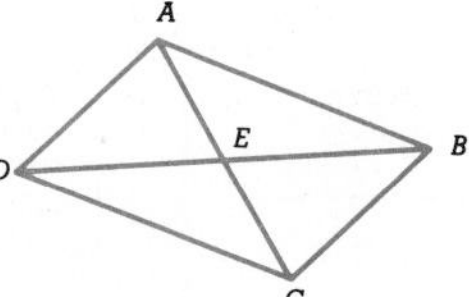

Exercises 13–16

7 **Written** **Prove each of the following.**

1. Theorem 7–8
2. If both pairs of opposite angles of a quadrilateral are congruent, then the quadrilateral is a parallelogram.
3. If one pair of opposite angles of a quadrilateral are congruent and one pair of opposite sides are parallel, then the quadrilateral is a parallelogram.
4. If quadrilateral $EFGH$ has $\angle G \cong \angle E$ and $\overline{FG} \cong \overline{GH} \cong \overline{HE}$, then the quadrilateral is parallelogram.
5. **Given:** $\overline{AE} \cong \overline{CE}$, $\angle ECD \cong \angle EAB$
   Prove: Quadrilateral $ABCD$ is a parallelogram.
6. **Given:** $\overline{BA} \parallel \overline{CD}$, $\angle DBC \cong \angle ADB$
   Prove: Quadrilateral $ABCD$ is a parallelogram.

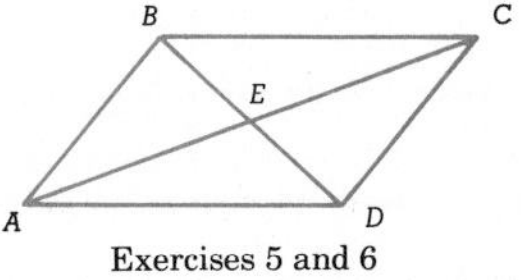

Exercises 5 and 6

222 *Polygons*

6. *Exploratory Exercises* can be used in class to review or clarify concepts.

7. *Written Exercises* provide ample practice to facilitate mastery of the lesson objectives. Exercises progress in difficulty level from the beginning to the end of the exercise set. *Challenge Exercises* appear where appropriate.

8. *Review* and *Test* materials are provided to help students evaluate their progress. Each chapter includes a *Vocabulary, Chapter Summary, Chapter Review,* and a *Chapter Test. Cumulative Reviews* appear periodically to help students maintain geometric skills.

TEACHER FEATURES

The Teacher's Annotated Edition includes the Teacher's Guide and annotated pages from the student text.

Annotated Pages

1

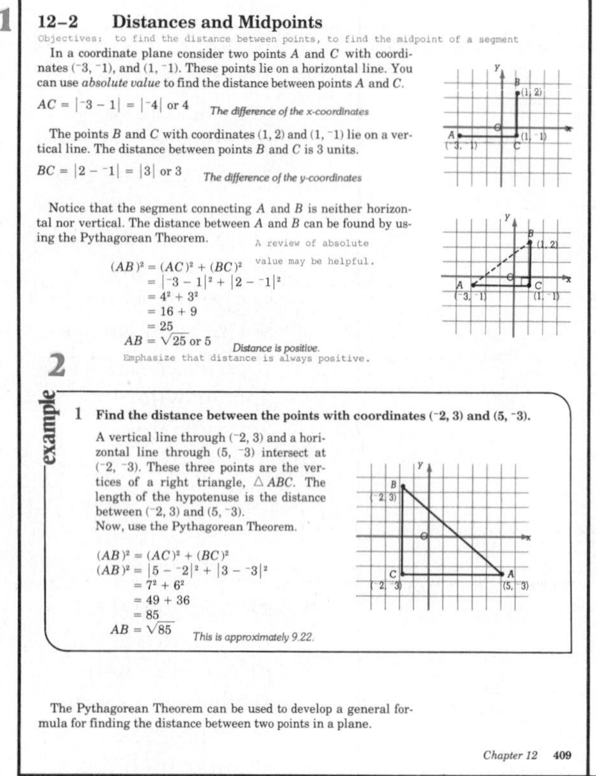

12–2 Distances and Midpoints

Objectives: to find the distance between points, to find the midpoint of a segment

In a coordinate plane consider two points A and C with coordinates $(^-3, ^-1)$, and $(1, ^-1)$. These points lie on a horizontal line. You can use *absolute value* to find the distance between points A and C.

$AC = |^-3 - 1| = |^-4|$ or 4 *The difference of the x-coordinates*

The points B and C with coordinates $(1, 2)$ and $(1, ^-1)$ lie on a vertical line. The distance between points B and C is 3 units.

$BC = |2 - ^-1| = |3|$ or 3 *The difference of the y-coordinates*

Notice that the segment connecting A and B is neither horizontal nor vertical. The distance between A and B can be found by using the Pythagorean Theorem. A review of absolute value may be helpful.

$$\begin{aligned}(AB)^2 &= (AC)^2 + (BC)^2\\ &= |^-3 - 1|^2 + |2 - ^-1|^2\\ &= 4^2 + 3^2\\ &= 16 + 9\\ &= 25\\ AB &= \sqrt{25} \text{ or } 5\end{aligned}$$

Distance is positive.
Emphasize that distance is always positive.

2

example

1 Find the distance between the points with coordinates $(^-2, 3)$ and $(5, ^-3)$.

A vertical line through $(^-2, 3)$ and a horizontal line through $(5, ^-3)$ intersect at $(^-2, ^-3)$. These three points are the vertices of a right triangle, $\triangle ABC$. The length of the hypotenuse is the distance between $(^-2, 3)$ and $(5, ^-3)$.
Now, use the Pythagorean Theorem.

$$\begin{aligned}(AB)^2 &= (AC)^2 + (BC)^2\\ (AB)^2 &= |5 - ^-2|^2 + |3 - ^-3|^2\\ &= 7^2 + 6^2\\ &= 49 + 36\\ &= 85\\ AB &= \sqrt{85}\end{aligned}$$

This is approximately 9.22.

The Pythagorean Theorem can be used to develop a general formula for finding the distance between two points in a plane.

Chapter 12 409

EN: Ex: 1, 4, 7, 10; Wr: 1-29 odds, 31-35; AV: Ex: 1-11 odds, Wr: 1-15; p. 408, Wr: 2-18 evens

exercises 3

FN: Ex: 1-12, Wr: 1-15; p. 408, Wr: 2-18 evens

Exploratory **Find the distance between each of the following pairs of points.**

1. (5, 0), (12, 0) 7
2. (0, 3), (0, 6) 3
3. $(^-6, 0), (^-2, 0)$ 4
4. (1, 2), (3, 4) $2\sqrt{2}$
5. (2, 3), (5, 7) 5
6. $(^-1, ^-2), (^-3, ^-4)$ $2\sqrt{2}$

Find the coordinates of the midpoint of each segment that has endpoints with the following coordinates. 4

7. (0, 4), (0, 0) (0,2)
8. (6, 0), (13, 0) $\left(\frac{19}{2}, 0\right)$
9. $(^-3, 2), (^-5, 6)$ $(^-4,4)$
10. $(^-1, ^-2), (^-3, ^-6)$ $(^-2,^-4)$
11. $(4, 6), (^-2, ^-3)$ $\left(1, \frac{3}{2}\right)$
12. $(^-1, ^-7), (6, 1)$ $\left(\frac{5}{2}, ^-3\right)$

Written **Find the distance between each of the following pairs of points.**

1. (2, 3), (8, 9) $6\sqrt{2}$
2. (15, 0), (0, 15) $15\sqrt{2}$
3. (1, 1), (8, 8) $7\sqrt{2}$
4. $(^-7, ^-5), (^-10, ^-9)$ 5
5. (0, 3), (5, 7) $\sqrt{41}$
6. $(^-2, ^-6), (^-6, ^-2)$ $4\sqrt{2}$
7. $(4, 6), (0, ^-4)$ $2\sqrt{29}$
8. $(6, 0), (^-4, ^-8)$ $2\sqrt{41}$
9. (0, 0), (3, 4) 5
10. $(0, 0), (p, q)$ $\sqrt{p^2 + q^2}$
11. $(a, c), (c, a)$ $|a - c|\sqrt{2}$
12. $(0, r), (0, ^-r)$ $2|r|$
13. $(4, a), (^-8, b)$ $\sqrt{144 + (a - b)^2}$
14. $\left(\frac{2}{3}, \frac{4}{5}\right), \left(\frac{1}{3}, \frac{2}{5}\right)$ $\frac{1}{15}\sqrt{61}$
15. (0.2, 0.7), (0.4, 0.9) $\frac{1}{5}\sqrt{2}$

16–30. Find the coordinates of the midpoint of each segment that has endpoints with the coordinates given in written exercises 1–15. 16. (5,6) 17. (7.5,7.5) 18. (4.5,4.5) 19. (-8.5,-7) 20. (2.5,5) 21. (-4,-4) 22. (2,1) 23. (1,-4) 24. (1.5,2)

31. The vertices of a rectangle have the coordinates $(4, 1), (^-5, 1), (^-5, ^-3)$, and $(4, ^-3)$. Find the perimeter of the rectangle. 26
32. Find the area of the rectangle in exercise 31. 36
33. Find the measure of each diagonal of the rectangle in exercise 31. $\sqrt{97}$ for each diagonal
34. Find the coordinates of the center of a circle whose diameter has endpoints with coordinates $(^-6, ^-8)$, and (5, 7). (-0.5,-0.5)
35. The center of a circle has coordinates $(^-8, 3)$. One endpoint of a diameter has coordinates (5, 4). Find the coordinates of the other endpoint of the diameter. (-21,2)

25. $\left(\frac{p}{2}, \frac{q}{2}\right)$ 26. $\left(\frac{a+c}{2}, \frac{c+a}{2}\right)$ 27. (0,0) 28. $\left(-2, \frac{a+b}{2}\right)$ 29. $\left(\frac{1}{2}, \frac{3}{5}\right)$ 30. (0.3,0.8)

Uses in Banking **computers**

Banks use computers to store data as well as to keep account of daily transactions. For example, when a checking account is opened, the computer assigns a number to the account. As deposits are made and withdrawals are completed, the computer keeps a running total by adding or subtracting as necessary. The computer processes this information at such a rate of speed that the time of processing is reduced from weeks to minutes.

Savings accounts, loans, and savings clubs are all kept up-to-date using a computer. Computers also make 24-hour self-service windows possible. In some areas, customers are able to make purchases using a special plastic credit card that deducts the amount from the customer's checking account.

412 Coordinates

1. *Objectives* are stated at the beginning of each lesson.

2. *Teaching Suggestions* and hints appear periodically in the margin notes. *Additional suggestions* are found in the Teacher's Notes.

3. *Suggested daily assignments* are provided for fundamental, average, and enriched classes.

4. *Answers* are provided for all exercises. Answers that do not appear on the annotated pages can be found in the Teacher's Answer Key.

Teacher's Guide

Assignment Guide
(T10–T11)

Information concerning gearing the course for students of different abilities is included as well as a Suggested Time Schedule.

Teacher's Notes
(T12–T25)

The Teacher Notes include a chapter overview and notes for each lesson.

Tests (T26–T40)

An independent test for each chapter is included in the testing portion. Answers to these tests follow the tests.
(T41–T48)

Teacher's Answer Key
(T50–T144)

The Teacher Answer Key provides answers that do not appear on the annotated pages.

ASSIGNMENT GUIDE

This textbook is designed for high school geometry classes. The textbook is organized so that each chapter can be covered in two to three weeks. This allows approximately one and one-fourth days per lesson, one day for review, and one day for the chapter test. Chapters 13, 14, and the Appendix are optional. Most classes should be able to cover the majority of the text in 170 class periods.

Each lesson in the textbook includes suggested daily assignments for three ability levels: enriched, average, and fundamental. These assignments are meant to provide general guidelines for using the text. Specific assignments can be designated by each teacher to meet individual classroom or school requirements. The chart on the next page gives an approximate time schedule for each of the ability levels.

Enriched Course

This course is for students who can master concepts after only a few examples and exerc suggested cises, abou exercises f for all 14 Review.

Average (

This cou mastery of concepts w assignmen most of the from speci approach w Suggested allotted for

Fu

T and less cise Mo gest for cou

T10

TEACHER'S NOTES

Chapter 1 Points, Lines, and Planes

Chapter Overview This chapter introduces the basic terms of geometry, giving their meaning and notation. The chapter includes terms such as point, line, and plane. Terms such as theorem, postulate, conditional, and definition relating to proofs are also discussed. The techniques for planning and writing proofs are also illustrated.

Lesson Notes

1-1 This section identifies the basic geometric terms of line, point, and plane. The students should be shown the correct notation so they can use it

p	q	$p \rightarrow q$	$q \rightarrow p$	$p \leftrightarrow q$ $(p \rightarrow q) \wedge (q \rightarrow p)$
T	T	T	T	T
T	F	F	T	F
F	T	T	F	F
F	F	T	T	T

1-4 This section states the basic postulates about points, lines, and planes. Euclid set up his system with the Incidence Postulates. Much of the terminology used may lead to some difficulties. Terms such as "exactly one," "at least one," and "not more than one" should be carefully analyzed.

Independent Chapter Tests

Independent Test for Chapter 1

Draw and label a diagram to show each of the following.

1. $\overleftrightarrow{EF}$ and $\overleftrightarrow{GH}$ intersect at R.
2. $\overleftrightarrow{CD}$ contains S and T.
3. m and n intersect at T.
4. Plane $\mathcal{J}$ contains $\overleftrightarrow{TS}$ and C.

Determine whether or *not* each of the following statements is a good definition. If *not*, tell why. Assume the terms in each statement are previously defined.

5. The points lie on the same line.
6. Points are coplanar if and only if they lie in the same plane.

Rewrite each of the following conditional statements in if-then form. Then write the converse of each.

7. Skew lines do not intersect.
8. A rhombus is a quadrilateral.

h is the

·l if and

ain $\overline{AB}$. lanes.

ılate, or

is equi

Teacher's Answer Key

CHAPTER 1 POINTS, LINES, AND PLANES

PAGES 3–4 WRITTEN

13. any one of $\overleftrightarrow{AF}$, $\overleftrightarrow{FA}$, $\overleftrightarrow{FB}$, $\overleftrightarrow{BF}$, n, $\overleftrightarrow{BA}$ **14.** any one of $\overleftrightarrow{AE}$, $\overleftrightarrow{AD}$, $\overleftrightarrow{DE}$, $\overleftrightarrow{ED}$, $\overleftrightarrow{EA}$, $\overleftrightarrow{DA}$ **15.** none **16.** B **17.** 2 pairs of A, E, D **18.** 2 pairs of D, H, C **19.** any three of $\overleftrightarrow{AF}$, $\overleftrightarrow{FB}$, $\overleftrightarrow{AB}$, $\overleftrightarrow{FA}$, $\overleftrightarrow{BF}$, $\overleftrightarrow{BA}$ **20.** any three of $\overleftrightarrow{BG}$, $\overleftrightarrow{GC}$, m, $\overleftrightarrow{GB}$, $\overleftrightarrow{CG}$, $\overleftrightarrow{CB}$ **21.** any three of: plane AFE, plane AFG, plane AFD, plane AFH, plane AFC, plane ABE, plane ABG, plane ABD, plane ABH, plane ABC, plane AEF, plane AEB, etc.

PAGES 7–8 WRITTEN

19. not a good definition:—does not state distinguishing properties **20.** not a good definition:—does not state distinguishing properties **21.** not a good definition:—not identifying set to which term belongs—not stating distinguishing properties—not reversible **22.** not a good definition:—not concise (do not need to say 3 angles) **23.** not a good definition: —does not identify set to which term belongs, does not name the term being defined **24.** good

2. If a figure is a square, then it is not a triangle. If a figure is not a triangle, then it is a square. **3.** If a figure is a square, then it is a rectangle. If a figure is a rectangle, then it is a square. **4.** If a number is an integer, then it is a real number. If a number is a real number, then it is an integer. **5.** If $x < 0$, then $5x > 6x$. If $5x > 6x$, then $x < 0$. **6.** If $2n + 1 = 5$, then $n = 2$. If $n = 2$, then $2n + 1 = 5$. **7.** If it rains, then it pours. If it pours, then it rains. **8.** If you want a new account, then phone for it. If you phone for a new account, then you want a new account. **9.** If two lines intersect, then they are contained in exactly one plane. If two lines are contained in exactly one plane, then they intersect. **10.** If two angles are vertical, then they are congruent. If two angles are congruent, then they are vertical. **11.** If there is smoke, then there is fire. If there is fire, then there is smoke. **12.** If you show me a genius, then I'll show you a scholar. If I show you a scholar, then you'll show me a genius. **23.–28.** Answers will vary. Sample answers are as follows. **23.** If three points are collinear, then they lie on one line. **24.** If $2x = 4$, then $x = 20$. **25.** If three points are collinear, then they are

SPECIAL FEATURES

Special features in the student text provide interesting and useful extra topics.

Careers

Career pages present relevant, interesting careers and show how geometry is used.

Excursions in Geometry

Excursions in Geometry provide short topics in the development and use of geometry, as well as puzzles and games.

Algebra Review

Algebra Reviews help students to maintain and use algebraic concepts.

Computers

Computer features provide information concerning both the historical background of computers and current uses of computers.

Calculators

Calculator features show students how to use a calculator.

Topics in Geometry

The Topics in Geometry pages provide information concerning different approaches to Geometry.

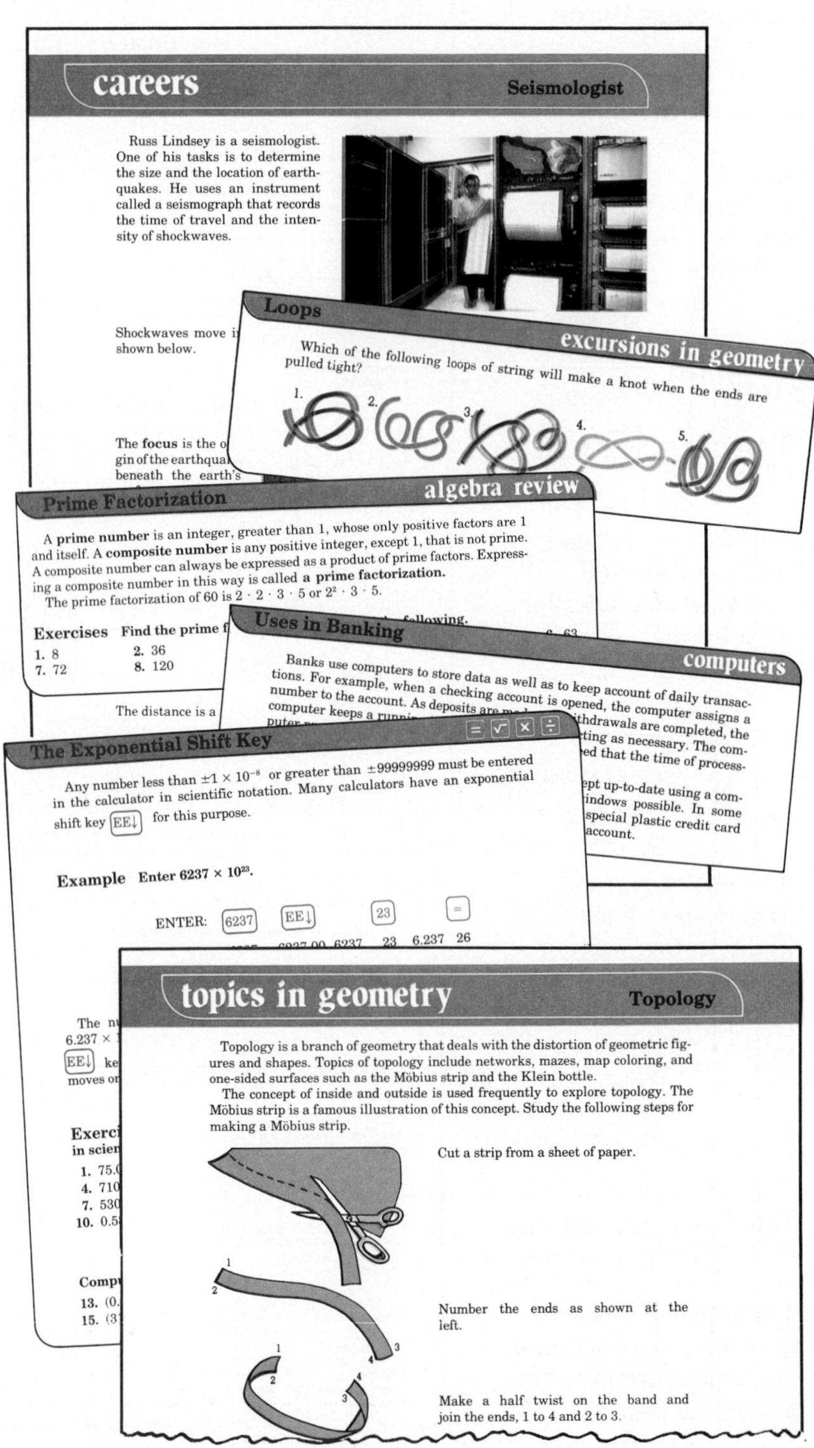

careers
Seismologist
Russ Lindsey is a seismologist. One of his tasks is to determine the size and the location of earthquakes. He uses an instrument called a seismograph that records the time of travel and the intensity of shockwaves.
Loops
excursions in geometry
Which of the following loops of string will make a knot when the ends are pulled tight?
Prime Factorization
algebra review
A prime number is an integer, greater than 1, whose only positive factors are 1 and itself. A composite number is any positive integer, except 1, that is not prime. A composite number can always be expressed as a product of prime factors. Expressing a composite number in this way is called a prime factorization.
The prime factorization of 60 is 2 · 2 · 3 · 5 or 2² · 3 · 5.
Uses in Banking
computers
The Exponential Shift Key
Any number less than ±1 × 10⁻⁸ or greater than ±99999999 must be entered in the calculator in scientific notation. Many calculators have an exponential shift key EE↓ for this purpose.
Example Enter 6237 × 10²³.
ENTER: 6237 EE↓ 23 =
topics in geometry
Topology
Topology is a branch of geometry that deals with the distortion of geometric figures and shapes. Topics of topology include networks, mazes, map coloring, and one-sided surfaces such as the Möbius strip and the Klein bottle.
The concept of inside and outside is used frequently to explore topology. The Möbius strip is a famous illustration of this concept. Study the following steps for making a Möbius strip.
Cut a strip from a sheet of paper.
Number the ends as shown at the left.
Make a half twist on the band and join the ends, 1 to 4 and 2 to 3.

ADDITIONAL FEATURES

Integer Equations: Addition and Subtraction

Solve each equation.

1. $7 + 5 = x$ 12
2. $6 + 4 = x$ 10
3. $8 + 9 = x$ 17
4. $19 + 20 = x$ 39
5. $13 + 15 = x$ 28
6. $45 + 24 = x$ 69
7. $38 + 16 = x$ 54
8. $96 + 52 = x$ 148
9. $77 + 9 = x$ 86
10. $104 + 47 = x$ 151
11. $83 + 86 = x$ 169
12. $27 + 34 = x$ 61
13. $636 + 104 = x$ 740
14. $108 + 597 = x$ 705
15. $302 + 969 = x$ 1271
16. $47 + 38 + 76 = x$ 161
17. $29 + 62 + 35 = x$ 126
18. $51 + 89 + 96 = x$ 236
19. $20 + 63 + 57 = x$ 140
20. $34 + 49 + 72 = x$ 155
21. $66 + 28 + 92 = x$ 186

22. ⁻8 +
25. 0 +
28. ⁻40
31. ⁻66
34. ⁻152
37. ⁻709
40. ⁻746
43. ⁻11
46. ⁻10
49. ⁻8 +
52. 24 +
55. 40 +
58. ⁻16
61. ⁻204

Solve ea

64. 47 –

Postulates and Theorems

Chapter 1: Points, Lines, and Planes

Postulate 1–1	Through any two points there is exactly one line. (14)
Postulate 1–2	Through any three points not on the same line there is exactly one plane. (14)
Postulate 1–3	A line contains at least two points. (15)
Postulate 1–4	A plane contains at least three points not on the same line. (15)
Postulate 1–5	If two points lie in a plane, then the entire line containing those two points lies in that plane. (15)
Postulate 1–6	If two planes intersect, then their intersection is a line. (15)
Theorem 1–1	If there is a line and a point not on the line, then there is exactly one

oth

ne.
eal

hat,
and

is a
een

Selected Answers

CHAPTER 1 POINTS, LINES, AND PLANES

Page 3 Exploratory 1. point 3. line 5. plane 7. line 9. plane 11. point

Page 3 Written 13. $\overleftrightarrow{AF}$, $\overleftrightarrow{FB}$, *n* 15. none 21. plane *AFE*, plane *ABC*, plane *DEH* 23. infinitely many 25. three

Page 7 Exploratory 1. false 3. false 5. true 7. false 9. false 11. true

Page 16 Exploratory 1. Postulate 1–1 3. Postulate 1–4 5. Postulate 1–4 7. Postulate 1–1 9. Postulate 1–6

Page 16 Written 1. true 3. false 5. true 11. 1 13. 3 15. 4 17. 15 19. 1 21. infinitely many

Page 20 Exploratory 1. theorem, given, prove statement, diagram, and proof

The Language of BASIC

BASIC is a frequently used computer language. BASIC is an abbreviation for Beginner's All-purpose Symbolic Instruction Code. In BASIC, some operation symbols are the same as those in algebra.

In BASIC, raising to a power is usually indicated by ↑.

Algebra	BASIC	Algebra	BASIC
+	+	÷	/
–	–	=	=
×	*	5^2	5 ↑ 2

Variables may be represented by a letter or by a letter and a numeral. A, B, X, C1, D2, and M5 are examples of variables in BASIC. *Check your manual to see if your computer allows other variable names.*

In BASIC an operation symbol *cannot* be omitted. For example, A times B must be written A * B, *not* AB as allowed in algebra.

The computer performs operations in the same order as in algebra.

Order of Operations in BASIC

1. **Do all operations in parentheses, from the innermost parentheses outward.**
2. **Evaluate all powers from left to right.**
3. **Do all multiplications and/or divisions from left to right.**
4. **Do all additions and/or subtractions from left to right.**

The order of operations is shown in the following example.

example

1 Evaluate 18/3 – (6 + 2) * 3 ↑ 2 + 4.

18/3 – (6 + 2) * 3 ↑ 2 + 4 = 18/3 – 8 * 3 ↑ 2 + 4 — *Do operations in parentheses.*
= 18/3 – 8 * 9 + 4 — *Evaluate powers.*
= 6 – 72 + 4 — *Do the division and multiplication.*
= ⁻62 — *Do the addition and subtraction.*

The value of the expression is ⁻62.

Diagnostic Skills Review

In this review, on pages 517–534, algebraic skills are systematically broken down. Problems can be assigned periodically throughout the year.

Postulates and Theorems

Found on pages 536–547 is a complete listing, chapter-by-chapter, of all postulates and theorems presented in *Merrill Geometry*.

Selected Answers

In this section found on pages 570–596, answers to selected problems are provided to allow students to check their progress as they work the exercises.

Appendix: BASIC

The BASIC appendix on pages 500–516 provides a short course in the BASIC programming language. Topics covered include the language of BASIC, variables, FOR-NEXT, IF-THEN statements, and BASIC functions.

ASSIGNMENT GUIDE

This textbook is designed for high school geometry classes. The textbook is organized so that each chapter can be covered in two to three weeks. This allows approximately one and one-fourth days per lesson, one day for review, and one day for the chapter test. Chapters 13, 14, and the Appendix are optional. Most classes should be able to cover the majority of the text in 170 class periods.

Each lesson in the textbook includes suggested daily assignments for three ability levels: enriched, average, and fundamental. These assignments are meant to provide general guidelines for using the text. Specific assignments can be designated by each teacher to meet individual classroom or school requirements. The chart on the next page gives an approximate time schedule for each of the ability levels.

Enriched Course

This course is for students who can master concepts after only a few examples and exercises. These students benefit from challenge activities and exercises. The suggested daily assignment for a lesson usually includes a few Exploratory Exercises, about half of the Written Exercises, most of the Challenge Exercises, and some exercises from special features. In the Suggested Time Schedule, days are allotted for all 14 chapters and the Appendix. Two days are allotted for each Cumulative Review.

Average Course

This course is for students who need many examples and exercises to facilitate mastery of the concepts. These students need occasional review exercises to retain concepts with some Challenge Exercises for added motivation. The suggested daily assignment for a lesson usually includes about half of the Exploratory Exercises, most of the Written Exercises, occasional Challenge Exercises, and some exercises from special features. Most assignments for the Written Exercises reflect a spiral approach with exercises from both the present lesson and the previous lesson. In the Suggested Time Schedule, days are allotted for all of Chapters 1–13. Two days are allotted for each Cumulative Review.

Fundamental Course

This course is for students who need additional practice to master the concepts and need frequent review to maintain skills. The suggested daily assignment for a lesson usually includes all of the Exploratory Exercises, many of the Written Exercises, occasional Challenge Exercises, and some exercises from special features. Most assignments for the Written Exercises reflect a spiral approach. In the Suggested Time Schedule, days are allotted for Chapters 1–12. Three days are allotted for each Cumulative Review. These reviews are important for students in this course.

Abbreviations

The following is a list of abbreviations used throughout the text in the suggested daily assignments.

AR	Algebra Review
AV	Average Course
C	Careers Exercises
Cal	Calculators Exercises
Ch	Challenge Exercises
E	Excursions in Geometry Exercises
EN	Enriched Course
Ex	Exploratory Exercises
FN	Fundamental Course
TG	Topics in Geometry Exercises
Wr	Written Exercises

SUGGESTED TIME SCHEDULE

Chapter	Number of Lessons	Suggested Number of Teaching Days		
		Enriched	Average	Fundamental
1	7	10	11	11
2	6	10	12	13
3	6	10	11	12
4	8	12	14	14
5	5	9	10	11
6	6	10	12	13
7	8	12	14	15
8	7	10	12	13
9	7	10	11	12
10	8	12	15	15
11	8	12	12	13
12	8	11	12	12
13	6	10	12	—
14	6	11	—	—
Appendix	5	9	—	—
Cumulative Reviews		8	8	12
Semester Reviews and Tests		4	4	4
Total Number of Days		170	170	170

TEACHER'S NOTES

Chapter 1 Points, Lines, and Planes

Chapter Overview This chapter introduces the basic terms of geometry, giving their meaning and notation. The chapter includes terms such as point, line, and plane. Terms such as theorem, postulate, conditional, and definition relating to proofs are also discussed. The techniques for planning and writing proofs are also illustrated.

Lesson Notes

1-1 This section identifies the basic geometric terms of line, point, and plane. The students should be shown the correct notation so they can use it throughout the course. Terminology such as "contain" and "lies on" should be discussed. Students should be able to use such terms in discussing points, lines, and planes. It may be helpful to use physical models when presenting these concepts. It is sometimes easier to understand geometry if figures are drawn and models are shown.

1-2 It is important to note the characteristics of a good definition.
1. Name the term being defined. **2.** Use only undefined terms or previously defined terms. **3.** Identify the set to which the term belongs. **4.** State the properties which distinguish the term from others in the set. **5.** Make it reversible. **6.** Make it concise. A discussion of some non-mathematical definitions will help students understand the guidelines. To make a definition reversible the "if and only if" form (biconditional) is used. This concept will be discussed more in the next section.

1-3 Being familiar with conditionals is helpful for interpreting advertisements. Have students clip magazine ads and listen to television commercials. Practically all theorems and postulates presented in this text are conditionals written in "if-then" form. This form helps make proofs of theorems more easily understood.

At this time, truth tables may be introduced. Analyze the biconditional using non-mathematical examples. For example, "Terry will win the race if and only if it is raining." The following truth table can be used where p is "Terry will win the race," and q is "it is raining."

p	q	$p \rightarrow q$	$q \rightarrow p$	$p \leftrightarrow q$ $(p \rightarrow q) \wedge (q \rightarrow p)$
T	T	T	T	T
T	F	F	T	F
F	T	T	F	F
F	F	T	T	T

1-4 This section states the basic postulates about points, lines, and planes. Euclid set up his system with the Incidence Postulates. Much of the terminology used may lead to some difficulties. Terms such as "exactly one," "at least one," and "not more than one" should be carefully analyzed. As new terms appear, carefully explain their geometric meaning. To make sure students can identify the hypothesis and conclusion of any conditional, discuss drawings for each postulate. Physical models, such as the corner of the classroom, two pieces of paper with a pencil, or a book with the desk top can be used for the exercises.

1-5 The five main parts of a formal proof are *the theorem, the given, the prove statement, a diagram,* and *the proof* with statements and reasons. Students should be able to state the theorem, the given, the prove statement, and draw a diagram. It is important that they can translate the theorem into these other elements. Drawing a diagram will be helpful in determining what is needed in order to prove a theorem.

1-6 This section gives a guide for writing a formal proof by taking a theorem and explaining the reasoning processes. The idea of reaching a conclusion, given certain conditions, should be stressed. Suggest the students make a list of the terms in the given and then check the definitions in the glossary, page 550. Also, the students should be made aware of the list of theorems and postulates on pages 536–547. This list will help students determine which ones may be needed.

1-7 This section presents other forms of the conditional. *Negation, inverse,* and *contrapositive* are discussed. A discussion of the *converse* may be included as the contrapositive of the inverse. Truth tables may be used to show the relationship among the forms of the conditional.

p	q	$\sim p$	$\sim q$	conditional $p \to q$	converse $q \to p$	inverse $\sim p \to \sim q$	contrapositive $\sim q \to \sim p$
T	T	F	F	T	T	T	T
T	F	F	T	F	T	T	F
F	T	T	F	T	F	F	T
F	F	T	T	T	T	T	T

Note that the converse and inverse have the same truth values as the conditional and contrapositive.

Chapter 2 Measure

Chapter Overview This chapter reviews basic algebraic operations involving fractions, decimals, and signed numbers. The properties of real numbers are reviewed and then used in relation to the measure of segments.

Lesson Notes

2-1 Students are given a review of the number line and the real number system. It may be helpful to review absolute value in relation to adding and subtracting signed numbers.

2-2 Measure and measurement are discussed. It is important to note that measure is part of a measurement. A measurement consists of a numeral, the measure, and a unit, the unit of measure. Given a desk 32 inches wide, *32 inches* wide is a *measurement. 32* is the *measure* and *inches* is the *unit of measure*. Stressing the distinction is necessary so that certain properties of real numbers can be applied in the measure of a distance.

2-3 This section introduces segments and some of the properties used with segments. Two segments can be congruent and thus have the same measure. Only measures can be equal. The definition of midpoint stated deals with equality. Thus, the measure of segments must be used when working with midpoint.

2-4 The properties of the real number system are reviewed using examples from algebra and geometry. Stress the reflexive, symmetric, and transitive properties of equality. These properties are very important in the study of geometry.

T-proofs or 2-column proofs are introduced in this lesson.

2-5 The focus of this lesson is on congruent segments. Make sure the students understand the difference between midpoint and bisector. The midpoint is the point that separates the segment into two parts. The bisector is the line or segment that intersects the segment at its midpoint.

The excursion following this section discusses significant digits. Significant digits are those which best represent the value of a measurement. Zeros that serve only to locate decimal points are *not* significant.

2-6 The properties of inequality are discussed in this section. It would be helpful to have the students solve some inequalities. Examples like the following could be used.

Solve each inequality. (Answers are in parentheses.)

1. $6 - y < 4$ ($y > 2$) **2.** $^-9 + n > 6$ ($n > 15$) **3.** $6n + 5 > 5n$ ($n > {}^-5$)

4. $\frac{a}{4} > 5$ ($a > 20$) **5.** $\frac{c}{^-8} > {}^-3$ ($c < 24$) **6.** $^-5 \leq \frac{d}{2}$ ($^-10 \leq d$)

7. $6x > {}^-24$ ($x > {}^-4$) **8.** $^-4y \leq 36$ ($y \geq {}^-9$) **9.** $9b \geq 6b + 18$ ($b \geq 6$)

10. $3(c + 4) \leq 16 - c$ ($c \leq 1$) **11.** $^-5 + x > {}^-8(x + 4)$ ($x > {}^-3$)

Chapter 3 Angles and Perpendiculars

Chapter Overview A definition of an angle is given with an explanation of the terms: ray, vertex, and side. The units of measure and the method of measuring are explained. Each student will need a protractor. Obtuse, acute, and right angles are defined and discussed in relation to one another.

Lesson Notes

3-1 Each student should be able to explain each term in the definition of an angle. Since an angle is defined in terms of *noncollinear* rays, the concept of *straight angle* can be illustrated by opposite rays. Make sure students understand that naming an angle by its vertex is sometimes not sufficient as in the case when there is more than one angle formed at a given vertex.

3-2 Each student will need a protractor for this section. The difference between measure and measurement should be reviewed. An example of the *measurement* of an angle is *40°*. ***40*** is the *measure* and the ***degree*** is the *unit of measure*. The notation $m\angle ABC = 40$ is read "the measure of angle ABC is 40". Students could do some research on different units of measure for angles and reflex angles.

3-3 Students have a tendency to confuse the definitions of complementary and supplementary. Make sure students understand these relationships since these concepts are used frequently in proofs.

The geometric topic after this section discusses flow proofs, an alternative to the two-column proof. Sample flow proofs are included in the excursion for Theorems 3-2 and 3-3. Flow proofs can be written in either vertical or horizontal form. A flow proof may be easier to follow as the steps involving substitution feed into the appropriate statement. It may be helpful for the students to have the option of using either flow proofs or two-column proofs in proving theorems.

Given: Two intersecting lines forming $\angle 1$, $\angle 2$, $\angle 3$, and $\angle 4$; $\angle 1$ is a right angle.
Prove: $\angle 2$, $\angle 3$, and $\angle 4$ are right angles.

Flow Proof:

<u>Two intersecting lines forming $\angle 1$, $\angle 2$, $\angle 3$, and $\angle 4$.</u> $\xrightarrow{1}$ {$\angle 1$ and $\angle 2$ form a linear pair. $\angle 1$ and $\angle 4$ form a linear pair.} <u>$\angle 1$ is a right angle.</u} $\xrightarrow{2}$

$\xrightarrow{2}$ {$\angle 2$ is a right angle. $\angle 4$ is a right angle.} $\xrightarrow{2}$ $\angle 3$ is a right angle.
$\xrightarrow{1}$ {$\angle 3$ and $\angle 4$ form a linear pair.}

1. Definition of linear pair
2. Theorem 3-7

3-4 A variety of theorems in this section lead to conclusions involving right angles. The recognition of vertical angles is very important for many proofs.

A flow proof for Theorem 3-9 appears at the bottom of this page. Note that <u>given</u> statements are <u>underlined.</u>

3-5 It is important to note that the definition of perpendicular lines does not state an angle measure. The definition includes the concept of a right angle being formed and that 90° angles are formed. When discussing Theorem 3-12 note that "in a plane" is a *necessary* statement. Skew lines could form infinitely many perpendiculars if that restriction were not in the theorem.

The following is a flow proof for Theorem 3-13.

Given: $\overleftrightarrow{PQ} \perp \overleftrightarrow{QR}$
Prove: $\angle PQR \cong \angle RQS$; $\angle PQR \cong \angle PQT$; $\angle TQS \cong \angle RQS$; $\angle TQS \cong \angle PQT$

Flow Proof:

<u>$\overleftrightarrow{PQ} \perp \overleftrightarrow{QR}$</u> $\xrightarrow{1}$ {$\angle PQR$, $\angle RQS$, $\angle SQT$ and $\angle TQP$ are right angles.} $\xrightarrow{2}$ {$\angle PQR \cong \angle RQS$; $\angle PQR \cong \angle PQT$; $\angle TQS \cong \angle RQS$; $\angle TQS \cong \angle PQT$}

1. Definition of Perpendicular Lines and Theorem 3-9
2. Theorem 3-6

3-6 A study of perpendicular planes is necessary to build a basis for solid geometry. Using physical models will be helpful while studying this section. It is difficult for some students to imagine three-dimensional figures. Paper folding may be a very helpful exercise at this time. The proofs involving three dimensions may be difficult. It is essential for students to use diagrams and clearly state the given and prove.

Chapter 4 Congruent Triangles

Chapter Overview This chapter explains the types of triangles and their definitions, which are used in many theorems. Besides these classifications, the different segments related to a triangle, such as altitude, angle bisector, and median are defined. These segments are used as auxiliary lines in proving some theorems.

The relative position of collinear points is assumed to agree with the diagrams. Lesson 5-2 in the next chapter places greater emphasis on the assumptions that can be made with diagrams.

Lesson Notes

4-1 A good understanding of triangles is essential to many future theorems. In this section a triangle is formally defined. Students should be able to identify the types of triangles. This knowledge is essential for proving many theorems. Exercises 31–34 can be used as a review of basic algebraic properties used in equation solving.

4-2 The paper folding experiment is an intuitive way to introduce the fact that the sum of the measures of the angles of any triangle is 180. This theorem will be proven in Chapter 6 on parallels.

4-3 To discuss congruent figures, examples from architecture can be used. Correspondence is important in the definitions and theorems which relate to congruent triangles. The students should be careful in writing the order of vertices in a congruence. Also, the order of vertices is important for other concepts such as similarity.

4-4 The three major tests for triangle congruence are SSS, SAS, and ASA. Most students will need to do all the exercises in order to become proficient in using all three. Flow proofs also may be used to help develop an understanding of congruence. As in the previous section, restate the importance of ordering the vertices properly.

4-5 Theorem 4-5, AAS, is presented. Make a clear distinction between ASA and AAS. Note also why SSA and AAA are not tests for congruence. Use counterexamples to disprove SSA and AAA.

4-6 In this section, the special segments of a triangle are defined. Medians, altitudes, and bisectors can be helpful in completing proofs. Note the difference among the three types of segments. You may want to discuss how these segments are related in an equilateral triangle, in an isosceles triangle, and in a right triangle.

4-7 Isosceles triangles are discussed and used to illustrate how an auxiliary line will help in a proof. Many of the proofs of theorems are left as exercises. This leaves the option of using them either for class discussion or for practice. If they are not assigned or discussed, the students should at least outline or plan a proof. Practice is very important at this point.

Theorem 4-6 can be proven in a less direct way than what is presented in the text. That is, flip $\triangle PQR$ over and prove $\triangle PQR \cong \triangle RQP$ by SAS.

4-8 Theorems 4-11, 4-12, and 4-13 deal with right triangles. Emphasize that the existence of a right triangle must be established before these theorems can be used. Once existence has been established, these theorems will save time in proving congruence of right triangles.

Chapter 5 Triangle Inequalities

Chapter Overview Relationships of interior and exterior angles are discussed using the Inequality Theorem. Also, this theorem is useful in establishing relationships between sides. The Triangle Inequality Theorem helps establish the basis for many theorems.

Lesson Notes

5-1 It is important to note that the exterior angles of a triangle are not vertical to the interior angles of the triangle. This concept will be new to most students, so there may be some need to stress the differences. This section is a good place to review the properties of inequalities.

5-2 It is sometimes difficult to determine what information is given in diagrams and to recognize overlapping figures. Stress the information that can be assumed from a diagram (existence, relative position, and intersections). Any properties listed, or congruences given, must be either written out, given, or proven. Make sure students understand that information which <u>cannot</u> be used.

5-3 Students must be able to identify the sides opposite an angle in a triangle. This lesson emphasizes the relationships between the sides and the angles of triangles. Example 1 uses a paragraph proof as opposed to a two-column proof or a flow proof. You may want to discuss such a proof in more detail by using other theorems in this section as illustrations.

5-4 The Triangle Inequality is one of the more important theorems in geometry. Using a compass or straws, students can experiment with segments to help them come to the desired conclusion of the theorem. A generalization from this theorem is: given two sides of a triangle, the length of the third side must lie between the sum and difference of the two given lengths. It should be possible for the students to determine whether three given numbers can be the measures of the sides of a triangle.

5-5 The Hinge Theorem and its converse may require much explanation before students can understand and apply it. Using a chalkboard compass is recommended as a model of a hinge. You may need to provide assistance and/or limit the number of proofs assigned in the exercises.

Chapter 6 Parallels

Chapter Overview Theorems and postulates for parallel lines are proven in this chapter. Angle congruences depending on parallel lines are explained and defined. Indirect proof is presented. Also included in this chapter is a discussion of distance in relation to parallel lines.

Lesson Notes

6-1 Students should understand that a transversal is a line in a plane intersecting two lines in two distinct points. All these lines are in the same plane and thus, the difference between parallel lines, transversals, and skew lines. Skew lines can be demonstrated by using physical models. Students should be able to identify the types of angles formed by two lines and a transversal (corresponding, alternate interior or exterior, alternate exterior or interior, consecutive).

6-2 In writing an *indirect proof,* it is important to note that the *conclusion* of the theorem is *negated.* Either paragraph form or standard statement-reason form can be used for the indirect proof. Indirect proof can be difficult and students may need a great deal of assistance. Stating the contradiction in postulate form can be helpful. A Contradiction Postulate that could be used is as follows.

The statement "p and not q" is false *if and only if* the statement "if p, then q" is true.

6-3 Students should be able to determine if lines are parallel. In doing this, students can apply theorems proven in the text. Even though Theorems 6-6 and 6-7 can be proven directly, they offer good examples for indirect proofs.

6-4 A discussion of other geometries, which assume that there are no or many parallels through the given point to the given line, may help to better understand the importance of the Parallel Postulate. Note that the Angle Sum Theorem for triangles is proven in Example 2 although it was introduced in Chapter 4.

6-5 Students must be able to recognize and use properties of parallel and perpendicular lines in various positions. It may be necessary to re-draw some of the figures by omitting some of the lines. Also suggest rotating figures as an aid to solving problems.

6-6 Students are asked to approach proofs in several stages. Identification of the hypothesis and conclusion is a first step. Drawing a labeled figure is a second step. After stating the given and prove statement, outline the proof and then write a formal proof. A *flow proof* is a useful model that makes the transition to paragraph proofs much easier.

A flow proof for Theorem 6-15 is given at the bottom of this page.

Given: $\ell \parallel m$
Prove: $AC = BD$

Flow Proof:

^{1}A lies on ℓ. $\xrightarrow{2}$ $\overline{AC} \perp m$; ^{5}Draw $\overline{AD}$. $\xrightarrow{4}$ $\angle ACD$ is a right angle. $\xrightarrow{6}$ $\triangle ACD$ is a right triangle.

^{1}B lies on ℓ. $\xrightarrow{2}$ $\overline{BD} \perp m$; $\ell \parallel m$ $\xrightarrow{3}$ $\overline{BD} \perp \ell$ $\xrightarrow{4}$ $\angle DBA$ is a right angle. $\xrightarrow{6}$ $\triangle DBA$ is a right triangle.

$\ell \parallel m \xrightarrow{7} \angle BAD \cong \angle ADC$

$^{8}\overline{AD} \cong \overline{AD}$

$\xrightarrow{9} \triangle ACD \cong \triangle DBA \xrightarrow{10} \overline{AC} \cong \overline{BD} \xrightarrow{11} AC = BD$

1. Postulate 1-3
2. Theorem 6-14
3. Theorem 6-13
4. Theorem 3-11
5. Postulate 1-1
6. Definition of Right Triangle
7. Theorem 6-10
8. Theorem 2-2
9. Theorem 4-11: HA
10. Definition of Congruent Triangles
11. Definition of Congruent Segments

Chapter 7 Polygons

Chapter Overview Polygons are defined and classified. This chapter includes many proofs concerning parallelograms and trapezoids. You may want to limit the number of proofs assigned. Some kind of student grouping on homework assignments may insure each problem is solved so that all students could benefit from all the theorems.

Lesson Notes

7-1 This text deals mainly with convex polygons. However, it is important to note the difference between convex and concave polygons. It is also important to identify regular polygons. Again, stress the order of the vertices in designating polygons. It might be interesting to do some research into the names of polygons with more than twelve sides.

7-2 The theorem for the sum of the measures of the angles of convex polygons is discussed. A discovery exercise may help the students better understand this theorem. Have them draw several polygons and measure the interior angles.

The problem-solving procedure is important to stress. Emphasize the need to refer back to the original problem to be sure the answer is reasonable.

An induction proof for Theorem 7-1 follows. Theorem 7-1 states that if a convex polygon has n sides, and S is the sum of the degree measure of its angles, then $S = (n - 2)180$.
(a) In this theorem $n \geq 3$ so we must show that the first case, $n = 3$ is true.

$$S = (3 - 2)180 = 180$$

By the Angle Sum Theorem, we know this is true.
(b) Assume that the formula is true for $n = k$. Thus, $S_k = (k - 2)180$. The sum of the series for $(k + 1)$ terms can be found by adding 180. We get:

$$(1)\ S_{k+1} = (k - 2)180 + 180$$

Applying the formula for $n = (k + 1)$:

$$(2)\ S_{k+1} = [(k + 1) - 2]180$$

Substitute (1) into (2). Then, using algebra, the identity can be verified.

$$(k - 2)180 + 180 \stackrel{?}{=} [(k + 1) - 2]180$$
$$[(k - 2) + 1]180 \stackrel{?}{=} [(k + 1) - 2]180$$
$$(k - 1)180 = (k - 1)180$$

(c) The formula is valid for $n = 3$ (the first case). The assumption that the formula holds for $n = k$, leads to the conclusion that the formula holds for $n = k + 1$. Thus, the formula $S = (n - 2)180$ is true for all $n \geq 3$.

7-3 Review the concepts of congruent triangles and congruent angles formed by a transversal and two parallel lines. The review should be done in regard to parallelograms and diagonals.

7-4 This lesson emphasizes tests for parallelograms. An alternative to doing only formal proofs would be to give the hypothesis of each of the theorems and make suggested conclusions. These exercises may be time consuming. Perhaps assigning only part of the exercises or dividing the class into groups will help.

7-5 The properties of special parallelograms such as rectangles, rhombi, and squares are presented. For most students, the properties discussed will be a review. The term rhombus may be new for some students.

7-6 Finding trapezoidal designs in the real world may help in identifying trapezoids. Tables, roofs, and lampshades utilize the shape of a trapezoid. Make sure the students see a proof of Theorem 7-14 (written exercise 42).

7-7 The concepts discussed in this section are probably familiar to most students. The arithmetic practice will be helpful; therefore, all the exercises could be assigned for this review.

A proof for Theorem 7-17 follows. Theorem 7-17 states that if a regular n-gon has perimeter P units, and a side measure s units, then $P = ns$.
(a) By induction, $P = 3s$ where $n = 3$. A regular triangle (equilateral triangle) has three congruent sides. Therefore, $3s$ must be the perimeter.
(b) Assume that the formula is true for $n = k$. Thus, $P_k = ks$. The sum of the series for $(k + 1)$ terms can be found by adding s.

$$P_k = ks + s$$

Applying the formula for $n = (k + 1)$ we get

$$P_{k+1} = (k + 1)s$$

Verifying the identity,

$ks + s = (k + 1)s$ Distributive Property to P_k
$(k + 1)s = (k + 1)s$ $P_k = P_{k+1}$

(c) The formula is valid for $n = 3$ (the first case). The assumption that the formula holds for $n = k$ leads to the conclusion that the formula holds for $n = k + 1$. Thus, the formula $P = ns$ is true for all $n \geq 3$.

7-8 Physical models are very helpful in discussing regular polyhedra. Some time may be spent in sketching solids and constructing physical models.

Euler's formula, $F + V = E + 2$ can be related to network theory. The formula $R + C = A + 2$ can stand for the following. The number of regions of a network (R) plus the number of corners (C) is equal to the number of arcs (A) plus 2. Using paper and pencil ask students to trace a design without lifting their pencils. The figures drawn are networks. They can be related to topological topics such as the seven bridges of Konigsberg. The problem is the following: is it possible to travel through the city and cross each of the seven bridges without recrossing any one of them?

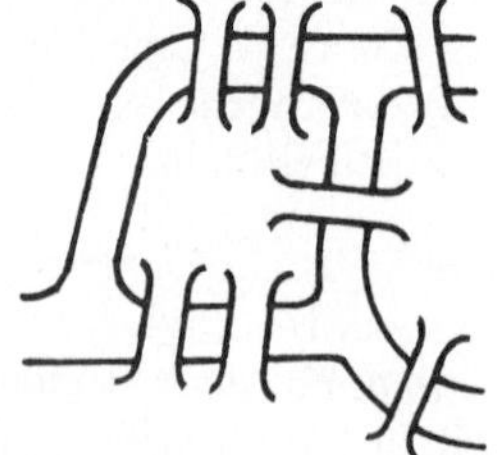

Chapter 8 Similarity

Chapter Overview The properties and applications of ratios and proportions are discussed. These topics are related to similar polygons with an emphasis on triangle similarity. Problem-solving techniques are also discussed and related to problems dealing with similarity.

Lesson Notes

8-1 The relationship between ratio and proportion is stressed. Since a percent is a ratio, percents are discussed and may need to be reviewed. In order to discuss real life problems, students could bring in articles from newspapers or magazines that involve ratios.

8-2 Properties of proportions are reviewed. Stress the idea that these concepts are called theorems and can thus be proven. The ratio of the length to the width of the Golden Rectangle is actually an irrational number. We are using an approximation in our discussion. It may be interesting for the students to do more research on this ratio and Fibonacci numbers.

8-3 The notion of similar polygons can be difficult for some students. Using the idea of <u>same shape</u> may help. Point out that congruent polygons are also similar. Remind the students about the correct correspondence. In working with proportions, it is important to name the congruent angles in order to set up the correct proportion.

8-4 The importance of similar triangles is stressed. Students will need practice in setting up the proper proportions. Redrawing overlapping triangles helps clarify the proportion.

8-5 Review the theorems on parallel lines prior to starting this section. The relationship between parallel lines and proportions is discussed. Stress the theorems present in this section because they will be needed for future areas of study such as trapezoids and their medians. Emphasize the importance of drawing diagrams.

8-6 Students should review altitude, median, and angle bisectors of a triangle. The theorems in this section are related to these topics. Time should be spent in planning the proofs for the theorems before they are actually done.

8-7 There are many uses of similarity in everyday life situations. Trigonometry is based on similarity. An interesting approach to this section would be to do some of the problems as experiments. Shadow reckoning is easily done outdoors. Perhaps some students could make a hypsometer and use it to determine distance.

Chapter 9 Right Triangles

Chapter Overview Square roots are reviewed in anticipation of using them for the geometric mean and the Pythagorean Theorem. The trigonometric ratios: sine, cosine, and tangent are introduced. After the students become acquainted with reading the Trigonometric Ratios table, page 549, problems involving applications are presented. You may want to encourage students to use calculators in doing the exercises in this chapter.

Lesson Notes

9-1 Before starting this section a review of prime factorization would be helpful. Square roots are discussed with the emphasis on the positive root or principal root since measure of distance involves only positive numbers. Rationalizing the denominators may be a concept in need of much practice. The time spent to insure a confidence in finding square roots will be most helpful in preparation for the remainder of the chapter.

9-2 A thorough understanding of the geometric mean will help in the understanding of the proof of the Pythagorean Theorem presented in section 9-3. The relationship between Theorems 9-2 and 9-3 should be discussed.

9-3 There are many proofs of the Pythagorean Theorem. The one presented in this section involves the geometric mean. It is important to stress that the Pythagorean Theorem applies only to right triangles.

President Garfield's proof of the Pythagorean Theorem is shown below. The proof involves finding the area of trapezoids and triangles. These concepts are discussed in Chapter 11; therefore, you may want to present this proof after Chapter 11.

Given: $\triangle ABC$ is a right triangle.

Prove: $AC^2 + BC^2 = AB^2$

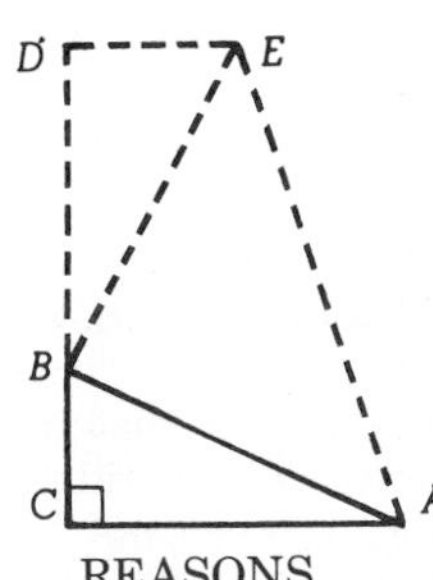

Proof:

STATEMENTS	REASONS
1. $\triangle ABC$ is a right triangle.	1. Given
2. Extend $\overline{CB}$ to D where $BD = AC$.	2. Postulate 1-1, Postulate 2-3
3. Draw $\overline{DE} \perp \overline{CB}$ where $DE = BC$.	3. Theorem 3-12, Postulate 2-3
4. $\overline{BD} \cong \overline{AC}$; $\overline{DE} \cong \overline{BC}$	4. Definition of Congruent Segments
5. $\triangle BED \cong \triangle ABC$	5. Theorem 4-12
6. $\overline{BE} \cong \overline{AB}$	6. CPCTC
7. $BE = AB$	7. Definition of Congruent Segments
8. $\overline{DE} \parallel \overline{CA}$	8. Theorem 6-8
9. Polygon $ACDE$ is a a trapezoid.	9. Definition of Trapezoid
10. $\triangle ABE$ is one half of a square with side AB.	10. Definition of Square
11. Area of $ACDE$ = $\frac{1}{2}(AC + DE)CD$	11. Theorem 11-4
12. Area of $\triangle ABE$ = $\frac{1}{2}(AB^2)$	12. Theorem 11-1
13. Area of $\triangle ABC$ = $\frac{1}{2}(AC)(BC)$ Area of $\triangle BED$ = $\frac{1}{2}(BD)(ED)$	13. Theorem 11-3
14. $\frac{1}{2}(AC + DE)CD - \frac{1}{2}(AC)(BC) - \frac{1}{2}(BD)(ED) = \frac{1}{2}(AB^2)$	14. Postulate 11-3, Postulate 2-7, and Postulate 2-9
15. $\frac{1}{2}(AC + BC)(AC + BC) - \frac{1}{2}(AC)(BC) - \frac{1}{2}(AC)(BC) = \frac{1}{2}(AB^2)$	15. Postulate 2-9, Definition of Between
16. $(AC + BC)^2 - (AC)(BC) - (AC)(BC) = AB^2$	16. Postulate 2-8
17. $AC^2 + 2(AC)(BC) + BC^2 - 2(AC)(BC) = AB^2$	17. Postulate 2-14, Postulate 2-9
18. $AC^2 + BC^2 = AB^2$	18. Postulates 2-10, 2-11, 2-12, 2-9

9-4 The 30°–60° and 45°–45° right triangles are discussed. These special triangles have useful relationships. The students should be able to derive these relationships for themselves.

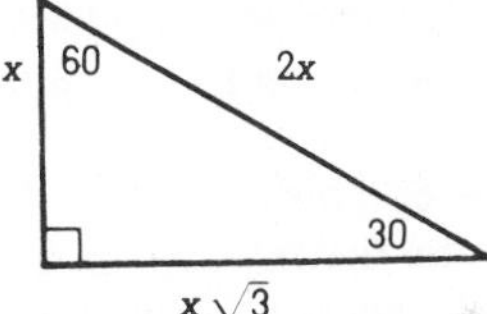

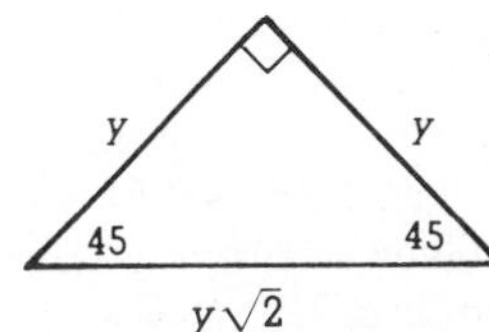

9-5 The trigonometric ratios of sine, cosine, and tangent are developed in terms of right triangles. Stress the fact that the ratios are dependent upon the measure of an angle and not on the length of the sides of the right triangle. A helpful mnemonic device for remembering the equations for sine, cosine, and tangent is SOH–CAH–TOA.

$$\underline{S}\text{ine} = \frac{\text{Opposite}}{\underline{H}\text{ypotenuse}} \qquad \underline{C}\text{osine} = \frac{\underline{A}\text{djacent}}{\underline{H}\text{ypotenuse}}$$

$$\underline{T}\text{angent} = \frac{\underline{O}\text{pposite}}{\underline{A}\text{djacent}}$$

9-6 As an extension of using the Trigonometric Ratios table, you may want to introduce interpolation. In doing this you will need to discuss minute measurement in relation to degree. Another extension for this section is to discuss the use of calculators with trigonometric functions.

9-7 This section uses practical applications as examples of the use of trigonometry. The popular example of surveying is presented. Bring surveying instruments to class and have students do some simple calculating. Further research on other applications would be beneficial.

Chapter 10 Circles and Spheres

Chapter Overview The basic concepts and properties of circles are discussed. The terms of arc and chord are related and used in finding various lengths and angle measures. The concept of circles is extended to the three-dimensional figures named spheres. The attempt to relate circles and spheres, and understand each one in terms of another is helpful throughout the study of geometry.

Lesson Notes

10-1 Parts of a circle are identified and defined. Note that the plural of radius is radii. The definition of a circle and the theorems concerning circles use the terms "in a plane." Stress the need for this restriction since relationships discussed would not otherwise be valid. For example, skew lines would contradict many theorems.

The first part of the proof of Theorem 10-1 involves identifying the point in the interior of the circle as being contained on a chord. Thus, by definition of a chord, this point is on a segment that intersects the circle in two points. Therefore, the line that contains that segment intersects the circle in two points. The second part of the proof involves proving that *only* two points are intersected. To prove this, use Postulate 1-1, which states that given the interior point and one point of intersection, only one line can be drawn containing both points. Therefore, the second point of intersection must be the *only* other point on the circle that lies on the given line.

10-2 In the discussion of measure of an arc, degree measure is the only measure defined. Perhaps it should be mentioned that there also is a measure of arc length. We do have arcs with degree measures greater than 180, but we do not refer to an angle with degree measure greater than 180. In naming arcs, stress the need for a *major arc* to be named by three letters whereas *minor arcs* are usually named by only two letters.

10-3 The theorems for congruent triangles, segment bisectors, perpendiculars, the Pythagorean Theorem, and distance from a point should be reviewed. Remind the students that distance means the perpendicular distance. In using the theorems concerning the arc of a chord, we mean the minor arc. In discussing congruent chords and intercepting congruent arcs stress the need for congruent circles.

The proofs in exercises 15–29 should be discussed since they round out the relationships between congruent arcs and chords.

10-4 Stress the need for an inscribed angle to have its vertex <u>on</u> the circle. This helps avoid confusion between inscribed angles and central angles. A review of isosceles triangles and the Exterior Angle Theorem will help.

10-5 Make sure the distinction between a tangent line and the trigonometric tangent function is clear. It may be interesting to do some research on circular functions as related to trigonometry.

10-6 The theorems in this section can be easily confused. A listing of the hypotheses and conclusions in table form may help the students to more clearly see the relationships. Stress the need to clearly identify the intercepted arcs.

10-7 A review of the conditions required for similar triangles would help before starting this section. In order to be better prepared to use Theorem 10-17, the following review of proportions is recommended.

1. $\frac{h}{6} = \frac{2}{12}$ (1) **2.** $\frac{u}{12} = \frac{3}{36}$ (1) **3.** $\frac{x}{6} = \frac{15}{18}$ (5)
4. $\frac{4}{11} = \frac{12}{x}$ (33) **5.** $\frac{b}{9} = \frac{28}{36}$ (7) **6.** $\frac{5}{7} = \frac{t}{21}$ (15)

In Example 2, the solution $^-11.95$ is rejected. Emphasize the need to reject negative numbers since distance is nonnegative.

10-8 Point out the many terms and ideas related to circles that can be used when studying spheres. The more interrelationships that can be found, the more clearly spheres will be understood. For example, hemispheres relate to semicircles, and the chords of a sphere relate to chords of a circle.

Chapter 11 Area and Volume

Chapter Overview Areas of polygons are defined. Formulas for the areas of triangles, parallelograms, and trapezoids are proven by using the formula for the area of a rectangle. Volume of solids is defined. This topic is extended to include Cavalieri's Principle.

Lesson Notes

11-1 The postulates listed in this section establish the basis for the work on area in this chapter. The formulas for area of a rectangle and a square are given. The exercises involve simple computational skills. A review of multiplication skills could be helpful.

11-2 Remind the students that the area of a figure actually means *the measure* of the area. Theorems 11-3 and 11-4 are proven in exercises 27 and 28. All the students would benefit from a discussion of these proofs.

11-3 An apothem is the perpendicular segment from the center of the regular polygon to the midpoint of any side of the polygon. To find the measure of the apothem, the tangent can be used. The angle formed at the vertex is bisected, and the tangent ratio can be found by using the table on page 549. This ratio is set equal to $a \div \frac{s}{2}$, where a is the apothem and s is the measure of the side.

11-4 When discussing the *measure* of the circumference, or the *measure* of the perimeter, the measures are referred to as the circumference and perimeter. Also when it is obvious that the radius refers to a number we will use "radius" rather than "radius measuring." Stress the fact that π is an irrational number. The students could research various aspects of π including its origin and the number of places to which π has been computed.

11-5 In finding surface area we refer to "the measure of the height" as "height". Physical models will be extremely helpful so that the students can visualize surface area. The problems in this section involve a good deal of computation. You may wish to permit students to use calculators for these and other similar exercises.

11-6 The formulas in this section should be discussed carefully. Drawing a figure of the individual faces will help the students to understand the formulas. As in the previous section, the computation tends to become involved. Emphasize the need to do the work accurately and to use the correct formula.

11-7 Volume is defined, and as in previous sections when discussing the *measure* of volume, use the term "volume." In the Volume Postulate a discussion of the solid region as space may help to more clearly explain volume. Stress the need to find the area of the base of a solid (other than a sphere) in order to find the volume of a figure.

11-8 Cavalieri's Principle involves cross sectional area in finding figures with the same volume. This principle is useful when finding volumes of figures that are not regular solids. Exercises 17–20 are applications of this principle.

Chapter 12 Coordinates

Chapter Overview This chapter discusses distance, midpoint, lines, circles, and solids using coordinates. Coordinate proofs are introduced. It is important to note that coordinates can be useful in studying the relationship between parallel and perpendicular lines.

Lesson Notes

12-1 Review graphing of a point, stressing the order of x and y in the ordered pair. Students should be able to identify linear equations. If students have a question as to whether an equation is linear, they should rewrite the equation in standard form, $Ax + By = C$.

The following is an example similar to exercises 13–18. The coordinates of three vertices of a rectangle are (4, 2), (4, $^-4$), and ($^-1$, 2). Graph them. Then, find the fourth vertex. Draw a segment parallel to $\overline{BC}$ through A *and* another parallel to $\overline{AB}$ through C. The point of intersection, D, is the fourth vertex. The coordinates for D are ($^-1$, $^-4$).

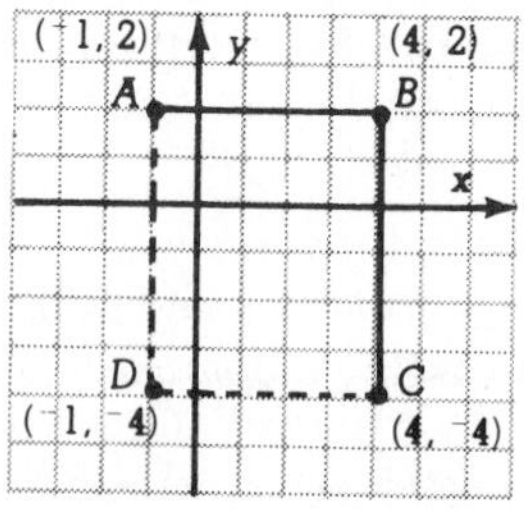

12-2 Review the Distance Postulate in Chapter 2 before beginning this section. Since the Pythagorean Theorem is the basis for the distance formula, a review of the Pythagorean Theorem may be necessary. Exercises 31–35 are applications of the Distance and Midpoint Postulates. It would be beneficial for all students to see the work involved in solving these exercises.

12-3 Students should be reminded to be careful when using the slope formula. Corresponding x and y coordinates must be placed carefully in the formula. Vertical and horizontal slopes should be discussed so that students understand how they differ. In stating Theorems 12-3 and 12-4, note that both theorems involve two lines. In some texts two nonvertical lines are perpendicular if and only if their slopes are negative reciprocals. In this text, the product of the slopes of two nonvertical lines is $^-1$ if and only if they are perpendicular.

12-4 Practice should be given in deciding which approach to use to find a linear equation. The resulting equation would be most useful if it is written in slope-intercept form. This form makes graphing an equation less difficult.

12-5 Emphasize that solving a system of equations graphically usually yields only an approximate solution. Algebraic solutions will yield more exact solutions. It is important to note that some systems will not have a unique solution as in the case of coincident lines. Also some systems have no solution as in the case of parallel lines.

12-6 An application of the distance formula develops an equation for the graph of a circle. An extension of this section could be to have the student show that the general equation of a circle is $Ax^2 + Bx + Cy^2 + Dy + E = 0$. Then give them an equation of a circle in a form such as $x^2 - 6x + y^2 - 8y - 11 = 0$. Convert to the general equation, $(x - 3)^2 + (y - 4^2) = 36$, by completing the square and factoring. Equations of other figures such as an ellipse could also be shown.

12-7 Stress the importance of minimizing the number of variables introduced. Students should practice <u>how</u> to choose the coordinates of the vertices. Coordinate proofs can be very difficult if the coordinates of the vertices are poorly chosen.

12-8 Models should be used to help demonstrate graphing of an ordered triple. Erector sets would be useful since the figures constructed would allow students to see within the three-dimensional figure. Relate the two-dimensional coordinate system to the three-dimensional coordinate system. Stress the equation of a sphere being an extension of the equation of a circle.

Chapter 13 Loci and Constructions

Chapter Overview The main constructions of geometry are demonstrated in this chapter. Each student will need a straightedge and a compass. Loci are described and used to solve problems.

Lesson Notes

13-1 Stress the need for only a straightedge (a plastic identification card, a credit card, and so on) and compass in doing constructions. No measurement is involved since measurement is only as exact as the instrument with which a length is measured. Justification for each construction is important. Make sure the students understand the justifications. In demonstrating these constructions, a chalkboard compass will be needed. Emphasize the need for accuracy with the compass. Some of the constructions in this section involve angles, so a review of angle and angle bisectors may be helpful.

13-2 This section demonstrates constructions for perpendicular and parallel lines. A review of the theorems concerning these topics may be needed since the justifications depend on those theorems. Nonformal paragraph proofs are adequate for this justification. Sometimes the justifications of one construction will help to understand how to justify another construction. For *Construction* 4 the arcs intersecting the given line could be one single arc. Written exercise 6 requests another method for doing *Construction* 7. Draw a line and a point not on the line.

Then, construct a perpendicular line from the point to the given line. Label this line ***m***. Any line perpendicular to ***m*** in the plane will be parallel to ℓ by Theorem 6-8. Therefore, construct a line perpendicular to ***m*** at *P*. This line is parallel to ℓ through *P*.

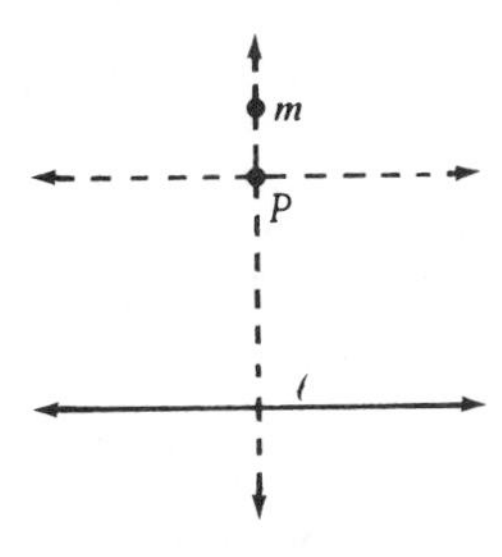

13-3 A review of concepts related to circles is important before beginning the constructions in this section. Accuracy is necessary. Practicing with the use of the compass would help. Emphasize how to find the center of a circle given only an arc. *Construction* 10 can be used for this construction. Review inscribed and circumscribed polygons.

13-4 A review of proportions may be necessary before doing this section. The geometric mean and the theorem of similar triangles should be clearly understood. Review Theorem 9-2, which states that the altitude of a right triangle from the right angle is the geometric mean between the measure of the two segments of the hypotenuse. As in all constructions, practice is recommended to develop accuracy.

13-5 Emphasize that the word "locus" means a location or path. Locus implies an *if and only if* situation. Note that the distance between points and lines is the perpendicular distance. This is an important concept to review. A gradual transition from two dimensions to three may help avoid the difficulty some students have in working with the space problems. Transformations may be used in explaining locus but such a discussion would be more clear after Chapter 14.

13-6 Drawing diagrams is essential to a better understanding of this section. When problems have more than one condition, it will be more clear if you break down the components into their separate parts. Additional help may be necessary in order for all the students to feel at ease with these problems.

Chapter 14 Transformations

Chapter Overview Transformations, such as mappings, dilations, translations, and rotations, give us another approach to geometric relationships. This method of establishing relationships may be of interest to the students. Before starting this chapter you may want to acquire some copies of the art of M. C. Escher.

Lesson Notes

14-1 Visuals are necessary when working with transformations. Encourage the use of diagrams. Stress the need for proper ordering of letters. Similarity and congruence are two important elements of transformations. Students should be able to identify an isometry.

14-2 One way of illustrating a reflection is by using a mirror. Mirrors provide a visual interpretation. Stress the fact that symmetry must exist in a reflection. Students should be encouraged to look for lines of symmetry in nature and architecture. Bring in some photos from magazines and have the students decide whether the pictures are symmetrical and indicate any lines of symmetry.

14-3 A translation is a movement in one direction. Stress the preservation of collinearity, angle measure, distance, and betweenness of points. Translations are examples of isometries.

14-4 Even though a rotation is the composite of two reflections, it can be thought of as swinging around a point (pivot) on a fixed arm. This can be illustrated by tacking a piece of string to a piece of cardboard and rotating a triangle. Students should be able to name the angle of rotation.

14-5 Composites of three or more reflections may be rather difficult for students to understand. Show several examples to help clarify the concept before introducing glide reflections. The exercises give practice in identifying composite reflections.

14-6 A dilation is not an isometry. Rather, it is a similarity transformation. An illustration of a dilation is the shadow cast on the ground by an airplane with the sun as the focal point of the dilation. This would be an enlargement. Students with a background in photography may be acquainted with another type of dilation called a reduction. Some experimenting with shadows and cameras may be interesting for an outdoor activity.

Appendix: BASIC

Appendix Overview This appendix gives the students an opportunity to write and run programs. Students will be able to write simple programs. The main topics include assignment of variables, IF-THEN statements, FOR-NEXT loops, and BASIC functions. Computer systems vary in several ways such as sign-on and sign-off procedures, stop procedures, spacing used in printouts, and so on. This should be kept in mind when using this section with your particular situation.

Lesson Notes

The Language of BASIC Simple statements and operational symbols used in BASIC are introduced. It should be noted that this language is similar to algebra with respect to the order of operations. Some calculators use the same order as well. Try the first example using a calculator and compare. Computers only do the operations they are told to do. Stress the need to be accurate in writing programs. Some of the examples of programs are not intended for computer use but only to illustrate the statements. In writing a program the numbers 10, 20, and so on are used as line numbers to allow for easy insertion of additional statements.

Two other programming languages are FORTRAN and PASCAL. Students could research these as well as BASIC to see why a certain language may be more appropriate for a specific use.

Assignment of Variables Emphasize that variables written to the right of an equals sign must be previously defined. Also, the variables to the left of an equals sign cannot include operations, such as A*A. The LET statement may give students difficulty because in algebra, statements such as $x = x + 1$ are invalid. However, in BASIC LET X = X + 1 is a valid statement. Students should be shown that there may be more than one valid program to accomplish a given task.

IF-THEN Statements An IF-THEN statement instructs the computer what to do next based on the results of a comparison. When the programmer does not know beforehand where a loop will end, an IF-THEN statement is used. Make clear to the students when the condition tested is false, the computer executes the next line. If the condition is true, it branches to the THEN line. The students should also discuss the unconditional branching statement GO TO. It is important to distinguish between conditional and unconditional branching in a computer program. The counting process can be accomplished by using a counter and setting it equal to either 0 or 1 at the onset of the program.

FOR-NEXT Loops The FOR-NEXT loop is a very important and useful set of statements in programming especially in keeping count for the programmer. Emphasize that loops may be nested but may not cross. If the word STEP is omitted, the computer will automatically increment by one. Point out that the NEXT statement must come after the FOR statement. Have students pretend to be the computer and write the step-by-step process called for in the program. The FOR-NEXT loop is very similar to the DO loop and CONTINUE statements in FORTRAN.

BASIC Functions The BASIC functions of ABS(X), SQR(X), and INT(X) are explained. Before discussing ABS(X) a review of absolute value would be helpful. Emphasize the format of the statements involving these three functions. These are only a few of the functions used in BASIC. Some research can be done to find other functions and to give practical examples of their use.

Independent Chapter Tests

Independent Test for Chapter 1

Draw and label a diagram to show each of the following.

1. $\overleftrightarrow{EF}$ and $\overleftrightarrow{GH}$ intersect at R.
2. $\overleftrightarrow{CD}$ contains S and T.
3. $\boldsymbol{m}$ and $\boldsymbol{n}$ intersect at T.
4. Plane $\mathscr{L}$ contains $\overleftrightarrow{TS}$ and C.

Determine whether or *not* each of the following statements is a good definition. If *not*, tell why. Assume the terms in each statement are previously defined.

5. The points lie on the same line.
6. Points are coplanar if and only if they lie in the same plane.

Rewrite each of the following conditional statements in if-then form. Then write the converse of each.

7. Skew lines do not intersect.
8. A rhombus is a quadrilateral.

Rewrite each of the following statements as two if-then statements, one of which is the converse of the other.

9. Points lie in the same plane if and only if they are coplanar.
10. Two lines in a plane are parallel if and only if they do *not* intersect.

Answer each of the following.

11. How many planes are determined by three noncollinear points?
12. Suppose two different planes contain $\overline{AB}$. Describe the intersection of the planes.

Draw and label a diagram to illustrate each of the following given statements.

13. Given: $\overleftrightarrow{AB}$ and $\mathscr{L}$ intersect at C.
14. Given: $\mathscr{A}$ and $\mathscr{L}$ intersect at $\boldsymbol{n}$.

For each of the following, fill in the blank with a reason. Use a definition, a postulate, or a proven theorem.

15. A and B are two points. — Given
    $\boldsymbol{m}$ is the only line through A and B. — ________________
16. $\boldsymbol{m}$ is a line and G is a point *not* on $\boldsymbol{m}$. — Given
    ℓ is the only plane that contains $\boldsymbol{m}$ and G. — ________________

Write the inverse and contrapositive for each of the following statements.

17. If a figure is a square, then it is a polygon.
18. If a triangle is equilateral, then it is equiangular.

Independent Test for Chapter 2

Change each fraction or mixed numeral to decimal form.

1. $\frac{4}{5}$ **2.** $-\frac{17}{20}$ **3.** $2\frac{3}{10}$ **4.** $-1\frac{1}{8}$

Change each repeating decimal to a fraction in simplest form.

5. $0.\overline{8}$ **6.** $^-1.\overline{3}$ **7.** $0.\overline{45}$ **8.** $^-8.0\overline{6}$

Use the number line below to find each measure.

9. DE **10.** AC **11.** BF **12.** AE

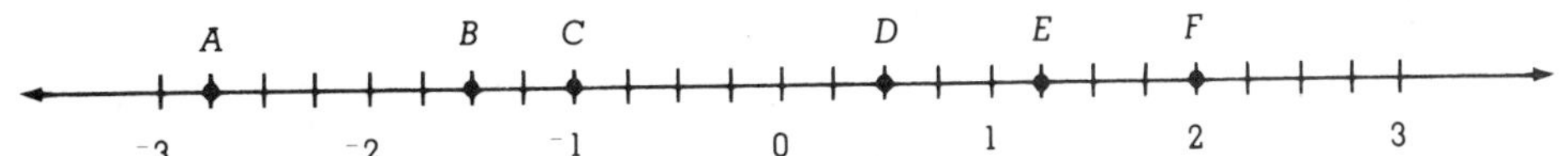

Use the number line above to solve each of the following.

13. Show that C is between B and D.

14. Show the D is the midpoint of $\overline{CF}$.

15. Show that C is *not* the midpoint of $\overline{AD}$.

16. Show that F is *not* between C and E.

State the missing reasons for each of the following proofs.

17. Given: $2x + 8 = {}^-6$
Prove: $x = {}^-7$
Proof:

STATEMENTS	REASONS
1. $2x + 8 = {}^-6$	1. ________
2. $2x + 8 - 8 = {}^-6 - 8$	2. ________
3. $2x = {}^-14$	3. ________
4. $\frac{2x}{2} = \frac{^-14}{2}$	4. ________
5. $x = {}^-7$	5. ________

18. Given: $\overline{PQ} \cong \overline{RS}$; $\overline{RS} \cong \overline{TV}$
Prove: $\overline{PQ} \cong \overline{TV}$
Proof:

P Q R S T V

STATEMENTS	REASONS
1. $\overline{PQ} \cong \overline{RS}$; $\overline{RS} \cong \overline{TV}$	1. ________
2. $PQ = RS$; $RS = TV$	2. ________
3. $PQ = TV$	3. ________
4. $\overline{PQ} \cong \overline{TV}$	4. ________

19. Prove that if $8 - 2y > {}^-12$, then $y < 10$.

Independent Test for Chapter 3

Use the figure to answer each of the following.

1. $\angle 2$ and $\angle DBC$ name the same angle. Write *yes* or *no*.
2. Name the vertex of $\angle 3$.
3. Write another name for $\angle 1$.
4. Name the sides of $\angle 4$.
5. Name a point interior to $\angle FBD$.

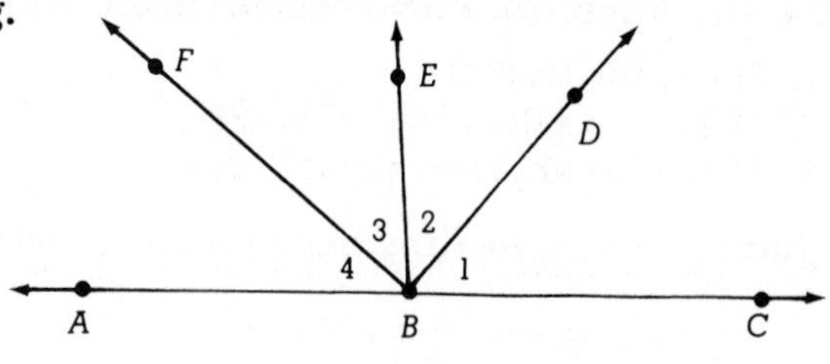

Exercises 1–5

In the figure, $m\angle GHK = 96$, $m\angle IHJ = 42$, and $\angle JHK \cong \angle IHJ$.

6. Find $m\angle JHK$.
7. Find $m\angle KHI$.
8. Find $m\angle JHG$.

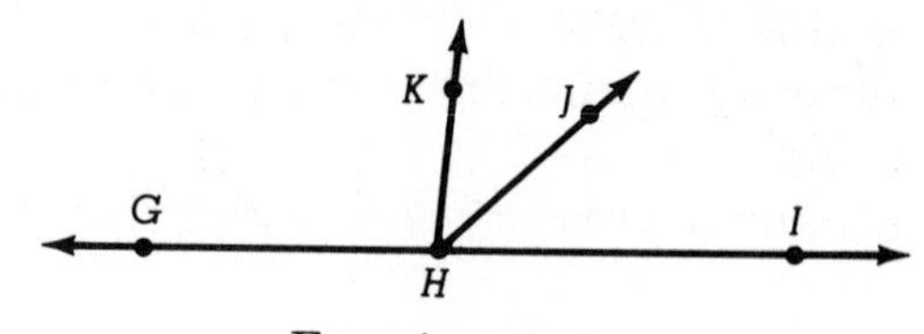

Exercises 6–8

9. Complete the reasons for the following proof.
   Given: $\angle A$ is the complement of $\angle B$.
   $\angle C$ is the complement of $\angle B$.
   Prove: $\angle A \cong \angle C$
   Proof:

STATEMENTS	REASONS
1. $\angle A$ is the complement of $\angle B$. $\angle C$ is the complement of $\angle B$.	1. ________
2. $m\angle A + m\angle B = 90$ $m\angle C + m\angle B = 90$	2. ________
3. $m\angle A + m\angle B = m\angle C + m\angle B$	3. ________
4. $m\angle A \cong \angle C$	4. ________
5. $\angle A \cong \angle C$	5. ________

10. Two angles form a linear pair. The degree measure of one of the angles is three times the degree measure of the other angle. Find the degree measures of both angles.
11. Prove that if two lines intersect to form supplementary vertical angles, then the lines are perpendicular.

In the figure, $\overline{AD} \perp \overline{DB}$, $\overline{AD} \perp \overline{DC}$, and $\overline{DC} \perp \overline{DB}$.

12. Name the dihedral angle with edge $\overleftrightarrow{CD}$.
13. Name the edge for $\angle B\text{-}\overleftrightarrow{AD}\text{-}C$.
14. Name a plane angle for $\angle C\text{-}\overleftrightarrow{DB}\text{-}A$.

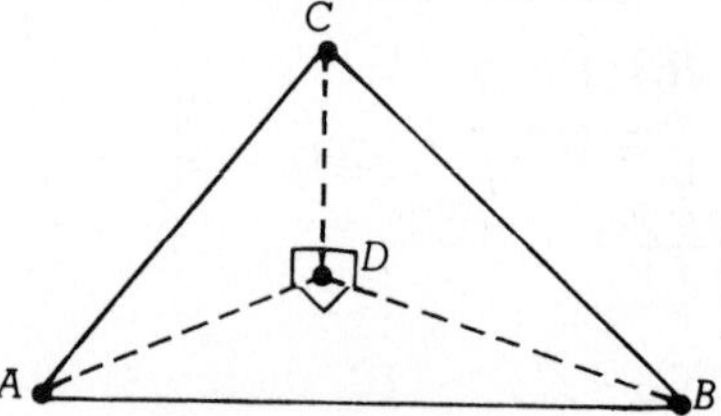

Independent Test for Chapter 4

Use the figure to answer each of the following.

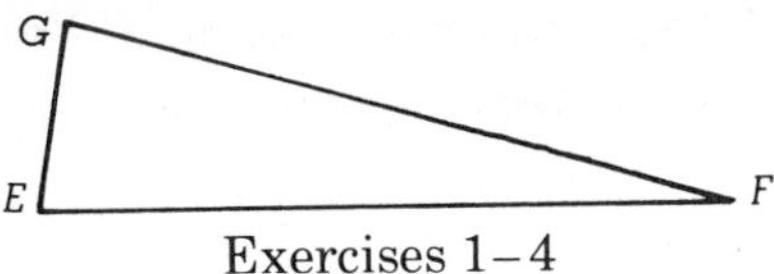

Exercises 1–4

1. Name the triangle.
2. Name the sides of the triangle.
3. Name the angles of the triangle.
4. Suppose $\triangle EFG$ is an isosceles triangle with $\overline{GF} \cong \overline{EF}$. Solve for x and find the measure of each side given that $GF = 2x - 9$, $EG = -\frac{1}{2}x + 14$, and $EF = \frac{1}{2}x + 15$.
5. Given $\triangle ABC$ in which $\angle B$ is a right angle and $m\angle A = 47$, find $m\angle C$.

Suppose $\triangle DFE \cong \triangle GFH$. For each of the following, name the corresponding part.

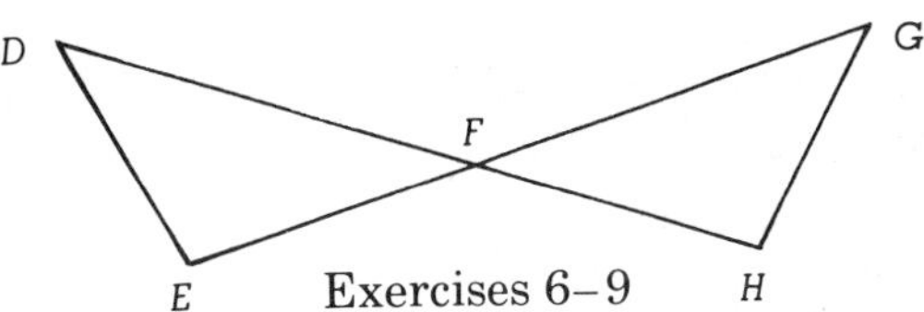

Exercises 6–9

6. $\overline{DF}$
7. $\angle H$
8. $\overline{GH}$
9. $\angle DFE$

Prove each of the following.

10. Given: $\overline{AC} \cong \overline{EC}$;
    C is the midpoint of $\overline{BD}$.
    Prove: $\overline{AB} \cong \overline{ED}$

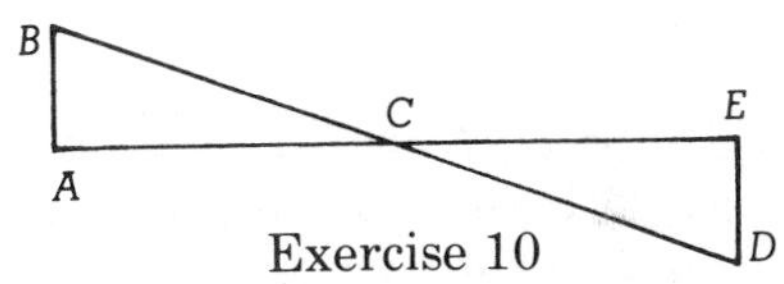

Exercise 10

11. Given: $\angle 1$ is the complement of $\angle 2$;
    $\angle 3$ is the complement of $\angle 2$;
    $\angle 2 \cong \angle 4$
    Prove: $\overline{AB} \cong \overline{CD}$

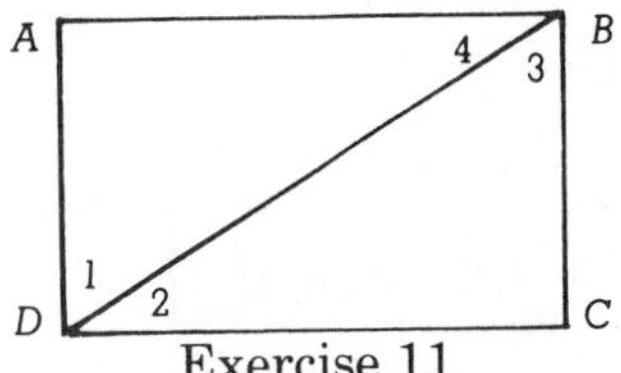

Exercise 11

12. Given: $\overline{DE} \cong \overline{EF}$;
    $\angle DGE \cong \angle FGE$
    Prove: $\overline{EG}$ bisects $\angle DEF$.

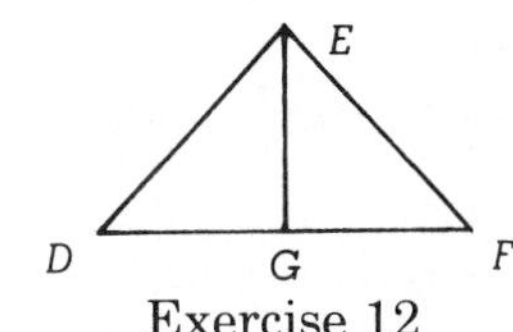

Exercise 12

13. Given: T is the midpoint of $\overline{PS}$;
    $\overline{PQ} \cong \overline{SR}$;
    $\angle 1 \cong \angle 2$
    Prove: $\triangle PQT \cong \triangle SRT$

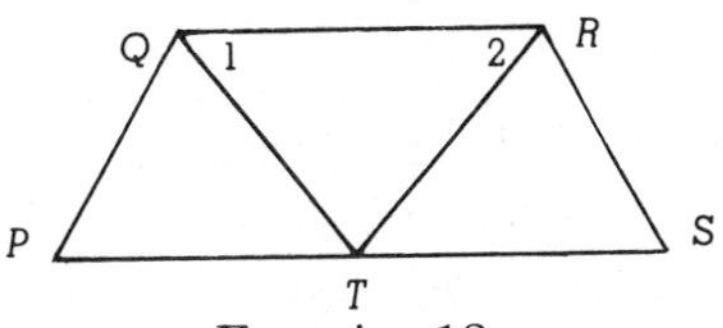

Exercise 13

14. Given: $\overline{XZ} \perp \overline{WY}$; $\overline{XZ}$ bisects $\angle WXY$.
    Prove: $\triangle WXZ \cong \triangle YXZ$

X
W
Y
Z
Exercise 14

Independent Test for Chapter 5

Use the information given in the figure to find the value of each of the following.

1. a
2. b
3. c
4. d
5. f
6. g
7. h
8. j

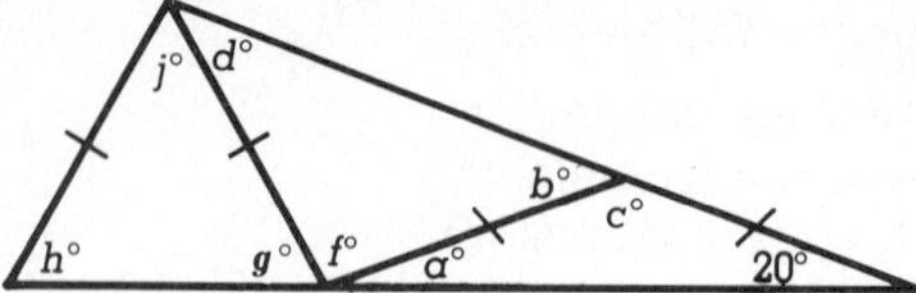

Using the figure, determine whether or *not* the following statements can be assumed.

9. $\overline{BE} + \overline{ED} = BD$
10. $\overline{BD} \cong \overline{AC}$
11. $\angle AEB$ and $\angle CED$ are vertical angles.
12. $\overline{AB} \cong \overline{CD}$
13. $\angle BEC$ and $\angle CED$ form a linear pair.
14. $\overline{AC}$ bisects $\angle BAD$.
15. E is between A and C.

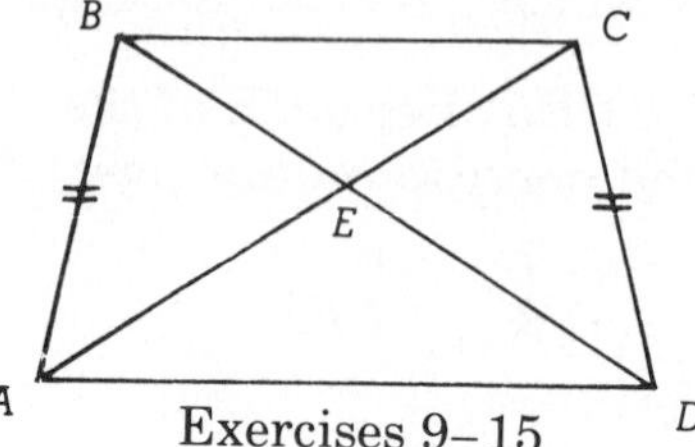

Exercises 9–15

16. Given: $\overline{BC} \cong \overline{DC}$;
    $m\angle ABC < m\angle ADC$
    Prove: $DA < BA$

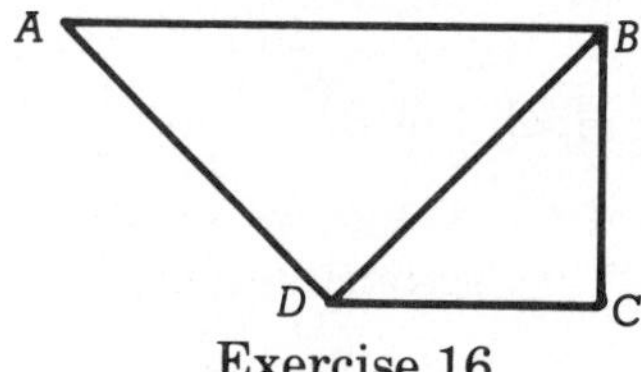

Exercise 16

For each of the following, determine whether or *not* it is possible to draw a triangle with sides of the given measures.

17. 8, 6, 6
18. 17, 4, 12
19. 168, 47, 124

Prove each of the following.

20. Given: $\triangle XWZ \cong \triangle ZYX$
    Prove: $XW < YX + XZ$

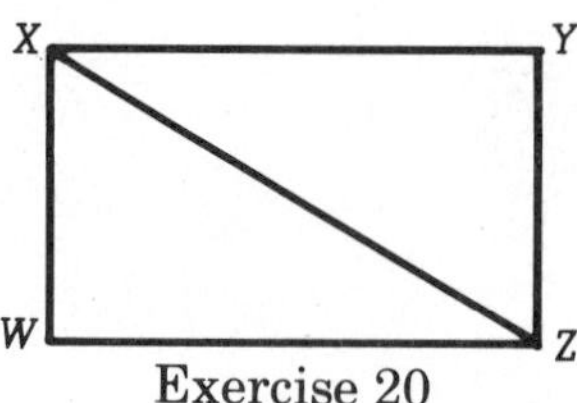

Exercise 20

21. Given: $\overline{AB} \cong \overline{DC}$;
    $m\angle ABC > m\angle DCB$
    Prove: $AC > DB$

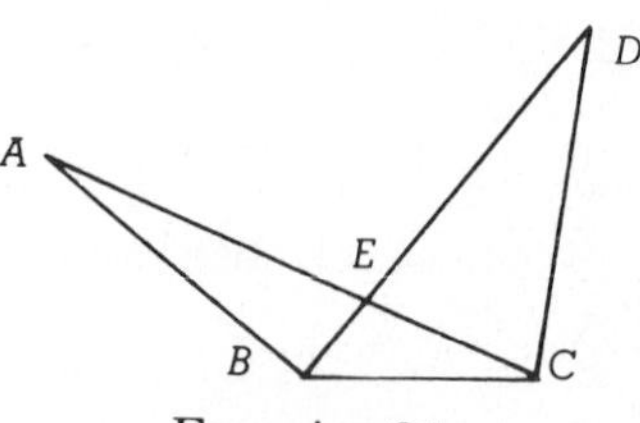

Exercise 21

Independent Test for Chapter 6

Using the diagram at the right, find an example for each of the following.

1. Two noncoplanar lines
2. Two parallel lines
3. Two segments that are not parallel
4. Two coplanar lines that intersect
5. Two parallel lines and a transversal
6. Two skew lines

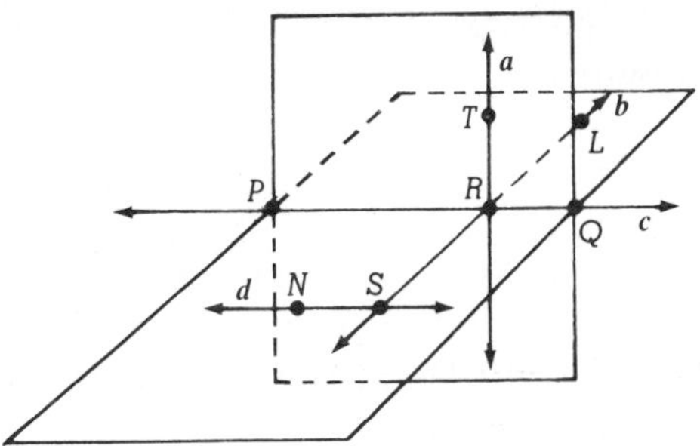

7. Write an indirect proof for the following. In a plane, if two lines are parallel to the same line, they are parallel to each other.

Prove each of the following.

8. Given: $\overline{AB} \cong \overline{CD}$;
 $\overline{BC} \cong \overline{DA}$
 Prove: $\overline{AB} \parallel \overline{CD}$

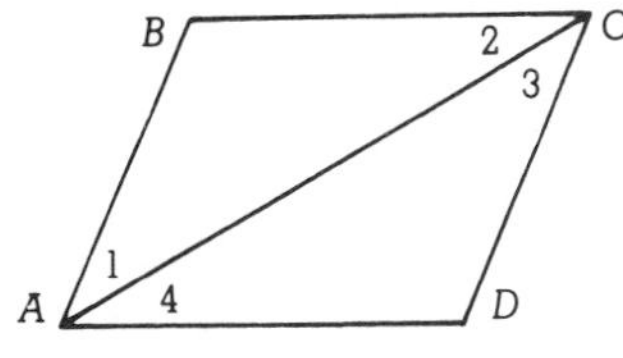

Exercise 8

9. Given: $\angle 4$ and $\angle 7$ are supplementary.
 Prove: $\ell \parallel m$

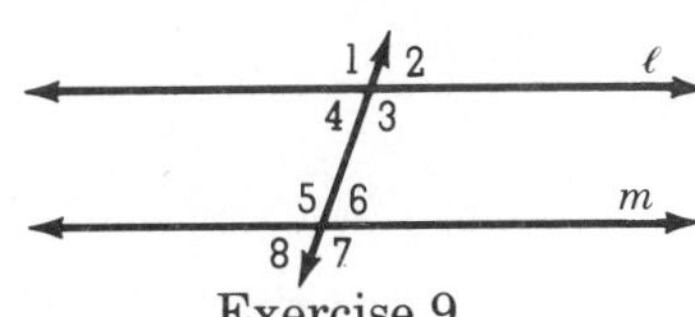

Exercise 9

In the diagram, $\overline{AC} \parallel \overline{DF}$ and $\overline{AB} \parallel \overline{DE}$. Find the degree measure for each of the following.

10. $\angle 2$
11. $\angle 1$
12. $\angle 3$
13. $\angle A$
14. $\angle 4$
15. $\angle D$

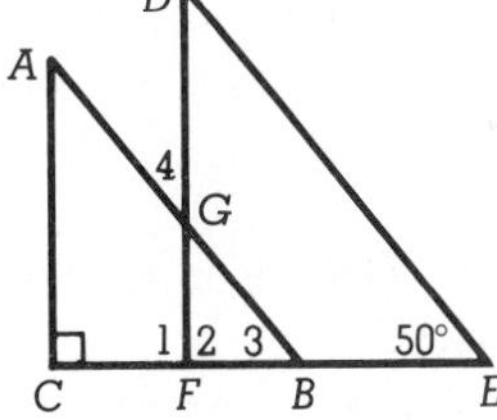

Exercises 10–15

Prove each of the following.

16. Given: $\overline{DE} \parallel \overline{AC}$;
 $\overline{BA} \cong \overline{BC}$
 Prove: $\angle 1 \cong \angle 2$

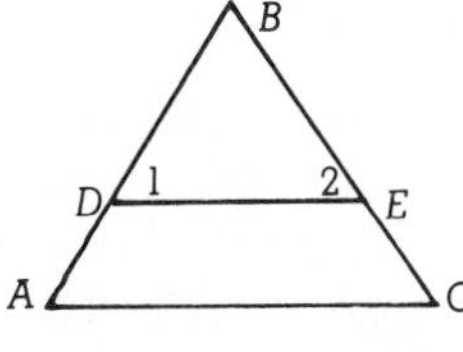

Exercise 16

17. Given: $\angle A$ and $\angle C$ are right angles;
 $AD = BC$
 Prove: $\overline{AD} \parallel \overline{BC}$

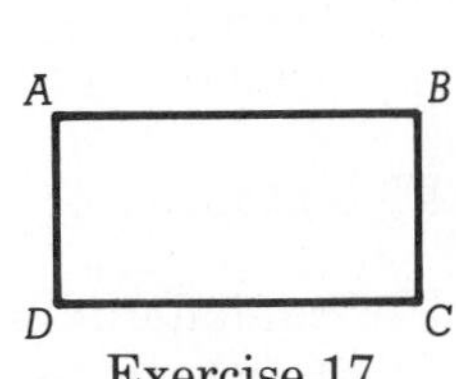

Exercise 17

Independent Test for Chapter 7

Use polygon *PQRSTV* to answer each of the following.

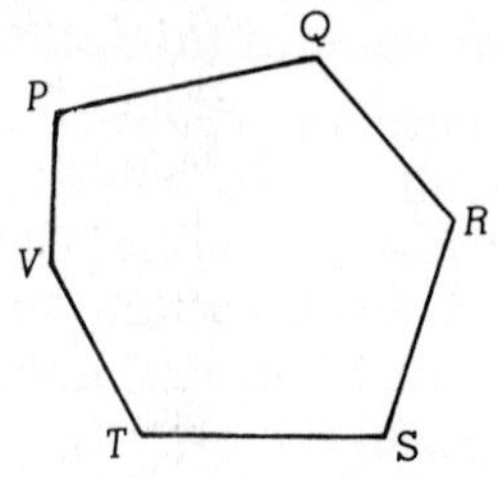

1. Name the vertices of the polygon.
2. Name the angles of the polygon.
3. Name the sides of the polygon.
4. Classify the polygon by the number of sides.
5. Classify the polygon as convex or concave.
6. Classify the polygon as regular or not regular.

Solve each problem.

7. Find the sum of the degree measures of the angles of a heptagon.
8. The sum of the degree measures of the angles of a convex polygon is 1620. Find the number of sides.

Use ▱*ABCD* for each of the following.

9. If $AE = 6$, find EC.
10. If $BD = 11.5$, find ED.
11. If $m\angle BAD = 75$, find $m\angle ADC$.
12. If $AE = 2x + 6$ and $AC = 7x + 9$, find the value of x.

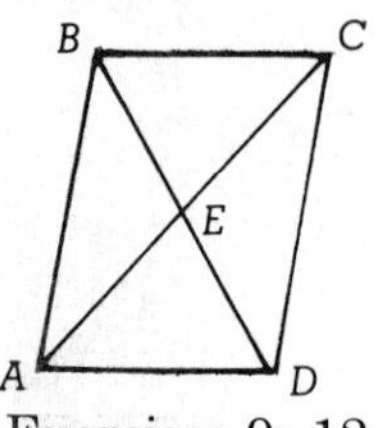

Exercises 9–12

Prove each of the following.

13. Given: $\overline{AB} \cong \overline{BC}$; $\overline{BE}$ and $\overline{CF}$ bisect each other.
    Prove: Quadrilateral *ABEF* is a parallelogram.

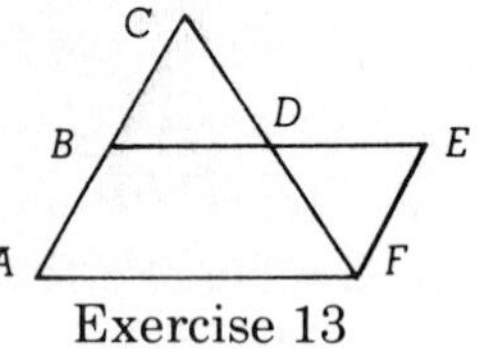

Exercise 13

14. Given: Quadrilateral *PQRS* is a square.
    Prove: $\angle QPR \cong \angle RPS$

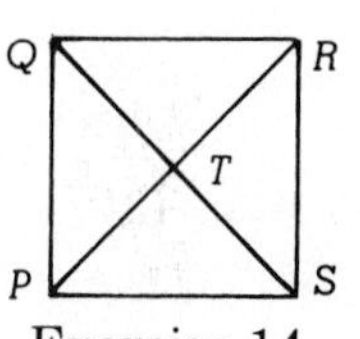

Exercise 14

Solve each problem.

15. The bases of a trapezoid have lengths of 16.5 meters and 8.1 meters. Find the length of the median.
16. The degree measure of one angle of an isosceles trapezoid is 71. Find the degree measures of the other three angles.
17. Find the perimeter of a rectangle whose length is 6.7 centimeters and whose width is 4.3 centimeters.
18. The perimeter of a regular octagon is 32 feet. Find the length of each side of the octagon.
19. Suppose four equilateral triangles intersect at a common vertex. Can a regular polyhedron be formed that includes these triangles? Write *yes* or *no*. If *yes*, name the polyhedron.

Independent Test for Chapter 8

Solve each of the following proportions using cross products.

1. $\frac{7}{8} = \frac{49}{a}$ **2.** $\frac{2.5}{42} = \frac{x}{5.04}$ **3.** $\frac{x+5}{x-3} = \frac{7}{3}$ **4.** $\frac{1-2n}{2} = \frac{n+7}{9}$

Suppose the measures of corresponding sides of the polygons at the right are proportional. For each of the following, find AB.

5. $AD = 5$, $PS = 2$, $PQ = 4$
6. $RS = 6$, $QP = 4$, $DC = 9$
7. $CB = 5.4$, $RQ = 1.5$, $PQ = 2.2$
8. $QP = 1\frac{1}{2}$, $PS = 2\frac{1}{3}$, $AD = 2\frac{1}{3}$

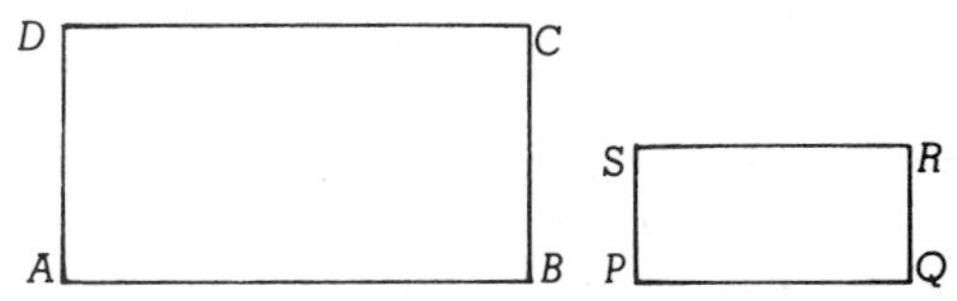

A corresponds to *P* *B* corresponds to *Q*
C corresponds to *R* *D* corresponds to *S*

For each of the following, write *yes* or *no*. Then, explain your answer.

9. All isosceles trapezoids are similar.
10. All regular pentagons are similar.
11. Congruent polygons are similar.
12. All squares are similar.

13. Given: $\overline{BD} \parallel \overline{AE}$
Prove: $\triangle ACE \sim \triangle BCD$

For each of the following, use the figure at the right and the given information to find the value of x.

14. $\overline{AC} \parallel \overline{FD}$
$FA = x + 6$
$DC = x + 9$
$EF = 3$
$ED = 4$

15. $\overline{FB} \parallel \overline{EC}$
$AF = x$
$AB = x - 2$
$BC = 1$
$FE = 5$

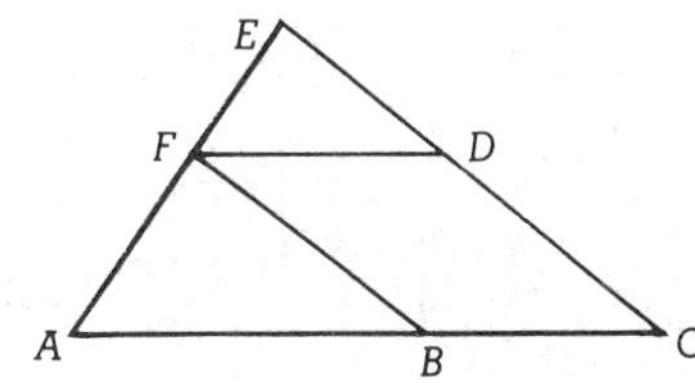

Solve each problem.

16. Suppose $\triangle ABC \sim \triangle DEF$. If $AB = 6$, $DE = 4$, and the perimeter of $\triangle ABC$ is 12, find the perimeter of $\triangle DEF$.

17. The perimeters of two similar triangles are 24.4 and 100. Suppose a median of the first triangle measures 6.1. Find the measure of the corresponding median in the second triangle.

18. Use similar triangles to find the distance between the helicopter and the ground.

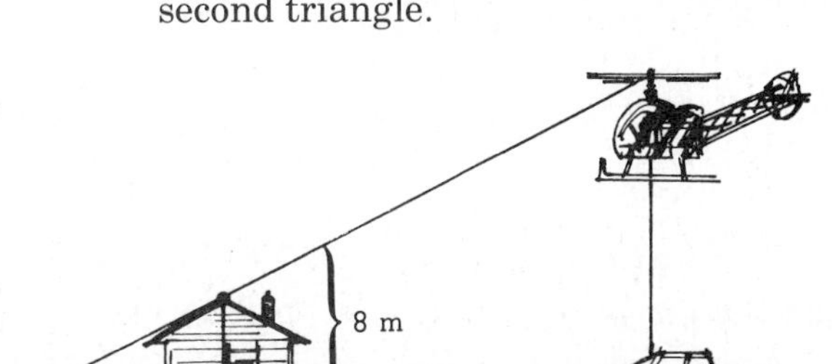

Independent Test for Chapter 9

Write the principal square root of each of the following.

1. 36 **2.** 81 **3.** 1.69 **4.** 14,400 **5.** $\frac{4}{49}$

Simplify each of the following and determine whether the answer is a rational number or an irrational number.

6. $\sqrt{96}$ **7.** $\sqrt{120}$ **8.** $\sqrt{10} \cdot \sqrt{40}$ **9.** $\sqrt{\frac{5}{2}}$

Find the geometric mean for each pair of numbers.

10. 9 and 4 **11.** 8 and 10 **12.** $\frac{1}{9}$ and 4 **13.** $\frac{1}{4}$ and $\frac{3}{8}$

Use the figure at the right to answer each of the following. Approximate each answer to the nearest tenth.

14. Find QS if $PS = 8$ and $SR = 5$.
15. Find PQ if $PR = 4$ and $PS = 2$.
16. Find QR if $PS = 5$ and $SR = 3$.
17. Find QP if $SP = 9.5$ and $SR = 3$.

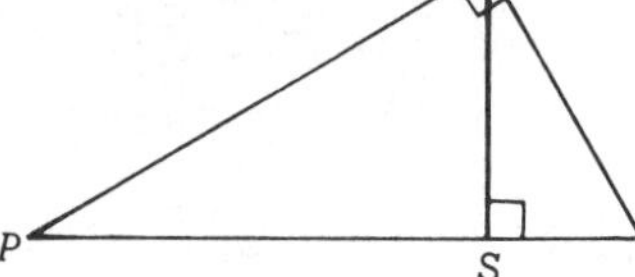

For each of the following, determine whether or *not* it is possible to draw a right triangle with sides of the given measures. Write *yes* or *no*.

18. 25, 24, 8 **19.** 4, $7\frac{1}{2}$, $8\frac{1}{2}$ **20.** 5.1, 8.5, 6.8

Find the value of x to the nearest tenth.

21.

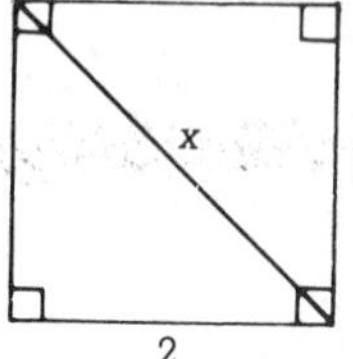

22.

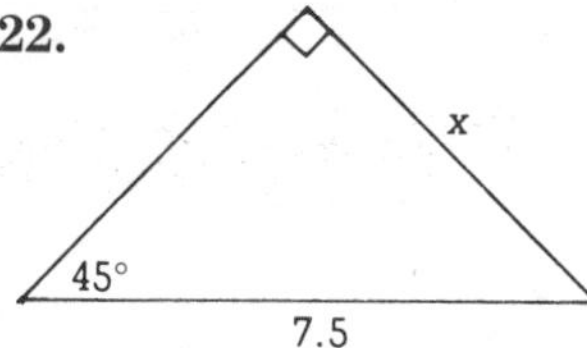

23.

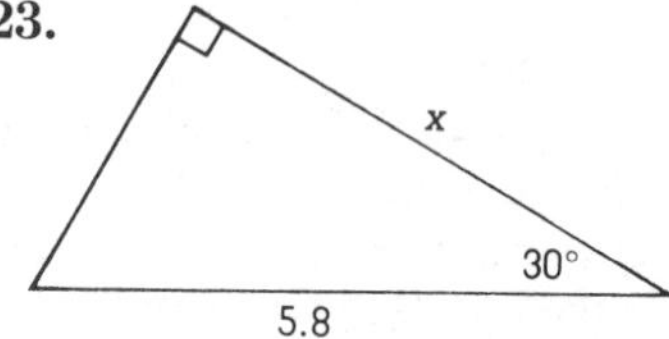

24. For the triangle at the right, express the sine, cosine, and tangent of each acute angle to the nearest hundredth.

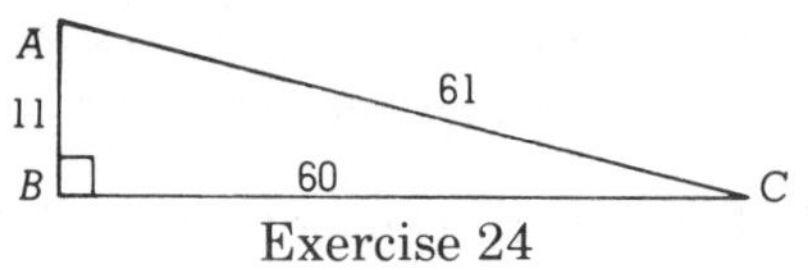

Exercise 24

Use the table at the back of the book to find the value of the following ratios.

25. sin 8° **26.** cos 27° **27.** tan 67° **28.** cos 41°

Use a triangle similar to $\triangle DEF$ to help answer each problem.

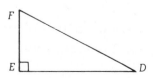

29. Given $m\angle F = 52$ and $ED = 7.5$, find FE to the nearest tenth.

30. Given $FD = 9.6$ and $FE = 2.7$, find $m\angle D$ to the nearest degree.

Independent Test for Chapter 10

For each of the following, write *yes* or *no*.

1. A chord of a circle is always a diameter of the circle.
2. A tangent of a circle intersects the circle in two points.

Answer the following if in ⊙P, $m\angle APB = 25$, $m\angle CPB = 93$, and $\overline{AD}$ and $\overline{BE}$ are diameters.

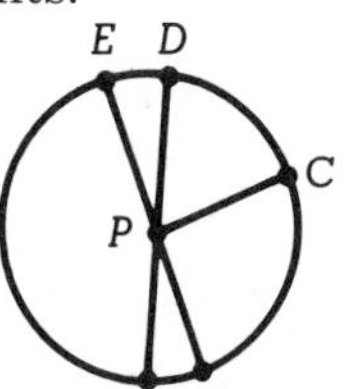

Exercises 3–8

3. Find $m\widehat{AB}$.
4. Find $m\widehat{AC}$.
5. Find $m\widehat{DA}$.
6. Find $m\widehat{DC}$.
7. Find $m\widehat{ECA}$.
8. Find $m\widehat{AE}$.

9. Suppose a chord of a circle is 30 meters long and is 20 meters from the center of the circle. Find the length of the radius.

10. Given: ⊙A;
$\overline{AF} \perp \overline{BC}$;
$\overline{AG} \perp \overline{DE}$;
$\angle FAB \cong \angle GAE$
Prove: $\widehat{CB} \cong \widehat{DE}$

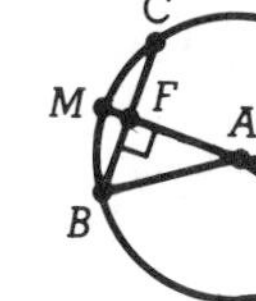

Exercise 10

Find each of the following if in ⊙M, $m\widehat{AB} = 108$, $m\widehat{BC} = 60$, and $m\widehat{CD} = 88$.

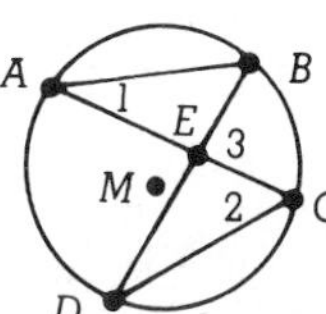

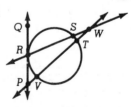

Exercises 11–14

11. $m\angle 1$
12. $m\widehat{AD}$
13. $m\angle 2$
14. $m\angle 3$

For each of the following, find the value of *y*. Assume *C* is the center of each circle.

15.

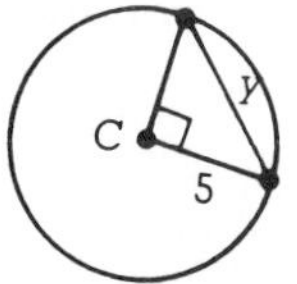

16.

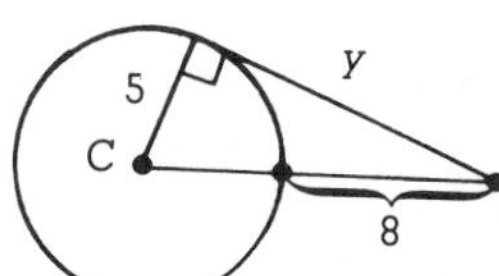

17.

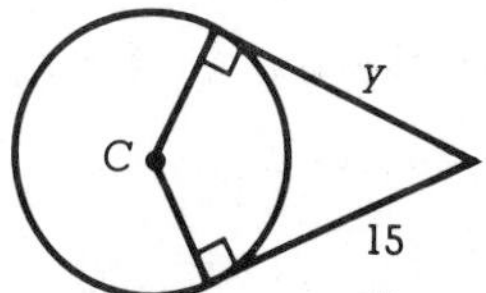

In the figure, $m\widehat{RS} = 136$, $m\widehat{RV} = 83$, $m\widehat{VT} = 96$, and $\overleftrightarrow{QR}$ is a tangent. Find each of the following.

18. $m\angle QRS$
19. $m\angle PRS$
20. $m\widehat{ST}$
21. $m\angle VWR$

For the following, find the value of *z*. Segments that appear tangent are tangent.

22.

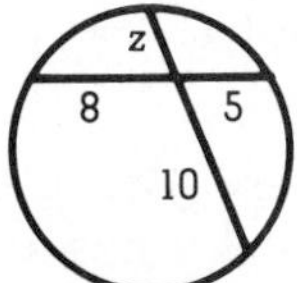

23.

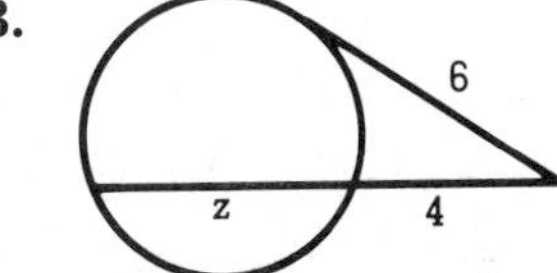

24.

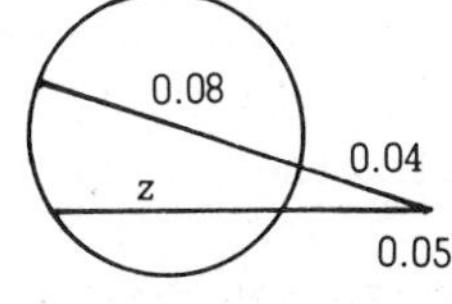

For each of the following, write *yes* or *no*.

25. Two spheres may intersect in a circle.
26. A line intersects a sphere in at most two points.

Independent Test for Chapter 11

Find the area of each rectangle described below.

1. 8 meters by 16 meters
2. 3.6 centimeters by 0.8 centimeters
3. $5\frac{1}{3}$ yards by $7\frac{5}{6}$ yards
4. y kilometers by $(y - 1)$ kilometers

Find the area of each of the following regions.

5. 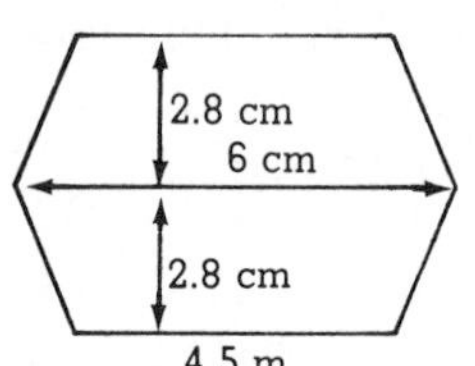

6. 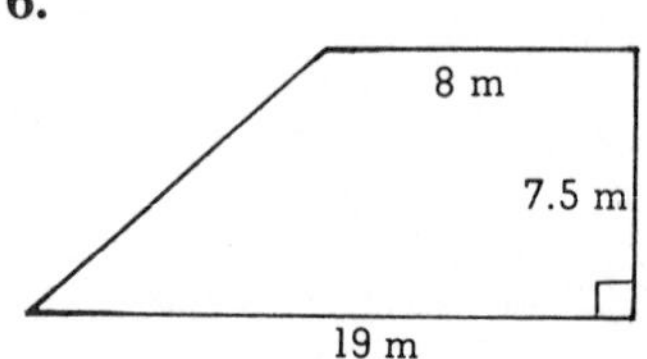

7. 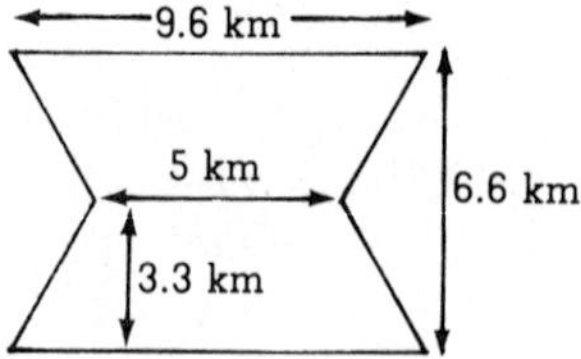

Find the area of each of the following. Round each answer to the nearest tenth.

8. a square inscribed in a circle with radius of 8 meters
9. a regular hexagon with an apothem of 25 centimeters
10. an equilateral triangle with an apothem of 3 feet and each side 5 feet long
11. a regular pentagon with a perimeter of $26\frac{1}{2}$ inches and an apothem of 5 inches

For each of the following, use 3.14 for π and round to the nearest tenth.

12. Find the circumference of a circle with a radius of 40.5 centimeters.
13. Find the area of a circle inscribed in a square whose sides are 9.6 meters.
14. Find the area of a sector of a circle, if the measurement of the central angle is 72° and the radius of the circle is 10 inches.
15. Find the lateral area of a regular pentagonal prism if its base has sides of 12.5 centimeters and its height is 19.2 centimeters.
16. Find the total surface area of a right cylindrical tank if it is 18 meters tall and has a radius of 5.1 meters.
17. Find the lateral area of a pyramid with an equilateral triangular base, if each side is 9 feet long and its slant height is 14 feet.
18. Find the total surface area of a right circular cone with a diameter of 14.4 meters and a slant height of 17 meters.
19. Find the volume of a right prism if its height is 9 centimeters and it has square bases with sides of 2.5 centimeters.
20. Find the volume of a right circular cone with a height of 9 meters and a base radius of 0.8 meters.
21. Find the volume of a sphere with a radius of 6 centimeters.

Independent Test for Chapter 12

Graph each of the following linear equations.

1. $y = x$
2. $x + y = {}^-3$
3. $y = {}^-3x + 1$
4. ${}^-3x + 2y = 4$

Find the distance between each of the following.

5. (4,7), (4,5)
6. (5,7), (⁻3,1)
7. (⁻1,0), (⁻5,8)

Determine the coordinates of each segment that has endpoints with the coordinates given below.

8. (4,0), (6,10)
9. (⁻5,⁻3), (⁻7,3)
10. $\left(\frac{1}{4}, -\frac{1}{2}\right), \left(1, {}^-1\frac{1}{2}\right)$

Determine the slope of the lines passing through the following pairs of points whose coordinates are given below.

11. (6,⁻1), (0,5)
12. (⁻4,⁻3), (⁻4,1)
13. (8,⁻2), (3,2)
14. Determine the value of r so that a line through $(r,6)$ and $({}^-3,r)$ has a slope of $\frac{1}{2}$.
15. Find the slope of any line parallel to a line passing through points with coordinates of (9,5) and (⁻3,6).

Write an equation of the line satisfying the given conditions.

16. $m = 6$, y-intercept is ⁻1
17. $m = -\frac{5}{8}$, through a point at (1,2)
18. parallel to the x-axis, through a point at (0,⁻4)
19. perpendicular to the graph of $y = {}^-2x + 4$, through a point at (6,4)

Solve each system of equations.

20. $y - x = {}^-10$
 $2y + 6 = x$
21. $x - 3y = 5$
 $2x + 3y = {}^-8$
22. $2x - 3y = {}^-5$
 $x - y = 4$

Answer each of the following.

23. Write the equation of the circle whose center is at (⁻4,2) and whose diameter is 2.
24. Determine the center and the measure of the radius for the circle whose equation is $(x + 8)^2 + (y - 7)^2 = 81$.

For each of the following theorems, name the given, the prove statement, and draw a diagram you would use in a formal proof using coordinate geometry.

25. The diagonals of a square are congruent and perpendicular.
26. The median of an isosceles trapezoid is parallel to the bases.

Answer each of the following.

27. Find the distance between (6,0,⁻5) and (10,⁻2,⁻4).
28. Determine the midpoint of the segment whose endpoints are (6,⁻1,4) and (9,⁻2,⁻5).
29. Determine the center and the measure of the radius for the sphere whose equation is $(x + 3)^2 + (y + 4)^2 + z^2 = 64$.
30. Write the equation of the sphere whose center is at (⁻1,5,⁻4) and whose radius is 6.

Independent Test for Chapter 13

On a piece of paper, draw and label two segments like the segments shown below. Then, construct segments for each of the following.

1. $a + b$
2. $3a - b$

On a piece of paper, draw and label two angles like the angles shown below. Then, construct angles with each of the following degree measures.

3. $x - y$
4. $\frac{1}{2}y + x$

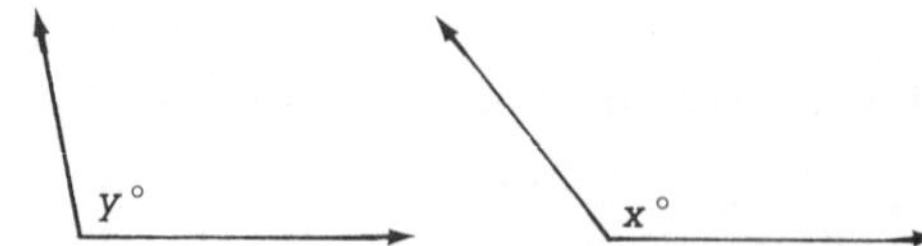

Complete each of the following.

5. Draw a segment. Label it $\overline{MN}$. Construct the perpendicular bisector of $\overline{MN}$.
6. Draw a segment. Label it $\overline{AB}$. Construct an isosceles right triangle, $\triangle ABC$, with a hypotenuse congruent to $\overline{AB}$.
7. Draw a circle. Label the center X. Draw a point exterior to the circle. Label it P. Construct a tangent to $\odot X$ containing P.
8. Construct an equilateral triangle. Circumscribe a circle about the triangle.

On a piece of paper, draw and label three segments like the segments shown below. Then, for each of the following, construct a segment with measure x so that the given proportion holds.

9. $\frac{a}{b} = \frac{x}{c}$
10. $\frac{b}{x} = \frac{c}{b}$
11. Construct the geometric mean of segments b and c.

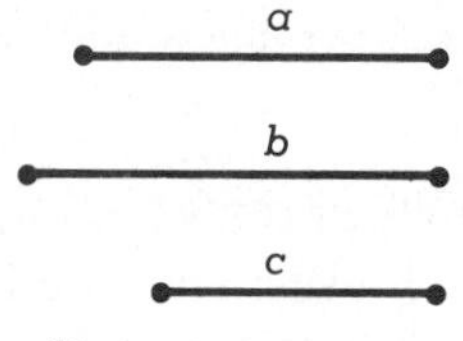

Exercises 9–11

Describe the locus for each of the following.

12. all points in a plane that are 2.5 meters from a given line n
13. all points in space that are 4.5 centimeters from a given point B
14. the intersection of a plane and a line
15. all the points in a plane equidistant from three points

Independent Test for Chapter 14

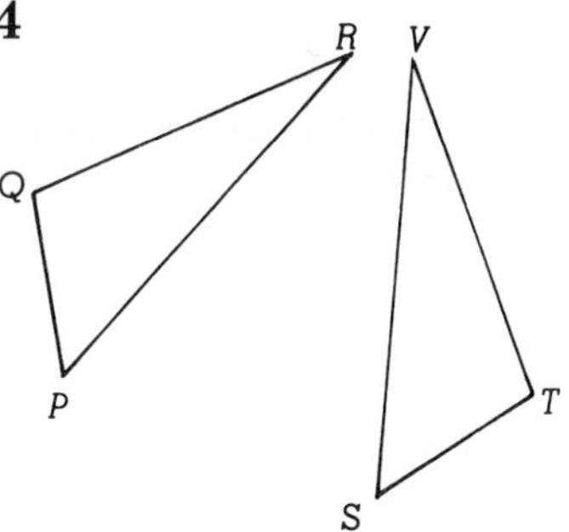

Exercises 1–8

Suppose $\triangle PQR \rightarrow \triangle STV$ and is an isometry. Name the preimage for each of the following.

1. T
2. $\overline{VT}$
3. $\angle SVT$
4. $\triangle TVS$

For each of the following, name a part congruent to the given part.

5. $\angle P$
6. $\overline{QR}$
7. $\overline{PQ}$
8. $\angle RPQ$

Copy each of the following. Then, draw the reflection image of each figure with respect to ℓ.

9.
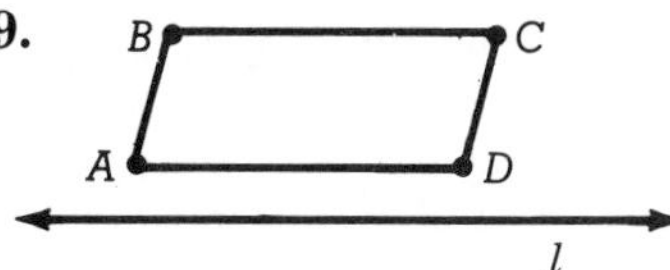

10.
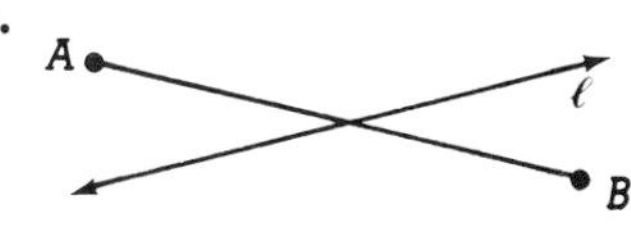

11.
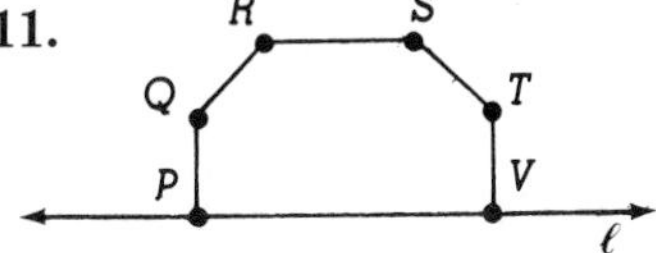

Copy each of the following. Then, draw the translation image of each figure with respect to the parallel lines m and n.

12.
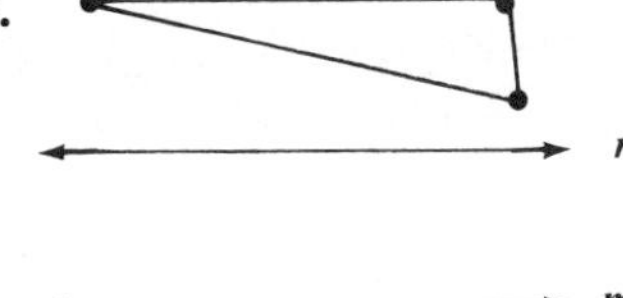

13.
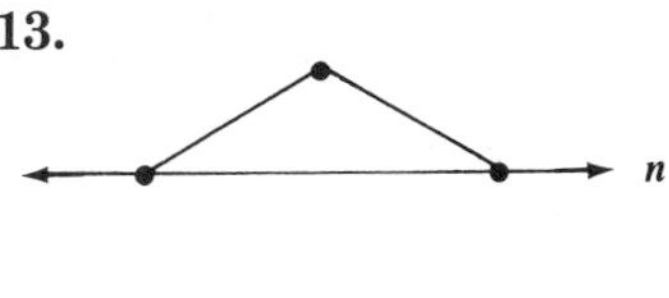

14.
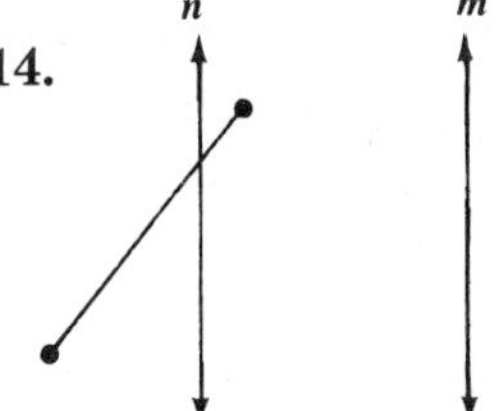

Use the figure to solve each of the following.

15. Find the degree measure of the angle of rotation.
16. Copy the figure at the right. Then, draw the rotation image with respect to ℓ and m.

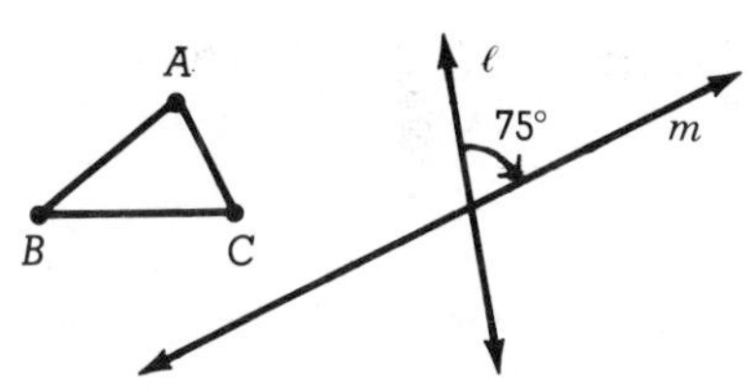

Name the kind of isometry that maps one figure onto the other.

17.
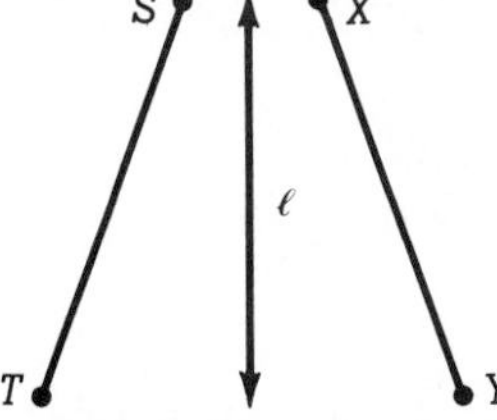

18.
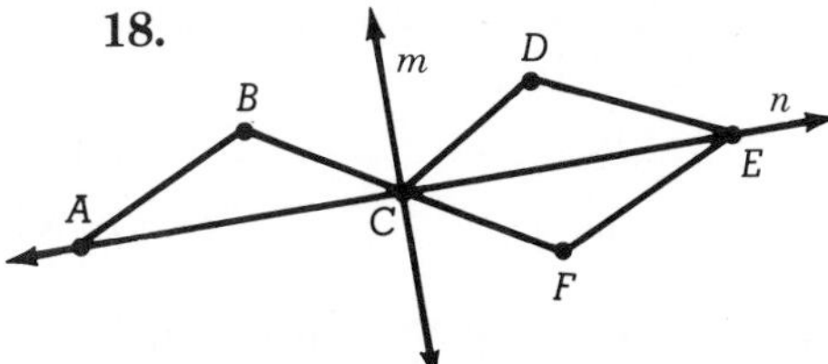

19.
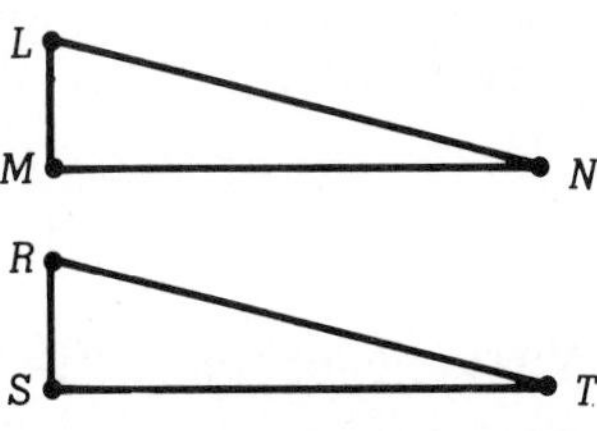

A dilation image with center C and a scale factor k maps P onto R and Q onto S. Find k for each of the following conditions.

20. $CP = 6$, $CR = 18$
21. $RS = 14$, $PQ = 7$
22. $CS = 1$, $CQ = 2$

Independent Test for Appendix

Write an expression in BASIC for each of the following.

1. $3x - 1$

2. $6x^2 - 2x + 1$

3. $\frac{2 + a}{3b}$

4. 2^{r+6}

Evaluate each of the following expressions.

5. 2 * 4 + 6 ↑ 2

6. 3 + 18/(2 * 3)

7. (3 + 4) ↑ 3 − 10

8. ((4 * 2) + 6)/7

Express each of the following using E notation.

9. 1,230,007

10. 0.000358

For each of the following, write a BASIC program using the given values of X, Y, and Z to compute and print the value of A.

11. X = 3, Y = 5, Z = ⁻4
A = 2X + 4Y − X · Z

12. X = ⁻1, Y = 10, Z = 2
A = (X − Y)(Z + X)

Let D = 3, E = 4, and Y = 9. State the line number of the statement that control will go to after the IF-THEN statement is executed.

13.
```
10  IF Y > 6 THEN 40
20  PRINT Y
```

14.
```
10  IF D = E THEN 100
15  PRINT D + E
```

15.
```
30  IF E * Y < D ↑ 2 THEN 95
38  PRINT D ↑ 2
```

16.
```
55  IF Y = E + 5 THEN 85
60  PRINT Y
```

Find the error in each of the following programs. Then, write a correct program and write the output of each corrected program.

17.
```
10  LET X = 2
20  FOR N = 1 TO 5
30      PRINT N + X
40  NEXT X
50  END
```

18.
```
10  FOR A = 1 TO 5 STEP 2
20      FOR B = 0 TO 6 STEP 3
30          PRINT A,B
40      NEXT A
50  NEXT B
60  END
```

Let A = 9, B = ⁻2, and C = ⁻0.36. Write the output for each of the following PRINT statements.

19. 10 PRINT SQR (A)

20. 40 PRINT INT (B)

21. 25 PRINT ABS(INT (C))

22. 30 PRINT SQR(ABS(C))

Write programs in BASIC to solve each of the following.

23. Find the perimeter and area of a rectangle whose length is 12 inches and whose width is 7 inches.

24. Use the Pythagorean Theorem to find the measure of a leg of a right triangle with a hypotenuse of 10 centimeters and a leg of 8 centimeters.

Answers to Independent Tests

Chapter 1 (T26)

1. 2.

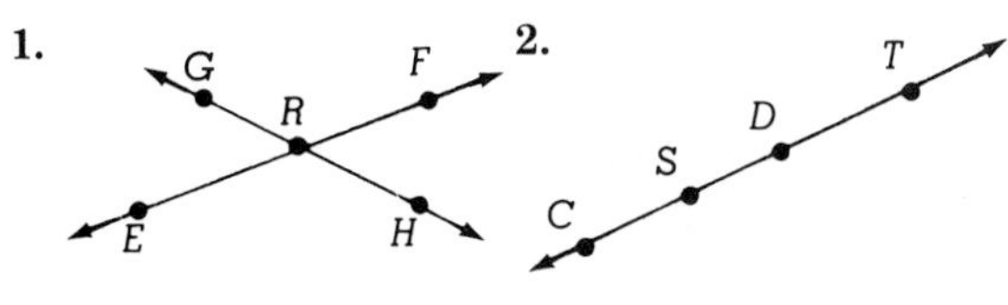

3. 4.

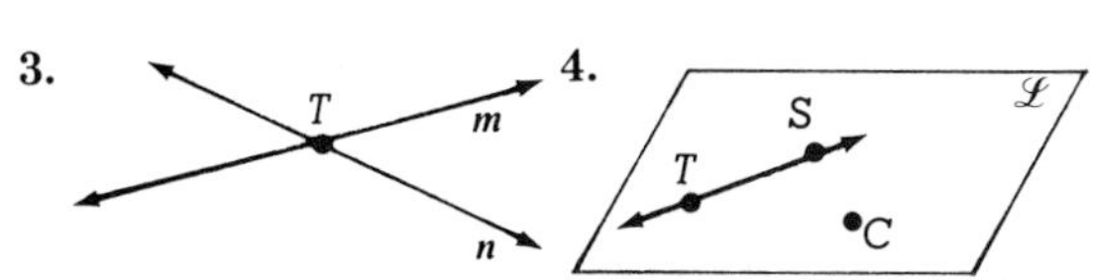

5. This is not a good definition because it does not name the term being defined. **6.** This is a good definition. **7.** If lines are skew, then they do not intersect. If lines do not intersect, then they are skew. **8.** If a figure is a rhombus, then it is a quadrilateral. If a figure is a quadrilateral, then it is a rhombus. **9.** If points lie in the same plane, then they are coplanar. If points are coplanar, then they lie in the same plane. **10.** If two lines in a plane are parallel, then they do not intersect. If two lines in a plane do not intersect, then they are parallel. **11.** one **12.** $\overleftrightarrow{AB}$

13.

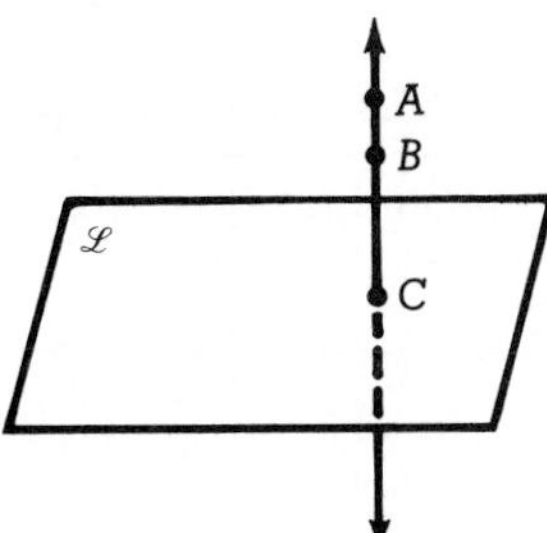

14.

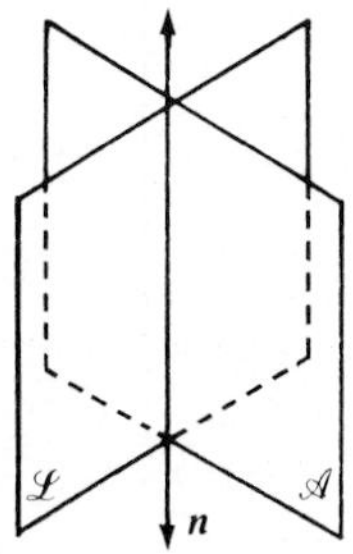

15. Postulate 1-1 **16.** Theorem 1-1 **17.** If a figure is not a square, then it is not a polygon. If a figure is not a polygon, then it is not a square. **18.** If a triangle is not equilateral, then the triangle is not equiangular. If a triangle is not equiangular, then the triangle is not equilateral.

Chapter 2 (T27)

1. 0.8 **2.** $^-0.85$ **3.** 2.3 **4.** $^-1.125$ **5.** $\frac{8}{9}$ **6.** $-\frac{4}{3}$ **7.** $\frac{5}{11}$ **8.** $-\frac{121}{15}$ **9.** $\frac{3}{4}$ **10.** $1\frac{3}{4}$ **11.** $3\frac{1}{2}$ **12.** 4

13.

$$BC + CD \stackrel{?}{=} BD$$
$$|^-1\tfrac{1}{2} - {}^-1| + |^-1 - \tfrac{1}{2}| \stackrel{?}{=} |^-1\tfrac{1}{2} - \tfrac{1}{2}|$$
$$\tfrac{1}{2} + 1\tfrac{1}{2} \stackrel{?}{=} 2$$
$$2 = 2$$

14.

$$CD + DF \stackrel{?}{=} CF$$
$$|^-1 - \tfrac{1}{2}| + |\tfrac{1}{2} - 2| \stackrel{?}{=} |^-1 - 2|$$
$$1\tfrac{1}{2} + 1\tfrac{1}{2} \stackrel{?}{=} 3$$
$$3 = 3$$
$$CD \stackrel{?}{=} DF$$
$$|^-1 - \tfrac{1}{2}| \stackrel{?}{=} |\tfrac{1}{2} - 2|$$
$$1\tfrac{1}{2} = 1\tfrac{1}{2}$$

15.

$$AC \stackrel{?}{=} CD$$
$$|^-2\tfrac{3}{4} - {}^-1| \stackrel{?}{=} |^-1 - \tfrac{1}{2}|$$
$$1\tfrac{3}{4} \neq 1\tfrac{1}{2}$$

16.

$$CF + FE \stackrel{?}{=} CE$$
$$|^-1 - 2| + |2 - 1\tfrac{1}{4}| \stackrel{?}{=} |^-1 - 1\tfrac{1}{4}|$$
$$3 + \tfrac{3}{4} \stackrel{?}{=} 2\tfrac{1}{4}$$
$$3\tfrac{3}{4} \neq 2\tfrac{1}{4}$$

17-1. Given **17-2.** Postulate 2-7 **17-3.** Postulates 2-13 and 2-9 **17-4.** Postulate 2-8 **17-5.** Postulates 2-13 and 2-9 **18-1.** Given **18-2.** Definition of Congruent Segments **18-3.** Postulate 2-9 **18-4.** Definition of Congruent Segments

19.

STATEMENTS	REASONS
1. $8 - 2y > {}^-12$	1. Given
2. ${}^-8 + 8 - 2y > {}^-8 - 12$	2. Postulate 2-16
3. ${}^-2y > {}^-20$	3. Postulates 2-13 and 2-9
4. $\frac{{}^-2y}{{}^-2} < \frac{{}^-20}{{}^-2}$	4. Postulate 2-17
5. $y < 10$	5. Postulates 2-13 and 2-9

Chapter 3 (T28) **1.** no **2.** B **3.** $\angle DBC, \angle CBD$ **4.** $\overrightarrow{BA}, \overrightarrow{BF}$ **5.** E **6.** 42 **7.** 84 **8.** 138 **9-1.** Given **9-2.** Definition of Complementary Angles **9-3.** Postulate 2-9 **9-4.** Postulates 2-7, 2-13, and 2-9 **9-5.** Definition of Congruent Angles

10. $x + 3x = 180$
$4x = 180$
$x = 45$
$3x = 135$

11. Given: $\angle 1$ and $\angle 3$ are vertical angles. $\angle 1$ and $\angle 3$ are supplementary.
Prove: $\ell \perp m$

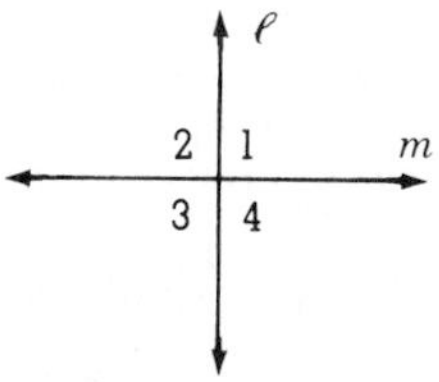

STATEMENTS	REASONS
1. $\angle 1$ and $\angle 3$ are vertical angles. $\angle 1$ and $\angle 3$ are supplementary.	1. Given
2. $\angle 1 \cong \angle 3$	2. Theorem 3-10
3. $\angle 1$ is a right angle.	3. Theorem 3-8
4. $\ell \perp m$	4. Definition of Perpendicular Lines

12. $\angle A\text{-}\overleftrightarrow{CD}\text{-}B$ **13.** $\overleftrightarrow{AD}$ **14.** $\angle CDA$

Chapter 4 (T29) **1.** $\triangle EFG$ **2.** $\overline{EF}, \overline{FG}, \overline{EG}$ **3.** $\angle E, \angle F, \angle G$

4. $2x - 9 = \frac{1}{2}x + 15$
$\frac{3}{2}x = 24$
$x = 16$

$GF = 2(16) - 9$
$= 32 - 9$
$= 23$

$EG = -\frac{1}{2}(16) + 14$
$= {}^-8 + 14$
$= 6$

$EF = \frac{1}{2}(16) + 15$
$= 8 + 15$
$= 23$

5. $90 + 47 + m\angle C = 180$
$m\angle C = 43$
6. $\overline{GF}$ **7.** $\angle E$ **8.** $\overline{DE}$ **9.** $\angle GFH$

10.

STATEMENTS	REASONS
1. $\overline{AC} \cong \overline{EC}$; C is the midpoint of $\overline{BD}$.	1. Given
2. $\overline{BC} \cong \overline{DC}$	2. Theorem 2-5
3. $\angle BCA \cong \angle DCE$	3. Theorem 3-10
4. $\triangle ABC \cong \triangle EDC$	4. Postulate 4-2
5. $\overline{AB} \cong \overline{ED}$	5. CPCTC

11.

STATEMENTS	REASONS
1. $\angle 1$ is the complement of $\angle 2$. $\angle 3$ is the complement of $\angle 2$. $\angle 2 \cong \angle 4$	1. Given
2. $\overline{BD} \cong \overline{DB}$	2. Theorem 2-2
3. $\angle 1 \cong \angle 3$	3. Theorem 3-4
4. $\triangle ABD \cong \triangle CDB$	4. Postulate 4-3
5. $\overline{AB} \cong \overline{CD}$	5. CPCTC

12.

STATEMENTS	REASONS
1. $\overline{DE} \cong \overline{EF}$; $\angle DGE \cong \angle FGE$	1. Given
2. $\angle EDG \cong \angle EFG$	2. Theorem 4-6
3. $\triangle DEG \cong \triangle FEG$	3. Theorem 4-5
4. $\angle DEG \cong \angle FEG$	4. CPCTC
5. $\overline{EG}$ bisects $\angle DEF$.	5. Definition of Angle Bisector of a Triangle

13.

STATEMENTS	REASONS
1. T is the midpoint of $\overline{PS}$; $\overline{PQ} \cong \overline{SR}$ $\angle 1 \cong \angle 2$	1. Given
2. $\overline{PT} \cong \overline{ST}$	2. Theorem 2-5
3. $\overline{QT} \cong \overline{RT}$	3. Theorem 4-9
4. $\triangle PQT \cong \triangle SRT$	4. Postulate 4-1

14.

STATEMENTS	REASONS
1. $\overline{XZ} \perp \overline{WY}$; $\overline{XZ}$ bisects $\angle WXY$.	1. Given
2. $\angle XZW$ and $\angle XZY$ are right angles.	2. Theorem 3-11
3. $\triangle WXZ$ and $\triangle YXZ$ are right triangles.	3. Definition of Right Triangle
4. $\overline{XZ} \cong \overline{XZ}$	4. Theorem 2-2
5. $\angle WXZ \cong \angle YXZ$	5. Definition of Angle Bisector
6. $\triangle WXZ \cong \triangle YXZ$	6. Theorem 4-13

Chapter 5 (T30) **1.** 20 **2.** 40 **3.** 140 **4.** 40 **5.** 100 **6.** 60 **7.** 60 **8.** 60 **9.** yes **10.** no **11.** yes **12.** yes **13.** yes **14.** no **15.** yes

16. STATEMENTS	REASONS
1. $\overline{BC} \cong \overline{DC}$; $m\angle ABC < m\angle ADC$	1. Given
2. $\angle CBC \cong \angle CDB$	2. Theorem 4-6
3. $m\angle CBD = m\angle CDB$	3. Definition of Congruent Angles
4. $m\angle CBD + m\angle DBA = m\angle CBA$; $m\angle CDB + m\angle BDA = m\angle CDA$	4. Postulate 3-3
5. $m\angle CBD + m\angle DBA < m\angle CDB + m\angle BDA$	5. Postulate 2-9
6. $m\angle CDB + m\angle DBA < m\angle CDB + m\angle BDA$	6. Postulate 2-9
7. $m\angle DBA < m\angle BDA$	7. Postulate 2-16 Postulate 2-9,
8. $DA < BA$	8. Theorem 5-5

17. yes **18.** no **19.** yes

20. STATEMENTS	REASONS
1. $\triangle XWZ \cong \triangle ZYX$	1. Given
2. $\overline{WZ} \cong \overline{YX}$	2. CPCTC
3. $WZ = YX$	3. Definition of Congruent Segments
4. $XW < WZ + XZ$	4. Theorem 5-8
5. $XW < YX + XZ$	5. Postulate 2-9

21. STATEMENTS	REASONS
1. $\overline{AB} \cong \overline{DC}$; $m\angle ABC > m\angle DCB$	1. Given
2. $\overline{BC} \cong \overline{BC}$	2. Theorem 2-2
3. $AC > DB$	3. Theorem 5-9

Chapter 6 (T31) **1.** *a,d* **2.** *c,d* **3.** $\overline{PR},\overline{TR}$; $\overline{PR},\overline{SR}$; $\overline{NS},\overline{SR}$; $\overline{NS},\overline{TR}$; $\overline{SR},\overline{TR}$ **4.** *b,c; a,c; b,d; a,b* **5.** *c,d,b* **6.** *a,d*

7. Given: $\ell \parallel m$, $m \parallel n$

Prove: $\ell \parallel n$

Proof:

Step 1: Assume $\ell \nparallel n$.

Step 2: Then, ℓ and n intersect at a point, say P. But, $\ell \parallel m$ and $m \parallel n$. Therefore, through P there are two lines parallel to m. The Parallel Postulate has been contradicted.

Step 3: The original assumption, $\ell \nparallel n$, is false.

Step 4: Thus $\ell \parallel n$.

8. STATEMENTS	REASONS
1. $\overline{AB} \cong \overline{CD}$; $\overline{BC} \cong \overline{DA}$	1. Given
2. $\overline{CA} \cong \overline{AC}$	2. Theorem 2-2
3. $\triangle ABC \cong \triangle CDA$	3. Postulate 4-1
4. $\angle 1 \cong \angle 3$	4. CPCTC
5. $\overline{AB} \parallel \overline{CD}$	5. Theorem 6-4

9. STATEMENTS	REASONS
1. $\angle 4$ and $\angle 7$ are supplementary.	1. Given
2. $\angle 4$ and $\angle 3$ are supplementary.	2. Postulate 3-4
3. $\angle 7 \cong \angle 3$	3. Theorem 3-2
4. $\ell \parallel m$	4. Theorem 6-5

10. 90 **11.** 90 **12.** 50 **13.** 40 **14.** 40 **15.** 40

16. STATEMENTS	REASONS
1. $\overline{DE} \parallel \overline{AC}$; $\overline{BA} \cong \overline{BC}$	1. Given
2. $\angle A \cong \angle C$	2. Theorem 4-6
3. $\angle 1 \cong \angle A$; $\angle 2 \cong \angle C$	3. Theorem 6-9
4. $\angle 1 \cong \angle 2$	4. Postulate 2-9

17. STATEMENTS	REASONS
1. $\angle A$ and $\angle C$ are right angles; $\overline{AD} = \overline{BC}$	1. Given
2. $\overline{AB} \parallel \overline{DC}$	2. Theorem 6-15
3. $\overline{AD} \perp \overline{AB}$; $\overline{BC} \perp \overline{CD}$	3. Definition of Perpendicular Lines
4. $\overline{BC} \perp \overline{AB}$	4. Theorem 6-13
5. $\overline{AD} \parallel \overline{BC}$	5. Theorem 6-8

Chapter 7 (T32) **1.** *P,Q,R,S,T,V* **2.** $\angle P, \angle Q, \angle R, \angle S, \angle T, \angle V$ **3.** $\overline{PQ},\overline{QR},\overline{RS},\overline{ST},\overline{TV},\overline{VP}$ **4.** hexagon **5.** convex **6.** not regular

7. $S = (7 - 2)180$
$= (5)180$
$= 900$

8. $1620 = (n - 2)180$
$1620 = 180n - 360$
$1980 = 180n$
$11 = n$

9. 6 10. 5.75 11. 105

12. $\frac{1}{2}(7x + 9) = 2x + 6$
$7x + 9 = 4x + 12$
$3x = 3$
$x = 1$

13. STATEMENTS	REASONS
1. $\overline{AB} \cong \overline{BC}$; $\overline{BE}$ and $\overline{CF}$ bisect each other.	1. Given
2. D is the midpoint of $\overline{BE}$ and $\overline{CF}$.	2. Definition of Segment Bisector
3. $\overline{BD} \cong \overline{ED}$; $\overline{CD} \cong \overline{FD}$	3. Definition of Midpoint
4. $\angle CDB \cong \angle FDE$	4. Theorem 3-10
5. $\triangle CDB \cong \triangle FDE$	5. Postulate 4-2
6. $\overline{BC} \cong \overline{EF}$	6. CPCTC
7. $\overline{AB} \cong \overline{EF}$	7. Postulate 2-9
8. $\angle BCD \cong \angle EFD$	8. CPCTC
9. $\overline{AC} \parallel \overline{EF}$	9. Theorem 6-4
10. Quadrilateral $ABEF$ is a parallelogram.	10. Theorem 7-8

14. STATEMENTS	REASONS
1. Quadrilateral $PQRS$ is a square.	1. Given
2. $\overline{QR} \cong \overline{SR}$; $\overline{PQ} \cong \overline{PS}$	2. Definition of Square
3. $\overline{PR} \cong \overline{PR}$	3. Theorem 2-2
4. $\triangle PQR \cong \triangle PSR$	4. Postulate 4-1
5. $\angle QPR \cong \angle RPS$	5. CPCTC

15. $x = \frac{1}{2}(16.5 + 8.1)$
$x = \frac{1}{2}(24.6)$
$x = 12.3$
12.3 meters

16. 71;109;109

17. $P = 2(6.7) + 2(4.3)$
$= 13.4 + 8.6$
$= 22$
22 centimeters

18. $s = \frac{32}{8}$
$s = 4$
4 feet

19. yes; octahedron

Chapter 8 (T33)

1. $7a = 392$
$a = 45$

2. $12.6 = 42x$
$0.3 = x$

3. $3x + 15 = 7x - 21$
$^-4x = {}^-36$
$x = 9$

4. $9 - 18n = 2n + 14$
$^-20n = 5$
$n = -\frac{5}{20}$ or $-\frac{1}{4}$

5. $\frac{5}{2} = \frac{AB}{4}$
$20 = 2(AB)$
$10 = AB$

6. $\frac{9}{6} = \frac{AB}{4}$
$36 = 6(AB)$
$6 = AB$

7. $\frac{5.4}{1.5} = \frac{AB}{2.2}$
$11.88 = 1.5(AB)$
$7.92 = AB$

8. $\frac{2\frac{1}{3}}{2\frac{1}{3}} = \frac{AB}{1\frac{1}{2}}$
$\frac{7}{2} = \frac{7}{3}(AB)$
$\frac{3}{2} = AB$

9. No. Their corresponding angles do not have to be congruent. 10. Yes. Their corresponding angles are congruent. 11. Yes. Their corresponding angles are congruent. 12. Yes. Their corresponding angles are congruent.

13. STATEMENTS	REASONS
1. $\overline{BD} \parallel \overline{AE}$	1. Given
2. $\angle CDB \cong \angle CEA$; $\angle CBD \cong \angle CAE$	2. Theorem 6-9
3. $\triangle ACE \sim \triangle BCD$	3. Postulate 8-1

14. $\frac{3}{x + 6} = \frac{4}{x + 9}$
$3x + 27 = 4x + 24$
$3 = x$

15. $\frac{5}{x} = \frac{1}{x - 2}$
$5x - 10 = x$
$4x = 10$
$x = \frac{10}{4}$ or $\frac{5}{2}$

16. $\frac{6}{4} = \frac{12}{x}$
$6x = 48$
$x = 8$

17. $\frac{24.4}{100} = \frac{6.1}{x}$
$24.4x = 610$
$x = 25$

18. $\frac{40}{185} = \frac{8}{x}$
$40x = 1480$
$x = 37$
37 meters

Chapter 9 (T34) 1. 6 2. 9 3. 1.3 4. 120 5. $\frac{2}{7}$ 6. $4\sqrt{6}$, irrational 7. $2\sqrt{30}$, irrational

8. 20, rational **9.** $\frac{\sqrt{10}}{2}$, irrational

10. $\frac{9}{x} = \frac{x}{4}$
$x^2 = 36$
$x = 6$

11. $\frac{8}{x} = \frac{x}{10}$
$x^2 = 80$
$x = 4\sqrt{5}$

12. $\frac{\frac{1}{9}}{x} = \frac{x}{4}$
$x^2 = \frac{4}{9}$
$x = \frac{2}{3}$

13. $\frac{\frac{1}{4}}{x} = \frac{x}{\frac{3}{8}}$
$x^2 = \frac{3}{32}$
$x = \frac{\sqrt{6}}{8}$

14. $\frac{PS}{QS} = \frac{QS}{SR}$
$\frac{8}{QS} = \frac{QS}{5}$
$(QS)^2 = 40$
$QS \approx 6.3$

15. $\frac{PR}{PQ} = \frac{PQ}{PS}$
$\frac{4}{PQ} = \frac{PQ}{2}$
$(PQ)^2 = 8$
$PQ \approx 2.8$

16. $\frac{PR}{QR} = \frac{QR}{SR}$
$\frac{8}{QR} = \frac{QR}{3}$
$(QR)^2 = 24$
$QR \approx 4.9$

17. $\frac{PR}{QP} = \frac{QP}{PS}$
$\frac{12.5}{QP} = \frac{QP}{9.5}$
$(QP)^2 = 118.75$
$QP \approx 10.9$

18. $25^2 \stackrel{?}{=} 24^2 + 8^2$
$625 \stackrel{?}{=} 576 + 64$
$625 \neq 640$
no

19. $\left(8\frac{1}{2}\right)^2 \stackrel{?}{=} 4^2 + \left(7\frac{1}{2}\right)^2$
$\frac{289}{4} \stackrel{?}{=} 16 + \frac{225}{4}$
$\frac{289}{4} = \frac{289}{4}$
yes

20. $8.5^2 \stackrel{?}{=} 5.1^2 + 6.8^2$
$72.25 \stackrel{?}{=} 26.01 + 46.24$
$72.25 = 72.25$
yes

21. 2.8

22. 5.3 **23.** 5.0 **24.** $\sin A = \frac{60}{61} \approx 0.98$, $\cos A = \frac{11}{61} \approx 0.18$, $\tan A = \frac{60}{11} \approx 5.45$, $\sin C = \frac{11}{61} \approx 0.18$, $\cos C = \frac{60}{61} \approx 0.98$, $\tan C = \frac{11}{60} \approx 0.18$

25. 0.1392 **26.** 0.8910 **27.** 2.3559 **28.** 0.7547

29. $\tan F = \frac{ED}{FE}$
$\tan 52° = \frac{7.5}{FE}$
$1.2799 = \frac{7.5}{FE}$
$1.2799(FE) = 7.5$
$FE \approx 5.9$

30. $\sin D = \frac{FE}{FD}$
$\sin D = \frac{2.7}{9.6}$
$\sin D = 0.28125$
$m\angle D \approx 16$

Chapter 10 (T35) **1.** no **2.** no **3.** 25 **4.** 118 **5.** 180 **6.** 62 **7.** 205 **8.** 155

9. $r^2 = 15^2 + 20^2$
$r^2 = 225 + 400$
$r^2 = 625$
$r = 25$
25 meters

10.

STATEMENTS	REASONS
1. $\odot A$; $\overline{AF} \perp \overline{BC}$; $\overline{AG} \perp \overline{DE}$; $\angle FAB \cong \angle GAE$	1. Given
2. $\overline{AB} \cong \overline{AE}$	2. Definition of Circle
3. $\angle BFA$ and $\angle EGA$ are right angles.	3. Definition of Perpendicular Lines
4. $\triangle BFA$ and $\triangle EGA$ are right triangles.	4. Definition of Right Triangle
5. $\triangle BFA \cong \triangle EGA$	5. Theorem 4-11
6. $\overline{BF} \cong \overline{EG}$	6. CPCTC
7. $\overline{BF} \cong \overline{FC}$ $\overline{EG} \cong \overline{GD}$	7. Theorem 10-4
8. $BF = EG$ $BF = FC$ $EG = GD$	8. Definition of Congruent Segments
9. $BF + FC = BC$ $EG + GD = ED$	9. Definition of Between
10. $BF + BF = BC$ $EG + EG = ED$	10. Postulate 2-9
11. $2(BF) = BC$ $2(EG) = ED$	11. Postulate 2-9
12. $2(EG) = BC$	12. Postulate 2-9
13. $BC = ED$	13. Postulate 2-9
14. $\overline{BC} \cong \overline{ED}$	14. Definition of Congruent Segments
15. $\widehat{CB} \cong \widehat{DE}$	15. Theorem 10-3

11. 30 **12.** 104 **13.** 52 **14.** 82

15. $y^2 = 5^2 + 5^2$
$y^2 = 25 + 25$
$y^2 = 50$
$y = 5\sqrt{2}$

16. $13^2 = y^2 + 5^2$
$169 = y^2 + 25$
$144 = y^2$
$12 = y$

17. 15 **18.** 68 **19.** 112 **20.** 45 **21.** 19

22. $8 \cdot 5 = 10z$
$40 = 10z$
$4 = z$

23. $6^2 = 4(z + 4)$
$36 = 4z + 16$
$20 = 4z$
$5 = z$

24. $0.04(0.08 + 0.04) = 0.05(0.05 + z)$
$0.0048 = 0.0025 + 0.05z$
$0.0023 = 0.05z$
$0.046 = z$

25. yes **26.** yes

Chapter 11 (T36)

1. $A = 8 \times 16$
$= 128$
128 m²

2. $A = 3.6 \times 0.8$
$= 2.88$
2.88 cm²

3. $A = 5\frac{1}{3} \times 7\frac{5}{6}$
$= 41\frac{7}{9}$
$41\frac{7}{9}$ yd²

4. $A = y(y - 1)$
$= y^2 - y$
$(y^2 - y)$km²

5. $A = 2\left(\frac{1}{2}(2.8)(4.5 + 6)\right)$
$= 2(1.4)(10.5)$
$= 29.4$
29.4 cm²

6. $A = \frac{1}{2}(7.5)(8 + 19)$
$= (3.75)(27)$
$= 101.25$
101.25 m²

7. $A = 2\left(\frac{1}{2}(3.3)(5 + 9.6)\right)$
$= 2(1.65)(14.6)$
$= 48.18$
48.18 km²

8. $s^2 + s^2 = 16^2$
$2s^2 = 256$
$s^2 = 128$
$A = 128$
128 m²

9. $\frac{1}{2}s = \frac{25}{\sqrt{3}}$
$s = \frac{50\sqrt{3}}{2}$
$P = 6\left(\frac{50\sqrt{3}}{3}\right)$
$= 100\sqrt{3}$
$A = \frac{1}{2}(25)(100\sqrt{3})$
$= 1250\sqrt{3}$
≈ 2165.0
2165.0 cm²

10. $p = 15$
$A = \frac{1}{2}(3)(15)$
$= 22.5$
22.5 ft²

11. $A = \frac{1}{2}\left(26\frac{1}{2}\right)(5)$
$= 66.25$
66.3 in.²

12. $C = 2(3.14)(40.5)$
$= 254.34$
254.3 cm

13. $r = \frac{9.6}{2}$
$r = 4.8$
$A = 3.14(4.8)^2$
$= 72.3456$
72.3 m²

14. $A = \frac{72}{360}(314)(10)^2$
$= 0.2(3.14)(100)$
$= 62.8$
62.8 in.²

15. $p = 5(12.5)$
$= 62.5$
$L = (62.5)(19.2)$
$= 1200$
1200 cm²

16. $T = 2(3.14)(5.1)(18) + 2(3.14)(5.1)^2$
$= 576.504 + 163.3428$
$= 739.8468$
739.8 m²

17. $P = 3(9)$
$= 27$
$L = \frac{1}{2}(27)(14)$
$= 189$
189 ft²

18. $T = (3.14)(7.2)(17) + (3.14)(7.2)^2$
$= 384.336 + 162.7776$
$= 547.1136$
547.1 m²

19. $B = (2.5)^2$
$= 6.25$
$V = (6.25)(9)$
$= 56.25$
56.3 cm³

20. $B = (3.14)(0.8)^2$
$= 2.0096$
$V = \frac{1}{3}(2.0096)(9)$
$= 6.0288$
6.0 m³

21. $V = \frac{4}{3}(3.14)(6)^3$
$= 904.32$
904.3 cm³

Chapter 12 (T37)

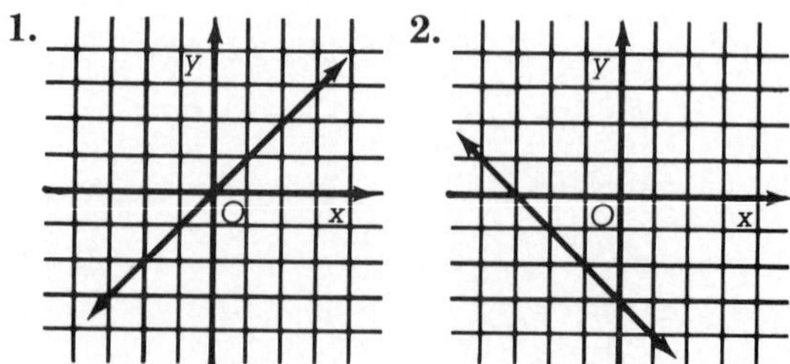

3. 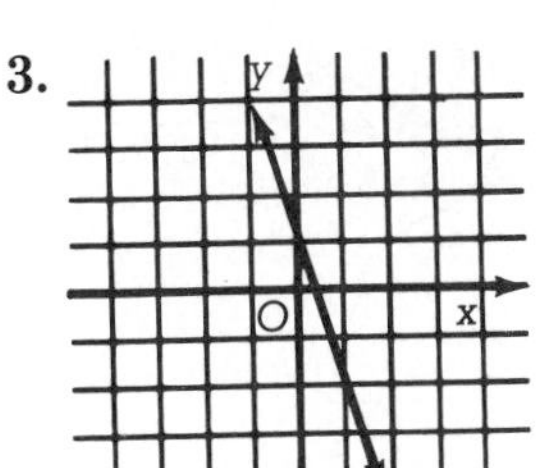

4. 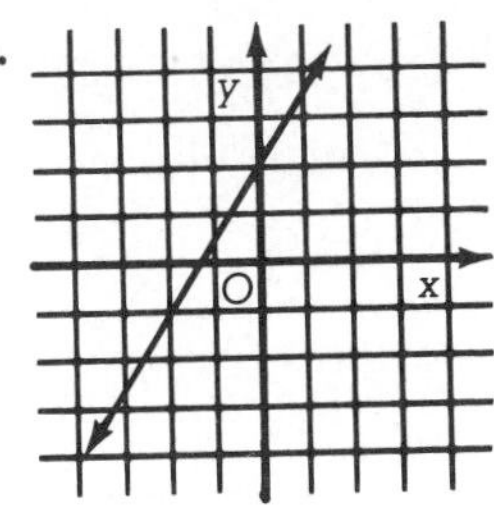

5. $d = \sqrt{(4-4)^2 + (5-7)^2}$
$= \sqrt{0 + 4}$
$= \sqrt{4}$
$= 2$

6. $d = \sqrt{({}^-3-5)^2 + (1-7)^2}$
$= \sqrt{64 + 36}$
$= \sqrt{100}$
$= 10$

7. $d = \sqrt{({}^-5 - {}^-1)^2 + (8-0)^2}$
$= \sqrt{16 + 64}$
$= \sqrt{80}$
$= 4\sqrt{5}$

8. $\left(\frac{4+6}{2}, \frac{0+10}{2}\right)$
$\left(\frac{10}{2}, \frac{10}{2}\right)$
$(5, 5)$

9. $\left(\frac{{}^-5 + {}^-7}{2}, \frac{{}^-3+3}{2}\right)$
$\left(\frac{{}^-12}{2}, \frac{0}{2}\right)$
$({}^-6, 0)$

10. $\left(\frac{\frac{1}{4}+1}{2}, \frac{\frac{{}^-1}{2} + {}^-1\frac{1}{2}}{2}\right)$
$\left(\frac{1\frac{1}{4}}{2}, \frac{{}^-2}{2}\right)$
$\left(\frac{5}{8}, {}^-1\right)$

11. $m = \frac{5 - {}^-1}{0-6}$
$= \frac{5+1}{{}^-6}$
$= \frac{6}{{}^-6}$
$= {}^-1$

12. $m = \frac{1 - {}^-3}{{}^-4 - {}^-4}$
$= \frac{1+3}{{}^-4+4}$
$= \frac{4}{0}$
undefined slope

13. $m = \frac{2 - {}^-2}{3-8}$
$= \frac{2+2}{{}^-5}$
$= -\frac{4}{5}$

14. $\frac{1}{2} = \frac{r-6}{{}^-3-r}$
$2r - 12 = {}^-3 - r$
$3r = 9$
$r = 3$

15. $m = \frac{6-5}{{}^-3-9}$
$= -\frac{1}{12}$

16. $y = 6x - 1$

17. $2 = -\frac{5}{8}(1) + b$
$2\frac{5}{8} = b$
$y = -\frac{5}{8}x + 2\frac{5}{8}$

18. $y = {}^-4$

19. $m = \frac{1}{2}$
$4 = \frac{1}{2}(6) + b$
$4 = 3 + b$
$1 = b$
$y = \frac{1}{2}x + 1$

20. $y - (2y + 6) = {}^-10$
$y - 2y - 6 = {}^-10$
${}^-y - 6 = {}^-10$
${}^-y = {}^-4$
$y = 4$

21. $x - 3y = 5$
$2x + 3y = {}^-8$
$3x = {}^-3$
$x = {}^-1$
${}^-1 - 3y = 5$
${}^-3y = 6$
$y = {}^-2$
$({}^-1, {}^-2)$

22. $2x - 3y = {}^-5$
${}^-2x + 2y = {}^-8$
${}^-y = {}^-13$
$y = 13$
$x - 13 = 4$
$x = 17$
$(17, 13)$

23. $(x+4)^2 + (y-2)^2 = 1$

24. $({}^-8, 7), r = 9$

25. Given: $ABCD$ is a square with diagonals $\overline{AC}$ and $\overline{BD}$.
Prove: $\overline{AC} \cong \overline{BD}$; $\overline{AC} \perp \overline{BD}$

26. Given: $ABCD$ is an isosceles trapezoid with median $\overline{EF}$.
Prove: $\overline{EF} \parallel \overline{AB}$; $\overline{EF} \parallel \overline{CD}$

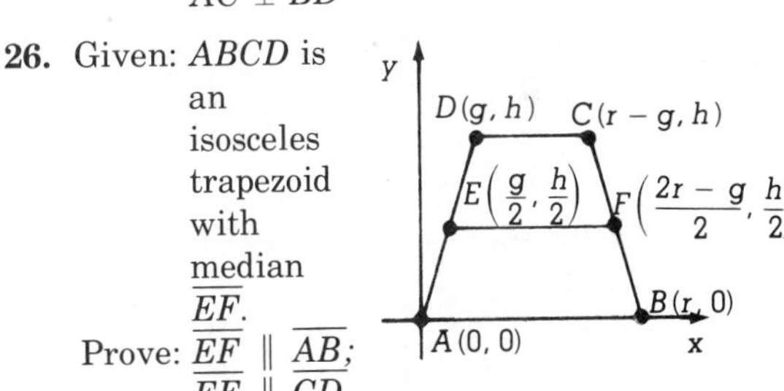

27. $d = \sqrt{(10-6)^2 + ({}^-2-0)^2 + ({}^-4 - {}^-5)^2}$
$= \sqrt{16 + 4 + 1}$
$= \sqrt{21}$

28. $\left(\frac{6+9}{2}, \frac{{}^-1 + {}^-2}{2}, \frac{4 + {}^-5}{2}\right)$
$\left(\frac{15}{2}, -\frac{3}{2}, -\frac{1}{2}\right)$

29. $({}^-3, {}^-4, 0), r = 8$

30. $(x+1)^2 + (y-5)^2 + (z+4)^2 = 36$

Chapter 13 (T38)

1\.

2\.

3\.

4\.

5\.

6\.

7\.

8\.

9\.

10\.

11\.

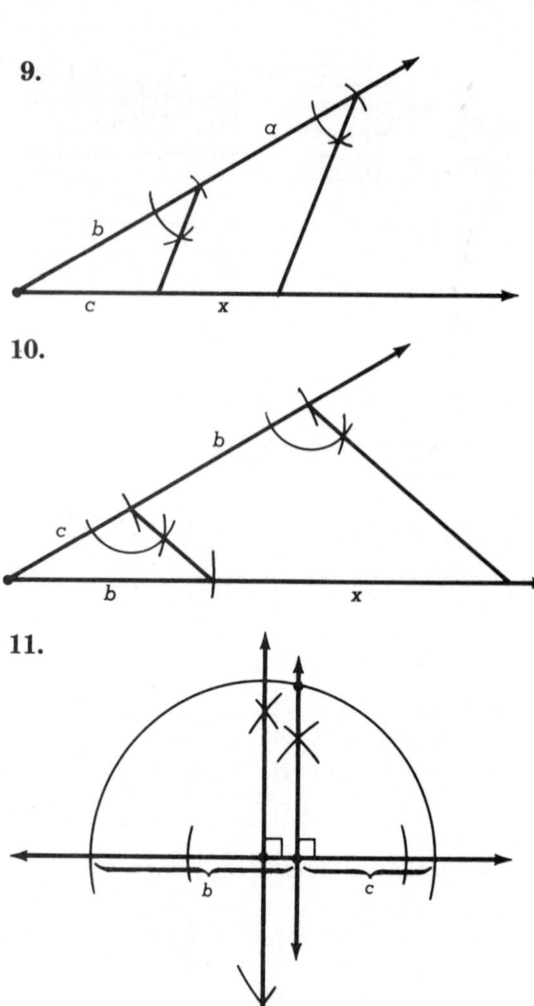

12\. a pair of lines parallel to n and 2.5 meters from n. **13.** a sphere with center B and a radius of 4.5 centimeters **14.** one point or the entire line **15.** the point where the perpendicular bisectors of each of the segments connecting the points intersect

Chapter 14 (T39) **1.** Q **2.** $\overline{RQ}$ **3.** $\angle PRQ$ **4.** $\triangle QRP$ **5.** $\angle S$ **6.** $\overline{TV}$ **7.** $\overline{ST}$ **8.** $\angle VST$

9.

10.

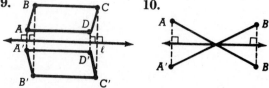

11.

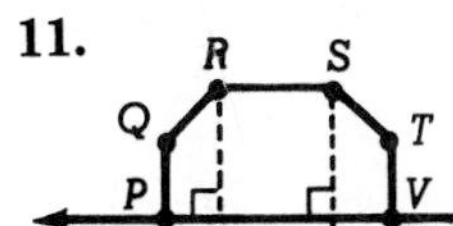

12.

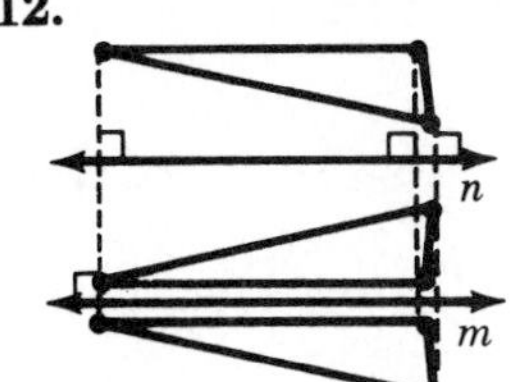

13.

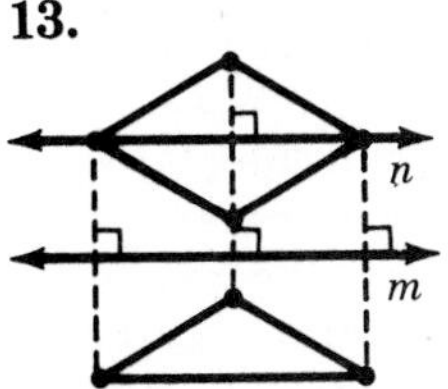

14.

15. 150 **16.**

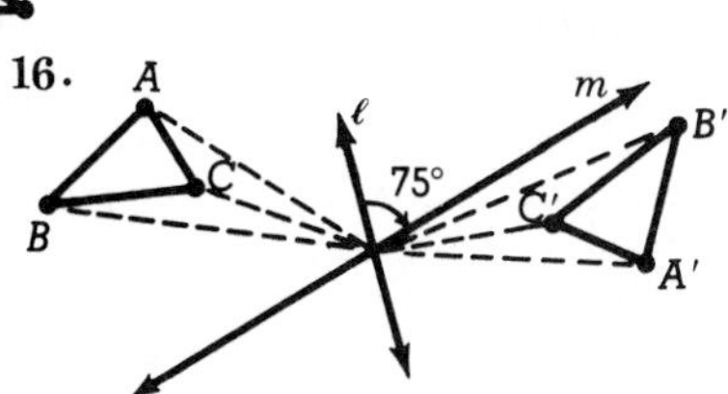

17. reflection **18.** rotation **19.** translation

20. $18 = 6k$, $3 = k$ **21.** $14 = 7k$, $2 = k$

22. $1 = 2k$, $\frac{1}{2} = k$

Appendix (T40) **1.** 3 * X − 1
2. 6 * X ↑ 2 − 2 * X + 1 **3.** (2 + A)/(3 * B)
4. 2 ↑ (R + 6) **5.** 44 **6.** 6 **7.** 333 **8.** 2
9. 1.230007E + 06 **10.** −3.58E − 04

11.
```
10 READ X, Y, Z
20 DATA 3, 5, −4
30 LET A = 2 * X + 4 * Y − X * Z
40 PRINT A
50 END
```

12.
```
10 READ X, Y, Z
20 DATA −1, 10, 2
30 LET A = (X − Y) * (Z + X)
40 PRINT A
50 END
```

13. 40 **14.** 15 **15.** 38 **16.** 85

17. The variable in the NEXT statement should be N not X.
```
10 Let X = 2
20 FOR N = 1 TO 5
30     PRINT N + X
40 NEXT N
50 END
```
output:
```
3
4
5
6
7
```

18. The variables in statements 40 and 50 are reversed.
```
10 FOR A = 1 TO 5 STEP 2
20     FOR B = 0 TO 6 STEP 3
30         PRINT A,  B
40     NEXT B
50 NEXT A
60 END
```
output:
```
1    0
1    3
1    6
3    0
3    3
3    6
5    0
5    3
5    6
```

19. 3 **20.** −2 **21.** 3 **22.** .6

23.
```
10 READ L,W
20 DATA 12,  7
30 LET P = 2 * L + 2 * W
40 LET A = L * W
50 PRINT P,  A
60 END
```

24.
```
10 READ A,  C
20 DATA 8,  10
30 LET B = SQR(C ↑ 2 − A ↑ 2)
40 PRINT B
50 END
```

Teacher's Answer Key

CHAPTER 1 POINTS, LINES, AND PLANES

PAGES 3–4 WRITTEN

13. any one of $\overleftrightarrow{AF}$, $\overleftrightarrow{FA}$, $\overleftrightarrow{FB}$, $\overleftrightarrow{BF}$, ***n***, $\overleftrightarrow{BA}$ **14.** any one of $\overleftrightarrow{AE}$, $\overleftrightarrow{AD}$, $\overleftrightarrow{DE}$, $\overleftrightarrow{ED}$, $\overleftrightarrow{EA}$, $\overleftrightarrow{DA}$ **15.** none **16.** *B* **17.** 2 pairs of *A, E, D* **18.** 2 pairs of *D, H, C* **19.** any three of $\overleftrightarrow{AF}$, $\overleftrightarrow{FB}$, $\overleftrightarrow{AB}$, $\overleftrightarrow{FA}$, $\overleftrightarrow{BF}$, $\overleftrightarrow{BA}$ **20.** any three of $\overleftrightarrow{BG}$, $\overleftrightarrow{GC}$, ***m***, $\overleftrightarrow{GB}$, $\overleftrightarrow{CG}$, $\overleftrightarrow{CB}$ **21.** any three of: plane *AFE,* plane *AFG,* plane *AFD,* plane *AFH,* plane *AFC,* plane *ABE,* plane *ABG,* plane *ABD,* plane *ABH,* plane *ABC,* plane *AEF,* plane *AEB,* etc.

PAGES 7–8 WRITTEN

19. not a good definition:—does not state distinguishing properties **20.** not a good definition:—does not state distinguishing properties **21.** not a good definition:—not identifying set to which term belongs—not stating distinguishing properties—not reversible **22.** not a good definition:—not concise (do not need to say 3 angles) **23.** not a good definition: —does not identify set to which term belongs, does not name the term being defined **24.** good **25.** good **26.** good **27.** Answers will vary for exercises 27–28. A sample is provided for each as follows: A definition is reversible if and only if it could be written using the words "if and only if." The term being defined (reversible) is named. It is assumed all other words are undefined or previously defined. The term reversible belongs to the set of definitions. Some definitions do not use the words "if and only if." The property distinguishes reversible definitions from other definitions. The words "if and only if" make it reversible. The definition is as concise as possible. **28.** A definition is concise if and only if it contains as few words as possible. The term "concise" is named. It is assumed all other words are undefined or previously defined. The term concise belongs to the set of definitions. Some definitions do not use as many words as possible. This property distinguishes concise definitions from other definitions. The words "if and only if" make it reversible. The definition is as concise as possible.

PAGES 12–13 WRITTEN

1. If lines are parallel, then they do not intersect. If lines do not intersect, then they are parallel. **2.** If a figure is a square, then it is not a triangle. If a figure is not a triangle, then it is a square. **3.** If a figure is a square, then it is a rectangle. If a figure is a rectangle, then it is a square. **4.** If a number is an integer, then it is a real number. If a number is a real number, then it is an integer. **5.** If $x < 0$, then $5x > 6x$. If $5x > 6x$, then $x < 0$. **6.** If $2n + 1 = 5$, then $n = 2$. If $n = 2$, then $2n + 1 = 5$. **7.** If it rains, then it pours. If it pours, then it rains. **8.** If you want a new account, then phone for it. If you phone for a new account, then you want a new account. **9.** If two lines intersect, then they are contained in exactly one plane. If two lines are contained in exactly one plane, then they intersect. **10.** If two angles are vertical, then they are congruent. If two angles are congruent, then they are vertical. **11.** If there is smoke, then there is fire. If there is fire, then there is smoke. **12.** If you show me a genius, then I'll show you a scholar. If I show you a scholar, then you'll show me a genius. **23.–28.** Answers will vary. Sample answers are as follows. **23.** If three points are collinear, then they lie on one line. **24.** If $2x = 4$, then $x = 20$. **25.** If three points are collinear, then they are coplanar. **26.** If you live in Illinois, then you live in Chicago. **27.** The Cubs have just won the 1982 World Series! **28.** Geometry is fun! **29.** If points are collinear, then they lie on the same line. If points lie on the same line, then they are collinear. **30.** If points are coplanar, then they lie in the same plane. If points lie in the same plane, then they are coplanar. **31.** If two line segments are congruent, then they have the same length. If two line segments have the same length, then they are congruent. **32.** If two angles are congruent, then they have the same measure. If two angles have the same measure, then they are congruent. **33.** If two angles are supplementary, then the sum of their measures is 180. If the sum of the measures of two angles is 180, then the angles are supplementary. **34.** If two angles are complementary, then the sum of their measures is 90. If the sum of the measures of two angles is 90, then the angles are complementary.

PAGE 21 WRITTEN

1. Given: Lines ℓ and ***m*** intersect at *A*.

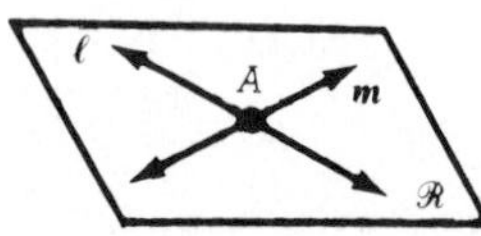

Prove: Plane $\mathcal{R}$ contains ℓ and $\boldsymbol{m}$.

2. Given: Lines ℓ and $\boldsymbol{m}$ intersect.
Prove: ℓ and $\boldsymbol{m}$ intersect at point A.

3. Given: Line ℓ and plane $\mathcal{M}$ intersect. Plane $\mathcal{M}$ does not contain ℓ.
Prove: ℓ and $\mathcal{M}$ intersect at A.

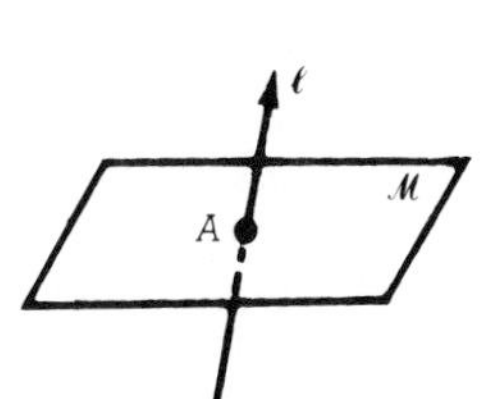

4. Given: Points A, B, C, and D are collinear.
Prove: A, B, C, and D are coplanar.

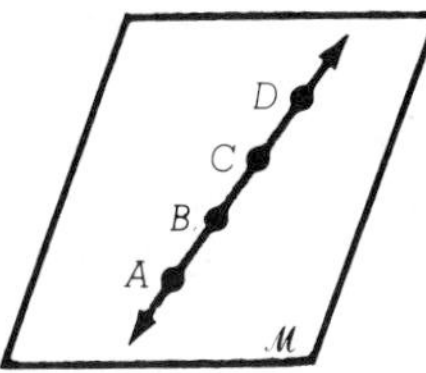

15. Point Q is not on line $\boldsymbol{m}$. **16.** Lines ℓ and $\boldsymbol{m}$ intersect. **17.** Planes $\mathcal{A}$ and $\mathcal{B}$ intersect in a line. **18.** Points R, P, and Q are noncollinear. **19.** $\overleftrightarrow{PQ}$ and $\overleftrightarrow{QR}$ intersect at Q. **20.** Point P is not in plane $\mathcal{A}$. **21.** A line intersects a plane at point P. **22.** Line ℓ lies in plane $\mathcal{M}$. **23.** $\overleftrightarrow{AB}$ intersects $\overleftrightarrow{CB}$ at B. Plane $\mathcal{M}$ contains $\overleftrightarrow{AB}$ but not $\overleftrightarrow{CB}$.

PAGES 24–25 WRITTEN

19. Given: Planes $\mathcal{L}$ and $\mathcal{M}$ intersect.
Prove: The intersection of $\mathcal{L}$ and $\mathcal{M}$ contains at least two points, A and B.

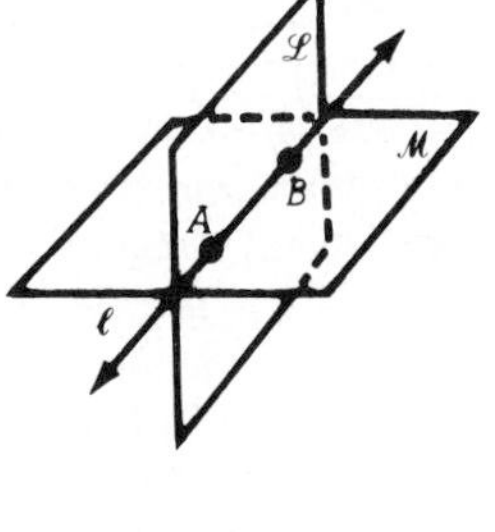

20. Given: Lines ℓ and $\boldsymbol{m}$ intersect at P.
Prove: Plane $\mathcal{R}$ contains both ℓ and $\boldsymbol{m}$.

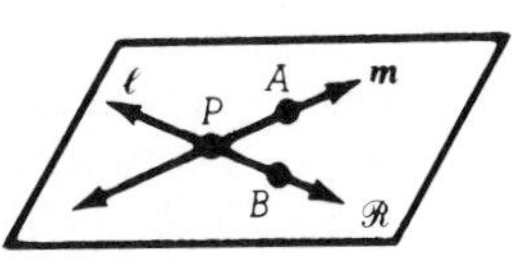

21. Given: Lines ℓ and $\boldsymbol{m}$ intersect at P.
Prove: ℓ and $\boldsymbol{m}$ contain P, A, and B.

22. Given: Plane $\mathcal{M}$
Prove: $\mathcal{M}$ contains $\overleftrightarrow{AB}$, $\overleftrightarrow{BC}$, and $\overleftrightarrow{AC}$.

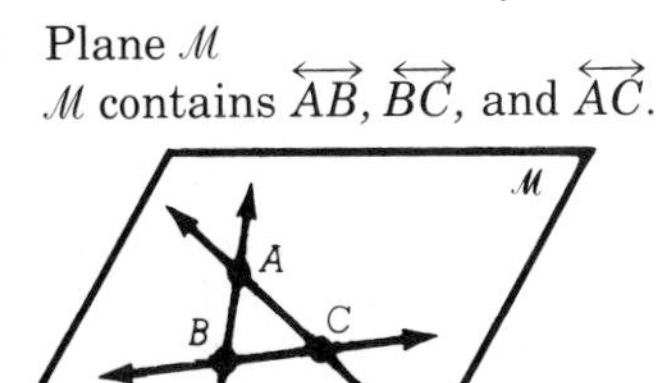

PAGE 28 EXPLORATORY

1. A figure is not a triangle. **2.** Two points do not lie in a plane. **3.** Three points are noncollinear. **4.** A figure is not a polygon. **5.** $\mathcal{M}$ does not intersect $\mathcal{N}$. **6.** $\overleftrightarrow{AB}$ intersects $\mathcal{M}$. **7.** ℓ lies in $\mathcal{M}$. **8.** ℓ does not intersect $\boldsymbol{t}$; ℓ is parallel to $\boldsymbol{t}$; ℓ is skew to $\boldsymbol{t}$. **9.** P, Q, and R are coplanar. **10.** A, B, and C are collinear. **11.** Two points lie in the same plane. **12.** Two lines lie in the same plane.

PAGE 29 WRITTEN

25. *Inverse:* If it does not rain, then the grass does not get wet. *Contrapositive:* If the grass does not get wet, then it does not rain. **26.** *Inverse:* If $3x \neq 12$, then $x \neq 4$. *Contrapositive:* If $x \neq 4$, then $3x \neq 12$. **27.** *Inverse:* If you do not live in Texas, then you are not an American. *Contrapositive:* If you are not an American, then you do not live in Texas. **28.** *Inverse:* If you do not ride a bicycle, then you do not have strong legs. *Contrapositive:* If you do not have strong legs, then you do not ride a bicycle. **29.** *Inverse:* If two lines are not perpendicular, then the two lines do not intersect. *Contrapositive:* If two lines do not intersect, then the two lines are not perpendicular. **30.** *Inverse:* If a triangle has no right angle, then it is not a right triangle. *Contrapositive:* If a triangle is not a right triangle, then it has no right angle. **31.** *Inverse:* If n is not even (odd) then n^2 is not even (odd). *Contrapositive:* If n^2 is not even (odd) then n is not even (odd). **32.** *Inverse:* If a number is not rational, then it is not real. *Contrapositive:* If a number is not real, then it is not rational. **33.** *Inverse:* If an animal is not a chimpanzee, then it is not a mammal.

Contrapositive: If an animal is not a mammal, then it is not a chimpanzee. **34.** *Inverse:* If you do not practice hard, then you will not make the team. *Contrapositive:* If you did not make the team, then you did not practice hard.
35. *Inverse:* If lines are not parallel, then the lines intersect. *Contrapositive:* If lines intersect, then the lines are not parallel. **36.** *Inverse:* If a figure is not a square, then it is a triangle. *Contrapositive:* If a figure is a triangle, then it is not a square. **37.** *Inverse:* If a figure is not a square, then it is not a rectangle. *Contrapositive:* If a figure is not a rectangle, then it is not a square. **38.** *Inverse:* If a number is not an integer, then it is not a real number. *Contrapositive:* If a number is not a real number, then it is not an integer. **39.** *Inverse:* If $x \not< 0$, then $5x \not> 6x$. *Contrapositive:* If $5x \not> 6x$, then $x \not< 0$. **40.** *Inverse:* If $2n + 1 \neq 5$, then $n \neq 2$. *Contrapositive:* If $n \neq 2$, then $2n + 1 \neq 5$.
41. *Inverse:* If today is not Friday, then it is Sunday. *Converse:* If today is not Sunday, then it is Friday. *Contrapositive:* If today is Sunday, then it is not Friday. **42.** *Inverse:* If you do not want a job, then do not learn how a computer works. *Converse:* If you learn how a computer works, then you want a job. *Contrapositive:* If you do not learn how a computer works, then you do not want a job.

PAGES 31–32 CHAPTER REVIEW

5. Points are noncoplanar points if and only if they do not lie in the same plane. **6.** The term defined is not named. The set to which the term belongs is not identified. Distinguishing properties are not stated. It is not reversible.
7. If an angle has a degree measure of 90, then the angle is a right angle. *Hypothesis:* an angle has a degree measure of 90. *Conclusion:* the angle is a right angle. **8.** If a triangle has at least two sides with the same length, then it is isosceles. *Hypothesis:* a triangle has at least two sides with the same length. *Conclusion:* it is isosceles. **9.** If an angle is right, it measures 90°. **10.** If a triangle is isosceles, then it has at least two sides with the same length. **11.** Lines are skew lines if and only if they are not coplanar. **12.** Lines are concurrent if and only if they have one point in common. **21.** *Inverse:* If it is not green, then it is yellow. *Contrapositive:* If it is yellow, then it is not green. **22.** *Inverse:* If the sun does not shine, then the sky is not blue. *Contrapositive:* If the sky is not blue, then the sun does not shine.

23. *Inverse:* If $2x \neq 8$, then $x \neq 4$. *Contrapositive:* If $x \neq 4$, then $2x \neq 8$. **24.** *Inverse:* If two points do not exist, then a line does not exist. *Contrapositive:* If a line does not exist, then two points do not exist. **25.** *Inverse:* If the month is not May, then it is June. (FALSE) *Converse:* If the month is not June, then it is May. (FALSE) *Contrapositive:* If the month is June, then the month is not May. (TRUE)

PAGE 33 CHAPTER TEST

7. If you can drive a car, then you are 16 years old. *Hypothesis:* you can drive a car. *Conclusion:* you are 16 years old. **8.** If a number is an integer, then it is a real number. *Hypothesis:* a number is an integer. *Conclusion:* it is a real number. **9.** If a triangle has three sides with the same measure, then it is equilateral. *Hypothesis:* a triangle has three sides with the same measure. *Conclusion:* it is equilateral. **10.** If an angle is a right angle, then it is not obtuse. *Hypothesis:* an angle is a right angle. *Conclusion:* it is not obtuse. **11.** If you are 16 years old, then you can drive a car. **12.** If a number is a real number, then it is an integer. **13.** If a triangle is equilateral, then it has three sides with the same measure. **14.** If an angle is not obtuse, then it is a right angle. **15.** *Inverse:* If two lines do not intersect, then they are parallel. *Contrapositive:* If two lines are parallel, then ~~they~~ do not intersect. **16.** *Inverse:* If it does not snow, then the ground is not white. *Contrapositive:* If the ground is not white, then it did not snow.
17. *Inverse:* If points are noncollinear, then they do not lie on the same line. *Contrapositive:* If points do not lie on the same line, then they are noncollinear. **18.** *Inverse:* If you do not ride a bicycle, then you do not have strong legs. *Contrapositive:* If you do not have strong legs, then you do not ride a bicycle.

19. Given: Lines ℓ and p intersect at M.
Prove: At least one plane $\mathscr{A}$ contains ℓ and p.

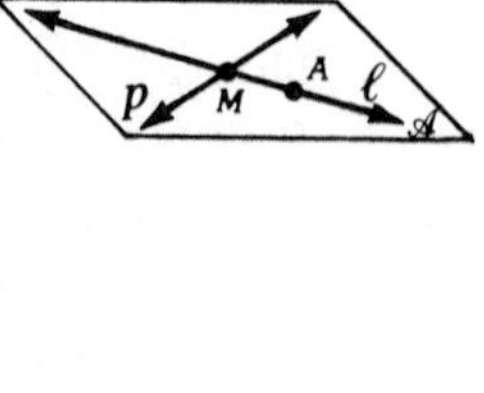

20. Given: Lines s and t intersect at R.
Prove: s and t contain P, Q, and R.

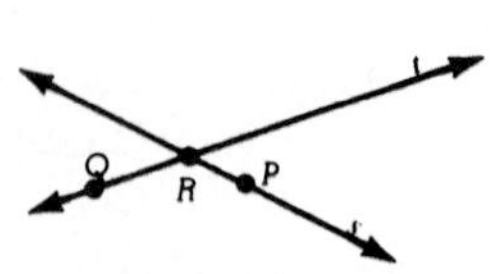

CHAPTER 2 MEASURE

PAGES 46–47 WRITTEN

21. $RT + TS \stackrel{?}{=} RS$
$|1 - 7| + |7 - 3| \stackrel{?}{=} |1 - 3|$
$6 + 4 \stackrel{?}{=} 2$
$10 \neq 2$

Since the three points do not satisfy condition 2 of the definition of between, T is *not* between R and S.

22. $VQ + QR \stackrel{?}{=} VR$
$|^-2 - 8| + |^-2 - 1| \stackrel{?}{=} |1 - 8|$
$10 + 3 \stackrel{?}{=} 7$
$13 \neq 7$

Since the three points do not satisfy condition 2 of the definition of between, Q is *not* between V and R.

23. $PN \stackrel{?}{=} NS$
$|^-9 - {}^-7| \stackrel{?}{=} |^-9 - 3|$
$2 \neq 12$

Since $PN \neq NS$, N is *not* the midpoint of $\overline{PS}$. Note that it also would have been sufficient to show $PN + NS \neq PS$.

24. $PR \stackrel{?}{=} RS$
$|^-7 - 1| \stackrel{?}{=} |1 - 3|$
$8 \neq 2$

Since $PR \neq RS$, R is *not* the midpoint of $\overline{PS}$.

25. There are two conditions to be met.

1. Show that Q is between P and S. Assume from the figure that all 3 points are collinear.
   $PQ + QS \stackrel{?}{=} PS$
   $|^-7 - {}^-2| + |^-2 - 3| \stackrel{?}{=} |^-7 - 3|$
   $5 + 5 \stackrel{?}{=} 10$
   $10 = 10$
2. Show that $PQ = QS$.
   $PQ \stackrel{?}{=} QS$
   $|^-7 - {}^-2| \stackrel{?}{=} |^-2 - 3|$
   $5 = 5$

   Since both conditions are met, Q is the midpoint of $\overline{PS}$.

26. There are two conditions to be met.

1. Show that S is between Q and V. Assume from the figure that all 3 points are collinear.
   $QS + SV \stackrel{?}{=} QV$
   $|^-2 - 3| + |3 - 8| \stackrel{?}{=} |^-2 - 8|$
   $5 + 5 \stackrel{?}{=} 10$
   $10 = 10$
2. Show that $QS = SV$.
   $QS \stackrel{?}{=} SV$
   $|^-2 - 3| \stackrel{?}{=} |3 - 8|$
   $5 = 5$

   Since both conditions are met, S is the midpoint of $\overline{QV}$.

27. $TM = MP$
$|7 - x| = |x - {}^-7|$
$7 - x = x + 7$
$0 = 2x$
$0 = x$

$\therefore$ the coordinate of M is 0. The symbol $\therefore$ is an abbreviation for thus or therefore.

28. $SM = MN$
$|3 - x| = |x - {}^-9|$
$3 - x = x + 9$
$^-6 = 2x$
$^-3 = x$

$\therefore$ the coordinate of M is $^-3$.

29. $NP + PQ \stackrel{?}{=} NQ$
$|^-9 - {}^-7| + |^-7 - {}^-2| \stackrel{?}{=} |^-9 - {}^-2|$
$|^-2| + |^-5| \stackrel{?}{=} |^-7|$
$2 + 5 \stackrel{?}{=} 7$
$7 = 7$

30. $QT - QS \stackrel{?}{=} ST$
$|^-2 - 7| - |^-2 - 3| \stackrel{?}{=} |3 - 7|$
$|^-9| - |^-5| \stackrel{?}{=} |^-4|$
$9 - 5 \stackrel{?}{=} 4$
$4 = 4$

31. $RV - ST \stackrel{?}{=} RS + TV$
$|1 - 8| - |3 - 7| \stackrel{?}{=} |1 - 3| + |7 - 8|$
$|^-7| - |^-4| \stackrel{?}{=} |^-2| + |^-1|$
$7 - 4 \stackrel{?}{=} 2 + 1$
$3 = 3$

32. $QR + RS + ST \stackrel{?}{=} QT$
$|^-2 - 1| + |1 - 3| + |3 - 7| \stackrel{?}{=} |^-2 - 7|$
$|^-3| + |^-2| + |^-4| \stackrel{?}{=} |^-9|$
$3 + 2 + 4 \stackrel{?}{=} 9$
$9 = 9$

33. $TM = MN$
$|7 - x| = |x - {}^-9|$
$7 - x = x + 9$
$^-2 = 2x$
$^-1 = x$

$\therefore$ the coordinate of M is $^-1$.

34. $QR + RS \stackrel{?}{=} ST + TV$
$|^-2 - 1| + |1 - 3| \stackrel{?}{=} |3 - 7| + |7 - 8|$
$|^-3| + |^-2| \stackrel{?}{=} |^-4| + |^-1|$
$3 + 2 \stackrel{?}{=} 4 + 1$
$5 = 5$

35. 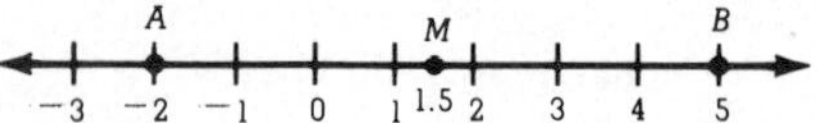

$AM = |{}^{-}2 - 1.5| = 3.5$
by the distance postulate
$MB = |1.5 - 5| = 3.5$
by the distance postulate
Since $AM = MB$, M is the midpoint of $\overline{AB}$ by the definition of midpoint.

36. 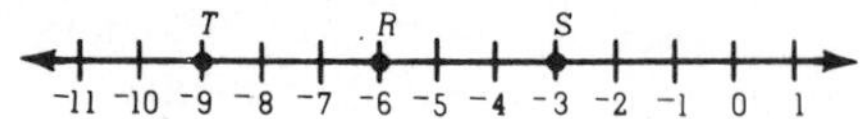

$TR = |{}^{-}9 - {}^{-}6| = 3$
by the distance postulate
$RS = |{}^{-}6 - {}^{-}3| = 3$
by the distance postulate
Since $TR = RS$, R is the midpoint of $\overline{TS}$ by the definition of midpoint.

37. 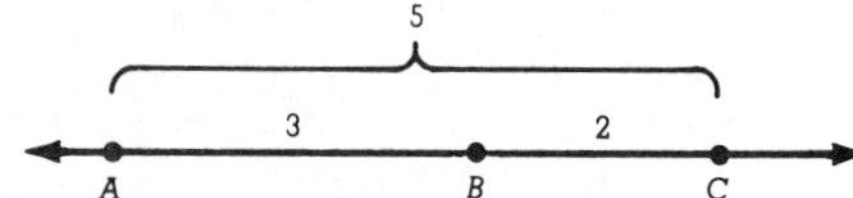

definition of between

38. 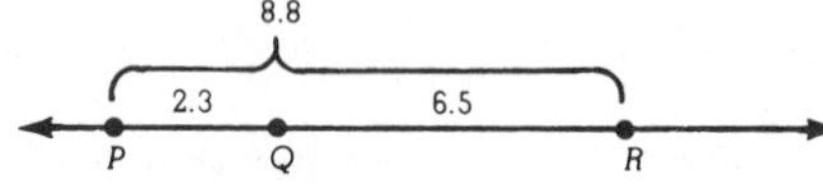

definition of between

39. 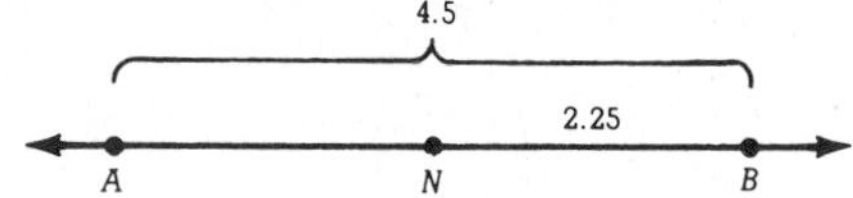

definition of midpoint, substitution, multiplicative identity, distributive, division property of equality, definition of between

40. 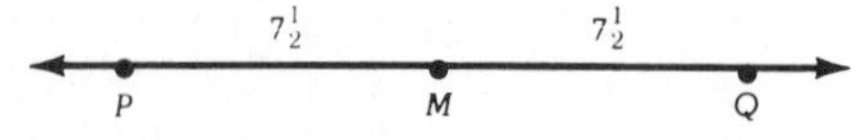

definition of midpoint

41. 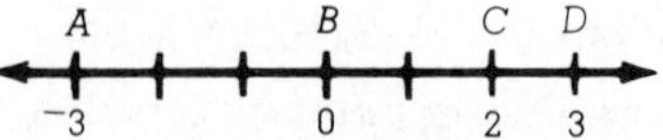

distance postulate, definition of midpoint

42. 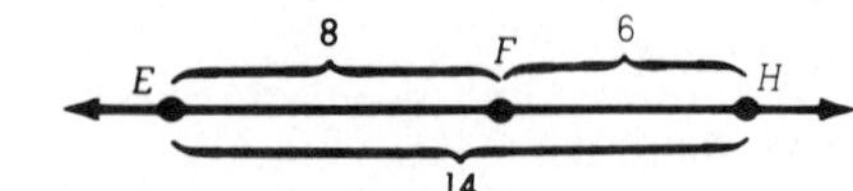

definition of between

PAGES 56–57 WRITTEN

11. M is the midpoint of $\overline{PQ}$. 12. $\overline{PM} \cong \overline{MQ}$
13. If $\overline{PM} \cong \overline{MQ}$, then M is the midpoint of $\overline{PQ}$.
14. False.

where $PM = MQ$

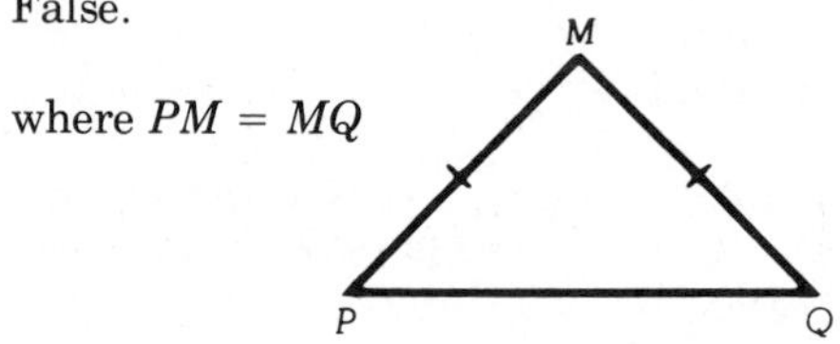

15. $\overline{PQ}$ is bisected at point M.

16.

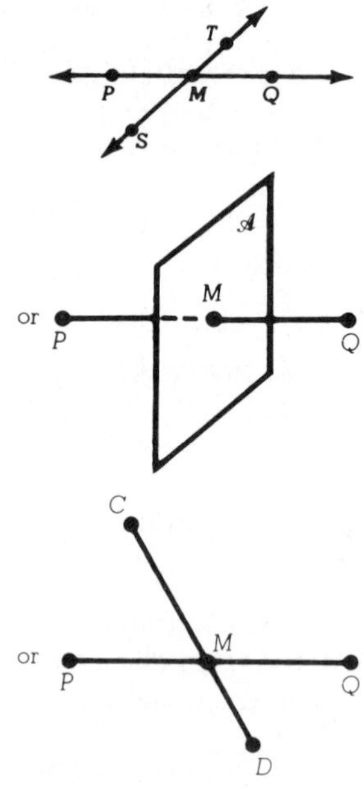

17. $\overline{PQ}$ is bisected at point M. 18. $\overline{PM} \cong \overline{MQ}$
19. $\overline{PM} \cong \overline{MQ}$

Sample solutions for **20–22** are as follows:

20. A segment, line, or plane bisects a segment if and only if it intersects that segment at its midpoint only. **21.** M is the midpoint of $\overline{PQ}$ if and only if M is between P and Q and $PM = MQ$. **22.** M is the midpoint of $\overline{PQ}$ if and only if M is between P and Q and $\overline{PM} \cong \overline{MQ}$.

23. Use definitions of bisect, midpoint and congruence of segments, or midpoint theorem.

24. Given: $\overline{PQ}$ is bisected at point M.
Prove: $\overline{PM} \cong \overline{MQ}$
Proof:

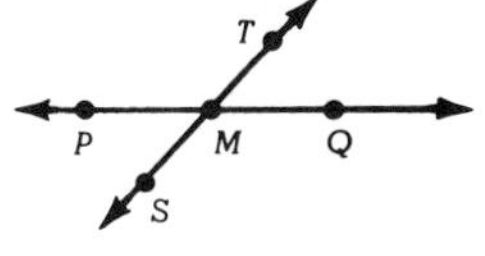

STATEMENTS	REASONS
1. $\overline{PQ}$ is bisected at point M.	1. Given
2. M is the midpoint of $\overline{PQ}$.	2. Definition of Bisect
3. $\overline{PM} \cong \overline{MQ}$	3. Theorem 2-5

25. Given: $\overline{AB}$
Prove: $\overline{AB} \cong \overline{AB}$
Proof:

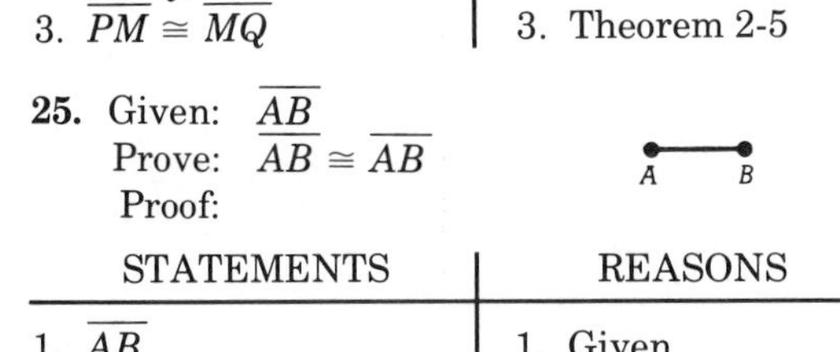

STATEMENTS	REASONS
1. $\overline{AB}$	1. Given
2. $AB = AB$	2. Reflexive Prop. of Equality
3. $\overline{AB} \cong \overline{AB}$	3. Definition of Congruent Segments

26. Given: $\overline{AB} \cong \overline{BC}$, and $\overline{BC} \cong \overline{CD}$
Prove: $\overline{AB} \cong \overline{CD}$
Proof:

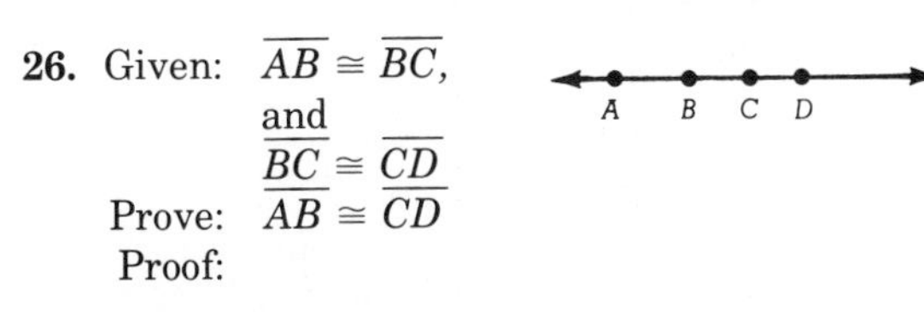

STATEMENTS	REASONS
1. $\overline{AB} \cong \overline{BC}$; $\overline{BC} \cong \overline{CD}$	1. Given
2. $AB = BC$; $BC = CD$	2. Definition of Congruent Segments
3. $AB = CD$	3. Transitive Prop. of Equality
4. $\overline{AB} \cong \overline{CD}$	4. Definition of Congruent Segments

27. Given: M is between P and Q; $\overline{PM} \cong \overline{MQ}$
Prove: M is the midpoint of $\overline{PQ}$.
Proof:

STATEMENTS	REASONS
1. M is between P and Q.	1. Given
2. $\overline{PM} \cong \overline{MQ}$	2. Given
3. $PM = MQ$	3. Definition of Congruent Segments
4. M is the midpoint of $\overline{PQ}$.	4. Definition of Midpoint

28. Given: $\overline{LP}$ bisects $\overline{RS}$ at M.
Prove: $\overline{RM} \cong \overline{MS}$
Proof:

STATEMENTS	REASONS
1. $\overline{LP}$ bisects $\overline{RS}$ at M.	1. Given
2. M is the midpoint of $\overline{RS}$.	2. Definition of Bisect
3. $\overline{RM} \cong \overline{MS}$	3. Midpoint Theorem

PAGE 60 WRITTEN

13. Given: $3x + 7 > 43$
Prove: $x > 12$
Proof:

STATEMENTS	REASONS
1. $3x + 7 > 43$	1. Given
2. $3x > 36$	2. Subtraction Prop. of Inequality; Substitution
3. $x > 12$	3. Division Prop. of Inequality; Substitution

14. Given: $2t - 9 < 21$
Prove: $t < 15$
Proof:

STATEMENTS	REASONS
1. $2t - 9 < 21$	1. Given
2. $2t < 30$	2. Addition Prop. of Inequaltiy; Substitution
3. $t < 15$	3. Division Prop. of Inequality; Substitution

15. Given: $11 - 5y < {}^-77$
Prove: $y > 17.6$
Proof:

STATEMENTS	REASONS
1. $11 - 5y < {}^-77$	1. Given
2. ${}^-5y < {}^-88$	2. Subtraction Prop. of Inequality; Substitution
3. $y > 17.6$	3. Division Prop. of Inequality; Substitution

16. Given: $8 - 3x < 44$
Prove: $x > {}^-12$
Proof:

STATEMENTS	REASONS
1. $8 - 3x < 44$	1. Given
2. ${}^-3x < 36$	2. Subtraction Prop. of Inequality; Substitution
3. $x > {}^-12$	3. Division Prop. of Inequality; Substitution

17. Given: $9(x + 2) < 72$
Prove: $x < 6$
Proof:

STATEMENTS	REASONS
1. $9(x + 2) < 72$	1. Given
2. $9x + 18 < 72$	2. Distributive Prop. of Multiplication over Addition; Substitution
3. $9x < 54$	3. Subtraction Prop. of Inequality; Substitution
4. $x < 6$	4. Division Prop. of Inequality; Substitution

18. Given: $5(5z - 3) > 60$
Prove: $z > 3$
Proof:

STATEMENTS	REASONS
1. $5(5z - 3) > 60$	1. Given
2. $25z - 15 > 60$	2. Distributive Prop. of Multiplication over Subtraction; Substitution
3. $25z > 75$	3. Addition Prop. of Inequality; Substitution
4. $z > 3$	4. Division Prop. of Inequality; Substitution

PAGES 63–64 CHAPTER REVIEW

21.
$$PQ + QR \stackrel{?}{=} PR$$
$$|{}^-2\tfrac{1}{2} - {}^-1| + |{}^-1 - 0| \stackrel{?}{=} |{}^-2\tfrac{1}{2} - 0|$$
$$|{}^-1\tfrac{1}{2}| + |{}^-1| \stackrel{?}{=} |{}^-2\tfrac{1}{2}|$$
$$1\tfrac{1}{2} + 1 \stackrel{?}{=} 2\tfrac{1}{2}$$
$$2\tfrac{1}{2} = 2\tfrac{1}{2}$$
Q is between P and R.

22.
$$RQ + QT \stackrel{?}{=} RT$$
$$|0 - {}^-1| + |{}^-1 - 2\tfrac{1}{2}| \stackrel{?}{=} |0 - 2\tfrac{1}{2}|$$
$$|1| + |{}^-3\tfrac{1}{2}| \stackrel{?}{=} |{}^-2\tfrac{1}{2}|$$
$$1 + 3\tfrac{1}{2} \stackrel{?}{=} 2\tfrac{1}{2}$$
$$4\tfrac{1}{2} \neq 2\tfrac{1}{2}$$
Q is not between R and T.

23.
$$QS \stackrel{?}{=} ST$$
$$|{}^-1 - 1| \stackrel{?}{=} |1 - 2\tfrac{1}{2}|$$
$$|{}^-2| \stackrel{?}{=} |{}^-1\tfrac{1}{2}|$$
$$2 \neq 1\tfrac{1}{2}$$
S is not the midpoint of Q and T.

24. We can assume $R, P,$ and T are collinear.

$$PR + RT \overset{?}{=} PT$$
$$|{}^-2\tfrac{1}{2} - 0| + |0 - 2\tfrac{1}{2}| \overset{?}{=} |{}^-2\tfrac{1}{2} - 2\tfrac{1}{2}|$$
$$|{}^-2\tfrac{1}{2}| \quad + \quad |{}^-2\tfrac{1}{2}| \quad \overset{?}{=} \quad |{}^-5|$$
$$2\tfrac{1}{2} \quad + \quad 2\tfrac{1}{2} \quad \overset{?}{=} \quad 5$$
$$5 = 5$$

R is the midpoint of P and T since $PR = RT$, $|{}^-2^1/_2 - 0| = |0 - 2^1/_2|$.

PAGE 65 CHAPTER TEST

15. We can assume $B, A,$ and E are collinear.

$$AB + BE \overset{?}{=} AE$$
$$|{}^-2\tfrac{2}{5} - {}^-1\tfrac{1}{5}| + |{}^-1\tfrac{1}{5} - 1| \overset{?}{=} |{}^-2\tfrac{2}{5} - 1|$$
$$|{}^-1\tfrac{1}{5}| \quad + \quad |{}^-2\tfrac{1}{5}| \quad \overset{?}{=} \quad |{}^-3\tfrac{2}{5}|$$
$$1\tfrac{1}{5} \quad + \quad 2\tfrac{1}{5} \quad \overset{?}{=} \quad 3\tfrac{2}{5}$$
$$3\tfrac{2}{5} = 3\tfrac{2}{5}$$

B is between A and E.

16. We can assume $C, B,$ and D are collinear.

$$BC + CD \overset{?}{=} BD$$
$$|{}^-1\tfrac{1}{5} - {}^-\tfrac{2}{5}| + |-\tfrac{2}{5} - \tfrac{2}{5}| \overset{?}{=} |{}^-1\tfrac{1}{5} - \tfrac{2}{5}|$$
$$|-\tfrac{4}{5}| \quad + \quad |-\tfrac{4}{5}| \quad \overset{?}{=} \quad |-\tfrac{8}{5}|$$
$$\tfrac{4}{5} \quad + \quad \tfrac{4}{5} \quad \overset{?}{=} \quad \tfrac{8}{5}$$
$$\tfrac{8}{5} = \tfrac{8}{5}$$

C is between B and D.

$$BC \overset{?}{=} CD$$
$$|{}^-1\tfrac{1}{5} - {}^-\tfrac{2}{5}| \overset{?}{=} |-\tfrac{2}{5} - \tfrac{2}{5}|$$
$$|-\tfrac{4}{5}| \quad \overset{?}{=} \quad |-\tfrac{4}{5}|$$
$$\tfrac{4}{5} = \tfrac{4}{5}$$

C is the midpoint of $\overline{BD}$.

18.

STATEMENTS	REASONS
1. $P, M,$ and Q are collinear; $PM + MQ = PQ$	1. Given
2. M is between P and Q.	2. Definition of Between
3. $\overline{PM} \cong \overline{MQ}$	3. Given
4. $PM = MQ$	4. Definition of Congruent Segments
5. M is the midpoint of $\overline{PQ}$.	5. Definition of Midpoint

CHAPTER 3 ANGLES AND PERPENDICULARS

PAGE 74 WRITTEN

27. Given: $\angle A$
Prove: $\angle A \cong \angle A$
Proof:

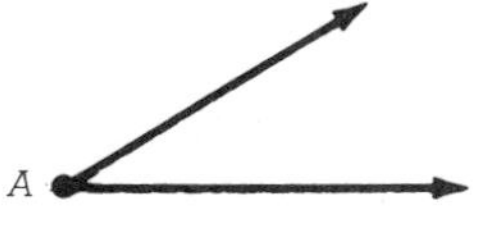

STATEMENTS	REASONS
1. $\angle A$	1. Given
2. $\angle A$ such that $m\angle A = r$	2. Postulate 3-1
3. $r = r$	3. Postulate 2-4
4. $m\angle A = m\angle A$	4. Postulate 2-9
5. $\angle A \cong \angle A$	5. Definition of Congruent Angles

28. Given: $\angle ABC \cong \angle RST$
Prove: $\angle RST \cong \angle ABC$
Proof:

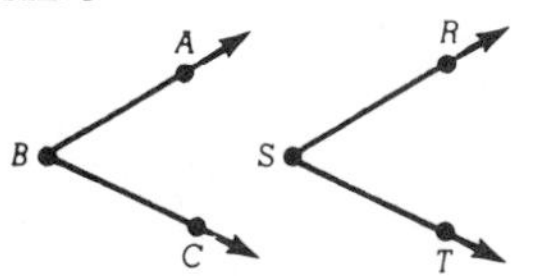

STATEMENTS	REASONS
1. $\angle ABC \cong \angle RST$	1. Given
2. $m\angle ABC = m\angle RST$	2. Definition of Congruent Angles
3. $m\angle RST = m\angle ABC$	3. Postulate 2-5
4. $\angle RST \cong \angle ABC$	4. Definition of Congruent Angles

29. Given: $\angle ABC \cong \angle RPQ$; $\angle RPQ \cong \angle STV$
Prove: $\angle ABC \cong \angle STV$

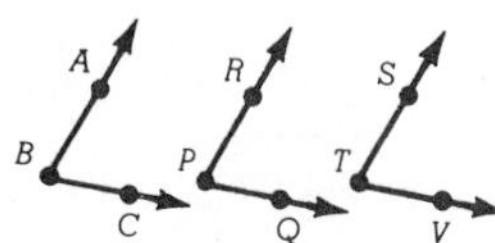

Proof:

STATEMENTS	REASONS
1. $\angle ABC \cong \angle RPQ$; $\angle RPQ \cong \angle STV$	1. Given
2. $m\angle ABC = m\angle RPQ$; $m\angle RPQ = m\angle STV$	2. Definition of Congruent Angles
3. $m\angle ABC = m\angle STV$	3 Postulate 2-6
4. $\angle ABC \cong \angle STV$	4. Definition of Congruent Angles

PAGE 79 EXPLORATORY

1. Two sides of adjacent angles lie on a line.

2.

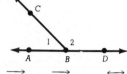

3. $\overrightarrow{BA}$ and $\overrightarrow{BD}$ lie on $\overleftrightarrow{AD}$. **4.** The angles are supplementary. **5.** $\angle ABC$ and $\angle DBC$ are supplementary. **6.** linear pair **7.** Postulate 3-4: Supplement Postulate, or Postulate 3-3: Angle Addition Postulate **8.** Show the two angles are a linear pair and then apply the Supplement Postulate.

PAGE 79 WRITTEN

14.

STATEMENTS	REASONS
1. $\angle 1 \cong \angle 2$; $\angle 1$ and $\angle 2$ are supplementary.	1. Given
2. $m\angle 1 + m\angle 2 = 180$	2. Definition of Supplementary Angles
3. $m\angle 1 = m\angle 2$	3. Definition of Congruent Angles
4. $m\angle 1 + m\angle 1 = 180$	4. Postulate 2-9
5. $2m\angle 1 = 180$	5. Postulate 2-14
6. $m\angle 1 = 90$	6. Postulate 2-8
7. $m\angle 2 = 90$	7. Postulate 2-9

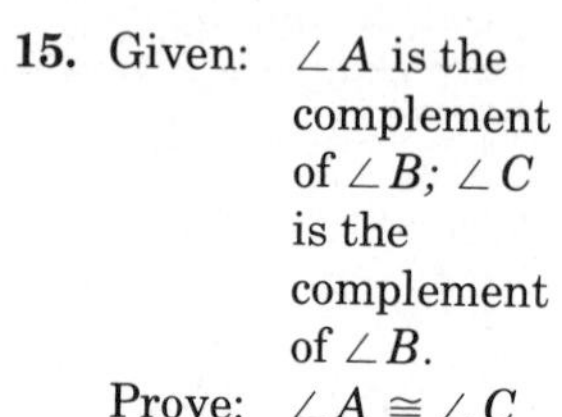

15. Given: $\angle A$ is the complement of $\angle B$; $\angle C$ is the complement of $\angle B$.
Prove: $\angle A \cong \angle C$
Proof:

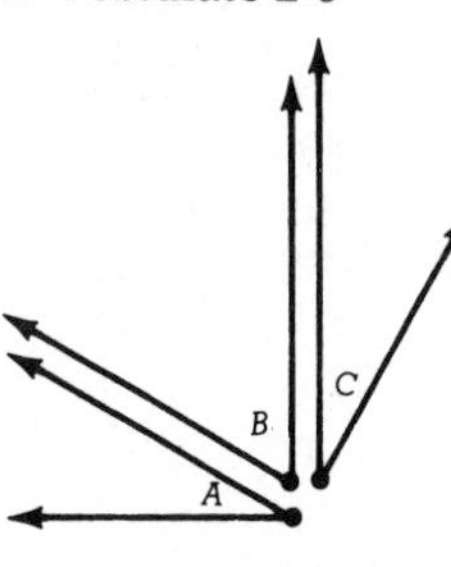

STATEMENTS	REASONS
1. $\angle A$ is the complement of $\angle B$; $\angle C$ is the complement of $\angle B$.	1. Given
2. $m\angle A + m\angle B = 90$; $m\angle C + m\angle B = 90$	2. Definition of Complementary Angles
3. $m\angle A + m\angle B = m\angle C + m\angle B$	3. Postulate 2-9
4. $m\angle A = m\angle C$	4. Postulate 2-7
5. $\angle A \cong \angle C$	5. Definition of Congruent Angles

16. Given: $\angle A$ is the complement of $\angle B$; $\angle C$ is the complement of $\angle D$; $\angle B \cong \angle D$
Prove: $\angle A \cong \angle C$
Proof:

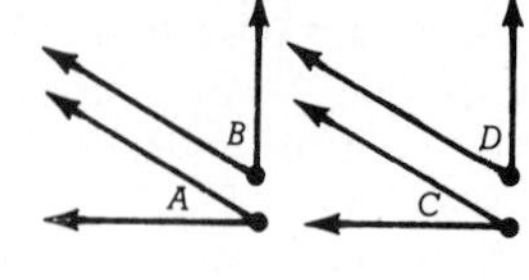

STATEMENTS	REASONS
1. $\angle A$ is the complement of $\angle B$; $\angle C$ is the complement of $\angle D$.	1. Given
2. $m\angle A + m\angle B = 90$; $m\angle C + m\angle D = 90$	2. Definition of Complementary Angles
3. $m\angle A + m\angle B = m\angle C + m\angle D$	3. Postulate 2-9
4. $\angle B \cong \angle D$	4. Given
5. $m\angle B = m\angle D$	5. Definition of Congruent Angles
6. $m\angle A + m\angle B = m\angle C + m\angle B$	6. Postulate 2-9
7. $m\angle A = m\angle C$	7. Postulate 2-7
8. $\angle A \cong \angle C$	8. Definition of Congruent Angles

PAGE 80 FLOW PROOFS

10. Given: $\angle A$ is complementary to $\angle B$; $\angle C$ is complementary to $\angle B$.
Prove: $\angle A \cong \angle C$

$\angle A$ is complementary to $\angle B$
$\angle C$ is complementary to $\angle B$ $\xrightarrow{1}$
$m\angle A + m\angle B = 180$
$m\angle C + m\angle B = 180$ $\xrightarrow{2}$
$m\angle A + m\angle B = m\angle C + m\angle B \xrightarrow{3} m\angle A = m\angle C \xrightarrow{4}$
$\angle A \cong \angle C$

1. Definition of Complementary Angles
2. Substitution
3. Subtraction Property of Equality
4. Definition of Congruent Angles

PAGE 83 EXPLORATORY

13. H: An angle with degree measure 90 and a right angle; **C:** The angles are congruent. **14. H:** Two angles are vertical angles; **C:** The angles are congruent. **15. H:** Two angles are right angles; **C:** The angles are supplementary. **16. H:** Two angles are congruent and supplementary; **C:** Each angle is a right angle. **17. H:** One angle in a linear pair is a right angle; **C:** The other angle also is a right angle. **18. H:** Two angles are right angles; **C:** The angles are congruent.

PAGE 84 WRITTEN

3.

STATEMENTS	REASONS
1. $\angle 2 \cong \angle 6$	1. Given
2. $\angle 3$ and $\angle 2$ are vertical angles; $\angle 6$ and $\angle 7$ are vertical angles.	2. Definition of Vertical Angles
3. $\angle 3 \cong \angle 2$; $\angle 6 \cong \angle 7$	3. Theorem 3-10
4. $\angle 3 \cong \angle 6$	4. Theorem 3-1
5. $\angle 3 \cong \angle 7$	5. Theorem 3-1

4.

STATEMENTS	REASONS
1. $\angle 2$ and $\angle 3$ are supplementary; $\angle 2 \cong \angle 3$	1. Given
2. $\angle 2$ and $\angle 3$ are right angles.	2. Theorem 3-8
3. $\angle 5$ and $\angle 7$ are right angles.	3. Theorem 3-9

5.

STATEMENTS	REASONS
1. $\angle A$ and $\angle C$ are complementary.	1. Given
2. $m\angle A + m\angle C = 90$	2. Definition of Complementary Angles
3. $\angle 1 \cong \angle C$; $\angle 2 \cong \angle A$	3. Given
4. $m\angle 1 = m\angle C$; $m\angle 2 = m\angle A$	4. Definition of Congruent Angles
5. $m\angle 1 + m\angle 2 = 90$	5. Postulate 2-9
6. $m\angle 1 + m\angle 2 = m\angle ABC$	6. Postulate 3-3
7. $m\angle ABC = 90$	7. Postulate 2-9
8. $\angle ABC$ is a right angle.	8. Definition of Right Angle

6.

STATEMENTS	REASONS
1. $\angle 2$ and $\angle 3$ are complementary.	1. Given
2. $m\angle 2 + m\angle 3 = 90$	2. Definition of Complementary Angles
3. $\angle 1$ and $\angle 2$ are vertical angles; $\angle 3$ and $\angle 4$ are vertical angles.	3. Definition of Vertical Angles
4. $\angle 1 \cong \angle 2$; $\angle 3 \cong \angle 4$	4. Theorem 3-10
5. $m\angle 1 = m\angle 2$; $m\angle 3 = m\angle 4$	5. Definition of Vertical Angles
6. $m\angle 1 + m\angle 4 = 90$	6. Postulate 2-9
7. $\angle 1$ and $\angle 4$ are complementary.	7. Definition of Complementary Angles

7. Given: $m\angle A = 90$; $\angle B$ is a right angle.
Prove: $\angle A \cong \angle B$
Proof:

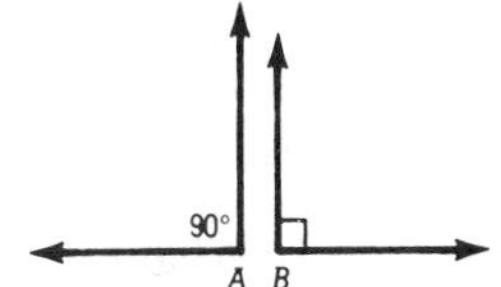

STATEMENTS	REASONS
1. $m\angle A = 90$; $\angle B$ is a right angle.	1. Given
2. $m\angle B = 90$	2. Definition of Right Angle
3. $m\angle A = m\angle B$	3. Postulate 2-9
4. $\angle A \cong \angle B$	4. Definition of Congruent Angles

8. Given: $\angle A$ and $\angle B$ are right angles.
Prove: $\angle A$ and $\angle B$ are supplementary.
Proof:

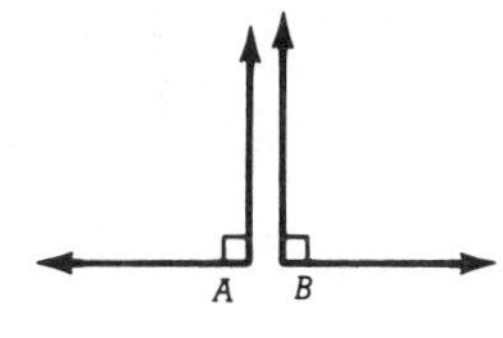

STATEMENTS	REASONS
1. $\angle A$ and $\angle B$ are right angles.	1. Given
2. $m\angle A = 90$; $m\angle B = 90$	2. Definition of Right Angle
3. $m\angle A + m\angle B = 180$	3. Postulate 2-7
4. $\angle A$ is supplementary to $\angle B$.	4. Definition of Supplementary Angles

9. Given: $\angle 1$ is a right angle; $\angle 1$ and $\angle 2$ form a linear pair.
Prove: $\angle 2$ is a right angle.
Proof:

STATEMENTS	REASONS
1. $\angle 1$ and $\angle 2$ form a linear pair.	1. Given
2. $\angle 1$ and $\angle 2$ are supplementary.	2. Postulate 3-4
3. $m\angle 1 + m\angle 2 = 180$	3. Definition of Supplementary Angles
4. $\angle 1$ is a right angle.	4. Given
5. $m\angle 1 = 90$	5. Definition of Right Angle
6. $90 + m\angle 2 = 180$	6. Postulate 2-9
7. $m\angle 2 = 90$	7. Postulate 2-7
8. $\angle 2$ is a right angle.	8. Definition of Right Angle

10. Given: $\angle A$ and $\angle B$ are right angles.
Prove: $\angle A \cong \angle B$
Proof:

STATEMENTS	REASONS
1. $\angle A$ and $\angle B$ are right angles.	1. Given
2. $m\angle A = 90$; $m\angle B = 90$	2. Definition of Right Angle
3. $m\angle A = m\angle B$	3. Postulate 2-9
4. $\angle A \cong \angle B$	4. Definition of Congruent Angles

PAGE 89 WRITTEN

2. Given: $\ell \perp m$
Prove: $\angle 1$, $\angle 2$, $\angle 3$, and $\angle 4$ are right angles.
Proof:

STATEMENTS	REASONS
1. $\ell \perp m$	1. Given
2. $\angle 1$ is a right angle.	2. Definition of Perpendicular Lines
3. $\angle 1$, $\angle 2$, $\angle 3$, and $\angle 4$ are right angles.	3. Theorem 3-9

3. Given: $\overrightarrow{BA} \perp \overrightarrow{BC}$
Prove: $\angle 1$ and $\angle 2$ are complementary.
Proof:

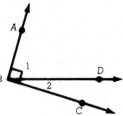

STATEMENTS	REASONS
1. $\overrightarrow{BA} \perp \overrightarrow{BC}$	1. Given
2. $\angle ABC$ is a right angle.	2. Definition of Perpendicular Lines
3. $m\angle ABC = 90$	3. Definition of Right Angle
4. $m\angle 1 + m\angle 2 = m\angle ABC$	4. Postulate 3-3
5. $m\angle 1 + m\angle 2 = 90$	5. Postulate 2-9
6. $\angle 1$ and $\angle 2$ are complementary.	6. Definition of Complementary Angles.

4.

STATEMENTS	REASONS
1. $\angle X$ and $\angle Z$ are complementary.	1. Given
2. $m\angle X + m\angle Z = 90$	2. Definition of Complementary Angles
3. $\angle 1 \cong \angle Z$; $\angle 2 \cong \angle X$	3. Given
4. $m\angle 1 = m\angle Z$; $m\angle 2 = m\angle X$	4. Definition of Congruent Angles
5. $m\angle 2 + m\angle 1 = 90$	5. Postulate 2-9
6. $m\angle 2 + m\angle 1 = m\angle ZYX$	6. Postulate 3-3
7. $m\angle ZYX = 90$	7. Postulate 2-9
8. $\angle ZYX$ is a right angle.	8. Definition of Right Angle
9. $\overleftrightarrow{XY} \perp \overleftrightarrow{YZ}$	9. Definition of Perpendicular Lines

5.

STATEMENTS	REASONS
1. $\overline{AB} \perp \overline{AD}$; $\overline{BC} \perp \overline{CD}$; $\angle 2 \cong \angle 4$	1. Given
2. $\angle DAB$ and $\angle DCB$ are right angles.	2. Definition of Perpendicular Lines
3. $m\angle DAB = 90$; $m\angle DCB = 90$	3. Definition of Right Angle

4. $m\angle 2 = m\angle 4$	4. Definition of Congruent Angles
5. $m\angle 1 + m\angle 2 = m\angle DAB$; $m\angle 3 + m\angle 4 = m\angle DCB$	5. Postulate 3-3
6. $m\angle 1 + m\angle 2 = 90$; $m\angle 3 + m\angle 4 = 90$	6. Postulate 2-9
7. $m\angle 1 + m\angle 2 = m\angle 3 + m\angle 4$	7. Postulate 2-9
8. $m\angle 1 + m\angle 2 = m\angle 3 + m\angle 2$	8. Postulate 2-9
9. $m\angle 1 = m\angle 3$	9. Postulate 2-7
10. $\angle 1 \cong \angle 3$	10. Definition of Congruent Angles

PAGE 93 WRITTEN

13. Given: Lines ℓ and m intersect at point P. $\overleftrightarrow{AB}$ is perpendicular to ℓ and m at point P.

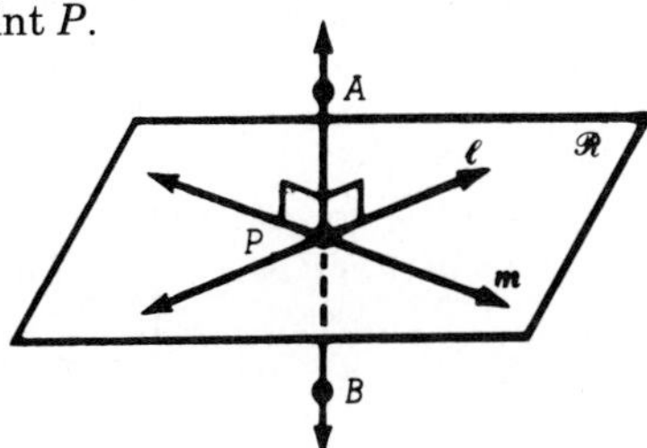

Prove: ℓ and m determine Plane $\mathcal{R}$; $\overleftrightarrow{AB} \perp \mathcal{R}$

14. Given: $\ell \perp \mathcal{M}$; $\mathcal{P}$ contains ℓ.

Prove: $\mathcal{P} \perp \mathcal{M}$

Proof:

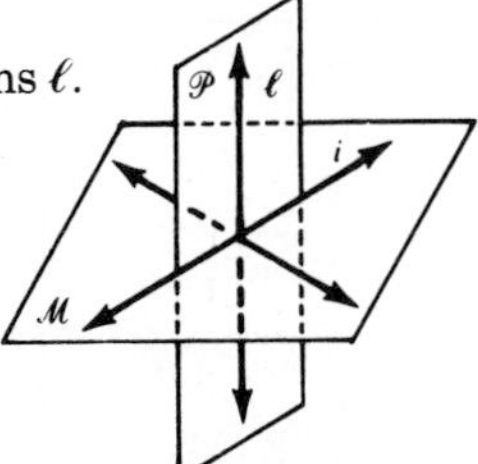

STATEMENTS	REASONS
1. $\ell \perp \mathcal{M}$; $\mathcal{P}$ contains ℓ.	1. Given
2. $\ell \perp i$	2. Definition of a Line Perpendicular to a Plane
3. $\mathcal{P} \perp \mathcal{M}$	3. Definition of Perpendicular Planes

15. Given: $\mathcal{P} \perp \mathcal{M}$

Prove: $\angle A - \overleftrightarrow{BX} - C$, $\angle C - \overleftrightarrow{BX} - P$, $\angle P - \overleftrightarrow{BX} - M$, and $\angle M - \overleftrightarrow{BX} - A$ are right dihedral angles.

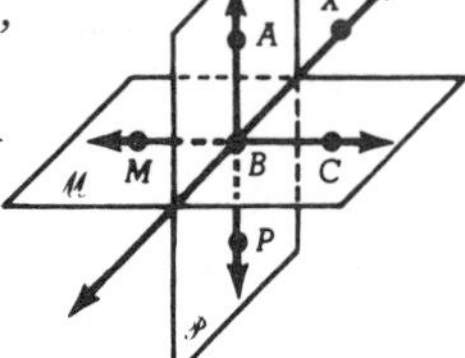

Proof:

STATEMENTS	REASONS
1. $\mathcal{P} \perp \mathcal{M}$	1. Given
2. $\mathcal{P}$ and $\mathcal{M}$ contain line $\overleftrightarrow{BX}$.	2. Postulate 1-6
3. $\overleftrightarrow{BA} \perp \overleftrightarrow{BX}$; $\overleftrightarrow{BC} \perp \overleftrightarrow{BX}$	3. Theorem 3-12
4. $\overleftrightarrow{BA} \perp \mathcal{M}$	4. Definition of Perpendicular Planes
5. $\overleftrightarrow{BC} \perp \mathcal{P}$	5. Definition of Perpendicular Planes
6. $\overleftrightarrow{BA} \perp \overleftrightarrow{BC}$	6. Definition of a Line Perpendicular to a Plane
7. $\angle ABC$, $\angle CBP$, $\angle MBP$, and $\angle ABM$ are right angles.	7. Theorem 3-11
8. $\angle A - \overleftrightarrow{BX} - C$, $\angle C - \overleftrightarrow{BX} - P$, $\angle P - \overleftrightarrow{BX} - M$, and $\angle M - \overleftrightarrow{BX} - A$ are right dihedral angles.	8. Definition of Right Dihedral Angle

16. Given: $\mathcal{P}$ intersects $\mathcal{M}$ at $\overleftrightarrow{AB}$; $\angle V - \overleftrightarrow{AB} - R$ is a right dihedral angle.

Prove: $\mathcal{P} \perp \mathcal{M}$

Proof:

STATEMENTS	REASONS
1. $\mathcal{P}$ intersects $\mathcal{M}$ at $\overleftrightarrow{AB}$; $\angle V - \overleftrightarrow{AB} - R$ is a right dihedral angle.	1. Given
2. $\overleftrightarrow{BR} \perp \overleftrightarrow{AB}$	2. Definition of Right Dihedral Angle

3. $\overleftrightarrow{BR} \perp \mathcal{M}$	3. Definition of a Line Perpendicular to a Plane
4. $\mathcal{P} \perp \mathcal{M}$	4. Definition of Perpendicular Planes

PAGE 98 CHAPTER REVIEW

18. Given: $\angle 1 \cong \angle 2$; $m\angle 1 + m\angle 2 = 90$

Prove: $m\angle 1 = 45$; $m\angle 2 = 45$

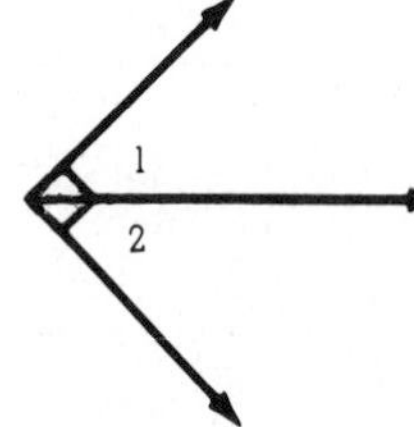

Proof:

STATEMENTS	REASONS
1. $\angle 1 \cong \angle 2$; $m\angle 1 + m\angle 2 = 90$	1. Given
2. $m\angle 1 = m\angle 2$	2. Definition of Congruent Angles
3. $m\angle 1 + m\angle 1 = 90$	3. Postulate 2-9
4. $2m\angle 1 = 90$	4. Postulate 2-12; Postulate 2-14; Postulate 2-9
5. $m\angle 1 = 45$	5. Postulate 2-8
6. $m\angle 2 = 45$	6. Postulate 2-9

19.

STATEMENTS	REASONS
1. $\angle AXB$ is a right angle.	1. Given
2. $m\angle AXB = 90$	2. Definition of Right Angle
3. $\angle AXD \cong \angle AXB$	3. Given
4. $m\angle AXD = m\angle AXB$	4. Definition of Congruent Angles
5. $m\angle AXD = 90$	5. Postulate 2-9 or Postulate 2-6
6. $\angle AXD$ is a right angle.	6. Definition of Right Angle

20.

STATEMENTS	REASONS
1. $\angle AXB$ and $\angle DXC$ are supplementary.	1. Given
2. $\angle AXB$ and $\angle DXC$ are vertical angles; $\angle AXD$ and $\angle BXC$ are vertical angles.	2. Definition of Vertical Angles
3. $\angle AXB \cong \angle DXC$; $\angle AXD \cong \angle BXC$	3. Theorem 3-10
4. $\angle AXB$ is a right angle.	4. Theorem 3-8
5. $\angle AXD$ and $\angle BXC$ are right angles.	5. Theorem 3-9
6. $m\angle AXD = 90$; $m\angle BXC = 90$	6. Definition of Right Angle
7. $m\angle AXD + m\angle BXC = 180$	7. Postulate 2-7
8. $\angle AXD$ and $\angle BXC$ are supplementary.	8. Definition of Supplementary Angles

21.

STATEMENTS	REASONS
1. $\overline{PR} \perp \overline{RS}$; $\angle 2 \cong \angle 3$; $\angle 1 \cong \angle 4$	1. Given
2. $m\angle 2 = m\angle 3$; $m\angle 1 = m\angle 4$	2. Definition of Congruent Angles
3. $m\angle 1 + m\angle 2 = m\angle SRP$	3. Postulate 3-3
4. $\angle SRP$ is a right angle.	4. Definition of Perpendicular Lines
5. $m\angle SRP = 90$	5. Definition of Right Angle
6. $m\angle 1 + m\angle 2 = 90$	6. Postulate 2-9 or Postulate 2-6
7. $m\angle 3 + m\angle 4 = 90$	7. Postulate 2-9 or Postulate 2-6
8. $\angle 3$ and $\angle 4$ are complementary angles.	8. Definition of Complementary Angles

22.

STATEMENTS	REASONS
1. $\overline{PR} \perp \overline{RS}$; $\overline{PQ} \perp \overline{QS}$; $\angle 1 \cong \angle 4$	1. Given
2. $m\angle 1 \cong m\angle 4$	2. Definition of Congruent Angles
3. $\angle SRP$ and $\angle SQP$ are right angles.	3. Definition of Perpendicular Lines
4. $m\angle SRP = 90$; $m\angle SQP = 90$	4. Definition of Right Angle
5. $m\angle 1 + m\angle 2 = m\angle SRP$; $m\angle 3 + m\angle 4 = m\angle SQP$	5. Postulate 3-3
6. $m\angle 1 + m\angle 2 = 90$; $m\angle 3 + m\angle 4 = 90$	6. Postulate 2-9
7. $m\angle 1 + m\angle 2 = m\angle 3 + m\angle 4$	7. Postulate 2-9 or Postulate 2-6

8. $m\angle 1 + m\angle 2 = m\angle 3 + m\angle 1$	8. Postulate 2-9
9. $m\angle 2 = m\angle 3$	9. Postulate 2-7
10. $\angle 6$ and $\angle 2$ are a linear pair; $\angle 5$ and $\angle 3$ are a linear pair.	10. Definition of Linear Pair
11. $\angle 6$ and $\angle 2$ are supplementary; $\angle 5$ and $\angle 3$ are supplementary.	11. Postulate 3-4
12. $\angle 2 \cong \angle 3$	12. Definition of Congruent Angles
13. $\angle 6 \cong \angle 5$	13. Theorem 3-3

PAGE 99 CHAPTER TEST

20. Given: $\angle 1$ and $\angle 2$ are vertical angles; $\angle 1$ is a right angle.
Prove: $\angle 2$ is a right angle.
Proof:

STATEMENTS	REASONS
1. $\angle 1$ and $\angle 2$ are vertical angles.	1. Given
2. $\angle 1 \cong \angle 2$	2. Theorem 3-10
3. $m\angle 1 = m\angle 2$	3. Definition of Congruent Angles
4. $\angle 1$ is a right angle.	4. Given
5. $m\angle 1 = 90$	5. Definition of a Right Angle
6. $m\angle 2 = 90$	6. Postulate 2-9
7. $\angle 2$ is a right angle.	7. Definition of Right Angle

21. Given: $\angle 1 \cong \angle 2$
$\angle 1$ and $\angle 2$ are supplementary.
A, B, and C are collinear.
Prove: $\overrightarrow{BD} \perp \overrightarrow{BA}$; $\overrightarrow{BD} \perp \overrightarrow{BC}$
Proof:

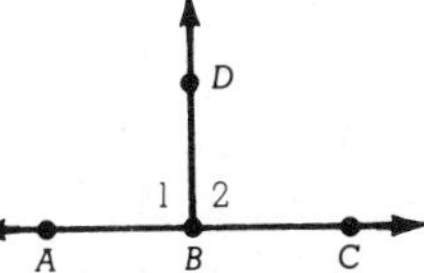

STATEMENTS	REASONS
1. $\angle 1 \cong \angle 2$ $\angle 1$ and $\angle 2$ are supplementary. A, B, and C are collinear.	1. Given
2. $\angle 1$ and $\angle 2$ are right angles.	2. Theorem 3-8
3. $\overrightarrow{BD} \perp \overrightarrow{BA}$; $\overrightarrow{BD} \perp \overrightarrow{BC}$	3. Definition of Perpendicular Lines

22. Given: Lines ℓ and m intersect at A; $\angle 1 \cong \angle 2$
Prove: $\ell \perp m$
Proof:

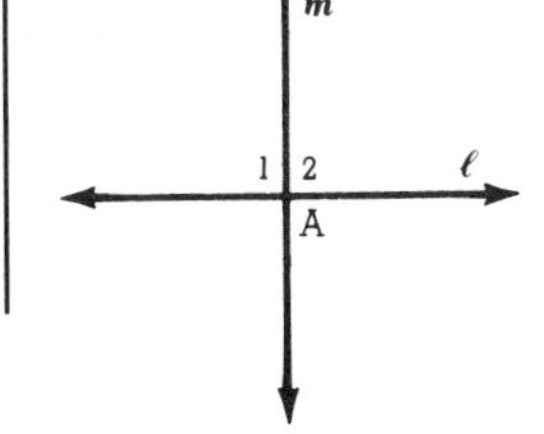

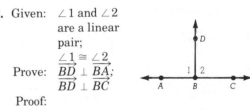

STATEMENTS	REASONS
1. ℓ and m intersect at A; $\angle 1 \cong \angle 2$	1. Given
2. $\angle 1$ and $\angle 2$ are a linear pair.	2. Definition of Linear Pair
3. $\angle 1$ and $\angle 2$ are supplementary.	3. Postulate 3-4
4. $\angle 1$ is a right angle.	4. Theorem 3-8
5. $\ell \perp m$	5. Definition of Perpendicular Lines

23. Given: $\angle 1$ and $\angle 2$ are a linear pair; $\angle 1 \cong \angle 2$
Prove: $\overrightarrow{BD} \perp \overrightarrow{BA}$; $\overrightarrow{BD} \perp \overrightarrow{BC}$
Proof:

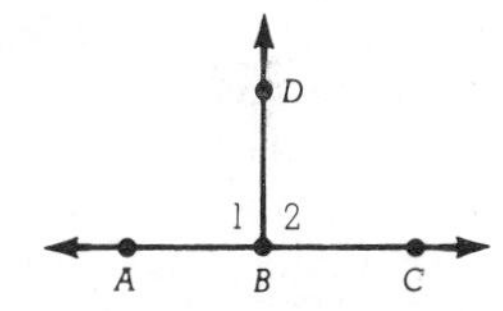

STATEMENTS	REASONS
1. $\angle 1$ and $\angle 2$ are a linear pair.	1. Given
2. $\angle 1$ and $\angle 2$ are supplementary.	2. Postulate 3-4
3. $\angle 1 \cong \angle 2$	3. Given
4. $\angle 1$ and $\angle 2$ are right angles.	4. Theorem 3-8
5. $\overrightarrow{BD} \perp \overrightarrow{BA}$; $\overrightarrow{BD} \perp \overrightarrow{BD}$	5. Definition of Perpendicular Lines

PAGES 100–101 CUMULATIVE REVIEW

30. Given: ℓ intersects m; $\angle 1$ and $\angle 2$ are supplementary.
Prove: $\angle 3$ and $\angle 4$ are supplementary.

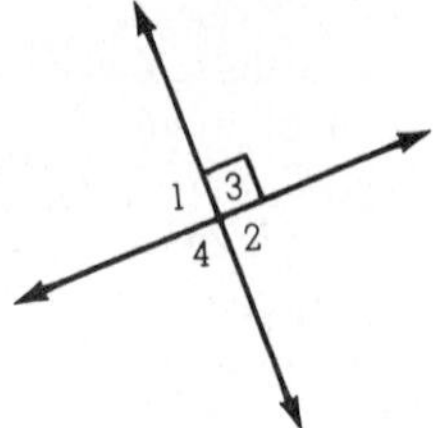

31. Given: $\angle 1 \cong \angle 2$; $\angle 1$ and $\angle 2$ are a linear pair.

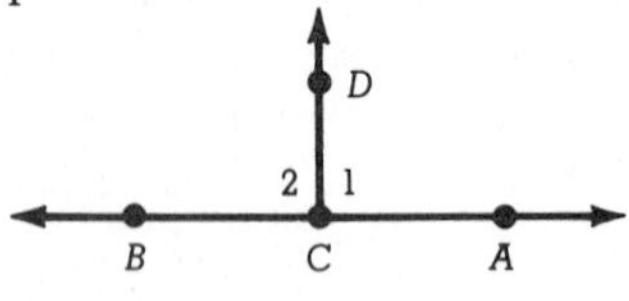

Prove: $\overline{DC} \perp \overline{BA}$

CHAPTER 4 CONGRUENT TRIANGLES

PAGE 106 WRITTEN

See students work for exercises **15–22.** Samples are shown as follows.
15. A figure is a triangle if and only if it is formed by three noncollinear segments called sides where the endpoint of a side is an endpoint of exactly one other side. **16.** A triangle is a right triangle if and only if one of its angles is a right angle.
17. A triangle is an obtuse triangle if and only if one of its angles is an obtuse angle. **18.** A triangle is an acute triangle if and only if all its angles are acute. **19.** A triangle is an equiangular triangle if and only if all its angles are congruent. **20.** A triangle is an equilateral triangle if and only if all its sides are congruent.
21. A triangle is an isosceles triangle if and only if two of its sides are congruent. **22.** A triangle is a scalene triangle if and only if no two of its sides are congruent.

PAGE 109 WRITTEN

9. *No;* if two angles were right angles, then by Theorem 4-1, the degree measure of the third angle would have to be zero. But this violates the Angle Measure Postulate. **10.** *No;* if two angles were obtuse, then by Theorem 4-1 the third angle would have to have a negative degree measure, which violates the Angle Measure Postulate.

11. Given: Equiangular triangle ABC
Prove: $m\angle A = 60$; $m\angle B = 60$; $m\angle C = 60$

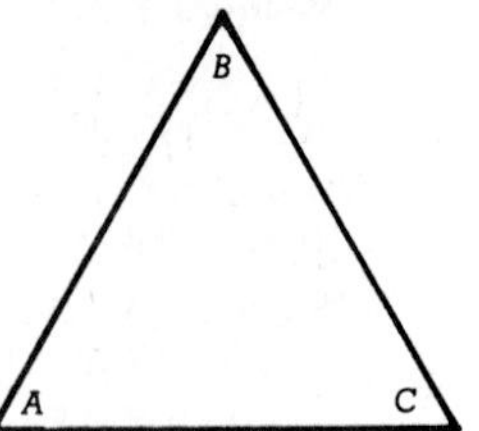

Proof:

STATEMENTS	REASONS
1. $\triangle ABC$ is equiangular.	1. Given
2. $m\angle A = m\angle B = m\angle C$	2. Definition of Equiangular Triangle
3. $m\angle A + m\angle B + m\angle C = 180$	3. Theorem 4-1
4. $m\angle A + m\angle A + m\angle A = 180$	4. Postulate 2-9
5. $3m\angle A = 180$	5. Postulate 2-14
6. $m\angle A = 60$	6. Postulate 2-8
7. $m\angle B = 60$; $m\angle C = 60$	7. Postulate 2-9

12. Given: $\triangle SRT$ is a right triangle; $\angle R$ is a right angle.
Prove: $\angle S$ and $\angle T$ are complementary.

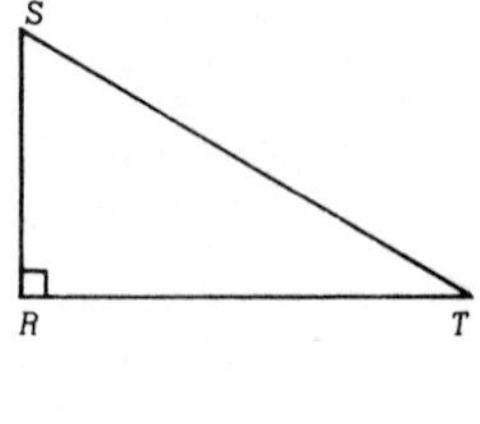

Proof:

STATEMENTS	REASONS
1. $\triangle SRT$ is a right triangle; $\angle R$ is a right angle.	1. Given
2. $m\angle R = 90$	2. Definition of Right Angle
3. $m\angle R + m\angle S + m\angle T = 180$	3. Theorem 4-1
4. $90 + m\angle S + m\angle T = 180$	4. Postulate 2-9
5. $m\angle S + m\angle T = 90$	5. Postulate 2-7
6. $\angle S$ and $\angle T$ are complementary.	6. Definition of Complementary Angles

19. Given: $\angle Q$ and $\angle T$ are right angles.
Prove: $m\angle P = m\angle S$
Proof:

STATEMENTS	REASONS
1. $\angle Q$ and $\angle T$ are right angles.	1. Given
2. $\angle P$ is complementary to $\angle QRP$; $\angle S$ is complementary to $\angle SRT$.	2. Theorem 4-3
3. $\angle QRP \cong \angle TRS$	3. Theorem 3-10
4. $\angle P \cong \angle S$	4. Theorem 3-5
5. $m\angle P = m\angle S$	5. Definition of Congruent Angles

20. Given: $\angle P$ and $\angle T$ are right angles; $m\angle QRS = 70$; $m\angle SRT = 55$
Prove: $m\angle Q = m\angle S$
Proof:

STATEMENTS	REASONS
1. $\angle P$ and $\angle T$ are right angles; $m\angle QRS = 70$; $m\angle SRT = 55$	1. Given
2. $m\angle SRT + m\angle S = 90$	2. Theorem 4-3
3. $m\angle S + 55 = 90$	3. Postulate 2-9
4. $m\angle S = 35$	4. Postulate 2-7
5. $m\angle TRS + m\angle SRQ = m\angle TRQ$	5. Postulate 3-3
6. $\angle TRQ$ and $\angle PRQ$ are a linear pair.	6. Definition of Linear Pair
7. $\angle TRQ$ and $\angle PRQ$ are supplementary.	7. Postulate 3-4
8. $m\angle TRQ + m\angle PRQ = 180$	8. Definition of Supplementary Angles
9. $m\angle TRS + m\angle SRQ + m\angle PRQ = 180$	9. Postulate 2-9
10. $55 + 70 + m\angle PRQ = 180$	10. Postulate 2-9
11. $m\angle QRP = 55$	11. Postulate 2-7
12. $m\angle QRP + m\angle Q = 90$	12. Theorem 4-3
13. $55 + m\angle Q = 90$	13. Postulate 2-9
14. $m\angle Q = 35$	14. Postulate 2-7
15. $m\angle Q = m\angle S$	15. Postulate 2-9

21. Given: Equiangular $\triangle ABC$
Prove: $\angle 1 \cong \angle 2 \cong \angle 3$

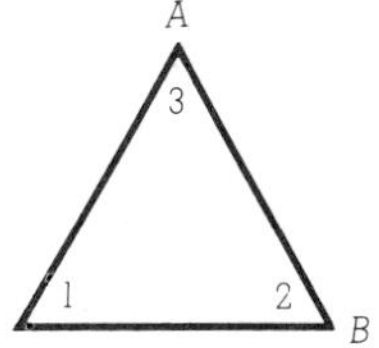

Proof:

STATEMENTS	REASONS
1. Equiangular $\triangle ABC$	1. Given
2. $m\angle 1 = 60$; $m\angle 2 = 60$; $m\angle 3 = 60$	2. Theorem 4-2
3. $m\angle 1 = m\angle 2 = m\angle 3$	3. Postulate 2-9
4. $\angle 1 \cong \angle 2 \cong \angle 3$	4. Definition of Congruent Angles

PAGE 115 WRITTEN

29. Given: $\triangle ABC$
Prove: $\triangle ABC \cong \triangle ABC$

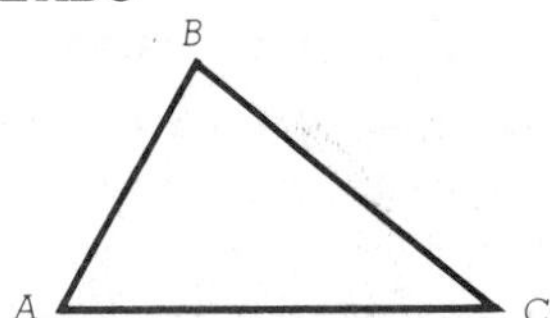

Proof:

STATEMENTS	REASONS
1. $\triangle ABC$	1. Given
2. $\angle A \cong \angle A$; $\angle B \cong \angle B$; $\angle C \cong \angle C$	2. Theorem 3-1
3. $\overline{AB} \cong \overline{AB}$; $\overline{BC} \cong \overline{BC}$; $\overline{AC} \cong \overline{AC}$	3. Theorem 2-2
4. $\triangle ABC \cong \triangle ABC$	4. Definition of Congruent Triangles

30. Given: $\triangle ABC \cong \triangle DEF$
Prove: $\triangle DEF \cong \triangle ABC$

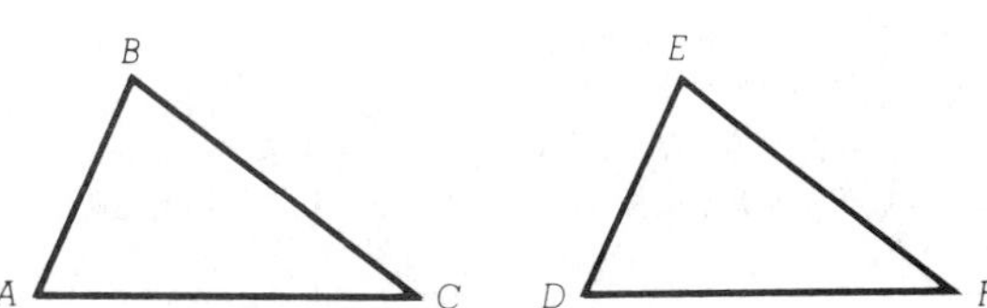

Proof:

STATEMENTS	REASONS
1. $\triangle ABC \cong \triangle DEF$	1. Given
2. $\angle A \cong \angle D$; $\angle B \cong \angle E$; $\angle C \cong \angle F$; $\overline{AB} \cong \overline{DE}$; $\overline{BC} \cong \overline{EF}$; $\overline{AC} \cong \overline{DF}$	2. Definition of Congruent Triangles
3. $\angle D \cong \angle A$; $\angle E \cong \angle F$; $\angle F \cong \angle C$	3. Theorem 3-1
4. $\overline{DE} \cong \overline{AB}$; $\overline{EF} \cong \overline{BC}$; $\overline{DF} \cong \overline{AC}$	4. Theorem 2-3
5. $\triangle DEF \cong \triangle ABC$	5. Definition of Congruent Triangles

31. Given: $\triangle ABC \cong \triangle DEF$; $\triangle DEF \cong \triangle XYZ$
Prove: $\triangle ABC \cong \triangle XYZ$

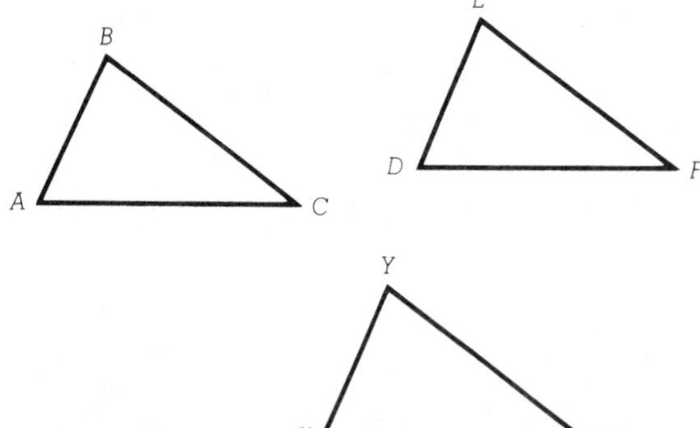

Proof:

STATEMENTS	REASONS
1. $\triangle ABC \cong \triangle DEF$; $\triangle DEF \cong \triangle XYZ$	1. Given
2. $\angle A \cong \angle D$; $\angle B \cong \angle E$; $\angle C \cong \angle F$; $\overline{AB} \cong \overline{DE}$; $\overline{BC} \cong \overline{EF}$; $\overline{AC} \cong \overline{DF}$; $\angle D \cong \angle X$; $\angle E \cong \angle Y$; $\angle F \cong \angle Z$; $\overline{DE} \cong \overline{XY}$; $\overline{EF} \cong \overline{YZ}$; $\overline{DF} \cong \overline{XZ}$	2. Definition of Congruent Triangles
3. $\angle A \cong \angle X$; $\angle B \cong \angle Y$; $\angle C \cong \angle Z$	3. Theorem 3-1
4. $\overline{AB} \cong \overline{XY}$; $\overline{BC} \cong \overline{YZ}$; $\overline{AC} \cong \overline{XZ}$	4. Theorem 2-4
5. $\triangle ABC \cong \triangle XYZ$	5. Definition of Congruent Triangles

PAGE 119 WRITTEN

1. STATEMENTS	REASONS
1. $\angle 1 \cong \angle 2$; R is the midpoint of $\overline{PT}$; $\angle P$ and $\angle T$ are right angles.	1. Given
2. $\angle P \cong \angle T$	2. Theorem 3-6
3. $PR = RT$	3. Definition of Midpoint
4. $\overline{PR} \cong \overline{RT}$	4. Definition of Congruent Segments
5. $\triangle QPR \cong \triangle STR$	5. ASA
6. $\overline{QP} \cong \overline{ST}$	6. Definition of Congruent Triangles

2. STATEMENTS	REASONS
1. $\overline{QP} \cong \overline{ST}$; R is the midpoint of PT; $\angle P$ and $\angle T$ are right angles.	1. Given
2. $\angle P \cong \angle T$	2. Theorem 3-6
3. $PR = RT$	3. Definition of Midpoint
4. $\overline{PR} \cong \overline{RT}$	4. Definition of Congruent Segments
5. $\triangle QPR \cong \triangle STR$	5. SAS
6. $\overline{QR} \cong \overline{SR}$	6. Definition of Congruent Triangles

3. STATEMENTS	REASONS
1. $\angle 1 \cong \angle 2$; $\angle P$ and $\angle T$ are right angles; $\overline{QR} \cong \overline{SR}$	1. Given
2. $\triangle QPR$ and $\triangle STR$ are right triangles.	2. Definition of Right Triangle
3. $\angle 1$ and $\angle Q$ are complementary; $\angle 2$ and $\angle S$ are complementary.	3. Theorem 4-3
4. $\angle Q \cong \angle S$	4. Theorem 3-5
5. $\triangle QPR \cong \triangle STR$	5. ASA
6. $\overline{PR} \cong \overline{TR}$	6. Definition of Congruent Triangles

4.

STATEMENTS	REASONS
1. $\overline{AD} \cong \overline{CB}$; $\overline{DC} \cong \overline{BA}$	1. Given
2. $\overline{AC} \cong \overline{CA}$	2. Theorem 2-2
3. $\triangle ADC \cong \triangle CBA$	3. SSS
4. $\angle 2 \cong \angle 5$	4. Definition of Congruent Triangles

5.

STATEMENTS	REASONS
1. $\angle 1 \cong \angle 6$; $\angle 3 \cong \angle 4$	1. Given
2. $\overline{AC} \cong \overline{CA}$	2. Theorem 2-2
3. $\triangle ADC \cong \triangle CBA$	3. ASA
4. $\overline{AD} \cong \overline{CB}$	4. Definition of Congruent Triangles

6.

STATEMENTS	REASONS
1. $\angle 3 \cong \angle 4$; $\overline{DC} \cong \overline{BA}$	1. Given
2. $\overline{AC} \cong \overline{CA}$	2. Theorem 2-2
3. $\triangle ADC \cong \triangle CBA$	3. SAS
4. $\angle 1 \cong \angle 6$	4. Definition of Congruent Triangles

7.

STATEMENTS	REASONS
1. $\overline{AC} \cong \overline{EC}$; $\angle A \cong \angle E$	1. Given
2. $\angle 1$ and $\angle 2$ are vertical angles.	2. Definition of Vertical Angles
3. $\angle 1 \cong \angle 2$	3. Theorem 3-10
4. $\triangle ABC \cong \triangle EDC$	4. ASA
5. $\overline{AB} \cong \overline{ED}$	5. Definition of Congruent Triangles

8.

STATEMENTS	REASONS
1. $\overline{AC} \cong \overline{EC}$; $\angle A \cong \angle E$	1. Given
2. $\angle 1$ and $\angle 2$ are vertical angles.	2. Definition of Vertical Angles
3. $\angle 1 \cong \angle 2$	3. Theorem 3-10
4. $\triangle ABC \cong \triangle EDC$	4. ASA
5. $\overline{BC} \cong \overline{DC}$	5. Definition of Congruent Triangles

9.

STATEMENTS	REASONS
1. $\overline{AC} \cong \overline{EC}$; $\overline{BC} \cong \overline{DC}$	1. Given
2. $\angle 1$ and $\angle 2$ are vertical angles.	2. Definition of Vertical Angles
3. $\angle 1 \cong \angle 2$	3. Theorem 3-10
4. $\triangle ABC \cong \triangle EDC$	4. SAS
5. $\angle A \cong \angle E$	5. Definition of Congruent Triangles

10.

STATEMENTS	REASONS
1. $\overline{AC} \cong \overline{EC}$; $\overline{BC} \cong \overline{DC}$	1. Given
2. $\angle 1$ and $\angle 2$ are vertical angles.	2. Definition of Vertical Angles
3. $\angle 1 \cong \angle 2$	3. Theorem 3-10
4. $\triangle ABC \cong \triangle EDC$	4. SAS
5. $\angle B \cong \angle D$	5. Definition of Congruent Triangles

29. $m\angle 1 + m\angle 2 + m\angle PVT = 180$; Theorem 4-1
$m\angle 1 = m\angle 2$; Definition of Congruent Angles
$m\angle 1 + m\angle 1 + m\angle PVT = 180$; Postulate 2-9
$30 + 30 + m\angle PVT = 180$; Postulate 2-9
$m\angle PVT = 120$; Postulate 2-7

30. $m\angle 3 = m\angle 4$; Definition of Congruent Angles
$95 = m\angle 4$; Postulate 2-9
$m\angle 4 + m\angle 6 = 180$; Postulate 3-4
$95 + m\angle 6 = 180$; Postulate 2-9
$m\angle 6 = 85$; Postulate 2-7

PAGE 120 CHALLENGE

1.

STATEMENTS	REASONS
1. $\overline{AB} \cong \overline{XY}$; $\overline{AC} \cong \overline{XP}$; $\angle A \cong \angle X$; $\angle ABC \cong \angle XYZ$	1. Given
2. $\triangle ABC \cong \triangle XYP$	2. SAS

2. Since $\triangle ABC \cong \triangle XYP$, $\angle ABC \cong \angle XYP$ by CPCTC.

PAGE 123 WRITTEN

1.

STATEMENTS	REASONS
1. $\overline{BC} \cong \overline{DC}$; $\angle A \cong \angle E$; $\angle 1 \cong \angle 2$	1. Given
2. $\triangle ABC \cong \triangle EDC$	2. AAS
3. $\overline{AC} \cong \overline{EC}$	3. CPCTC

2.

STATEMENTS	REASONS
1. $\overline{BC} \cong \overline{DC}$; $\angle A \cong \angle E$; $\angle 1 \cong \angle 2$	1. Given
2. $\triangle ABC \cong \triangle EDC$	2. AAS
3. $\overline{AB} \cong \overline{ED}$	3. CPCTC

3.

STATEMENTS	REASONS
1. $\angle A \cong \angle E$; $\overline{AC} \cong \overline{EC}$; $\angle 1 \cong \angle 2$	1. Given
2. $\triangle ABC \cong \triangle EDC$	2. ASA
3. $\angle B \cong \angle D$	3. CPCTC

4.

STATEMENTS	REASONS
1. $\overline{AC} \cong \overline{EC}$; $\overline{BC} \cong \overline{DC}$; $\angle 1 \cong \angle 2$	1. Given
2. $\triangle ABC \cong \triangle EDC$	2. SAS
3. $\angle B \cong \angle D$	3. CPCTC

5.

STATEMENTS	REASONS
1. $\angle A \cong \angle C$; $\angle 1 \cong \angle 2$	1. Given
2. $\overline{BD} \cong \overline{BD}$	2. Theorem 2-2
3. $\triangle ABD \cong \triangle CBD$	3. AAS
4. $\overline{AD} \cong \overline{CD}$	4. CPCTC
5. $AD = CD$	5. Definition of Congruent Segments
6. D is the midpoint of $\overline{AC}$.	6. Definition of Midpoint
7. $\overline{BD}$ bisects $\overline{AC}$.	7. Definition of Segment Bisector

6.

STATEMENTS	REASONS
1. $\angle A \cong \angle C$; $\overline{BD} \perp \overline{AC}$	1. Given
2. $\angle 3 \cong \angle 4$	2. Theorem 3-13
3. $\overline{BD} \cong \overline{BD}$	3. Theorem 2-2
4. $\triangle ABD \cong \triangle CBD$	4. AAS
5. $\overline{AB} \cong \overline{CB}$	5. CPCTC

7.

STATEMENTS	REASONS
1. $\overline{AB} \cong \overline{CB}$; $\overline{BD}$ bisects $\overline{AC}$.	1. Given
2. D is the midpoint of $\overline{AC}$.	2. Definition of Segment Bisector
3. $\overline{AD} \cong \overline{CD}$	3. Theorem 2-5
4. $\overline{BD} \cong \overline{BD}$	4. Theorem 2-2
5. $\triangle ABD \cong \triangle CBD$	5. SSS
6. $\angle A \cong \angle C$	6. CPCTC

8.

STATEMENTS	REASONS
1. $\angle 1 \cong \angle 2$; $\angle 3$ and $\angle 4$ are right angles.	1. Given
2. $\angle 3 \cong \angle 4$	2. Theorem 3-6
3. $\overline{BD} \cong \overline{BD}$	3. Theorem 2-2
4. $\triangle ABD \cong \triangle CBD$	4. ASA
5. $\overline{AD} \cong \overline{CD}$	5. CPCTC

9.

STATEMENTS	REASONS
1. J is the midpoint of $\overline{GK}$; $\angle H$ is a right angle; $\angle L$ is a right angle.	1. Given
2. $\overline{GJ} \cong \overline{KJ}$	2. Theorem 2-5
3. $\angle H \cong \angle L$	3. Theorem 3-6
4. $\angle HJG$ and $\angle LJK$ are vertical angles.	4. Definition of Vertical Angles
5. $\angle HJG \cong \angle LJK$	5. Theorem 3-10
6. $\triangle GHJ \cong \triangle KLJ$	6. AAS
7. $\overline{HG} \cong \overline{LK}$	7. CPCTC

10.

STATEMENTS	REASONS
1. J is the midpoint of $\overline{HL}$; $\angle G \cong \angle K$	1. Given
2. $\overline{HJ} \cong \overline{LJ}$	2. Theorem 2-5
3. $\angle HJG$ and $\angle LJK$ are vertical angles.	3. Definition of Vertical Angles
4. $\angle HJG \cong \angle LJK$	4. Theorem 3-10
5. $\triangle GHJ \cong \triangle KLJ$	5. AAS
6. $\angle H \cong \angle L$	6. CPCTC

11.

STATEMENTS	REASONS
1. $\overline{PS}$ and $\overline{SR}$ are in $\mathcal{M}$; $\overline{QS} \perp \mathcal{M}$; $\angle P \cong \angle R$	1. Given
2. $\overline{QS} \perp \overline{PS}$; $\overline{QS} \perp \overline{RS}$	2. Definition of a Line Perpendicular to a Plane
3. $\angle QSP$ and $\angle QSR$ are right angles.	3. Definition of Perpendicular Lines
4. $\angle QSP \cong \angle QSR$	4. Theorem 3-6
5. $\overline{QS} \cong \overline{QS}$	5. Theorem 2-2

6. $\triangle PSQ \cong \triangle RSQ$	6. AAS
7. $\overline{QP} \cong \overline{QR}$	7. CPCTC

12. STATEMENTS	REASONS
1. $\overline{PS}$ and $\overline{SR}$ are in $\mathscr{M}$; $\overline{QS} \perp \mathscr{M}$; $\angle P \cong \angle R$	1. Given
2. $\overline{QS} \perp \overline{PS}$; $\overline{QS} \perp \overline{RS}$	2. Definition of a Line Perpendicular to a Plane
3. $\angle QSP$ and $\angle QSR$ are right angles.	3. Definition of Perpendicular Lines
4. $\angle QSP \cong \angle QSR$	4. Theorem 3-6
5. $\overline{QS} \cong \overline{QS}$	5. Theorem 2-2
6. $\triangle PSQ \cong \triangle RSQ$	6. AAS
7. $\overline{PS} \cong \overline{RS}$	7. CPCTC

PAGE 127 WRITTEN

11. STATEMENTS	REASONS
1. $\overline{AB}$ is an altitude of $\triangle ABD$; $\overline{CD}$ is an altitude of $\triangle BCD$; $\overline{BC} \cong \overline{AD}$; $\overline{CD} \cong \overline{AD}$; $\overline{AB} \cong \overline{CD}$	1. Given
2. $\overline{BD} \cong \overline{BD}$	2. Theorem 2-2
3. $\triangle ABD \cong \triangle CBD$	3. SSS
4. $\angle ABD \cong \angle CBD$	4. CPCTC
5. $\overline{BD}$ bisects $\angle ABC$.	5. Definition of Angle Bisector

12. STATEMENTS	REASONS
1. $\overline{PR}$ is an altitude of $\triangle PQR$; R is the midpoint of $\overline{QT}$ and $\overline{PS}$.	1. Given
2. $\overline{QR} \cong \overline{RT}$; $\overline{PR} \cong \overline{RS}$	2. Theorem 2-5
3. $\angle QRP \cong \angle TRS$	3. Definition of Vertical Angles; Theorem 3-10
4. $\triangle QPR \cong \triangle TSR$	4. SAS
5. $m\angle QPR = 90$	5. Definition of Altitude of a Triangle; Definition of Perpendicular Lines; Definition of Right Angle
6. $\angle QPR \cong \angle TSR$	6. CPCTC
7. $m\angle QPR = m\angle TSR$	7. Definition of Congruent Angles
8. $m\angle TSR = 90$	8. Postulate 2-9
9. $\overline{RS}$ is perpendicular to $\overline{ST}$.	9. Definition of Right Angle; Definition of Perpendicular Lines
10. $\overline{RS}$ is an altitude of $\triangle RST$.	10. Definition of Altitude of a Triangle

13. Given: Isosceles $\triangle ABC$; $\overline{AB} \cong \overline{CB}$; $\overline{BD}$ is a median.

Prove: $\overline{BD}$ bisects $\angle ABC$.

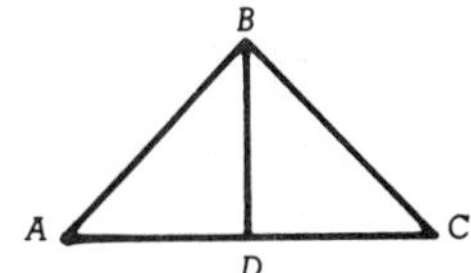

Proof:

STATEMENTS	REASONS
1. Isosceles $\triangle ABC$; $\overline{AB} \cong \overline{CB}$; $\overline{BD}$ is a median.	1. Given
2. D is the midpoint of $\overline{AC}$.	2. Definition of Median of a Triangle
3. $\overline{AD} \cong \overline{DC}$	3. Theorem 2-5
4. $\overline{BD} \cong \overline{BD}$	4. Theorem 2-2
5. $\triangle ABD \cong \triangle CBD$	5. SSS
6. $\angle ABD \cong \angle CBD$	6. CPCTC
7. $\overline{BD}$ bisects $\angle ABC$.	7. Definition of Bisector of an Angle

14. Given: Isosceles $\triangle ABC$; $\overline{BD}$ is a median; $\overline{AB} \cong \overline{CB}$

Prove: $\overline{BD}$ is an altitude.

Proof:

STATEMENTS	REASONS
1. Isosceles $\triangle ABC$; $\overline{BD}$ is a median; $\overline{AB} \cong \overline{CB}$	1. Given
2. D is the midpoint of $\overline{AC}$.	2. Definition of Median
3. $\overline{AD} \cong \overline{CD}$	3. Theorem 2-5

STATEMENTS	REASONS
4. $\overline{BD} \cong \overline{BD}$	4. Theorem 2-2
5. $\triangle ABD \cong \triangle CBD$	5. SSS
6. $\angle ADB \cong \angle CDB$	6. CPCTC
7. $\overline{AC} \perp \overline{BD}$	7. Theorem 3-14
8. $\overline{BD}$ is an altitude.	8. Definition of Altitude of a Triangle

15. Given: $\triangle ABC$; $\overline{CD}$ is a median; $\overline{CD}$ is an altitude.
Prove: $\triangle ABC$ is isosceles.
Proof:

STATEMENTS	REASONS
1. $\triangle ABC$; $\overline{CD}$ is a median; $\overline{CD}$ is an altitude.	1. Given
2. D is the midpoint of $\overline{AB}$.	2. Definition of Median
3. $\overline{AD} \cong \overline{BD}$	3. Theorem 2-5
4. $\overline{CD} \perp \overline{AB}$	4. Definition of Altitude of a Triangle
5. $\angle ADC$ and $\angle BDC$ are right angles.	5. Theorem 3-11
6. $\angle ADC \cong \angle BDC$	6. Theorem 3-6
7. $\overline{CD} \cong \overline{CD}$	7. Theorem 2-2
8. $\triangle ADC \cong \triangle BDC$	8. SAS
9. $\overline{AC} \cong \overline{BC}$	9. CPCTC
10. $\triangle ABC$ is isosceles.	10. Definition of Isosceles Triangle

16. Given: $\triangle ABC$; $\overline{BD}$ is a median; $\overline{BD}$ is an altitude.
Prove: $\overline{BD}$ is an angle bisector of $\angle ABC$.

Proof:

STATEMENTS	REASONS
1. $\triangle ABC$; $\overline{BD}$ is a median; $\overline{BD}$ is an altitude.	1. Given
2. $\overline{BD} \cong \overline{BD}$	2. Theorem 2-2
3. D is the midpoint of $\overline{AC}$.	3. Definition of Median of a Triangle
4. $\overline{AD} \cong \overline{CD}$	4. Definition of Midpoint
5. $\overline{BD} \perp \overline{AC}$	5. Definition of Altitude of a Triangle
6. $\angle ADB \cong \angle CDB$	6. Theorem 3-13
7. $\triangle ADB \cong \triangle CDB$	7. SAS
8. $\angle ABD \cong \angle CBD$	8. CPCTC
9. $\overline{BD}$ bisects $\angle ABC$.	9. Definition of Angle Bisector of a Triangle

17. Given: $\overrightarrow{BD}$ bisects $\angle ABC$; $\overline{DE}$ is an altitude of $\triangle ADB$; $\overline{DF}$ is an altitude of $\triangle CDB$.
Prove: $\overline{DE} \cong \overline{DF}$

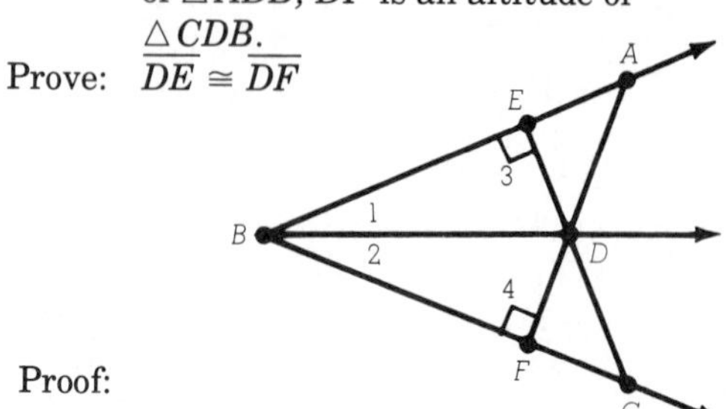

Proof:

STATEMENTS	REASONS
1. $\overrightarrow{BD}$ bisects $\angle ABC$; $\overline{DE}$ is an altitude of $\triangle ADB$; $\overline{DF}$ is an altitude of $\triangle CDB$.	1. Given
2. $\angle 1 \cong \angle 2$	2. Definition of Angle Bisector of a Triangle
3. $\overline{DE} \perp \overline{AB}$; $\overline{DF} \perp \overline{BC}$	3. Definition of Altitude of a Triangle
4. $\angle 3$ and $\angle 4$ are right angles.	4. Theorem 3-11
5. $\angle 3 \cong \angle 4$	5. Theorem 3-6
6. $\overline{BD} \cong \overline{BD}$	6. Theorem 2-2
7. $\triangle EBD \cong \triangle FBD$	7. AAS
8. $\overline{DE} \cong \overline{DF}$	8. CPCTC

18. Given: $\triangle ACD \cong \triangle EFG$; $\overline{DB}$ and $\overline{GH}$ are medians.
Prove: $\overline{DB} \cong \overline{GH}$
Proof:

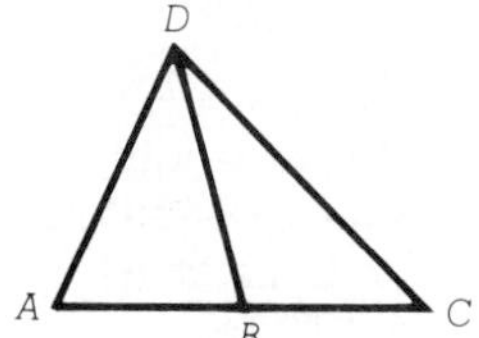

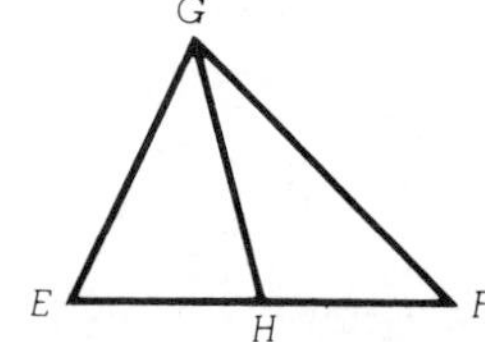

STATEMENTS	REASONS
1. $\triangle ACD \cong \triangle EFG$; $\overline{DB}$ and $\overline{GH}$ are medians.	1. Given
2. B is the midpoint of $\overline{AC}$; H is the midpoint of $\overline{EF}$.	2. Definition of Median of a Triangle
3. $AB = BC$; $EH = HF$	3. Definition of Midpoint
4. $AB + BC = AC$; $EH + HF = EF$	4. Definition of Between
5. $\overline{AC} \cong \overline{EF}$; $\overline{AD} \cong \overline{EG}$; $\angle A \cong \angle E$	5. CPCTC
6. $AC = EF$	6. Definition of Congruent Segments
7. $AB + BC = EH + HF$	7. Postulate 2-9
8. $AB + AB = EH + EH$	8. Postulate 2-9
9. $2AB = 2EH$	9. Postulate 2-12; Postulate 2-14; Postulate 2-9
10. $AB = EH$	10. Postulate 2-8
11. $\overline{AB} \cong \overline{EH}$	11. Definition of Congruent Segments
12. $\triangle ADB \cong \triangle EGH$	12. SAS
13. $\overline{DB} \cong \overline{GH}$	13. CPCTC

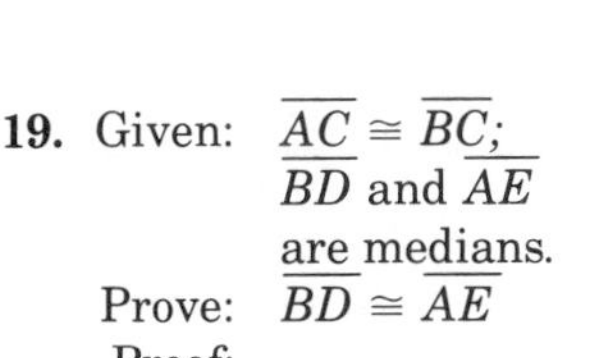

19. Given: $\overline{AC} \cong \overline{BC}$; $\overline{BD}$ and $\overline{AE}$ are medians.
Prove: $\overline{BD} \cong \overline{AE}$
Proof:

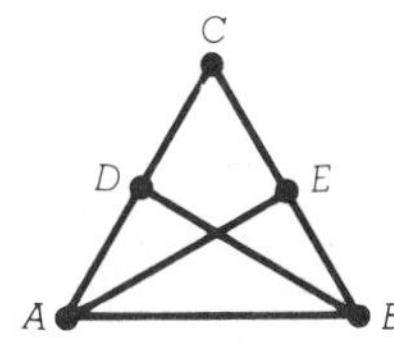

STATEMENTS	REASONS
1. $\overline{AC} \cong \overline{BC}$; $\overline{BD}$ and $\overline{AE}$ are medians.	1. Given
2. $AC = BC$	2. Definition of Congruent Segments
3. $AD + DC = AC$; $BE + EC = BC$	3. Definition of Between
4. $AD + DC = BE + EC$	4. Postulate 2-9
5. D is the midpoint of $\overline{AC}$; E is the midpoint of $\overline{BC}$.	5. Definition of Median of a Triangle

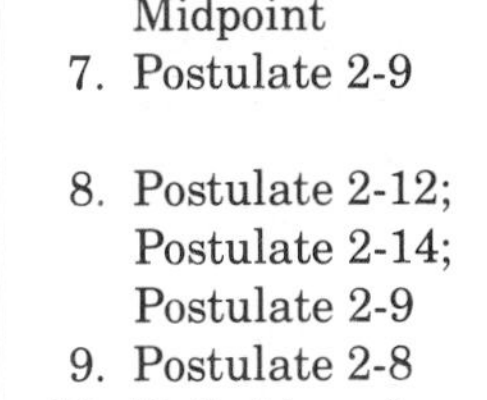

STATEMENTS	REASONS
6. $AD = DC$; $BE = EC$	6. Definition of Midpoint
7. $DC + DC = EC + EC$	7. Postulate 2-9
8. $2DC = 2EC$	8. Postulate 2-12; Postulate 2-14; Postulate 2-9
9. $DC = EC$	9. Postulate 2-8
10. $\overline{DC} \cong \overline{EC}$	10. Definition of Congruent Segments
11. $\angle C \cong \angle C$	11. Theorem 3-1
12. $\triangle DCB \cong \triangle ECA$	12. SAS
13. $\overline{BD} \cong \overline{AE}$	13. CPCTC

20. Given: $\angle ABC$ with bisector $\overrightarrow{BD}$.
Prove: $\overrightarrow{BD}$ is the only bisector of $\angle ABC$.
Proof:

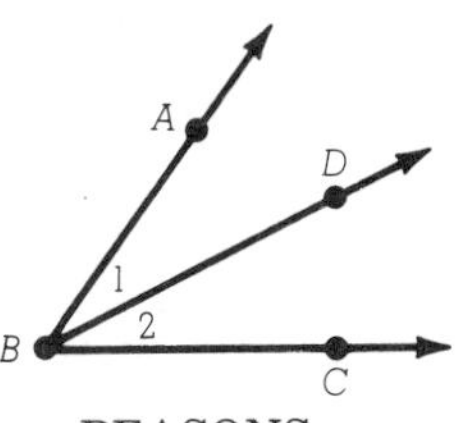

STATEMENTS	REASONS
1. $\overrightarrow{BD}$ bisects $\angle ABC$.	1. Given
2. $\angle 1 \cong \angle 2$	2. Definition of Angle Bisector of a Triangle
3. $m\angle 1 = m\angle 2$	3. Definition of Congruent Angles
4. $m\angle 1 = x$	4. Postulate 3-1
5. $m\angle 2 = x$	5. Postulate 2-9
6. $\overrightarrow{BD}$ is the only bisector of $\angle ABC$.	6. Postulate 3-2

PAGE 128 CHALLENGE

1. It is isosceles. **2.** It is isosceles. **3.** It is obtuse. **4.** It is equilateral. **5.** The three *medians* of any triangle intersect in one point in the interior of the triangle; The *altitudes* of an *acute* triangle intersect at one point in the interior of the triangle; The *altitudes* of a *right* triangle intersect at the vertex of the right angle; The lines containing the *altitudes* of an *obtuse* triangle intersect at one point in the exterior of the triangle; The *angle bisectors* of any triangle intersect at one point in the interior of the triangle.

PAGE 131 WRITTEN

10. *Yes* **11.** *No*; $\overline{PQ}$ has exactly one midpoint, X, but $\overline{RX}$ is not necessarily perpendicular to

$\overline{PQ}$. **12.** *No;* $\angle R$ has exactly one bisector, but that bisector may not bisect $\overline{PQ}$. **13.** *Yes* **14.** *Yes* **15.** *No;* since $\overline{QP}$ intersects $\overline{PR}$, $\overline{XY}$ cannot be perpendicular to both.

16. STATEMENTS	REASONS
1. $\overline{PQ} \cong \overline{PS}$; $\overline{QR} \cong \overline{SR}$	1. Given
2. Draw $\overline{PR}$.	2. Postulate 1-1
3. $\overline{PR} \cong \overline{PR}$	3. Theorem 2-2
4. $\triangle PQR \cong \triangle PSR$	4. SSS
5. $\angle Q \cong \angle S$	5. CPCTC

17. STATEMENTS	REASONS
1. $\overline{AB} \cong \overline{BC}$	1. Given
2. $\angle 1 \cong \angle 2$	2. Theorem 4-6
3. $\angle 1$ and $\angle 3$ are a linear pair; $\angle 2$ and $\angle 4$ are a linear pair.	3. Definition of Linear Pair
4. $\angle 1$ and $\angle 3$ are supplementary; $\angle 2$ and $\angle 4$ are supplementary.	4. Postulate 3-4
5. $\angle 3 \cong \angle 4$	5. Theorem 3-3

18. STATEMENTS	REASONS
1. $\overline{PQ} \cong \overline{RS}$; $\overline{PS} \cong \overline{RQ}$	1. Given
2. Draw $\overline{SQ}$.	2. Postulate 1-1
3. $\overline{SQ} \cong \overline{QS}$	3. Theorem 2-2
4. $\triangle QSP \cong \triangle SQR$	4. SSS
5. $\angle P \cong \angle R$	5. CPCTC

19. STATEMENTS	REASONS
1. $\overline{ZT} \cong \overline{ZR}$; $\overline{TX} \cong \overline{RY}$	1. Given
2. $\angle 2 \cong \angle 3$	2. Theorem 4-6
3. $\angle 1$ and $\angle 2$ are a linear pair; $\angle 3$ and $\angle 4$ are a linear pair.	3. Definition of Linear Pair
4. $\angle 1$ and $\angle 2$ are supplementary; $\angle 3$ and $\angle 4$ are supplementary.	4. Postulate 3-4
5. $\angle 1 \cong \angle 4$	5. Theorem 3-3
6. $\triangle XTZ \cong \triangle YRZ$	6. SAS
7. $\angle 5 \cong \angle 7$	7. CPCTC

20. STATEMENTS	REASONS
1. $\overline{AB} \cong \overline{CB}$; $\overline{AD} \cong \overline{CD}$	1. Given
2. Draw $\overline{BD}$.	2. Postulate 1-1
3. $\overline{BD} \cong \overline{BD}$	3. Theorem 2-3
4. $\triangle BAD \cong \triangle BCD$	4. SSS
5. $\angle A \cong \angle C$	5. CPCTC

21. Given: $\overline{AB} \cong \overline{BC}$; $\overline{BC} \cong \overline{AC}$; $\overline{AC} \cong \overline{AB}$

Prove: $\triangle ABC$ is equiangular.

Proof:

STATEMENTS	REASONS
1. $\overline{AB} \cong \overline{BC}$; $\overline{BC} \cong \overline{AC}$; $\overline{AC} \cong \overline{AB}$	1. Given
2. $\angle A \cong \angle B$; $\angle B \cong \angle C$; $\angle C \cong \angle A$	2. Theorem 4-6
3. $\triangle ABC$ is equiangular.	3. Definition of Equiangular Triangles

22. Given: $\overline{AB} \cong \overline{BC}$; $\overline{BC} \cong \overline{AC}$; $\overline{AC} \cong \overline{AB}$

Prove: $m\angle A = 60$; $m\angle B = 60$; $m\angle C = 60$

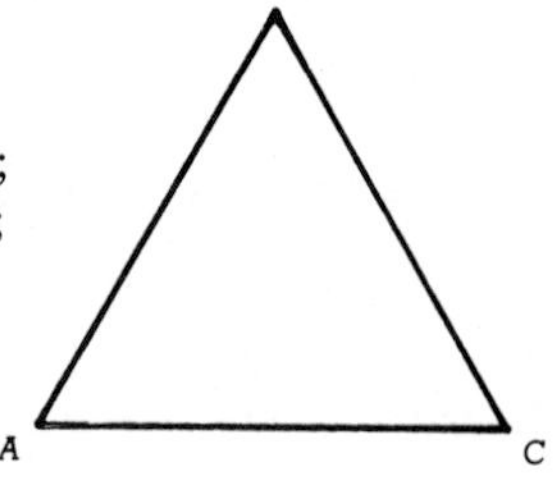

Proof:

STATEMENTS	REASONS
1. $\overline{AB} \cong \overline{BC}$; $\overline{BC} \cong \overline{AC}$; $\overline{AC} \cong \overline{AB}$	1. Given
2. $\angle A \cong \angle B$; $\angle B \cong \angle C$; $\angle C \cong \angle A$	2. Theorem 4-7
3. $m\angle A = m\angle B$; $m\angle B = m\angle C$; $m\angle C = m\angle A$	3. Definition of Congruent Angles
4. $m\angle A + m\angle B + m\angle C = 180$	4. Theorem 4-1
5. $m\angle A + m\angle A + m\angle A = 180$	5. Postulate 2-9
6. $3m\angle A = 180$	6. Postulate 2-14
7. $m\angle A = 60$	7. Postulate 2-8
8. $m\angle B = 60$; $m\angle C = 60$	8. Postulate 2-9

23. Given: $\triangle PQR$; $\angle P \cong \angle R$
Prove: $\overline{PQ} \cong \overline{RQ}$

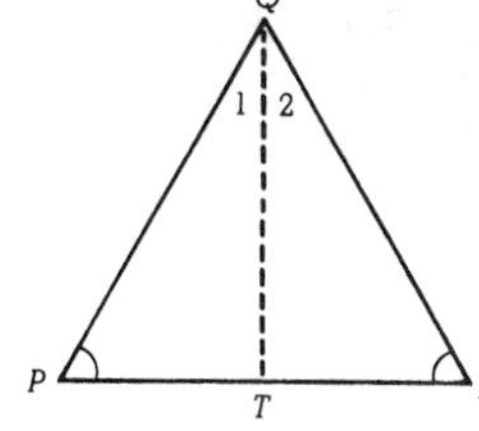

Proof:

STATEMENTS	REASONS
1. Let $\overline{QT}$ bisect $\angle PQR$.	1. Auxiliary line; Definition of Angle Bisector
2. $\angle P \cong \angle R$	2. Given
3. $\angle 1 \cong \angle 2$	3. Definition of an Angle Bisector of a Triangle
4. $\overline{QT} \cong \overline{QT}$	4. Theorem 2-2
5. $\triangle PQT \cong \triangle RQT$	5. AAS
6. $\overline{PQ} \cong \overline{RQ}$	6. CPCTC

PAGE 135 WRITTEN

1.

STATEMENTS	REASONS
1. $\angle Q$ and $\angle S$ are right angles; $\angle 1 \cong \angle 2$	1. Given
2. $\triangle QRP$ and $\triangle SPR$ are right triangles.	2. Definition of Right Triangle
3. $\overline{PR} \cong \overline{RP}$	3. Theorem 2-2
4. $\triangle QRP \cong \triangle SPR$	4. HA
5. $\overline{QP} \cong \overline{SR}$	5. CPCTC

2.

STATEMENTS	REASONS
1. $\angle Q$ and $\angle S$ are right angles; $\angle 1 \cong \angle 2$	1. Given
2. $\triangle QRP$ and $\triangle SPR$ are right triangles.	2. Definition of Right Triangle
3. $\overline{PR} \cong \overline{RP}$	3. Theorem 2-2
4. $\triangle QRP \cong \triangle SPR$	4. HA
5. $\overline{QR} \cong \overline{SP}$	5. CPCTC

3.

STATEMENTS	REASONS
1. $\angle Q$ and $\angle S$ are right angles; $\overline{QP} \cong \overline{SR}$	1. Given
2. $\triangle QRP$ and $\triangle SPR$ are right triangles.	2. Definition of Right Triangle
3. $\overline{PR} \cong \overline{RP}$	3. Theorem 2-2
4. $\triangle QRP \cong \triangle SPR$	4. HL
5. $\overline{QR} \cong \overline{SP}$	5. CPCTC

4.

STATEMENTS	REASONS
1. $\angle Q$ and $\angle S$ are right angles; $\overline{QP} \cong \overline{SR}$	1. Given
2. $\triangle QRP$ and $\triangle SPR$ are right triangles.	2. Definition of Right Triangle
3. $\overline{PR} \cong \overline{RP}$	3. Theorem 2-2
4. $\triangle QRP \cong \triangle SPR$	4. HL
5. $\angle 4 \cong \angle 3$	5. CPCTC

5.

STATEMENTS	REASONS
1. $\overline{BA} \perp \overline{AE}$; $\overline{DE} \perp \overline{AE}$; C is the midpoint of $\overline{AE}$; $\angle ABC \cong \angle EDC$	1. Given
2. $\overline{AC} \cong \overline{EC}$	2. Theorem 2-5
3. $\angle A$ and $\angle E$ are right angles.	3. Theorem 3-11
4. $\triangle BAC$ and $\triangle DEC$ are right triangles.	4. Definition of Right Triangle
5. $\triangle BAC \cong \triangle DEC$	5. LA
6. $\angle 1 \cong \angle 2$	6. CPCTC

6.

STATEMENTS	REASONS
1. $\overline{AC} \cong \overline{EC}$; $\angle 3 \cong \angle 4$; $\angle A$ and $\angle E$ are right angles.	1. Given
2. $\triangle ABC$ and $\triangle EDC$ are right triangles.	2. Definition of Right Triangle
3. $\overline{BC} \cong \overline{DC}$	3. Theorem 4-9
4. $\triangle BAC \cong \triangle DEC$	4. HL
5. $\angle 1 \cong \angle 2$	5. CPCTC

7.

STATEMENTS	REASONS
1. $\overline{BD} \perp \overline{XC}$; X is the midpoint of $\overline{BD}$.	1. Given
2. $\angle 5 \cong \angle 6$	2. Theorem 3-13
3. $\overline{BX} \cong \overline{DX}$	3. Theorem 2-5
4. $\overline{XC} \cong \overline{XC}$	4. Theorem 2-2
5. $\triangle BXC \cong \triangle DXC$	5. SAS or LL
6. $\angle 3 \cong \angle 4$	6. CPCTC

8.

STATEMENTS	REASONS
1. $\overline{CB} \cong \overline{CD}$; $\angle 5 \cong \angle 6$	1. Given
2. $\angle 3 \cong \angle 4$	2. Theorem 4-6
3. $\triangle BXC \cong \triangle DXC$	3. AAS

9. Given: $\triangle ABC$ and $\triangle RPQ$ are right triangles; $\angle A$ and $\angle R$ are right angles; $\overline{BC} \cong \overline{PQ}$; $\angle B \cong \angle P$

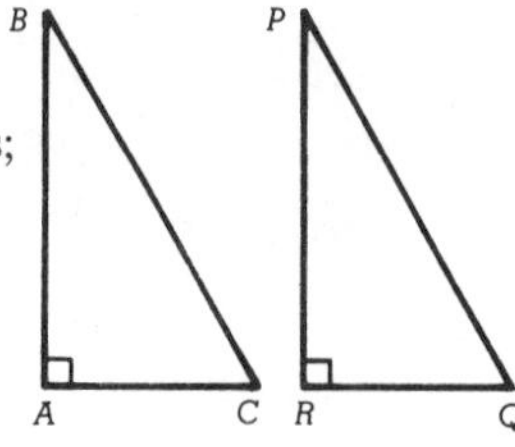

Prove: $\triangle ABC \cong \triangle RPQ$

Proof:

STATEMENTS	REASONS
1. $\triangle ABC$ and $\triangle RPQ$ are right triangles; $\angle A$ and $\angle R$ are right angles; $\overline{BC} \cong \overline{PQ}$; $\angle B \cong \angle P$	1. Given
2. $\angle A \cong \angle R$	2. Theorem 3-6
3. $\triangle ABC \cong \triangle RPQ$	3. AAS

10. Given: $\triangle MPQ$ and $\triangle RTV$ are right triangles; $\angle M$ and $\angle R$ are right angles; $\overline{MP} \cong \overline{RT}$; $\overline{MQ} \cong \overline{RV}$

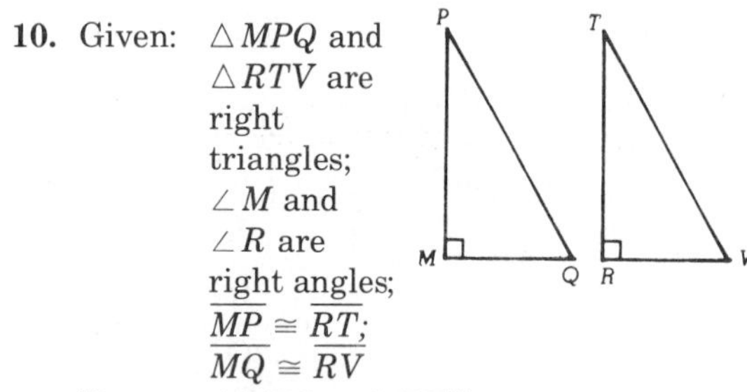

Prove: $\triangle MPQ \cong \triangle RTV$

Proof:

STATEMENTS	REASONS
1. $\triangle MPQ$ and $\triangle RTV$ are right triangles; $\angle M$ and $\angle R$ are right angles; $\overline{MP} \cong \overline{RT}$; $\overline{MQ} \cong \overline{RV}$	1. Given
2. $\angle M \cong \angle R$	2. Theorem 3-6
3. $\triangle MPQ \cong \triangle RTV$	3. SAS

11. *CASE I:*

Given: $\angle B$ and $\angle E$ are right angles; $\angle C \cong \angle F$; $\overline{BC} \cong \overline{EF}$

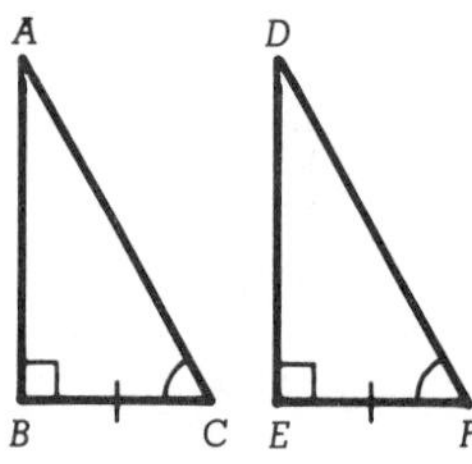

Prove: $\triangle ABC \cong \triangle DEF$

Proof:

STATEMENTS	REASONS
1. $\angle B$ and $\angle E$ are right angles; $\angle C \cong \angle F$; $\overline{BC} \cong \overline{EF}$	1. Given
2. $\angle B \cong \angle E$	2. Theorem 3-6
3. $\triangle ABC \cong \triangle DEF$	3. ASA

CASE II:

Given: $\angle A \cong \angle D$; $\overline{BC} \cong \overline{EF}$; $\angle B$ and $\angle E$ are right angles.

Prove: $\triangle ABC \cong \triangle DEF$

Proof:

STATEMENTS	REASONS
1. $\angle A \cong \angle D$; $\overline{BC} \cong \overline{EF}$; $\angle B$ and $\angle E$ are right angles.	1. Given
2. $\angle B \cong \angle E$	2. Theorem 3-6
3. $\triangle ABC \cong \triangle DEF$	3. AAS

PAGES 137–138 CHAPTER REVIEW

15.

STATEMENTS	REASONS
1. $\overline{AC}$ and $\overline{BD}$ bisect each other.	1. Given
2. E is the midpoint of $\overline{AC}$ and $\overline{BD}$.	2. Definition of Bisector of a Segment
3. $\overline{BE} \cong \overline{DE}$; $\overline{AE} \cong \overline{EC}$	3. Theorem 2-5
4. $\angle BEA$ and $\angle DEC$ are vertical angles.	4. Definition of Vertical Angles
5. $\angle BEA \cong \angle DEC$	5. Theorem 3-10
6. $\triangle BEA \cong \triangle DEC$	6. SAS
7. $\overline{AB} \cong \overline{CD}$	7. CPCTC

16.

STATEMENTS	REASONS
1. E is the midpoint of $\overline{AC}$; $\angle 1 \cong \angle 2$	1. Given
2. $\overline{AE} \cong \overline{CE}$	2. Theorem 2-5
3. $\angle BEC$ and $\angle DEA$ are vertical angles.	3. Definition of Vertical Angles
4. $\angle BEC \cong \angle DEA$	4. Theorem 3-10
5. $\triangle BEC \cong \triangle DEA$	5. ASA
6. $\angle 3 \cong \angle 4$	6. CPCTC

17.

STATEMENTS	REASONS
1. $\overline{PR} \perp \overline{QS}$; $\angle Q \cong \angle S$	1. Given
2. $\angle 3 \cong \angle 4$	2. Theorem 3-13
3. $\overline{PR} \cong \overline{PR}$	3. Theorem 2-2

STATEMENTS	REASONS
4. $\triangle SRP \cong \triangle QRP$	4. AAS
5. $\overline{SR} \cong \overline{QR}$	5. CPCTC
6. $SR = QR$	6. Definition of Congruent Segments
7. R is the midpoint of $\overline{QS}$.	7. Definition of Midpoint

18.

STATEMENTS	REASONS
1. $\overline{PQ} \cong \overline{PS}$; $\overline{PR}$ bisects $\overline{QS}$.	1. Given
2. R is the midpoint of $\overline{QS}$.	2. Definition of Bisector of a Segment
3. $\overline{QR} \cong \overline{SR}$	3. Theorem 2-5
4. $\overline{PR} \cong \overline{PR}$	4. Theorem 2-2
5. $\triangle PRS \cong \triangle PRQ$	5. SSS
6. $\angle 1 \cong \angle 2$	6. CPCTC

19.

STATEMENTS	REASONS
1. $\overline{AB} \cong \overline{CB}$; $\overline{BP}$ bisects $\angle ABC$.	1. Given
2. $\angle 1 \cong \angle 2$	2. Definition of Bisector of an Angle
3. $\overline{BP} \cong \overline{BP}$	3. Theorem 2-2
4. $\triangle ABP \cong \triangle CBP$	4. SAS
5. $\overline{AP} \cong \overline{CP}$	5. CPCTC
6. $AP = CP$	6. Definition of Congruent Segments
7. P is the midpoint of $\overline{AC}$.	7. Definition of Midpoint of a Segment
8. $\overline{BP}$ is a median of $\triangle ABC$.	8. Definition of Median of a Triangle

20.

STATEMENTS	REASONS
1. $\overline{BC} \cong \overline{BA}$; $\overline{PB}$ is a median of $\triangle ABC$.	1. Given
2. P is the midpoint of $\overline{AC}$.	2. Definition of Median of a Triangle
3. $\overline{AP} \cong \overline{CP}$	3. Theorem 2-5
4. $\overline{BP} \cong \overline{BP}$	4. Theorem 2-2
5. $\triangle ABP \cong \triangle CBP$	5. SSS
6. $\angle 3 \cong \angle 4$	6. CPCTC
7. $\overline{BP} \perp \overline{AC}$	7. Theorem 3-14
8. $\overline{PB}$ is an altitude of $\triangle ABC$.	8. Definition of Altitude of a Triangle

21.

STATEMENTS	REASONS
1. $\angle A \cong \angle D$; $\overline{AB} \cong \overline{DC}$; E is the midpoint of $\overline{AD}$.	1. Given
2. $\overline{AE} \cong \overline{DE}$	2. Theorem 2-5
3. $\triangle BAE \cong \triangle CDE$	3. SAS
4. $\overline{BE} \cong \overline{CE}$	4. CPCTC
5. $\angle 3 \cong \angle 4$	5. Theorem 4-6

22.

STATEMENTS	REASONS
1. $\angle A$ and $\angle C$ are right angles; $\angle 2 \cong \angle 4$	1. Given
2. $\triangle BAD$ and $\triangle DCB$ are right triangles.	2. Definition of Right Triangle
3. $\overline{BD} \cong \overline{DB}$	3. Theorem 2-2
4. $\triangle BAD \cong \triangle DCB$	4. HA
5. $\overline{AB} \cong \overline{CB}$	5. CPCTC

PAGE 139 CHAPTER TEST

16.

STATEMENTS	REASONS
1. $\triangle ABC$ is equilateral; $\angle 1 \cong \angle 6$; $\angle 2 \cong 3$; $\angle 4 \cong \angle 5$	1. Given
2. $\overline{AB} \cong \overline{CB}$	2. Definition of Equilateral Triangle
3. $\overline{BD} \cong \overline{BD}$	3. Theorem 2-2
4. $\triangle ABD \cong \triangle CBD$	4. SAS
5. $\overline{AD} \cong \overline{CD}$	5. CPCTC

17.

STATEMENTS	REASONS
1. $\angle L$ and $\angle N$ are right angles; $\overline{LP} \cong \overline{NM}$	1. Given
2. $\overline{MP} \cong \overline{PM}$	2. Theorem 2-2
3. $\triangle PLM$ and $\triangle MNP$ are right triangles.	3. Definition of Right Triangle
4. $\triangle PLM \cong \triangle MNP$	4. HL
5. $\overline{LM} \cong \overline{NP}$	5. CPCTC

18.

STATEMENTS	REASONS
1. $\angle L$ and $\angle N$ are right angles; $\overline{LM} \cong \overline{NP}$	1. Given
2. $\triangle PLM$ and $\triangle MNP$ are right triangles.	2. Definition of Right Triangle

3. $\overline{PM} \cong \overline{MP}$	3. Theorem 2-2
4. $\triangle PLM \cong \triangle MNP$	4. HL
5. $\angle 1 \cong \angle 2$	5. CPCTC
6. $m\angle 1 = m\angle 2$	6. Definition of Congruent Angles
7. $m\angle N + m\angle 2 + m\angle 3 = 180$	7. Theorem 4-1
8. $m\angle 2 + m\angle 3 = 90$	8. Postulate 2-7; Postulate 2-9
9. $m\angle 1 + m\angle 3 = 90$	9. Postulate 2-9
10. $m\angle 1 + m\angle 3 = m\angle LMN$	10. Postulate 3-3
11. $m\angle LMN = 90$	11. Postulate 2-9;
12. $\angle LMN$ is a right angle.	12. Definition of Right Angle

CHAPTER 5 TRIANGLE INEQUALITIES

PAGE 144 WRITTEN

15.

STATEMENTS	REASONS
1. $\angle 1 \cong \angle 2$	1. Given
2. $\angle 1$ and $\angle 3$ are a linear pair; $\angle 4$ and $\angle 2$ are a linear pair.	2. Definition of Linear Pair
3. $\angle 1$ and $\angle 3$ are supplementary; $\angle 4$ and $\angle 2$ are supplementary.	3. Postulate 3-4
4. $\angle 3 \cong \angle 4$	4. Theorem 3-3
5. $\overline{PQ} \cong \overline{RQ}$	5. Theorem 4-9
6. $\triangle PQR$ is isosceles.	6. Definition of Isosceles Triangle

16.

STATEMENTS	REASONS
1. $m\angle 1 > m\angle 3$	1. Given
2. $m\angle 3 > m\angle 2$	2. Theorem 5-3
3. $m\angle 1 > m\angle 2$	3. Postulate 2-18

17.

STATEMENTS	REASONS
1. P, Q, and N are collinear.	1. Given
2. $m\angle 1 > m\angle 2$ in $\triangle QON$, $m\angle 2 > m\angle 3$ in $\triangle PQO$.	2. Theorem 5-3
3. $m\angle 1 > m\angle 3$	3. Postulate 2-18

18.

STATEMENTS	REASONS
1. $\overline{NM} \cong \overline{MO}$, N, O, and K are collinear; N, M, and L are collinear.	1. Given
2. $m\angle 1 > m\angle KNL$ in $\triangle KLN$.	2. Theorem 5-3
3. $\angle 2 \cong \angle KNL$	3. Theorem 4-6
4. $m\angle 2 \cong m\angle KNL$	4. Definition of Congruent Angles
5. $m\angle 1 > m\angle 2$	5. Postulate 2-9

19. Given: $\triangle PQR$; $\angle 1$ is an exterior angle of $\triangle PQR$.

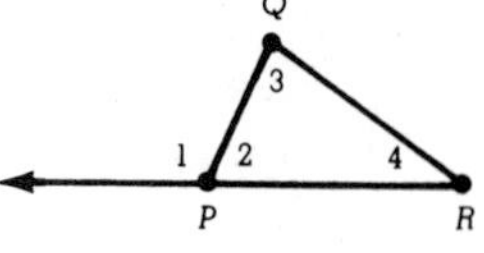

Prove: $m\angle 1 = m\angle 3 + m\angle 4$

Proof:

STATEMENTS	REASONS
1. $\angle 1$ is an exterior angle of $\triangle PQR$.	1. Given
2. $\angle 1$ and $\angle 2$ are a linear pair.	2. Definition of a Linear Pair
3. $m\angle 1 + m\angle 2 = 180$	3. Postulate 3-4
4. $m\angle 2 + m\angle 3 + m\angle 4 = 180$	4. Theorem 4-1
5. $m\angle 1 + m\angle 2 = m\angle 2 + m\angle 3 + m\angle 4$	5. Postulate 2-9
6. $m\angle 1 = m\angle 3 + m\angle 4$	6. Postulate 2-7

22.

STATEMENTS	REASONS
1. $b = x + c$	1. Given
2. $y = b + c$	2. Theorem 5-1
3. $y = x + c + c$	3. Postulate 2-9
4. $y > x$	4. Theorem 5-2

23.

STATEMENTS	REASONS
1. $\overline{PQ} \cong \overline{PS}$	1. Given
2. $\angle 1 \cong \angle 2$	2. Theorem 4-6
3. $m\angle 1 = m\angle 2$	3. Definition of Congruent Angles
4. $m\angle SQR = m\angle 1 + m\angle 3$	4. Postulate 3-3
5. $m\angle SQR = m\angle 2 + m\angle 3$	5. Postulate 2-9
6. $m\angle SQR > m\angle 2$	6. Theorem 5-2

PAGE 150 WRITTEN

28.

STATEMENTS	REASONS
1. $\overline{PM} \cong \overline{QO}$, $\angle MPQ \cong \angle OQP$	1. Given
2. $\overline{PQ} \cong \overline{QP}$	2. Theorem 2-2
3. $\triangle MPQ \cong \triangle OQP$	3. SAS
4. $\angle 1 \cong \angle 2$	4. CPCTC
5. $\overline{PN} \cong \overline{QN}$	5. Theorem 4-9

29.

STATEMENTS	REASONS
1. $\overline{XW} \perp \overline{WZ}$, $\overline{YZ} \perp \overline{WZ}$	1. Given
2. $\angle XWZ$ and $\angle YZW$ are right angles.	2. Definition of Perpendicular Lines
3. $\triangle XWZ$ and $\triangle YZW$ are right triangles.	3. Definition of Right Triangle
4. $\overline{XW} \cong \overline{ZY}$	4. Given
5. $\overline{WZ} \cong \overline{WZ}$	5. Theorem 2-2
6. $\triangle XWZ \cong \triangle YZW$	6. LL
7. $\angle WXZ \cong \angle ZYW$	7. CPCTC
8. $\angle XPW \cong \angle YPZ$	8. Theorem 3-10
9. $\triangle XWP \cong \triangle YZP$	9. AAS
10. $\overline{XP} \cong \overline{YP}$	10. CPCTC

PAGES 154–155 WRITTEN

1. Given: $\triangle PQR$, $PQ > QR$

Prove: $m\angle 2 > m\angle 1$

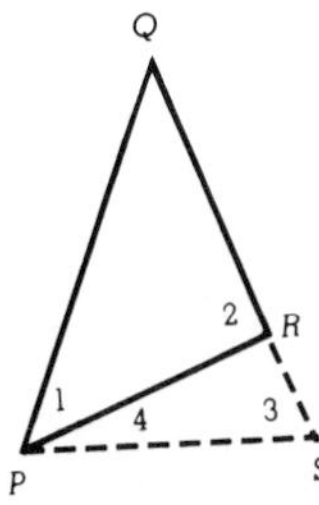

Proof:

STATEMENTS	REASONS
1. $\triangle PQR$, $PQ > QR$	1. Given
2. Extend $\overline{QR}$ to S so that $\overline{QS} \cong \overline{PQ}$.	2. Postulate 2-2
3. $\angle QPS \cong \angle QSP$	3. Theorem 4-6
4. $m\angle QPS = m\angle 1 + m\angle 4$	4. Postulate 3-3
5. $m\angle QPS = m\angle QSP$	5. Definition of Congruent Angles
6. $m\angle QSP = m\angle 1 + m\angle 4$	6. Postulate 2-9
7. $m\angle 2 = m\angle 3 + m\angle 4$	7. Theorem 5-1
8. $m\angle 2 = m\angle 1 + m\angle 4 + m\angle 4$	8. Postulate 2-9
9. $m\angle 2 > m\angle 1$	9. Theorem 5-2

2. *CASE I:*

Given: $\overline{AB} \perp \mathscr{M}$; $\overline{AC}$ is any other segment joining A and $\mathscr{M}$.

Prove: $AC > AB$

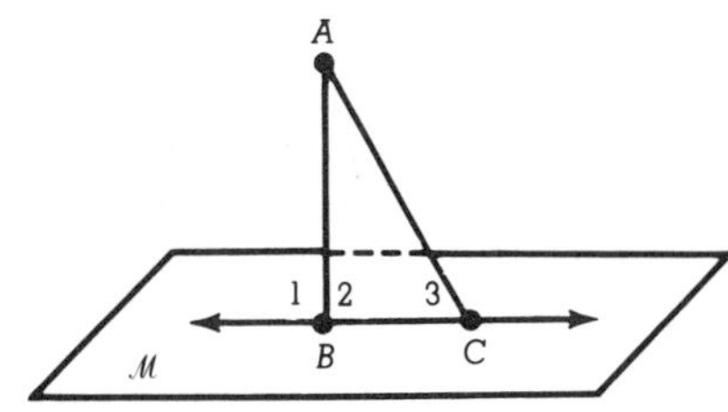

Proof:

STATEMENTS	REASONS
1. $\overline{AB} \perp \mathscr{M}$	1. Given
2. Draw $\overleftrightarrow{BC}$.	2. Postulate 1-1
3. $\overleftrightarrow{BC}$ is in $\mathscr{M}$.	3. Postulate 1-5
4. $\overline{AB} \perp \overleftrightarrow{BC}$	4. Definition of a Line Perpendicular to a Plane
5. $\angle 1 \cong \angle 2$	5. Theorem 3-13
6. $m\angle 1 > m\angle 3$	6. Theorem 5-3
7. $m\angle 1 = m\angle 2$	7. Definition of Congruent Angles
8. $m\angle 2 > m\angle 3$	8. Postulate 2-9
9. $AC > AB$	9. Theorem 5-5

CASE II:

Given: Point B is a point in $\mathscr{M}$; A is not in $\mathscr{M}$; $AC > AB$ for all other points C in $\mathscr{M}$.

Prove: $\overline{AB} \perp \mathscr{M}$

Proof:

STATEMENTS	REASONS
1. $AC > AB$ for all other points C in $\mathscr{M}$.	1. Given
2. Draw $\overleftrightarrow{BC}$	2. Postulate 1-1
3. $\overleftrightarrow{BC}$ is in $\mathscr{M}$.	3. Postulate 1-5
4. $\overline{AB} \perp \overleftrightarrow{BC}$ for all points $C \neq B$ in $\mathscr{M}$.	4. Theorem 5-6
5. $\overline{AB} \perp \mathscr{M}$	5. Definition of a Line Perpendicular to a Plane

3.

STATEMENTS	REASONS
1. $\triangle ABC$, $\angle A$ is a right angle.	1. Given
2. $m\angle A = 90$	2. Definition of Right Angle
3. $\angle B$ and $\angle C$ are complementary.	3. Theorem 4-3
4. $m\angle B + m\angle C = 90$	4. Definition of Complementary Angles
5. $m\angle A = m\angle B + m\angle C$	5. Postulate 2-9
6. $m\angle A > m\angle C$	6. Theorem 5-2
7. $BC > BA$	7. Theorem 5-5

4.

STATEMENTS	REASONS
1. $\triangle ABC$, $\angle A$ is a right angle.	1. Given
2. $m\angle A = 90$	2. Definition of Right Angle
3. $\angle B$ and $\angle C$ are complementary.	3. Theorem 4-3
4. $m\angle B + m\angle C = 90$	4. Definition of Complementary Angles
5. $m\angle A = m\angle B + m\angle C$	5. Postulate 2-9
6. $m\angle A > m\angle B$	6. Theorem 5-2
7. $BC > AC$	7. Theorem 5-5

5.

STATEMENTS	REASONS
1. $\triangle PQR$; $QR > QP$, $\overline{PR} \cong \overline{PQ}$	1. Given
2. $PR = QP$	2. Definition of Congruent Segments
3. $QR > PR$	3. Postulate 2-9

6.

STATEMENTS	REASONS
1. $\triangle PQR$, $QR > QP$, $\overline{PR} \cong \overline{PQ}$	1. Given
2. $PR = QP$	2. Definition of Congruent Segments
3. $QR > PR$	3. Postulate 2-9
4. $m\angle P > m\angle Q$	4. Theorem 5-4

7.

STATEMENTS	REASONS
1. $TE > AE$, $m\angle P > m\angle PAE$	1. Given
2. $AE > PE$	2. Theorem 5-5
3. $TE > PE$	3. Postulate 2-18

8.

STATEMENTS	REASONS
1. $\overline{AE} \cong \overline{EK}$	1. Given
2. $\angle K \cong \angle EAK$	2. Theorem 4-6
3. $m\angle K = m\angle EAK$	3. Definition of Congruent Angles
4. $m\angle 1 > m\angle K$	4. Theorem 5-3
5. $m\angle 1 > m\angle EAK$	5. Postulate 2-9
6. $m\angle EAK > m\angle 2$	6. Theorem 5-3
7. $m\angle 1 > m\angle 2$	7. Postulate 2-18

PAGES 158–159 WRITTEN

7.

STATEMENTS	REASONS
1. $\angle ABC \cong \angle ACB$	1. Given
2. $AD + AC > CD$	2. Theorem 5-8
3. $\overline{AB} \cong \overline{AC}$	3. Theorem 4-9
4. $AB = AC$	4. Definition of Congruent Segments
5. $AD + AB > CD$	5. Postulate 2-9

8.

STATEMENTS	REASONS
1. $\triangle PTS \cong \triangle QRS$	1. Given
2. $PS + ST > PT$	2. Theorem 5-8
3. $\overline{PT} \cong \overline{QS}$, $\overline{ST} \cong \overline{SR}$	3. CPCTC
4. $ST = SR$, $PT = QS$	4. Definition of Congruent Segments
5. $PS + SR > QS$	5. Postulate 2-9
6. $PS + SR = PR$	6. Definition of Between
7. $PR > QS$	7. Postulate 2-9

9.

STATEMENTS	REASONS
1. $\overline{ED}$ bisects $\overline{AC}$, $\overline{ED} \perp \overline{AC}$	1. Given
2. $\angle EDA$ and $\angle EDC$ are right angles.	2. Theorem 3-11
3. D is the midpoint of $\overline{AC}$.	3. Definition of Segment Bisector
4. $\overline{AD} \cong \overline{CD}$	4. Theorem 2-5
5. $\overline{ED} \cong \overline{ED}$	5. Theorem 2-2
6. $\triangle AED \cong \triangle CED$	6. LL
7. $BE + AE > BA$	7. Theorem 5-8
8. $\overline{AE} \cong \overline{CE}$	8. CPCTC
9. $AE = CE$	9. Definition of Congruent Segments

10. $BE + CE > BA$	10. Postulate 2-9
11. $BE + CE = BC$	11. Definition of Between
12. $BC > BA$	12. Postulate 2-9

10. STATEMENTS	REASONS
1. $MN = MQ$; M is between N and P.	1. Given
2. $NM + MP = NP$	2. Definition of Between
3. $NO + OP > NP$	3. Theorem 5-8
4. $NO + OP > NM + MP$	4. Postulate 2-9
5. $QM + MP > QP$	5. Theorem 5-8
6. $MN + MP > QP$	6. Postulate 2-9
7. $NO + OP > QP$	7. Postulate 2-18

11. STATEMENTS	REASONS
1. $\triangle GRC$; $\overline{RA}$ is an altitude.	1. Given
2. $\overline{RA} \perp \overleftrightarrow{GC}$	2. Definition of Altitude
3. $RC > RA$	3. Theorem 5-6

12. STATEMENTS	REASONS
1. $\triangle SKY$	1. Given
2. $SY + KY > SK$	2. Theorem 5-8
3. $SK < SY + KY$	3. Postulate 2-15
4. $SK - KY < SY$	4. Postulate 2-16

13. STATEMENTS	REASONS
1. $\triangle ABC$; $\overline{AD}$, $\overline{BE}$, and $\overline{CF}$ are altitudes.	1. Given
2. $\overline{AD} \perp \overline{CD}$, $\overline{CF} \perp \overline{AF}$, $\overline{BE} \perp \overline{AC}$	2. Definition of Altitude
3. $AB > AD$, $BC > BE$, $AC > CF$	3. Theorem 5-6
4. $AB = AD + x$ where $x > 0$, $BC = BE + y$ where $y > 0$, $AC = CF + z$ where $z > 0$	4. Theorem 5-2
5. $AB + BC + AC = AD + x + BE + y + CF + z$	5. Postulate 2-7
6. $AB + BC + AC = AD + BE + CF + x + y + z$	6. Postulate 2-10
7. $AB + BC + AC > AD + BE + CF$	7. Theorem 5-2

14. STATEMENTS	REASONS
1. $\triangle DAB$ and $\triangle DAC$	1. Given
2. $DA + AB > DB$ $DC + CB > DB$ $AB + CB > AC$ $DC + DA > AC$	2. Theorem 5-8
3. $DA + AB + DC + CB + AB + CB + DC + DA > DB + DB + CA + CA$	3. Postulate 2-16; Postulate 2-18
4. $2DA + 2AB + 2BC + 2CD > 2DB + 2CA$	4. Postulate 2-14
5. $DA + AB + BC + CD > DB + CA$	5. Postulate 2-17

PAGES 162–163 WRITTEN

1. STATEMENTS	REASONS
1. $\overline{PQ} \cong \overline{SQ}$	1. Given
2. $\overline{QR} \cong \overline{QR}$	2. Theorem 2-2
3. $m\angle PQR = m\angle PQT + m\angle SQR$	3. Postulate 3-3
4. $m\angle PQR > m\angle SQR$	4. Theorem 5-2
5. $PR > SR$	5. Theorem 5-9

2. STATEMENTS	REASONS
1. $\overline{PQ} \cong \overline{RS}$, $QR < PS$	1. Given
2. $\overline{QS} \cong \overline{QS}$	2. Theorem 2-2
3. $m\angle 3 < m\angle 1$	3. Theorem 5-10

3. STATEMENTS	REASONS
1. $\overline{AB} \cong \overline{BC}$, $m\angle 4 > m\angle 3$	1. Given
2. $\overline{BD} \cong \overline{BD}$	2. Theorem 2-2
3. $AD > CD$	3. Theorem 5-9

4. STATEMENTS	REASONS
1. $\overline{AB} \cong \overline{BC}$, $AD > CD$	1. Given
2. $\overline{BD} \cong \overline{BD}$	2. Theorem 2-2
3. $m\angle 4 > m\angle 3$	3. Theorem 5-10

5. STATEMENTS	REASONS
1. D is the midpoint of $\overline{AC}$, $AB > CB$	1. Given
2. $\overline{CD} \cong \overline{AD}$	2. Theorem 2-5
3. $\overline{BD} \cong \overline{BD}$	3. Theorem 2-2
4. $m\angle 1 > m\angle 2$	4. Theorem 5-10

6. STATEMENTS	REASONS
1. $\overline{BD}$ bisects $\overline{AC}$.	1. Given
2. D is the midpoint of $\overline{AC}$.	2. Definition of Segment Bisector
3. $\overline{AD} \cong \overline{CD}$	3. Theorem 2-5
4. $\overline{BD} \cong \overline{BD}$	4. Theorem 2-2
5. $AB > CB$	5. Given
6. $m\angle 1 > m\angle 2$	6. Theorem 5-10
7. $m\angle > m\angle 3$	7. Theorem 5-3
8. $m\angle 1 > m\angle 3$	8. Postulate 2-18

7. STATEMENTS	REASONS
1. $\overline{BD}$ bisects $\overline{AC}$; $AB > CB$	1. Given
2. D is the midpoint of $\overline{AC}$.	2. Definition of Segment Bisector
3. $\overline{CD} \cong \overline{AD}$	3. Theorem 2-6
4. $\overline{BD} \cong \overline{BD}$	4. Theorem 2-2
5. $m\angle 1 > m\angle 2$	5. Theorem 5-10
6. $m\angle 2 > m\angle A$	6. Theorem 5-3
7. $m\angle 1 > m\angle A$	7. Postulate 2-18

8. STATEMENTS	REASONS
1. $\overline{PR} = \overline{PQ}$; $SQ > SR$	1. Given
2. Draw $\overline{PS}$.	2. Postulate 1-1
3. $\overline{PS} \cong \overline{PS}$	3. Theorem 2-2
4. $m\angle 2 > m\angle 1$	4. Theorem 5-10

9. STATEMENTS	REASONS
1. $\triangle TER$; $\overline{TR} \cong \overline{EU}$	1. Given
2. $\overline{TU} \cong \overline{TU}$	2. Theorem 2-2
3. $m\angle 1 > m\angle 2$	3. Theorem 5-3
4. $TE > RU$	4. Theorem 5-9

10. STATEMENTS	REASONS
1. $\triangle FCE$; $\overline{AE}$ bisects $\overline{FC}$; $m\angle CAE = 50$	1. Given
2. $\angle CAE$ and $\angle EAF$ are a linear pair.	2. Definition of Linear Pair
3. $\angle CAE$ and $\angle EAF$ are supplementary.	3. Postulate 3-4
4. $m\angle CAE + m\angle EAF = 180$	4. Definition of Supplementary Angles
5. $50 + m\angle EAF = 180$	5. Postulate 2-9
6. $m\angle EAF = 130$	6. Postulate 2-7
7. $m\angle CAE + 80 = 130$	7. Postulate 2-7
8. $m\angle CAE + 80 = m\angle EAF$	8. Postulate 2-9
9. $m\angle EAF > m\angle CAE$	9. Theorem 5-2
10. $\overline{FA} \cong \overline{AC}$	10. Theorem 2-6
11. $\overline{AE} \cong \overline{AE}$	11. Theorem 2-2
12. $FE > EC$	12. Theorem 5-9
13. $m\angle C > m\angle F$	13. Theorem 5-4

11. STATEMENTS	REASONS
1. $\overline{ER} \cong \overline{EC}$; $\overline{GE} \cong \overline{AE}$; $RA > RG$; $m\angle CEA > m\angle REA$	1. Given
2. $\overline{EA} \cong \overline{EA}$	2. Theorem 2-2
3. $AC > RA$	3. Theorem 5-9
4. $AC > RG$	4. Postulate 2-18

12. STATEMENTS	REASONS
1. $\overline{ER} \cong \overline{EC}$; $\overline{GE} \cong \overline{AE}$; $RA > RG$; $m\angle CEA > m\angle REA$	1. Given
2. $\overline{ER} \cong \overline{ER}$	2. Theorem 2-2
3. $m\angle AER > m\angle REG$	3. Theorem 5-10
4. $m\angle CEA > m\angle GER$	4. Postulate 2-18

13. STATEMENTS	REASONS
1. $\overline{PQ} \cong \overline{AB}$; $\overline{PR} \cong \overline{AC}$; $m\angle P = m\angle A$	1. Given
2. $\angle P \cong \angle A$	2. Definition of Congruent Angles
3. $\triangle QPR \cong \triangle BAC$	3. SAS
4. $\overline{QR} \cong \overline{BC}$	4. CPCTC
5. $QR = BC$	5. Definition of Congruent Segments

14. STATEMENTS	REASONS
1. $\overline{PQ} \cong \overline{AB}$; $\overline{PR} \cong \overline{AC}$; $m\angle P < m\angle A$	1. Given
2. $QR < BC$	2. Theorem 5-9

PAGE 164 CHALLENGE

1. STATEMENTS	REASONS
1. On $\triangle PQR$, draw $\overrightarrow{PS}$ so that $\angle SPR \cong \angle BAC$, $\overline{PS} \cong \overline{AB}$, and S lies on $\overline{QR}$.	1. Postulate 2-2
2. $\overline{PR} \cong \overline{AC}$	2. Given
3. $\triangle PSR \cong \triangle ABC$	3. SAS
4. $\overline{SR} \cong \overline{BC}$	4. CPCTC

5. $SR = BC$	5. Definition of Congruent Segments
6. $QS + SR = QR$	6. Definition of Between
7. $QR > SR$	7. Theorem 5-2
8. $QR > BC$	8. Postulate 2-9

2. STATEMENTS	REASONS
1. On $\triangle PQR$, draw $\overrightarrow{PS}$ so that $\angle SPR \cong \angle BAC$ and $\overline{PS} \cong \overline{AB}$. Let T be the intersection of $\overrightarrow{PS}$ and $\overrightarrow{QR}$.	1. Postulate 2-2
2. $\overline{PQ} \cong \overline{AB}$	2. Given
3. $\overline{PS} \cong \overline{PQ}$	3. Theorem 2-4
4. On $\triangle QPT$, draw $\overrightarrow{PV}$ so that $\angle QPT$ is bisected and V lies on $\overline{QR}$.	4. Postulate 2-2; Postulate 3-1
5. $\angle QPV \cong \angle VPT$	5. Definition of Angle Bisector
6. $\overline{PV} \cong \overline{PV}$	6. Theorem 2-2
7. $\triangle QPV \cong \triangle SPV$	7. SAS
8. $\overline{QV} \cong \overline{SV}$	8. CPCTC
9. $QV = SV$	9. Definition of Congruent Segments
10. $VR + VS > SR$	10. Theorem 5-8
11. $VR + QV > SR$	11. Postulate 2-9
12. $VR + QV = QR$	12. Definition of Between
13. $QR > SR$	13. Postulate 2-9
14. $\overline{PR} \cong \overline{AC}$	14. Given
15. $\triangle SPR \cong \triangle BAC$	15. SAS
16. $\overline{SR} \cong \overline{BC}$	16. CPCTC
17. $SR = BC$	17. Definition of Congruent Segments
18. $QR > BC$	18. Postulate 2-9

Pages 167–168 CHAPTER REVIEW

23. STATEMENTS	REASONS
1. $\overline{AK} \cong \overline{AC}$	1. Given
2. $\angle 2 \cong \angle C$	2. Theorem 4-6
3. $m\angle 2 = m\angle C$	3. Definition of Congruent Angles
4. $m\angle 1 > m\angle C$	4. Theorem 5-3
5. $m\angle 1 > m\angle 2$	5. Postulate 2-9

24. STATEMENTS	REASONS
1. $\triangle APE$ is equilateral.	1. Given
2. $\overline{AP} \cong \overline{PE}$	2. Definition of Equilateral Triangle
3. $\angle A \cong \angle APE$	3. Theorem 4-6
4. $m\angle A = m\angle APE$	4. Definition of Congruent Angles
5. $m\angle APQ + m\angle QPE = m\angle APE$	5. Postulate 3-3
6. $m\angle APE > \angle APQ$	6. Theorem 5-2
7. $m\angle A > m\angle APQ$	7. Postulate 2-9
8. $PQ > QA$	8. Theorem 5-5

33. STATEMENTS	REASONS
1. $\triangle XYZ$	1. Given
2. $XY < YZ + XZ$	2. Theorem 5-8
3. $XY - YZ < XZ$	3. Postulate 2-16

34. STATEMENTS	REASONS
1. $\overline{AB} \cong \overline{CB}$; $m\angle ABE > m\angle CBE$	1. Given
2. $\overline{BE} \cong \overline{BE}$	2. Theorem 2-2
3. $AE > CE$	3. Theorem 5-9

35. STATEMENTS	REASONS
1. $AD > BC$	1. Given
2. $m\angle ABD > m\angle BAC$	2. Theorem 5-3

PAGE 169 CHAPTER TEST

17. STATEMENTS	REASONS
1. $m\angle 7 = 90$	1. Given
2. $m\angle 5 > m\angle 7$	2. Theorem 5-3
3. $m\angle 7 > m\angle 9$	3. Theorem 5-3
4. $m\angle 5 > m\angle 9$	4. Postulate 2-18
5. $m\angle 9 > m\angle 4$	5. Theorem 5-3
6. $m\angle 5 > m\angle 4$	6. Postulate 2-18

18. STATEMENTS	REASONS
1. $\overline{PR} \cong \overline{PT}$; $m\angle 2 > m\angle 3$	1. Given
2. $\overline{PS} \cong \overline{PS}$	2. Theorem 2-2
3. $RS > TS$	3. Theorem 5-9

19. STATEMENTS	REASONS
1. $m\angle 8 = 90$	1. Given
2. $m\angle 10 > m\angle 8$	2. Theorem 5-3
3. $m\angle 10 > 90$	3. Postulate 2-9
4. $\angle V$ and $\angle VPS$ are complementary.	4. Theorem 4-3

5. $m\angle V + m\angle VPS = 90$	5. Definition of Complementary Angles
6. $90 > m\angle V$	6. Theorem 5-2
7. $m\angle 10 = 90 + c$	7. Theorem 5-2
8. $m\angle 10 = m\angle V + m\angle VPS + c$	8. Postulate 2-9
9. $m\angle 10 > m\angle V$	9. Theorem 5-2
10. $PV > PT$	10. Theorem 5-5

20.

STATEMENTS	REASONS
1. $\overline{NO} \cong \overline{QP}$; $PN > OQ$	1. Given
2. $\overline{OP} \cong \overline{OP}$	2. Theorem 2-2
3. $m\angle NOP > m\angle OPQ$	3. Theorem 5-10
4. $MP > MO$	4. Theorem 5-5

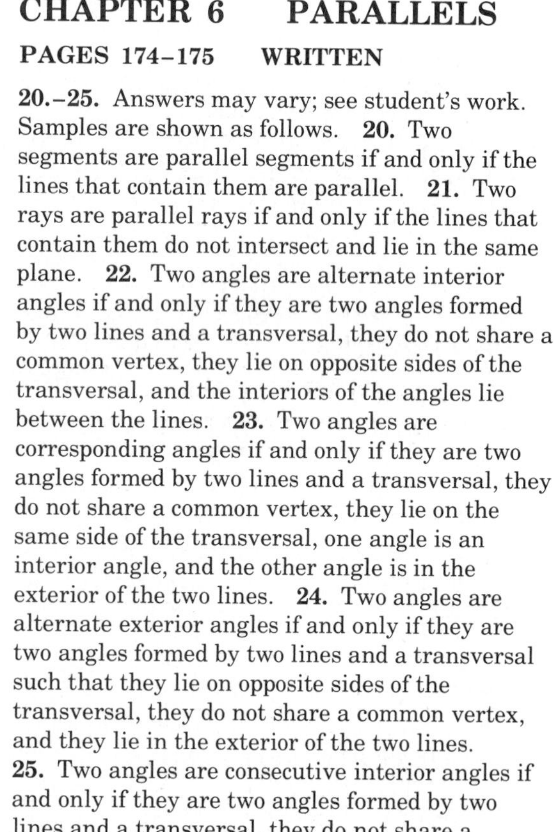

CHAPTER 6 PARALLELS

PAGES 174–175 WRITTEN

20.–25. Answers may vary; see student's work. Samples are shown as follows. **20.** Two segments are parallel segments if and only if the lines that contain them are parallel. **21.** Two rays are parallel rays if and only if the lines that contain them do not intersect and lie in the same plane. **22.** Two angles are alternate interior angles if and only if they are two angles formed by two lines and a transversal, they do not share a common vertex, they lie on opposite sides of the transversal, and the interiors of the angles lie between the lines. **23.** Two angles are corresponding angles if and only if they are two angles formed by two lines and a transversal, they do not share a common vertex, they lie on the same side of the transversal, one angle is an interior angle, and the other angle is in the exterior of the two lines. **24.** Two angles are alternate exterior angles if and only if they are two angles formed by two lines and a transversal such that they lie on opposite sides of the transversal, they do not share a common vertex, and they lie in the exterior of the two lines. **25.** Two angles are consecutive interior angles if and only if they are two angles formed by two lines and a transversal, they do not share a common vertex, they lie on the same side of the transversal, and their interiors lie between the lines.

26. Given: $\angle 3 \cong \angle 7$
Prove: $\angle 1 \cong \angle 5$; $\angle 2 \cong \angle 6$; $\angle 4 \cong \angle 8$

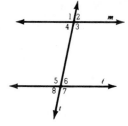

Proof:

STATEMENTS	REASONS
1. $\angle 3 \cong \angle 7$	1. Given
2. $\angle 2 \cong \angle 3$; $\angle 7 \cong \angle 6$	2. Theorem 3-10
3. $\angle 2 \cong \angle 6$	3. Theorem 3-1
4. $\angle 1$ and $\angle 3$ are a linear pair; $\angle 5$ and $\angle 7$ are a linear pair; $\angle 2$ and $\angle 4$ are a linear pair; $\angle 6$ and $\angle 8$ are a linear pair.	4. Given
5. $\angle 1$ and $\angle 3$ are supplementary; $\angle 5$ and $\angle 7$ are supplementary; $\angle 2$ and $\angle 4$ are supplementary; $\angle 6$ and $\angle 8$ are supplementary.	5. Postulate 3-4
6. $\angle 1 \cong \angle 5$; $\angle 4 \cong \angle 8$	6. Theorem 3-3

27. Given: $\angle 3$ and $\angle 5$ are supplementary.
Prove: $\angle 4$ and $\angle 6$ are supplementary.

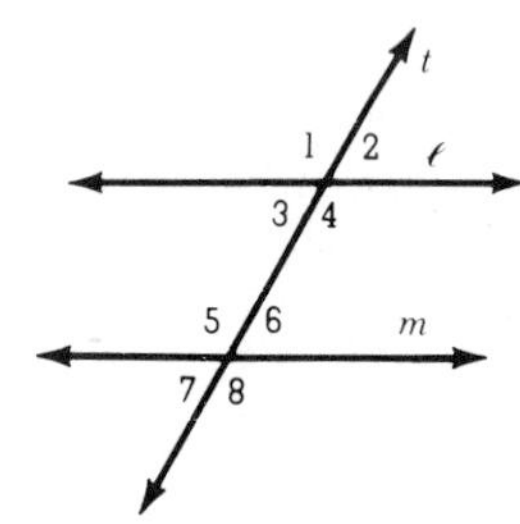

Proof:

STATEMENTS	REASONS
1. $\angle 3$ and $\angle 5$ are supplementary.	1. Given
2. $m\angle 3 + m\angle 5 = 180$	2. Definition of Supplementary Angles
3. $\angle 3$ and $\angle 4$ are a linear pair; $\angle 5$ and $\angle 6$ are a linear pair.	3. Given

4. $\angle 3$ and $\angle 4$ are supplementary; $\angle 5$ and $\angle 6$ are supplementary.	4. Postulate 3-4
5. $m\angle 3 + m\angle 4 = 180$; $m\angle 5 + m\angle 6 = 180$	5. Definition of Supplementary Angles
6. $m\angle 3 + m\angle 4 + m\angle 5 + m\angle 6 = 360$	6. Postulate 2-7
7. $m\angle 4 + m\angle 6 = 180$	7. Postulate 2-9; Postulate 2-7
8. $\angle 4$ and $\angle 6$ are supplementary.	8. Definition of Supplementary Angles

PAGE 175 CHALLENGE

1. *No.* Suppose a line was parallel to itself ($\ell \parallel \ell$), then the intersection of ℓ with ℓ should be the empty set. This is not true. **2.** *Yes.* If $\ell \parallel m$, then ℓ and m are in the same plane and do not intersect. Thus, $m \parallel \ell$. **3.** *Yes.* If $\ell \parallel m$ and $m \parallel p$, and ℓ and p are different lines, then $\ell \parallel p$.

PAGE 175 ALGEBRA REVIEW

1. $(y + 5)(y - 5)$ **2.** $(x + y)(x - y)(x^2 + y^2)$
3. $(x - 5)(x - 2)$ **4.** $r(r + 4s)(r + 2s)$
5. $(2m + 3)(5m + 2)$ **6.** $(7b - 5)(3b + 4)$
7. $x^2 - 2xy + x - 2y = x(x - 2y) + (x - 2y) = (x + 1)(x - 2y)$ **8.** $3a^2 + 12ab - 2a - 8b = 3a(a + 4b) - 2(a + 4b) = (3a - 2)(a + 4b)$
9. $^{-}b^2 + 8b + a^2 - 16 = a^2 - b^2 + 8b - 16 = a^2 - (b^2 - 8b + 16) = a^2 - (b - 4)^2 = (a + b - 4)(a - b + 4)$ **10.** $r^2 + 4rs + 4s^2 - 9y^2 = (r + 2s)^2 - (3y)^2 = (r + 2s + 3y)(r + 2s - 3y)$
11. $(3y - 7)(y - 4)$ **12.** $64a^2 - 1 = (4a)^3 - 1^3 = (4a - 1)(16a^2 + 4a + 1)$

PAGES 178–179 EXPLORATORY

1.–12. See student's work. Samples are shown as follows. **1.** The leaves of a plant are in groups of three, and the plant is not poison ivy. **2.** A mushroom is red, and it is not poisonous. **3.** The radio does not play well, and it is not defective. **4.** The lamp will not turn on, and the light bulb is not defective. **5.** The two lines intersect, and they intersect in no points. **6.** A line not in a plane intersects a plane, and they intersect in more than one point. **7.** A right triangle has more than two acute angles. **8.** A triangle has more than one obtuse angle. **9.** In a plane, two lines are parallel to the same line and are not parallel to each other. **10.** Two lines not in the same plane do not intersect, and they are not skew lines. **11.** The measures of two angles of a triangle are unequal, and the measures of the sides opposite those angles are equal (in the same order). **12.** Two sides of one triangle are congruent to two sides of another triangle, but the lengths of the third sides are unequal, and the measures of the angles included between the pairs of congruent sides are equal (in the same order).

PAGES 179–180 WRITTEN

1. Two lines in the same plane are cut by a transversal so a pair of alternate exterior angles are congruent, and the two lines are not parallel. **2.** Two lines in the same plane are cut by a transversal so a pair of consecutive interior angles are supplementary, and the two lines are not parallel. **3.** A plane and a line not in the plane intersect, and they intersect in more than one point. **4.** There is a line and a point not on the line, and there is more than one plane that contains them. **5.** A transversal intersects two parallel lines, and both pairs of alternate interior angles formed are not congruent. **6.** Two lines intersect, and more than one plane contains them.

7. Assumption: $\triangle ABC$ is a right triangle with right angle C and $\triangle ABC$ has more than two acute angles.

(a) Assumption
(b) Definition of Acute Angle
(c) Given
(d) Definition of Right Angle
(e) Postulate 2-15
(f) The prior statement, (d), contradicts the comparison property, (e). Therefore, the initial assumption must have been false.

8. Assumption: Lines ℓ and m intersect in more than one point.

(a) Assumption
(b) Assumption
(c) Postulate 1-1
(d) The prior statement, (b), contradicts Postulate 1-1, (c). Therefore, the initial assumption must have been false.

9. Given: $\triangle ABC$

Prove: $\triangle ABC$ has at most one obtuse angle C.

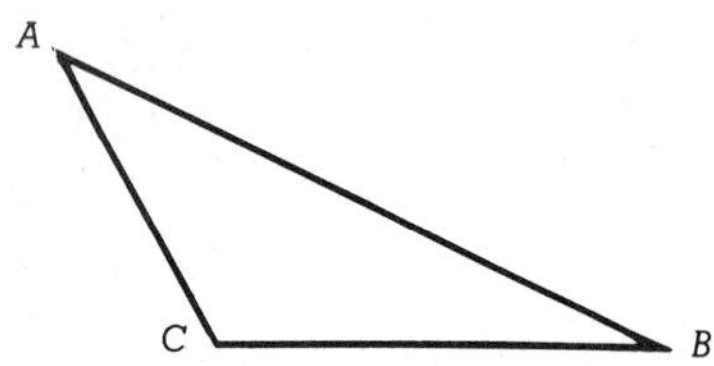

Assumption for Indirect Proof:
$\triangle ABC$ has more than one obtuse angle.

Proof:

STATEMENTS	REASONS
1. $\angle A$ and $\angle B$ are obtuse.	1. Assumption
2. $m\angle A > 90$ and $m\angle B > 90$	2. Definition of Obtuse Angle
3. $m\angle A + m\angle B > 180$	3. Postulate 2-16
4. $m\angle A + m\angle B + m\angle C = 180$	4. Theorem 4-1
5. $m\angle A + m\angle B < 180$	5. Theorem 5-2

Step 5 contradicts Step 3. Thus, $\triangle ABC$ has at most one obtuse angle.

10. Given: line ℓ and plane $\mathcal{P}$ intersect. Line ℓ is not in plane $\mathcal{P}$.

Prove: Line ℓ and plane $\mathcal{P}$ intersect in no more than one point.

Assumption for Indirect Proof:
Line ℓ is not in plane $\mathcal{P}$, and ℓ and $\mathcal{P}$ intersect in more than one point (A and B).

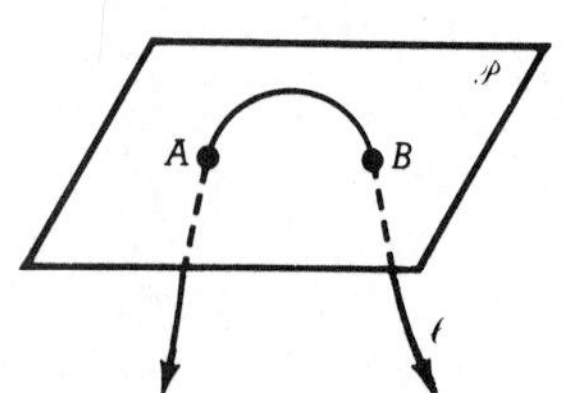

Proof:

STATEMENTS	REASONS
1. Line ℓ is not in plane $\mathcal{P}$, and ℓ and $\mathcal{P}$ intersect in different points (A and B).	1. Assumption
2. ℓ is in $\mathcal{P}$.	2. Postulate 1-5

Step 2 contradicts Step 1. The original assumption that ℓ and $\mathcal{P}$ intersect in more than one point must be false. Thus, ℓ and $\mathcal{P}$ intersect in no more than one point.

PAGE 184 WRITTEN

1.

STATEMENTS	REASONS
1. $\angle R$ and $\angle S$ are supplementary; $\angle Q \cong \angle S$	1. Given
2. $m\angle R + m\angle S = 180$	2. Definition of Supplementary Angles
3. $m\angle Q = m\angle S$	3. Definition of Congruent Angles
4. $m\angle R + m\angle Q = 180$	4. Postulate 2-9
5. $\angle R$ and $\angle Q$ are supplementary.	5. Definition of Supplementary Angles
6. $\overline{QP} \parallel \overline{RS}$	6. Theorem 6-6

2.

STATEMENTS	REASONS
1. $\angle Q$ and $\angle R$ are supplementary; $\angle S \cong \angle Q$	1. Given
2. $m\angle Q + m\angle R = 180$	2. Definition of Supplementary Angles
3. $m\angle S = m\angle Q$	3. Definition of Congruent Angles
4. $m\angle S + m\angle R = 180$	4. Postulate 2-9
5. $\angle S$ and $\angle R$ are supplementary.	5. Definition of Supplementary Angles
6. $\overline{QR} \parallel \overline{PS}$	6. Theorem 6-6

3.

STATEMENTS	REASONS
1. $\angle 1 \cong \angle 3$; $\overline{AD} \cong \overline{CB}$	1. Given
2. $\overline{AC} \cong \overline{AC}$	2. Theorem 2-2
3. $\triangle ADC \cong \triangle CBA$	3. SAS
4. $\overline{DC} \cong \overline{BA}$	4. CPCTC

4.

STATEMENTS	REASONS
1. $\overline{AD} \cong \overline{CB}$; $\overline{DC} \cong \overline{BA}$	1. Given
2. $\overline{AC} \cong \overline{AC}$	2. Theorem 2-2
3. $\triangle ADC \cong \triangle CBA$	3. SSS
4. $\angle 2 \cong \angle 4$	4. CPCTC
5. $\overline{DC} \parallel \overline{AB}$	5. Theorem 6-4

5.

STATEMENTS	REASONS
1. $\overline{MP} \cong \overline{MQ}$; $\angle 1 \cong \angle N$	1. Given
2. $\angle 2 \cong \angle 1$	2. Theorem 4-6
3. $\angle 2 \cong \angle N$	3. Theorem 3-1
4. $\overline{PQ} \parallel \overline{LN}$	4. Theorem 6-5

6.

STATEMENTS	REASONS
1. $\overline{MP} \cong \overline{MQ}$; $\angle L$ and $\angle 4$ are supplementary.	1. Given
2. $\angle 1 \cong \angle 2$	2. Theorem 4-6
3. $\angle 2$ and $\angle 4$ are a linear pair.	3. Definition of Linear Pair
4. $\angle 2$ and $\angle 4$ are supplementary.	4. Postulate 3-4
5. $\angle 1$ and $\angle 4$ are supplementary.	5. Postulate 2-9
6. $\angle 1 \cong \angle L$	6. Theorem 3-2
7. $\overline{PQ} \parallel \overline{LN}$	7. Theorem 6-5

7.

STATEMENTS	REASONS
1. $\angle 1 \cong \angle 2$	1. Given
2. $\overline{BC} \parallel \overline{FE}$	2. Theorem 6-4

8.

STATEMENTS	REASONS
1. $\overline{AF} \perp \overline{AD}$; $\overline{CD} \perp \overline{AD}$	1. Given
2. $\overline{AF} \parallel \overline{AD}$	2. Theorem 6-8

9.

STATEMENTS	REASONS
1. $\angle F$ and $\angle 2$ are complementary; $\angle C$ and $\angle 1$ are complementary.	1. Given
2. $m\angle F + m\angle 2 = 90$; $m\angle C + m\angle 1 = 90$	2. Definition of Complementary Angles
3. $m\angle F + m\angle 2 + m\angle A = 180$; $m\angle C + m\angle 1 + m\angle D = 180$	3. Theorem 4-1
4. $m\angle A = 90$; $m\angle D = 90$	4. Postulate 2-9; Postulate 2-7
5. $\overline{AF} \perp \overline{AD}$; $\overline{CD} \perp \overline{AD}$	5. Definitions of Right Angle and Perpendicular Lines
6. $\overline{AF} \parallel \overline{CD}$	6. Theorem 6-8

10. Given: $\angle 2$ and $\angle 3$ are supplementary.
Prove: $\ell \parallel m$

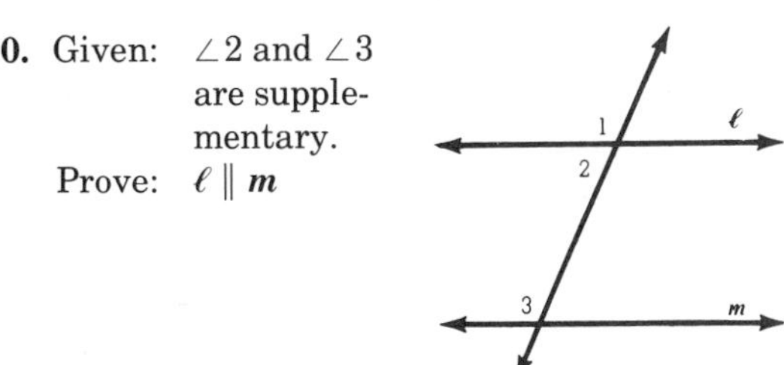

Proof:

STATEMENTS	REASONS
1. $\angle 2$ and $\angle 3$ are supplementary.	1. Given
2. $\angle 1$ and $\angle 2$ are a linear pair.	2. Definition of Linear Pair
3. $\angle 1$ and $\angle 2$ are supplementary.	3. Postulate 3-4
4. $\angle 1 \cong \angle 3$	4. Theorem 3-2
5. $\ell \parallel m$	5. Theorem 6-4

11. Given: $\angle 1 \cong \angle 2$
Prove: $\ell \parallel m$

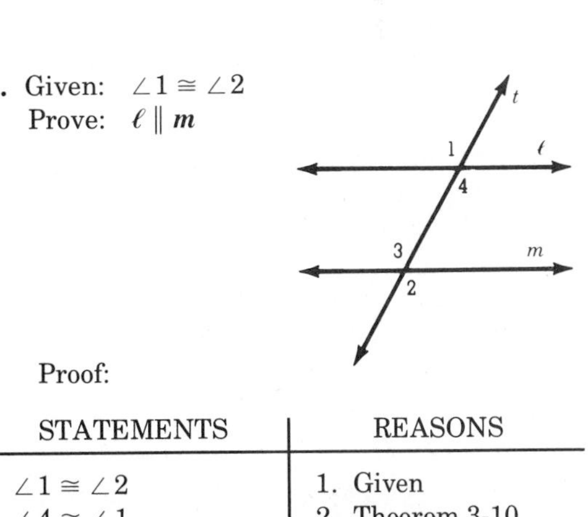

Proof:

STATEMENTS	REASONS
1. $\angle 1 \cong \angle 2$	1. Given
2. $\angle 4 \cong \angle 1$	2. Theorem 3-10
3. $\angle 4 \cong \angle 2$	3. Theorem 3-1
4. $\ell \parallel m$	4. Theorem 6-5

12. Given: $\angle ABD \cong \angle BEF$;
$\overleftrightarrow{BC}$ bisects $\angle ABD$;
$\overleftrightarrow{EH}$ bisects $\angle BEF$.
Prove: $\overline{BC} \parallel \overline{EH}$

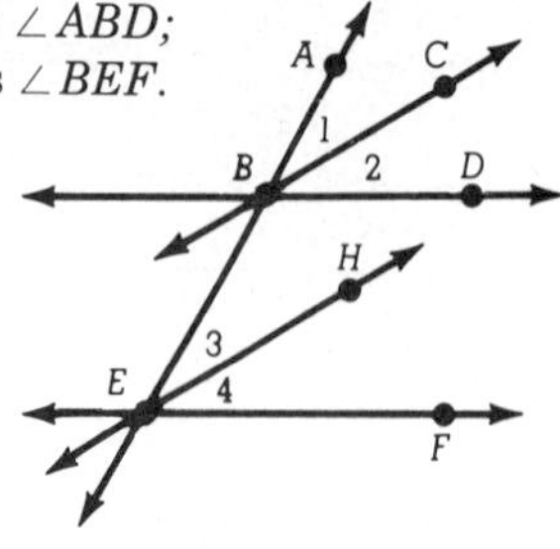

Proof:

STATEMENTS	REASONS
1. $\angle ABD \cong \angle BEF$; $\overleftrightarrow{BC}$ bisects $\angle ABD$; $\overleftrightarrow{EH}$ bisects $\angle BEF$.	1. Given
2. $m\angle 1 + m\angle 2 = m\angle ABD$; $m\angle 3 + m\angle 4 = m\angle BEF$	2. Postulate 3-3
3. $m\angle ABD = m\angle BEF$	3. Definition of Congruent Angles
4. $m\angle 1 + m\angle 2 = m\angle 3 + m\angle 4$	4. Postulate 2-9
5. $\angle 1 \cong \angle 2$; $\angle 3 \cong \angle 4$	5. Definition of Angle Bisector
6. $m\angle 1 = m\angle 2$; $m\angle 3 = m\angle 4$	6. Definition of Congruent Angles
7. $m\angle 1 + m\angle 1 = m\angle 3 + m\angle 3$	7. Postulate 2-9
8. $2m\angle 1 = 2m\angle 3$	8. Postulate 2-14
9. $m\angle 1 = m\angle 3$	9. Postulate 2-8
10. $\angle 1 \cong \angle 3$	10. Definition of Congruent Angles
11. $\overline{BC} \parallel \overline{EH}$	11. Theorem 6-5

PAGES 188–189 EXPLORATORY

1. Any 4 pairs of the following:
   $\angle 4$; $\angle 6$; ***t***; $\angle 2$, $\angle 12$, ℓ
   $\angle 3$, $\angle 5$, ***t***; $\angle 3$, $\angle 9$, ℓ
   $\angle 12$, $\angle 14$, ***s***; $\angle 6$, $\angle 16$, ***m***
   $\angle 11$, $\angle 13$, ***s***; $\angle 7$, $\angle 13$, ***m***
2. Any 4 of the following:
   $\angle 1$, $\angle 5$, ***t***; $\angle 9$, $\angle 13$, ***s***; $\angle 1$, $\angle 9$, ℓ;
   $\angle 5$, $\angle 13$, ***m***
   $\angle 2$, $\angle 6$, ***t***; $\angle 10$, $\angle 14$, ***s***; $\angle 2$, $\angle 10$, ℓ;
   $\angle 6$, $\angle 14$, ***m***
   $\angle 4$, $\angle 8$, ***t***; $\angle 12$, $\angle 16$, ***s***; $\angle 4$, $\angle 12$, ℓ;
   $\angle 8$, $\angle 16$, ***m***
   $\angle 3$, $\angle 7$, ***t***; $\angle 11$, $\angle 15$, ***s***; $\angle 3$, $\angle 11$, ℓ;
   $\angle 7$, $\angle 15$, ***m***
3. Any 4 of the following:
   $\angle 4$, $\angle 5$, ***t***; $\angle 2$, $\angle 9$, ℓ
   $\angle 3$, $\angle 6$, ***t***; $\angle 3$, $\angle 12$, ℓ
   $\angle 12$, $\angle 13$, ***s***; $\angle 6$, $\angle 13$, ***m***
   $\angle 11$, $\angle 14$, ***s***; $\angle 7$, $\angle 16$, ***m***
4. Any 4 of the following:
   $\angle 1$, $\angle 7$, ***t***; $\angle 9$, $\angle 15$, ***s***; $\angle 4$, $\angle 10$, ℓ;
   $\angle 5$, $\angle 15$, ***m***
   $\angle 2$, $\angle 8$, ***t***; $\angle 10$, $\angle 16$, ***s***; $\angle 1$, $\angle 11$, ℓ;
   $\angle 8$, $\angle 14$, ***m***

PAGE 189 WRITTEN

19. Given: $\ell \parallel m$
Prove: $\angle 4 \cong \angle 5$;
$\angle 3 \cong \angle 6$
Assumption for Indirect Proof:
$\angle 4 \not\cong \angle 5$ and $\ell \parallel m$

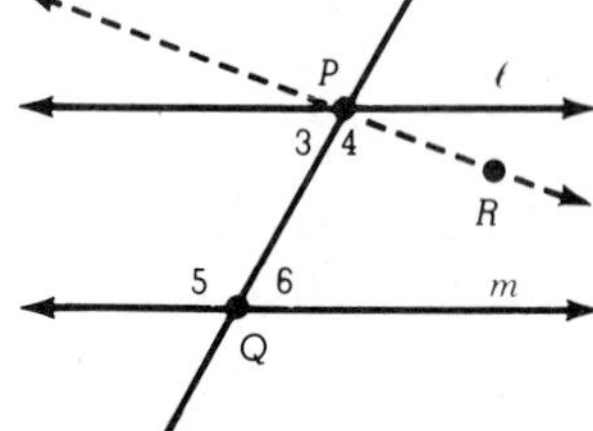

Proof:

STATEMENTS	REASONS
1. $\angle 4 \not\cong \angle 5$	1. Assumption
2. Draw $\overleftrightarrow{PR}$ so that $m\angle QPR = m\angle 5$.	2. Postulate 3-2
3. $\angle QPR \cong \angle 5$	3. Definition of Congruent Angles
4. $\overleftrightarrow{PR} \parallel m$	4. Theorem 6-4
5. $\ell \parallel m$	5. Given

Steps 4 and 5 contradict the Parallel Postulate since $\overleftrightarrow{PR}$ and ℓ are different lines that contain P and are both parallel to m.
The original assumption is false.
Since $\angle 4 \cong \angle 5$, then $\angle 3 \cong \angle 6$ by Theorem 6-1.

20. Given: $\ell \parallel m$
Prove: $\angle 1$ and $\angle 2$ are supplementary; $\angle 3$ and $\angle 4$ are supplementary.

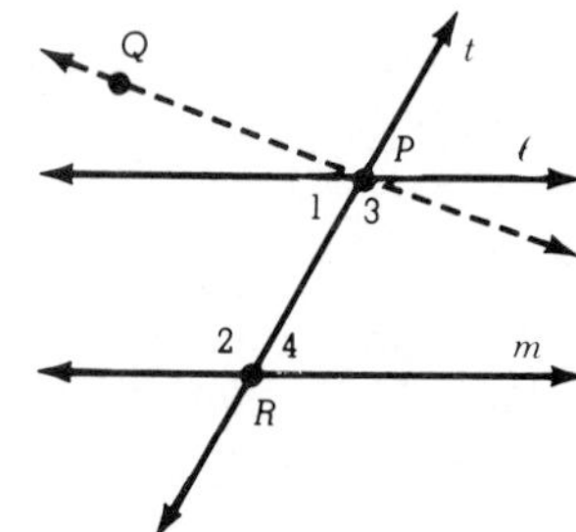

Assumption for Indirect Proof:
$\angle 1$ is not supplementary to $\angle 2$ and $\ell \parallel m$.

Proof:

STATEMENTS	REASONS
1. $\angle 1$ is not supplementary to $\angle 2$.	1. Assumption
2. Draw $\overleftrightarrow{PQ}$ such that $m\angle QPR = 180 - m\angle 2$.	2. Theorem 3-2
3. $m\angle QPR + m\angle 2 = 180$	3. Postulate 2-7
4. $\angle QPR$ and $\angle 2$ are supplementary.	4. Definition of Supplementary Angles
5. $\overleftrightarrow{QP} \parallel m$	5. Theorem 6-6
6. $\ell \parallel m$	6. Given

Steps 5 and 6 contradict the Parallel Postulate since $\overleftrightarrow{PQ}$ and ℓ are different lines that contain P and are both parallel to m.
The original assumption is false.
Since $\angle 1$ and $\angle 2$ are supplementary, $\angle 3$ and $\angle 4$ are supplementary by exercise 27, p. 175.

21. Given: $\ell \parallel m$
Prove: $\angle 1 \cong \angle 4$; $\angle 2 \cong \angle 3$

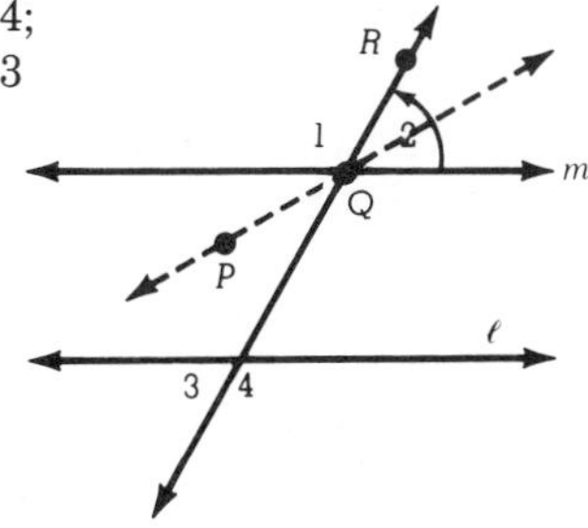

Assumption for Indirect Proof:
$\angle 1 \not\cong \angle 4$ and $\ell \parallel m$

Proof:

STATEMENTS	REASONS
1. $\angle 1 \not\cong \angle 4$	1. Assumption
2. Draw $\overleftrightarrow{PQ}$ so that $m\angle PQR = m\angle 4$.	2. Theorem 3-2
3. $\angle PQR \cong \angle 4$	3. Definition of Congruent Angles
4. $\overleftrightarrow{PQ} \parallel \ell$	4. Theorem 6-7
5. $\ell \parallel m$	5. Given

Steps 4 and 5 contradict the Parallel Postulate since $\overleftrightarrow{PQ}$ and m are different lines that contain Q and are both parallel to ℓ.
The original assumption is false. Thus, $\angle 1 \cong \angle 4$.

STATEMENTS	REASONS
6. $\angle 1$ and $\angle 2$ are a linear pair; $\angle 3$ and $\angle 4$ are a linear pair.	6. Definition of Linear Pair
7. $\angle 1$ and $\angle 2$ are supplementary; $\angle 3$ and $\angle 4$ are supplementary.	7. Postulate 3-4
8. $\angle 2 \cong \angle 3$	8. Theorem 3-3

22. Given: $\ell \parallel m$; $m \parallel n$
Prove: $\ell \parallel n$

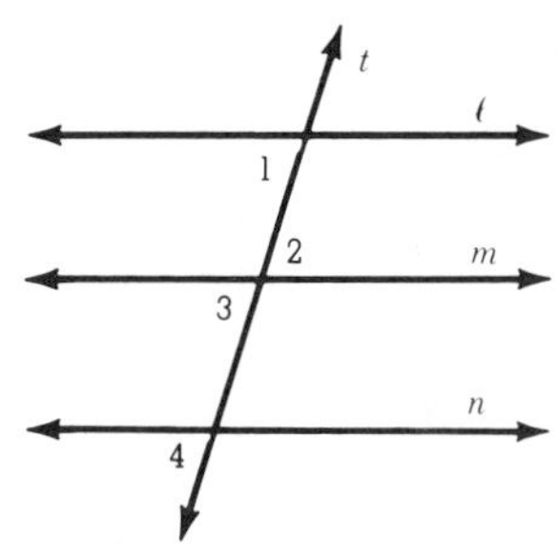

Proof:

STATEMENTS	REASONS
1. $\ell \parallel m$; $m \parallel n$	1. Given
2. $\angle 1 \cong \angle 3$; $\angle 3 \cong \angle 4$	2. Theorem 6-9
3. $\angle 1 \cong \angle 4$	3. Theorem 3-1
4. $\ell \parallel n$	4. Theorem 6-5

PAGES 193–194 WRITTEN

1. STATEMENTS	REASONS
1. $\overline{AB} \parallel \overline{CD}$; $\overline{BD} \perp \overline{CD}$; $\overline{AB} \perp \overline{AD}$	1. Given
2. Draw $\overleftrightarrow{BD}$.	2. Postulate 1-1
3. $\angle A$ and $\angle C$ are right angles.	3. Definition of Perpendicular Lines
4. $\angle A \cong \angle C$	4. Theorem 3-6
5. $\angle ABD \cong \angle CDB$	5. Theorem 6-10
6. $\overline{BD} \cong \overline{BD}$	6. Theorem 2-2
7. $\triangle ABD \cong \triangle CDB$	7. AAS
8. $\angle CBD \cong \angle BDA$	8. CPCTC
9. $\overline{BC} \parallel \overline{AD}$	9. Theorem 6-4

2.

STATEMENTS	REASONS
1. $\overline{BC} \parallel \overline{AD}$; $\overline{CD} \perp \overline{BC}$; $\overline{AB} \perp \overline{AD}$	1. Given
2. Draw $\overline{BD}$.	2. Postulate 1-1
3. $\angle A$ and $\angle C$ are right angles.	3. Definition of Perpendicular Lines
4. $\triangle BAD$ and $\triangle CDB$ are right triangles.	4. Definition of Right Triangle
5. $\overline{BD} \cong \overline{BD}$	5. Theorem 2-2
6. $\angle CBD \cong \angle ADB$	6. Theorem 6-10
7. $\triangle BAD \cong \triangle DCB$	7. HA
8. $\angle ABD \cong \angle CDB$	8. CPCTC
9. $\overline{AB} \parallel \overline{CD}$	9. Theorem 6-4

3.

STATEMENTS	REASONS
1. $\overline{QS} \parallel \overline{PT}$; $\angle T$ is a right angle.	1. Given
2. $\overline{PT} \perp \overline{RT}$	2. Definition of Perpendicular Lines
3. $\overline{QS} \perp \overline{RT}$	3. Theorem 6-13
4. $\angle 2$ is a right angle.	4. Theorem 3-11
5. $\triangle RQS$ is a right triangle.	5. Definition of Right Triangle

4.

STATEMENTS	REASONS
1. $\overline{QS} \parallel \overline{PT}$; $\angle T$ is a right angle.	1. Given
2. $\overline{RT} \perp \overline{PT}$	2. Definition of Perpendicular Lines
3. $\overline{RT} \perp \overline{QS}$	3. Theorem 6-13
4. $\overline{RS} \perp \overline{QS}$	4. $\overline{RS}$ is a segment of $\overline{RT}$.

5.

STATEMENTS	REASONS
1. $\overline{BA} \parallel \overline{ED}$; $\overline{BA} \cong \overline{DE}$	1. Given
2. $\angle B \cong \angle D$; $\angle A \cong \angle E$	2. Theorem 6-10
3. $\triangle ABC \cong \triangle EDC$	3. ASA
4. $\overline{EC} \cong \overline{AC}$	4. CPCTC

6.

STATEMENTS	REASONS
1. $\overline{BA} \parallel \overline{ED}$; C is the midpoint of $\overline{BD}$.	1. Given
2. $\overline{BC} \cong \overline{CD}$	2. Theorem 2-5
3. $\angle B \cong \angle D$; $\angle A \cong \angle E$	3. Theorem 6-10
4. $\triangle ABC \cong \triangle EDC$	4. AAS
5. $\overline{EC} \cong \overline{AC}$	5. CPCTC

7.

STATEMENTS	REASONS
1. $\overline{QS} \parallel \overline{PT}$; $\triangle QRS$ is equilateral; R is the midpoint of $\overline{PT}$.	1. Given
2. $\overline{QR} \cong \overline{SR}$	2. Definition of Equilateral Triangle
3. $\angle SQR \cong \angle QSR$	3. Theorem 4-6
4. $\angle PRQ \cong \angle SQR$; $\angle QSR \cong \angle SRT$	4. Theorem 6-10
5. $\angle PRQ \cong \angle QSR$	5. Theorem 3-1
6. $\angle PRQ \cong \angle SRT$	6. Theorem 3-1
7. $\overline{PR} \cong \overline{TR}$	7. Theorem 2-5
8. $\triangle PQR \cong \triangle TSR$	8. SAS
9. $\overline{PQ} \cong \overline{TS}$	9. CPCTC

8.

STATEMENTS	REASONS
1. $\overline{QS} \parallel \overline{PT}$; $\triangle QRS$ is equilateral; R is the midpoint of $\overline{PT}$.	1. Given
2. $\triangle PQR \cong \triangle TSR$	2. See exercise 7, steps 1–8.
3. $\angle P \cong \angle T$	3. CPCTC

9.

STATEMENTS	REASONS
1. $\overline{BC} \parallel \overline{AE}$; $\angle 1 \cong \angle 2$; $\angle 3 \cong \angle 4$	1. Given
2. $\angle ABC$ and $\angle BAE$ are supplementary.	2. Theorem 6-11
3. $m\angle ABC + m\angle BAE = 180$	3. Definition of Supplementary Angles
4. $m\angle ABC = m\angle 1 + m\angle 2$; $m\angle BAE = m\angle 3 + m\angle 4$	4. Postulate 3-3
5. $m\angle 1 + m\angle 2 + m\angle 3 + m\angle 4 = 180$	5. Postulate 2-9
6. $m\angle 1 = m\angle 2$; $m\angle 3 = m\angle 4$	6. Definition of Congruent Angles
7. $m\angle 2 + m\angle 2 + m\angle 3 + m\angle 3 = 180$	7. Postulate 2-9
8. $m\angle 2 + m\angle 3 = 90$	8. Postulate 2-14; Postulate 2-8; Postulate 2-9
9. $m\angle 2 + m\angle 3 + m\angle BDA = 180$	9. Theorem 4-1
10. $90 + m\angle BDA = 180$	10. Postulate 2-9
11. $m\angle BDA = 90$	11. Postulate 2-7

12. $\overline{BD} \perp \overline{AD}$	12. Definition of Right Angle; Definition of Perpendicular Lines

10. STATEMENTS	REASONS
1. $\overline{AB} \parallel \overline{CE}$; $\overline{BD} \cong \overline{AD}$	1. Given
2. $\angle 2 \cong \angle 3$	2. Theorem 4-6
3. $\angle 3 \cong \angle ADE$; $\angle BDC \cong \angle 2$	3. Theorem 6-10
4. $\angle BDC \cong \angle ADE$	4. Theorem 3-1

PAGE 197 EXPLORATORY

1. a line and a point not on the line

2. m •P

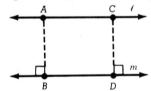

3. Given: line m and point P not on m **4.** There is exactly one line through the point that is perpendicular to the given line. **5.** Prove: there is exactly one line through P perpendicular to m. **6.** There is at least one line through P perpendicular to m. There is at most one line through P perpendicular to m. **7.** In a plane, if two lines are parallel, then they are everywhere equidistant. In a plane, if two lines are everywhere equidistant, then they are parallel.

8. A C ℓ B D m

PAGES 197–199 WRITTEN

11. Given: A point is on the bisector of an angle.

12.

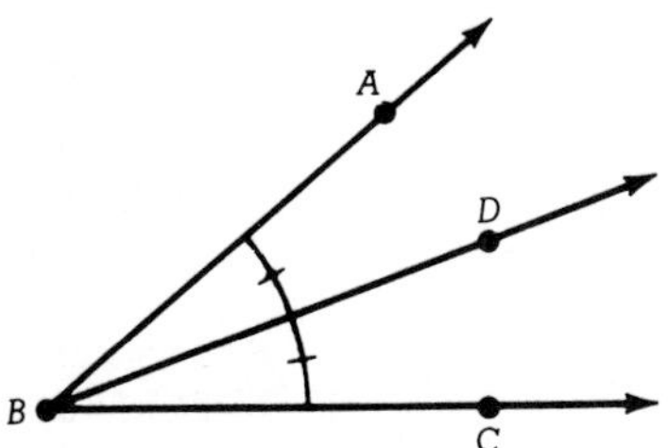

13. Pick any point on the angle bisector and draw lines through that point perpendicular to the sides of the angle. Show the two triangles formed are congruent and use CPCTC to show equidistance.

14. Given: $\overrightarrow{BD}$ bisects $\angle ABC$; Point D is any point on $\overrightarrow{BD}$.
Prove: $AD = CD$

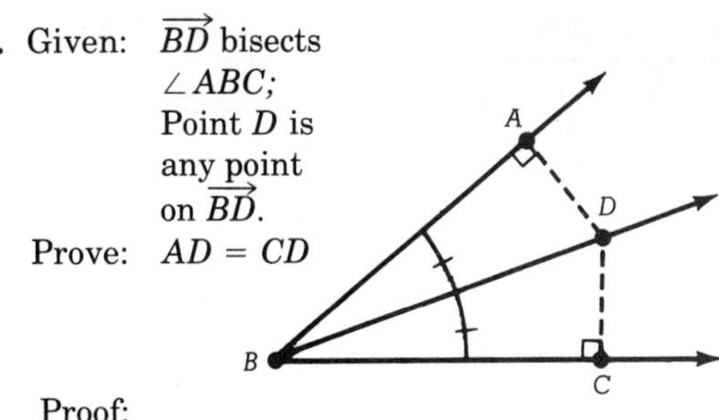

Proof:

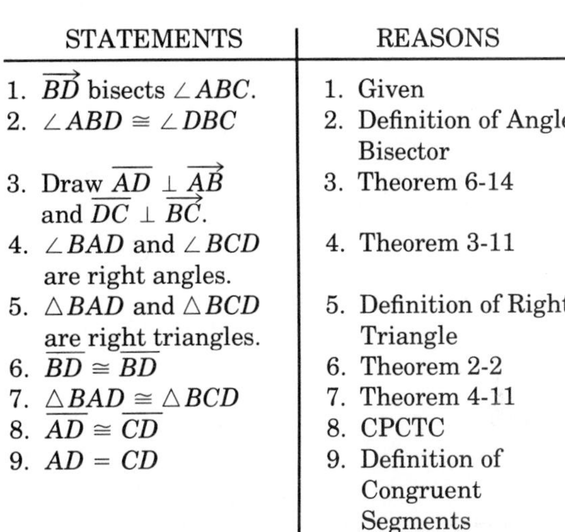

STATEMENTS	REASONS
1. $\overrightarrow{BD}$ bisects $\angle ABC$.	1. Given
2. $\angle ABD \cong \angle DBC$	2. Definition of Angle Bisector
3. Draw $\overline{AD} \perp \overrightarrow{AB}$ and $\overline{DC} \perp \overrightarrow{BC}$.	3. Theorem 6-14
4. $\angle BAD$ and $\angle BCD$ are right angles.	4. Theorem 3-11
5. $\triangle BAD$ and $\triangle BCD$ are right triangles.	5. Definition of Right Triangle
6. $\overline{BD} \cong \overline{BD}$	6. Theorem 2-2
7. $\triangle BAD \cong \triangle BCD$	7. Theorem 4-11
8. $\overline{AD} \cong \overline{CD}$	8. CPCTC
9. $AD = CD$	9. Definition of Congruent Segments

15. If a point in the interior of the angle is equidistant from the sides of the angle, then that point is on the bisector of that angle.

16. Draw lines through the point perpendicular to each side. Draw the ray from the vertex through the point. Prove the triangles are congruent by HL. By CPCTC and Definition of Angle Bisector, show that the point is on the angle bisector.

17. Given: $AD = CD$
Prove: $\overrightarrow{BD}$ is the bisector of $\angle ABC$.

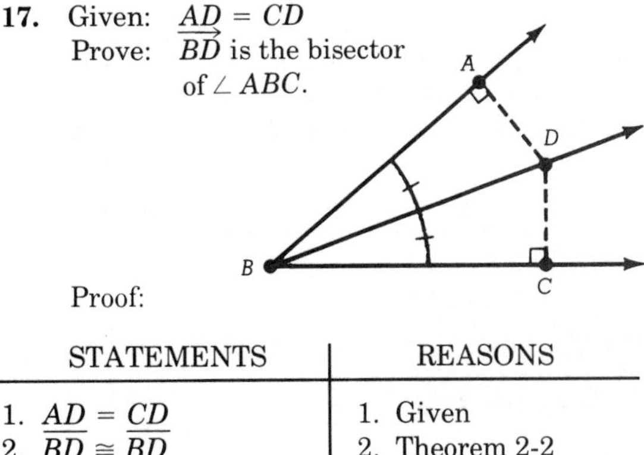

Proof:

STATEMENTS	REASONS
1. $AD = CD$	1. Given
2. $\overline{BD} \cong \overline{BD}$	2. Theorem 2-2

3. $\overline{AD} \perp \overline{AB}$; $\overline{DC} \perp \overline{BC}$	3. Definition of the Distance Between a Point and a Line
4. $\angle BAD$ and $\angle BCD$ are right angles.	4. Theorem 3-11
5. $\triangle BAD$ and $\triangle BCD$ are right triangles.	5. Definition of Right Triangle
6. $\triangle BAD \cong \triangle BCD$	6. Postulate 4-4
7. $\angle ABD \cong \angle CBD$	7. CPCTC
8. $\overrightarrow{BD}$ bisects $\angle ABC$.	8. Definition of Angle Bisector

18. A ray with its endpoint on the vertex of an angle and containing a point in the interior of the angle is the bisector of that angle if and only if a point on the ray and in the interior of the angle is equidistant from the sides of the angle.

19. STATEMENTS	REASONS
1. $\overline{AD} \parallel \overline{BC}$	1. Given
2. $\angle 3 \cong \angle 2$	2. Theorem 6-9
3. $\angle 1$ and $\angle 2$ are right angles.	3. Given
4. $\angle 3$ is a right angle.	4. Postulate 2-9
5. $\angle 1$ and $\angle ABC$ form a linear pair.	5. Definition of Linear Pair
6. $\angle ABC$ is a right angle.	6. Theorem 3-7
7. Draw $\overleftrightarrow{AC}$.	7. Postulate 1-1
8. $\overline{AC} \cong \overline{AC}$	8. Theorem 2-2
9. $\angle DAC \cong \angle BCA$	9. Theorem 6-10
10. $\triangle DAC \cong \triangle BCA$	10. AAS
11. $\overline{AD} \cong \overline{BC}$	11. CPCTC

20. $CD = 10$ feet $\quad AD = 15$ feet

PAGE 199 CHALLENGE

1. *No,* they may be skew. **2.** *Yes,* answers may vary. **3.** Select any point on one of the planes. Determine the line that contains that point and is perpendicular to the other plane. Find the distance between the point of intersection of the line and the plane and the original point.
4. *Yes,* for the same reason that parallel lines are equidistant.

PAGE 199 EXCURSION

1. Epimenides is a Cretan. If all Cretans lie, then he lies—a contradiction. **2.** "This statement is false" implies the statement is true—a contradiction. **3.** If the catalog lists itself, then it is listing a catalog that lists itself. This contradicts a catalog that does *not* list itself.

PAGES 201–202 CHAPTER REVIEW

7. Given: $\triangle ABC$ is a right triangle.
Prove: $\triangle ABC$ has only one right angle.

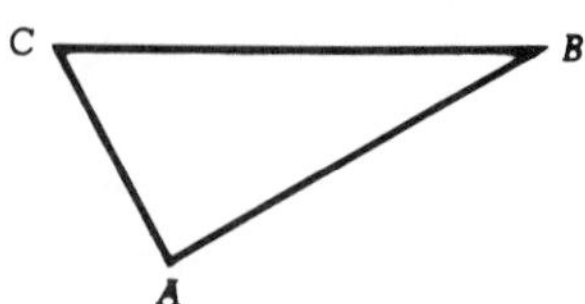

Assumption for Indirect Proof:
$\triangle ABC$ is a right triangle, and $\angle A$ and $\angle C$ are right angles.

Proof:

STATEMENTS	REASONS
1. $\triangle ABC$ is a right triangle; $\angle A$ and $\angle C$ are right angles.	1. Assumption
2. $m\angle A = 90$; $m\angle C = 90$	2. Definition of Right Angle
3. $m\angle A + m\angle C = 180$	3. Postulate 2-7
4. $m\angle A + m\angle B + m\angle C = 180$	4. Theorem 4-1

Steps 3 and 4 imply that $m\angle B = 0$. This is a contradiction of the definition of a triangle. Thus, $\triangle ABC$ has but one right angle.

8. Given: Line ℓ and plane $\mathcal{P}$ intersect; ℓ is not in $\mathcal{P}$.
Prove: ℓ and $\mathcal{P}$ intersect in no more than one point.

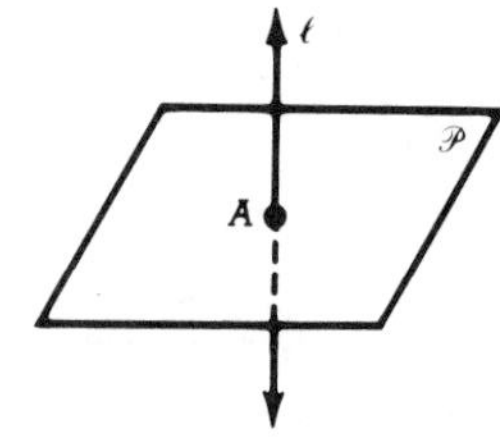

Assumption for Indirect Proof:
ℓ is not in $\mathcal{P}$; ℓ and $\mathcal{P}$ intersect in more than one point, (A and B)

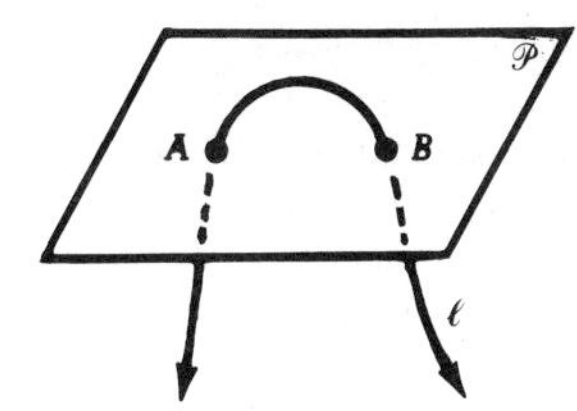

Proof:

STATEMENTS	REASONS
1. ℓ is not in $\mathscr{P}$, and ℓ and $\mathscr{P}$ intersect in different points, (A and B).	1. Assumption
2. ℓ is in $\mathscr{P}$.	2. Postulate 1-5

Step 2 contradicts step 1. The original assumption that ℓ and $\mathscr{P}$ intersect in different points must be false.
Thus, ℓ and $\mathscr{P}$ intersect in no more than one point.

9.

STATEMENTS	REASONS
1. T is the midpoint of $\overline{QS}$ and $\overline{PR}$.	1. Given
2. $\overline{QT} \cong \overline{TS}$; $\overline{PT} \cong \overline{TR}$	2. Theorem 2-5
3. $\angle 1 \cong \angle 3$	3. Theorem 3-10
4. $\triangle QPT \cong \triangle SRT$	4. SAS
5. $\angle QPT \cong \angle SRT$	5. CPCTC
6. $\overline{QP} \parallel \overline{RS}$	6. Theorem 6-4

10.

STATEMENTS	REASONS
1. $\triangle QPT \cong \triangle SRT$	1. Given
2. $\overline{QT} \cong \overline{ST}$; $\overline{PT} \cong \overline{RT}$	2. CPCTC
3. $\angle 2 \cong \angle 4$	3. Theorem 3-10
4. $\triangle QTR \cong \triangle STP$	4. SAS
5. $\angle RQT \cong \angle PST$	5. CPCTC
6. $\overline{QR} \parallel \overline{PS}$	6. Theorem 6-4

12.

STATEMENTS	REASONS
1. $\overline{DE} \parallel \overline{AC}$; E is the midpoint of $\overline{BC}$; $\overline{EF} \cong \overline{BE}$	1. Given
2. $\overline{BE} \cong \overline{EC}$	2. Theorem 2-5
3. $\angle EFC \cong \angle DEF$	3. Theorem 6-10
4. $\angle BED \cong \angle C$	4. Theorem 6-9
5. $\overline{EF} \cong \overline{EC}$	5. Theorem 2-4
6. $\angle EFC \cong \angle C$	6. Theorem 4-6
7. $\angle BED \cong \angle EFC$	7. Theorem 3-1
8. $\angle BED \cong \angle DEF$	8. Theorem 3-1
9. $\overline{DE} \cong \overline{DE}$	9. Theorem 2-2
10. $\triangle BED \cong \triangle FED$	10. SAS
11. $\overline{DF} \cong \overline{DB}$; $\angle BDE \cong \angle FDE$	11. CPCTC
12. $\angle BDE \cong \angle A$	12. Theorem 6-9
13. $\angle DFA \cong \angle FDE$	13. Theorem 6-10
14. $\angle A \cong \angle FDE$	14. Theorem 3-1
15. $\angle A \cong \angle DFA$	15. Theorem 3-1
16. $\overline{DA} \cong \overline{DF}$	16. Theorem 4-9
17. $\overline{DA} \cong \overline{BD}$	17. Theorem 2-4
18. D is the midpoint of $\overline{AB}$.	18. Theorem 2-5

13. Given: $\overline{AC} \perp m$; $\overline{BD} \perp \ell$; $AC = BD$
Prove: $\ell \parallel m$

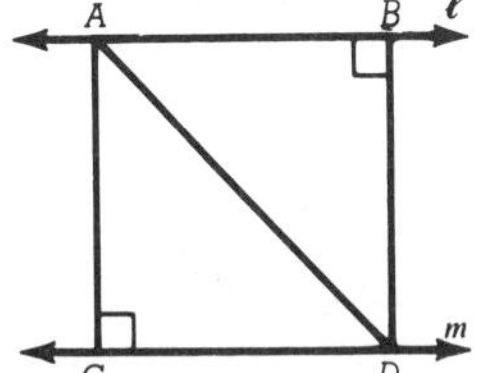

Proof:

STATEMENTS	REASONS
1. Draw $\overline{AD}$.	1. Postulate 1-1
2. $\overline{AC} \perp m$; $\overline{BD} \perp \ell$	2. Given
3. $\angle ACD$ is a right angle; $\angle DBA$ is a right angle.	3. Theorem 3-11
4. $\triangle ACD$ is a right triangle; $\triangle DBA$ is a right triangle.	4. Definition of Right Triangle
5. $AC = BD$	5. Given
6. $\overline{AC} \cong \overline{BD}$	6. Definition of Congruent Segments
7. $\overline{AD} \cong \overline{AD}$	7. Theorem 2-2
8. $\triangle ACD \cong \triangle DBA$	8. Postulate 4-4
9. $\angle BAD \cong \angle CDA$	9. CPCTC
10. $\ell \parallel m$	10. Theorem 6-4

14. Given: $\ell \parallel m$; $\overline{AC} \perp m$; $\overline{BD} \perp m$
Prove: $AC = BD$

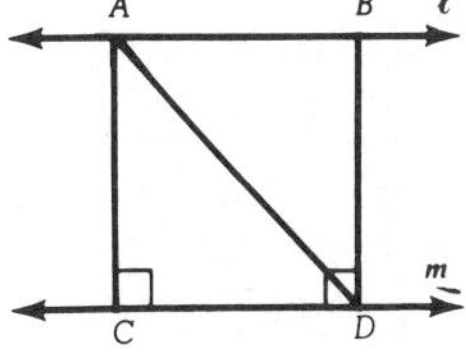

Proof:

STATEMENTS	REASONS
1. Draw $\overline{AD}$.	1. Postulate 1-1
2. $\overline{AC} \perp m$	2. Given
3. $\angle ACD$ is a right angle.	3. Theorem 3-11
4. $\triangle ACD$ is a right triangle.	4. Definition of Right Triangle
5. $\ell \parallel m$; $\overline{BD} \perp m$	5. Given

6. $\overline{BD} \perp \ell$	6. Theorem 6-14
7. $\angle DBA$ is a right angle.	7. Theorem 3-11
8. $\triangle DBA$ is a right triangle.	8. Definition of Right Triangle.
9. $\angle BAD \cong \angle ADC$	9. Theorem 6-10
10. $\overline{AD} \cong \overline{AD}$	10. Theorem 2-2
11. $\triangle ACD \cong \triangle DBA$	11. HA
12. $\overline{AC} \cong \overline{BD}$	12. CPCTC
13. $AC = BD$	13. Definition of Congruent Segments

PAGE 203 CHAPTER TEST

1. $\overline{AE} \parallel \overline{BF}$; $\overline{BF} \parallel \overline{CD}$; $\overline{AE} \parallel \overline{CD}$; $\overline{AB} \parallel \overline{EF}$; $\overline{BC} \parallel \overline{DF}$; $\overline{AC} \parallel \overline{ED}$ **2.** $\overleftrightarrow{AB} \parallel \overleftrightarrow{EF}$, trans. $\overleftrightarrow{AE}$ or $\overleftrightarrow{BF}$; $\overleftrightarrow{AE} \parallel \overleftrightarrow{BF}$, trans. $\overleftrightarrow{AB}$ or $\overleftrightarrow{EF}$; $\overleftrightarrow{AC} \parallel \overleftrightarrow{ED}$, trans. $\overleftrightarrow{AE}$ or $\overleftrightarrow{CD}$; $\overleftrightarrow{AE} \parallel \overleftrightarrow{CD}$, trans. $\overleftrightarrow{AC}$ or $\overleftrightarrow{ED}$; $\overleftrightarrow{BC} \parallel \overleftrightarrow{DF}$, trans. $\overleftrightarrow{BF}$ or $\overleftrightarrow{CD}$; $\overleftrightarrow{BF} \parallel \overleftrightarrow{CD}$, trans. $\overleftrightarrow{BC}$ or $\overleftrightarrow{DF}$ **3.** $\overrightarrow{AB}, \overrightarrow{CD}$; $\overrightarrow{AB}, \overrightarrow{FD}$; $\overrightarrow{AB}, \overrightarrow{ED}$; $\overrightarrow{BF}, \overrightarrow{ED}$; $\overrightarrow{BF}, \overrightarrow{AC}$; etc. **4.** $\overrightarrow{AE}, \overrightarrow{AC}$, etc. **5.** $\overrightarrow{AE}, \overrightarrow{AC}$, etc.
6. See exercise 3.

7. Given: $\triangle ABC$; $m\angle A < m\angle B$
Prove: $BC < AC$

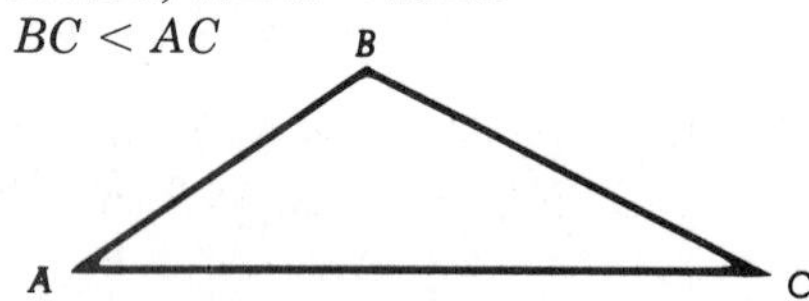

Assumption for Indirect Proof:
In $\triangle ABC$, $m\angle A < m\angle B$, and $BC > AC$.

Proof:

STATEMENTS	REASONS
1. $\triangle ABC$; $m\angle A < m\angle B$; $BC > AC$	1. Assumption
2. $BC = AC$ or $BC > AC$	2. Postulate 2-15
3. $\overline{BC} \cong \overline{AC}$ or $BC > AC$	3. Definition of Congruent Segments
4. $\angle A \cong \angle B$ or $m\angle A > m\angle B$	4. Theorem 4-6; Theorem 5-4
5. $m\angle A = m\angle B$ or $m\angle A > m\angle B$	5. Definition of Congruent Segments

Step 5 contradicts step 1.
Thus $BC < AC$.

8. Given: Line ℓ; P is on ℓ.

Prove: There is exactly one line perpendicular to ℓ through P.

Proof of Existence:

STATEMENTS	REASONS
1. Line ℓ; P is on ℓ.	1. Given
2. Draw another point on ℓ and call it F.	2. Postulate 1-3
3. In a half plane with edge ℓ, there is a point A such that $m\angle APF = 90$.	3. Postulate 3-2
4. $\angle APF$ is a right angle.	4. Definition of Right Angle
5. Draw the line through P and A.	5. Postulate 1-1
6. $\overleftrightarrow{PA} \perp \ell$	6. Definition of Perpendicular Lines

Proof of Uniqueness: By Indirect Method

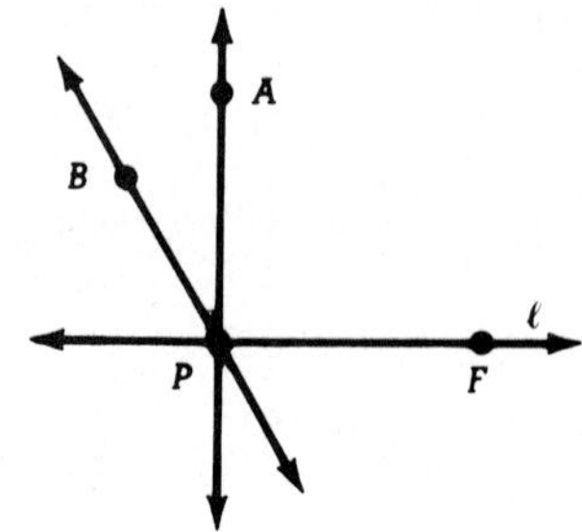

STATEMENTS	REASONS
7. There are two different lines $\overleftrightarrow{AP}$ and $\overleftrightarrow{BP}$ which are perpendicular to ℓ.	7. Assumption
8. $\angle BPF$ and $\angle APF$ are right angles.	8. Theorem 3-11
9. $m\angle BPF = 90$; $m\angle APF = 90$	9. Definition of Right Angle
10. B and A are on the same line.	10. Theorem 3-12

Since two different lines both contain B and P, Postulate 1-1 is contradicted. The assumption is false. There is at most one line perpendicular to ℓ through P.

9. STATEMENTS	REASONS
1. $\triangle ABC \cong \triangle DEF$	1. Given
2. $\angle A \cong \angle EDF$	2. CPCTC
3. $\overline{AB} \parallel \overline{DE}$	3. Theorem 6-5

10. STATEMENTS	REASONS
1. $\overline{AB} \parallel \overline{DE}$; $\triangle ABC$ is a right triangle; $\angle B$ and $\angle E$ are right angles.	1. Given
2. $\angle ABC \cong \angle E$	2. Theorem 3-6
3. $\angle DGC \cong \angle ABC$	3. Theorem 6-9
4. $\angle DGC \cong \angle E$	4. Theorem 3-1
5. $\overline{BC} \parallel \overline{EF}$	5. Theorem 6-5

11. STATEMENTS	REASONS
1. $\angle 2 \cong \angle 5$; $\angle 1 \cong \angle 4$	1. Given
2. $m\angle 2 = m\angle 5$; $m\angle 1 = m\angle 4$	2. Definition of Congruent Angles
3. $m\angle 1 + m\angle 2 = m\angle 4 + m\angle 5$	3. Postulate 2-7
4. $m\angle 1 + m\angle 2 = m\angle DAB$; $m\angle 4 + m\angle 5 = m\angle ACG$	4. Postulate 3-3
5. $m\angle DAB = m\angle ACG$	5. Postulate 2-9
6. $\angle DAB \cong \angle ACG$	6. Definition of Congruent Angles
7. $\overrightarrow{AB} \parallel \overrightarrow{CG}$	7. Theorem 6-5

12. STATEMENTS	REASONS
1. $\overrightarrow{AB} \parallel \overrightarrow{CG}$; $\angle 2 \cong \angle 5$	1. Given
2. $\angle DAB \cong \angle ACG$	2. Theorem 6-9
3. $m\angle DAB = m\angle ACG$; $m\angle 2 = m\angle 5$	3. Definition of Congruent Angles
4. $m\angle DAB = m\angle 1 + m\angle 2$; $m\angle ACG = m\angle 4 + m\angle 5$	4. Postulate 3-3
5. $m\angle 1 + m\angle 2 = m\angle 4 + m\angle 5$	5. Postulate 2-9
6. $m\angle 1 = m\angle 4$	6. Postulate 2-7
7. $\angle 1 \cong \angle 4$	7. Definition of Congruent Angles
8. $\overrightarrow{AE} \parallel \overrightarrow{CB}$	8. Theorem 6-5

PAGES 204–205 CUMULATIVE REVIEW

11. STATEMENTS	REASONS
1. $\overline{DB} \perp \overline{AC}$	1. Given
2. $\angle DBA \cong \angle DBC$	2. Theorem 3-13
3. $\overline{DB} \cong \overline{DB}$	3. Theorem 2-2
4. B is the midpoint of $\overline{AC}$.	4. Given
5. $\overline{AB} \cong \overline{BC}$	5. Theorem 2-5
6. $\triangle DBA \cong \triangle DBC$	6. SAS
7. $\overline{AD} \cong \overline{CD}$	7. CPCTC

12. STATEMENTS	REASONS
1. $\overline{SW} \perp \overline{RS}$; $\overline{SW} \perp \overline{WV}$	1. Given
2. $\angle RST$ is a right angle; $\angle VWT$ is a right angle.	2. Definition of Perpendicular Lines
3. $\angle RST \cong \angle VWT$	3. Theorem 3-6
4. T is the midpoint of $\overline{SW}$.	4. Given
5. $\overline{ST} \cong \overline{TW}$	5. Theorem 2-5
6. $\angle STR \cong \angle WTV$	6. Theorem 3-10
7. $\triangle RST \cong \triangle VWT$	7. ASA

27.–31. Answers may vary. Samples are shown as follows. **27.** $\overleftrightarrow{SV} \parallel \overleftrightarrow{PR}$, $\overleftrightarrow{SV} \parallel \overleftrightarrow{PQ}$, $\overleftrightarrow{SV} \parallel \overleftrightarrow{QR}$, $\overleftrightarrow{WS} \parallel \overleftrightarrow{PR}$, $\overleftrightarrow{WS} \parallel \overleftrightarrow{PQ}$, $\overleftrightarrow{WS} \parallel \overleftrightarrow{QR}$, $\overleftrightarrow{WV} \parallel \overleftrightarrow{PR}$, $\overleftrightarrow{WV} \parallel \overleftrightarrow{PQ}$, $\overleftrightarrow{WV} \parallel \overleftrightarrow{QR}$ **28.** $\overrightarrow{SV} \parallel \overrightarrow{PR}$, $\overrightarrow{SV} \parallel \overrightarrow{PQ}$, $\overrightarrow{SV} \parallel \overrightarrow{QR}$, $\overrightarrow{WS} \parallel \overrightarrow{PR}$, $\overrightarrow{WS} \parallel \overrightarrow{PQ}$, $\overrightarrow{WS} \parallel \overrightarrow{QR}$, $\overrightarrow{WV} \parallel \overrightarrow{PR}$, $\overrightarrow{WV} \parallel \overrightarrow{PQ}$, $\overrightarrow{WV} \parallel \overrightarrow{QR}$ **29.** $\overleftrightarrow{SV}$ and $\overleftrightarrow{TQ}$, $\overleftrightarrow{WV}$ and $\overleftrightarrow{TQ}$, $\overleftrightarrow{WS}$ and $\overleftrightarrow{TQ}$ **30.** $\overleftrightarrow{SV}$ and $\overleftrightarrow{TQ}$, $\overleftrightarrow{WV}$ and $\overleftrightarrow{TQ}$, $\overleftrightarrow{WS}$ and $\overleftrightarrow{TQ}$ **31.** $\overleftrightarrow{SV} \parallel \overleftrightarrow{PR}$ with $\overleftrightarrow{WP}$ as a transversal. See exercise 27 for all ways of varying the parallel lines.

32. Given: $\angle 1$ and $\angle 2$ are supplementary; $\angle 3$ and $\angle 4$ are supplementary; $\angle 3 \cong \angle 2$

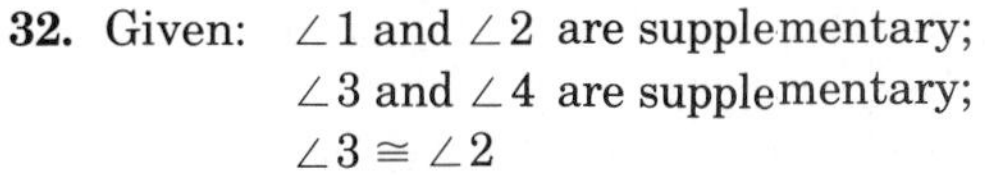

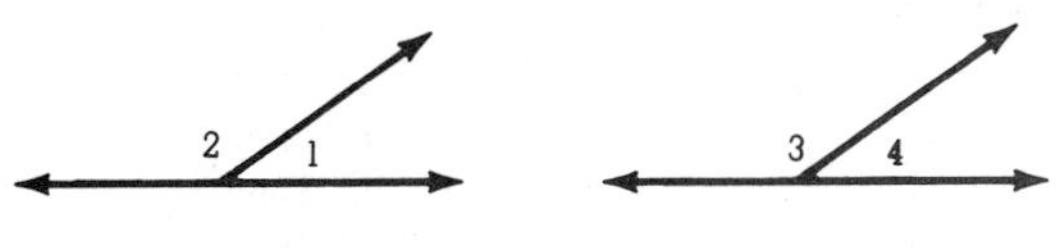

Prove: $\angle 1 \cong \angle 4$
Assumption for Indirect Proof: Suppose $\angle 1 \not\cong \angle 4$.

33. Given: $\triangle ABC$; $\angle C$ is a right angle.
Prove: $\angle A$ and $\angle B$ are complementary.
Assumption for Indirect Proof: Suppose $\angle A$ and $\angle B$ are not complementary.

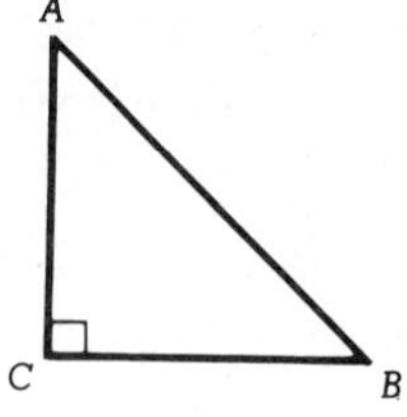

34. STATEMENTS	REASONS
1. $\overleftrightarrow{AD} \parallel \overleftrightarrow{BC}$; $\overleftrightarrow{AB} \parallel \overleftrightarrow{DC}$	1. Given
2. $\angle 6 \cong \angle 4$	2. Theorem 6-10
3. $\angle 4 \cong \angle 1$	3. Theorem 6-10
4. $\angle 6 \cong \angle 1$	4. Theorem 3-1
5. $m\angle 6 = m\angle 1$	5. Definition of Congruent Angles
6. $m\angle 6 = 110$	6. Given
7. $m\angle 1 = 110$	7. Postulate 2-9

35. STATEMENTS	REASONS
1. $\triangle BGD \cong \triangle GDF$	1. Given
2. $\angle BGD \cong \angle GDF$	2. CPCTC
3. $\overline{DF} \parallel \overline{BC}$	3. Theorem 6-4
4. $\angle GCF$ and $\angle DFC$ are supplementary.	4. Theorem 6-11

CHAPTER 7 POLYGONS

PAGE 210 WRITTEN

15. A, B, C, D, E **16.** $\angle A, \angle B, \angle C, \angle D, \angle E$
17. $\overline{AB}, \overline{BC}, \overline{CD}, \overline{DE}, \overline{EA}$ **18.** pentagon
19. convex **20.** not regular **21.** Any of the following 5 pairs: $\angle A, \angle B$; $\angle B, \angle C$; $\angle C, \angle D$; $\angle D, \angle E$; $\angle E, \angle A$ **22.** Any of the following 5 pairs: $\overline{AB}, \overline{BC}$; $\overline{BC}, \overline{CD}$; $\overline{CD}, \overline{DE}$; $\overline{DE}, \overline{AE}$; $\overline{AE}, \overline{AB}$
23. A pair of angles of a polygon is consecutive if and only if the two angles share a common side.
24. A pair of sides of a polygon is consecutive if and only if the two sides share a common endpoint.

PAGE 213 EXPLORATORY

11. An angle is an exterior angle of a convex polygon if and only if the angle forms a linear pair with one of the interior angles of the polygon.

PAGES 214–215 WRITTEN

46. $S = (n - 2)180$
If $n = 5$,
$S = (5 - 2)180$
$S = 3(180)$
$S = 540$

47. S = sum of the measures of the interior angles; n = number of sides

$$S = \frac{180(n-2)}{n}$$
$$S = \frac{180(4-2)}{4}$$
$$S = 90$$

exterior angle $= 180 - 90 = 90$
4 exterior angles $= 4(90)$ or 360

48. n = number of sides

Each interior angle $= \dfrac{180(n-2)}{n}$

Each exterior angle $= 180 - \dfrac{180(n-2)}{n}$

The sum of all exterior angles, one at each vertex

$$= n\left(180 - \frac{180(n-2)}{n}\right)$$
$$= 180n - 180(n - 2)$$
$$= 180n - 180n + 360$$
$$= 360$$

49. n = number of sides

Each interior angle $= \dfrac{180 - (n-2)}{n}$

Each exterior angle $= 180 - \dfrac{180(n-2)}{n}$

The sum of all exterior angles, two at each vertex

$$= 2n\left(180 - \frac{180(n-2)}{n}\right)$$
$$= 360n - 360(n - 2)$$
$$= 360n - 360n + 720$$
$$= 720$$

PAGES 218–219 WRITTEN

13. Given: $\square ABCD$
Prove: $\angle BCD \cong \angle DAB$; $\angle ABC \cong \angle CDA$

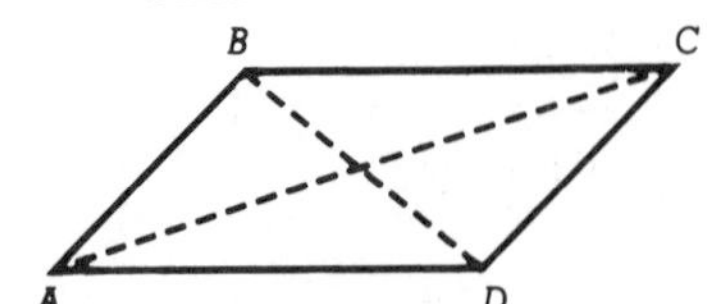

Proof:

STATEMENTS	REASONS
1. $\square ABCD$	1. Given
2. Draw $\overline{AC}$ and $\overline{BD}$.	2. Postulate 1-1

3. $\triangle BCD \cong \triangle DAB$; $\triangle ABC \cong \triangle CDA$	3. Theorem 7-3
4. $\angle BCD \cong \angle DAB$; $\angle ABC \cong \angle CDA$	4. CPCTC

14. Given: $\square ABCD$
Prove: $\overline{BC} \cong \overline{DA}$; $\overline{AB} \cong \overline{CD}$

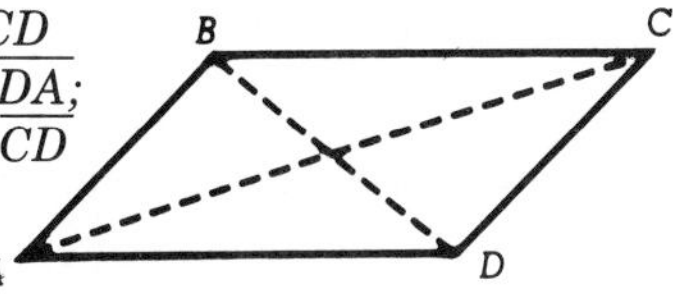

Proof:

STATEMENTS	REASONS
1. $\square ABCD$	1. Given
2. Draw $\overline{BD}$ and $\overline{AC}$.	2. Postulate 1-1
3. $\triangle BCD \cong \triangle DAB$; $\triangle ABC \cong \triangle CDA$	3. Theorem 7-3
4. $\overline{BC} \cong \overline{DA}$; $\overline{AB} \cong \overline{CD}$	4. CPCTC

15. Given: $\square HIJK$
Prove: $\angle HKJ$ is supplementary to $\angle IJK$.
Proof:

STATEMENTS	REASONS
1. $\square HIJK$	1. Given
2. $\overline{HK} \parallel \overline{IJ}$	2. Definition of Parallelogram
3. $\angle HKJ$ is supplementary to $\angle IJK$.	3. Theorem 6-11

16.

STATEMENTS	REASONS
1. $\square ABCD$; $\overline{DE} \perp \overline{AC}$; $\overline{BF} \perp \overline{AC}$	1.Given
2. $\overline{DE} \parallel \overline{BF}$	2. Theorem 6-8

17.

STATEMENTS	REASONS
1. $\square ABCD$; $\overline{DE} \perp \overline{AC}$; $\overline{BF} \perp \overline{AC}$	1. Given
2. $\triangle ABC \cong \triangle CDA$	2. Theorem 7-3
3. $\overline{BC} \cong \overline{DA}$; $\angle DAE \cong \angle BCF$	3. CPCTC
4. $\angle AED$ and $\angle CFB$ are right angles.	4. Theorem 3-11
5. $\angle AED \cong \angle CFB$	5. Theorem 3-6
6. $\triangle ADE \cong \triangle CBF$	6. AAS
7. $\overline{DE} \cong \overline{BF}$	7. CPCTC

PAGE 219 CHALLENGE

1.

STATEMENTS	REASONS
1. $\square PQST$; $\overrightarrow{RP}$ bisects $\angle QPT$; $\overrightarrow{VS}$ bisects $\angle QST$.	1. Given
2. $\angle Q \cong \angle T$; $\angle QST \cong \angle QPT$	2. Theorem 7-4
3. $m\angle QST = m\angle QPT$	3. Definition of Congruent Angles
4. $m\angle QST = m\angle QSV + m\angle VST$; $m\angle QPT = m\angle QPR + m\angle RPV$	4. Postulate 3-3
5. $m\angle QSV = m\angle VST$; $m\angle QPR = m\angle RPV$	5. Definitions of Angle Bisector and Congruent Angles
6. $m\angle QST = 2m\angle VST$; $m\angle QPT = 2m\angle QPR$	6. Postulate 2-9; Postulate 2-14
7. $m\angle VST \cong m\angle QPR$	7. Postulate 2-9; Postulate 2-8
8. $\angle VST \cong \angle QPR$	8. Definition of Congruent Angles
9. $\overline{QP} \cong \overline{ST}$	9. Theorem 7-5
10. $\triangle QPR \cong \triangle TSV$	10. Postulate 4-3; ASA
11. $\angle QRP \cong \angle SVT$	11. CPCTC
12. $\overline{QS} \parallel \overline{PT}$	12. Definition of Parallelogram
13. $\angle QRP \cong \angle RPT$	13. Theorem 6-10
14. $\angle SVT \cong \angle RPT$	14. Theorem 3-1
15. $\overline{RP} \parallel \overline{VS}$	15. Theorem 6-5

2.

STATEMENTS	REASONS
1.–10.	1.–10. Same as those in exercise 1.
11. $\overline{RP} \cong \overline{VS}$	11. CPCTC

PAGE 222 EXPLORATORY

7. *yes;* Theorem 6-4, Theorem 7-8 **8.** *no;* still must prove $\overline{QR} \parallel \overline{PS}$ **9.** *no; TR* $\neq 5$ **10.** *yes;* Theorem 6-4, Definition of Parallelogram **11.** *yes;* Theorem 6-6, Theorem 7-1, Definition of Parallelogram **12.** *no;* opposite sides are not congruent. **13.** *yes;* Theorem 7-9 **14.** *no;* opposite sides are not necessarily congruent. **15.** *yes;* CPCTC, Theorem 7-7, Theorem 6-4 **16.** *yes;* Theorem 6-4, Theorem 7-8

PAGES 222–223 WRITTEN

1. Given: Quadrilateral $ABCD$; $\overline{AB} \cong \overline{CD}$; $\overline{AB} \parallel \overline{CD}$

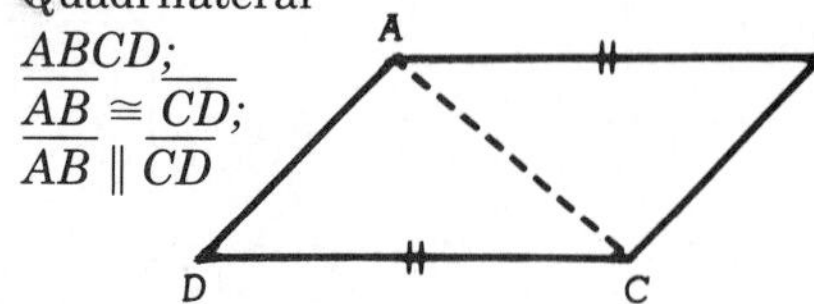

Prove: Quadrilateral $ABCD$ is a parallelogram.

Proof:

STATEMENTS	REASONS
1. $\overline{AB} \cong \overline{CD}$; $\overline{AB} \parallel \overline{CD}$	1. Given
2. Draw $\overline{AC}$.	2. Postulate 1-1
3. $\angle BAC \cong \angle DCA$	3. Theorem 6-10
4. $\overline{AC} \cong \overline{AC}$	4. Theorem 2-2
5. $\triangle ABC \cong \triangle CDA$	5. SAS
6. $\overline{BC} \cong \overline{DA}$	6. CPCTC
7. Quadrilateral $ABCD$ is a parallelogram.	7. Theorem 7-7

2. Given: $\angle A \cong \angle C$; $\angle D \cong \angle B$

Prove: Quadrilateral $ABCD$ is a parallelogram.

Proof:

STATEMENTS	REASONS
1. $\angle A \cong \angle C$; $\angle D \cong \angle B$	1. Given
2. $m\angle A = m\angle C$; $m\angle D = m\angle B$	2. Definition of Congruent Angles
3. $m\angle A + m\angle B + m\angle C + m\angle D = 360$	3. Theorem 7-1
4. $m\angle A + m\angle A + m\angle D + m\angle D = 360$	4. Postulate 2-9
5. $2m\angle A + 2m\angle D = 360$	5. Postulate 2-14
6. $m\angle A + m\angle D = 180$	6. Postulate 2-8
7. $\angle A$ and $\angle D$ are supplementary.	7. Definition of Supplementary Angles
8. $\overline{AB} \parallel \overline{DC}$	8. Theorem 6-6
9. $m\angle A + m\angle B = 180$	9. Postulate 2-9
10. $\angle A$ and $\angle B$ are supplementary.	10. Definition of Supplementary Angles
11. $\overline{AD} \parallel \overline{BC}$	11. Theorem 6-6
12. Quadrilateral $ABCD$ is a parallelogram.	12. Definition of Parallelogram

3. Given: Quadrilateral $ABCD$; $\angle A \cong \angle C$; $\overline{AB} \parallel \overline{CD}$

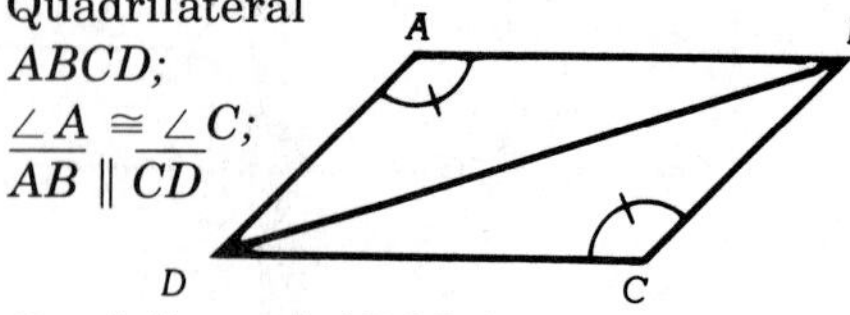

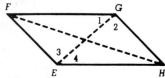

Prove: Quadrilateral $ABCD$ is a parallelogram.

Proof:

STATEMENTS	REASONS
1. Quadrilateral $ABCD$; $\angle A \cong \angle C$; $\overline{AB} \parallel \overline{CD}$	1. Given
2. Draw $\overline{BD}$.	2. Postulate 1-1
3. $\angle ABD \cong \angle CDB$	3. Theorem 6-10
4. $\overline{BD} \cong \overline{BD}$	4. Theorem 2-2
5. $\triangle ABD \cong \triangle CDB$	5. AAS
6. $\overline{AB} \cong \overline{CD}$; $\overline{AD} \cong \overline{CB}$	6. CPCTC
7. Quadrilateral $ABCD$ is a parallelogram.	7. Theorem 7-7

4. Given: Quadrilateral $EFGH$; $\angle G \cong \angle E$; $\overline{FG} \cong \overline{GH} \cong \overline{HE}$

Prove: Quadrilateral $EFGH$ is a parallelogram.

Proof:

STATEMENTS	REASONS
1. Quadrilateral $EFGH$; $\angle G \cong \angle E$; $\overline{FG} \cong \overline{GH} \cong \overline{HE}$	1. Given
2. Draw $\overline{FH}$ and $\overline{EG}$.	2. Postulate 1-1
3. $\angle 2 \cong \angle 4$	3. Definition of Isosceles Triangle; Theorem 4-6
4. $\angle 1 + \angle 2 = \angle G$; $\angle 3 + \angle 4 = \angle E$	4. Theorem 4-1
5. $\angle 1 + \angle 2 = \angle 3 + \angle 4$	5. Postulate 2-9

6. $\angle 1 + \angle 2 = \angle 3 + \angle 2$	6. Postulate 2-9
7. $\angle 1 \cong \angle 3$	7. Postulate 2-7
8. $\overline{EF} \cong \overline{FG}$	8. Theorem 4-9
9. Quadrilateral *EFGH* is a parallelogram.	9. Theorem 7-7

5. STATEMENTS	REASONS
1. $\overline{AE} \cong \overline{CE}$; $\angle ECD \cong \angle EAB$	1. Given
2. $\angle AEB \cong \angle CED$	2. Theorem 3-10
3. $\triangle AEB \cong \triangle CED$	3. ASA
4. $\overline{AB} \cong \overline{CD}$; $\angle BAE \cong \angle DCE$	4. CPCTC
5. $\overline{AB} \parallel \overline{CD}$	5. Theorem 6-4
6. Quadrilateral *ABCD* is a parallelogram.	6. Theorem 7-8

6. STATEMENTS	REASONS
1. $\overline{BA} \parallel \overline{CD}$; $\angle DBC \cong \angle ADB$	1. Given
2. $\overline{BC} \parallel \overline{AD}$	2. Theorem 6-4
3. Quadrilateral *ABCD* is a parallelogram.	3. Definition of Parallelogram

7. STATEMENTS	REASONS
1. $\triangle PQR \cong \triangle STV$; $\overline{PR} \parallel \overline{VS}$	1. Given
2. $\overline{PR} \cong \overline{SV}$	2. CPCTC
3. Quadrilateral *PRSV* is a parallelogram.	3. Theorem 7-8

8. STATEMENTS	REASONS
1. $\square PQST$; $\overline{QR} \cong \overline{TV}$	1. Given
2. $\overline{QP} \cong \overline{ST}$	2. Theorem 7-5
3. $\angle Q \cong \angle T$	3. Theorem 7-4
4. $\triangle QPR \cong \triangle TSV$	4. SAS
5. $\overline{PR} \cong \overline{SV}$; $\angle QRP \cong \angle TVS$	5. CPCTC
6. $\overline{QS} \parallel \overline{PT}$	6. Definition of Parallelogram
7. $\angle TVS \cong \angle RSV$	7. Theorem 6-10
8. $\angle QRP \cong \angle RSV$	8. Theorem 3-1
9. $\overline{PR} \parallel \overline{VS}$	9. Theorem 6-5
10. Quadrilateral *PRSV* is a parallelogram.	10. Theorem 7-8

9. STATEMENTS	REASONS
1. *E, F, G* and *H* are midpoints of $\overline{AB}, \overline{BC}, \overline{CD}$, and $\overline{DA}$ respectively, in $\square ABCD$.	1. Given
2. $\overline{AB} \cong \overline{DC}$; $\overline{BC} \cong \overline{AD}$	2. Theorem 7-5
3. $AB = DC$; $BC = AD$	3. Definition of Congruent Segments
4. $AE + EB = AB$; $DG + GC = DC$; $BF + FC = BC$; $AH + HD = AD$	4. Definition of Between
5. $AE + EB = DG + GC$; $BF + FC = AH + HD$	5. Postulate 2-9
6. $AE = EB$; $DG = GC$; $BF = FC$; $AH = HD$	6. Definition of Midpoint
7. $AE + AE = GC + GC$; $EB + EB = DG + DG$; $BF + BF = HD + HD$; $FC + FC = AH + AH$	7. Postulate 2-9
8. $2AE = 2GC$; $2EB = 2DG$; $2BF = 2HD$; $2FC = 2AH$	8. Postulate 2-14
9. $AE = GC$; $EB = DG$; $BF = HD$; $FC = AH$	9. Postulate 2-8
10. $\overline{AE} \cong \overline{GC}$; $\overline{EB} \cong \overline{DG}$; $\overline{BF} \cong \overline{HD}$; $\overline{FC} \cong \overline{AH}$	10. Definition of Congruent Segments
11. $\angle B \cong \angle D$; $\angle A \cong \angle C$	11. Theorem 7-4
12. $\triangle AEH \cong \triangle CGF$; $\triangle EBF \cong \triangle GDH$	12. SAS
13. $\overline{EH} \cong \overline{GF}$; $\overline{EF} \cong \overline{GH}$	13. CPCTC
14. Quadrilateral *EFGH* is a parallelogram.	14. Theorem 7-7

10. STATEMENTS	REASONS
1. $\overline{AF} \cong \overline{CF}$; $\overline{BE} \cong \overline{GD}$; F is the midpoint of $\overline{EG}$.	1. Given
2. $AF = CF$	2. Definition of Congruent Segments
3. F is the midpoint of $\overline{AC}$.	3. Definition of Midpoint
4. $\overline{AF}$ and $\overline{EG}$ bisect each other.	4. Definition of Bisector of a Segment
5. Quadrilateral $AECG$ is a parallelogram.	5. Theorem 7-9
6. $\overline{EC} \parallel \overline{AG}$	6. Definition of Parallelogram
7. $\overline{EC} \cong \overline{AG}$	7. Theorem 7-5
8. $EC = AG$; $BE = GD$	8. Definition of Congruent Segments
9. $BE + EC = AG + GD$	9. Postulate 2-7
10. $BE + EC = BC$; $AG + GD = AD$	10. Definition of Between
11. $BC = AD$	11. Postulate 2-9
12. $\overline{BC} \cong \overline{AD}$	12. Definition of Congruent Segments
13. Quadrilateral $ABCD$ is a parallelogram.	13. Theorem 7-8

11. STATEMENTS	REASONS
1. $\overline{AB} \cong \overline{BC}$; D is the midpoint of $\overline{CF}$; D is the midpoint of $\overline{BE}$.	1.Given
2. $\overline{CD} \cong \overline{DF}$; $\overline{BD} \cong \overline{DE}$	2. Theorem 2-5
3. $\angle CDB \cong \angle FDE$	3. Theorem 3-10
4. $\triangle CBD \cong \triangle FED$	4. SAS
5. $\overline{BC} \cong \overline{EF}$; $\angle CBD \cong \angle FED$	5. CPCTC
6. $\overline{AB} \cong \overline{EF}$	6. Theorem 2-4
7. $\overline{AB} \parallel \overline{EF}$	7. Theorem 6-4
8. Quadrilateral $ABEF$ is a parallelogram.	8. Theorem 7-8

12. STATEMENTS	REASONS
1. $\overline{FB} \perp \overline{AC}$; $\overline{FD} \perp \overline{CE}$; $\overline{FB} \perp \overline{FD}$	1. Given
2. $\angle FBC$, $\angle BFD$, and $\angle CDF$ are right angles.	2. Definition of Perpendicular Lines
3. $m\angle FBC = 90$; $m\angle BFD = 90$; $m\angle CDF = 90$	3. Definition of Right Angle
4. $m\angle FBC + m\angle BFD = 180$; $m\angle FDC + m\angle BFD = 180$	4. Postulate 2-7
5. $\angle FBC$ and $\angle BFD$ are supplementary; $\angle FDC$ and $\angle BFD$ are supplementary.	5. Definition of Supplementary Angles
6. $\overline{BF} \parallel \overline{CD}$; $\overline{BC} \parallel \overline{FD}$	6. Theorem 6-6
7. Quadrilateral $FBCD$ is a parallelogram.	7. Definition of Parallelogram

13. STATEMENTS	REASONS
1. $\angle ABF \cong \angle EDF$; $\overline{FD} \parallel \overline{AC}$	1. Given
2. $\angle ABF \cong \angle BFD$	2. Theorem 6-10
3. $\angle BFD \cong \angle EDF$	3. Theorem 3-1
4. $\overline{CD} \parallel \overline{BF}$	4. Theorem 6-4
5. Quadrilateral $FBCD$ is a parallelogram.	5. Definition of Parallelogram

14. STATEMENTS	REASONS
1. $\square ACEF$; $\overline{BG} \parallel \overline{CD}$; $\angle G \cong \angle F$	1. Given
2. $\angle C \cong \angle F$	2. Theorem 7-4
3. $\angle C \cong \angle G$	3. Theorem 3-1
4. $\angle C$ is supplementary to $\angle CBG$.	4. Theorem 6-11
5. $\angle G$ is supplementary to $\angle CBG$.	5. Postulate 2-9
6. $\overline{DG} \parallel \overline{CB}$	6. Theorem 6-6
7. Quadrilateral $BCDG$ is a parallelogram.	7. Definition of Parallelogram

15. STATEMENTS	REASONS
1. $\square BCDG$; $\angle E \cong \angle A$; $\overline{CE} \parallel \overline{AF}$	1. Given
2. $\angle A$ is supplementary to $\angle C$.	2. Theorem 6-11
3. $\angle E$ is supplementary to $\angle C$.	3. Postulate 2-9
4. $\overline{AC} \parallel \overline{EF}$	4. Theorem 6-6
5. Quadrilateral $ACEF$ is a parallelogram.	5. Definition of Parallelogram

PAGE 226 EXPLORATORY

1. rectangle, (square) **2.** parallelogram, (rectangle, rhombus, square) **3.** parallelogram, (rectangle, rhombus, square) **4.** parallelogram, (rectangle, rhombus, square) **5.** rhombus, (square) **6.** rectangle, (square) **7.** rhombus, (square) **8.** square

PAGES 226–228 WRITTEN

21. Given: Square *ABCD*
Prove: $\overline{AC}$ and $\overline{BD}$ bisect each other.
Proof:

STATEMENTS	REASONS
1. Square *ABCD*	1. Given
2. Quadrilateral *ABCD* is a rectangle.	2. Definition of Square
3. Quadrilateral *ABCD* is a parallelogram.	3. Definition of Rectangle
4. $\overline{AC}$ and $\overline{BD}$ bisect each other.	4. Theorem 7-6

22. Given: Square *RSQT*
Prove: $\overline{RT} \perp \overline{QS}$
Proof:

STATEMENTS	REASONS
1. Square *RSQT*	1. Given
2. Quadrilateral *RSQT* is a rectangle with all 4 sides congruent.	2. Definition of Square
3. Quadrilateral *RSQT* is a parallelogram.	3. Definition of Rectangle
4. Quadrilateral *RSQT* is a rhombus.	4. Definition of Rhombus
5. $\overline{RT} \perp \overline{QS}$	5. Theorem 7-12

23. Given: Quadrilateral *LMNO* is a parallelogram; $\angle O$ is a right angle.
Prove: Quadrilateral *LMNO* is a rectangle.
Proof:

STATEMENTS	REASONS
1. Quadrilateral *LMNO* is a parallelogram; $\angle O$ is a right angle.	1. Given
2. $\overline{LO} \perp \overline{ON}$	2. Definition of Perpendicular Lines
3. $\overline{LM} \parallel \overline{ON}$	3. Definition of Parallelogram
4. $\overline{LO} \perp \overline{LM}$	4. Theorem 6-13
5. $\angle L$ is a right angle.	5. Definition of Perpendicular Lines
6. $\angle O \cong \angle M$; $\angle L \cong \angle N$	6. Theorem 7-4
7. $m\angle O = 90$; $m\angle L = 90$	7. Definition of Right Angle
8. $m\angle M = 90$; $m\angle N = 90$	8. Postulate 2-9
9. $\angle M$ and $\angle N$ are right angles.	9. Definition of Right Angle
10. Quadrilateral *LMNO* is a rectangle.	10. Definition of Rectangle

24. Given: $\square TXYZ$; $\overline{TY} \perp \overline{XZ}$
Prove: $\square TXYZ$ is a rhombus.
Proof:

STATEMENTS	REASONS
1. $\square TXYZ$; $\overline{TY} \perp \overline{XZ}$	1. Given
2. $\angle TSX$, $\angle XSY$, $\angle TSZ$, and $\angle ZSY$ are right angles.	2. Theorem 3-11
3. $\angle TSX \cong \angle XSY$; $\angle TSX \cong \angle TSZ$; $\angle TSZ \cong \angle ZSY$; $\angle XSY \cong \angle ZSY$	3. Theorem 3-6
4. $\overline{TY}$ and $\overline{XZ}$ bisect each other.	4. Theorem 7-6
5. $\overline{TS} \cong \overline{SY}$; $\overline{XS} \cong \overline{SZ}$	5. Theorem 2-6
6. $\overline{TS} \cong \overline{TS}$; $\overline{XS} \cong \overline{XS}$; $\overline{SZ} \cong \overline{SZ}$; $\overline{SY} \cong \overline{SY}$	6. Theorem 2-2
7. $\triangle TSX \cong \triangle YSX$; $\triangle YSX \cong \triangle YSZ$; $\triangle YSZ \cong \triangle TSZ$; $\triangle TSZ \cong \triangle TSX$	7. SAS
8. $\overline{TX} \cong \overline{YX}$; $\overline{YX} \cong \overline{YZ}$; $\overline{YZ} \cong \overline{TZ}$; $\overline{TZ} \cong \overline{TX}$	8. CPCTC
9. $\square TXYZ$ is a rhombus.	9. Definition of Rhombus

25. Given: $\square EFGH$; $\overline{EF} \cong \overline{FG}$
Prove: $\square EFGH$ is a rhombus.

Proof:

STATEMENTS	REASONS
1. ▱$EGFH$; $\overline{EF} \cong \overline{FG}$	1. Given
2. $\overline{GH} \cong \overline{EF}$; $\overline{FG} \cong \overline{EH}$	2. Theorem 7-5
3. $\overline{GH} \cong \overline{EH}$	3. Theorem 2-4
4. ▱$EFGH$ is a rhombus.	4. Definition of Rhombus

26. Given: Quadrilateral $ABCD$ is a rhombus.
Prove: $\overline{AC} \perp \overline{BD}$

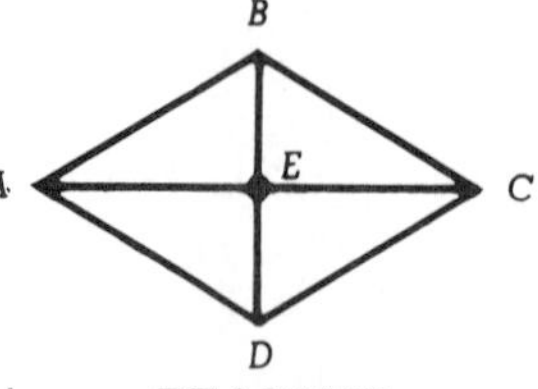

Proof:

STATEMENTS	REASONS
1. Quadrilateral $ABCD$ is a rhombus.	1. Given
2. Quadrilateral $ABCD$ is a parallelogram.	2. Definition of Rhombus
3. $\overline{AB} \cong \overline{BC}$	3. Definition of Rhombus
4. $\overline{BD}$ bisects $\overline{AC}$ at E.	4. Theorem 7-6
5. $\overline{AE} \cong \overline{CE}$	5. Theorem 2-6
6. $\overline{BE} \cong \overline{BE}$	6. Theorem 2-2
7. $\triangle ABE \cong \triangle CBE$	7. SSS
8. $\angle BEA \cong \angle BEC$	8. CPCTC
9. $\angle BEA$ and $\angle BEC$ form a linear pair.	9. Definition of Linear Pair
10. $m\angle BEA + m\angle BEC = 180$	10. Postulate 3-4
11. $m\angle BEA = m\angle BEC$	11. Definition of Congruent Angles
12. $2m\angle BEA = 180$	12. Postulate 2-9; Postulate 2-14
13. $m\angle BEA = 90$	13. Postulate 2-8
14. $m\angle BEC = 90$	14. Postulate 2-9
15. $\overline{AC} \perp \overline{BD}$	15. Definition of Perpendicular Lines

27. Given: ▱$EFGH$; $\overline{EG}$ bisects $\angle E$ and $\angle G$; $\overline{FH}$ bisects $\angle F$ and $\angle H$.

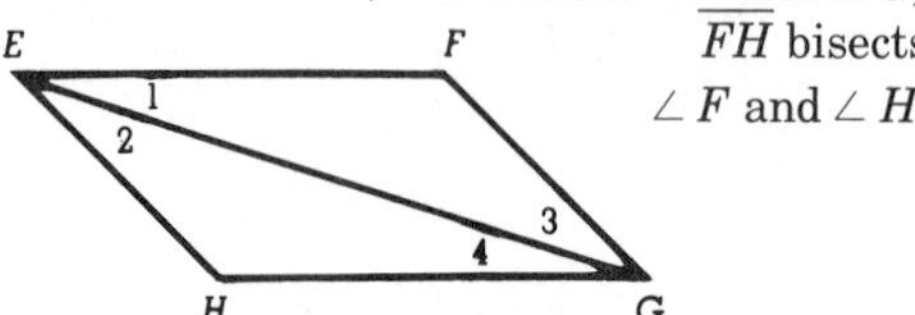

Prove: $EFGH$ is a rhombus.

Proof:

STATEMENTS	REASONS
1. ▱$EFGH$	1. Given
2. $\overline{EF} \cong \overline{GH}$; $\overline{FG} \cong \overline{HE}$	2. Theorem 7-5
3. $\overline{EG}$ bisects $\angle E$ and $\angle G$.	3. Given
4. $\angle 1 \cong \angle 2$; $\angle 3 \cong \angle 4$	4. Definition of Angle Bisector
5. $\overline{EG} \cong \overline{EG}$	5. Theorem 2-2
6. $\triangle EFG \cong \triangle EHG$	6. ASA
7. $\overline{EF} \cong \overline{EH}$	7. CPCTC
8. $\overline{EF} \cong \overline{FG} \cong \overline{GH} \cong \overline{HE}$	8. Theorem 2-4
9. ▱$EFGH$ is a rhombus.	9. Definition of Rhombus

28. Given: ▱$YNKR$; $\overline{NR} \cong \overline{YK}$
Prove: ▱$YNKR$ is a rectangle.

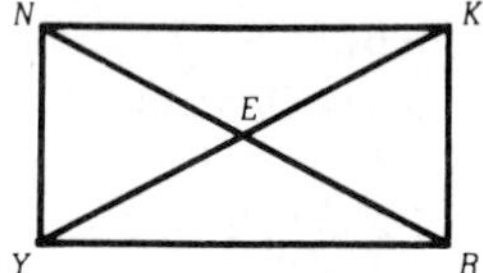

Proof:

STATEMENTS	REASONS
1. ▱$YNKR$; $\overline{NR} \cong \overline{YK}$	1. Given
2. $\overline{NY} \cong \overline{KR}$	2. Theorem 7-5
3. $\overline{NK} \cong \overline{NK}$	3. Theorem 2-2
4. $\triangle YNK \cong \triangle RKN$	4. SSS
5. $\angle N \cong \angle K$	5. CPCTC
6. $m\angle N = m\angle K$	6. Definition of Congruent Angles
7. $\overline{NY} \parallel \overline{KR}$	7. Definition of Parallelogram
8. $\angle N$ is supplementary to $\angle K$.	8. Theorem 6-11
9. $m\angle N + m\angle K = 180$	9. Definition of Supplementary Angles
10. $m\angle N + m\angle N = 180$	10. Postulate 2-9
11. $2m\angle N = 180$	11. Postulate 2-14
12. $m\angle N = 90$	12. Postulate 2-8
13. $m\angle K = 90$	13. Postulate 2-9
14. $\angle N$ and $\angle K$ are right angles.	14. Definition of Right Angle
15. $\angle N \cong \angle R$; $\angle K \cong \angle Y$	15. Theorem 7-4
16. $\angle R$ and $\angle Y$ are right angles.	16. Postulate 2-9
17. ▱$YNKR$ is a rectangle.	17. Definition of Rectangle

PAGE 228 CHALLENGE

1.

STATEMENTS	REASONS
1. $PRTW$ is a square; Q is the midpoint of $\overline{PR}$; S is the midpoint of $\overline{RT}$; V is the midpoint of $\overline{TW}$; X is the midpoint of $\overline{PW}$.	1. Given
2. $PRTW$ is a rectangle; $\overline{RT} \cong \overline{TW}$; $\overline{WP} \cong \overline{RP}$; $\overline{TW} \cong \overline{WP}$; $\overline{RP} \cong \overline{RT}$	2. Definition of Square
3. $\angle R$, $\angle T$, $\angle W$, and $\angle P$ are right angles.	3. Definition of Rectangle
4. Draw $\overline{QS}$, $\overline{SV}$, $\overline{QX}$, and $\overline{XV}$.	4. Postulate 1-1
5. $\triangle RSQ$, $\triangle PQX$, $\triangle XVW$, and $\triangle STV$ are right triangles.	5. Definition of Right Triangle
6. $RT = TW$; $WP = RP$; $TW = WP$; $RP = RT$	6. Definition of Congruent Segments
7. $RS + ST = RT$; $TV + VW = TW$; $WX + XP = WP$; $PQ + QR = RP$	7. Definition of Between
8. $RS = ST$; $TV = VW$; $WX = XP$; PQ $= QR$	8. Definition of Midpoint
9. $RS + RS = RT$; $QR + QR = RP$; $ST + ST = RT$; $TV + TV = TW$; $VW + VW = TW$; $WX + WX = WP$; $XP + XP = WP$; $PQ + PQ = RP$	9. Postulate 2-9
10. $2RS = RT$; $2VW = TW$; $2QR = RP$; $2WX = WP$; $2ST = RT$; $2XP = WP$; $2TV = TW$; $2PQ = RP$	10. Postulate 2-14
11. $2QR = 2RS$; $2VW = 2WX$; $2ST = 2TV$; $2XP = 2PQ$	11. Postulate 2-9; Steps 6 and 10
12. $QR = RS$; $VW = WX$; $ST = TV$; $XP = PQ$	12. Postulate 2-8
13. $QR = RS = ST = TV = VW = WX = XP = PQ$	13. Postulate 2-6; Step 8
14. $\overline{QR} \cong \overline{RS} \cong \overline{ST} \cong \overline{TV} \cong \overline{VW} \cong \overline{WX} \cong \overline{XP} \cong \overline{PQ}$	14. Definition of Congruent Segments
15. $\triangle QRS \cong \triangle STV \cong \triangle VWX \cong \triangle XPQ$	15. LL
16. $\overline{QS} \cong \overline{SV} \cong \overline{VX} \cong \overline{XQ}$	16. CPCTC
17. $QSVW$ is a rhombus.	17. Definition of Rhombus
18. $\overline{QV} \perp \overline{SX}$	18. Theorem 7-12

2.

STATEMENTS	REASONS
1. $\square ABCD$ is a rhombus; $\overline{AF} \cong \overline{BG}$; $\overline{BG} \cong \overline{CH}$; $\overline{CH} \cong \overline{DE}$; $\overline{DE} \cong \overline{AF}$	1. Given
2. $AF = BG$; $BG = CH$; $CH = DE$; $DE = AF$	2. Definition of Congruent Segments
3. $\overline{BC} \cong \overline{CD} \cong \overline{AD} \cong \overline{AB}$	3. Definition of Rhombus
4. $BC = CD = AD = AB$	4. Definition of Congruent Segments
5. G lies between B and C; F lies between A and B; E lies between A and D; H lies between D and C.	5. Given
6. $BG + GC = BC$; $AF + FB = AB$; $DH + HC = DC$; $AE + ED = AD$	6. Definition of Between
7. $BG + GC = AF + FB = DH + HC = AE + ED$	7. Postulate 2-9

8. $BG + GC = BG + FB = DH + BG = AE + AF$	8. Postulate 2-9
9. $BG + GC = BG + FB = DH + BG = AE + BG$	9. Postulate 2-6
10. $GC = FB = DH = AE$	10. Postulate 2-7
11. $\overline{GC} \cong \overline{FB} \cong \overline{DH} \cong \overline{AE}$	11. Definition of Congruent Segments
12. $\angle B \cong \angle D$; $\angle A \cong \angle C$	12. Theorem 7-4
13. $\triangle FBG \cong \triangle HDE$; $\triangle GCH \cong \triangle EAF$	13. SAS
14. $\overline{FG} \cong \overline{HE}$; $\overline{GH} \cong \overline{FE}$	14. CPCTC
15. Quadrilateral $EFGH$ is a parallelogram.	15. Theorem 7-7

PAGE 232 EXPLORATORY

13. Since $\overline{AB} \parallel \overline{CD}$, $\angle 1$ and $\angle 3$ are supplementary. However, $\angle 3 \cong \angle 4$ since the trapezoid is isosceles. Therefore, $\angle 1$ and $\angle 4$ are supplementary.

PAGES 233–234 WRITTEN

33. Given: Trapezoid $ABCD$; $\overline{AD} \cong \overline{BC}$
Prove: $\angle B$ and $\angle D$ are supplementary; $\angle A$ and $\angle C$ are supplementary.
Proof:

STATEMENTS	REASONS
1. Trapezoid $ABCD$; $\overline{AD} \cong \overline{BC}$	1. Given
2. $\angle A \cong \angle B$; $\angle D \cong \angle C$	2. Theorem 7-13
3. $\overline{AB} \parallel \overline{DC}$	3. Definition of Trapezoid
4. $\angle A$ and $\angle D$ are supplementary; $\angle B$ and $\angle C$ are supplementary.	4. Theorem 6-11
5. $\angle B$ and $\angle D$ are supplementary; $\angle A$ and $\angle C$ are supplementary.	5. Postulate 2-9

34.

STATEMENTS	REASONS
1. $\overline{LM} \parallel \overline{RN}$; $\overline{LR} \cong \overline{MN}$; $\overline{RP} \perp \overline{LM}$; $\overline{NQ} \perp \overline{LM}$	1. Given
2. $\angle LPR$ and $\angle MQN$ are right angles.	2. Definition of Perpendicular Lines
3. $\triangle LPR$ and $\triangle MQN$ are right triangles.	3. Definition of Right Triangle
4. $\overline{PR} \parallel \overline{QN}$	4. Theorem 6-8
5. $\square PQNR$	5. Definition of Parallelogram
6. $\overline{PR} \cong \overline{QN}$	6. Theorem 7-5
7. $\triangle LRP \cong \triangle MNQ$	7. HL

35.

STATEMENTS	REASONS
1. $\overline{LM} \parallel \overline{RN}$; $\overline{LR} \cong \overline{MN}$; $\overline{RP} \perp \overline{LM}$; $\overline{NQ} \perp \overline{LM}$	1. Given
2. Quadrilateral $LMNR$ is an isosceles trapezoid.	2. Definition of Isosceles Trapezoid
3. $\angle RLP \cong \angle NMQ$	3. Theorem 7-13

36.

STATEMENTS	REASONS
1. $\overline{RT} \parallel \overline{PW}$; $\overline{TX} \parallel \overline{RP}$; Q is the midpoint of $\overline{PR}$; V is the midpoint of $\overline{SW}$.	1. Given
2. $\overline{SV} \cong \overline{WV}$	2. Theorem 2-6
3. $\angle T \cong \angle VXW$; $\angle TSV \cong \angle VWX$	3. Theorem 6-10
4. $\triangle STV \cong \triangle WXV$	4. AAS
5. $\overline{TV} \cong \overline{XV}$	5. CPCTC
6. $TV = XV$	6. Definition of Congruent Segments
7. V is the midpoint of of $\overline{TX}$.	7. Definition of Midpoint

37. See proof of exercise 36, steps 1–4.

38.

STATEMENTS	REASONS
1. $\overline{RT} \parallel \overline{PW}$; $\overline{TX} \parallel \overline{RP}$; Q is the midpoint of $\overline{PR}$; V is the midpoint of $\overline{SW}$.	1. Given
2. $\overline{QV}$ is the median of trapezoid $PRSW$.	2. Definition of Median

3. $\overline{QV} \parallel \overline{RT}$	3. Theorem 7-15
4. Quadrilateral *QRTV* is a parallelogram.	4. Definition of Parallelogram

39.

STATEMENTS	REASONS
1. $\overline{RT} \parallel \overline{PW}$; $\overline{TX} \parallel \overline{RP}$; Q is the midpoint of $\overline{PR}$; V is the midpoint of $\overline{SW}$.	1. Given
2. $\overline{QV}$ is a median of trapezoid *RSWP*.	2. Definition of Median
3. $\overline{QV} \parallel \overline{PW}$	3. Theorem 7-15

40.

STATEMENTS	REASONS
1. Trapezoid *RSPT* is isosceles.	1. Given
2. $\angle R \cong \angle S$	2. Theorem 7-13
3. $\overline{RQ} \cong \overline{SQ}$	3. Theorem 4-9
4. $\triangle RSQ$ is isosceles.	4. Definition of Isosceles Triangle

41.

STATEMENTS	REASONS
1. $\triangle PQT$ is isosceles; $\overline{TP} \parallel \overline{RS}$	1. Given
2. $\overleftrightarrow{RQ}$ and $\overleftrightarrow{SQ}$ intersect	2. Definition of Triangle
3. $\overleftrightarrow{RQ} \nparallel \overleftrightarrow{SQ}$	3. Definition of Parallel Lines
4. $\overline{RQ} \nparallel \overline{SQ}$	4. Definition of Parallel Segments
5. Quadrilateral *RSPT* is a trapezoid.	5. Definition of Trapezoid

42. Given: Isosceles trapezoid *ABCD*; $\overline{AD} \cong \overline{BC}$
Prove: $\overline{AC} \cong \overline{BD}$
Proof:

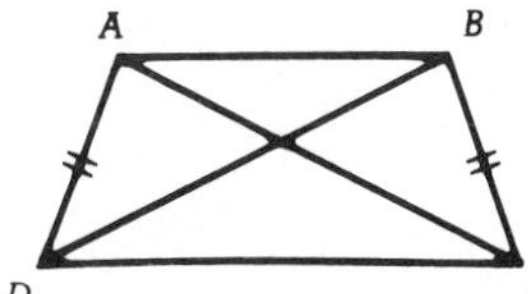

STATEMENTS	REASONS
1. Isosceles trapezoid *ABCD*; $\overline{AD} \cong \overline{BC}$	1. Given
2. $\angle ADC \cong \angle BCD$	2. Theorem 7-13
3. $\overline{DC} \cong \overline{DC}$	3. Theorem 2-2
4. $\triangle ADC \cong \triangle BCD$	4. SAS
5. $\overline{AC} \cong \overline{BD}$	5. CPCTC

43. Given: Trapezoid *ABCD*; $\angle A \cong \angle D$; $\angle ABC \cong \angle C$

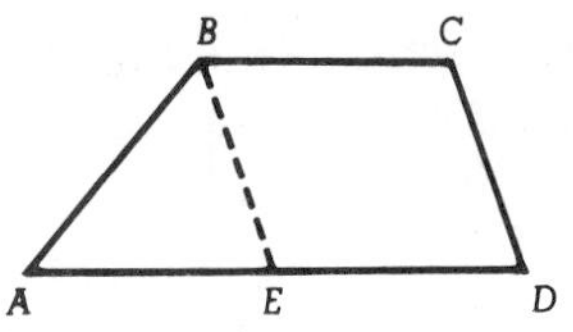

Prove: Trapezoid *ABCD* is isosceles.
Proof:

STATEMENTS	REASONS
1. Trapezoid *ABCD*; $\angle A \cong \angle D$; $\angle ABC \cong \angle C$	1. Given
2. Through B, draw a line $\overline{BE} \parallel \overline{CD}$.	2. Postulate 6-1
3. $\angle D \cong \angle AEB$	3. Theorem 6-9
4. $\angle A \cong \angle AEB$	4. Theorem 3-1
5. $\overline{AB} \cong \overline{BE}$	5. Theorem 4-9
6. $\overline{BC} \parallel \overline{AD}$	6. Definition of Trapezoid
7. $\square BCDE$	7. Definition of Parallelogram
8. $\overline{BE} \cong \overline{CD}$	8. Theorem 7-5
9. $\overline{AB} \cong$ CD	9. Theorem 2-4
10. Trapezoid *ABCD* is isosceles.	10. Definition of Isosceles Trapezoid

PAGE 235 TOPICS IN GEOMETRY

1. The sum of the measures of the angles of a quadrilateral is less than 360. **2.**

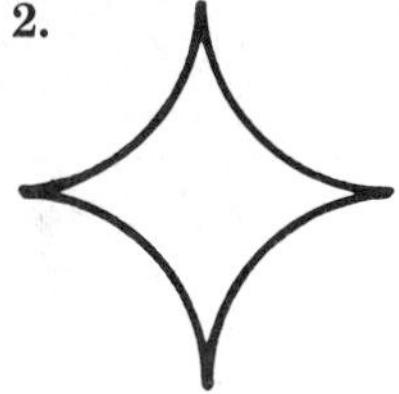

3. Suggested reference: History of Mathematics, Vol. II, D. E. Smith, Dover Publications, Inc., N.Y., N.Y., 1958.

PAGE 242 EXPLORATORY

1. Faces: $\triangle ABD$, $\triangle BCD$, $\triangle ADC$, $\triangle ABC$
Edges: $\overline{AB}, \overline{BC}, \overline{AC}, \overline{BD}, \overline{CD}, \overline{AD}$
Vertices: A, B, C, D

2. Faces: $\triangle AFD$, $\triangle ACF$, $\triangle EDF$, $\triangle ECF$, $\triangle ABD$, $\triangle ABC$, $\triangle DBE$, $\triangle CBE$
Edges: $\overline{AB}, \overline{BE}, \overline{AD}, \overline{AC}, \overline{BD}, \overline{BC}, \overline{DF}, \overline{FC}, \overline{AF}, \overline{DE}, \overline{CE}, \overline{EF}$
Vertices: A, B, C, D, E, F

3. Faces: Quadrilaterals *ABCD*, *EFGH*, *ABFE*, *DCGH*, *ADHE*, *BCGF*
Edges: $\overline{AD}, \overline{DC}, \overline{BC}, \overline{AB}, \overline{EH}, \overline{HG}, \overline{FG}, \overline{EF}, \overline{AE}, \overline{DH}, \overline{CG}, \overline{BF}$
Vertices: A, B, C, D, E, F, G, H

PAGE 242 EXCURSION

$F + V = E + 2$: **17.** $4 + 4 = 6 + 2$
18. $6 + 8 = 12 + 2$ **19.** $8 + 6 = 12 + 2$

PAGES 245–246 CHAPTER REVIEW

1. Q, R, S, T, U **2.** $\overline{QR}, \overline{RS}, \overline{ST}, \overline{TU}, \overline{UQ}$
3. $\angle Q, \angle R, \angle S, \angle T, \angle U$ **4.** pentagon
5. convex **6.** regular

20. STATEMENTS	REASONS
1. $\angle 1$ and $\angle 2$ are supplementary; $\angle 2 \cong \angle 3$	1. Given
2. $\angle 1$ and $\angle QPS$ are a linear pair.	2. Definition of Linear Pair
3. $\angle 1$ and $\angle QPS$ are supplementary.	3. Postulate 3-4
4. $\angle QPS \cong \angle 2$	4. Theorem 3-2
5. $\overline{QP} \parallel \overline{RS}$	5. Theorem 6-5
6. $\overline{QR} \parallel \overline{PS}$	6. Theorem 6-4
7. Quadrilateral *PQRS* is a parallelogram.	7. Definition of Parallelogram

21. STATEMENTS	REASONS
1. $\square ABCD$; $\overline{AE} \cong \overline{CF}$	1. Given
2. $\overline{BC} \parallel \overline{AD}$; $\overline{AB} \parallel \overline{CD}$	2. Definition of Parallelogram
3. $\angle BAC \cong \angle ACD$; $\angle BCA \cong \angle CAD$	3. Theorem 6-10
4. $\overline{AB} \cong \overline{DC}$; $\overline{BC} \cong \overline{AD}$	4. Theorem 7-5
5. $\triangle AEB \cong \triangle CFD$; $\triangle AED \cong \triangle CFB$	5. SAS
6. $\overline{BE} \cong \overline{DF}$; $\overline{DE} \cong \overline{BF}$	6. CPCTC
7. Quadrilateral *EBFD* is a parallelogram.	7. Theorem 7-7

29. STATEMENTS	REASONS
1. $\overline{BC} \parallel \overline{AD}$; $\overline{AB} \nparallel \overline{CD}$; $\overline{AB} \cong \overline{DC}$	1. Given
2. Quadrilateral *ABCD* is an isosceles trapezoid.	2. Definition of Isosceles Trapezoid
3. $\overline{AC} \cong \overline{DB}$	3. Theorem 7-14
4. $\overline{AD} \cong \overline{AD}$	4. Theorem 2-2
5. $\triangle ACD \cong \triangle DBA$	5. SSS
6. $\angle CAD \cong \angle BDA$	6. CPCTC
7. $\overline{AE} \cong \overline{DE}$	7. Theorem 4-9
8. $\triangle AED$ is isosceles.	8. Definition of Isosceles Triangle

30. STATEMENTS	REASONS
1. $\overline{RS} \parallel \overline{PV}$; $\overline{QT}$ is a median of trapezoid *PRSV*.	1. Given
2. Draw $\overline{RM} \parallel \overline{SV}$; extend $\overline{PV}$ to *M*; extend $\overline{QT}$ to *N*.	2. Postulate 6-1; Auxillary Lines
3. $\overline{QT} \parallel \overline{RS}$; $\overline{QT} \parallel \overline{PV}$	3. Theorem 7-15
4. $\overline{RN} \cong \overline{ST}$; $\overline{TV} \cong \overline{NM}$	4. Theorem 6-15
5. $\overline{ST} \cong \overline{TV}$	5. Definition of Median
6. $\overline{RN} \cong \overline{TV}$	6. Postulate 2-9
7. $\overline{RS} \cong \overline{MV}$	7. Given
8. Quadrilateral *RSVM* is a parallelogram.	8. Definition of Parallelogram
9. $\angle RMP \cong \angle VSR$	9. Theorem 7-4
10. $\angle RWQ \cong \angle TWV$	10. Theorem 3-10
11. $\angle RMP \cong \angle RNW$; $\angle VSR \cong \angle WTV$	11. Theorem 6-9
12. $\angle RNW \cong \angle WTV$	12. Postulate 2-18; Steps 9 and 11
13. $\triangle RWN \cong \triangle VWT$	13. AAS
14. $\overline{RW} \cong \overline{WV}$	14. CPCTC
15. *W* is the midpoint of $\overline{RV}$.	15. Definition of Midpoint

PAGE 247 CHAPTER TEST

11. STATEMENTS	REASONS
1. $\overline{AC} \cong \overline{BD}$; $\square ABCD$	1. Given
2. $\overline{AB} \cong \overline{DC}$	2. Theorem 7-5
3. $\overline{AD} \cong \overline{AD}$	3. Theorem 2-2
4. $\triangle ADC \cong \triangle DAB$	4. SSS
5. $\angle DAB \cong \angle ADC$	5. CPCTC
6. $m\angle DAB = m\angle ADC$	6. Definition of Congruent Angles
7. $\overline{AB} \parallel \overline{DC}$	7. Definition of Parallelogram
8. $\angle DAB$ and $\angle ADC$ are supplementary.	8. Theorem 6-11
9. $m\angle DAB + m\angle ADC = 180$	9. Definition of Supplementary Angles
10. $2m\angle DAB = 180$	10. Postulate 2-9; Postulate 2-14
11. $m\angle DAB = 90$	11. Postulate 2-8
12. $m\angle ADC = 90$	12. Postulate 2-9
13. $\angle ADC \cong \angle ABC$; $\angle DAB \cong \angle BCD$	13. Theorem 7-4

14. $m\angle ADC = m\angle ABC$; $m\angle DAB = m\angle BCD$	14. Definition of Congruent Angles
15. $m\angle ABC = 90$; $m\angle BCD = 90$	15. Postulate 2-9
16. $\angle DAB$, $\angle ADC$, $\angle ABC$ and $\angle BCD$ are right angles.	16. Definition of Right Angle
17. $\square ABCD$ is a rectangle.	17. Definition of Rectangle

12. STATEMENTS	REASONS
1. $\square LMNP$; $\overline{MP} \perp \overline{LN}$	1. Given
2. $\angle LOM$ and $\angle MON$ are right angles.	2. Theorem 3-11
3. $\triangle LOM$ and $\triangle MON$ are right triangles.	3. Definition of Right Triangle
4. $\overline{MP}$ bisects $\overline{LN}$.	4. Theorem 7-6
5. $\overline{LO} \cong \overline{ON}$	5. Theorem 2-6
6. $\overline{MO} \cong \overline{MO}$	6. Theorem 2-2
7. $\triangle LOM \cong \triangle NOM$	7. SAS
8. $\overline{LM} \cong \overline{NM}$	8. CPCTC
9. $\overline{LM} \cong \overline{PN}$; $\overline{MN} \cong \overline{LP}$	9. Theorem 7-5
10. $\overline{LM} \cong \overline{MN} \cong \overline{NP} \cong \overline{LP}$	10. Theorem 2-4
11. $\square LMNO$ is a rhombus.	11. Definition of Rhombus

13. STATEMENTS	REASONS
1. $\overline{BC} \parallel \overline{AD}$; $\overline{AB} \nparallel \overline{CD}$; $\overline{AB} \cong \overline{DC}$	1. Given
2. Quadrilateral $ABCD$ is an isosceles trapezoid.	2. Definition of Isosceles Trapezoid
3. $\overline{BD} \cong \overline{CA}$	3. Theorem 7-14
4. $\overline{BC} \cong \overline{BC}$	4. Theorem 2-2
5. $\triangle ABC \cong \triangle DCB$	5. SSS

14. STATEMENTS	REASONS
1. $\overline{PQ} \parallel \overline{RS}$; $\overline{PQ} \cong \overline{RS}$; T is the midpoint of $\overline{QP}$; V is the midpoint of $\overline{RS}$.	1. Given
2. $PT = TQ$; $VS = RV$	2. Theorem 2-5
3. $PQ = PT + TQ$; $RS = RV + VS$	3. Definition of Between
4. $PQ = RS$	4. Definition of Congruent Segments
5. $PT + TQ = RV + VS$	5. Postulate 2-9
6. $TQ + TQ = RV + RV$	6. Postulate 2-9
7. $2TQ = 2RV$	7. Postulate 2-14
8. $TQ = RV$	8. Postulate 2-8
9. $\overline{TQ} \cong \overline{RV}$	9. Definition of Congruent Segments
10. Quadrilateral $TQRV$ is a parallelogram.	10. Theorem 7-8

CHAPTER 8 SIMILARITY

PAGES 251–252 WRITTEN

31. STATEMENTS	REASONS
1. $ad = bc$; $b \neq 0$; $d \neq 0$	1. Given
2. $ad \cdot \frac{1}{b} \cdot \frac{1}{d} = bc \cdot \frac{1}{b} \cdot \frac{1}{d}$	2. Theorem 2-8
3. $a \cdot \frac{1}{b} \cdot d \cdot \frac{1}{d} = b \cdot \frac{1}{b} \cdot c \cdot \frac{1}{d}$	3. Postulate 2-11; Postulate 2-10
4. $a \cdot \frac{1}{b} \cdot 1 = 1 \cdot c \cdot \frac{1}{d}$	4. Postulate 2-13
5. $a \cdot \frac{1}{b} = c \cdot \frac{1}{d}$	5. Postulate 2-12
6. $\frac{a}{b} = \frac{c}{d}$	6. Postulate 2-9

PAGES 256–257 WRITTEN

Remind students that terms in exercises 7-12 are defined only with *nonzero* denominators.

7. STATEMENTS	REASONS
1. $\frac{a}{b} = \frac{c}{d}$	1. Given
2. $ad = bc$	2. Theorem 8-1
3. $\frac{ad}{cd} = \frac{bc}{cd}$	3. Postulate 2-8
4. $\frac{a}{c} = \frac{b}{d}$	4. Postulate 2-12; Postulate 2-9

8. STATEMENTS	REASONS
1. $\frac{a}{b} = \frac{c}{d}$	1. Given
2. $ad = bc$	2. Theorem 8-1
3. $bc = ad$	3. Postulate 2-5
4. $\frac{b}{a} = \frac{d}{c}$	4. Theorem 8-1

9.

STATEMENTS	REASONS
1. $\frac{a}{b} = \frac{c}{d}$	1. Given
2. $\frac{a}{b} - 1 = \frac{c}{d} - 1$	2. Postulate 2-7
3. $b \cdot \frac{1}{b}$ or $\frac{b}{b} = 1$; $d \cdot \frac{1}{d}$ or $\frac{d}{d} = 1$	3. Postulate 2-13
4. $\frac{a}{b} - \frac{b}{b} = \frac{c}{d} - \frac{d}{d}$	4. Postulate 2-9
5. $\frac{a-b}{b} = \frac{c-d}{d}$	5. Postulate 2-14

10.

STATEMENTS	REASONS
1. $\frac{a-b}{b} = \frac{c-d}{d}$	1. Given
2. $\frac{a}{b} - \frac{b}{b} = \frac{c}{d} - \frac{d}{d}$	2. Postulate 2-14
3. $b \cdot \frac{1}{b}$ or $\frac{b}{b} = 1$; $d \cdot \frac{1}{d}$ or $\frac{d}{d} = 1$	3. Postulate 2-13
4. $\frac{a}{b} - 1 = \frac{c}{d} - 1$	4. Postulate 2-9
5. $\frac{a}{b} = \frac{c}{d}$	5. Postulate 2-7

11.

STATEMENTS	REASONS
1. $\frac{a}{b} = \frac{a+c}{b+d}$	1. Given
2. $a(b+d) = b(a+c)$	2. Theorem 8-1
3. $ab + ad = ba + bc$	3. Postulate 2-14
4. $^{-}ab + ab + ad = {}^{-}ab + ba + bc$	4. Postulate 2-7
5. $0 + ad = 0 + bc$	5. Postulate 2-13; Postulate 2-9
6. $ad = bc$	6. Postulate 2-12; Postulate 2-9
7. $\frac{a}{b} = \frac{c}{d}$	7. Theorem 8-1

12.

STATEMENTS	REASONS
1. $\frac{a}{b} = \frac{c}{d}$	1. Given
2. $ad = bc$	2. Theorem 8-1
3. $ad + cd = bc + dc$	3. Postulate 2-7; Postulate 2-10
4. $(a+c)d = (b+d)c$	4. Postulate 2-14
5. $\frac{a+c}{b+d} = \frac{c}{d}$	5. Theorem 8-1
6. $\frac{c}{d} = \frac{a+c}{b+d}$	6. Postulate 2-5

PAGES 260–261 EXPLORATORY

1. $\angle A \cong \angle D$, $\angle B \cong \angle E$, $\angle C \cong \angle F$; $\frac{AB}{DE} = \frac{BC}{EF} = \frac{AC}{DF}$ **2.** $\angle P \cong \angle A$, $\angle Q \cong \angle B$, $\angle R \cong \angle C$, $\angle S \cong \angle D$; $\frac{PQ}{AB} = \frac{QR}{BC} = \frac{RS}{CD} = \frac{PS}{AD}$ **3.** $\angle R \cong \angle L$, $\angle S \cong \angle M$, $\angle T \cong \angle N$, $\angle V \cong \angle O$, $\angle W \cong \angle P$, $\angle X \cong \angle Q$; $\frac{RS}{LM} = \frac{ST}{MN} = \frac{TV}{NO} = \frac{VW}{OP} = \frac{WX}{PQ} = \frac{XR}{QL}$ **4.** $\angle A \cong \angle N$, $\angle B \cong \angle M$, $\angle C \cong \angle L$, $\angle D \cong \angle P$; $\frac{AB}{NM} = \frac{BC}{ML} = \frac{CD}{LP} = \frac{DA}{PN}$

PAGES 261–262 WRITTEN

1. *True,* the angles are 60° and the sides are proportional. **2.** *False,* the angles are not necessarily congruent. **3.** *False,* the sides are not necessarily proportional. **4.** *True,* the angles are congruent, and the sides are proportional. **5.** *False,* the angles are not necessarily congruent. **6.** *True,* the angles are congruent, and the sides are in the ratio 1:1. **7.** *False,* the angles are not necessarily congruent. **8.** *False,* the angles are not necessarily congruent. **9.** *False,* the sides are proportional but not necessarily congruent. **10.** *True,* the sides are in the ratio of 1:1, and the angles are congruent.

15. Given: $\triangle ABC$
Prove: $\triangle ABC \sim \triangle ABC$

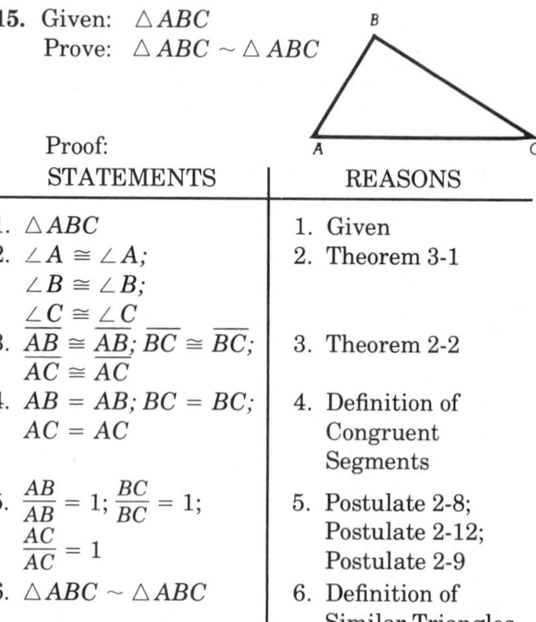

Proof:

STATEMENTS	REASONS
1. $\triangle ABC$	1. Given
2. $\angle A \cong \angle A$; $\angle B \cong \angle B$; $\angle C \cong \angle C$	2. Theorem 3-1
3. $\overline{AB} \cong \overline{AB}$; $\overline{BC} \cong \overline{BC}$; $\overline{AC} \cong \overline{AC}$	3. Theorem 2-2
4. $AB = AB$; $BC = BC$; $AC = AC$	4. Definition of Congruent Segments
5. $\frac{AB}{AB} = 1$; $\frac{BC}{BC} = 1$; $\frac{AC}{AC} = 1$	5. Postulate 2-8; Postulate 2-12; Postulate 2-9
6. $\triangle ABC \sim \triangle ABC$	6. Definition of Similar Triangles

16. Given: $\triangle ABC \sim \triangle RST$
Prove: $\triangle RST \sim \triangle ABC$

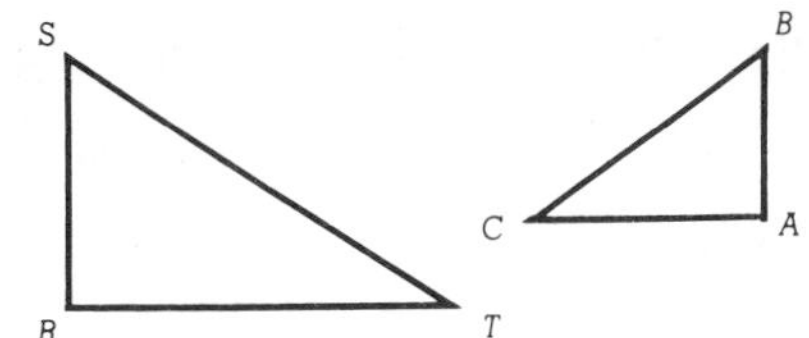

Proof:

STATEMENTS	REASONS
1. $\triangle ABC \sim \triangle RST$	1. Given
2. $\angle A \cong \angle R$; $\angle B \cong \angle S$; $\angle C \cong \angle T$; $\frac{AB}{RS} = \frac{BC}{ST} = \frac{CA}{TR}$	2. Definition of Similar Polygons
3. $\angle R \cong \angle A$; $\angle S \cong \angle B$; $\angle T \cong \angle C$	3. Theorem 3-1
4. $\frac{RS}{AB} = \frac{ST}{BC} = \frac{TR}{CA}$	4. Theorem 8-3
5. $\triangle RST \sim \triangle ABC$	5. Definition of Similar Polygons

17. Given: $\triangle ABC \sim \triangle RST$; $\triangle RST \sim \triangle PQM$
Prove: $\triangle ABC \sim \triangle PQM$

Proof:

STATEMENTS	REASONS
1. $\triangle ABC \sim \triangle RST$; $\triangle RST \sim \triangle PQM$	1. Given
2. $\angle A \cong \angle R$; $\angle B \cong \angle S$; $\angle C \cong \angle T$; $\angle R \cong \angle P$; $\angle S \cong \angle Q$; $\angle T \cong \angle M$	2. Definition of Similar Polygons
3. $\angle A \cong \angle P$; $\angle B \cong \angle Q$; $\angle C \cong \angle M$	3. Theorem 3-1
4. $\frac{AB}{RS} = \frac{BC}{ST} = \frac{CA}{TR}$; $\frac{RS}{PQ} = \frac{ST}{QM} = \frac{TR}{MP}$	4. Definition of Similar Polygons
5. $\dfrac{\frac{AB}{RS}}{\frac{RS}{PQ}} = \dfrac{\frac{BC}{ST}}{\frac{ST}{QM}} = \dfrac{\frac{CA}{TR}}{\frac{TR}{MP}}$	5. Postulate 2-8
6. $\frac{AB}{PQ} = \frac{BC}{QM} = \frac{CA}{MP}$	6. Simplification; Postulate 2-9
7. $\triangle ABC \sim \triangle PQM$	7. Definition of Similar Polygons

18. Given: $\triangle ABC \cong \triangle KLM$
Prove: $\triangle ABC \sim \triangle KLM$

Proof:

STATEMENTS	REASONS
1. $\triangle ABC \cong \triangle KLM$	1. Given
2. $\angle A \cong \angle K$; $\angle B \cong \angle L$; $\angle C \cong \angle M$; $\overline{AB} \cong \overline{KL}$; $\overline{BC} \cong \overline{LM}$; $\overline{CA} \cong \overline{MK}$	2. Definition of Congruent Triangles
3. $AB = KL$; $BC = LM$; $CA = MK$	3. Definition of Congruent Segments
4. $\frac{AB}{KL} = 1$; $\frac{BC}{LM} = 1$; $\frac{CA}{MK} = 1$	4. Postulate 2-8; Postulate 2-12; Postulate 2-9
5. $\triangle ABC \sim \triangle KLM$	5. Definition of Similar Polygons

PAGE 266 WRITTEN

3.

STATEMENTS	REASONS
1. $\angle D$ is a right angle; $\overline{BE} \perp \overline{AC}$	1. Given
2. $\angle ABE$ is a right angle.	2. Theorem 3-11
3. $\angle D \cong \angle ABE$	3. Theorem 3-6
4. $\angle A \cong \angle A$	4. Theorem 3-1
5. $\triangle ADC \sim \triangle ABE$	5. AA Similarity

4.

STATEMENTS	REASONS
1. $\overline{QS} \parallel \overline{PT}$	1. Given
2. $\angle SQR \cong \angle PTR$; $\angle QSR \cong \angle TPR$	2. Theorem 6-10
3. $\triangle QRS \sim \triangle TRP$	3. AA Similarity

5.

STATEMENTS	REASONS
1. $\angle Q$ is a right angle; $\square WSTV$ is a square.	1. Given
2. $\square WSTV$ is a rectangle.	2. Definition of Square
3. $\angle SWV$ and $\angle WVT$ are right angles.	3. Definition of Rectangle
4. $\angle SWP$ and $\angle TVR$ are right angles.	4. Theorem 3-9
5. $\angle SWP \cong \angle TVR$	5. Theorem 3-6

6. $\triangle SWP$ and $\triangle PQR$ are right triangles.	6. Definition of Right Triangle
7. $\angle P$ and $\angle PSW$ are complementary angles; $\angle P$ and $\angle R$ are complementary angles.	7. Theorem 4-3
8. $\angle PSW \cong \angle R$	8. Theorem 3-4
9. $\triangle PWS \sim \triangle TVR$	9. AA Similarity

6. STATEMENTS	REASONS
1. $\overline{PR} \cong \overline{TR}$; $\overline{VQ} \perp \overline{PR}$; $\overline{VS} \perp \overline{RT}$	1. Given
2. $\angle PQV$ and $\angle TSV$ are right angles.	2. Theorem 3-11
3. $\angle PQV \cong \angle TSV$	3. Theorem 3-6
4. $\angle P \cong \angle T$	4. Theorem 4-6
5. $\triangle PQV \sim \triangle TSV$	5. AA Similarity
6. $\frac{PQ}{TS} = \frac{VQ}{VS}$	6. Definition of Similar Polygons

7. Given: $\angle B \cong \angle E$; $\frac{AB}{DE} = \frac{BC}{EF}$

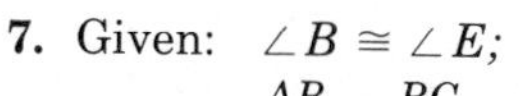

Prove: $\triangle ABC \sim \triangle DEF$

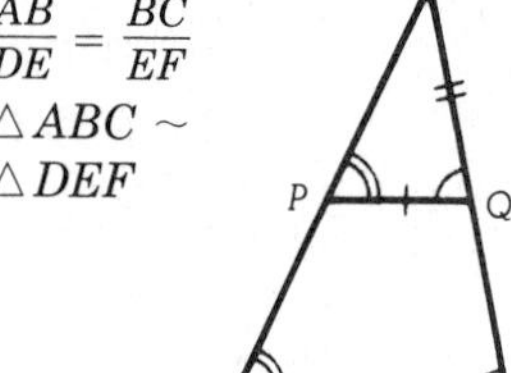

Proof:

STATEMENTS	REASONS
1. Draw $\overline{PQ} \parallel \overline{CB}$ so $\overline{PQ} \cong \overline{FE}$.	1. Postulate 6-1
2. $\angle APQ \cong \angle C$; $\angle AQP \cong \angle B$	2. Theorem 6-9
3. $\angle B \cong \angle E$	3. Given
4. $\angle AQP \cong \angle E$	4. Theorem 3-1
5. $\triangle ABC \sim \triangle AQP$	5. AA Similarity
6. $\frac{AB}{AQ} = \frac{BC}{QP}$	6. Definition of Similar Polygons
7. $\frac{AB}{DE} = \frac{BC}{EF}$	7. Given
8. $AB \cdot QP = AQ \cdot BC$; $AB \cdot EF = DE \cdot BC$	8. Theorem 8-1
9. $PQ = FE$	9. Definition of Congruent Segments
10. $AB \cdot EF = AQ \cdot BC$	10. Postulate 2-9
11. $AQ \cdot BC = DE \cdot BC$	11. Postulate 2-9
12. $AQ = DE$	12. Postulate 2-8
13. $\overline{AQ} \cong \overline{DE}$	13. Definition of Congruent Segments
14. $\triangle AQP \cong \triangle DEF$	14. SAS
15. $\triangle ABC \sim \triangle DEF$	15. Postulate 2-9

8. Given: $\triangle ABC$; $\triangle DEF$; $\angle B$ is a right angle; $\angle E$ is a right angle; $\frac{AB}{DE} = \frac{BC}{EF}$

Prove: $\triangle ABC \sim \triangle DEF$

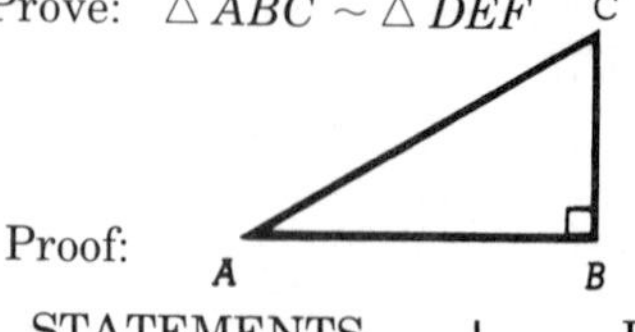

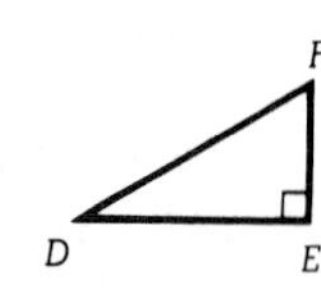

Proof:

STATEMENTS	REASONS
1. $\triangle ABC$; $\triangle DEF$; $\angle B$ is a right angle; $\angle E$ is a right angle; $\frac{AB}{DE} = \frac{BC}{EF}$	1. Given
2. $\angle B \cong \angle E$	2. Theorem 3-6
3. $\triangle ABC \sim \triangle DEF$	3. SAS Similarity

PAGE 275 WRITTEN

Answers will vary. Samples are shown as follows.
1. $\frac{TW}{LN} = \frac{TV}{LM}$; $\frac{VT}{LM} = \frac{VW}{MN}$; $\frac{TW}{LN} = \frac{VW}{MN}$; $\frac{TW}{LN} = \frac{TV + VX + TX}{LM + MO + LO}$; $\frac{TW}{LN} = \frac{WX}{NO}$; $\frac{TX}{LO} = \frac{WX}{NO}$; $\frac{TW}{LN} = \frac{TX}{LO}$; $\frac{TW}{LN} = \frac{VX}{MO}$ **2.** See answers to exercise 1.

9. Suppose $\triangle ABC \sim \triangle PQM$. Then, $\angle A \cong \angle P$ because they are corresponding angles. If $\overline{BD}$ and $\overline{QR}$ are altitudes of the triangles, then $\angle BDA$ and $\angle QRP$ are right angles and, therefore, congruent. By AA Similarity, $\triangle ABD \sim \triangle PQR$, which implies $\frac{BD}{QR} = \frac{BA}{QP}$.

10. Given: $\triangle ABC \sim \triangle PQM$; altitudes $\overline{BD}$ and $\overline{QR}$

Prove: $\frac{BD}{QR} = \frac{AB}{PQ} = \frac{BC}{QM} = \frac{AC}{PM}$

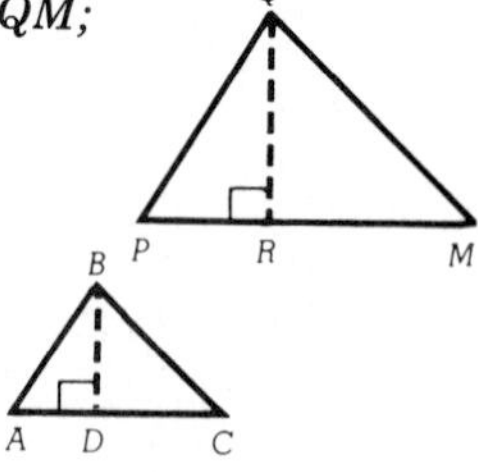

Proof:

STATEMENTS	REASONS
1. $\triangle ABC \sim \triangle PQM$	1. Given
2. $\angle A \cong \angle P$; $\frac{AB}{PQ} = \frac{BC}{QM} = \frac{AC}{PM}$	2. Definition of Similar Triangles

3. $\overline{BD}$ and $\overline{QR}$ are altitudes.	3. Given
4. $\angle BDA$ and $\angle QRP$ are right angles.	4. Definition of Altitude
5. $\angle BDA \cong \angle QRP$	5. Theorem 3-6
6. $\triangle ABD \sim \triangle PQR$	6. AA Similarity
7. $\frac{BD}{QR} = \frac{AB}{PQ}$	7. Definition of Similar Triangles
8. $\frac{BD}{QR} = \frac{AB}{PQ} = \frac{BC}{QM} = \frac{CA}{PM}$	8. Postulate 2-18

11. Suppose $\triangle RST \sim \triangle EFG$ and $\overline{RV}$ bisects $\angle SRT$ while $\overline{EH}$ bisects $\angle FEG$. $\angle SRV \cong \angle FEH$ and $\angle S \cong \angle F$. By AA Similarity, $\triangle SRV \sim \triangle FEH$, which implies $\frac{RV}{EH} = \frac{RS}{EF}$.

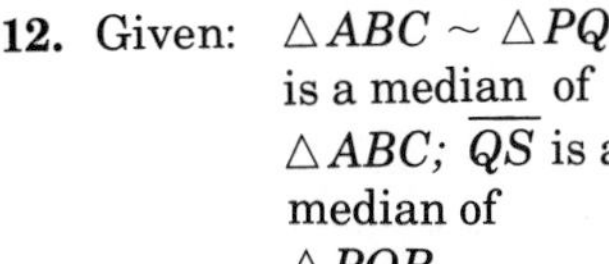

12. Given: $\triangle ABC \sim \triangle PQR$; $\overline{BD}$ is a median of $\triangle ABC$; $\overline{QS}$ is a median of $\triangle PQR$.

Prove: $\frac{BD}{QS} = \frac{BA}{QP}$

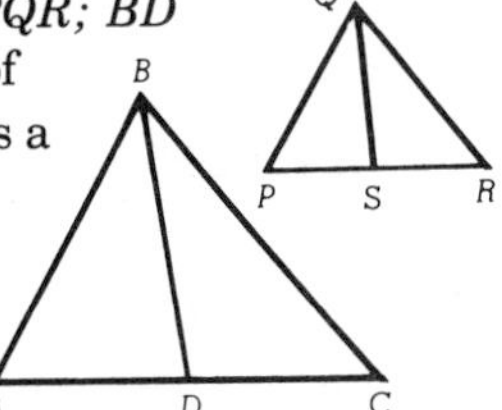

Proof:

STATEMENTS	REASONS
1. $\triangle ABC \sim \triangle PQR$; $\overline{BD}$ is a median of $\triangle ABC$; $\overline{QS}$ is a median of $\triangle PQR$.	1. Given
2. D is the midpoint of $\overline{AC}$; S is the midpoint of $\overline{PR}$.	2. Definition of Median
3. $AD = DC$; $PS = SR$	3. Definition of Midpoint
4. $\angle A \cong \angle P$; $\frac{AB}{PQ} = \frac{AC}{PR}$	4. Definition of Polygon
5. $AC = AD + DC$; $PR = PS + SR$	5. Definition of Between
6. $\frac{AB}{PQ} = \frac{AD + DC}{PS + SR}$	6. Postulate 2-9
7. $AD + DC = AD + AD$; $PS + SR = PS + PS$	7. Postulate 2-9
8. $AD + DC = 2AD$; $PS + SR = 2PS$	8. Postulate 2-14; Postulate 2-9
9. $\frac{AB}{PQ} = \frac{2AD}{2PS}$	9. Postulate 2-9
10. $AB \cdot 2PS = PQ \cdot 2AD$	10. Theorem 8-1
11. $AB \cdot PS = PQ \cdot AD$	11. Postulate 2-10; Postulate 2-8

12. $\frac{AB}{PQ} = \frac{AD}{PS}$	12. Theorem 8-1
13. $\triangle ABD \sim \triangle PQS$	13. SAS Similarity
14. $\frac{BD}{QS} = \frac{BA}{QP}$	14. Definition of Similar Polygons

PAGE 283 CHAPTER REVIEW

9.

STATEMENTS	REASONS
1. $\frac{a}{b} = \frac{c}{d}$	1. Given
2. $\frac{a-b}{b} = \frac{c-d}{d}$	2. Theorem 8-5
3. $\frac{a-b}{c-d} = \frac{b}{d}$	3. Theorem 8-2

10.

STATEMENTS	REASONS
1. $\frac{a+c}{b+d} = \frac{a}{b}$	1. Given
2. $\frac{a+c}{a} = \frac{b+d}{b}$	2. Theorem 8-2
3. $\frac{c}{a} = \frac{d}{b}$	3. Theorem 8-4
4. $\frac{c}{d} = \frac{a}{b}$	4. Theorem 8-2
5. $\frac{a}{b} = \frac{c}{d}$	5. Postulate 2-5

11. *Yes,* the corresponding angles are congruent. Also, the measures of the corresponding sides are proportional. **12.** *No,* corresponding sides can be proportional without being congruent.

15.

STATEMENTS	REASONS
1. $\frac{PR}{QS} = \frac{RS}{QP}$; $\overline{QR} \parallel \overline{PS}$; isosceles trapezoid $PQRS$	1. Given
2. $\angle QRP \cong \angle SPR$; $\angle RQS \cong \angle PSQ$	2. Theorem 6-10
3. $\triangle QRT \cong \triangle SPT$	3. AA Similarity
4. $\frac{QT}{ST} = \frac{RT}{PT}$	4. Definition of Similar Polygons
5. $\angle QTP \cong \angle STR$	5. Theorem 3-10
6. $\triangle QTP \sim \triangle STR$	6. SAS Similarity
7. $\angle QPT \cong \angle RST$	7. Definition of Similar Polygons
8. $\angle RQP \cong \angle QRS$	8. Theorem 7-13
9. $\triangle PQR \sim \triangle SRQ$	9. AA Similarity

16.

STATEMENTS	REASONS
1. $\overline{QR} \parallel \overline{PS}$	1. Given
2. $\angle RQT \cong \angle PST$; $\angle QRT \cong \angle SPT$	2. Theorem 6-10

3. $\triangle QRT \sim \triangle SPT$	3. AA Similarity
4. $\frac{QT}{TS} = \frac{TR}{PT}$	4. Definition of Similar Polygons

PAGE 285 CHAPTER TEST

9.

STATEMENTS	REASONS
1. $\triangle ABC \sim \triangle RSP$; D is the midpoint of $\overline{AC}$; Q is the midpoint of $\overline{PR}$; $\overline{TP}$ bisects $\angle SPQ$; $\overline{EC}$ bisects $\angle BCD$.	1. Given
2. $\angle RPS \cong \angle ACB$	2. Definition of Similar Triangle
3. $\frac{SQ}{BD} = \frac{SP}{BC}$	3. Theorem 8-17
4. $PQ = QR$; $DC = DA$	4. Theorem 2-5
5. $AD + DC = AC$; $PQ + QR = PR$	5. Definition of Between
6. $2DC = AC$; $2PQ = PR$	6. Postulate 2-14; Postulate 2-9
7. $\frac{PR}{CA} = \frac{SQ}{BD}$	7. Theorem 8-17
8. $\frac{2PQ}{2DC} = \frac{SQ}{BD}$	8. Postulate 2-9
9. $\frac{PQ}{DC} = \frac{SQ}{BD}$	9. Postulate 2-12; Postulate 2-13
10. $\triangle SPQ \sim \triangle BCD$	10. SSS Similarity
11. $\angle SQP \cong \angle BDC$	11. Definition of Similar Triangles
12. $\angle QPT \cong \angle TPS$; $\angle BCE \cong \angle ECD$	12. Definition of Angle Bisector
13. $m\angle QPT = m\angle TPS$; $m\angle BCE = m\angle ECD$	13. Definition of Congruent Angles
14. $m\angle QPT + m\angle TPS = m\angle SPR$; $m\angle BCE + m\angle ECD = \angle ACB$	14. Postulate 3-3
15. $m\angle QPT + m\angle TPS = m\angle BCE + m\angle ECD$	15. Steps 2, 14; Definition of Congruent Angles: Postulate 2-9
16. $2m\angle QPT = 2m\angle ECD$	16. Step 13; Postulate 2-9; Postulate 2-14
17. $m\angle QPT = m\angle ECD$	17. Postulate 2-12; Postulate 2-13
18. $\angle QPT \cong \angle ECD$	18. Definition of Congruent Angles
19. $\triangle PQT \sim \triangle CDE$	19. AA Similarity
20. $\frac{QT}{DE} = \frac{PQ}{CD}$	20. Definition of Similar Triangles
21. $\frac{QT}{DE} = \frac{SP}{BC}$	21. Steps 3, 9, 20; Postulate 2-18

10. Given: $\triangle ABC \sim \triangle MPR$

Prove: $\overline{BD}$ is the altitude of $\triangle ABC$; $\overline{PQ}$ is the altitude of $\triangle MPR$.

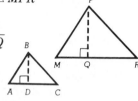

Prove: $\frac{BD}{PQ} = \frac{AB + BC + CA}{MP + PR + RM}$

Proof:

STATEMENTS	REASONS
1. $\triangle ABC \sim \triangle MPR$; $\overline{BD}$ is the altitude of $\triangle ABC$; $\overline{PQ}$ is the altitude of $\triangle MPR$.	1. Given
2. $\frac{BD}{PQ} = \frac{AB}{MP}$	2. Theorem 8-15
3. $\frac{AB}{MP} = \frac{AB + BC + CA}{MP + PR + RM}$	3. Theorem 8-14
4. $\frac{BD}{PQ} = \frac{AB + BC + CA}{MP + PR + RM}$	4. Postulate 2-9

CHAPTER 9 RIGHT TRIANGLES

PAGE 294 WRITTEN

29. Given: $\triangle ADC$; $\angle ADC$ is a right angle; $\overline{DB}$ is an altitude of $\triangle ADC$.

Prove: $\frac{AB}{DB} = \frac{DB}{CB}$

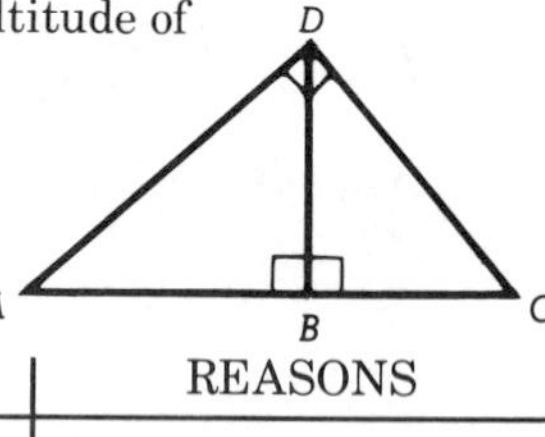

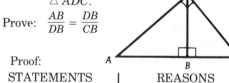

Proof:

STATEMENTS	REASONS
1. $\triangle ADC$; $\angle ADC$ is a right angle; $\overline{BD}$ is an altitude of $\triangle ADC$.	1. Given
2. $\triangle ADB \sim \triangle DCB$	2. Theorem 9-1
3. $\frac{AB}{DB} = \frac{DB}{CB}$	3. Definition of Similar Polygons

30. Given: $\triangle ADC$; $\angle ADC$ is a right angle; $\overline{DB}$ is an altitude of $\triangle ADC$.

Prove: $\frac{AB}{AD} = \frac{AD}{AC}$; $\frac{BC}{DC} = \frac{DC}{AC}$

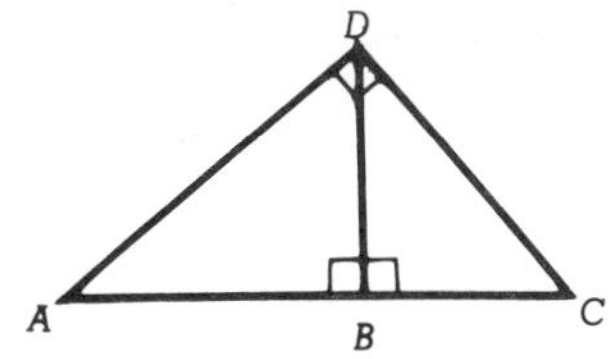

Proof:

STATEMENTS	REASONS
1. $\triangle ADC$; $\angle ADC$ is a right angle; $\overline{DB}$ is an altitude of $\triangle ADC$.	1. Given
2. $\triangle ABD \sim \triangle ADC$; $\triangle DBC \sim \triangle ADC$	2. Theorem 9-1
3. $\frac{AB}{AD} = \frac{AD}{AC}$; $\frac{BC}{DC} = \frac{DC}{AC}$	3. Definition of Similar Polygons

PAGE 298 WRITTEN

24. Given: $\triangle ABC, a^2 + b^2 = c^2; AB = c; BC = a; AC = b$

Prove: $\triangle ABC$ is a right triangle.

Proof:

STATEMENTS	REASONS
1. $\triangle ABC; a^2 + b^2 = c^2; AB = c; BC = a; AC = b$	1. Given
2. Draw $\triangle PQR$ with $PR = b$ and $RQ = a$ so that $PR \perp RQ$.	2. Postulate 2-2; Postulate 2-3; Postulate 3-2
3. Let $PQ = h$; $h^2 = a^2 + b^2$	3. Postulate 2-9; Theorem 9-4
4. $c^2 = h^2$	4. Postulate 2-6
5. $c = h$	5. Definition of Square Root
6. $AB = PQ$; $AC = PR$; $CB = RQ$	6. Postulate 2-9
7. $\overline{AB} \cong \overline{PQ}$; $\overline{AC} \cong \overline{PR}$; $\overline{CB} \cong \overline{RQ}$	7. Definition of Congruent Segments
8. $\triangle ABC \cong \triangle PQR$	8. SSS
9. $\angle C \cong \angle R$	9. CPCTC
10. $\angle R$ is a right angle.	10. Definition of Perpendicular Lines
11. $\angle C$ is a right angle.	11. Postulate 2-9
12. $\triangle ABC$ is a right triangle.	12. Definition of Right Triangle

PAGE 305 WRITTEN

1. $\sin A = \frac{30}{34} \approx 0.882$ $\quad \sin B = \frac{16}{34} \approx 0.471$
$\cos A = \frac{16}{34} \approx 0.471$ $\quad \cos B = \frac{30}{34} \approx 0.882$
$\tan A = \frac{30}{16} \approx 1.875$ $\quad \tan B = \frac{16}{30} \approx 0.533$

2. $\sin A = \frac{9}{41} \approx 0.220$ $\quad \sin B = \frac{40}{41} \approx 0.976$
$\cos A = \frac{40}{41} \approx 0.976$ $\quad \cos B = \frac{9}{41} \approx 0.220$
$\tan A = \frac{9}{40} \approx 0.225$ $\quad \tan B = \frac{40}{9} \approx 4.444$

3. $\sin A = \frac{63}{65} \approx 0.969$ $\quad \sin B = \frac{16}{65} \approx 0.246$
$\cos A = \frac{16}{65} \approx 0.246$ $\quad \cos B = \frac{63}{65} \approx 0.969$
$\tan A = \frac{63}{16} \approx 3.938$ $\quad \tan B = \frac{16}{63} \approx 0.254$

4. $\sin A = \frac{80}{89} \approx 0.899$ $\quad \sin B = \frac{39}{89} \approx 0.438$
$\cos A = \frac{39}{89} \approx 0.438$ $\quad \cos B = \frac{80}{89} \approx 0.899$
$\tan A = \frac{80}{39} \approx 2.051$ $\quad \tan B = \frac{39}{80} \approx 0.488$

5. $\sin A = \frac{4}{5} \approx 0.800$ $\quad \sin B = \frac{3}{5} \approx 0.600$
$\cos A = \frac{3}{5} \approx 0.600$ $\quad \cos B = \frac{4}{5} \approx 0.800$
$\tan A = \frac{4}{3} \approx 1.333$ $\quad \tan B = \frac{3}{4} \approx 0.750$

6. $\sin A = \frac{4.0}{4.1} \approx 0.976$ $\quad \sin B = \frac{0.9}{4.1} \approx 0.220$
$\cos A = \frac{0.9}{4.1} \approx 0.220$ $\quad \cos B = \frac{4.0}{4.1} \approx 0.976$
$\tan A = \frac{4.0}{0.9} \approx 4.444$ $\quad \tan B = \frac{0.9}{4.0} \approx 0.225$

PAGE 310 CALCULATOR EXCURSION

1. 7.503 16 **2.** 1.59 12 **3.** 6.7 16 **4.** 7.102 24 **5.** 5.675 31 **6.** ⁻1.592 12 **7.** 5.308 35 **8.** ⁻7.8 ⁻20 **9.** ⁻1.248 09 **10.** 5.8001 ⁻21 **11.** ⁻1.603 ⁻30 **12.** 7.2 32 **13.** 3.4506×10^8 (without rounding: 3.45056×10^8) **14.** 6.6228×10^{10} (without rounding: 6.6227895×10^{10}) **15.** 3.2106 (without rounding: 3.21056) **16.** 1.1204×10^5

PAGE 315 TOPICS IN GEOMETRY

1. See *Men of Mathematics*, E.T. Bell, Simon & Schuster, 1937, Chapter 26. **2.**

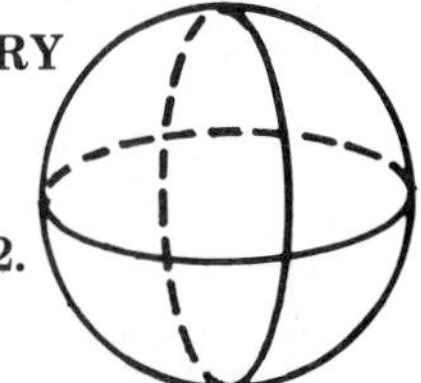

PAGES 317–318 CHAPTER REVIEW

26. $\sin A = \frac{2.0}{2.8} \approx 0.7$ $\quad \sin C = \frac{2.0}{2.8} \approx 0.7$
$\cos A = \frac{2.0}{2.8} \approx 0.7$ $\quad \cos C = \frac{2.0}{2.8} \approx 0.7$
$\tan A = \frac{2.0}{2.0} = 1.0$ $\quad \tan C = \frac{2.0}{2.0} = 1.0$

27. $\sin Q = \frac{15.0}{17.0} \approx 0.9$ $\quad \sin R = \frac{8.0}{17.0} \approx 0.5$
$\cos Q = \frac{8.0}{17.0} \approx 0.5$ $\quad \cos R = \frac{15.0}{17.0} \approx 0.9$
$\tan Q = \frac{15.0}{8.0} \approx 1.9$ $\quad \tan R = \frac{8.0}{15.0} \approx 0.5$

CHAPTER 10 CIRCLES AND SPHERES

PAGE 326 WRITTEN

11. Given: $\overline{AB}$ is a diameter of $\odot P$; $\overline{PC}$ is a radius of $\odot P$; $PC = r$; $AB = d$
Prove: $d = 2r$
Proof:

STATEMENTS	REASONS
1. $\overline{AB}$ is a diameter of $\odot P$; $\overline{PC}$ is a radius of $\odot P$.	1. Given
2. $AP = PC$; $PB = PC$	2. Definition of Circle
3. $AP + PB = AB$	3. Definition of Between
4. $AB = PC + PC$	4. Postulate 2-9
5. $PC = r$; $AB = d$	5. Given
6. $d = r + r$	6. Postulate 2-9
7. $d = 2r$	7. Postulate 2-9

12. Given: X is in the interior of $\odot P$.
Prove: There are points A and B on $\odot P$ such that X is between A and B.
Proof:

STATEMENTS	REASONS
1. X is in the interior of $\odot P$.	1. Given
2. Choose any point on $\odot P$ and call it A; Draw $\overleftrightarrow{AX}$.	2. Postulate 1-1
3. $\overleftrightarrow{AX}$ intersects $\odot P$ in exactly two points, A and B.	3. Theorem 10-1
4. X is between A and B.	4. Definition of Between

13.

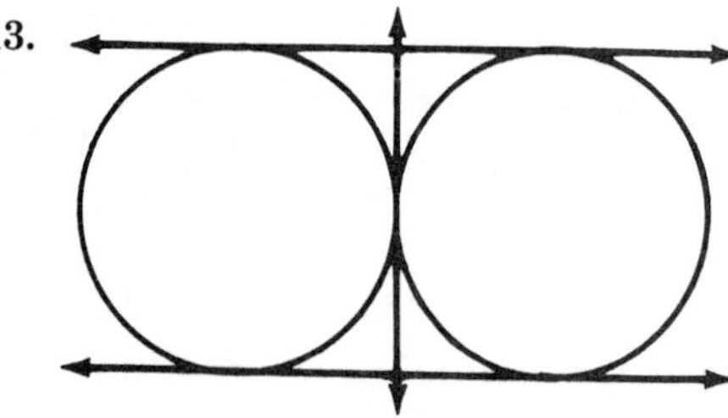

14.

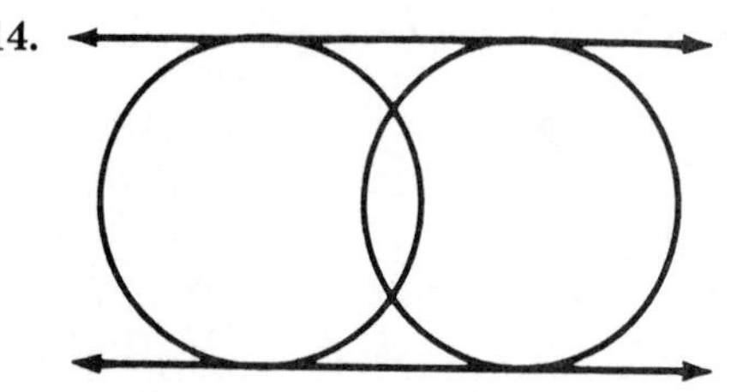

15.

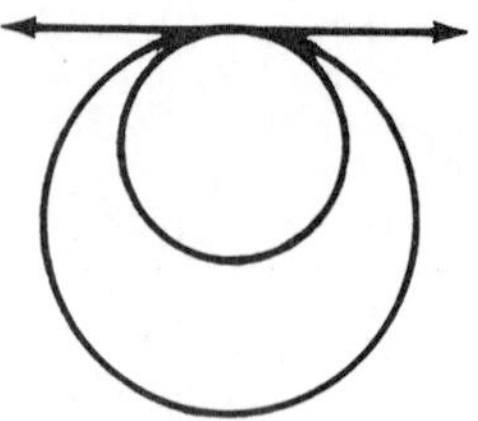

PAGES 329–330 WRITTEN

36. Given: $\odot P \cong \odot Q$; $\widehat{AB} \cong \widehat{CD}$
Prove: $\angle P \cong \angle Q$
Proof:

STATEMENTS	REASONS
1. $\odot P \cong \odot Q$; $\widehat{AB} \cong \widehat{CD}$	1. Given
2. $m\widehat{AB} = m\widehat{CD}$	2. Definition of Congruent Arcs
3. $m\widehat{AB} = m\angle P$; $m\widehat{CD} = m\angle Q$	3. Definition of Arc Measure
4. $m\angle P = m\angle Q$	4. Postulate 2-9
5. $\angle P \cong \angle Q$	5. Definition of Congruent Angles

37. Given: $\odot P \cong \odot Q$; $\angle P \cong \angle Q$
Prove: $\widehat{AB} \cong \widehat{CD}$
Proof:

STATEMENTS	REASONS
1. $\odot P \cong \odot Q$; $\angle P \cong \angle Q$	1. Given
2. $m\angle P = m\angle Q$	2. Definition of Congruent Angles
3. $m\angle P = m\widehat{AB}$; $m\angle Q = m\widehat{CD}$	3. Definition of Arc Measure
4. $m\widehat{AB} = m\widehat{CD}$	4. Postulate 2-9
5. $\widehat{AB} \cong \widehat{CD}$	5. Definition of Congruent Arcs

38. 156

PAGES 333–334 WRITTEN

15. Given: $\odot P$; $\overline{AB} \cong \overline{CD}$
Prove: $\widehat{AB} \cong \widehat{CD}$
Proof:

STATEMENTS	REASONS
1. $\odot P$; $\overline{AB} \cong \overline{CD}$	1. Given
2. Draw $\overline{AP}$, $\overline{BP}$, $\overline{CP}$, and $\overline{DP}$.	2. Postulate 1-1
3. $AP = DP$; $BP = CP$	3. Definition of Circle
4. $\overline{AP} \cong \overline{DP}$; $\overline{BP} \cong \overline{CP}$	4. Definition of Congruent Segments
5. $\triangle ABP \cong \triangle DCP$	5. SSS
6. $\angle APB \cong \angle DPC$	6. Definition of Congruent Triangles
7. $\widehat{AB} \cong \widehat{CD}$	7. Theorem 10-2

16. Given: $\odot P \cong \odot Q$; $\overline{AB} \cong \overline{CD}$
Prove: $\widehat{AB} \cong \widehat{CD}$
Proof:

STATEMENTS	REASONS
1. $\odot P \cong \odot Q$; $\overline{AB} \cong \overline{CD}$	1. Given
2. Draw $\overline{AP}$, $\overline{BP}$, $\overline{CQ}$, and $\overline{DQ}$.	2. Postulate 1-1
3. $\overline{AP} \cong \overline{CQ}$; $\overline{BP} \cong \overline{DQ}$	3. Definition of Congruent Circles
4. $\triangle APB \cong \triangle CQD$	4. SSS
5. $\angle P \cong \angle Q$	5. Definition of Congruent Triangles
6. $m\angle P = m\angle Q$	6. Definition of Congruent Angles
7. $\widehat{AB} \cong \widehat{CD}$	7. Theorem 10-2

17. Given: $\odot P$; $\overline{PX}$ bisects $\widehat{AB}$.
Prove: $\overline{PX}$ bisects $\overline{AB}$.

Proof:

STATEMENTS	REASONS
1. $\odot P$; $\overline{PX}$ bisects $\widehat{AB}$.	1. Given
2. $\widehat{AX} \cong \widehat{XB}$	2. Definition of Bisector of an Arc
3. Draw radii $\overline{AP}$ and $\overline{BP}$.	3. Postulate 1-1
4. $AP = BP$	4. Definition of Circle
5. $\overline{AP} \cong \overline{BP}$	5. Definition of Congruent Segments
6. $\overline{NP} \cong \overline{NP}$	6. Theorem 2-2
7. $\angle APX \cong \angle BPX$	7. Theorem 10-2
8. $\triangle APN \cong \triangle BPN$	8. SAS
9. $\overline{AN} \cong \overline{BN}$	9. Definition of Congruent Triangles
10. $AN = BN$	10. Definition of Congruent Segments
11. $\overline{PX}$ bisects $\overline{AB}$.	11. Definition of Segment Bisector

18. Given: $\overline{CD}$ is a diameter of $\odot P$; $\overline{AB} \perp \overline{CD}$
Prove: $\overline{CD}$ bisects $\overline{AB}$; $\overline{CD}$ bisects $\widehat{AB}$; $\overline{CD}$ bisects $\widehat{ACB}$.

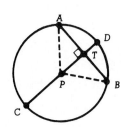

Proof:

STATEMENTS	REASONS
1. $\overline{CD}$ is a diameter of $\odot P$.	1. Given
2. Draw radii $\overline{AP}$, $\overline{BP}$.	2. Postulate 1-1
3. $AP = BP$	3. Definition of Circle
4. $\overline{AP} \cong \overline{BP}$	4. Definition of Congruent Segments
5. $\overline{PT} \cong \overline{PT}$	5. Theorem 2-2
6. $\overline{AB} \perp \overline{CD}$	6. Given
7. $\angle ATP$ and $\angle BTP$ are right angles.	7. Theorem 3-11
8. $\triangle ATP$ and $\triangle BTP$ are right triangles.	8. Definition of Right Triangle
9. $\triangle ATP \cong \triangle BTP$	9. HL
10. $\overline{AT} \cong \overline{BT}$; $\angle APT \cong \angle BPT$	10. Definition of Congruent Triangles
11. $AT = BT$	11. Definition of Congruent Segments
12. $\overline{CD}$ bisects $\overline{AB}$.	12. Definition of Segment Bisector
13. $\widehat{AB} \cong \widehat{DB}$	13. Theorem 10-2
14. $\angle CPA$ and $\angle APD$ form a linear pair; $\angle CPB$ and $\angle BPD$ form a linear pair.	14. Definition of Linear Pair
15. $\angle CPA$ and $\angle APD$ are supplementary; $\angle CPB$ and $\angle BPD$ are supplementary.	15. Postulate 3-4
16. $\angle CPA \cong \angle CPB$	16. Theorem 3-3
17. $\widehat{AC} \cong \widehat{BC}$	17. Theorem 10-2
18. $\overline{CD}$ bisects $\widehat{AB}$; $\overline{CD}$ bisects $\widehat{ACB}$.	18. Definition of Bisector of an Arc

19. Given: $\odot P$; $\overline{PE} \perp \overline{AB}$; $\overline{PF} \perp \overline{CD}$; $\overline{AB} \cong \overline{CD}$
Prove: $PE = PF$

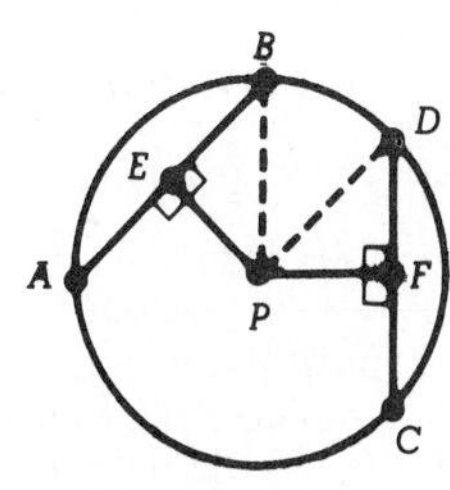

Proof:

STATEMENTS	REASONS
1. $\odot P$; $\overline{AB} \cong \overline{CD}$	1. Given
2. Draw radii $\overline{BP}$ and $\overline{DP}$.	2. Postulate 1-1
3. $BP = DP$	3. Definition of Circle
4. $\overline{PE} \perp \overline{AB}$; $\overline{PF} \perp \overline{CD}$	4. Given

STATEMENTS	REASONS
5. $\overline{PE}$ bisects $\overline{AB}$; $\overline{PF}$ bisects $\overline{CD}$.	5. Theorem 10-4
6. $AE = EB; DF = FC$	6. Definition of Segment Bisector
7. $AB = CD$	7. Definition of Congruent Segments
8. $AB = AE + EB$; $CD = DF + FC$	8. Definition of Between
9. $AE + EB = DF + FC$	9. Postulate 2-9
10. $EB + EB = DF + DF$	10. Postulate 2-9
11. $2EB = 2DF$	11. Postulate 2-9
12. $EB = DF$	12. Postulate 2-8; Postulate 2-9
13. $\overline{EB} \cong \overline{DF}$; $\overline{BP} \cong \overline{DP}$	13. Definition of Congruent Segments
14. $\angle BEP$ and $\angle DFP$ are right angles.	14. Theorem 3-11
15. $\triangle BEP$ and $\triangle DFP$ are right triangles.	15. Definition of Right Triangle
16. $\triangle BEP \cong \triangle DFP$	16. HL
17. $\overline{PE} \cong \overline{PF}$	17. Definition of Congruent Triangles
18. $PE = PF$	18. Definition of Congruent Segments

20. Given: $\odot P$; $\overline{PE} \perp \overline{AB}$; $\overline{PF} \perp \overline{CD}$; $PE = PF$
Prove: $\overline{AB} \cong \overline{CD}$
Proof:

STATEMENTS	REASONS
1. $\odot P$; $PE = PF$	1. Given
2. Draw radii $\overline{BP}$, $\overline{CP}$.	2. Postulate 1-1
3. $BP = CP$	3. Definition of Circle
4. $\overline{BP} \cong \overline{CP}$; $\overline{PE} \cong \overline{PF}$	4. Definition of Congruent Segments
5. $\overline{PE} \perp \overline{AB}$; $\overline{PF} \perp \overline{CD}$	5. Given
6. $\angle BEP$ and $\angle CFP$ are right angles.	6. Theorem 3-11
7. $\triangle BEP$ and $\triangle CFP$ are right triangles.	7. Definition of Right Triangle
8. $\triangle BEP \cong \triangle CFP$	8. HL
9. $\overline{EB} \cong \overline{FC}$	9. Definition of Congruent Triangles
10. $EB = FC$	10. Definition of Congruent Segments
11. $\overline{EP}$ bisects $\overline{AB}$; $\overline{FP}$ bisects $\overline{CD}$.	11. Theorem 10-4
12. $AE = EB; FC = FD$	12. Definition of Segment Bisector
13. $AB = AE + EB$; $CD = CF + FD$	13. Definition of Between
14. $AE + FC = EB + FD$	14. Postulate 2-7
15. $AE + EB = FC + FD$	15. Postulate 2-9
16. $AB = CD$	16. Postulate 2-9
17. $\overline{AB} \cong \overline{CD}$	17. Definition of Congruent Segments

21. Given: $\odot P$; $\overline{CD}$ is the perpendicular bisector of $\overline{AB}$.
Prove: $\overline{CD}$ is a diameter of $\odot P$.

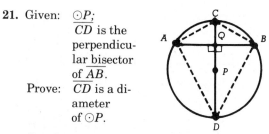

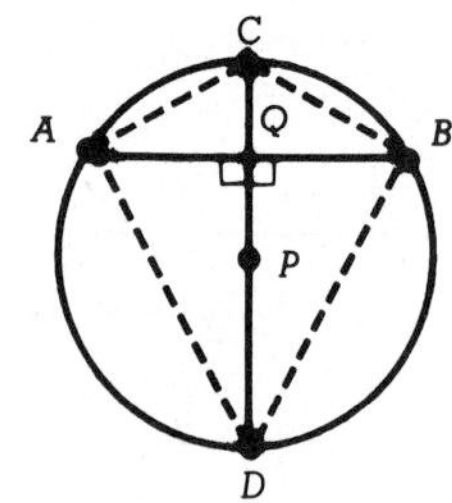

Proof:

STATEMENTS	REASONS
1. $\odot P$; $\overline{CD}$ is the perpendicular bisector of $\overline{AB}$.	1. Given
2. $\overline{AQ} \cong \overline{QB}$	2. Definition of Segment Bisector
3. Draw chords $\overline{AC}$, $\overline{CB}$, $\overline{BD}$, and $\overline{DA}$.	3. Postulate 1-1
4. $\overline{AQ} \cong \overline{AQ}$; $\overline{BQ} \cong \overline{BQ}$; $\overline{QD} \cong \overline{QD}$; $\overline{CQ} \cong \overline{CQ}$	4. Theorem 2-2
5. $\angle AQC$, $\angle AQD$, $\angle CQB$, and $\angle BQD$ are right angles.	5. Theorem 3-11
6. $\triangle AQC$, $\triangle AQD$, $\triangle CQB$, and $\triangle BQD$ are right triangles.	6. Definition of Right Triangle
7. $\triangle AQC \cong \triangle BQC$; $\triangle AQD \cong \triangle BQD$	7. LL
8. $\overline{AC} \cong \overline{BC}$; $\overline{AD} \cong \overline{BD}$	8. Definition of Congruent Triangles
9. $\overset{\frown}{AC} \cong \overset{\frown}{BC}$; $\overset{\frown}{AD} \cong \overset{\frown}{BD}$	9. Theorem 10-3
10. $m\overset{\frown}{AC} = m\overset{\frown}{BC}$; $m\overset{\frown}{AD} = m\overset{\frown}{BD}$	10. Definition of Congruent Arcs
11. $m\overset{\frown}{AC} + m\overset{\frown}{AD} = m\overset{\frown}{BC} + m\overset{\frown}{BD}$	11. Postulate 2-7; Postulate 2-9
12. $m\overset{\frown}{AC} + m\overset{\frown}{AD} = m\overset{\frown}{CAD}$; $m\overset{\frown}{BC} + m\overset{\frown}{BD} = m\overset{\frown}{CBD}$	12. Postulate 10-1
13. $m\overset{\frown}{CAD} = m\overset{\frown}{CBD}$	13. Postulate 2-9

14. $m\overset{\frown}{CAD} + m\overset{\frown}{CBD} = 360$	14. Definition of Arc Measure
15. $m\overset{\frown}{CAD} + m\overset{\frown}{CAD} = 360$	15. Postulate 2-9
16. $2m\overset{\frown}{CAD} = 360$	16. Postulate 2-9; Postulate 2-14
17. $m\overset{\frown}{CAD} = 180$	17. Postulate 2-8, Postulate 2-9
18. $\overset{\frown}{CAD}$ is a semicircle.	18. Definition of Arc Measure
19. $\overline{CD}$ is a diameter of $\odot P$.	19. Definition of Semicircle

22. Given: $\odot P$; $AB > CD$; $\overline{PM} \perp \overline{AB}$; $\overline{PQ} \perp \overline{CD}$

Prove: $PM < PQ$

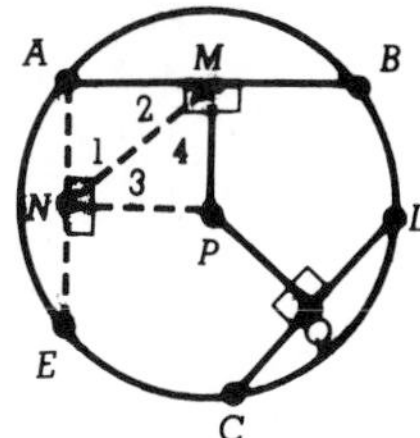

Proof:

STATEMENTS	REASONS
1. $\odot P$; $AB > CD$; $\overline{PM} \perp \overline{AB}$; $\overline{PQ} \perp \overline{CD}$	1. Given
2. Draw $\overline{AE}$ so that $AE = CD$.	2. Postulate 1-1
3. Draw $\overline{PN}$ so that $\overline{PN} \perp \overline{AE}$.	3. Postulate 1-1
4. Draw $\overline{MN}$.	4. Postulate 1-1
5. $\overline{PQ} \cong \overline{PN}$	5. Theorem 10-5
6. $PQ = PN$	6. Definition of Congruent Segments
7. $AM = MB$; $CQ = QD$; $AN = NE$	7. Theorem 10-4
8. $AN + NE = AE$; $AM + MB = AB$	8. Definition of Between
9. $AB > AE$	9. Postulate 2-9
10. $AM + MB > AN + NE$	10. Postulate 2-9
11. $2AM > 2AN$	11. Postulate 2-9
12. $AM > AN$	12. Postulate 2-17; Postulate 2-9
13. $\angle ANP$ and $\angle AMP$ are right angles.	13. Theorem 3-11
14. $\angle ANP \cong \angle AMP$	14. Theorem 3-6
15. $m\angle ANP = m\angle AMP$	15. Definition of Congruent Angles
16. $m\angle 1 + m\angle 3 = m\angle ANP$; $m\angle 2 + m\angle 4 = m\angle AMP$	16. Postulate 3-3
17. $m\angle 1 + m\angle 3 = m\angle 2 + m\angle 4$	17. Postulate 2-9
18. $m\angle 1 > m\angle 2$	18. Theorem 5-4
19. $m\angle 1 = m\angle 2 + c$, where $c > 0$.	19. Theorem 5-2
20. $m\angle 2 + c + m\angle 3 = m\angle 2 + m\angle 4$	20. Postulate 2-9
21. $c + m\angle 3 = m\angle 4$	21. Postulate 2-7
22. $m\angle 3 < m\angle 4$	22. Theorem 5-2
23. $PM < PN$	23. Theorem 5-5
24. $PM < PQ$	24. Postulate 2-9

23. STATEMENTS	REASONS
1. $\overline{AC}$ is a diameter; $\overline{AC} \perp \overline{BD}$	1. Given
2. $\overline{AC}$ bisects $\overset{\frown}{BCD}$.	2. Theorem 10-4
3. $\overset{\frown}{BC} \cong \overset{\frown}{DC}$	3. Definition of Bisector of an Arc

24. STATEMENTS	REASONS
1. $\overline{AC}$ is a diameter; $\overline{AC} \perp \overline{BC}$	1. Given
2. $\overline{AC}$ bisects $\overline{BD}$; $\overline{AC}$ bisects $\overset{\frown}{BCD}$.	2. Theorem 10-4
3. $\overline{EB} \cong \overline{ED}$	3. Definition of Segment Bisector
4. $\overset{\frown}{BC} \cong \overset{\frown}{DC}$	4. Definition of Bisector of an Arc
5. $\overline{BC} \cong \overline{DC}$	5. Theorem 10-3
6. $\overline{EC} \cong \overline{EC}$	6. Theorem 2-2
7. $\triangle EBC \cong \triangle EDC$	7. SSS

25. STATEMENTS	REASONS
1. $\overset{\frown}{PTS} \cong \overset{\frown}{QST}$; $\overline{RS} \cong \overline{RT}$	1. Given
2. $\overline{PS} \cong \overline{QT}$	2. Theorem 10-3
3. $PS = QT$; $RS = RT$	3. Definition of Congruent Segments
4. $PS = PR + RS$; $QT = QR + RT$	4. Definition of Between
5. $PR + RS = QR + RT$	5. Postulate 2-9
6. $PR = QR$	6. Postulate 2-7; Postulate 2-9
7. $\overline{PR} \cong \overline{QR}$	7. Definition of Congruent Segments
8. $\triangle PQR$ is isosceles.	8. Definition of Isosceles Triangle

26. STATEMENTS	REASONS
1. $\overline{RQ} \cong \overline{RP}$; $\overset{\frown}{QS} \cong \overset{\frown}{PT}$	1. Given
2. $m\overset{\frown}{QT} = m\overset{\frown}{QS} + m\overset{\frown}{ST}$; $m\overset{\frown}{PS} = m\overset{\frown}{PT} + m\overset{\frown}{ST}$	2. Postulate 10-1
3. $m\overset{\frown}{QS} = m\overset{\frown}{PT}$	3. Definition of Congruent Arcs

4. $m\overset{\frown}{QS} + m\overset{\frown}{ST} = m\overset{\frown}{PT} + m\overset{\frown}{ST}$	4. Postulate 2-7
5. $m\overset{\frown}{QT} = m\overset{\frown}{PS}$	5. Postulate 2-7; Postulate 2-9
6. $\overset{\frown}{QT} \cong \overset{\frown}{PS}$	6. Definition of Congruent Arcs
7. $\overline{QT} \cong \overline{PS}$	7. Theorem 10-3
8. $QT = PS; RQ = RP$	8. Definition of Congruent Segments
9. $QT = QR + RT;$ $PS = PR + RS$	9. Definition of Between
10. $RQ + RT = RP + RS$	10. Postulate 2-9
11. $RQ + RT = RQ + RS$	11. Postulate 2-9
12. $RT = RS$	12. Postulate 2-7; Postulate 2-9
13. $\overline{RT} \cong \overline{RS}$	13. Definition of Congruent Segments
14. $\triangle SRT$ is isosceles.	14. Definition of Isosceles Triangle

27.

STATEMENTS	REASONS
1. $\overline{FE}$ is a diameter of $\odot A$; $\overline{UT}$ is a diameter of $\odot P$; $\overline{FE} \perp \overline{BD}$; $\overline{UT} \perp \overline{QS}$; $\odot A \cong \odot P$; $\overline{BC} \cong \overline{QR}$	1. Given
2. $\overline{FE}$ bisects $\overline{BD}$; $\overline{UT}$ bisects $\overline{QS}$.	2. Theorem 10-4
3. $\overline{BC} \cong \overline{CD}$; $\overline{QR} \cong \overline{RS}$	3. Definition of Segment Bisector
4. $BC = CD;$ $QR = RS;$ $BC = QR$	4. Definition of Congruent Segments
5. $CD = RS$	5. Postulate 2-9
6. $BD = BC + CD;$ $QS = RS + QR$	6. Definition of Between
7. $BC + CD = RS + QR$	7. Postulate 2-7
8. $BD = QS$	8. Postulate 2-9
9. $\overline{BD} \cong \overline{QS}$	9. Definition of Congruent Segments
10. $\overset{\frown}{BD} \cong \overset{\frown}{QS}$	10. Theorem 10-3

28.

STATEMENTS	REASONS
1. $\overline{FE}$ is a diameter of $\odot A$; $\overline{UT}$ is a diameter of $\odot P$; $\overline{FE} \perp \overline{BD}$; $\overline{UT} \perp \overline{QS}$; $\overline{AE} \cong \overline{PT}$ $\overline{AC} \cong \overline{PR}$	1. Given
2. $\odot A \cong \odot P$	2. Definition of Congruent Circles
3. $\overline{AC} \cong \overline{PR}$	3. Given
4. $AC = PR$	4. Definition of Congruent Segments
5. $\overline{BD} \cong \overline{QS}$	5. Definition of the Distance Between a Point and a Line; Theorem 10-5
6. $BD = QS$	6. Definition of Congruent Segments
7. $BC + CD = BD;$ $QR + RS = QS$	7. Definition of Between
8. $BC + CD = QR + RS$	8. Postulate 2-9
9. $BC = CD;$ $QR = RS$	9. Theorem 10-4
10. $BC + BC = QR + QR$	10. Postulate 2-9
11. $2BC = 2QR$	11. Postulate 2-9
12. $BC = QR$	12. Postulate 2-8; Postulate 2-9
13. $\overline{BC} \cong \overline{QR}$	13. Definition of Congruent Segments

29.

STATEMENTS	REASONS
1. $\overline{FE}$ is a diameter of $\odot A$; $\overline{UT}$ is a diameter of $\odot P$; $\overline{FE} \perp \overline{BD}$; $\overline{UT} \perp \overline{QS}$; $\overline{AC} \cong \overline{PR}$; $\overline{CD} \cong \overline{RS}$	1. Given
2. Draw radii $\overline{AD}$ and $\overline{PS}$.	2. Postulate 1-1
3. $\angle ACD$ and $\angle PRS$ are right angles.	3. Theorem 3-11
4. $\triangle ACD$ and $\triangle PRS$ are right triangles.	4. Definition of Right Triangle
5. $\triangle ACD \cong \triangle PRS$	5. LL
6. $\angle EAD \cong \angle TPS$; $\overline{AD} \cong \overline{PS}$	6. Definition of Congruent Triangles
7. $\odot A \cong \odot P$	7. Definition of Congruent Circles
8. $\overset{\frown}{ED} \cong \overset{\frown}{TS}$	8. Theorem 10-2
9. $\overline{FE}$ bisects $\overset{\frown}{BD}$; $\overline{UT}$ bisects $\overset{\frown}{QS}$.	9. Theorem 10-4
10. $\overset{\frown}{BE} \cong \overset{\frown}{ED}$; $\overset{\frown}{QT} \cong \overset{\frown}{TS}$	10. Definition of Bisector of an Arc

11. $m\widehat{ED} = m\widehat{TS}$; $m\widehat{BE} = m\widehat{ED}$; $m\widehat{QT} = m\widehat{TS}$	11. Definition of Congruent Arcs
12. $m\widehat{BE} = m\widehat{QT}$	12. Postulate 2-9
13. $\widehat{BE} \cong \widehat{QT}$	13. Definition of Congruent Arcs

PAGES 338–339 WRITTEN

23. Given: $\odot X$ with diameter $\overline{AB}$; $\angle CAB$ is inscribed in $\odot X$.
Prove: $m\angle CAB = \frac{1}{2}m\widehat{BC}$

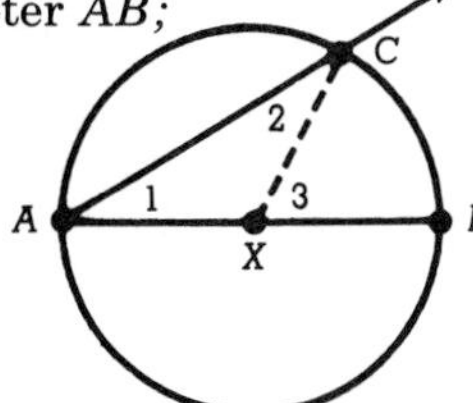

Proof:

STATEMENTS	REASONS
1. $\odot X$ with diameter $\overline{AB}$; $\angle CAB$ is inscribed in $\odot X$.	1. Given
2. Draw radius $\overline{XC}$.	2. Postulate 1-1
3. $AX = XC$	3. Definition of Circle
4. $\overline{AX} \cong \overline{XC}$	4. Definition of Congruent Segments
5. $\angle 1 \cong \angle 2$	5. Theorem 4-6
6. $m\angle 1 = m\angle 2$	6. Definition of Congruent Angles
7. $m\angle 1 + m\angle 2 = m\angle 3$	7. Theorem 5-1
8. $m\angle 1 + m\angle 1 = m\angle 3$	8. Postulate 2-9
9. $2m\angle 1 = m\angle 3$	9. Postulate 2-9
10. $m\angle 3 = m\widehat{CB}$	10. Defintion of Arc Measure
11. $2m\angle 1 = m\widehat{CB}$	11. Postulate 2-9
12. $m\angle 1 = \frac{1}{2}m\widehat{CB}$	12. Postulate 2-8; Postulate 2-9

24. Given: $\overline{BD}$ bisects inscribed angle $\angle ABC$.
Prove: $\widehat{AD} \cong \widehat{DC}$

STATEMENTS	REASONS
1. $\overline{BD}$ bisects inscribed angle $\angle ABC$.	1. Given
2. $\angle ABD \cong \angle DBC$	2. Definition of Angle Bisector
3. $m\angle ABD = m\angle DBC$	3. Definition of Congruent Angles
4. $m\angle ABD = \frac{1}{2}m\widehat{AD}$; $m\angle DBC = \frac{1}{2}m\widehat{DC}$	4. Theorem 10-6
5. $\frac{1}{2}m\widehat{AD} = \frac{1}{2}m\widehat{DC}$	5. Postulate 2-9
6. $m\widehat{AD} = m\widehat{DC}$	6. Postulate 2-8; Postulate 2-13
7. $\widehat{AD} \cong \widehat{DC}$	7. Definition of Congruent Arcs

25. Given: $\odot P$; $\widehat{AC} \cong \widehat{DF}$
Prove: $\angle ABC \cong \angle DEF$
Proof:

STATEMENTS	REASONS
1. $\odot P$; $\widehat{AC} \cong \widehat{DF}$	1. Given
2. $m\widehat{AC} = m\widehat{DF}$	2. Definition of Congruent Arcs
3. $\frac{1}{2}m\widehat{AC} = \frac{1}{2}m\widehat{DF}$	3. Postulate 2-8
4. $m\angle ABC = \frac{1}{2}m\widehat{AC}$; $m\angle DEF = \frac{1}{2}m\widehat{DF}$	4. Theorem 10-6
5. $m\angle ABC = m\angle DEF$	5. Postulate 2-9
6. $\angle ABC \cong \angle DEF$	6. Definition of Congruent Angles

The proof for two inscribed angles in two congruent circles is the same as the one given.

26. Given: $\odot X$ with inscribed quadrilateral $ABCD$.
Prove: $\angle A$ and $\angle C$ are supplementary; $\angle B$ and $\angle D$ are supplementary.
Proof:

STATEMENTS	REASONS
1. $\odot X$ with inscribed quadrilateral $ABCD$.	1. Given
2. $m\angle A = \frac{1}{2}m\widehat{BCD}$; $m\angle C = \frac{1}{2}m\widehat{BAD}$; $m\angle B = \frac{1}{2}m\widehat{ADC}$; $m\angle D = \frac{1}{2}m\widehat{ABC}$	2. Theorem 10-6
3. $m\widehat{BCD} + m\widehat{BAD} = 360$; $m\widehat{ADC} + m\widehat{ABC} = 360$	3. Definition of Arc Measure
4. $\frac{1}{2}(m\widehat{BCD} + m\widehat{BAD}) = \frac{1}{2}(360)$; $\frac{1}{2}(m\widehat{ADC} + m\widehat{ABC}) = \frac{1}{2}(360)$	4. Postulate 2-8

STATEMENTS	REASONS
5. $\frac{1}{2}m\overset{\frown}{BCD} + \frac{1}{2}m\overset{\frown}{BAD} = 180$; $\frac{1}{2}m\overset{\frown}{ADC} + \frac{1}{2}m\overset{\frown}{ABC} = 180$	5. Postulate 2-14; Postulate 2-9
6. $m\angle A + m\angle C = 180$; $m\angle B + m\angle D = 180$	6. Postulate 2-9
7. $\angle A$ and $\angle C$ are supplementary; $\angle B$ and $\angle D$ are supplementary.	7. Definition of Supplementary Angles

27.

STATEMENTS	REASONS
1. $\overline{ZY}$ is a diameter of $\odot A$; $\overset{\frown}{XY} \cong \overset{\frown}{ZW}$	1. Given
2. $\overset{\frown}{ZXY}$ and $\overset{\frown}{ZWY}$ are semicircles.	2. Definition of Semicircle
3. $m\overset{\frown}{ZXY} = 180$; $m\overset{\frown}{ZWY} = 180$	3. Definition of Arc Measure
4. $m\overset{\frown}{ZXY} = m\overset{\frown}{ZWY}$	4. Postulate 2-9
5. $m\overset{\frown}{ZXY} = m\overset{\frown}{ZX} + m\overset{\frown}{XY}$; $m\overset{\frown}{ZWY} = m\overset{\frown}{WY} + m\overset{\frown}{ZW}$	5. Postulate 10-1
6. $m\overset{\frown}{ZX} + m\overset{\frown}{XY} = m\overset{\frown}{WY} + m\overset{\frown}{ZW}$	6. Postulate 2-9
7. $m\overset{\frown}{XY} = m\overset{\frown}{ZW}$	7. Definition of Congruent Arcs
8. $m\overset{\frown}{ZX} = m\overset{\frown}{WY}$	8. Postulate 2-7; Postulate 2-9
9. $\frac{1}{2}m\overset{\frown}{ZX} = \frac{1}{2}m\overset{\frown}{WY}$	9. Postulate 2-8
10. $m\angle XYZ = \frac{1}{2}m\overset{\frown}{ZX}$; $m\angle WZY = \frac{1}{2}m\overset{\frown}{WY}$	10. Theorem 10-6
11. $m\angle XYZ = m\angle WZY$	11. Postulate 2-9
12. $\angle XYZ \cong \angle WZY$	12. Definition of Congruent Angles

28.

STATEMENTS	REASONS
1. $XY \parallel ZW$; $\overline{ZY}$ is a diameter of $\odot A$.	1. Given
2. $\angle XYZ \cong \angle YZW$	2. Theorem 6-10
3. $m\angle XYZ = m\angle YZW$	3. Definition of Congruent Angles
4. $\overset{\frown}{ZXY}$ and $\overset{\frown}{ZWY}$ are semicircles.	4. Definition of Semicircle
5. $m\overset{\frown}{ZXY} = 180$; $m\overset{\frown}{ZWY} = 180$	5. Definition of Arc Measure
6. $m\overset{\frown}{ZXY} = m\overset{\frown}{ZWY}$	6. Postulate 2-9
7. $m\overset{\frown}{ZX} + m\overset{\frown}{XY} = m\overset{\frown}{ZXY}$; $m\overset{\frown}{ZW} + m\overset{\frown}{WY} = m\overset{\frown}{ZWY}$	7. Postulate 10-1
8. $m\overset{\frown}{ZX} + m\overset{\frown}{XY} = m\overset{\frown}{ZW} + m\overset{\frown}{WY}$	8. Postulate 2-9
9. $m\angle XYZ = \frac{1}{2}m\overset{\frown}{ZX}$; $m\angle YZW = \frac{1}{2}m\overset{\frown}{WY}$	9. Theorem 10-6
10. $\frac{1}{2}m\overset{\frown}{ZX} = \frac{1}{2}m\overset{\frown}{WY}$	10. Postulate 2-9
11. $m\overset{\frown}{ZX} = m\overset{\frown}{WY}$	11. Postulate 2-8; Postulate 2-9
12. $m\overset{\frown}{XY} = m\overset{\frown}{ZW}$	12. Postulate 2-7; Postulate 2-9
13. $\overset{\frown}{XY} \cong \overset{\frown}{ZW}$	13. Definition of Congruent Arcs

29.

STATEMENTS	REASONS
1. $\overline{ZY}$ is a diameter of $\odot A$; $\overset{\frown}{XZ} \cong \overset{\frown}{YW}$	1. Given
2. $\angle XYZ \cong \angle YZW$	2. Theorem 10-7
3. $\overset{\frown}{ZXY}$ and $\overset{\frown}{ZWY}$ are semicircles.	3. Definition of Semicircle
4. $\angle X$ and $\angle W$ are right angles.	4. Theorem 10-8
5. $\angle X \cong \angle W$	5. Theorem 3-6
6. $\overline{ZY} \cong \overline{ZY}$	6. Theorem 2-2
7. $\triangle ZXY \cong \triangle YWZ$	7. AAS

PAGES 342–343 WRITTEN

22. Given: $\overleftrightarrow{CA}$ is tangent to $\odot X$ at A.
Prove: $\overline{XA} \perp \overleftrightarrow{CA}$

STATEMENTS	REASONS
1. $\overleftrightarrow{CA}$ is tangent to $\odot X$ at A.	1. Given
2. Choose point B (any point on $\overleftrightarrow{CA}$ except A) and draw $\overline{XB}$.	2. Postulate 1-1
3. $\overleftrightarrow{CA}$ intersects $\odot X$ at exactly one point, A.	3. Definition of Tangent
4. B lies in the exterior of $\odot X$.	4. Definition of Tangent
5. $XA < XB$	5. Definition of the Exterior of a Circle
6. $\overline{XA} \perp \overleftrightarrow{CA}$	6. Theorem 5-6

23. Given: $\odot X$ with radius $\overline{XA}$; $\overline{XA} \perp \overleftrightarrow{CA}$
Prove: $\overleftrightarrow{CA}$ is tangent to $\odot X$.

STATEMENTS	REASONS
1. $\odot X$ with radius $\overline{XA}$.	1. Given

STATEMENTS	REASONS
2. Choose point B (any point on $\overleftrightarrow{CA}$ except A) and draw $\overline{XB}$.	2. Postulate 1-1
3. $\overline{XA} \perp \overleftrightarrow{CA}$	3. Given
4. $XA < XB$	4. Theorem 5-6
5. B lies in the exterior of $\odot X$.	5. Definition of the Exterior of a Circle
6. $\overleftrightarrow{CA}$ is tangent to $\odot X$.	6. Definition of Tangent

24. Given: $\overline{AB}$ and $\overline{AC}$ are tangent to $\odot X$ at B and C.

Prove: $\overline{AB} \cong \overline{AC}$

Proof:

STATEMENTS	REASONS
1. $\overline{AB}$ and $\overline{AC}$ are tangent to $\odot X$ at B and C.	1. Given
2. Draw $\overline{XB}$, $\overline{XC}$, and $\overline{XA}$.	2. Postulate 1-1
3. $\overline{XB} \perp \overline{AB}$; $\overline{XC} \perp \overline{AC}$	3. Theorem 10-10
4. $\angle ABX$ and $\angle ACX$ are right angles.	4. Theorem 3-11
5. $\triangle ABX$ and $\triangle ACX$ are right triangles.	5. Definition of Right Triangle
6. $BX = CX$	6. Definition of Circle
7. $\overline{BX} \cong \overline{CX}$	7. Definition of Congruent Segments
8. $\overline{AX} \cong \overline{AX}$	8. Theorem 2-2
9. $\triangle ABX \cong \triangle ACX$	9. HL
10. $\overline{AB} \cong \overline{AC}$	10. Definition of Congruent Triangles

25.

STATEMENTS	REASONS
1. $\overleftrightarrow{AC}$ is tangent to $\odot P$; $\widehat{DB} \cong \widehat{BE}$	1. Given
2. $\angle APB \cong \angle CPB$	2. Theorem 10-2
3. $\overline{PB} \cong \overline{PB}$	3. Theorem 2-2
4. $\overline{PB} \perp \overleftrightarrow{AC}$	4. Theorem 10-10
5. $\angle ABP$ and $\angle CBP$ are right angles.	5. Theorem 3-11
6. $\angle ABP \cong \angle CBP$	6. Theorem 3-6
7. $\triangle ABP \cong \triangle CBP$	7. ASA
8. $\overline{AB} \cong \overline{CB}$	8. Definition of Congruent Triangles

26.

STATEMENTS	REASONS
1. $\overleftrightarrow{AC}$ is tangent to $\odot P$; $\angle PAB \cong \angle PCB$	1. Given
2. $\overline{PB} \cong \overline{PB}$	2. Theorem 2-2
3. $\overline{PB} \perp \overleftrightarrow{AC}$	3. Theorem 10-10
4. $\angle ABP$ and $\angle CBP$ are right angles.	4. Theorem 3-11
5. $\angle ABP \cong \angle CBP$	5. Theorem 3-6
6. $\triangle ABP \cong \triangle CBP$	6. AAS
7. $\angle APB \cong \angle CPB$	7. Definition of Congruent Triangles
8. $\widehat{DB} \cong \widehat{BE}$	8. Theorem 10-2

27.

STATEMENTS	REASONS
1. $\triangle APC$ is isosceles; $\widehat{DB} \cong \widehat{BE}$	1. Given
2. $\overline{AP} \cong \overline{CP}$	2. Definition of Isosceles Triangle
3. $\angle APB \cong \angle CPB$	3. Theorem 10-2
4. $\overline{PB} \cong \overline{PB}$	4. Theorem 2-2
5. $\triangle APB \cong \triangle CPB$	5. SAS
6. $\angle PBA \cong \angle PBC$	6. Definition of Congruent Triangles
7. $\overline{PB} \perp \overline{AC}$	7. Theorem 3-14
8. $\overleftrightarrow{AC}$ is tangent to $\odot P$.	8. Theorem 10-11

28.

STATEMENTS	REASONS
1. $\overleftrightarrow{AF}$ and $\overleftrightarrow{CF}$ are tangent to $\odot B$.	1. Given
2. $\overline{AF} \cong \overline{CF}$	2. Theorem 10-12
3. $\overline{BF} \cong \overline{BF}$	3. Theorem 2-2
4. $AB = CB$	4. Definition of Circle
5. $\overline{AB} \cong \overline{CB}$	5. Definition of Congruent Segments
6. $\triangle ABF \cong \triangle CBF$	6. SSS
7. $\angle AFD \cong \angle CFD$	7. Definition of Congruent Triangles
8. $\overline{DF} \cong \overline{DF}$	8. Theorem 2-2
9. $\triangle ADF \cong \triangle CDF$	9. SAS

29.

STATEMENTS	REASONS
1. $\overleftrightarrow{AF}$ and $\overleftrightarrow{CF}$ are tangent to $\odot B$.	1. Given
2. $\overline{AF} \cong \overline{CF}$	2. Theorem 10-2
3. $\overline{BF} \cong \overline{BF}$	3. Theorem 2-2
4. $AB = CB$	4. Definition of Circle
5. $\overline{AB} \cong \overline{CB}$	5. Definition of Congruent Segments
6. $\triangle ABF \cong \triangle CBF$	6. SSS
7. $\angle AFD \cong \angle CFD$	7. Definition of Congruent Triangles
8. $\overline{DF} \cong \overline{DF}$	8. Theorem 2-2
9. $\triangle ADF \cong \triangle CDF$	9. SAS

10. $\angle ADF \cong \angle CDF$	10. Definition of Congruent Triangles
11. $\overline{BF} \perp \overline{AC}$	11. Theorem 3-14

30.

STATEMENTS	REASONS
1. $\overleftrightarrow{WX}$, $\overleftrightarrow{XY}$, $\overleftrightarrow{YZ}$, and $\overleftrightarrow{ZW}$ are tangent to $\odot P$; $\overline{WX} \parallel \overline{ZY}$; $\overline{WZ} \parallel \overline{XY}$	1. Given
2. Quadrilateral $WXYZ$ is a parallelogram.	2. Definition of Parallelogram
3. $\angle XWZ \cong \angle XYZ$; $\angle WXY \cong \angle WZY$	3. Theorem 7-4
4. $\overline{PT} \perp \overline{WZ}$; $\overline{PQ} \perp \overline{WX}$	4. Theorem 10-10
5. $\angle PTW$ and $\angle WQP$ are right angles.	5. Theorem 3-11
6. $m\angle PTW = 90$; $m\angle WQP = 90$	6. Definition of Right Angle
7. $\overline{WT} \cong \overline{WQ}$	7. Theorem 10-12
8. $\overline{WT} \cong \overline{TP}$	8. Given
9. $TP = PQ$	9. Definition of Circle
10. $\overline{TP} \cong \overline{PQ}$	10. Definition of Congruent Segments
11. $\overline{WT} \cong \overline{WQ} \cong \overline{TP} \cong \overline{PQ}$	11. Postulate 2-9
12. Quadrilateral $WTPQ$ is a parallelogram.	12. Theorem 7-7
13. $m\angle QWT = m\angle QPT$	13. Theorem 7-4
14. $m\angle PTW + m\angle QWT + m\angle WQP + m\angle QPT = 360$	14. Theorem 7-1
15. $90 + m\angle QWT + 90 + m\angle QWT = 360$	15. Postulate 2-9
16. $2m\angle QWT + 180 = 360$	16. Postulate 2-9
17. $2m\angle QWT = 180$	17. Postulate 2-7; Postulate 2-9
18. $m\angle QWT = 90$	18. Postulate 2-8; Postulate 2-9
19. $m\angle XWZ = m\angle XYZ$	19. Definition of Congruent Angles
20. $m\angle XYZ = 90$	20. Postulate 2-9
21. $\angle WXY$ and $\angle XYZ$ are supplementary; $\angle XWZ$ and $\angle WZY$ are supplementary.	21. Theorem 6-11
22. $m\angle WXY + m\angle XYZ = 180$; $m\angle XWZ + m\angle WZY = 180$	22. Definition of Supplementary Angles
23. $m\angle WXY + 90 = 180$; $90 + m\angle WZY = 180$	23. Postulate 2-9
24. $m\angle WXY = 90$; $m\angle WZY = 90$	24. Postulate 2-7; Postulate 2-9
25. $\angle XWZ$, $\angle WXY$, $\angle XYZ$, and $\angle WZY$ are right angles.	27. Definition of Right Angle
26. Quadrilateral $WXYZ$ is a rectangle.	26. Definition of a Rectangle

31. Given: Hexagon $ABCDEF$ is circumscribed about $\odot P$ and inscribed in $\odot S$.

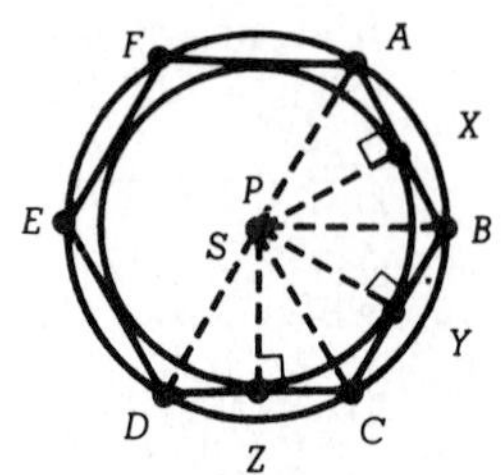

Prove: Hexagon $ABCDEF$ is regular.
Proof:

STATEMENTS	REASONS
1. Hexagon $ABCDEF$ is circumscribed about $\odot P$ and inscribed in $\odot S$.	1. Given
2. Draw radii $\overline{SA}$, $\overline{SB}$, $\overline{SC}$, $\overline{SD}$, $\overline{PX}$, $\overline{PY}$, and $\overline{PZ}$.	2. Postulate 1-1
3. $SA = SB = SC = SD = PX = PY = PZ$	3. Definition of Circle
4. $\overline{SA} \cong \overline{SB} \cong \overline{SC} \cong \overline{SD} \cong \overline{PX} \cong \overline{PY} \cong \overline{PZ}$	4. Definition of Congruent Segments
5. $\overline{PX} \perp \overline{AB}$; $\overline{PY} \perp \overline{BC}$; $\overline{PZ} \perp \overline{DC}$	5. Theorem 10-10
6. $\angle AXP$, $\angle BXP$, $\angle BYP$, $\angle CYP$, $\angle CZP$, and $\angle DZP$ are right angles.	6. Theorem 3-11
7. $\triangle AXP$, $\triangle BXP$, $\triangle BYP$, $\triangle CYP$, $\triangle CZP$, and $\triangle DZP$ are right triangles.	7. Definition of Right Triangle

8. $\triangle AXP \cong \triangle BXP \cong \triangle BYP \cong \triangle CYP \cong \triangle CZP \cong \triangle DZP$	8. HL
9. $\overline{AX} \cong \overline{BX} \cong \overline{BY} \cong \overline{CY} \cong \overline{CZ} \cong \overline{DZ}$; $\angle PAX \cong \angle PBX \cong \angle PBY \cong \angle PCY \cong \angle PCZ \cong \angle PDZ$	9. Definition of Congruent Triangles
10. $AX = BX = BY = CY = CZ = DZ$	10. Definition of Congruent Segments
11. $m\angle PAX = m\angle PBX = m\angle PBY = m\angle PCY = m\angle PCZ = m\angle PDZ$	11. Definition of Congruent Angles
12. $AX + XB = AB$; $BY + YC = BC$	12. Definition of Between
13. $AX + AX = AB$; $AX + AX = BC$	13. Postulate 2-9
14. $AB = BC$	14. Postulate 2-9
15. $\overline{AB} \cong \overline{BC}$	15. Definition of Congruent Segments
16. $m\angle ABC = m\angle PBX + m\angle PBY$; $m\angle BCD = m\angle PCY + m\angle PCZ$	16. Postulate 3-1
17. $m\angle ABC = m\angle PBX + m\angle PBX$; $m\angle BCD = m\angle PBX + m\angle PBX$	17. Postulate 2-9
18. $m\angle ABC = m\angle BCD$	18. Postulate 2-9
19. $\angle ABC \cong \angle BCD$	19. Definition of Congruent Angles
Repeat this procedure for all vertices and sides.	
20. Hexagon $ABCDEF$ is regular.	20. Definition of Regular Polygon

PAGES 346–347 WRITTEN

34. Given: Secants $\overleftrightarrow{AC}$ and $\overleftrightarrow{BD}$ intersect at X in the interior of $\odot P$.

Prove: $m\angle AXB = \frac{1}{2}(m\overset{\frown}{AB} + m\overset{\frown}{CD})$

STATEMENTS	REASONS
1. Secants $\overleftrightarrow{AC}$ and $\overleftrightarrow{BD}$ intersect at X in the interior of $\odot P$.	1. Given
2. Draw $\overline{BC}$.	2. Postulate 1-1
3. $m\angle XBC = \frac{1}{2}m\overset{\frown}{CD}$; $m\angle XCB = \frac{1}{2}m\overset{\frown}{AB}$	3. Theorem 10-6
4. $m\angle AXB = m\angle XCB + m\angle XBC$	4. Theorem 5-1
5. $m\angle AXB = \frac{1}{2}m\overset{\frown}{AB} + \frac{1}{2}m\overset{\frown}{CD}$	5. Postulate 2-9
6. $m\angle AXB = \frac{1}{2}(m\overset{\frown}{AB} + m\overset{\frown}{CD})$	6. Postulate 2-14

35. Given: Secant $\overleftrightarrow{AB}$; $\overleftrightarrow{CB}$ is tangent to $\odot P$ at B.

Prove: $m\angle EBA = \frac{1}{2}m\overset{\frown}{BA}$; $m\angle CBA = \frac{1}{2}m\overset{\frown}{BDA}$

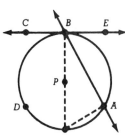

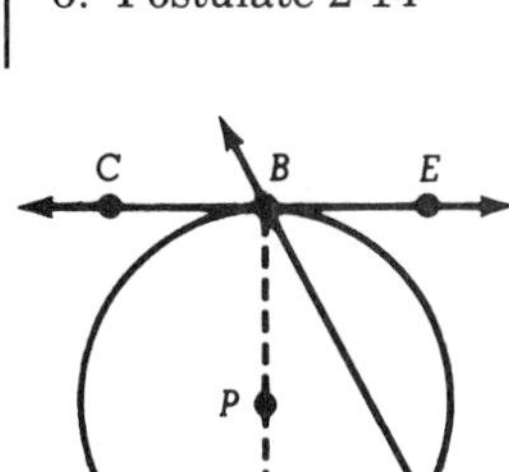

STATEMENTS	REASONS
1. Secant $\overleftrightarrow{AB}$; $\overleftrightarrow{CB}$ is tangent to $\odot P$ at B.	1. Given
2. Draw diameter $\overline{BF}$ and chord $\overline{FA}$.	2. Postulate 1-1
3. $m\angle EBA + m\angle ABF = m\angle EBF$	3. Postulate 3-3
4. $m\angle EBA = m\angle EBF - m\angle ABF$	4. Postulate 2-7; Postulate 2-9
5. $m\angle ABF = \frac{1}{2}m\overset{\frown}{AF}$	5. Theorem 10-6
6. $\overset{\frown}{FAB}$ and $\overset{\frown}{FDB}$ are semicircles.	6. Definition of Semicircle
7. $m\overset{\frown}{FAB} = 180$; $m\overset{\frown}{FDB} = 180$	7. Definition of Arc Measure
8. $\overline{BF} \perp \overleftrightarrow{CB}$	8. Theorem 10-10
9. $\angle EBF$ is a right angle.	9. Theorem 3-11
10. $m\angle EBF = 90$	10. Definition of Right Angle
11. $m\angle EBA = 90 - \frac{1}{2}m\overset{\frown}{AF}$	11. Postulate 2-9
12. $m\angle EBA = \frac{1}{2}(180) - m\overset{\frown}{AF}$	12. Postulate 2-9
13. $m\angle EBA = \frac{1}{2}(180 - m\overset{\frown}{AF})$	13. Postulate 2-14
14. $m\angle EBA = \frac{1}{2}(m\overset{\frown}{FAB} - m\overset{\frown}{AF})$	14. Postulate 2-9

15. $m\widehat{BA} + m\widehat{AF} = m\widehat{FAB}$	15. Postulate 10-1
16. $m\widehat{BA} = m\widehat{FAB} - m\widehat{AF}$	16. Postulate 2-7
17. $m\angle EBA = \frac{1}{2}m\widehat{BA}$	17. Postulate 2-9
18. $m\angle CBA = m\angle CBF + m\angle FBA$	18. Postulate 3-3
19. $\angle CBF$ is a right angle.	19. Theorem 3-11
20. $m\angle CBF = 90$	20. Definition of Right Angle
21. $m\angle CBA = 90 + \frac{1}{2}m\widehat{AF}$	21. Postulate 2-9
22. $m\angle CBA = \frac{1}{2}(180) + \frac{1}{2}m\widehat{AF}$	22. Postulate 2-9
23. $m\angle CBA = \frac{1}{2}(180 + m\widehat{AF})$	23. Postulate 2-14
24. $m\angle CBA = \frac{1}{2}(m\widehat{FDB} + m\widehat{AF})$	24. Postulate 2-9
25. $m\widehat{AF} + m\widehat{FDB} = m\widehat{BDA}$	25. Postulate 10-1
26. $m\angle CBA = \frac{1}{2}m\widehat{BDA}$	26. Postulate 2-9

36. Given: $\overleftrightarrow{AB}$ is tangent to $\odot X$ at A; secant $\overleftrightarrow{BD}$

Prove: $\frac{1}{2}(m\widehat{AD} - m\widehat{AC}) = m\angle ABD$

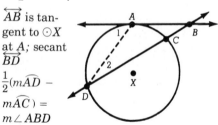

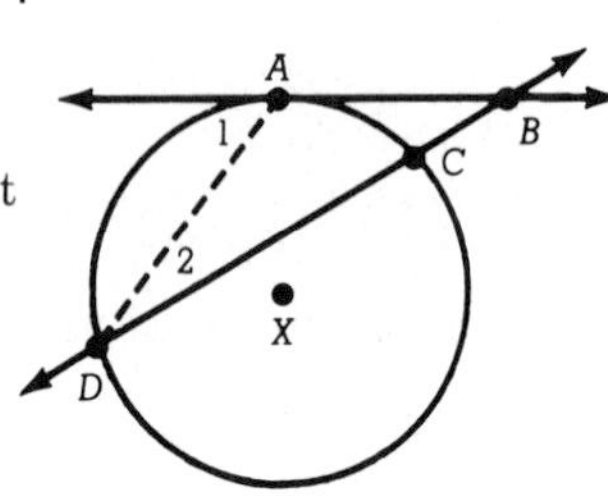

Proof:

STATEMENTS	REASONS
1. $\overleftrightarrow{AB}$ is tangent to $\odot X$ at A; secant $\overleftrightarrow{BD}$	1. Given
2. Draw $\overline{AD}$.	2. Postulate 1-1
3. $m\angle 1 = m\angle 2 + m\angle ABD$	3. Theorem 5-1
4. $m\angle 1 = \frac{1}{2}m\widehat{AD}$	4. Theorem 10-15
5. $m\angle 2 = \frac{1}{2}m\widehat{AC}$	5. Theorem 10-6
6. $\frac{1}{2}m\widehat{AD} = \frac{1}{2}m\widehat{AC} + m\angle ABD$	6. Postulate 2-9
7. $\frac{1}{2}m\widehat{AD} - \frac{1}{2}m\widehat{AC} = m\angle ABD$	7. Postulate 2-7; Postulate 2-9
8. $\frac{1}{2}(m\widehat{AD} - m\widehat{AC}) = m\angle ABD$	8. Postulate 2-14

37. Given: $\overleftrightarrow{AB}$ is tangent to $\odot X$ at A; $\overleftrightarrow{BC}$ is tangent to $\odot X$ at C.

Prove: $m\angle ABC = \frac{1}{2}(m\widehat{ADC} - m\widehat{AC})$

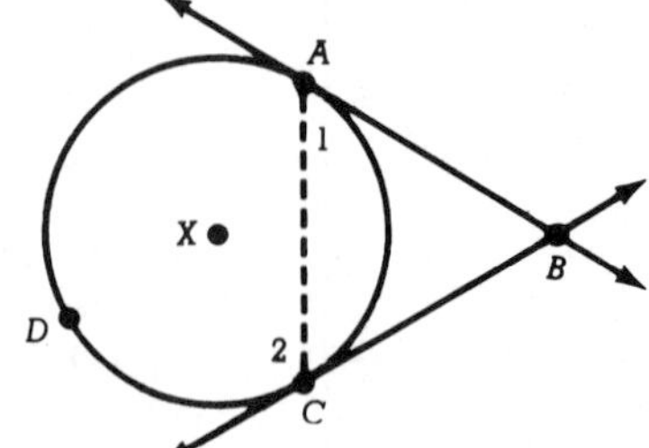

Proof:

STATEMENTS	REASONS
1. $\overleftrightarrow{AB}$ is tangent to $\odot X$ at A; $\overleftrightarrow{BC}$ is tangent to $\odot X$ at C.	1. Given
2. Draw $\overline{AC}$.	2. Postulate 1-1
3. $m\angle 1 = \frac{1}{2}m\widehat{AC}$; $m\angle 2 = \frac{1}{2}m\widehat{ADC}$	3. Theorem 10-15
4. $m\angle ABC + m\angle 1 = m\angle 2$	4. Theorem 5-1
5. $m\angle ABC + \frac{1}{2}m\widehat{AC} = \frac{1}{2}m\widehat{ADC}$	5. Postulate 2-9
6. $m\angle ABC = \frac{1}{2}m\widehat{ADC} - \frac{1}{2}m\widehat{AC}$	6. Postulate 2-7
7. $m\angle ABC = \frac{1}{2}(m\widehat{ADC} - m\widehat{AC})$	7. Postulate 2-9

38.

STATEMENTS	REASONS
1. $\overleftrightarrow{FA}$ is tangent to $\odot P$ and $\odot E$ at A; $\overline{AE} \perp \overline{EB}$	1. Given
2. $\overline{AE} \perp \overleftrightarrow{FA}$	2. Theorem 10-10
3. $\overleftrightarrow{FA} \parallel \overleftrightarrow{EB}$	3. Theorem 6-8
4. $\angle AEB$ is a right angle.	4. Theorem 3-11
5. $m\angle AEB = 90$	5. Definition of Right Angle
6. $AE = CE$	6. Definition of Circle
7. $\overline{AE} \cong \overline{CE}$	7. Definition of Congruent Segments
8. $\angle CAE \cong \angle ACE$	8. Theorem 4-6

9. $m\angle CAE = m\angle ACE$	9. Definition of Congruent Angles
10. $m\angle CAE + m\angle ACE + m\angle AEC = 180$	10. Theorem 4-1
11. $m\angle ACE + m\angle ACE + 90 = 180$	11. Postulate 2-9
12. $m\angle ACE + m\angle ACE = 90$	12. Postulate 2-7; Postulate 2-9
13. $2m\angle ACE = 90$	13. Postulate 2-9
14. $m\angle ACE = 45$	14. Postulate 2-8; Postulate 2-9
15. $\angle ACE \cong \angle FAC$	15. Theorem 6-10
16. $m\angle ACE = m\angle FAC$	16. Definition of Congruent Angles
17. $m\angle FAC = 45$	17. Postulate 2-9
18. $m\angle FAC = \frac{1}{2}m\widehat{AD}$	18. Theorem 10-15
19. $\frac{1}{2}m\widehat{AD} = 45$	19. Postulate 2-5; Postulate 2-9
20. $m\widehat{AD} = 90$	20. Postulate 2-8; Postulate 2-9

39.

STATEMENTS	REASONS
1. $\overleftrightarrow{FA}$ is tangent to $\odot P$ and to $\odot E$ at A.	1. Given
2. $m\angle CAF = \frac{1}{2}m\widehat{AC}$	2. Theorem 10-15
3. $2m\angle CAF = m\widehat{AC}$	3. Postulate 2-7; Postulate 2-9
4. $m\angle CEA = m\widehat{AC}$	4. Definition of Arc Measure
5. $2m\angle CAF = m\angle CEA$	5. Postulate 2-9
6. $m\angle CAF = \frac{1}{2}m\angle CEA$	6. Postulate 2-9

40.

STATEMENTS	REASONS
1. $\overline{RP} \perp \overline{QT}$; $\overline{RT} \perp \overline{QS}$	1. Given
2. $\angle PXT$ and $\angle SVT$ are right angles.	2. Theorem 3-11
3. $m\angle PXT = 90$; $m\angle SVT = 90$	3. Definition of Right Angle
4. $m\angle PXT = m\angle SVT$	4. Postulate 2-9
5. $m\angle PXT = \frac{1}{2}(m\widehat{PT} + m\widehat{QR})$; $m\angle SVT = \frac{1}{2}(m\widehat{ST} + m\widehat{QR})$	5. Theorem 10-13
6. $\frac{1}{2}(m\widehat{PT} + m\widehat{QR}) = \frac{1}{2}(m\widehat{ST} + m\widehat{QR})$	6. Postulate 2-9
7. $m\widehat{PT} + m\widehat{QR} = m\widehat{ST} + m\widehat{QR}$	7. Postulate 2-8; Postulate 2-9
8. $m\widehat{PT} = m\widehat{ST}$	8. Postulate 2-7; Postulate 2-9

41.

STATEMENTS	REASONS
1. $m\widehat{PT} = m\widehat{ST}$	1. Given
2. $m\widehat{PT} + m\widehat{QR} = m\widehat{ST} + m\widehat{QR}$	2. Postulate 2-7
3. $\frac{1}{2}(m\widehat{PT} + m\widehat{QR}) = \frac{1}{2}(m\widehat{ST} + m\widehat{QR})$	3. Postulate 2-8
4. $m\angle PXT = \frac{1}{2}(m\widehat{PT} + m\widehat{QR})$; $m\angle SVT = \frac{1}{2}(m\widehat{ST} + m\widehat{QR})$	4. Theorem 10-13
5. $m\angle PXT = m\angle SVT$	5. Postulate 2-9

42.

STATEMENTS	REASONS
1. $\widehat{NS} \cong \widehat{RT}$; $\widehat{SNM} \cong \widehat{TRM}$	1. Given
2. $m\widehat{NS} = m\widehat{RT}$; $m\widehat{SNM} = m\widehat{TRM}$	2. Definition of Congruent Arcs
3. $m\widehat{SNM} = m\widehat{NS} + m\widehat{MN}$; $m\widehat{TRM} = m\widehat{RT} + m\widehat{MR}$	3. Postulate 10-1
4. $m\widehat{NS} + m\widehat{MN} = m\widehat{RT} + m\widehat{MR}$	4. Postulate 2-9
5. $m\widehat{RT} + m\widehat{MN} = m\widehat{NS} + m\widehat{MR}$	5. Postulate 2-9
6. $\frac{1}{2}(m\widehat{RT} + m\widehat{MN}) = \frac{1}{2}(m\widehat{NS} + m\widehat{MR})$	6. Postulate 2-8
7. $m\angle MPQ = \frac{1}{2}(m\widehat{NS} + m\widehat{MR})$; $m\angle MQP = \frac{1}{2}(m\widehat{RT} + m\widehat{MN})$	7. Theorem 10-13
8. $m\angle MQP = m\angle MPQ$	8. Postulate 2-9
9. $\angle MQP \cong \angle MPQ$	9. Definition of Congruent Angles
10. $\overline{MP} \cong \overline{MQ}$	10. Theorem 4-9
11. $\triangle PMQ$ is isosceles.	11. Definition of Isosceles Triangle

43.

STATEMENTS	REASONS
1. $\widehat{NS} \cong \widehat{RT}$; $\angle NPS \cong \angle RQT$	1. Given

2. $\angle NPS$ and $\angle NPM$ are a linear pair; $\angle RQT$ and $\angle RQM$ are a linear pair.	2. Definition of Linear Pair
3. $\angle NPS$ and $\angle NPM$ are supplementary; $\angle RQT$ and $\angle RQM$ are supplementary.	3. Postulate 3-4
4. $\angle NPM \cong \angle RQM$	4. Theorem 3-3

PAGE 351 WRITTEN

19. Given: secant segments: $\overline{AC}$ and $\overline{CE}$
Prove: $AC \cdot BC = EC \cdot DC$

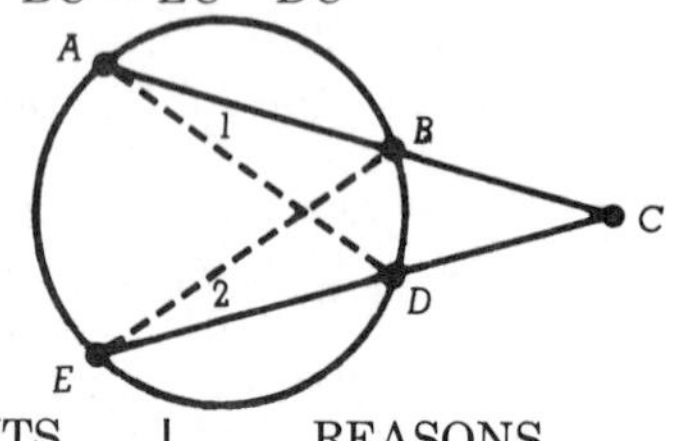

Proof:

STATEMENTS	REASONS
1. secant segments: $\overline{AC}$ and $\overline{CE}$	1. Given
2. Draw $\overline{BE}$ and $\overline{AD}$.	2. Postulate 1-1
3. $\angle C \cong \angle C$	3. Theorem 3-1
4. $m\widehat{BD} = m\widehat{BD}$	4. Postulate 2-4
5. $\widehat{BD} \cong \widehat{BD}$	5. Definition of Congruent Arcs
6. $\angle 1 \cong \angle 2$	6. Theorem 10-7
7. $\triangle ADC \sim \triangle EBC$	7. AA Similarity
8. $\frac{AC}{EC} = \frac{DC}{BC}$	8. Definition of Similar Polygons
9. $AC \cdot BC = EC \cdot DC$	9. Theorem 8-1

20. Given: $\overline{AB}$ is tangent to $\odot P$ at A; secant segment $\overline{DB}$
Prove: $(AB)^2 = DB \cdot CB$

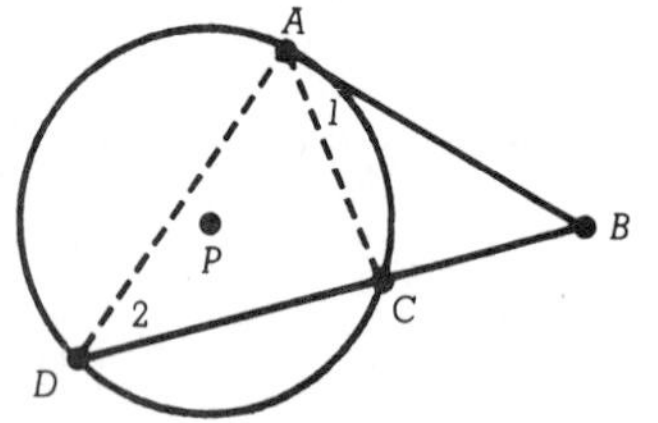

Proof:

STATEMENTS	REASONS
1. $\overline{AB}$ is tangent to $\odot P$ at A; secant segment $\overline{DB}$	1. Given
2. Draw $\overline{AD}$ and $\overline{AC}$.	2. Postulate 1-1
3. $m\angle 1 = \frac{1}{2}m\widehat{AC}$	3. Theorem 10-15
4. $m\angle 2 = \frac{1}{2}m\widehat{AC}$	4. Theorem 10-6
5. $m\angle 1 = m\angle 2$	5. Postulate 2-9
6. $\angle 1 \cong \angle 2$	6. Definition of Congruent Angles
7. $\angle B \cong \angle B$	7. Theorem 3-1
8. $\triangle ACB \sim \triangle DAB$	8. AA Similarity
9. $\frac{AB}{DB} = \frac{CB}{AB}$	9. Definition of Similar Polygons
10. $(AB)^2 = DB \cdot CB$	10. Theorem 8-1

21. STATEMENTS	REASONS
1. $\overleftrightarrow{CF}$ is tangent to $\odot P$ and to $\odot Q$ at F.	1. Given
2. $(CF)^2 = CA \cdot CB$ $(CF)^2 = CE \cdot CD$	2. Theorem 10-19
3. $CA \cdot CB = CE \cdot CD$	3. Postulate 2-9

22. STATEMENTS	REASONS
1. $\overrightarrow{GM}$ is tangent to $\odot R$ and to $\odot S$ at M.	1. Given
2. $(GM)^2 = GH \cdot GL$; $(GM)^2 = GJ \cdot GK$	2. Theorem 10-19
3. $GH \cdot GL = GJ \cdot GK$	3. Postulate 2-9

PAGES 355–356 WRITTEN

15–26. Answers may vary. Samples are shown as follows. **15.** A segment is a radius of a sphere if and only if its endpoints are the center of the sphere and a point on the sphere. **16.** A segment is a chord of a sphere if and only if its endpoints are points on the sphere. **17.** A circle is a great circle of a sphere if and only if the center of the circle is also the center of the sphere. **18.** A chord of a sphere is a diameter of the sphere if and only if the chord contains the center of the sphere. **19.** A point lies in the interior of a sphere if and only if the length of the segment joining the point to the center of the sphere is less than the length of a radius of the sphere. **20.** A point lies in the exterior of a sphere if and only if the length of the segment joining the point to the center of the sphere is greater than the length of a radius of the sphere. **21.** A line is tangent to a sphere if and only if the line intersects the sphere in exactly one point. **22.** A plane is tangent to the sphere if and only if the plane intersects the sphere in exactly one point. **23.** A line is a secant of a sphere if and only if it intersects the sphere in exactly two points. **24.** A set of points is a hemisphere if and only if it contains a great circle and all points of a sphere on "one side of" a great circle. **25.** Two spheres are congruent if and only if their radii are congruent. **26.** A set of points is an arc of a sphere if and only if the set of points is an arc of a great circle of the sphere.

35. STATEMENT	REASONS
1. $\overline{PR}$ and $\overline{QS}$ are diameters of sphere N. (N is the center of the sphere).	1. Given
2. $\overline{PR}$ and $\overline{QS}$ both contain the center of sphere N.	2. Definition of Diameter of a Sphere
3. There is exactly one plane, call it $\mathscr{A}$, that contains $\overline{PR}$ and $\overline{QS}$.	3. Theorem 1-2
4. There exists a plane $\mathscr{A}$ that intersects sphere N in a great circle.	4. Theorem 10-20
5. For any two points Y and Z on the circle, $YN = ZN$. (The circle of intersection has N as its center).	5. Definition of Sphere
6. $\overline{QS}$ and $\overline{PR}$ are diameters of $\odot N$.	6. Definition of a Diameter of a Circle
7. $\widehat{QRS}$, $\widehat{RSP}$, $\widehat{SPQ}$ and $\widehat{PQR}$ are semicircles.	7. Definition of Semicircle
8. $m\widehat{QRS} = m\widehat{RSP} = m\widehat{SPQ} = m\widehat{PQR} = 180$	8. Definition of Arc Measure
9. $\frac{1}{2}m\widehat{QRS} = \frac{1}{2}m\widehat{RSP} = \frac{1}{2}m\widehat{SPQ} = \frac{1}{2}m\widehat{PQR} = 90$	9. Postulate 2-8; Postulate 2-9
10. $m\angle RQP = \frac{1}{2}m\widehat{RSP}$; $m\angle SRQ = \frac{1}{2}m\widehat{SPQ}$; $m\angle RSP = \frac{1}{2}m\widehat{PQR}$; $m\angle SPQ = \frac{1}{2}m\widehat{QRS}$	10. Theorem 10-6
11. $m\angle RQP = 90$; $m\angle RSP = 90$; $m\angle SRQ = 90$; $m\angle SPQ = 90$	11. Postulate 2-9
12. $\angle RQP$, $\angle RSP$, $\angle SRQ$ and $\angle SPQ$ are right angles.	12. Definition of Right Angle
13. $QN = NS$; $PN = NR$	13. Definition of Sphere
14. N is the midpoint of $\overline{QS}$ and $\overline{PR}$.	14. Definition of Midpoint
15. $\overline{QS}$ and $\overline{PR}$ bisect each other.	15. Definition of Segment Bisector
16. Quadrilateral $QRSP$ is a parallelogram.	16. Theorem 7-9
17. Quadrilateral $QRSP$ is a rectangle.	17. Definition of Rectangle

PAGES 359–360 CHAPTER REVIEW

14. STATEMENTS	REASONS
1. $\overline{AB}$ is a diameter of $\odot E$; $\overline{AB} \perp \overline{CD}$	1. Given
2. $\overline{AB}$ bisects $\widehat{CBD}$.	2. Theorem 10-4
3. $\widehat{CB} \cong \widehat{DB}$	3. Definition of Bisector of an Arc

CHAPTER 11 AREA AND VOLUME

PAGE 365 EXPLORATORY

1. 1 cm × 24 cm
2 cm × 12 cm
3 cm × 8 cm
4 cm × 6 cm

2. 1 cm × 36 cm
2 cm × 18 cm
3 cm × 12 cm
4 cm × 9 cm
6 cm × 6 cm

PAGE 370 WRITTEN

27. Given: $\triangle ABC$; $\overline{BD} \perp \overleftrightarrow{AC}$; $AC = b$; $BD = h$

Prove: Area of $\triangle ABC = \frac{1}{2}bh$

Proof:

STATEMENTS	REASONS
1. $\triangle ABC$; $\overline{BD} \perp \overleftrightarrow{AC}$; $AC = b$; $BD = h$	1. Given
2. Draw $\overleftrightarrow{BE} \parallel \overline{AC}$ and $\overleftrightarrow{CE} \parallel \overline{AB}$.	2. Postulate 6-1
3. Quadrilateral $ABEC$ is a parallelogram.	3. Definition of Parallelogram
4. $\triangle ABC \cong \triangle ECB$	4. Theorem 7-3
5. Area $\triangle ABC$ = Area $\triangle ECB$	5. Postulate 11-2
6. Area $\triangle ABC$ + Area $\triangle ECB$ = Area ▱ $ABEC$	6. Postulate 11-3
7. Area ▱ $ABEC = bh$	7. Theorem 11-2
8. Area $\triangle ABC$ + Area $\triangle ABC = bh$	8. Postulate 2-9

9. 2(Area $\triangle ABC$) = bh	9. Postulate 2-9
10. Area $\triangle ABC = \frac{1}{2}bh$	10. Postulate 2-8; Postulate 2-12; Postulate 2-13; Postulate 2-19

28. Given: Trapezoid $ABCD$; $\overline{AB} = b_1$; $\overline{CD} = b^2$; $\overline{AE} = h$; $\overline{AE} \perp \overline{CD}$; $\overline{AE} \perp \overline{AB}$; $\overline{AB} \parallel \overline{CD}$

Prove: Area of trapezoid $ABCD = \frac{1}{2}h(b_1 + b_2)$

Proof:

STATEMENTS	REASONS
1. Trapezoid $ABCD$; $\overline{AB} = b_1$; $\overline{CD} = b_2$; $\overline{AE} = h$; $\overline{AE} \perp \overline{CD}$; $\overline{AE} \perp \overline{AB}$; $\overline{AB} \parallel \overline{CD}$	1. Given
2. Draw $\overline{AC}$, $\overleftrightarrow{AB}$, and $\overleftrightarrow{CD}$.	2. Postulate 1-1
3. Draw $\overline{CF} \perp \overleftrightarrow{AB}$.	3. Theorem 6-14
4. AE is the distance between E and $\overleftrightarrow{AF}$; CF is the distance between C and $\overleftrightarrow{AF}$.	4. Definition of Distance Between a Point and a Line
5. $AE = CF$	5. Theorem 6-15
6. $h = CF$	6. Postulate 2-9
7. Area $\triangle ADC = \frac{1}{2}b_2h$; Area $\triangle ABC = \frac{1}{2}b_1h$	7. Theorem 11-3
8. Area trapezoid $ABCD$ = Area $\triangle ABC$ + Area $\triangle ADC$	8. Postulate 11-3
9. Area trapezoid $ABCD = \frac{1}{2}b_1h + \frac{1}{2}b_2h$	9. Postulate 2-9
10. Area trapezoid $ABCD = \frac{1}{2}h(b_1 + b_2)$	10. Postulate 2-14

PAGES 374–375 WRITTEN

20. Given: Regular polygon $ABCDE$ inscribed about $\odot X$; $\overline{XN}$ is an apothem.

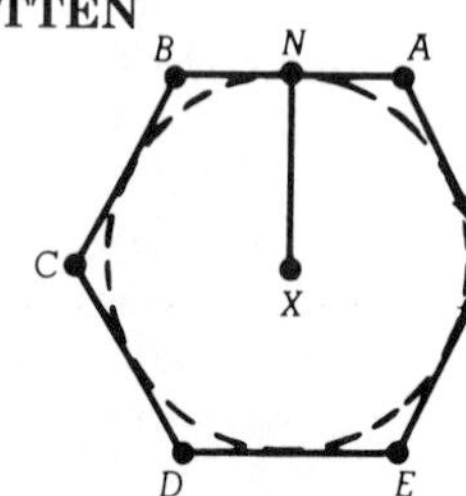

Prove: $\overline{XN} \perp \overline{BA}$

Proof:

STATEMENTS	REASONS
1. Regular polygon $ABCDE$ inscribed about $\odot X$; $\overline{XN}$ is an apothem.	1. Given
2. $\overline{XN}$ is a radius of $\odot X$.	2. Definition of Apothem
3. $\overline{AB}$ is tangent to $\odot X$.	3. Definition of Circle Inscribed in a Polygon
4. $\overline{XN} \perp \overline{BA}$	4. Theorem 10-10

21. Given: Regular pentagon $ABCDE$; apothem $\overline{XN}$ is of length a; $AB + BC + CD + DE + EA = p$

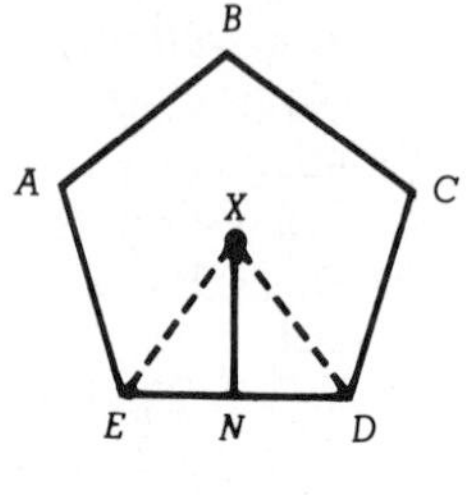

Prove: Area of $ABCDE = \frac{1}{2}ap$

Proof:

STATEMENTS	REASONS
1. Regular pentagon $ABCDE$; apothem $\overline{XN}$ is of length a; $AB + BC + CD + DE + EA = p$	1. Given
2. $\overline{XN} \perp \overline{ED}$	2. Theorem 11-6
3. Draw $\overline{XE}$, $\overline{XA}$, $\overline{XB}$, $\overline{XC}$, and $\overline{XD}$.	3. Postulate 1-1
4. $\overline{XE} \cong \overline{XA} \cong \overline{XB} \cong \overline{XC} \cong \overline{XD}$	4. Definition of Radius
5. $\overline{XB} \cong \overline{BC} \cong \overline{CD} \cong \overline{DE} \cong \overline{EA}$	5. Definition of Regular Polygon
6. $\triangle AXB \cong \triangle BXC \cong \triangle CXD \cong \triangle DXE \cong \triangle EXA$	6. SSS
7. $\overline{XN}$ is an altitude of $\triangle DXE$.	7. Definition of Altitude
8. Area of $\triangle DXE = \frac{1}{2}a(ED)$	8. Theorem 11-3
9. Area of $\triangle AXB$ + Area of $\triangle BXC$ + Area of $\triangle CXD$ + Area of $\triangle DXE$ + Area of $\triangle EXA$ = Area of pentagon $ABCDE$	9. Postulate 11-2

10. Area of pentagon $ABCDE = 5\left(\frac{1}{2}aED\right)$	10. Postulate 2-9; Postulate 2-7
11. $5(ED) = p$	11. Postulate 2-9
12. Area of pentagon $ABCDE = \frac{1}{2}ap$	12. Postulate 2-9

22. Given: $ABCDEF$ is a regular hexagon.
Prove: $m\angle 1 = m\angle 3 = m\angle 4 = m\angle 5 = m\angle 6 = \frac{360}{6}$
Proof:

STATEMENTS	REASONS
1. $ABCDEF$ is a regular hexagon.	1. Given
2. Draw $\overline{AX}, \overline{BX}, \overline{CX}, \overline{DX}, \overline{EX}$, and $\overline{FX}$.	2. Postulate 1-1
3. $\overline{AX} \cong \overline{BX} \cong \overline{CX} \cong \overline{DX} \cong \overline{EX} \cong \overline{FX}$	3. Definition of Radius
4. $\overline{AB} \cong \overline{BC} \cong \overline{CD} \cong \overline{DE} \cong \overline{EF}$	4. Definition of Regular Polygon
5. $\triangle AXB \cong \triangle BXC \cong \triangle CXD \cong \triangle DXE \cong \triangle EXF \cong \triangle FXA$	5. SSS
6. $\angle 1 \cong \angle 2 \cong \angle 3 \cong \angle 4 \cong \angle 5 \cong \angle 6$	6. CPCTC
7. $m\angle 1 + m\angle 2 + m\angle 3 + m\angle 4 + m\angle 5 + m\angle 6 = 360$	7. Definition of Arc Measure
8. $6(m\angle 1) = 360$	8. Postulate 2-9; Postulate 2-7
9. $m\angle 1 = \frac{360}{6}$	9. Postulate 2-8
10. $m\angle 1 = m\angle 2 = m\angle 3 = m\angle 4 = m\angle 5 = m\angle 6 = \frac{360}{6}$	10. Definition of Congruent Angles

23. Given: $\triangle ABC$ is equilateral.
Prove: $m\angle 1 = m\angle 2 = m\angle 3 = \frac{360}{3}$

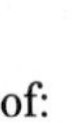

B
1
X 2
3
A
C

Proof:

STATEMENTS	REASONS
1. $\triangle ABC$ is equilateral.	1. Given
2. Draw $\overline{XA}, \overline{XB}$, and $\overline{XC}$.	2. Postulate 1-1
3. $\overline{XA} \cong \overline{XB} \cong \overline{XC}$	3. Definition of Radius
4. $\overline{AB} \cong \overline{BC} \cong \overline{CA}$	4. Definition of Regular Polygon
5. $\triangle AXB \cong \triangle BXC \cong \triangle CXA$	5. SSS
6. $\angle 1 \cong \angle 2 \cong \angle 3$	6. CPCTC
7. $m\angle 1 + m\angle 2 + m\angle 3 = 360$	7. Definition of Arc Measure
8. $3(m\angle 1) = 360$	8. Postulate 2-9; Postulate 2-7
9. $m\angle 1 = \frac{360}{3}$	9. Postulate 2-8
10. $m\angle 1 = m\angle 2 = m\angle 3 = \frac{360}{3}$	10. Definition of Congruent Angles

PAGE 380 EXCURSION

1.

below

above

2.

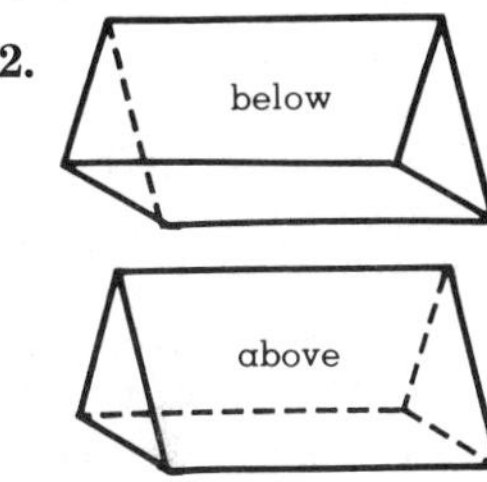

3.

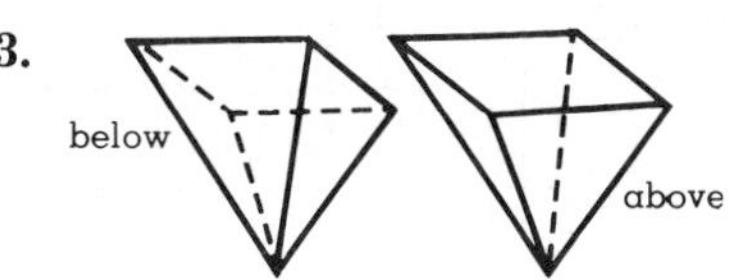

CHAPTER 12 COORDINATES

PAGE 408 WRITTEN

1.

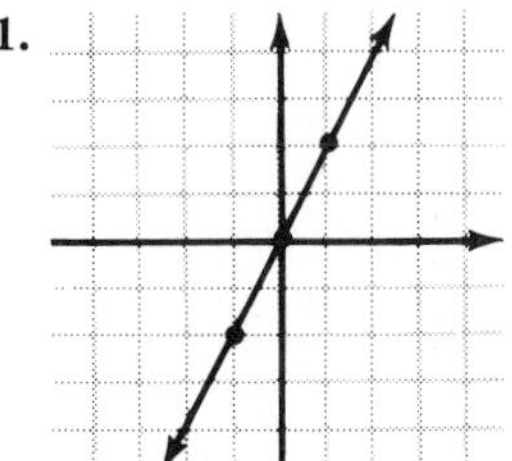

2.

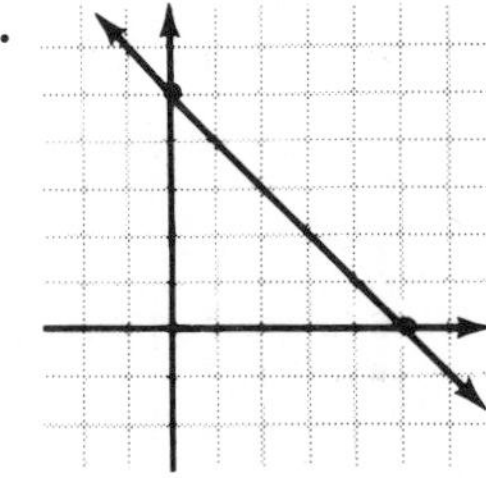

3.

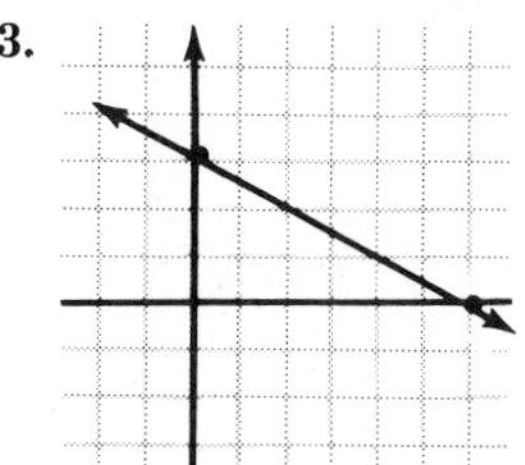

4.

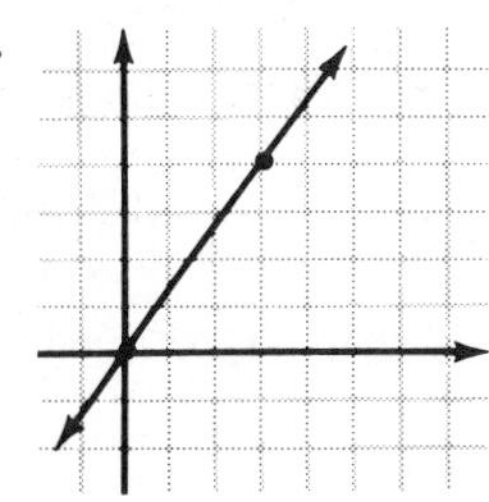

5.

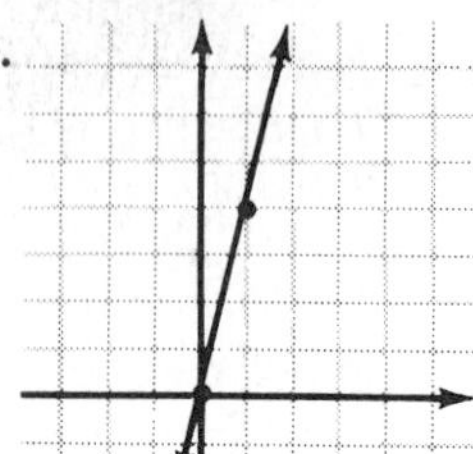

6.

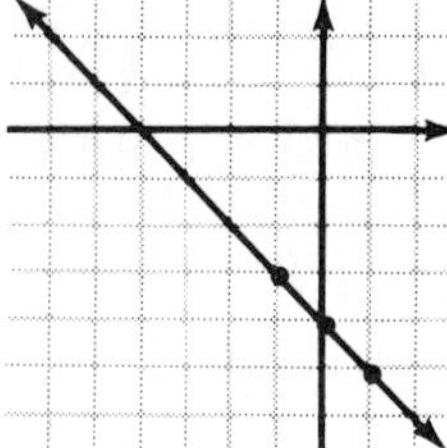

7.

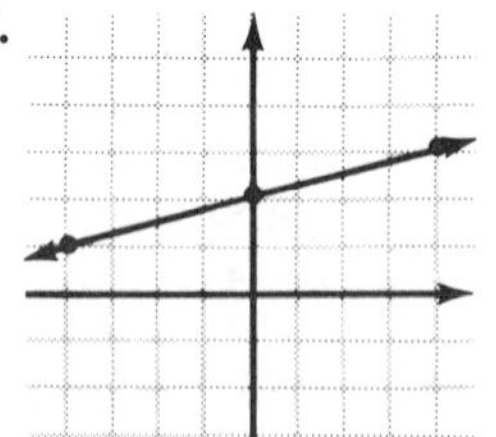

8.

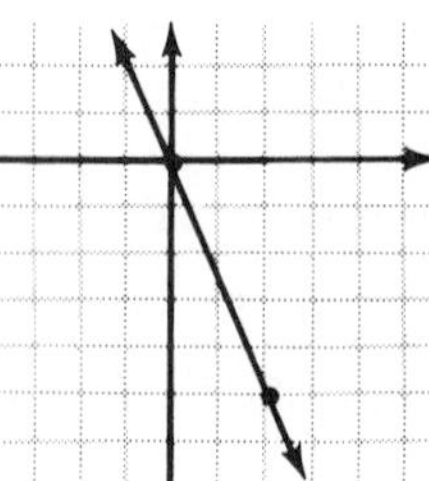

9.

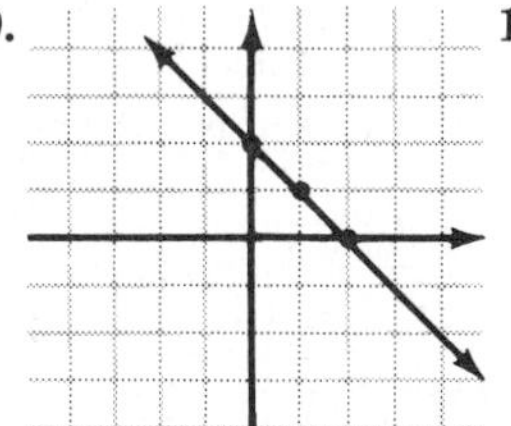

10.

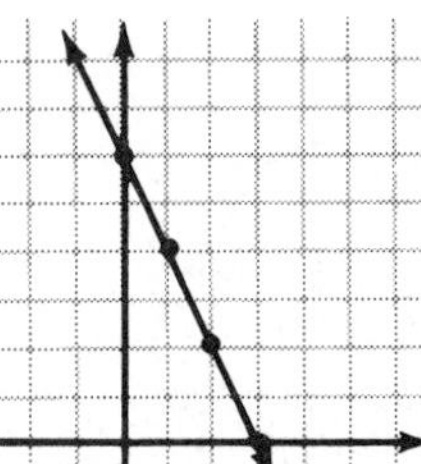

11.

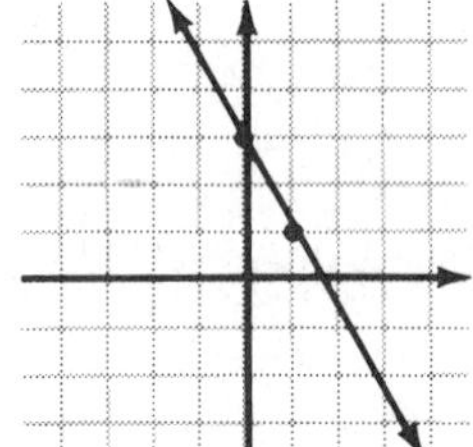

12.

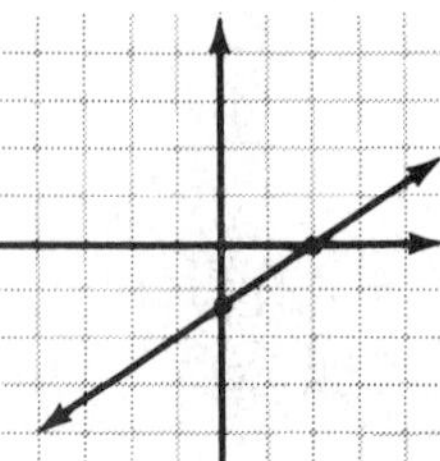

13.

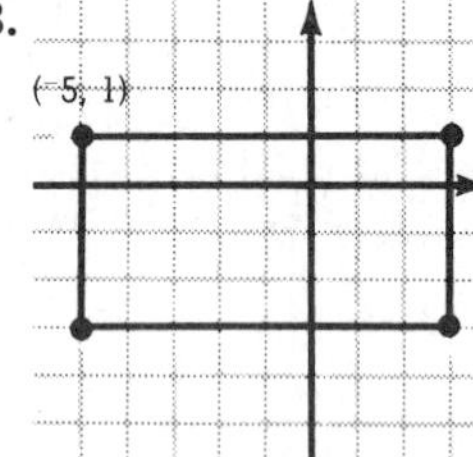

The graphs for exercises **14.–18.** are similar to the graph for exercise **13.**

PAGE 419 WRITTEN

26.

$$y - 6 = \frac{^-3}{7}(x - 3) \qquad y - 9 = \frac{^-3}{7}(x + 4)$$

$$7y - 42 = {}^-3(x - 3) \qquad 7y - 63 = {}^-3(x + 4)$$

$$7y - 42 = {}^-3x + 9 \qquad 7y - 63 = {}^-3x - 12$$

$$7y = {}^-3x + 51 \qquad 7y = {}^-3x + 51$$

PAGE 422 WRITTEN

1.

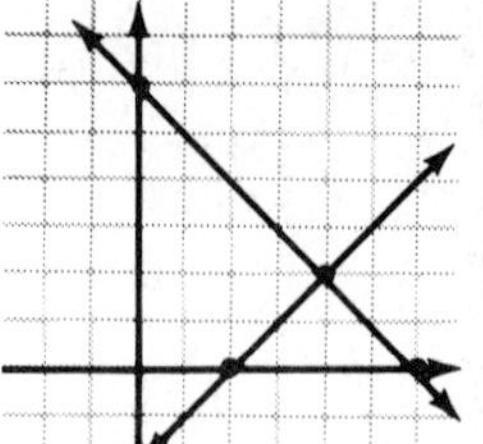

2.

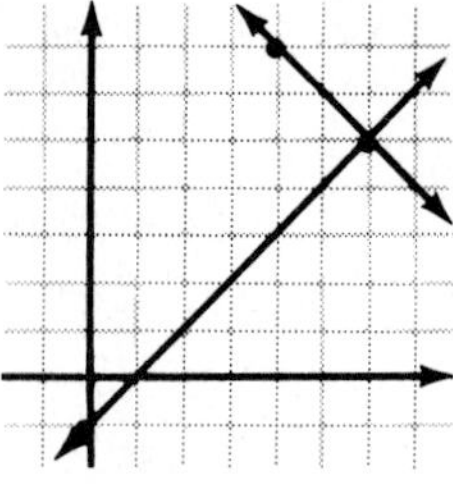

3.

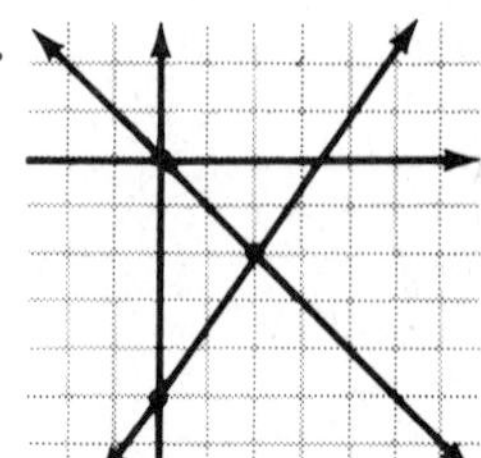

4.

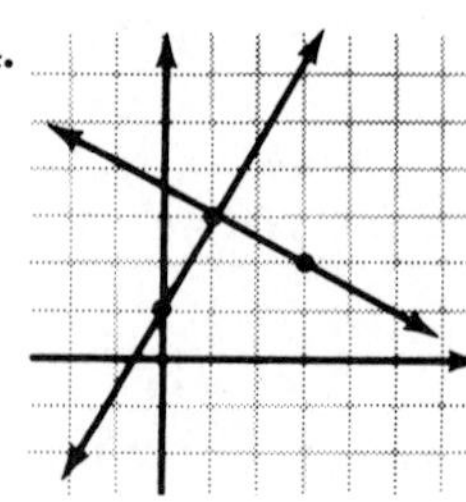

5.

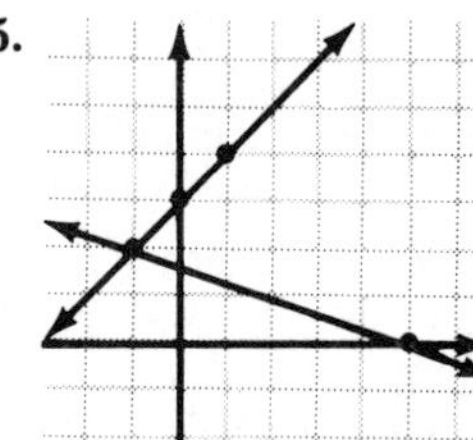

6.

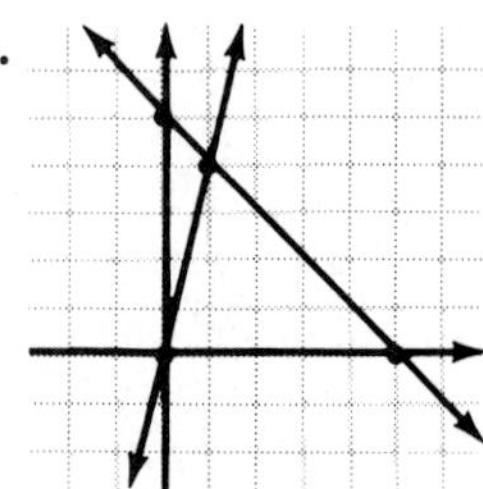

PAGE 422 ALGEBRA REVIEW

1. $x = {}^-2 \pm \sqrt{5}$ **2.** $x = \frac{5 \pm \sqrt{33}}{2}$ **3.** $x = \frac{^-3 \pm \sqrt{6}}{3}$

4. $x = \frac{7 \pm \sqrt{89}}{^-4}$ **5.** $x = 2 \pm \sqrt{14}$ **6.** $x = \frac{^-1 \pm \sqrt{13}}{2}$

PAGE 429 WRITTEN

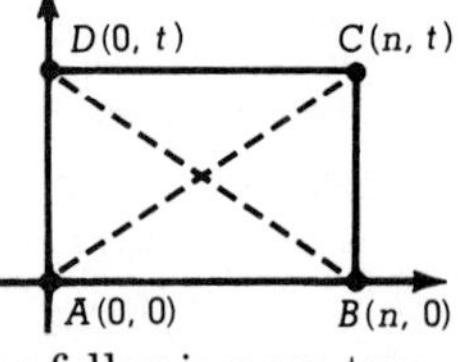

7. Given: rectangle $ABCD$

Prove: $\overline{BD} \cong \overline{AC}$

Proof:

By the distance formula, the following are true.

$BD = \sqrt{(n - 0)^2 + (0 - t)^2}$

$AC = \sqrt{(n - 0)^2 + (t - 0)^2}$

$BD = \sqrt{n^2 + t^2}$ $\qquad AC = \sqrt{n^2 + t^2}$

By substitution, $BD = AC$. By definition of congruent segments, $\overline{BD} \cong \overline{AC}$.

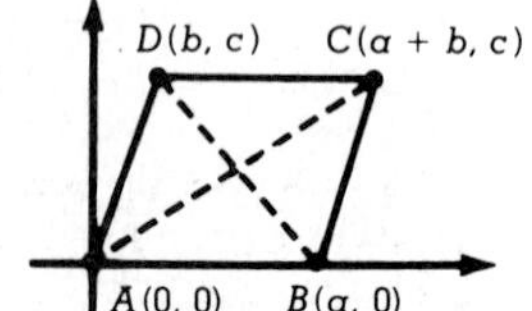

8. Given: rhombus $ABCD$

Prove: $\overline{AC} \perp \overline{DB}$

Proof:

$$m_1 = \text{slope of } \overline{AC} = \frac{c-0}{(a+b)-0} = \frac{c}{a+b}$$

$$m_2 = \text{slope of } \overline{DB} = \frac{c-0}{b-a}$$

$$m_1 \cdot m_2 = \frac{c}{a+b} \cdot \frac{c}{b-a} = \frac{c^2}{b^2-a^2}$$

Since $c^2 = b^2 - a^2$, $\frac{c^2}{b^2-a^2} = \frac{b^2-a^2}{b^2-a^2}$.

Therefore, $m_1 \cdot m_2 = {}^-1$.

By Theorem 12-4, $\overline{AC} \perp \overline{DB}$.

9. Given: Quadrilateral $ABCD$ is an isosceles trapezoid.

Prove: $\overline{AC} \cong \overline{BD}$

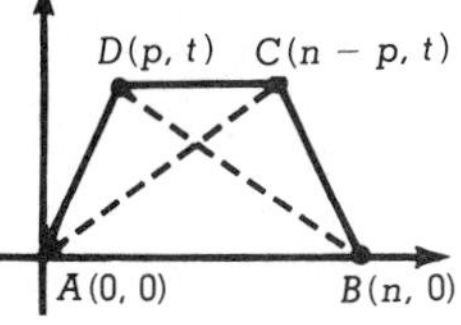

Proof:

$$AC = \sqrt{(n-p-0)^2 + (t-0)^2} = \sqrt{(n-p)^2 + t^2}$$

$$BD = \sqrt{(n-p)^2 + (0-t)^2} = \sqrt{(n-p)^2 + t^2}$$

By substitution, $AC = BC$. By definition of congruent segments, $\overline{AC} \cong \overline{BC}$.

10. Given: Quadrilateral $ABCD$ is a parallelogram.

Prove: $\overline{AC}$ and $\overline{BD}$ bisect each other.

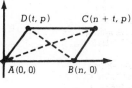

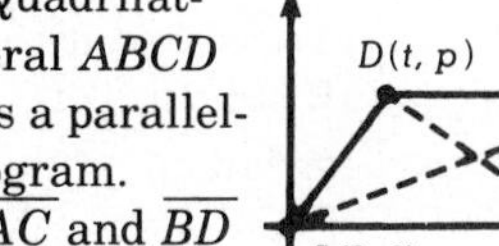

Proof:

$$\text{midpoint of } \overline{AC} = \left(\frac{n+t}{2}, \frac{p+0}{2}\right) = \left(\frac{n+t}{2}, \frac{p}{2}\right)$$

$$\text{midpoint of } \overline{BD} = \left(\frac{n+t}{2}, \frac{p}{2}\right)$$

Since $\overline{AC}$ and $\overline{BD}$ have the same midpoint, they bisect each other.

11. Given: Quadrilateral $ABCD$ is a parallelogram.

Prove: $\overline{AD} \cong \overline{BC}$; $\overline{AB} \cong \overline{DC}$

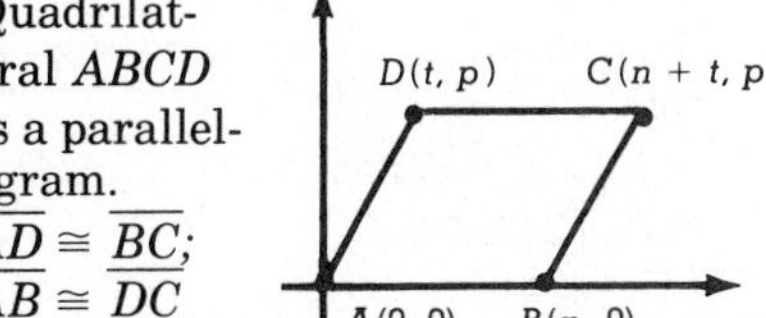

Proof:

$$AB = \sqrt{(n-0)^2 + (0-0)^2} = |n|$$

$$DC = \sqrt{(n+t-t)^2 + (p-p)^2} = |n|$$

$$AD = \sqrt{(t-0)^2 + (p-0)^2} = \sqrt{t^2 + p^2}$$

$$BC = \sqrt{(n+t-n)^2 + (p-0)^2} = \sqrt{t^2 + p^2}$$

By substitution, $AB = DC$ and $AD = BC$.

By definition of congruent segments, $\overline{AB} \cong \overline{DC}$ and $\overline{AD} \cong \overline{BC}$.

12. Given: Quadrilateral $ABCD$ is a rectangle; X, Y, Z, and W are midpoints of $\overline{AC}$, $\overline{AB}$, $\overline{BD}$, and $\overline{DC}$ respectively.

Prove: Quadrilateral $XYZW$ is a rhombus.

Proof:

By the midpoint formula:

$$X = \left(\frac{0+0}{2}, \frac{t+0}{2}\right) = \left(0, \frac{t}{2}\right)$$

$$Y = \left(\frac{n+0}{2}, \frac{0+0}{2}\right) = \left(\frac{n}{2}, 0\right)$$

$$Z = \left(\frac{n+n}{2}, \frac{t+0}{2}\right) = \left(n, \frac{t}{2}\right)$$

$$W = \left(\frac{n+0}{2}, \frac{t+t}{2}\right) = \left(\frac{n}{2}, t\right)$$

By definition of slope:

$$\text{slope of } \overleftrightarrow{XY} = \frac{\frac{t}{2} - 0}{0 - \frac{n}{2}} = \frac{{}^-t}{n}$$

$$\text{slope of } \overleftrightarrow{WZ} = \frac{t - \frac{t}{2}}{\frac{n}{2} - n} = \frac{\frac{t}{2}}{\frac{{}^-n}{2}} = -\frac{t}{n}$$

$$\text{slope of } \overleftrightarrow{XW} = \frac{t - \frac{t}{2}}{\frac{n}{2} - 0} = \frac{t}{n}$$

$$\text{slope of } \overleftrightarrow{YZ} = \frac{\frac{t}{2} - 0}{n - \frac{n}{2}} = \frac{t}{n}$$

By substitution:

slope of $\overleftrightarrow{XY}$ = slope of $\overleftrightarrow{WZ}$
slope of $\overleftrightarrow{XW}$ = slope of $\overleftrightarrow{YZ}$

By Theorem 12-3 and definition of parallel parts of lines, $\overline{XY} \parallel \overline{WZ}$ and $\overline{XW} \parallel \overline{YZ}$.

By definition of parallelogram, quadrilateral $XYZW$ is a parallelogram.

By the distance formula:

$$XY = \sqrt{\left(\frac{n}{2} - 0\right)^2 + \left(0 - \frac{t}{2}\right)^2} = \sqrt{\frac{n^2 + t^2}{4}}$$

$$YZ = \sqrt{\left(n - \frac{n}{2}\right)^2 + \left(\frac{t}{2} - 0\right)^2} = \sqrt{\frac{n^2 + t^2}{4}}$$

$$WZ = \sqrt{\left(n - \frac{n}{2}\right)^2 + \left(t - \frac{t}{2}\right)^2} = \sqrt{\frac{n^2 + t^2}{4}}$$

$$WX = \sqrt{\left(\frac{n}{2} - 0\right)^2 + \left(t - \frac{t}{2}\right)^2} = \sqrt{\frac{n^2 + t^2}{4}}$$

By substitution: $XY = YZ = WZ = WX$
By definition of congruent segments:
$\overline{XY} \cong \overline{YZ} \cong \overline{WZ} \cong \overline{WX}$
By definition of rhombus: quadrilateral $XYZW$ is a rhombus.

13. Given: trapezoid $ABDC$; median $\overline{MN}$

Prove: $MN = \frac{1}{2}(AB + CD)$

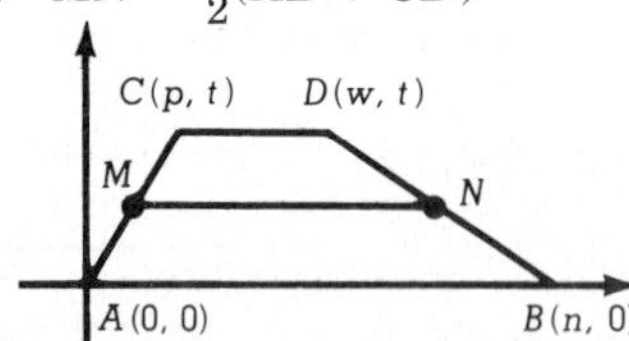

Proof:
By the definition of median of a trapezoid, M is the midpoint of $\overline{AC}$ and N is the midpoint of $\overline{BD}$.
By the midpoint formula:

$$M = \left(\frac{p + 0}{2}, \frac{t + 0}{2}\right) = \left(\frac{p}{2}, \frac{t}{2}\right)$$

$$N = \left(\frac{n + w}{2}, \frac{t + 0}{2}\right) = \left(\frac{n + w}{2}, \frac{t}{2}\right)$$

By the distance formula:

$$MN = \sqrt{\left(\frac{n + w}{2} - \frac{p}{2}\right)^2 + \left(\frac{t}{2} - \frac{t}{2}\right)^2} = \left|\frac{n + w - p}{2}\right|$$

$$= \frac{n + w - p}{2}$$

because $w > p$ and $n > 0$.

$$= \frac{1}{2}(n + w - p)$$

$AB = \sqrt{(n - 0)^2 + (0 - 0)^2} = |n| = n$ since $n > 0$
$CD = \sqrt{(w - p)^2 + (t - t)^2} = |w - p| = w - p$ since $w > p$

By substitution: $MN = \frac{1}{2}(AB + CD)$.

14. Given: Quadrilateral $ABCD$ is an isosceles trapezoid; Y, M, N, and W are midpoints of $\overline{DC}$, $\overline{AD}$, $\overline{AB}$, and $\overline{BC}$ respectively.

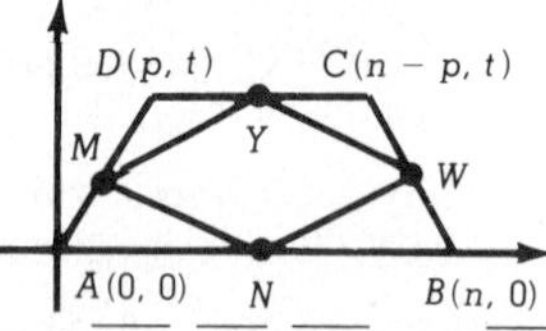

Prove: Quadrilateral $MNWY$ is a rhombus.
By midpoint formula:

$$Y = \left(\frac{n - p + p}{2}, \frac{t + t}{2}\right) = \left(\frac{n}{2}, t\right)$$

$$M = \left(\frac{p + 0}{2}, \frac{t + 0}{2}\right) = \left(\frac{p}{2}, \frac{t}{2}\right)$$

$$N = \left(\frac{n + 0}{2}, \frac{0 + 0}{2}\right) = \left(\frac{n}{2}, 0\right)$$

$$W = \left(\frac{n + n - p}{2}, \frac{t + 0}{2}\right) = \left(n - \frac{p}{2}, \frac{t}{2}\right)$$

By definition of slope:

$$\text{slope of } \overleftrightarrow{MN} = \frac{\frac{t}{2} - 0}{\frac{p}{2} - \frac{n}{2}} = \frac{t}{p - n}$$

$$\text{slope of } \overleftrightarrow{WY} = \frac{t - \frac{t}{2}}{\frac{n}{2} - n + \frac{p}{2}} = \frac{t}{p - n}$$

$$\text{slope of } \overleftrightarrow{MY} = \frac{t - \frac{t}{2}}{\frac{n}{2} - \frac{p}{2}} = \frac{t}{n - p}$$

$$\text{slope of } \overleftrightarrow{NW} = \frac{\frac{t}{2} - 0}{n - \frac{p}{2} - \frac{n}{2}} = \frac{t}{n - p}$$

By substitution: slope of $\overleftrightarrow{MN}$ = slope of $\overleftrightarrow{WY}$, slope of $\overleftrightarrow{MY}$ = slope of $\overleftrightarrow{NW}$
By Theorem 12-3 and definition of parallel parts of lines: $\overline{MN} \parallel \overline{WY}$ and $\overline{MY} \parallel \overline{NW}$.
By definition of parallelogram: quadrilateral $MNWY$ is a parallelogram.
By the distance formula:

$$MN = \sqrt{\left(\frac{p}{2} - \frac{n}{2}\right)^2 + \left(\frac{t}{2} - 0\right)^2} = \sqrt{\left(\frac{p - n}{2}\right)^2 + \left(\frac{t}{2}\right)^2}$$

$$NW = \sqrt{\left(n - \frac{p}{2} - \frac{n}{2}\right)^2 + \left(\frac{t}{2} - 0\right)^2} = \sqrt{\left(\frac{p - n}{2}\right)^2 + \left(\frac{t}{2}\right)^2}$$

$$WY = \sqrt{\left(\frac{n}{2} - n + \frac{p}{2}\right)^2 + \left(t - \frac{t}{2}\right)^2} = \sqrt{\left(\frac{p - n}{2}\right)^2 + \left(\frac{t}{2}\right)^2}$$

$$MY = \sqrt{\left(\frac{n}{2} - \frac{p}{2}\right)^2 + \left(t - \frac{t}{2}\right)^2} = \sqrt{\left(\frac{p - n}{2}\right)^2 + \left(\frac{t}{2}\right)^2}$$

By substitution: $MN = NW = WY = MY$
By definition of congruent segments:
$\overline{MN} \cong \overline{NW} \cong \overline{WY} \cong \overline{MY}$
By definition of rhombus: quadrilateral $MNWY$ is a rhombus.

PAGES 436–438 CHAPTER REVIEW

1.

2.

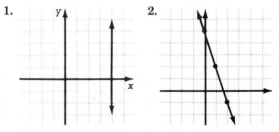

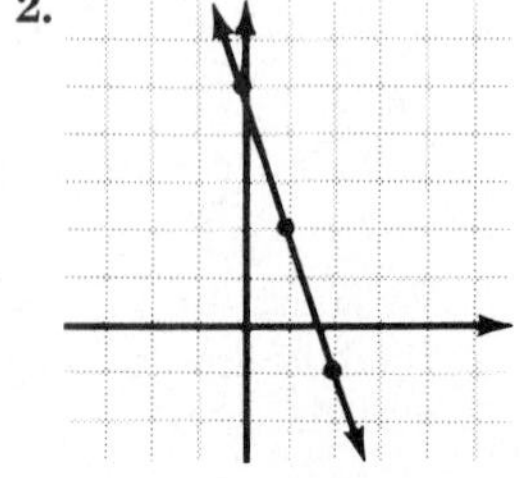

3.

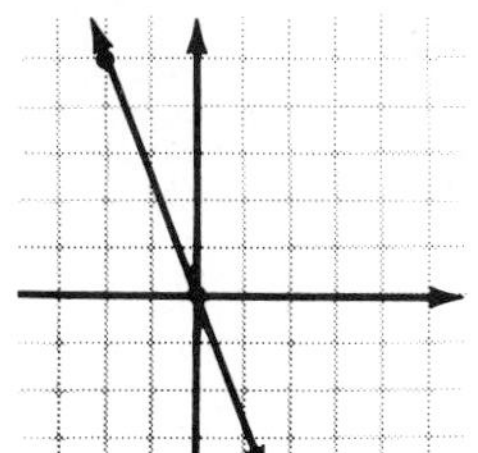

4.

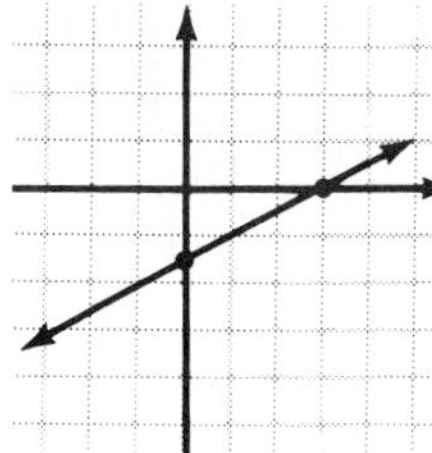

5.

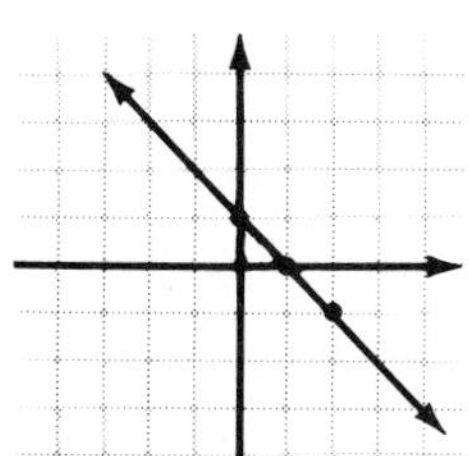

6.

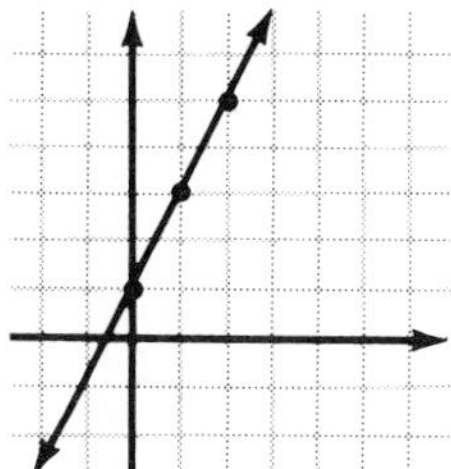

7.

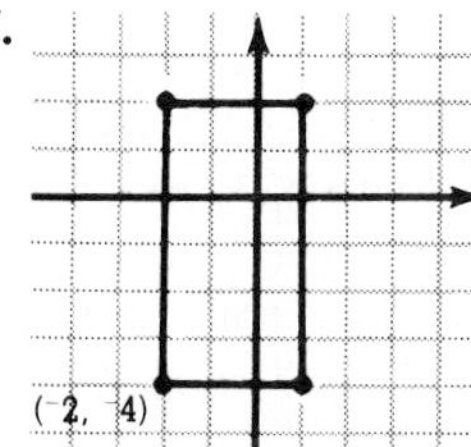

The graphs for exercises **8.–10.** are similar to the graph for exercise **7.**

44.

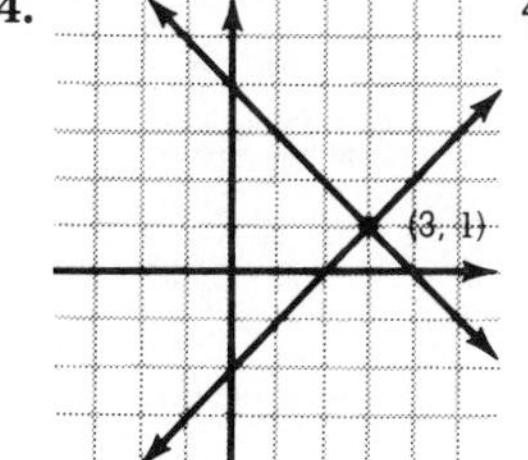

45.

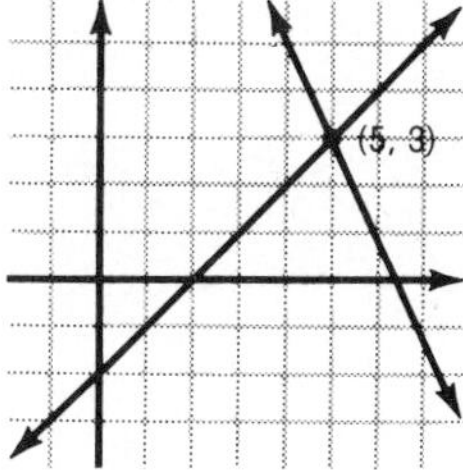

61. Given: rhombus $ABCD$
Prove: $\overline{BD} \perp \overline{AC}$

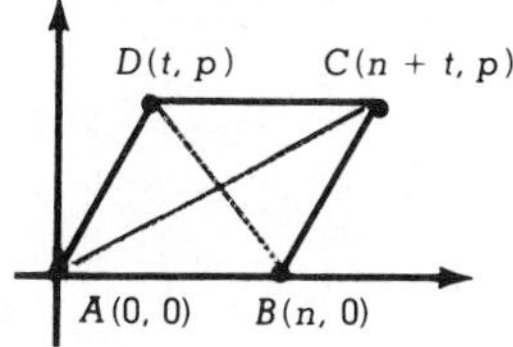

PAGE 439 CHAPTER TEST

1.

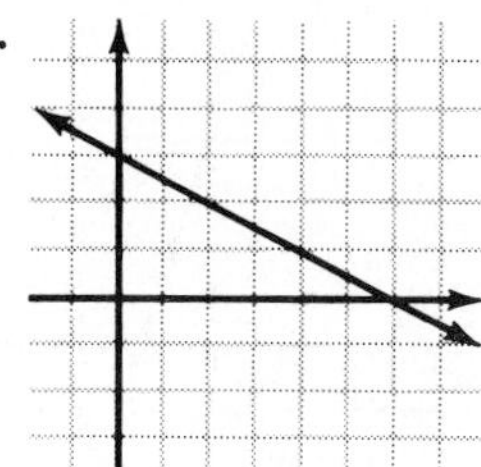

2.

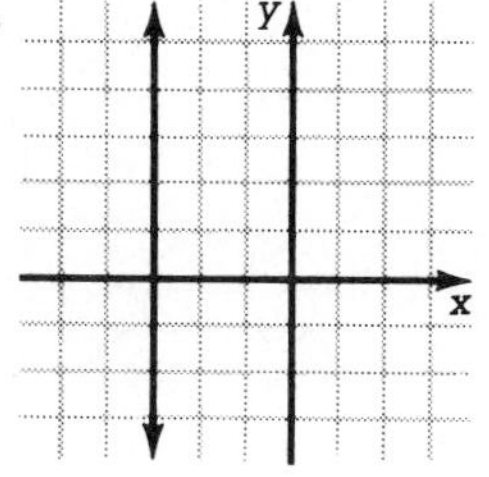

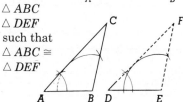

20. Given: rectangle $ABCD$
Prove: $\overline{AC} \cong \overline{BD}$

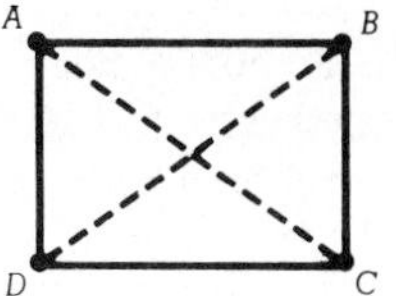

PAGES 440–441 CUMULATIVE REVIEW

1.

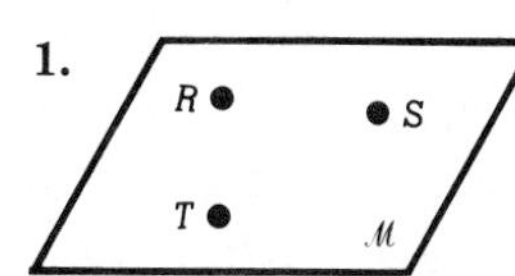

2. L M N

3. *Inverse:* If three points are not coplanar, then they do not lie in the same plane. *Contrapositive:* If three points do not lie in the same plane, then they are not coplanar.

4. *Inverse:* If it does not snow, then you may not ski. *Contrapositive:* If you may not ski, then it does not snow.

19. STATEMENTS	REASONS
1. $\triangle ABC \cong \triangle CDA$	1. Given
2. $\angle 3 \cong \angle 2$	2. CPCTC
3. $\overline{BC} \parallel \overline{DA}$	3. Theorem 6-4

20. STATEMENTS	REASONS
1. $\angle 2 \cong \angle 3$, $\angle 4 \cong \angle 1$	1. Given
2. $\overline{AC} \cong \overline{AC}$	2. Theorem 2-2
3. $\triangle ABC \cong \triangle CDA$	3. ASA
4. $\overline{AB} \cong \overline{CD}$	4. CPCTC

21. A B C D

CHAPTER 13 LOCI AND CONSTRUCTIONS

PAGE 446 EXPLORATORY

1. Given: $\overline{AB}$
Construct: Equilateral triangle with $\overline{AB}$ as one of its sides.

A B
A B

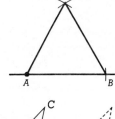

2. Given: $\triangle ABC$
Construct: $\triangle DEF$ such that $\triangle ABC \cong \triangle DEF$

C F
A B D E

3. Given: $\overline{AB}$
Construct: $\overline{CD}$ such that $CD = 2AB$

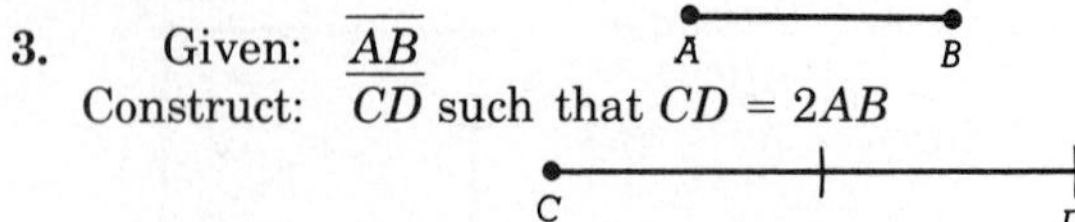

4. Given: $\overline{AB}$
Construct: $\overline{CD}$ such that $CD = 3AB$

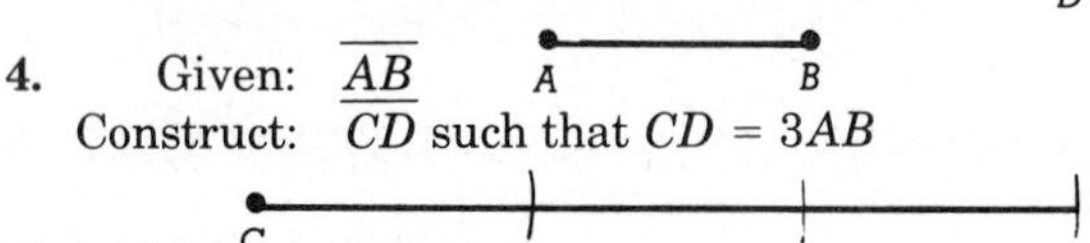

5. Given: $\overline{AB}$; $\overline{CD}$
Construct: $\overline{AD}$ such that $AD = AB + CD$

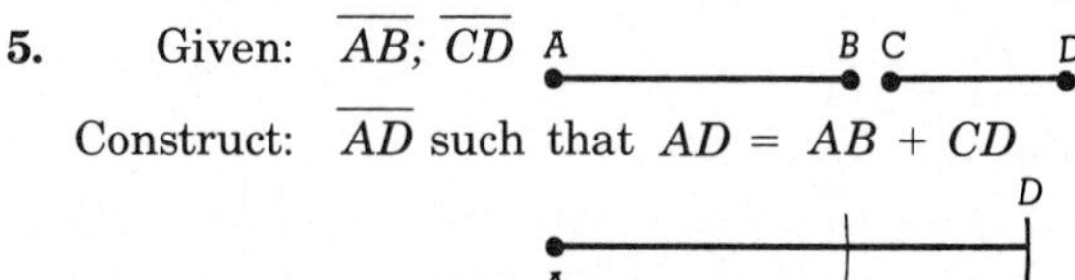

6. Given: $\angle ABC$
Construct: $\angle DEF$ such that $m\angle DEF = 2m\angle ABC$

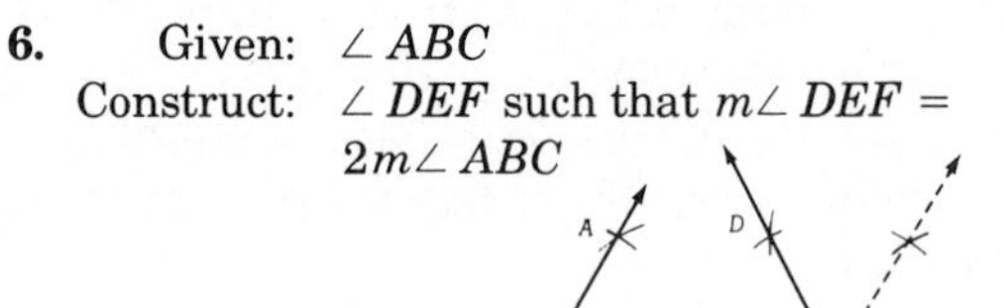

7. Given: $\angle ABC$
Construct: $\angle EFG$ such that $m\angle EFG = \frac{1}{2}m\angle ABC$

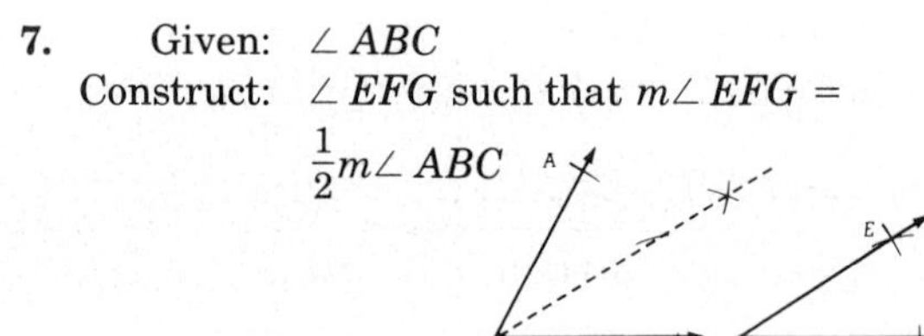

8. Given: $\angle ABC$; $\angle DEF$
Construct: $\angle HIJ$ such that $m\angle HIJ = m\angle ABC + m\angle DEF$

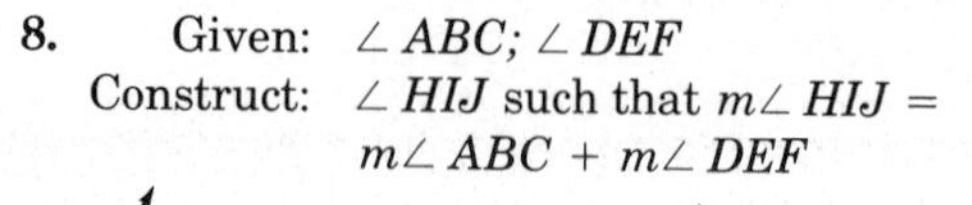

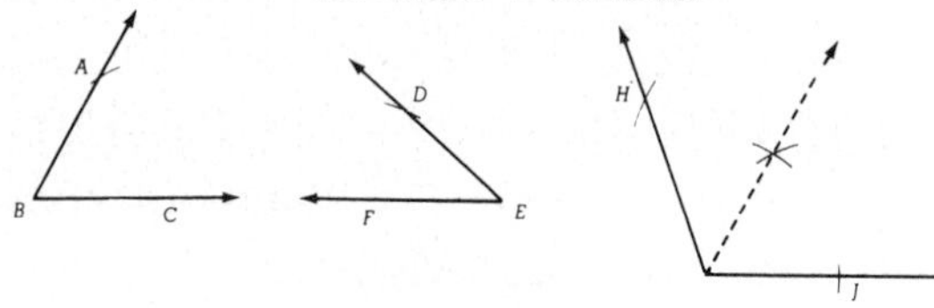

PAGE 446 WRITTEN

1. 2. 3. 4. 5.

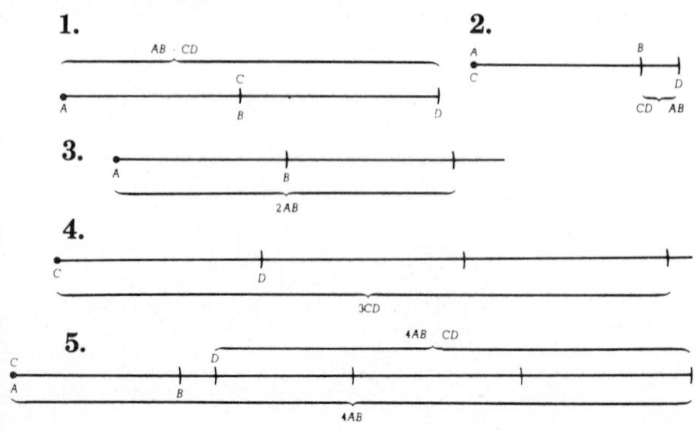

6.

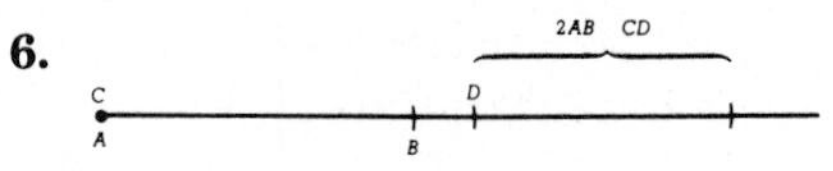

7.

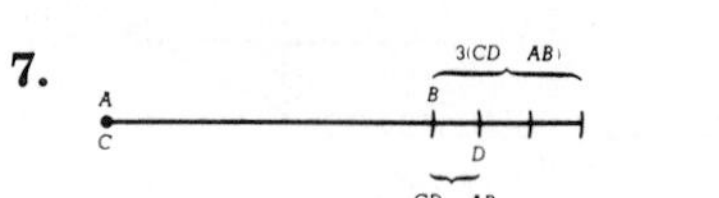

8.

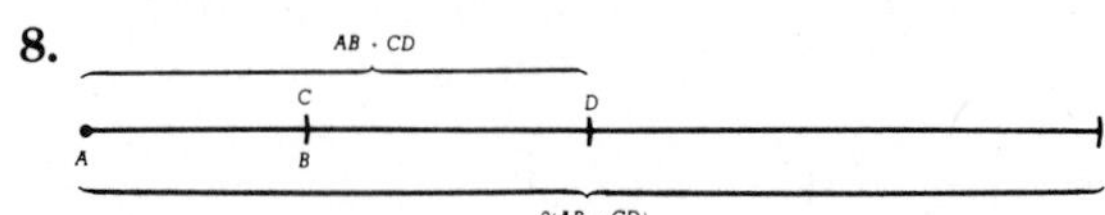

9. 10. 11.

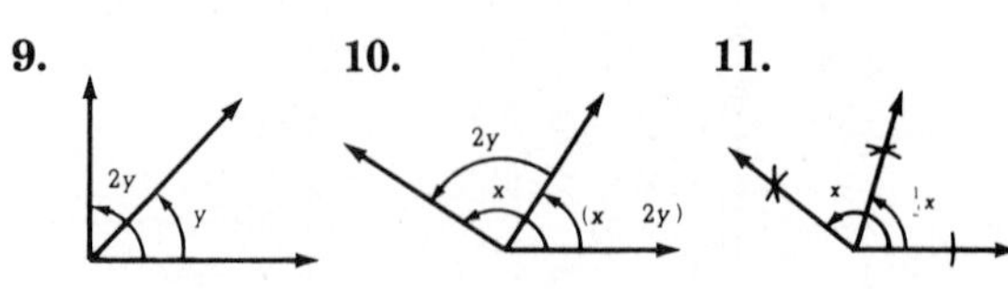

12. 13. 14.

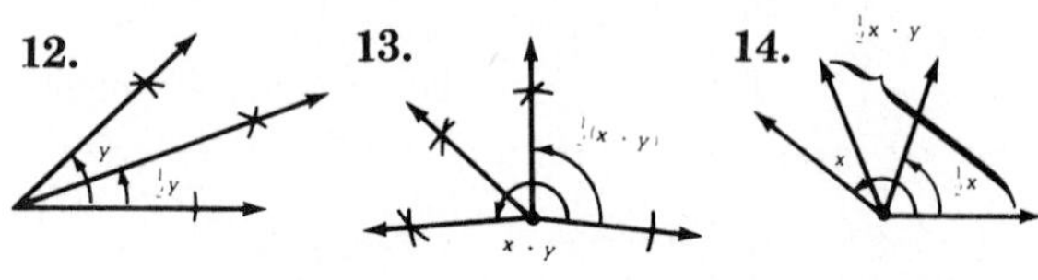

15. 16. 17.

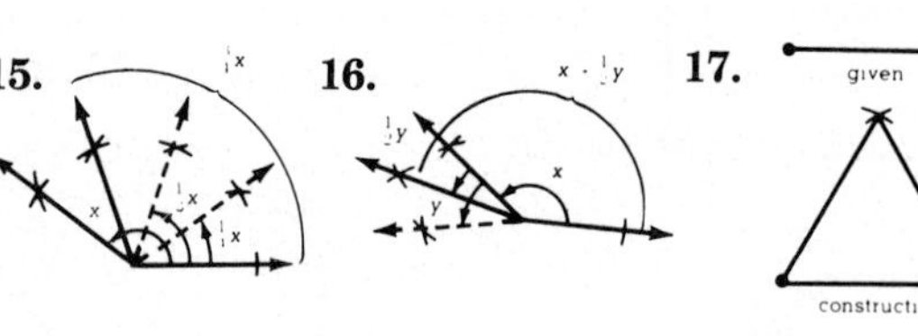

18.

19. Copy the 60° angle from exercise 17, and bisect it.

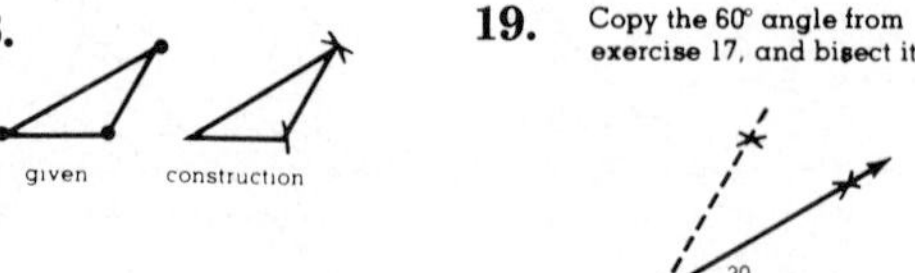

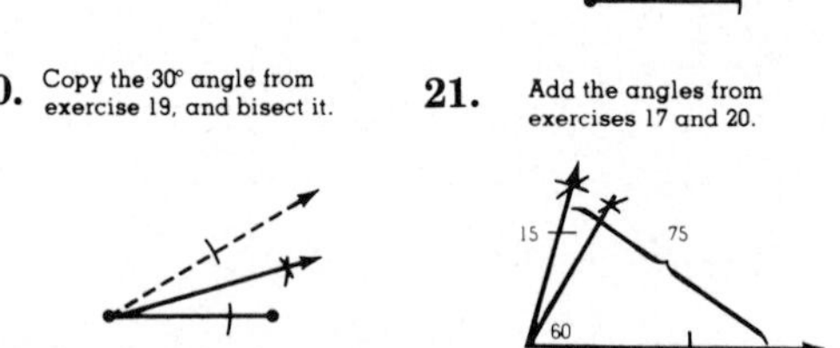

20. Copy the 30° angle from exercise 19, and bisect it.

21. Add the angles from exercises 17 and 20.

22. Add the angles from exercises 19 and 20.

23.

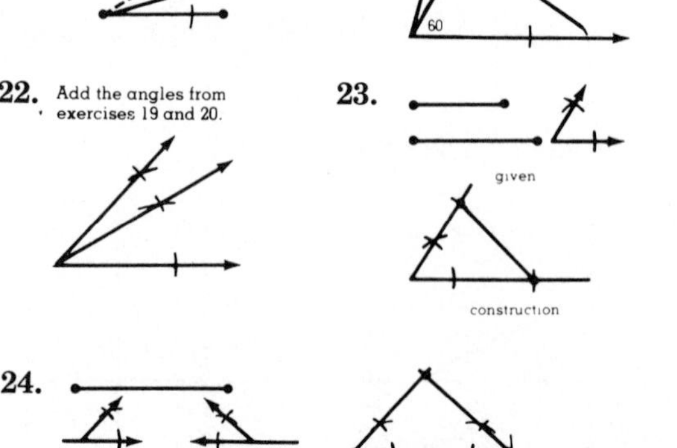

24.

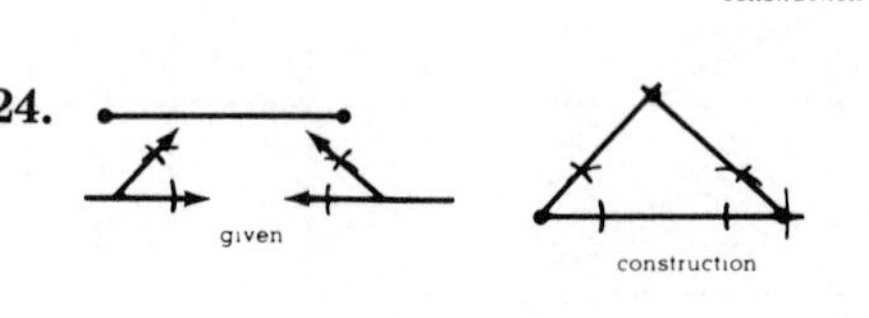

PAGE 446 CHALLENGE

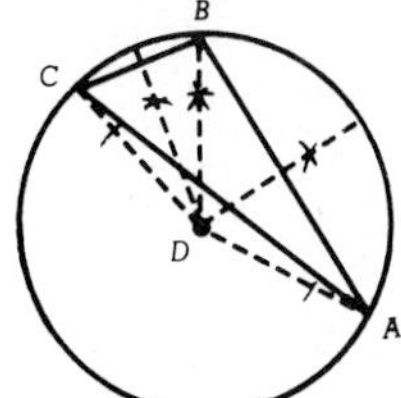

With a radius of the circle as one side, construct an angle, $\angle BDC$, having twice the measure of $\angle 1$. Adjacent to this angle construct an angle, $\angle BDA$, having twice the measure of $\angle 3$. By Theorem 10-6, $m\angle A = \frac{1}{2}(2m\angle 1)$ and $m\angle C = \frac{1}{2}(2m\angle 3)$.

PAGE 450 WRITTEN

1.

2.

3.

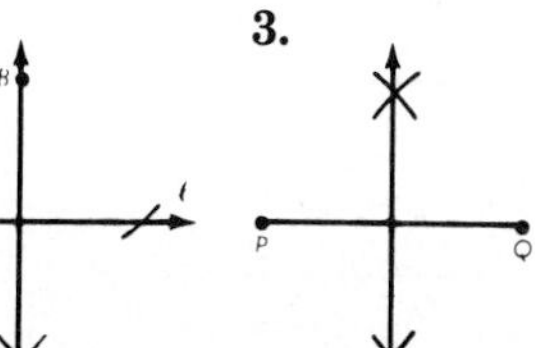

4.

5.

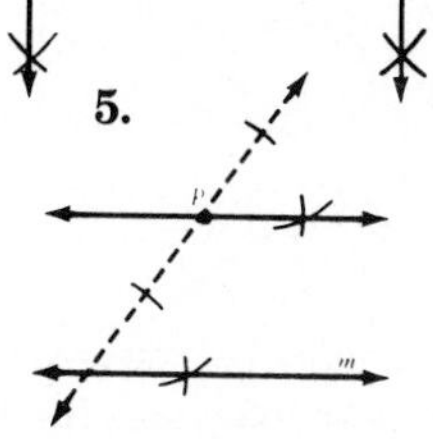

6. Given *P*; ***m***. Use *construction 4* to construct the line perpendicular to ***m*** through *P*. Call it ***ℓ***. Then use *construction 6* to construct the line perpendicular to ***ℓ*** through *P*.

7.

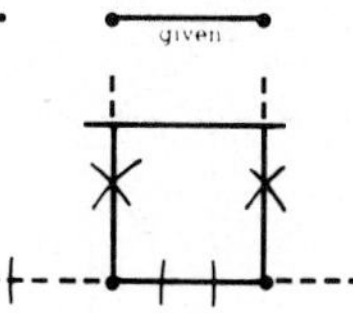

8.

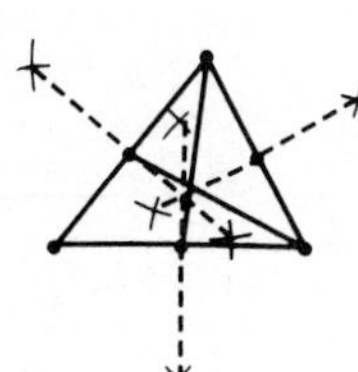

9.

10.

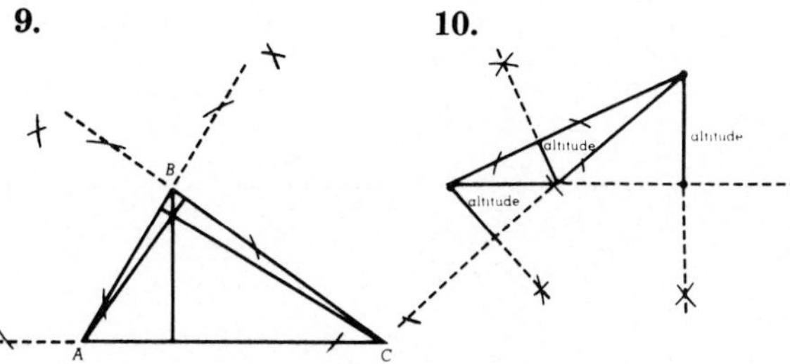

11.

12.

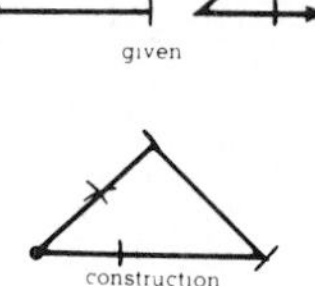

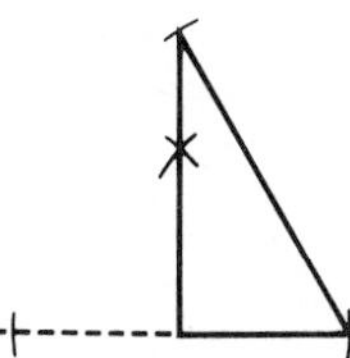

13.

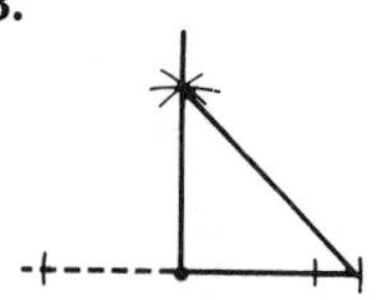

14.

15.

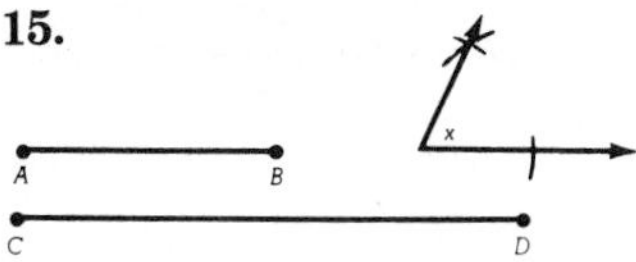

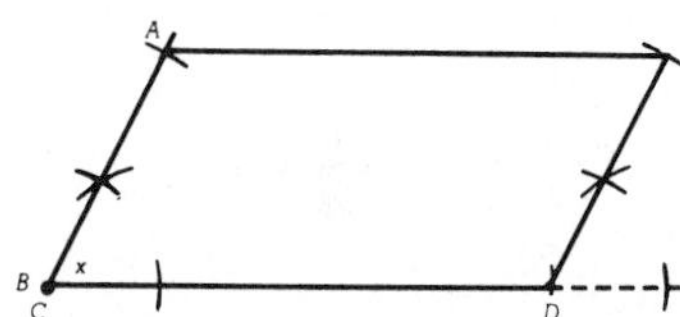

16. Use the segments from exercise 15 for exercises 16–19.

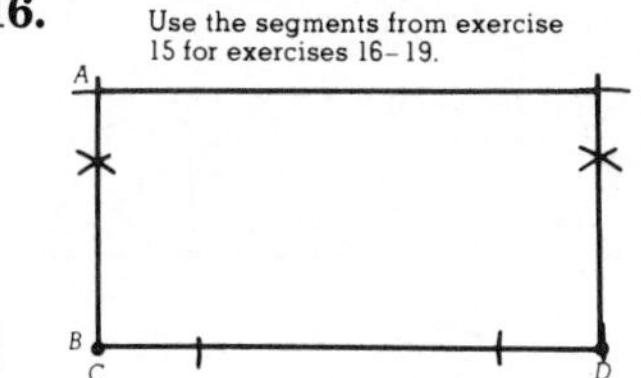

17.

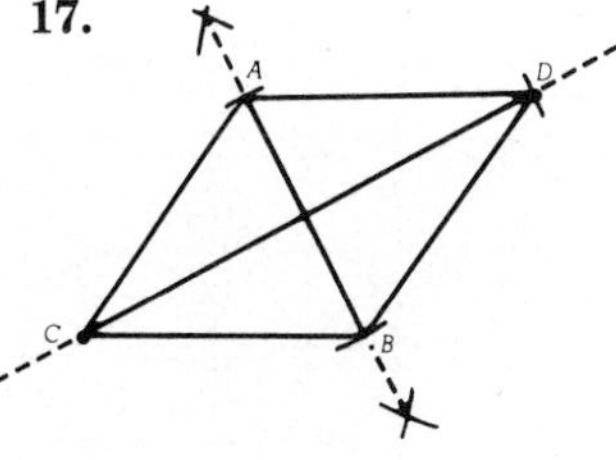

18.

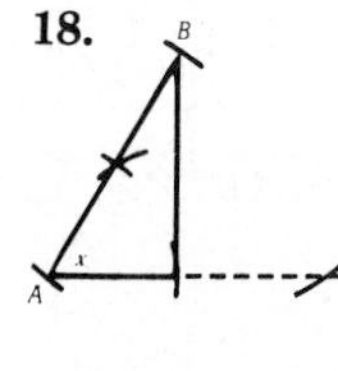

19.

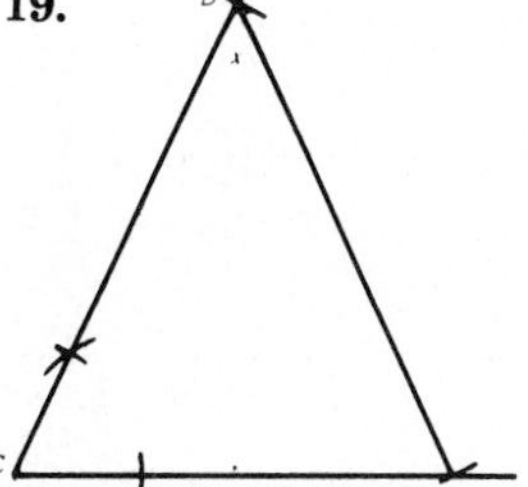

PAGE 453 WRITTEN

1.

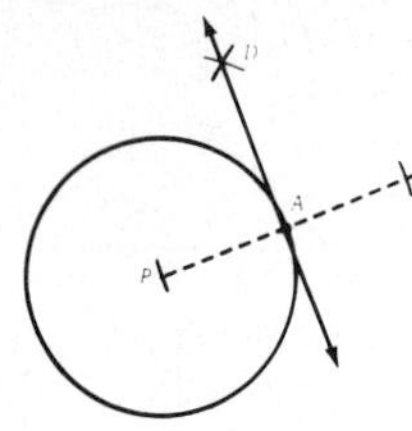

2.

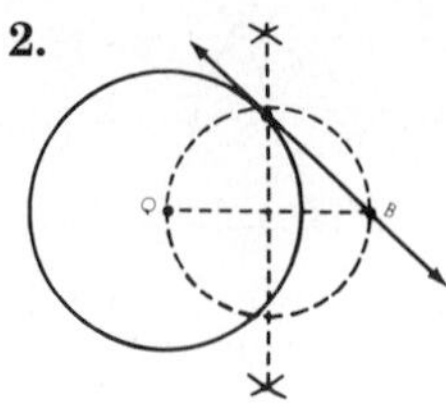

3.

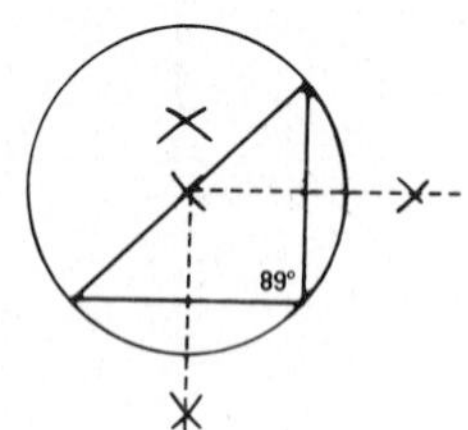

4.

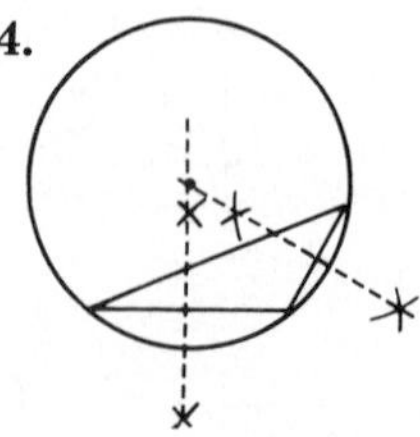

5.

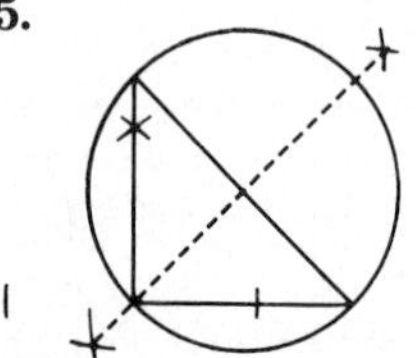

6.

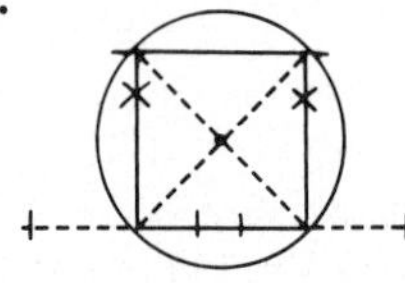

7.

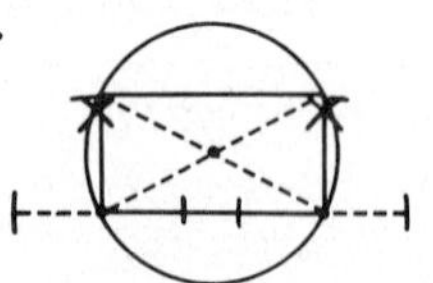

8.

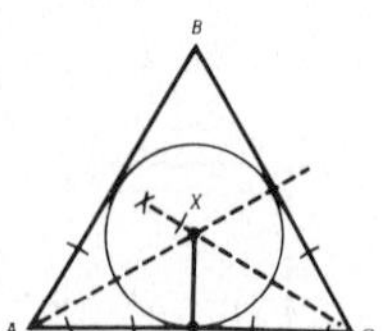

9.

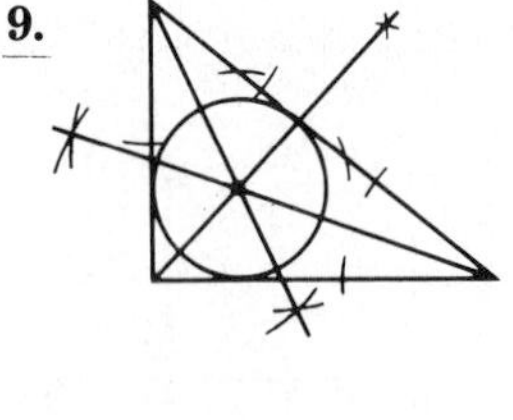

10.

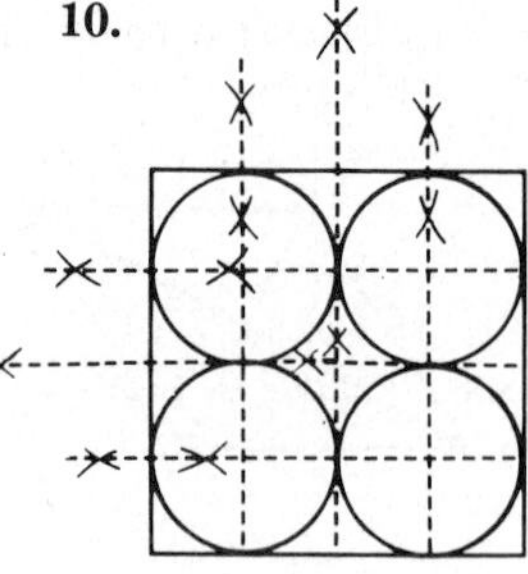

PAGE 456 WRITTEN

1.

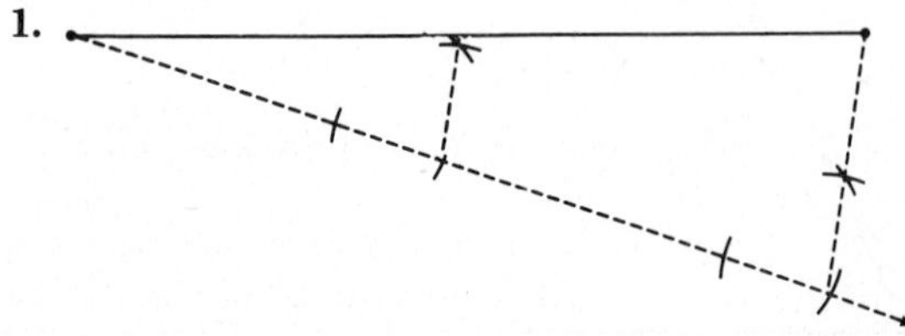

The answers to exercises **2.–7.** are similar to the answer to exercise **1.**

8.

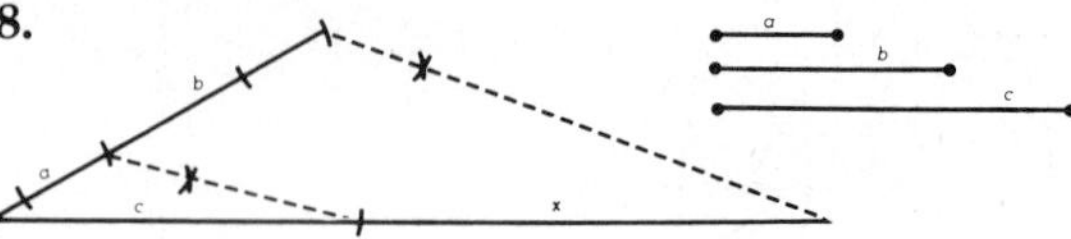

9.

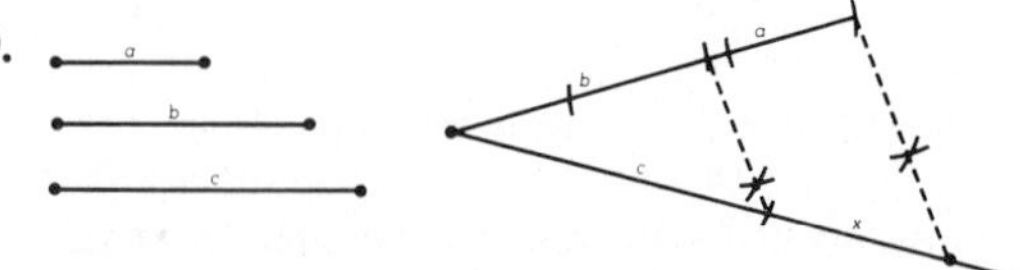

10.

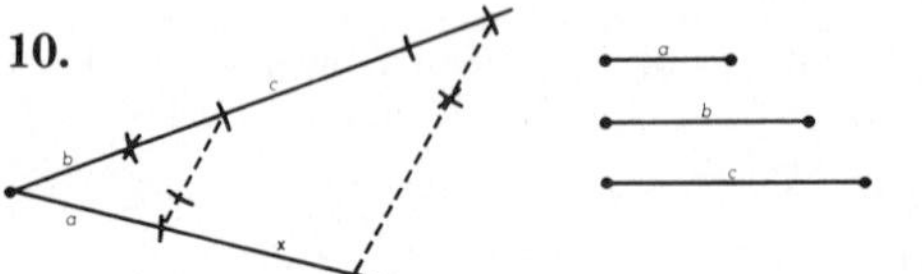

11.

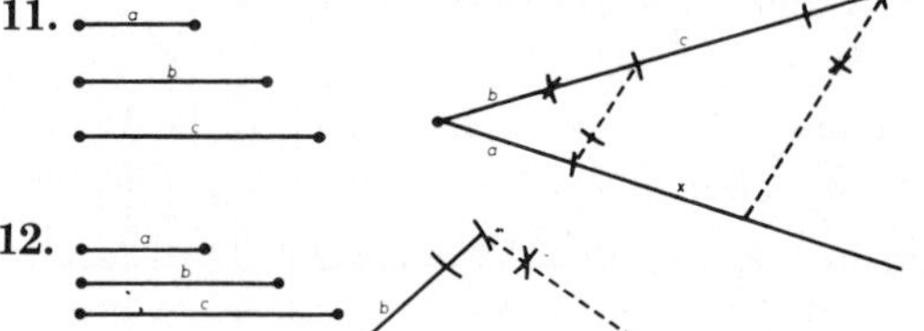

12.

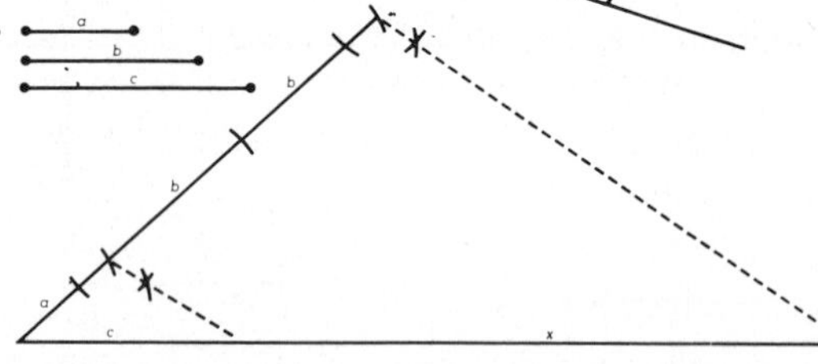

The answers to exercises **13.–15.** are similar to the answers to exercises **8.–12.**

16.

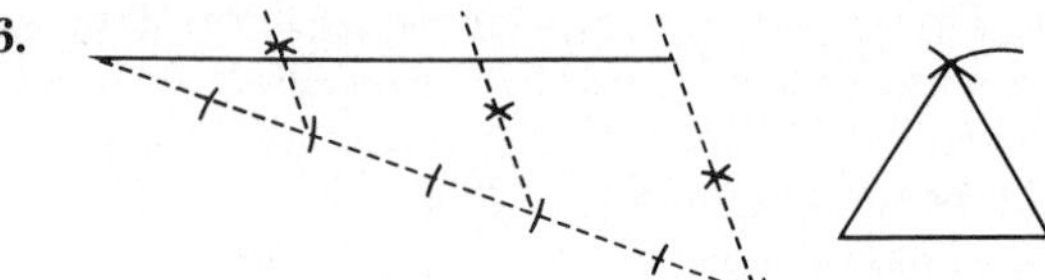

17.

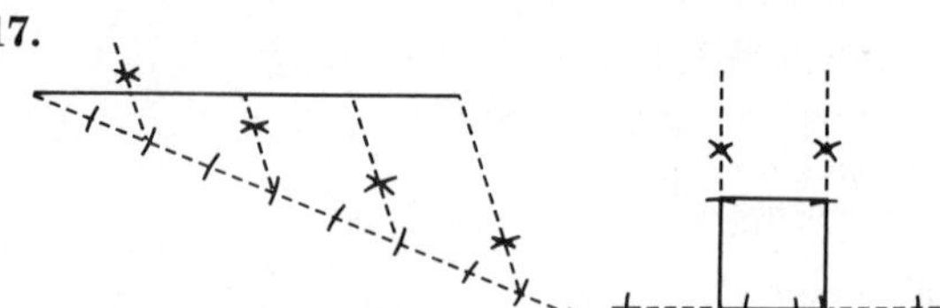

18. 19.

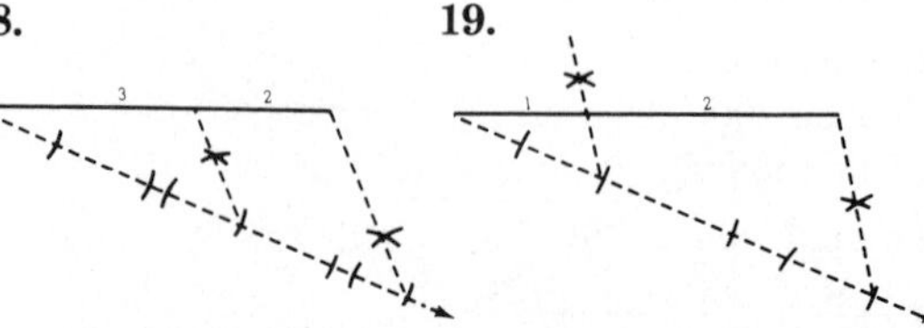

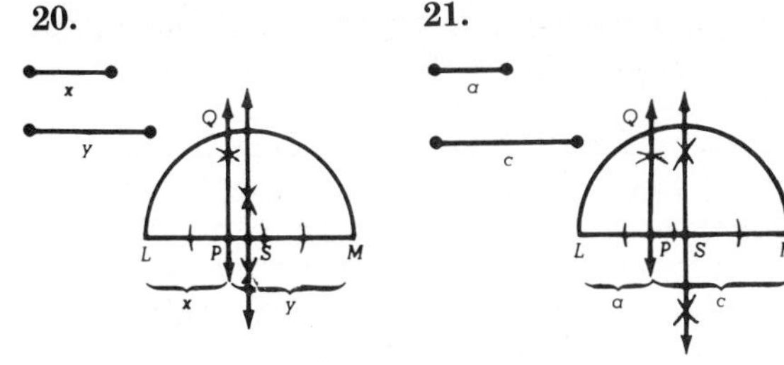

PAGE 460 EXPLORATORY

1. a circle with center C and radius of 1 mm; a sphere with center C and radius of 1 mm
2. a circle with center C and radius of 2 ft; a sphere with center C and radius of 2 ft
3. a circle with center C and radius of 3 m; a sphere with center C and radius of 3 m
4. a circle with center C and radius of 4 in.; a sphere with center C and radius of 4 in.
5. a circle with center C and radius of 40 m; a sphere with center C and radius of 40 m
6. a circle with center C and radius of 100 cm; a sphere with center C and radius of 100 cm
7. a circle with center C and radius of 1000 mm; a sphere with center C and radius of 1000 mm
8. a circle with center C and radius of x ft; a sphere with center C and radius of x ft
9. a pair of parallel lines coplanar with ℓ and each 1 inch from ℓ; a cylinder with axis ℓ and radius of 1 in.
10. a pair of parallel lines coplanar with ℓ and each 2 mm from ℓ; a cylinder with axis ℓ and radius of 2 mm
11. a pair of parallel lines coplanar with ℓ and each 3 inches from ℓ; a cylinder with axis ℓ and radius of 3 in.
12. a pair of parallel lines coplanar with ℓ and each 4 m from ℓ; a cylinder with axis ℓ and radius of 4 m
13. a pair of parallel lines coplanar with ℓ and each 40 cm from ℓ; a cylinder with axis ℓ and radius of 40 cm
14. a pair of parallel lines coplanar with ℓ and each 100 ft from ℓ; a cylinder with axis ℓ and radius of 100 ft
15. a pair of parallel lines coplanar with ℓ and each 1000 cm from ℓ; a cylinder with axis ℓ and radius of 1000 cm
16. a pair of parallel lines coplanar with ℓ and each 4 inches from ℓ; a cylinder with axis ℓ and radius of x inches

PAGE 460 WRITTEN

1.–20. Answers may vary. Samples are shown as follows.

1. a circle, concentric to the given circle, but with radius of 5 cm **2.** a circle, concentric to the given circle, with radius of 6 inches **3.** a one-inch square with diagonals collinear with the corresponding diagonals of the original square **4.** a nine-inch square with diagonals collinear with the corresponding diagonals of the original square **5.** the bisector of the angle **6.** the two perpendicular lines that contain the angle bisectors of the four angles formed by the original lines **7.** the line that is the perpendicular bisector of the segment with the given points as endpoints **8.** the line that is the perpendicular bisector of the segment with the centers of the circles as endpoints **9.** a circle, concentric to the given circle, with radius of 8 cm **10.** two circles, each concentric to the given circle, with radii of 2 cm and 8 cm **11.** a circle in the plane with the given point as its center and radius 7 inches **12.** all points on the line that is perpendicular to the given line at the given point in the plane except the given point itself **13.** all points on the bisector of the angles except the endpoint of the bisector **14.** two lines coplanar with and parallel to the given line each a distance of 15 mm from the given line **15.** all points on the line in the given plane that is the perpendicular bisector of the given base except the midpoint of the base **16.** all points in the plane that are on the circle with the given segment as a diameter except the endpoints of the given segment **17.** a cylinder with the given line as its axis and the given distance as its radius **18.** a plane perpendicular to the segment with the two given points as endpoints and passing through the midpoint of that segment **19.** two planes parallel to the given plane and each r units from the given plane **20.** all points on the line that is perpendicular to the given plane at the given point except the given point itself

PAGE 464 WRITTEN

1.–20. Answers may vary. Samples are shown as follows.

1. They may have no points of intersection; one or both lines may be tangents of the circle; one or both lines may be secants of the circle; number of

possible points of intersection: 0, 1, 2, 3, or 4 **2.** They may have no points of intersection; the line may be tangent to either circle; the line may be secant to the outer circle; the line may be secant to both circles; number of possible points of intersection: 0, 1, 2, 3, or 4 **3.** They may have no points of intersection; one or both lines may be tangent to the outer circle; one or both lines may be tangent to the inner circle; one or both lines may be secant to the outer circle; one or both lines may be secant to both circles; number of possible points of intersection as a result of all possible combinations: 0, 1, 2, 3, 4, 5, 6, or 7 **4.** They may have no points of intersection; the plane may be tangent to the sphere, or it may intersect the sphere in a circle; number of possible points of intersection: 0, 1, infinite **5.** They may have no points of intersection; one or both lines may be tangent to the sphere; one or both lines may be secant to the sphere; number of possible points of intersection: 0, 1, 2, 3, or 4 **6.** They may have no points of intersection; the circles may coincide; the circles may be tangent; the circles may intersect at two points; number of possible points of intersection: 0, 1, 2, or infinite **7.** They may have no points of intersection; they may be tangent; they may intersect in a circle; they may coincide; number of possible points of intersection: 0, 1, or infinite **8.** They may have no points of intersection; both planes may be tangent to the sphere; both planes may intersect the sphere in a circle; numbers of possible points of intersection: 0, 1, 2, 1 circle, 1 circle and 1 point, or 2 circles **9.** They may have no points of intersection; the plane may be tangent to the circle; the plane may intersect the circle at two points; the circle may lie in the plane; number of possible points of intersection: 0, 1, 2, or infinite **10.** They may have no points of intersection; the circle may lie on the sphere, the circle may intersect the sphere at two points: numbers of possible points: numbers of possible points of intersection: 0, 1, 2, or infinite **11.** The first locus is two parallel lines both coplanar with the given line and each 2 cm from the given line. The second locus is a circle with the given point as its center and radius of 5 cm. The locus of points meeting both conditions are the four points in common with the two parallel lines and the circle.
12. empty set **13.** The first locus is a cylinder with the given line as its axis with a radius of 2 in. The second locus is a sphere with the given point as the center and a radius of 5 in. The locus of points meeting both conditions is the two circles formed by the intersection of the sphere and cylinder. **14.** empty set **15.** the center of the circle determined by the three points **16.** The first locus is two parallel lines both coplanar to the given line and each the same distance away from the given line. The second locus is the perpendicular bisector in the plane of the segment joining the two given points. The locus of points meeting both conditions is the two points formed by the intersection of the two parallel lines and the perpendicular bisector. **17.** The first locus is the bisector of the given angle. The second locus is a circle in the given plane with the vertex as its center and a radius of 4 in. The locus of points meeting both conditions is a single point 4 in. from the vertex and on the bisector of the angle. **18.** Same answer as 17, but *the given distance* is substituted for *4 in.* **19.** The first locus is a line parallel to and in the same plane as the two given lines equidistant from both given lines. The second locus is two parallel lines, one in each half-plane determined by the given line, and each the same distance away from the given line. The locus of points meeting both conditions is either no points or a line, depending on whether the other line is parallel to the original two. **20.** The first locus is a line parallel to and in the same plane as the two given lines and equidistant from both given lines. The second locus is a circle with the given point as its center and with a radius of the given distance. The locus of points meeting both conditions is either zero, one, or two points depending on how the line and circle intersect.

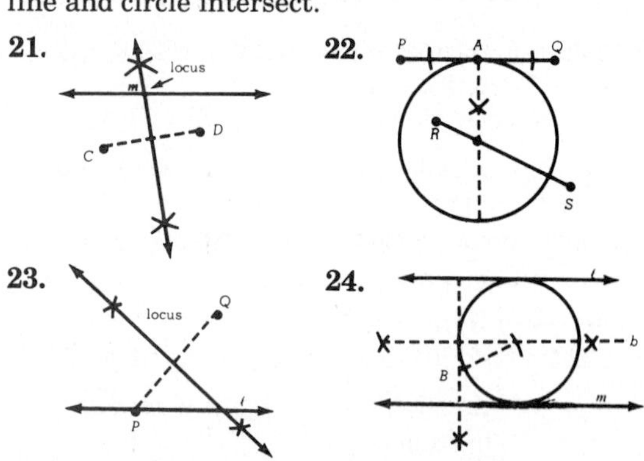

PAGE 467 CHAPTER REVIEW

1.

X W Y Z

XY ≅ WZ

The answers to exercises **2.–4.** are similar to the answer to exercise **1.**

5. 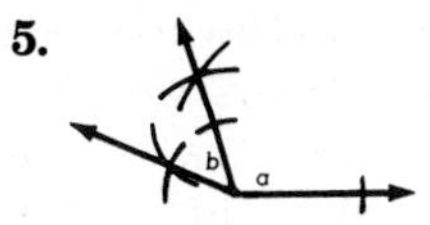

6. 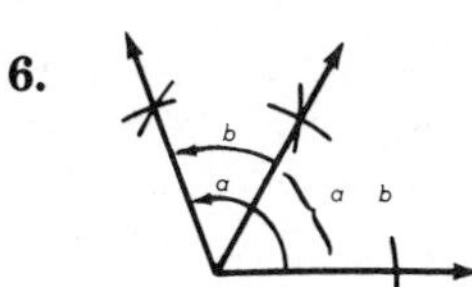

The answers to exercises **7.–8.** are similar to the answers to exercises **5–6.**

9. 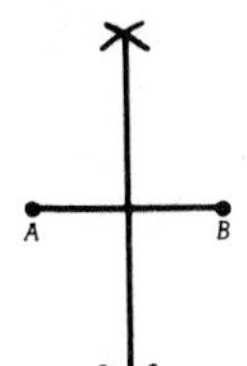

10. 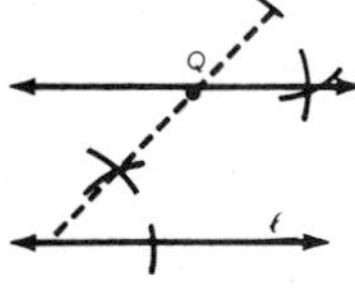

11. 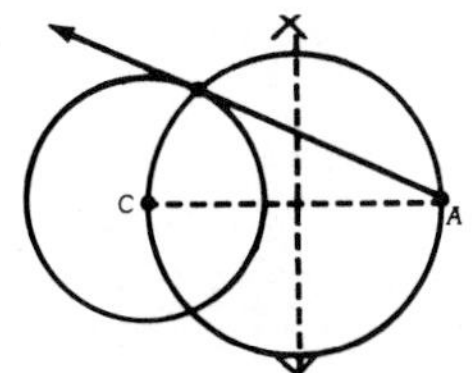

12. 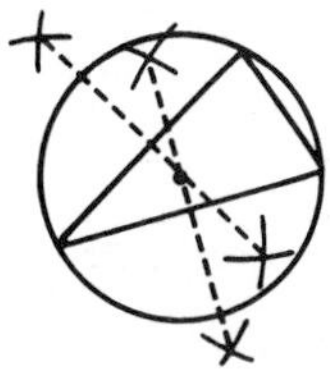

13. 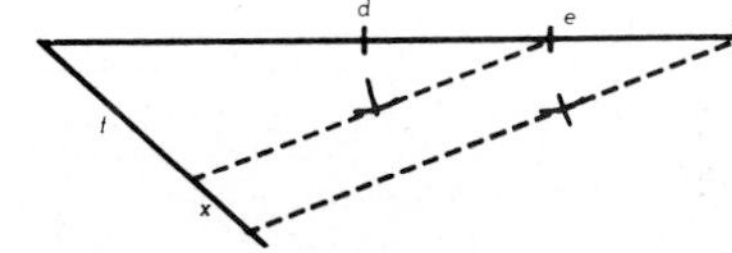

The answers to exercises **14.–16.** are similar to the answer to exercise **13.**

17. 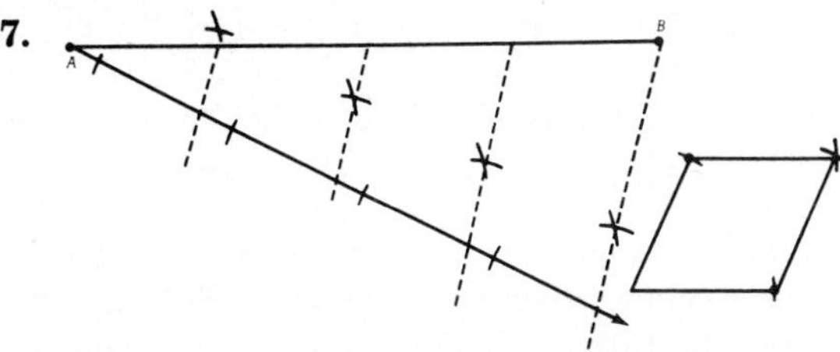

18. a circle in the plane with center C and radius 1 foot **19.** a sphere with center A and radius of 1 inch **20.** the center of the circle **21.** a circle in the plane with the given point as the center and radius of 11 cm **22.** none, one, two points, or entire circle **23.** none, one, or two points **24.** none, tangent to outer circle, tangent to inner circle, two points of outer circle, two points of each circle, both circles; thus they can intersect in 0, 1, 2, 3, 4 or infinite points **25.** none, one or both planes tangent to circle, one or both planes intersect circle at two points, the circle lies in one plane **26.** any line on a plane perpendicular to the given segment so that both the plane and the line pass through the midpoint of the segment. **27.** all points that are equidistant from both given perpendicular planes **28.**

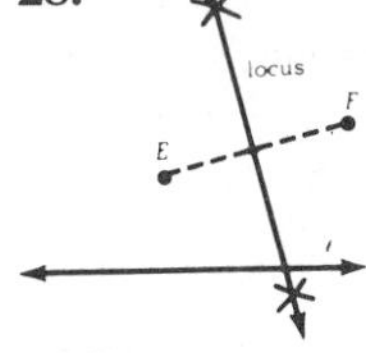

PAGE 469 CHAPTER TEST

1. 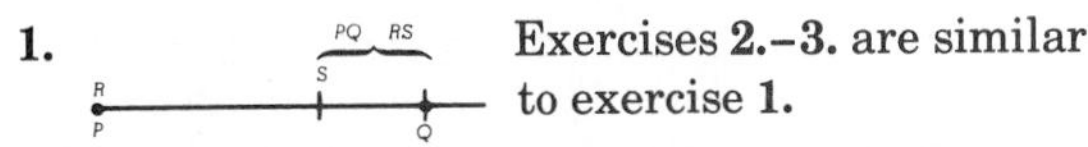

Exercises **2.–3.** are similar to exercise **1.**

4. 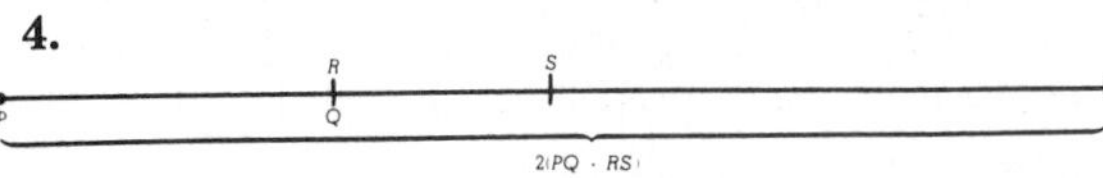

5. 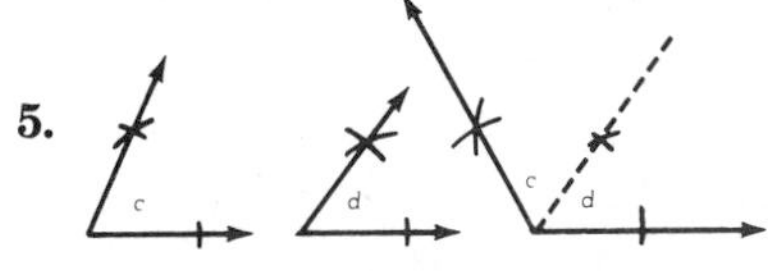

6. 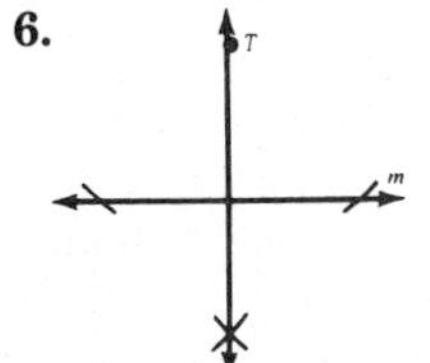

7. 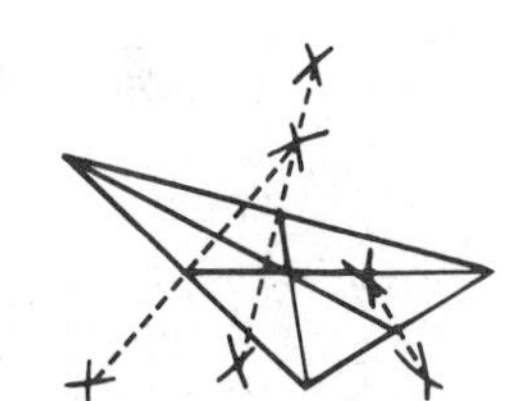

8. 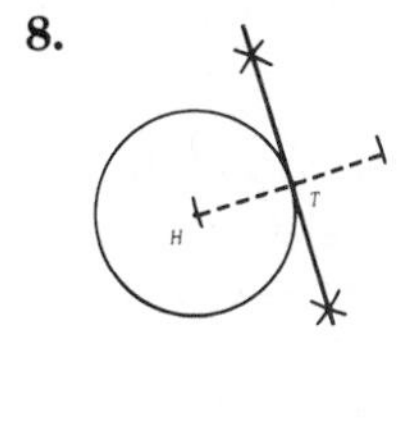

9. 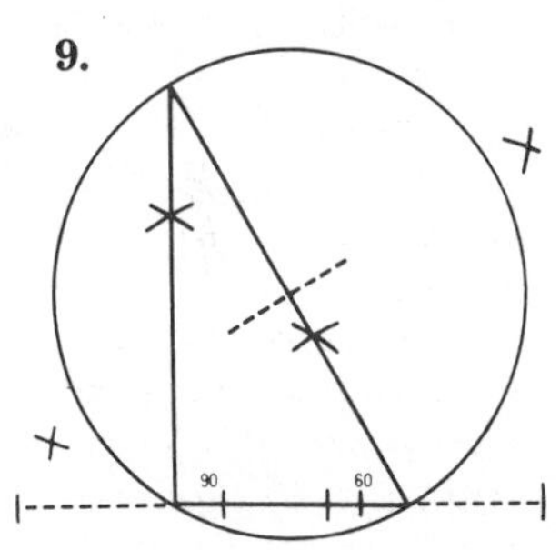

10. 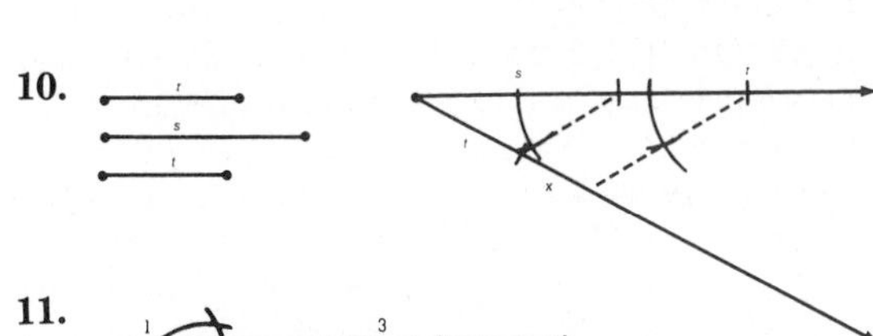

11. 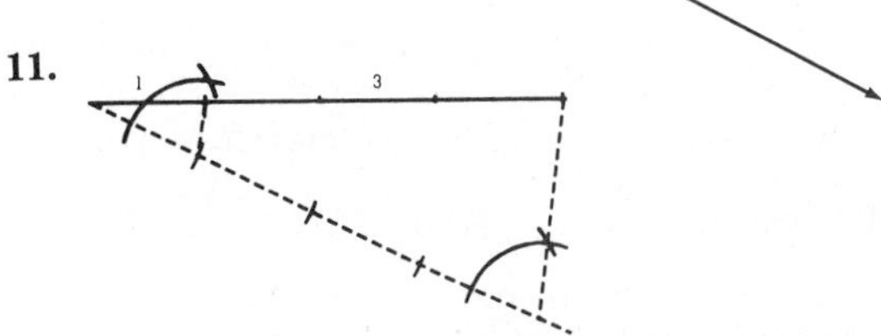

12. two parallel lines both coplanar to the given line, both parallel to the given line, and each a distance of 5 inches from the given line **13.** a circle in the given plane with center A and radius of 4 cm **14.** a sphere with center C and radius 3 m **15.** a cylinder with n as its axis and a radius of 10 feet **16.** none, the line tangent to outer sphere, the line tangent to inner sphere, the line intersecting both spheres at two points **17.** none, one or both planes tangent to the sphere, one or both planes intersecting the sphere in a circle(s) **18.** a line **19.** The first locus is a cylinder with the given line as the axis and a radius of 6 mm. The second locus is a sphere with the given points as the center and a radius of 10 mm. The locus of points satisfying both conditions is a pair of circles formed by the intersection of the cylinder and the sphere.

CHAPTER 14 TRANSFORMATIONS

PAGES 477–478 WRITTEN

1. The reflection images for exercises **2.–6.** are found in a manner similar to the image for exercise **1.**

13. The reflection images for exercises **14.–16.** are found in a manner similar to exercise **13.**

17. Exercises **18., 19., 20., 21.,** and **24.,** each have one line of symmetry. These lines are found in a manner similar to exercise **17.**

27. The points of symmetry for exercises **25., 32.,** and **34.** are found in a manner similar to exercise **27.**

PAGES 480–481 WRITTEN

7. blue to green **8.** none **9.** blue to green **10.** blue to green **11.** none **12.** blue to green **13.** green to red **14.** green to red **15.** green to red **16.** green to red **17.** none **18.** green to red

19.

20.

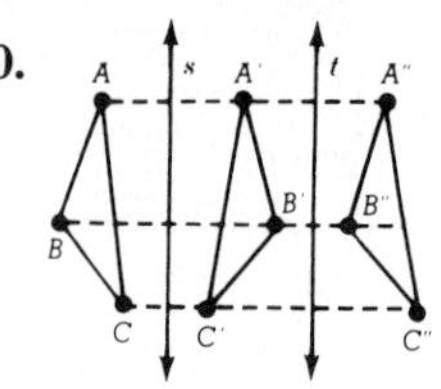

21.

22.

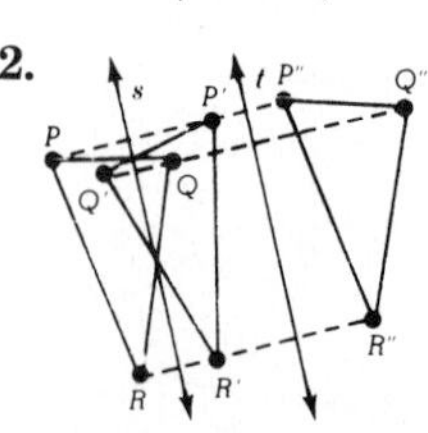

23.

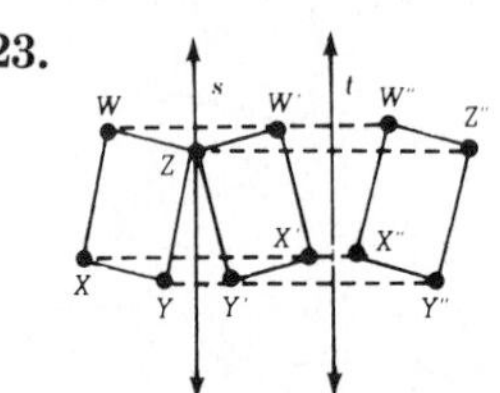

24.

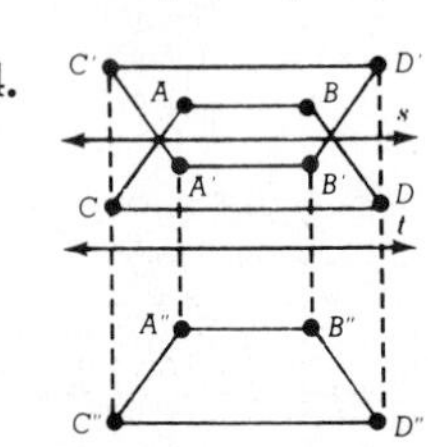

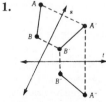

30. *Plan:* A translation is composed of two successive reflections. The first reflection with respect to ℓ preserves collinearity. The second reflection with respect to m preserves collinearity. Therefore, by transitivity, collinearity is preserved from preimage to image. **31.** *Plan:* A translation is composed of two successive reflections. The first reflection with respect to ℓ preserves betweenness of points. The second reflection with respect to m preserves betweenness of points. Therefore, by transitivity, betweenness of points is preserved from preimage to image. **32.** *Plan:* A translation is composed of two successive reflections. The first reflection with respect to ℓ preserves angle and distance measure. The second reflection with respect to m preserves angle and distance measure. Therefore, by transitivity, angle and distance measure is preserved from preimage to image.

PAGES 484–485 WRITTEN

1.

2.

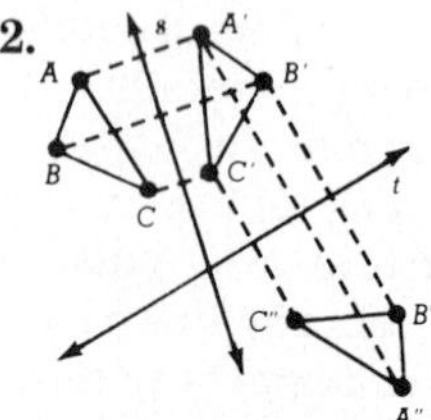

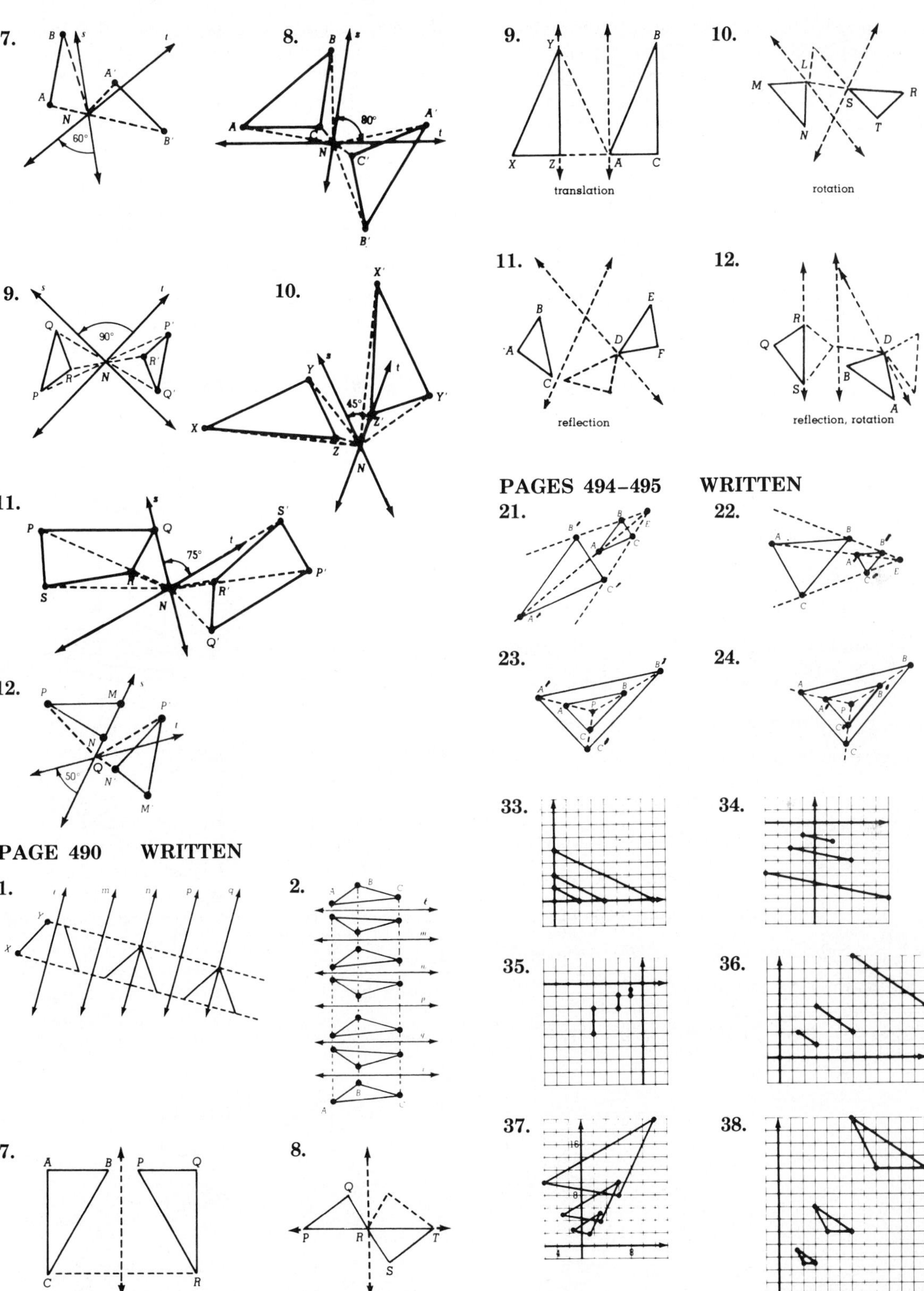
7.
8.
9.
translation
10.
rotation
9.
10.
11.
reflection
12.
reflection, rotation
11.
PAGES 494–495 WRITTEN
21.
22.
23.
24.
12.
33.
34.
PAGE 490 WRITTEN
1.
2.
35.
36.
37.
38.
7.
reflection
8.
rotation

39. 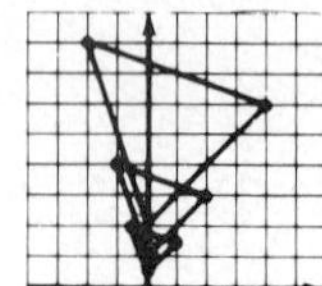

40. 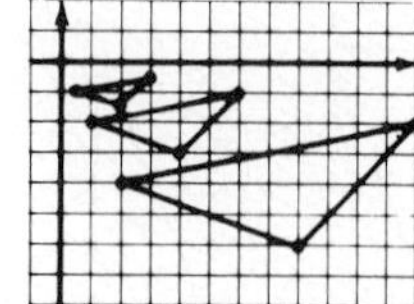

41. 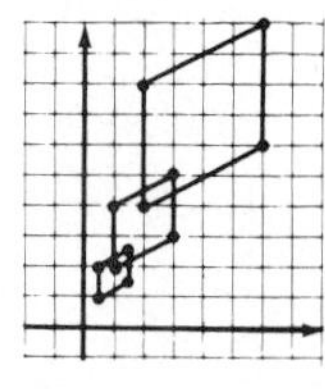

42. 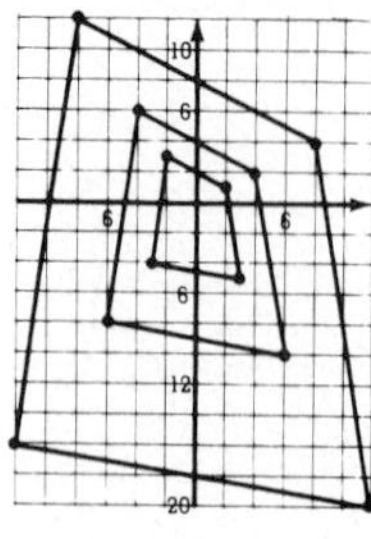

49. $\angle C \cong \angle C$ by the Reflexive Property; $CE = \frac{1}{2}CA$ and $CD = \frac{1}{2}CB$ from the Given; $\frac{CE}{CA} = \frac{1}{2}$ and $\frac{CD}{CB} = \frac{1}{2}$ by the Multiplication Property of Equality; $\triangle CED \sim \triangle CAB$ by SAS for similarity; $\frac{CE}{CA} = \frac{ED}{AB}$ by the Definition of Similar Triangles; $\frac{1}{2} = \frac{ED}{AB}$ by Substitution; $ED = \frac{1}{2}AB$ by the Multiplication Property of Equality.

50. $\angle C \cong \angle C$ by the Reflexive Property; $CE = k(CA)$ and $CD = k(CB)$ from the Given; $\frac{CE}{CA} = k$, $\frac{CD}{CB} = k$ by the Multiplication Property of Equality; $\triangle CEF \sim \triangle CAB$ by SAS for similarity; $\frac{CE}{CA} = \frac{ED}{AB}$ by the Definition of Similar Triangles; $k = \frac{ED}{AB}$ by Substitution; $ED = k(AB)$ by the Multiplication Property of Equality.

PAGES 497–498 CHAPTER REVIEW

9. 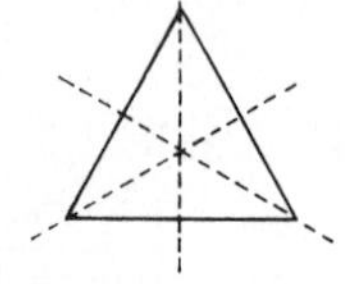

10. 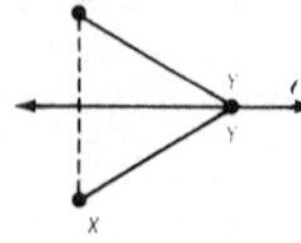

11. 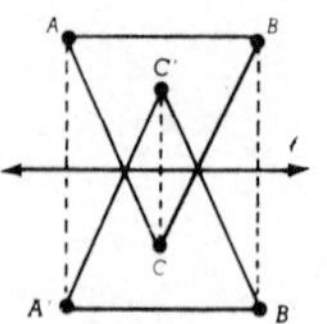

12. 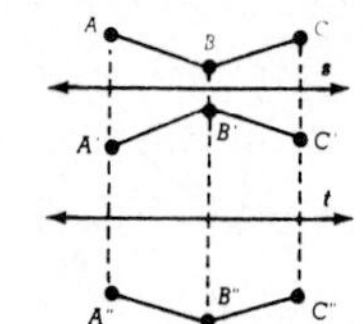

13. 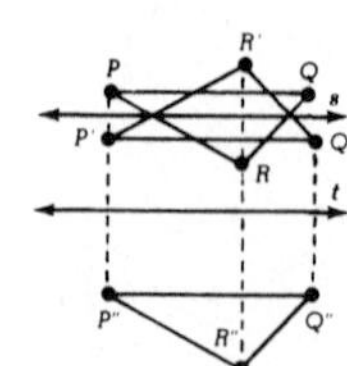

15. 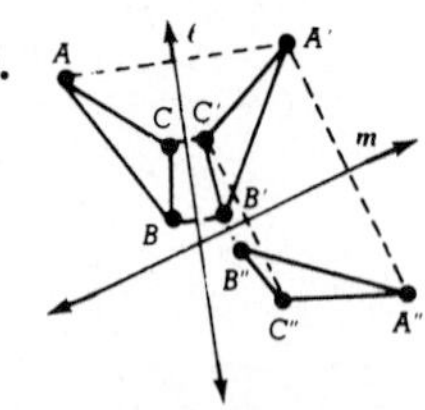

PAGE 499 CHAPTER TEST

13. 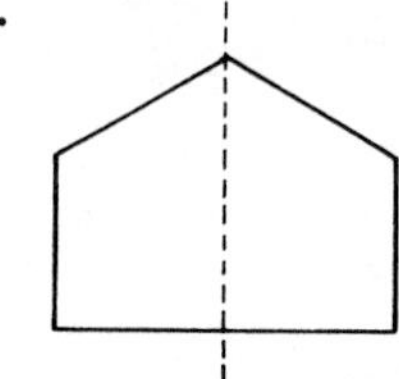

14. 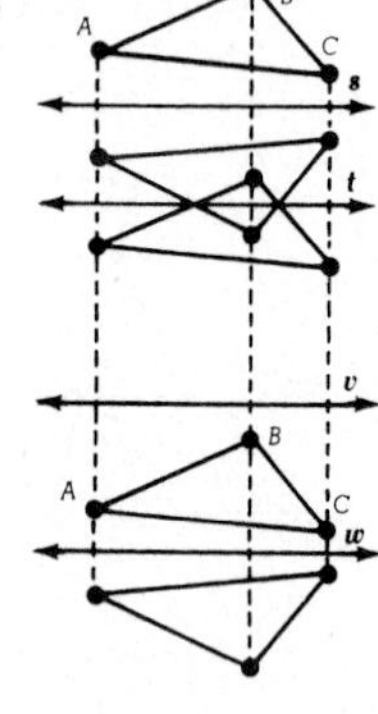

20. 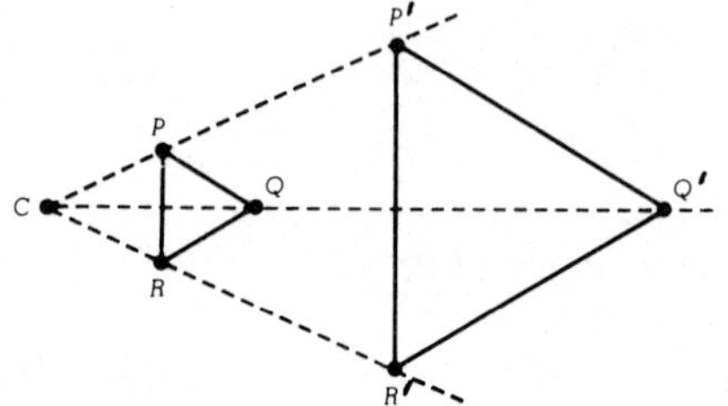

21. 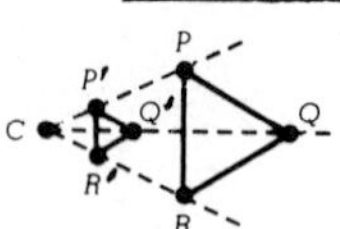

22. 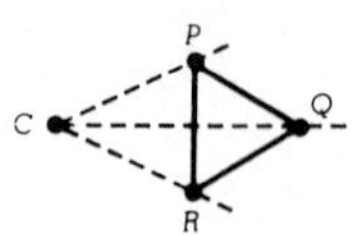

APPENDIX: BASIC

Page 503 Written

23.
```
10 READ A, B
20 DATA 5, 2
30 PRINT A^2 - B^2, (A - B)^2,
   A^2 + B^2, (A + B)^2
40 END
```

24.
```
10 READ R, PI
20 DATA 2.58, 3.14159
30 PRINT 2*PI*R, PI*R^2
40 END
```

25.
```
10 READ B, H
20 DATA 7.3, 4.8
30 PRINT B*H/2
40 END
```

26.
```
10 READ E
20 DATA 5.5
30 PRINT E^3, 6*E^2
40 END
```

27.
```
10 READ M
20 DATA 68
30 PRINT 90 - M, 180 - M
40 END
```

28.
```
10 READ A1, A2
20 DATA 48, 30
30 PRINT 180 - (A1 + A2)
40 END
```

29.
```
10 READ N
20 DATA 40
30 PRINT 180*(N - 2)
40 END
```

30.
```
10 READ A
20 DATA 168
30 PRINT 360/(180 - A)
40 END
```

31.
```
10 READ S1, S2, S3, S4, S5
20 DATA 16, 8.2, 4.3, 4.2, 4.1
30 PRINT S1 + S2 + S3 + S4 + S5
40 END
```

32.
```
10 READ B1, B2, H
20 DATA 10, 20, 6
30 PRINT H/2*(B1 + B2)
40 END
```

Pages 505-506 Written

25.
```
10 LET A = 5
20 LET B = 10
30 LET C = 4
40 LET X = 3*A + 5*B - 6*C
50 PRINT X
60 END
```

26.
```
10 LET A = 10
20 LET B = 2
30 LET C = 13
40 LET X = 3*A^2 - 4*(B + C)
50 PRINT X
60 END
```

27.
```
10 LET A = 2
20 LET B = -3
30 LET C = 11
40 LET X = A^2 - 4*B + C
50 PRINT X
60 END
```

28.
```
10 LET A = -1
20 LET B = 15
30 LET C = -4
40 LET X = (A*B)^2 - 5*C
50 PRINT X
60 END
```

29.
```
10 READ M1, M2, M3
20 DATA 1, 2, 3
30 LET C1 = 100*M1
40 LET C2 = 100*M2
50 LET C3 = 100*M3
60 PRINT C1, C2, C3
70 END
```

30.
```
10 READ N1, N2, N3, N4, N5
20 DATA 12, 254, 618, 29, 73
30 LET A = (N1 + N2 + N3 + N4 +
   N5)/5
40 PRINT A
50 END
```

31.
```
10 READ L, W
20 DATA 16, 6
30 LET P = 2*L + 2*W
40 PRINT P
50 END
```

32.
```
10 LET S = 7.5
20 LET A = S^2
30 PRINT A
40 END
```

33.
```
10 READ B, H
20 DATA 12, 5.5
30 LET A = B*H
40 PRINT A
50 END
```

34.
```
10 LET D = 14
20 LET PI = 3.14
30 LET C = PI*D
40 PRINT C
50 END
```

Consult the programming manual for your system to see how semicolons are used in PRINT statements.

35.
```
10 READ X1, Y1, X2, Y2
20 DATA 3, -6, 11, 5
30 LET MX = (X1 + X2)/2
40 LET MY = (Y1 + Y2)/2
50 PRINT "(";MX;", ";MY;")"
60 END
```

36.
```
10 READ X1, Y1, X2, Y2
20 DATA -4, 7, -1, -2
30 LET M = (Y2 - Y1)/(X2 - X1)
40 PRINT M
50 END
```

37.
```
10 LET A = 110
20 LET B = (180 - A)/2
30 PRINT B
40 END
```

38.
```
10 READ A1, A2
20 DATA 36, 98
30 LET AE = A1 + A2
40 PRINT AE
50 END
```

39.
```
10 LET N = 35
20 LET CA = 360/N
30 PRINT CA
40 END
```

40.
```
10 READ T, Q
20 DATA 3, 4
30 LET ST = (T - 2)*180
40 LET SQ = (Q - 2)*180
50 PRINT ST, SQ
60 END
```

41.
```
10 READ S, N, AP
20 DATA 6, 4, 3.5
30 LET A = 1/2*S*AP*N
40 PRINT A
50 END
```

42.
```
10 READ L, W, H
20 DATA 7.5, 4, 2.5
30 LET V = L*W*H
40 PRINT V
50 END
```

43.
```
10 READ B, P, H
20 DATA 6, 10, 10
30 LET T = P*H + 2*B
40 PRINT T
50 END
```

44.
```
10 READ R, H
20 DATA 8, 14
30 LET PI = 3.14
40 LET T = 2*PI*R*H + 2*PI*R^2
50 PRINT T
60 END
```

Pages 508-509 Written

12.
```
10 LET I = 10
20 PRINT I
30 LET I = I - 1
40 IF I > 0 THEN 20
50 END
```

13.
```
10 LET I = 1
20 LET E = 2*I
30 PRINT E
40 LET I = I + 1
50 IF E < 20 THEN 20
60 END
```

14.
```
10 READ A, B, C
20 DATA 4, 4, 4, 2, 5, 1, 4,
   7, 9, 6, 7, 20, 0, 0, 0
30 IF A = 0 THEN 110
40 IF A >= B + C THEN 90
50 IF B >= A + C THEN 90
60 IF C >= A + B THEN 90
70 PRINT A;", ";B;", ";C;" TRIANGLE
   EXISTS"
80 GOTO 10
90 PRINT A;", ";B;", ";C;" TRIANGLE
   DOESN'T EXIST"
100 GOTO 10
110 END
```

15.
```
10 READ A
20 DATA 17, 164, 39, 90, 111,
   85, 127, 45, 63, 0
30 IF A = 0 THEN 120
40 IF A < 90 THEN 80
50 IF A = 90 THEN 100
60 PRINT "OBTUSE"
70 GOTO 10
80 PRINT "ACUTE"
90 GOTO 10
100 PRINT "RIGHT"
110 GOTO10
120 END
```

16.
```
10 READ A, B
20 DATA 45, 60, 95, 20, 37,
   53, 124, 46, 90, 45, 23,
   49, 0, 0
30 IF A = 0 THEN 150
40 IF A = 90 THEN 110
45 IF B = 90 THEN 110
50 IF A > 90 THEN 130
55 IF B > 90 THEN 130
60 LET C = 180 - A - B
70 IF C = 90 THEN 110
80 IF C > 90 THEN 130
90 PRINT "ACUTE"
100 GOTO 10
110 PRINT "RIGHT"
120 GOTO 10
130 PRINT "OBTUSE"
140 GOTO 10
150 END
```

17.
```
10 READ A, B, C
20 DATA 3, 4, 5, 15, 20, 30,
   27, 36, 45, 2, 7, 9, 9, 40,
   41, 21, 28, 35, 0, 0, 0
30 IF A = 0 THEN 110
40 IF A^2 + B^2 = C^2 THEN 90
50 IF B^2 + C^2 = A^2 THEN 90
60 IF A^2 + C^2 = B^2 THEN 90
70 PRINT A;", ";B;", ";C;" IS
   NOT A RIGHT TRIANGLE"
80 GOTO 10
90 PRINT A;", ";B;", ";C;" IS
   A RIGHT TRIANGLE"
100 GOTO 10
110 END
```

18.
```
10 READ N
20 DATA 102, 43, 117, 204, 89,
   85, 155, 0
30 IF N = 0 THEN 90
40 LET M = 1
50 LET Z = 17*M
55 IF Z > 204 THEN 10
60 IF Z = N THEN 80
70 LET M = M + 1
```

```
   75 GOTO 50
   80 PRINT N;" IS A MULTIPLE OF 17"
   85 GOTO 10
   90 END
```

19.
```
   10 LET X = 1
   20 LET Y = 7*X
   30 IF Y > 500 THEN 70
   40 PRINT Y,
   50 LET X = X + 1
   60 GOTO 20
   70 END
```

20.
```
   10 LET P = 0
   15 LET X = 1
   20 LET Y = 6^X
   30 IF Y > 900000 THEN 75
   40 PRINT Y
   50 LET P = P + 1
   60 LET X = X + 1
   70 GOTO 20
   75 PRINT "THERE ARE ";P;" POWERS OF
      6 < 900000"
   80 END
```

21.
```
   10 READ X, Y
   20 DATA 1, 7, 3, 1, -1, 6, -4,
      -2, 1, 2, 4, .5, 0, 0
   30 IF X = 0 THEN 90
   40 IF 3*X + 6*Y = 15 THEN 70
   50 PRINT "(";X;", ";Y;") IS NOT
      ON THE LINE"
   60 GOTO 10
   70 PRINT "(";X;", ";Y;") IS ON
      THE LINE"
   80 GOTO 10
   90 END
```

22.
```
   10 READ X1, Y1, X2, Y2
   20 DATA 3, 5, 7, 6, 2, 1, 2, 6,
      -3, 4, 3, 8, -1, 7, 7, 7, -2,
      -10, 2, 10, 0, 0, 0, 0
   30 IF X1 = 0 THEN 90
   40 IF X2 - X1 = 0 THEN 70
   50 PRINT "SLOPE IS DEFINED"
   60 GOTO 10
   70 PRINT "SLOPE IS NOT DEFINED"
   80 GOTO 10
   90 END
```

23.
```
   10 READ N
   20 DATA 16, -90, 45, 6, 13, -42,
      -8, 0
   30 IF N = 0 THEN 120
   40 IF N > 10 THEN 80
   50 IF N < -10 THEN 100
   60 PRINT N
   70 GOTO 10
   80 PRINT N, N^2
   90 GOTO 10
  100 PRINT N, N^3
  110 GOTO 10
  120 END
```

24.
```
   10 READ A, B, C, D
   20 DATA 3, -7, 8, 5, -10, 25, 0,
      6, -1, -6, -11, -2, -5, 8, 4,
      13, 0, 0, 0, 0
   30 IF A = 0 THEN 130
   40 LET X = A
   50 IF X > B THEN 70
   60 LET X = B
   70 IF X > C THEN 90
   80 LET X = C
   90 IF X > D THEN 110
  100 LET X = D
  110 PRINT X
  120 GOTO 10
  130 END
```

25.
```
   10 READ A, B, C
   20 DATA 2, 1, 5, -3, 6, -7, 0, 10,
      6, 25, -4, 13, 21, -30, 2, 0,
      0, 0
   30 IF A + B = 0 THEN 160
   40 IF A < B THEN 90
   50 LET X = A
   60 LET A = B
   70 LET B = X
   80 IF B < C THEN 140
   90 LET X = B
  100 LET B = C
  110 LET C = X
  120 GOTO 40
  130 PRINT A, B, C
  140 GOTO 10
  150 END
```

Page 512 Written

1.
```
   10 FOR K = 1 TO 16 STEP 1
   20 PRINT K
   30 NEXT K
   40 END
```

2.
```
   10 FOR M = 3 TO 25 STEP 2
   20 PRINT M
   30 NEXT M
   40 END
```

3.
```
   10 LET X = 4
   20 FOR T = 1 TO 40 STEP 3
   30 PRINT T
   40 NEXT T
   50 END
```

4.
```
   10 FOR X = 1 TO 6 STEP 3
   20 FOR Y = 2 TO 44 STEP 2
   30 PRINT X*Y
   40 NEXT Y
   50 NEXT X
   60 END
```

8.
```
   INTEGER 10      SQUARE 100
   INTEGER 20      SQUARE 400
   INTEGER 30      SQUARE 900
   INTEGER 40      SQUARE 1600
   INTEGER 50      SQUARE 2500
   INTEGER 60      SQUARE 3600
   INTEGER 70      SQUARE 4900
   INTEGER 80      SQUARE 6400
   INTEGER 90      SQUARE 8100
   INTEGER 100     SQUARE 10000
```

9.
```
   10 LET S = 0
   20 FOR I = 1 TO 20
   30 LET C = I^3
   40 LET S = S + C
   50 NEXT I
   60 PRINT S
   70 END
```

```
10. 10 PRINT "ANGLE", "COMPLEMENT"
    20 FOR I = 0 TO 90 STEP 5
    30 LET C = 90 - I
    40 PRINT I, C
    50 NEXT I
    60 END

11. 10 FOR X = -3 TO 3
    20 LET Y = X^2 - X + 6
    30 PRINT "FOR X = ";X;", Y = ";Y
    40 NEXT X
    50 END

12. 10 PRINT "FAHRENHEIT", "CELSIUS"
    20 FOR F = 0 TO 100 STEP 2
    30 LET C = 5/9*(F - 32)
    40 PRINT F, C
    50 NEXT F
    60 END

13. 10 PRINT "LENGTH", "WIDTH",
       "PERIMETER", "AREA"
    20 FOR I = 1 TO 3
    30 READ L, W
    40 DATA 8, 5, 9.2, 3.4, 17, 18
    50 LET P = 2*L + 2*W
    60 LET A = L*W
    70 PRINT L, W, P, A
    80 NEXT I
    90 END

14. 10 FOR I = 1 TO 3
    20 READ X1, Y1, X2, Y2
    30 DATA 2, 5, 4, -6, 7, 8, -9,
       5, 4, 2.8, 3.6, -2.1
    40 LET M = (Y2 - Y1)/(X2 - X1)
    50 PRINT "THE SLOPE IS "; M
    60 NEXT I
    70 END

15. 10 PRINT "SIDES", "DIAGONALS"
    20 FOR N = 3 TO 25
    30 LET D = N*(N - 3)/2
    40 PRINT N, D
    50 NEXT N
    60 END

16. 10 PRINT "SIDES", "SUM OF ANGLES"
    20 FOR N = 3 TO 50
    30 LET S = (N - 2)*180
    40 PRINT N, S
    50 NEXT N
    60 END

17. 10 FOR A = 1 TO 20
    20 LET V = 2*3.14*A*(400 - A^2)
    30 PRINT A, V
    40 NEXT A
    50 END
```

Page 516 Written

```
 9. 10 PRINT "NUMBER", "ABSOLUTE VALUE"
    20 FOR I = 1 TO 5
    30 READ N
    40 DATA -2, 4.761, 0, -.11, 7.999
    50 PRINT N, ABS(N)
    60 NEXT I
    70 END

10. 10 FOR I = 1 TO 5
    20 READ N
    30 DATA 2, 4.761, 0, -3, 8
    40 IF N >= 0 THEN 60
    50 PRINT "THE SQUARE ROOT OF ";N;
       " DOESN'T EXIST"
    55 GOTO 70
    60 PRINT "THE SQUARE ROOT OF ";N;
       " IS ";SQR(N)
    70 NEXT I
    80 END

11. 10 LET S = 0
    20 FOR I = 1 TO 10
    30 LET X = INT(SQR(I))
    40 LET S = S + X
    50 NEXT I
    60 PRINT "THE SUM IS ";S
    70 END

12. 10 LET S = 0
    20 FOR I = 1 TO 10
    30 LET X = SQR(I)
    40 LET S = S + X
    50 NEXT I
    60 PRINT "THE SUM IS ";INT(S)
    70 END

13. 10 FOR I = 1 TO 6
    20 READ N
    30 DATA -6, -5, -1, 0, 2, 9
    40 IF N/2 <> INT(N/2) THEN 70
    50 PRINT N;" IS EVEN"
    60 GOTO 80
    70 PRINT N;" IS ODD"
    80 NEXT I
    90 END

14. 10 PRINT "LEG", "LEG", "HYPOTENUSE"
    20 FOR I = 1 TO 4
    30 READ A, B
    40 DATA 3, 4, 8, 15, 4, 4, 9, 10
    50 LET C = SQR(A^2 + B^2)
    60 PRINT A, B, C
    70 NEXT I
    80 END

15. 10 FOR I = 1 TO 2
    20 READ X1, Y1, X2, Y2
    30 DATA 1, 5, -7, 2, 2, -2.5,
       -11.7, -1
    40 LET D = SQR((X2 - X1)^2 +
       (Y2 - Y1)^2)
    50 PRINT D
    60 NEXT I
    70 END

16. 10 FOR I = 1 TO 3
    20 READ A, B, C
    30 DATA 4, 5, 7, 9, 40, 41, 20,
       21, 29
    40 IF C = SQR(A^2 + B^2) THEN 70
    50 PRINT A;", ";B;", ";C;" IS NOT A
       RIGHT TRIANGLE"
    60 GOTO 80
    70 PRINT A;", ";B;", ";C;" IS A
       RIGHT TRIANGLE"
    80 NEXT I
    90 END
```

2 3 4 5 6 7 8 9 10 11 12 13 14 15 — 89 88 87 86 85 84 83

Merrill
Geometry

Foster • Cummins • Yunker

Charles E. Merrill Publishing Co.
A Bell & Howell Company
Columbus, Ohio

Toronto • London • Sydney

About the Cover

The cover photograph shows a sculpture, "The Eagle" by Alexander Calder. This structure is made of structural steel and weighs 16 tons. It is located in front of the Texas American Bank Building in Fort Worth, Texas.

The photographer was Leo Touchet/Woodfin Camp & Associates.

ISBN 0-675-05219-X

ISBN 0-675-05218-1

Published by
Charles E. Merrill Publishing Co.
A Bell & Howell Company
Columbus, Ohio 43216

Printed in the United States of America

Authors

Alan G. Foster is head of the Mathematics Department at Addison Trail High School, Addison Illinois. He has taught mathematics courses at every level of the high school curriculum. Mr. Foster obtained his B.S. from Illinois State University and his M.A. in mathematics from the University of Illinois, with additional work at Northern Illinois University, Purdue, Northwestern, and Princeton. Mr. Foster is active in professional organizations at local, state, and national levels, frequently speaking or conducting workshops. He is a past president of the Illinois Council of Teachers of Mathematics. Mr. Foster is co-author of *Merrill Algebra One* and *Merrill Algebra Two*.

Jerry J. Cummins is head of the Mathematics Department at Proviso West High School, Hillside, Illinois. In addition to teaching experience at a junior high school and community college, he has taught mathematics courses at every level of the high school curriculum. Mr. Cummins obtained a B.S. in mathematics education and an M.S. in educational administration and supervision from Southern Illinois University. He also holds an M.S. in mathematics education from the University of Oregon. He has done additional graduate work at the Illinois Institute of Technology. Mr. Cummins has spoken on mathematics at the local, state, and national levels. He is past president of the Metropolitan Mathematics Club of Chicago and a past president of the Illinois Council of Teachers of Mathematics. Mr. Cummins is co-author of Merrill's *Programming in BASIC*.

Lee E. Yunker is head of the Mathematics Department at West Chicago Community High School, West Chicago, Illinois. He has taught mathematics courses at every level of the high school curriculum. Mr. Yunker obtained his B.S. from Elmhurst College and his M.Ed. in mathematics from the University of Illinois, with additional graduate work at the University of Illinois, Northwestern University, University of Montana, Northern Illinois University, and National College of Education. Mr. Yunker is very active in professional mathematics organizations at the local, state, and national levels frequently speaking or conducting workshops on a variety of topics. Mr. Yunker is a recipient of the Illinois Council of Teachers of Mathematics T.E. Rine Award for outstanding service and leadership to mathematics education. He is a co-author of *Merrill Advanced Mathematical Concepts*.

Consultants

Dr. Ralph Winston Cain
Associate Professor
Departments of Mathematics and Curriculum and Instruction
University of Texas
Austin, Texas

Dr. John Kenelly
Professor of Mathematical Sciences
Clemson University
Clemson, South Carolina

Reviewers

Karen Ardner
Mathematics Department Chairperson
Waite High School
Toledo, Ohio

Johanna L. Brown
Mathematics Department Chairperson
Swartz Creek Middle School
Swartz Creek, Michigan

Maureen A. Lister
Mathematics Teacher
Central High School
Providence, Rhode Island

James G. McGinnis
Mathematics/Science Teacher
Booker T. Washington High School
Tulsa, Oklahoma

Michael E. Mooberry
Mathematics Teacher
Lindbergh Junior High School
Long Beach, California

R. T. Mosman
Department Chairperson
South Salem High School
Salem, Oregon

Gloria H. Tuggle
Instructional Consultant, Mathematics
Memphis City Schools
Memphis, Tennessee

Frank Vigario
Mathematics Department Chairperson
Redwood High School
Visalia, California

Staff

Editorial
Project Editor: Cynthia Zengler
Assistant Project Editor: Jack Witherspoon
Assistant Editors: Cynthia Lindsay, Michael H. Thorne
Annamaria J. Doney
Photo Editor: Sue Marquart

Art
Project Artist: Dotte Turner Russell
Book Designer: Michael T. Henry
Illustrators: Lorraine Hitesman, James Hubbard
Artists: Lynn Norton, M. Lisy Boren

Photo Credits

xii, Hale Observatories; **1,** Gerard Photography; **9,** Allen Zak; **10,** Reprinted with permission of Ralston Purina Co., St. Louis, Mo.; **18,** Photo supplied by Dick Ruhl (APRO) Aerial Phenomena Research Org. Inc., Tucson, Ariz./N.Y.; **34,** Hickson-Bender Photography; **39,** Gerard Photography; **43,** IBM; **53,** Gerard Photography; **66,** Gerard Photography; **67,** Advertising Image Photography; **91,** Advertising Image Photography; **102,** Larry Hamill; **103,** L. D. Franga; **111,** Elaine Comer; **140,** William D. McKinney/FPG; **151,** Frank Balthis; **156,** Doug Martin; **170,** L. D. Franga; **171,** Roger Burnard; **181,** Tim Courlas; **185,** U.S. Bureau of Reclamation; **191,** Union Carbide Corporation; **195,** Tim Courlas; **206,** © Manley Photo/Shostal Associates; **216,** Larry Hamill; **229** top, Grumman Corp.; **229** bottom, Smithsonian Institution photo by Dane Penland; **230,** Kevin Roche, John Dinkeloo and Assoc.; **237,** Tim Courlas; **248,** Tim Courlas; **249,** Bill Barr for the Kansas City Kings; **253, 255,** File Photos; **258,** Doug Martin; **262,** Courtesy of General American Transportation Corporation, Chicago; **268,** David Germon; **286,** Advertising Image Photography; **306,** Eric Hoffhines; **312,** U.S. Forest Service; **322,** Roger Burnard; **323,** Photo courtesy of DEKALB AgResearch, Inc.; **328,** Russ Lappa; **352,** Dan McCoy/Rainbow; **355,** Tim Courlas; **362,** Tracy Borland; **363,** Advertising Image Photography; **391,** EPA Documerica; **396,** Jerry Bowling; **399,** Joey Jacques; **404,** George Schwartz/FPG; **423,** Jim Pickerell: Click/Chicago Ltd.; **430,** Camilla Smith/Rainbow; **442,** Doug Martin; **457,** Patty Jedick; **470,** Keith Turpie; **479,** Frank Lerner; **486,** Gerard Photography; **491** top, Doug Martin; **491** center, Fig. 4, Photos by Doug Martin, courtesy of MicroCenter, Columbus, Oh.; Fig. 1, 2, 3, 5 Reprinted from the MATHEMATICS TEACHER (vol. 75, pp. 16–19), © 1981 by the National Council of Teachers of Mathematics. Used by permission; **492,** Elaine Comer; **495,** File Photo; **500,** Tim Courlas.

Preface

Merrill Geometry was developed by experienced high school teachers for the classroom. Its goals are to develop student proficiency with geometric skills and to expand understanding of geometric concepts. This text promotes success, improves logical reasoning, and provides a complete course in high school geometry. To achieve these goals the following strategies are used.

Build a Solid Foundation. Geometric concepts are introduced intuitively by drawing upon students' past experience with geometry in real life. Students learn to organize their ideas and gradually are led to the concept of geometric proof. Once the needed background is built, students can progress successfully.

Utilize Sound Pedagogy. *Merrill Geometry* covers in logical sequence all topics generally presented at this level. Each concept presented is then used within that lesson and in later lessons. Concepts are introduced as they are needed.

Facilitate Learning. An appropriate reading level and a concise format make the text easy for students to read and use. Furthermore, many appealing photographs, illustrations, charts, graphs, and tables help students visualize the ideas presented.

Use Relevant, Real-Life Applications. Applications provide motivation by showing the practical value of concepts and the ways geometry prepares students for the future.

Merrill Geometry offers a variety of useful aids for the student studying geometry.

Student Annotations Help students to identify important concepts as they study.

Selected Answers Allow students to check their progress as they work. These answers are provided in the back of the book.

Vocabulary Lists Provide students with a list of important mathematical words.

Chapter Summaries Provide students with a listing of major concepts presented within each chapter.

Chapter Reviews Permit students to review each chapter by working sample problems from each lesson.

Chapter Tests Enable students to check their progress.

Cumulative Reviews Help students to maintain and reinforce geometric concepts.

Postulates and Theorems List Provide students with a listing of the postulates and theorems used in the text.

The following special features, which appear periodically throughout the text, provide interesting and useful extra topics.

Careers Depict a variety of people in different careers using mathematics. These features provide career alternatives that students may pursue.

Topics in Geometry Provide information concerning different approaches to geometry such as topology and elliptic geometry.

Algebra Reviews Help students to maintain and use algebraic concepts.

Calculators Instruct students in using a calculator.

Computers Provide information concerning both the historical background of computers and current uses of computers.

Excursions in Geometry Enliven and help maintain student interest by providing interesting side trips. Topics are varied and include glimpses into the development and uses of geometry as well as puzzles, games, and history.

BASIC Instructs students in writing programs using the BASIC computer language. This feature, provided in the Appendix, can be taught as a unit or interspersed throughout the year.

Students will find the practical, straightforward approach of *Merrill Geometry* both interesting and easy to understand. Teachers will find that the careful sequencing of topics and thorough mathematical treatment of essential ideas provide an effective course in high school geometry.

Contents

Points, Lines, and Planes — xii

1

LESSONS
1–1 Points, Lines, and Planes 1 **1–2** Definitions 5
1–3 Conditional Statements 10 **1–4** Postulates 14
1–5 Theorems 18 **1–6** Writing Proofs 22 **1–7** Inverses and Contrapositives 27

REVIEW AND TEST
Vocabulary 30 Chapter Summary 30 Chapter Review 31
Chapter Test 33

FEATURES
Excursions in Geometry: Apples and Oranges 4 Careers: Paralegal Aide 9 Calculators: Basic Functions 17 Topics in Geometry: Finite Geometry 26

Measure — 34

2

LESSONS
2–1 Number Lines 35 **2–2** Distance 39 **2–3** Segments 44
2–4 Properties of the Real Number System 48 **2–5** Congruent Segments 54 **2–6** Properties of Inequalities 58

REVIEW AND TEST
Vocabulary 61 Chapter Summary 61 Chapter Review 63
Chapter Test 65

FEATURES
Algebra Review: Percents 42 Computers: History of Computers 43
Excursions in Geometry: Length in the Metric System 47 Careers: Carpet Installer 53 Excursions in Geometry: Significant Digits 57

Angles and Perpendiculars 66

3

LESSONS
3–1 Rays and Angles 67 **3–2** Measuring Angles 71 **3–3** Pairs of Angles 76 **3–4** Right Angles 81 **3–5** Perpendiculars 86 **3–6** Perpendicular Planes 90

REVIEW AND TEST
Vocabulary 95 Chapter Summary 95 Chapter Review 97 Chapter Test 99 Cumulative Review 100

FEATURES
Excursions in Geometry: Radian Measure 75 Topics in Geometry: Flow Proofs 80 Calculators: Memory 85 Careers: Rescuer 94

Congruent Triangles 102

4

LESSONS
4–1 Triangles 103 **4–2** Angle Measures 107 **4–3** Congruence 112 **4–4** Tests for Congruence 116 **4–5** More Tests for Congruence 121 **4–6** Medians, Altitudes, and Bisectors 125 **4–7** Isosceles Triangles 129 **4–8** Right Triangles 133

REVIEW AND TEST
Vocabulary 136 Chapter Summary 136 Chapter Review 137 Chapter Test 139

FEATURES
Careers: Navigator 111 Excursions in Geometry: Seeing Patterns 120 Algebra Review: Prime Factorization 124 Computers: Input Equipment 128

Triangle Inequalities 140

5

LESSONS
5–1 Exterior Angles 141 **5–2** Using Diagrams 146 **5–3** Sides and Angles 152 **5–4** The Triangle Inequality 156 **5–5** The Hinge Theorem 160

REVIEW AND TEST
Vocabulary 166 Chapter Summary 166 Chapter Review 167 Chapter Test 169

FEATURES
Careers: Architect 151 Excursions in Geometry: Closed Curves 155 Excursions in Geometry: Triangles 164 Topics in Geometry: Projective Geometry 165

Parallels — 170

LESSONS
6–1 Parallels and Transversals 171 **6–2** Indirect Proof 176
6–3 Testing for Parallel Lines 181 **6–4** The Parallel Postulate 186
6–5 Using Parallels 191 **6–6** Distance 195

REVIEW AND TEST
Vocabulary 200 Chapter Summary 200 Chapter Review 201
Chapter Test 203 Cumulative Review 204

FEATURES
Algebra Review: Factoring 175 Excursions in Geometry: Classifying Ideas 180 Career: Soil Scientist 185 Computers: Computer Languages 190 Excursions in Geometry: Contradictions 199

Polygons — 206

7

LESSONS
7–1 Classifying Polygons 207 **7–2** Angles of Polygons 211
7–3 Parallelograms 216 **7–4** Tests for Parallelograms 220
7–5 Special Parallelograms 224 **7–6** Trapezoids 230
7–7 Perimeter 236 **7–8** Solids 240

REVIEW AND TEST
Vocabulary 243 Chapter Summary 243 Chapter Review 245
Chapter Test 247

FEATURES
Calculators: Finding Roots 215 Excursions in Geometry: Loops 219
Careers: Mineralogist 229 Topics in Geometry: Hyperbolic Geometry 235

Similarity — 248

LESSONS
8–1 Ratios and Proportions 249 **8–2** Properties of Proportions 254 **8–3** Similar Polygons 258 **8–4** Similar Triangles 263 **8–5** Proportional Parts 267 **8–6** Parts of Similar Polygons 272 **8–7** Using Similarity 276

REVIEW AND TEST
Vocabulary 281 Chapter Summary 281 Chapter Review 283
Chapter Test 285

FEATURES
Algebra Review: Factoring Equations 252 Careers: Advertising Designer 253 Excursions in Geometry: Pentagram 257

Right Triangles 9 — 286

LESSONS
9–1 Square Roots 287 **9–2** The Geometric Mean 291 **9–3** The Pythagorean Theorem 295 **9–4** Special Right Triangles 299 **9–5** Trigonometry 303 **9–6** Trigonometric Tables 307 **9–7** Using Trigonometry 311

REVIEW AND TEST
Vocabulary 316 Chapter Summary 316 Chapter Review 317 Chapter Test 319 Cumulative Review 320

FEATURES
Excursions in Geometry: Heron's Formula 302 Careers: Recreation Supervisor 306 Calculators: The Exponential Shift Key 310 Topics in Geometry: Elliptic Geometry 315

Circles and Spheres 10 — 322

LESSONS
10–1 Parts of Circles 323 **10–2** Angles and Arcs 327 **10–3** Arcs and Chords 331 **10–4** Inscribed Angles 335 **10–5** Tangents 340 **10–6** Measuring Angles 344 **10–7** Segments 348 **10–8** Spheres 353

REVIEW AND TEST
Vocabulary 357 Chapter Summary 357 Chapter Review 359 Chapter Test 361

FEATURES
Excursions in Geometry: Centers of Circles 326 Algebra Review: Radical Equations 330 Computers: Uses in Transportation 339 Careers: Seismologist 352

Area and Volume 11 — 362

LESSONS
11–1 Defining Area 363 **11–2** Area Formulas 367 **11–3** Regular Polygons 371 **11–4** Circles 376 **11–5** Surface Area 381 **11–6** More about Surface Area 387 **11–7** Defining Volume 391 **11–8** More about Volume 395

REVIEW AND TEST
Vocabulary 400 Chapter Summary 400 Chapter Review 401 Chapter Test 403

FEATURES
Excursions in Geometry: Pick's Theorem 366 Calculators: Trigonometric Functions 375 Excursions in Geometry: Drawing Figures 380 Topics in Geometry: Topology 386 Careers: Scuba Diving 399

Coordinates 404

12

LESSONS
12–1 Graphing 405 **12–2** Distances and Midpoints 409
12–3 Slope 413 **12–4** Equations for a Line 417 **12–5** Systems of Equations 420 **12–6** Circles 423 **12–7** Coordinate Proofs 426
12–8 Coordinates in Space 431

REVIEW AND TEST
Vocabulary 435 Chapter Summary 435 Chapter Review 436
Chapter Test 439 Cumulative Review 440

FEATURES
Excursions in Geometry: Creative Blocks 408 Computers: Uses in Banking 412 Algebra Review: Quadratic Formula 422 Careers: Drafter 430

Loci and Constructions 442

13

LESSONS
13–1 Basic Constructions 443 **13–2** Perpendiculars and Parallels 447
13–3 Circles 451 **13–4** Proportions 454 **13–5** Loci 458
13–6 Intersection of Loci 462

REVIEW AND TEST
Vocabulary 466 Chapter Summary 466 Chapter Review 467
Chapter Test 469

FEATURES
Careers: Carpenter 457 Topics in Geometry: Vectors 461 Calculators: [K] or Constant Key 465

Transformations 470

14

LESSONS
14–1 Mappings 471 **14–2** Reflections 474 **14–3** Translations 479
14–4 Rotations 482 **14–5** Composites 486 **14–6** Dilations 492

REVIEW AND TEST
Vocabulary 496 Chapter Summary 496 Chapter Review 497
Chapter Test 499

FEATURES
Computers: Futurists 473 Careers: Urban Designers 491 Excursions in Geometry: Transformations in Art and Nature 495

Appendix: BASIC 500

The Language of BASIC 501 Assignment of Variables 504 IF-THEN Statements 507 FOR-NEXT Loops 510 BASIC Functions 514

Diagnostic Skills Review 517

Symbols 535

Postulates and Theorems 536

Squares and Approximate Square Roots 548

Trigonometric Ratios 549

Glossary 550

Index 562

Selected Answers 570

chapter 1 Points, Lines, and Planes

In geometry, figures are used as models for real life phenomena. For example, a point is a model for the position of a star.

1–1 Points, Lines, and Planes

Objectives: to recognize and identify points, lines, and planes

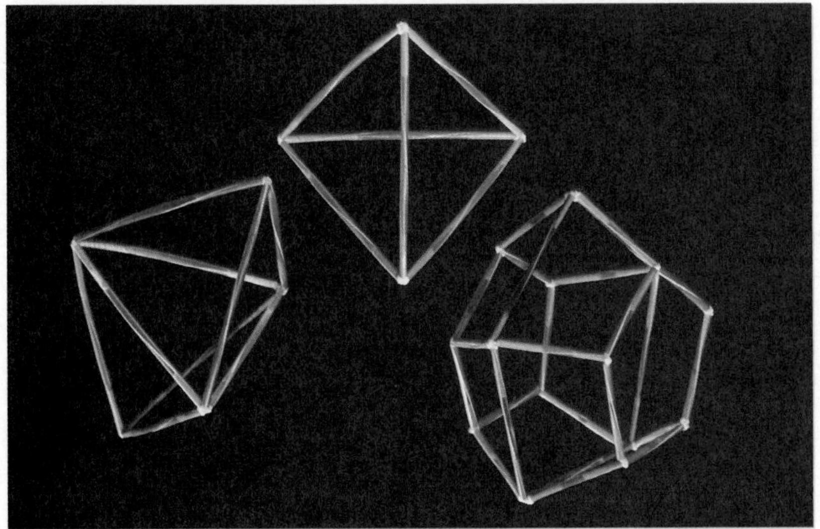

Points, lines, and **planes** are used in many ways. They are the basic terms of geometry.

Physical models of the concepts, including intersecting lines and planes, enhance discussion.

A location or a pinhole suggests the idea of a point. Points have no dimensions. Points are represented by dots and named by capital letters.

B
point *B*

A
point *A*

A point has no dimension.

C
point *C*

A flight path or a taut wire suggests the idea of a line. Lines extend indefinitely and have no thickness or width. Lines are represented by double arrows and named by lowercase letters. A line also can be named using double arrows over capital letters representing two points on the line.

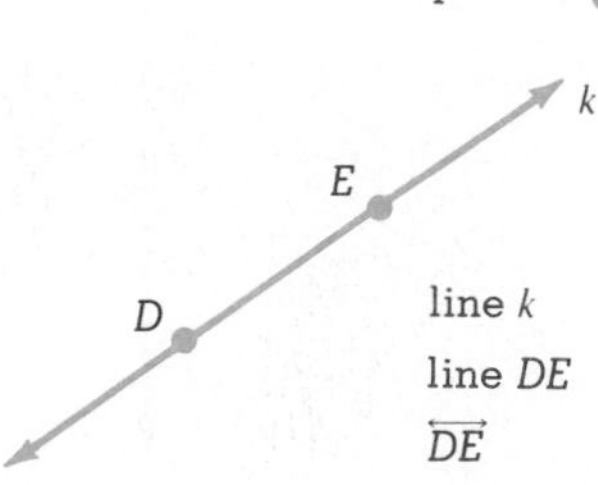

A line has one dimension.

A line, in plane geometry, means a straight line.

A flat map or a pane of glass in a window suggests the idea of a plane. A plane extends indefinitely in all directions and has no thickness. Planes are represented by four-sided figures and are named by capital script letters. Planes also can be named by using three points of the plane that are not on the same line.

A plane has two dimensions.

P
Q
S
$\mathscr{R}$

plane $\mathscr{R}$

plane *P, Q, S*

Two lines, or lines and planes **intersect** if they have points in common. For example, the two lines below intersect at point E.

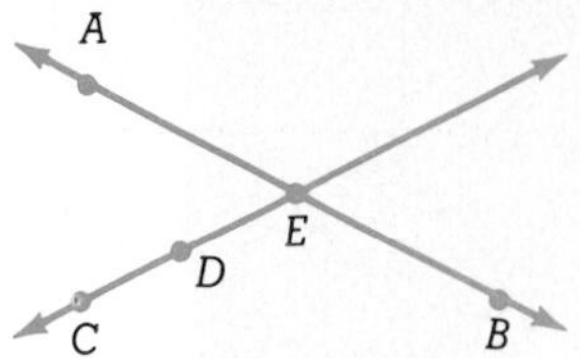

$\overleftrightarrow{AB}$ *intersects* $\overleftrightarrow{CD}$ *at E. The intersection of* $\overleftrightarrow{AB}$ *and* $\overleftrightarrow{CD}$ *is E.*

examples

1 Find the intersection of plane $\mathscr{A}$ and plane $\mathscr{B}$.

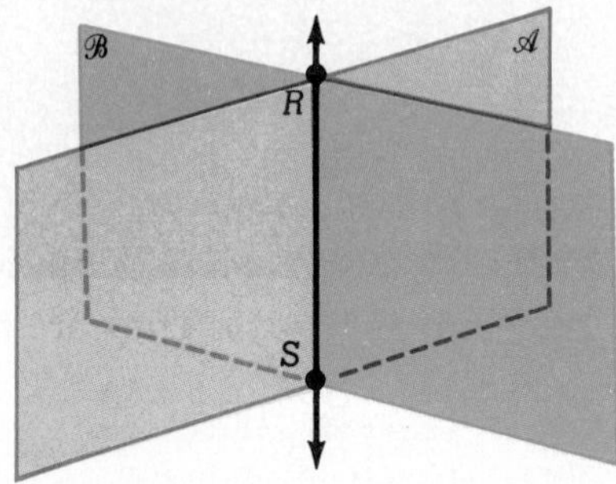

Plane $\mathscr{A}$ and plane $\mathscr{B}$ have $\overleftrightarrow{RS}$ in common. Their intersection is $\overleftrightarrow{RS}$.

2 Find the intersection of plane $\mathscr{A}$ and $\overleftrightarrow{TR}$.

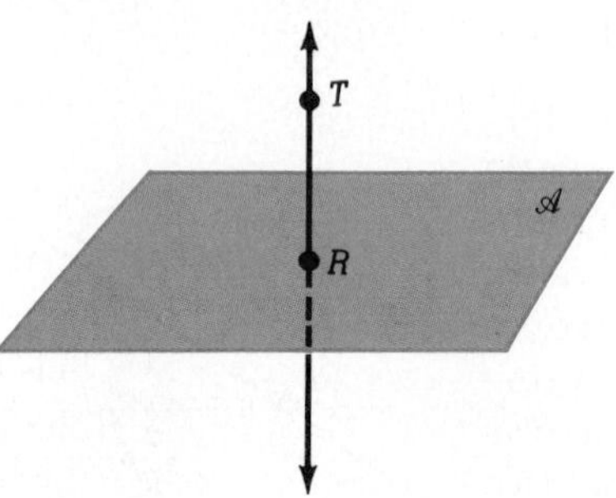

Plane $\mathscr{A}$ and $\overleftrightarrow{TR}$ have point R in common. Their intersection is point R.

All the points of $\overleftrightarrow{AB}$ are also points of $\mathscr{M}$. We say $\overleftrightarrow{AB}$ is in $\mathscr{M}$, or $\mathscr{M}$ **contains** $\overleftrightarrow{AB}$. Also, A **lies on** $\overleftrightarrow{AB}$ and is in $\mathscr{M}$. Alternatively, both $\overleftrightarrow{AB}$ and $\mathscr{M}$ contain A. Meter sticks and sheets of paper can be used to illustrate concepts of lines and planes.

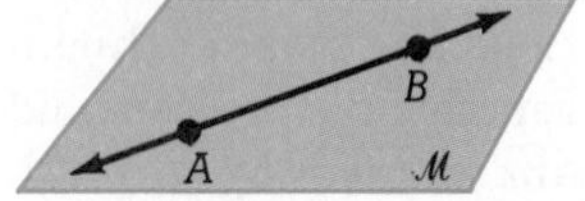

Lines contain points. *Points lie on lines and are in planes.*
Planes contain points and lines. *Lines are in planes.*

In geometry, points, lines, and planes are represented by figures or diagrams. We label these figures and diagrams to help visualize the relationships between the points, lines, and planes.

examples

3 **Draw and label a diagram to show $\overleftrightarrow{AB}$ and $\overleftrightarrow{CD}$ intersecting at P.**

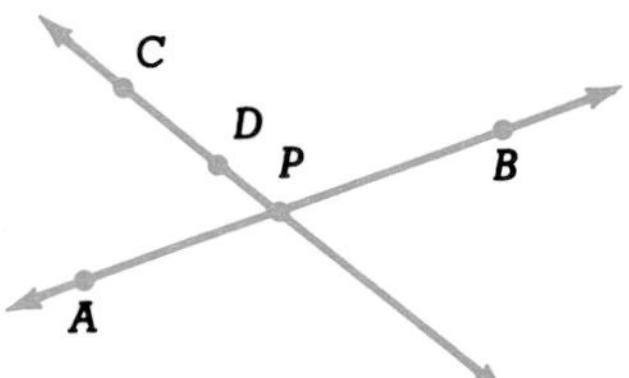

In the assignment guide EX: refers to Exploratory Exercises and WR: refers to Written Exercises

4 **Draw and label a diagram to show plane $\mathcal{N}$ contains m but not S.**

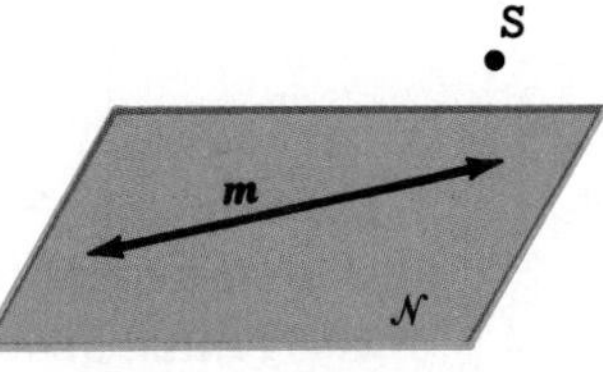

EN: refers to Enriched Course
AV: refers to Average Course
FN: refers to Fundamental Course

exercises

EN: WR: 2-26 evens; AV: EX: 1-13 odds; WR: 1-25 odds

Exploratory **Determine whether each of the following suggests a point, a line, or a plane.**

1. corner of a box point
2. side of a box plane
3. meeting of a wall and ceiling of a room 3. line
4. wall of a room plane
5. parking lot plane
6. guitar string line
7. vapor trail of an airplane line
8. grain of salt point
9. ceiling of a room plane
10. clothesline line
11. period at the end of a sentence point
12. star in the sky point
13. laser beam line
14. small town on a map point

FN: Ex: 1-14, Wr: 1-25 odds

Written **Draw and label a diagram to show each of the following.** See student's work.

1. Plane $\mathcal{L}$ and $\overleftrightarrow{CD}$ intersect at P.
2. ℓ and m intersect at R.
3. $\overleftrightarrow{RS}$ and plane $\mathcal{M}$ do *not* intersect.
4. $\overleftrightarrow{PQ}$, $\overleftrightarrow{RS}$, and plane $\mathcal{N}$ intersect at T.
5. Plane $\mathcal{L}$, plane $\mathcal{M}$, and plane $\mathcal{N}$ intersect at P.
6. Plane $\mathcal{M}$, plane $\mathcal{N}$, and plane $\mathcal{L}$ do *not* intersect.
7. P lies on $\overleftrightarrow{AB}$.
8. $\overleftrightarrow{AB}$ contains R.
9. t contains Q and R, but does *not* contain P and S.
10. A, B, and C lie on m but D does *not* lie on m.
11. Plane $\mathcal{M}$ contains n and R.
12. t contains P and lies in plane $\mathcal{N}$.

For answers to exercises 13-21, see the Teacher's Guide.

Use the figure for each of the following.

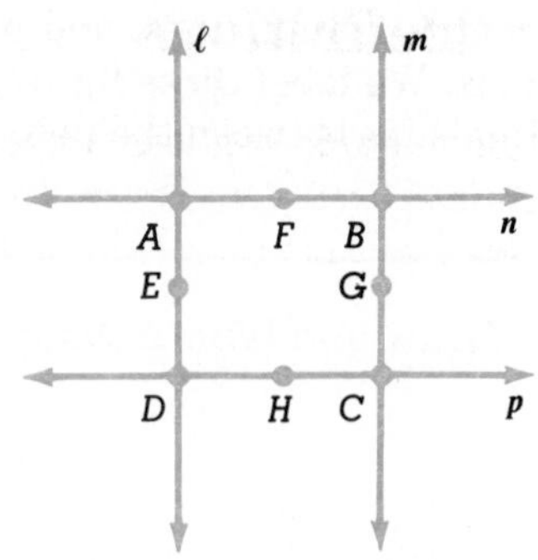

Exercises 13–21

13. Write another name for $\overleftrightarrow{AB}$.

14. Write another name for ℓ.

15. What points do $\overleftrightarrow{AD}$ and $\overleftrightarrow{BC}$ have in common?

16. What points do $\overleftrightarrow{AB}$ and m have in common?

17. Name two points that lie on $\overleftrightarrow{AD}$.

18. Name two points that lie on p.

19. Write three other names for n.

20. Write three other names for $\overleftrightarrow{BC}$.

21. Write three names for the plane that contains all the points and lines represented in the figure.

Answer the following.

22. Exactly one if $P \neq Q$. Infinitely many if $P = Q$.

23. infinitely many

22. Suppose P and Q are two points. How many lines can contain both P and Q?

23. Suppose P and Q are two points. How many planes can contain both P and Q?

24. Suppose P, Q, and R are three points *not* on the same line. How many lines can be drawn so that each line contains two of the points? 3

25. Think about a board or a piece of stiff cardboard. What is the *minimum* number of legs needed to support it in a fixed position? 3

26. Why does a tripod stand firm on uneven ground? Three different points, not all on one line, determine a plane.

Choose from the third box. If it is an apple, then the third box must be apples. Thus, the second box is apples & oranges, and the first box is oranges. Similarly, if the fruit is an orange, then the labels are apples & oranges, apples, and oranges.

Apples and Oranges — excursions in geometry

The three boxes shown below are labeled *apples, oranges,* and *apples and oranges*. Each label is incorrect. Suppose you may pull out one piece of fruit from one box. You are *not* allowed to reach around in the box or to peek. Tell from which box you would choose. Then, explain how to label the boxes correctly.

1–2 Definitions

Objectives: to recognize collinear and coplanar points; to recognize the characteristics of a good definition

To define a word, you use **undefined** terms or terms that have previously been defined. The basic terms of geometry—**point, line,** and **plane**—are undefined. They are used to define other terms of geometry.

An undefined term is a word which has a meaning that is readily understood.

The following definitions are based on points, lines, and planes.

Definition of Collinear Points

Points are collinear if and only if they lie on the same line.

Definition of Coplanar Points

Points are coplanar if and only if they lie in the same plane.

A model of a tetrahedron can enhance classroom discussion.

examples

1 In the figure, are points *A, E,* and *D* collinear?

Since points A, E, and D lie on $\overleftrightarrow{AD}$, they are collinear.

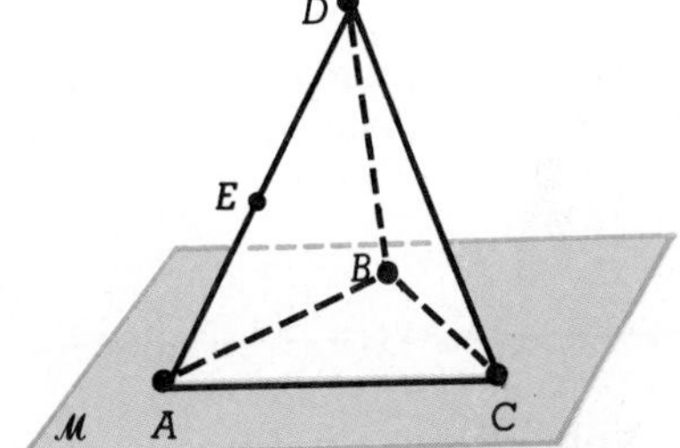

2 In the figure above, are points *A, B, C,* and *D* coplanar?

Points A, B, and C lie in plane $\mathcal{M}$, but point D does *not* lie in plane $\mathcal{M}$. Thus, the four points are *not* coplanar.

Definitions must be written very carefully. The following guidelines will help you write good definitions.

Guidelines for a Definition

1. **Name the term being defined.**
2. **Use only undefined terms or previously defined terms.**
3. **Identify the set to which the term belongs.**
4. **State the properties which distinguish the term from others in the set.**
5. **Make it reversible.**
6. **Make it concise.**

Reread the definition of collinear points. Notice that it satisfies all the guidelines for a good definition.

The term being defined is *collinear*.

Name the term being defined.

The definition uses *points* and *lines*. These terms are undefined.

Use only undefined terms or previously defined terms.

Collinear points belong to the set of *points*.

Identify the set to which the term belongs.

Collinear points *lie on the same line*. Some sets of points do *not* lie on the same line.

State the properties which distinguish the term from others in the set.

If points are collinear, then they lie on the same line.
If points lie on the same line, then they are collinear.
Notice how "points are collinear" and "lie on the same line" are reversed.

Make it reversible.

Studying conditional statements will help students learn to reverse statements.

Points are collinear if and only if they lie on the same line.
Notice this statement contains as few words as possible.

Make it concise.

Emphasize writing statements in "if-then" form.

example

3 Noncollinear points are points that are *not* collinear. Write a good definition for noncollinear points without using the word collinear.

The term being defined is *noncollinear* points.

Name the term being defined.

Use only *points* and *line*.

Use only undefined terms or previously defined terms.

Noncollinear points belong to the set of *points*.

Identify the set to which the term belongs.

Some sets of points do *not* lie on the same line. Collinear points *lie on the same line.*

State the properties which distinguish the term from others in its set.

If points are noncollinear, then they do *not* lie on the same line. If points do *not* lie on the same line, then they are noncollinear.

Make it reversible.

Points are noncollinear if and only if they do *not* lie on the same line.

Make it concise.

Reversing statements will be further developed in the next lesson.

example

4 The statement "they lie in the same plane" is *not* a good definition. Tell why. Assume the terms in the statement are previously defined.

The statement does *not* satisfy guidelines **1, 3,** and **5.**

1. It does *not* name the term being defined.
3. It does *not* identify the set to which the term belongs.
5. It is *not* reversible.

EN: Enriched
AV: Average
FN: Fundamental
Wr: Written
Ex: Exploratory

C: refers to Career page exercises
EN: Wr: 2-28 evens; p.9 C: 1-4; AV: Ex: 1-11 odds, Wr: 1-27 odds; pp. 3-4, Wr: 4, 8, 12, 16, 26

exercises

Exploratory **Use the figure to determine whether each of the following is *true* or *false*.** 1. false 2. true 3. false 4. true 5. true 6. true 7. false 8. true 9. false 10. false 11. true 12. true

1. A, B, and C are collinear.
2. A, B, and C are coplanar.
3. E, F, G, and H are coplanar.
4. A, F, E, and G are coplanar.
5. B, J, and K are coplanar.
6. C and G are collinear.
7. H, G, and D are collinear.
8. B, J, and C are collinear.
9. B, J, H, and G are coplanar.
10. B, J, H, and G are collinear.
11. G and H are collinear.
12. K and D are collinear.

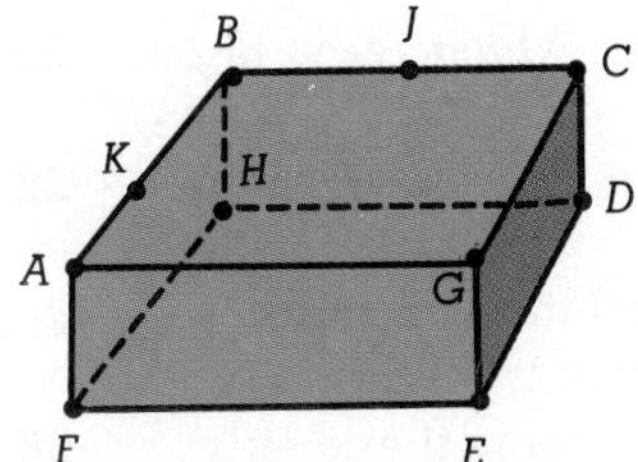

Exercises 1–12

FN: Ex: 1-12; Wr: 1-27 odds; pp. 3-4, Wr: 2-26 evens

Written **Points are noncollinear if and only if they do *not* lie on the same line. Use the figure to identify each of the following sets of points as collinear or noncollinear.**

1. F, G, E
2. A, J, E
3. B, F, A
4. H, B, A
5. C, J, E
6. K, G, C
7. F, D, B
8. J, K, E
9. A, J, C
10. B, G, E

1. collinear
2. noncollinear
3. noncollinear
4. collinear
5. collinear
6. noncollinear
7. noncollinear
8. noncollinear
9. noncollinear
10. noncollinear

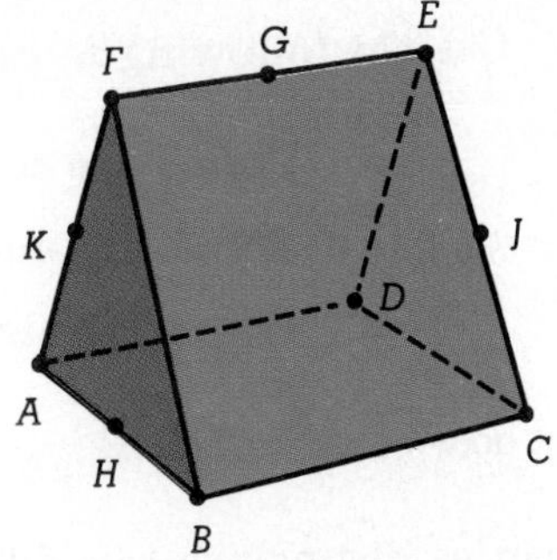

Exercises 1–10

Points are noncoplanar if and only if they do *not* lie in the same plane. Use the figure to identify each of the following sets of points as coplanar or noncoplanar.

11. *F, G, E, K*
12. *A, J, E, D*
13. *H, B, A, C*
14. *C, J, E, B*
15. *B, F, A, G*
16. *K, G, C, A*
17. *E, J, C, A*
18. *F, K, A, C*

11. noncoplanar

12. coplanar

13. coplanar

14. noncoplanar

15. coplanar

16. coplanar

17. coplanar

18. noncoplanar

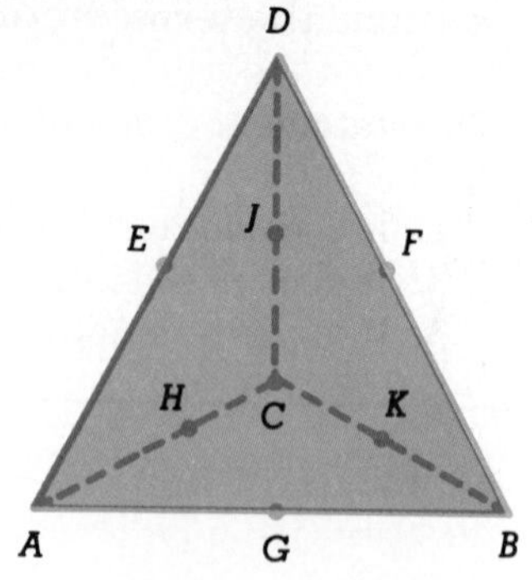

Exercises 11–18

For answers to exercises 19-28, see the Teacher's Guide.

Determine whether or *not* each of the following statements is a good definition. If *not*, tell why. Assume the terms in each statement are previously defined.

19. Skew lines are lines which are *not* coplanar.

20. A bedroom is a room where people sleep.

21. A person who lives in Detroit lives in Michigan.

22. A triangle is a polygon having three sides and three angles.

23. A diagonal of a quadrilateral separates the quadrilateral into two triangles.

24. Coinciding lines are lines which have all their points in common.

25. Points are noncoplanar points if and only if they do *not* lie in the same plane.

26. Points are collinear points if and only if they lie on the same line.

For each of the following, write your own definition. State how the definition satisfies the guidelines of a good definition.

27. reversible

28. concise

Challenge **Use the following sequence of definitions to answer the questions.**

(i) Points are costellar if and only if they are contravariant.

(ii) Points are contravariant if and only if they are semidiffused.

(iii) Points are semidiffused if and only if they are costellar.

1. To what set does costellar belong? points

2. What are the undefined terms being used to define contravariant?

2. points, semidiffused, costellar

3. What properties distinguish semidiffused points from the other points?

3. the property of costellar

4. Have costellar, contravariant, and semidiffused been defined? Explain. No. The sequence presents circular reasoning.

careers — Paralegal Aide

Jim Muir is a paralegal aide for the Tucson City prosecuting attorney's office. He is gathering information regarding a shoplifting case. He must find evidence to prove that Geri Kerman did shoplift at Levy's Department Store.

From the police report and witnesses, he has the following statements.

A. Geri Kerman was in the store at the time of the shoplifting.
B. Geri Kerman is 16 years old.
C. Geri Kerman has no receipt for the merchandise.
D. Geri Kerman attends high school.
E. Geri Kerman has blue eyes.
F. Geri Kerman was in the parking lot with the merchandise.

Suppose the definition of shoplifting is, *the removal of merchandise from a store by an individual(s) without proof of payment.* Then the information in statements **A, C,** and **F** can be used as evidence of shoplifting.

2. B, insufficient information. A could be in or out of seat.

Exercises For each of the following, answer the questions.

1. A *speeding violation* occurs when a motorist drives at a speed over the posted limit. Which person is speeding? B
   A. Bell Wilkins was driving 30 mph in a 35 mph zone.
   B. Jon Bunch was found driving 45 mph in a 20 mph zone.

2. Students are considered *late to class* if they are *not* in their seats when the bell rings. Which student is late?
   A. Bill is looking at the bulletin board when the bell rings.
   B. Sara is in her friend's seat when the bell rings.

3. An *olympic class swimmer* is a person who can swim the 100-meter backstroke in less than 01:02.00. Which person is an olympic class swimmer? B
   A. Kornelia Ender can swim the 100-meter freestyle in 00:55.65.
   B. Ulriche Richter can swim the 100-meter backstroke in 01:01.51.

4. *Supplementary angles* are two angles whose degree measures total 180. Which pair of angles are supplementary angles? B
   A. The degree measure of angle C is 50, and the degree measure of angle D is 40.
   B. The degree measure of angle R is 125, and the degree measure of angle S is 55.

1–3 Conditional Statements

Objective: to write statements in "if-then" or "if and only if" form

Conditional statements have two parts. One part can begin with *if*, and the other part can begin with *then*. The statement below is a conditional statement with *then* omitted.

If *you want a healthy cat,* then *start with a healthy kitten.*

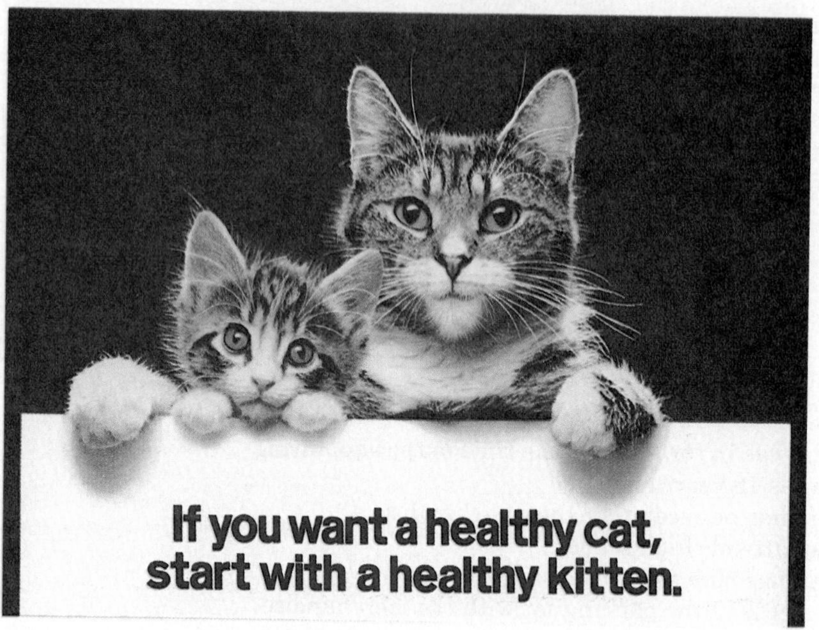
If you want a healthy cat,
start with a healthy kitten.

Conditional statements are written in many different ways, but all conditional statements can be written in *if-then* form. For example, the following statements can *all* be written as: *If you are a genius, then you are left-handed.*

You may want to introduce "if p then q," or "p → q."

All geniuses are left-handed.
You are left-handed if you are a genius.
You are a genius only if you are left-handed.
Being a genius implies you are left-handed.
You are left-handed when you are a genius.

example

1 **Rewrite the following conditional statement in if-then form.**

There is at least one plane that contains a line and a point *not* on the line.

If there is a line and a point *not* on the line, *then* there is at least one plane that contains them.

The part following *if* in a conditional statement is called the **hypothesis.** It tells what is to be *assumed.* The part following *then* in a conditional statement is called the **conclusion.** It tells the result, what is believed to follow from the assumption.

A conditional statement is false only when the hypothesis is true and the conclusion is false.

Conditional	If there is a line and a point *not* on the line, then there is at least one plane that contains them.
Hypothesis	there is a line and a point *not* on the line
Conclusion	there is at least one plane that contains them

Conditional statements may be true or false. Questions and exclamations are *not* conditional statements because usually they are *neither* true *nor* false.

Question	Who wrote *I Know Why the Caged Bird Sings?*
Exclamation	Be careful!

Given a conditional statement, a new statement can be formed by interchanging the hypothesis and conclusion. This new statement is called the **converse** of the conditional.

Statement	If it is raining, then there are clouds in the sky.
Converse	If there are clouds in the sky, then it is raining.

As the above example shows, the converse of a true statement may *not* be true.

2 Write the converse of the following true conditional statement. Is the converse a true statement?

If three points lie on the same line, then they are collinear.

Converse If three points are collinear, then they lie on the same line.

Yes, the converse is a true statement in this case.

A statement in *if and only if* form can be written as two conditional statements.

Two planes are parallel *if and only if* they do *not* intersect.

means

If two planes are parallel, then they do *not* intersect,
and if two planes do *not* intersect, then they are parallel.

Statements that can be written in *if and only if* form are called **biconditional statements.** All definitions are biconditional statements because they are reversible.

Not *all reversible statements are definitions.*

EN: Enriched
AV: Average
FN: Fundamental
Wr: Written
Ex: Exploratory

Ch: refers to Challenge Exercises

example

3 **Rewrite the following pair of statements as a single statement in *if and only if* form.**

If two lines are skew, then they do *not* intersect and are *not* in the same plane.

If two lines *do not* intersect and are *not* in the same plane, then they are skew.

Two lines are skew if and only if they do *not* intersect and are *not* in the same plane.

EN: Wr: 2-38 even; p. 8, Ch: 1-4; AV: Ex: 1-10, Wr: 1-37 odds; pp. 7-8, Wr: 6, 12, 18, 24, 32

exercises

The hypothesis is underlined, and the conclusion is circled.

Exploratory Identify the hypothesis and conclusion for each of the following.

1. If it rains, then the grass gets wet.
2. If a triangle has a right angle, then it is a right triangle.
3. If you live in Texas, then you are an American.
4. If you ride a bicycle, then you have strong legs.
5. If two lines are perpendicular, then the two lines intersect.
6. If $3x = 12$, then $x = 4$.
7. If n is even, then n^2 is even.
8. If a number is rational, then it is real.
9. If an animal is a chimpanzee, then it is a mammal.
10. If you practice hard, then you will make the team.

FN: Ex: 1-10, Wr: 1-37 odds; pp. 7-8, Wr: 2-28 evens

Written Rewrite each of the following conditional statements in if-then form. Then write the converse of each.

For answers to exercises 1-12, see the Teacher's Guide.

1. Parallel lines do *not* intersect.
2. A square is *not* a triangle.
3. A square is a rectangle.
4. All integers are real numbers.
5. $x < 0$ implies $5x > 6x$.
6. $2n + 1 = 5$ implies $n = 2$.
7. When it rains it pours.
8. If you want a new account, phone for it.
9. Two intersecting lines are contained in exactly one plane.
10. Two angles are congruent when they are vertical angles.
11. Where there is smoke, there is fire.
12. Show me a genius and I'll show you a scholar.

Remind students that conditional statements are not necessarily in if-then form.

Determine whether or *not* each of the following is a conditional statement. Write yes or no. Determine if each is *true, false,* or *neither*. Be prepared to justify your answer.

13. If it is blue, then it is *not* green.

14. If it is *not* green, then it is blue.

15. When animals are hungry, they eat.

16. A person who is crying is *not* happy.

17. Be home by twelve o'clock.

18. Define collinear points.

19. Every line contains at least two points.

20. Sugar is *not* always white.

21. How are points and lines different?

22. Why are some people afraid of high places?

13. yes; true (if based on a color wheel)

14. yes; false 15. yes; neither 16. yes; neither 17. no; neither

18. no; neither 19. yes; true 20. yes; true 21. no; neither 22. no; neither

Give an example for each of the following. Answers will vary.

23. A conditional and its converse that are both true

24. A conditional and its converse that are both false

25. A true conditional statement whose converse is false

26. A false conditional statement whose converse is true

27. An exclamation that is false

28. An exclamation that is true

Regarding Exercises 27-28, this type of sentence is not used in logic.

For answers to exercises 29-34, see the Teacher's Guide.

Rewrite each of the following statements as two if-then statements, one of which is the converse of the other.

29. Points are collinear if and only if they lie on the same line.

30. Points are coplanar if and only if they lie in the same plane.

31. Two segments are congruent if and only if they have the same measure.

32. Two angles are congruent if and only if they have the same measure.

33. Two angles are supplementary if and only if the sum of their degree measures is 180.

34. Two angles are complementary if and only if the sum of their degree measures is 90.

35. Two lines are perpendicular if and only if they intersect at right angles.

36. Two lines do not intersect if and only if they are parallel.

Rewrite the following pairs of statements as single statements using *if and only if*.

35. If two lines are perpendicular, then they intersect at right angles.

If two lines intersect at right angles, then they are perpendicular.

36. In a plane, if two lines do *not* intersect, then they are parallel.

In a plane, if two lines are parallel, then they do *not* intersect.

37. Two lines intersected by a transversal have alternate interior angles congruent if and only if the lines are parallel.

37. If two lines are intersected by a transversal so that alternate interior angles are congruent, then the lines are parallel.

If two lines are parallel and intersected by a transversal, then the alternate interior angles are congruent.

38. If two lines are parallel and intersected by a transversal, then the corresponding angles are congruent.

If two lines are intersected by a transversal so that corresponding angles are congruent, then the lines are parallel.

38. Two lines intersected by a transversal have corresponding angles congruent if and only if the lines are parallel.

1–4 Postulates

Objectives: to identify and use the basic postulates about points, lines, and planes

In order to play a game, you must know the rules. In order to study geometry, you must know the **postulates.**

The rules, or postulates, of geometry tell how different sets of points are related. Postulates are statements that are accepted as true.

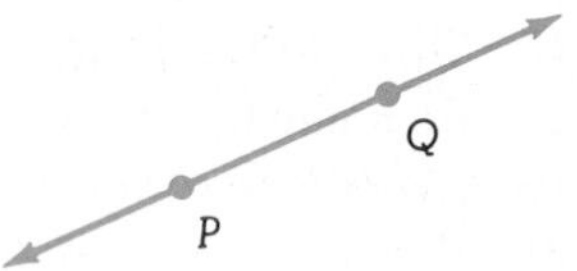

Postulate 1–1 relates points and lines. It guarantees that P and Q, for example, always determine a line.

Through any two points there is exactly one line. *Postulate 1–1*

Postulate 1–2 relates points and planes.

Point out that "exactly one" means at least one and no more than one.

Through any three points *not* on the same line there is exactly one plane. *Postulate 1–2*

examples

1 Given four points with no three collinear, how many lines can be drawn which contain any two of them?

For every two points there is exactly one line. Thus, for four points there are at most six lines that can be drawn.

In the figure, $\overleftrightarrow{AB}$, $\overleftrightarrow{BC}$, $\overleftrightarrow{CD}$, $\overleftrightarrow{AD}$, $\overleftrightarrow{BD}$, and $\overleftrightarrow{AC}$ can be drawn.

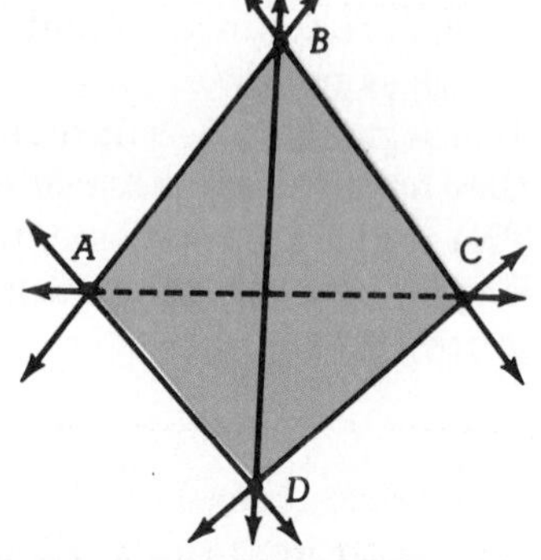

2 Given four noncoplanar points with no three collinear, how many planes can be drawn which contain any three of them?

For every three points *not* on the same line there is exactly one plane. Each face of the pyramid in the figure represents a plane containing three of the four points. The figure shows that there are, at most, four planes that can be drawn through the four points taken three at a time. The planes formed are the planes containing the following sets of points.

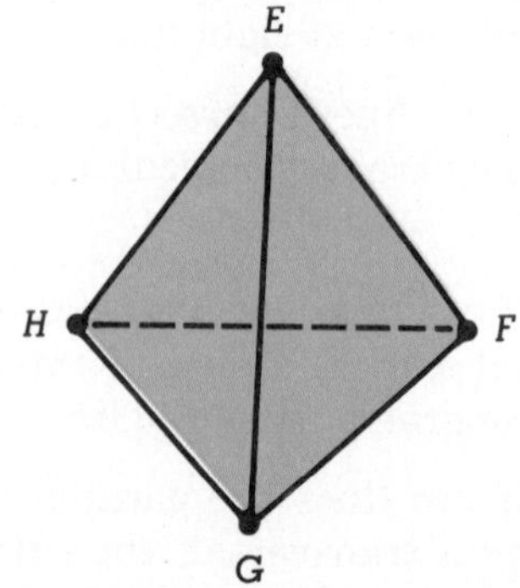

H, E, G $\quad$ G, E, F $\quad$ E, F, H $\quad$ F, G, H

Postulates 1–3 and 1–4 state the minimum number of points on a line and in a plane.

A line contains at least two points. *Postulate 1–3*

A plane contains at least three points not on the same line. *Postulate 1–4*

Postulate 1–5 relates points, lines, and planes.

If two points lie in a plane, then the entire line containing those two points lies in that plane. *Postulate 1–5*

example

3 Suppose three noncollinear points, *A, B,* and *C,* lie in the same plane. How many lines can be drawn containing any two of the points? Name the lines.

There are three lines that can be drawn.
They are $\overleftrightarrow{AB}$, $\overleftrightarrow{BC}$, and $\overleftrightarrow{AC}$.

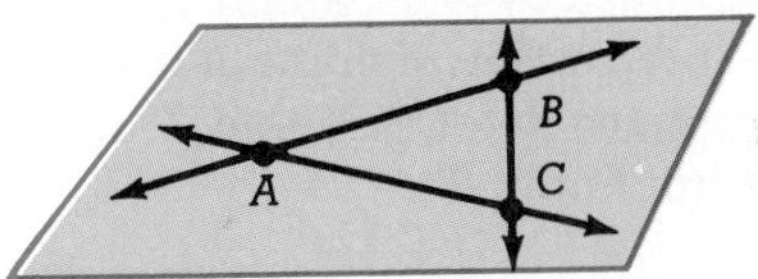

Postulate 1–6 relates lines and planes.

If two planes intersect, then their intersection is a line. *Postulate 1–6*

example

4 Suppose plane $\mathcal{M}$ contains noncollinear points *A, C,* and *E*. Suppose plane $\mathcal{N}$ contains noncollinear points *A, C,* and *D*. Name the intersection of the two planes.

The intersection of planes $\mathcal{N}$ and $\mathcal{M}$ is $\overleftrightarrow{AC}$.

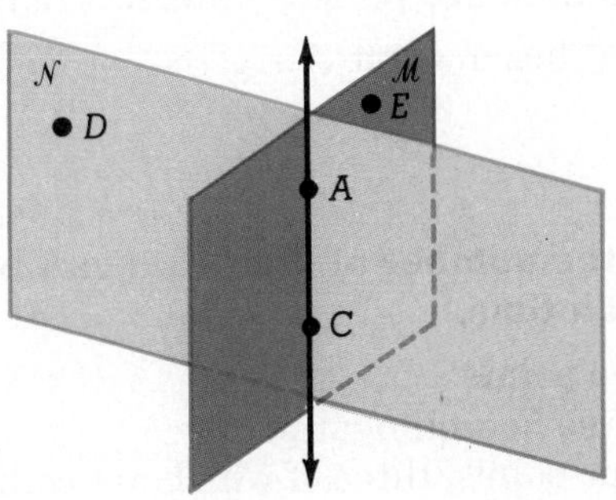

Ch: Challenge C: Careers Cal: Calculators

exercises

EN: Wr: 2-22 evens; p. 17, Cal: 1-8; AV: Ex: 1-10, Wr: 1-21 odds; pp. 12-13 Wr: 6, 12, 18, 24, 30

Exploratory **For each of the following statements, name the postulate that explains the relationship. Use the figure.**

EN: Enriched
AV: Average
FN: Fundamental
Ex: Exploratory
Wr: Written

1. Exactly one line contains Q and P.
2. The entire line containing R and S lies in plane $\mathcal{M}$.
3. There are at least three points in plane $\mathcal{M}$.
4. There are at least two points on $\overleftrightarrow{QP}$.
5. There is at least one point in plane $\mathcal{M}$ *not* on $\overleftrightarrow{RS}$.
6. Exactly one line contains R and S.
7. P and S lie on exactly one line.
8. Plane $\mathcal{M}$ is the only plane containing R, S, and T.
9. The intersection of plane $\mathcal{M}$ and the plane determined by Q, P, and R is $\overleftrightarrow{RP}$.
10. The intersection of plane $\mathcal{M}$ and the plane determined by Q, P, and T is the line through P and T.

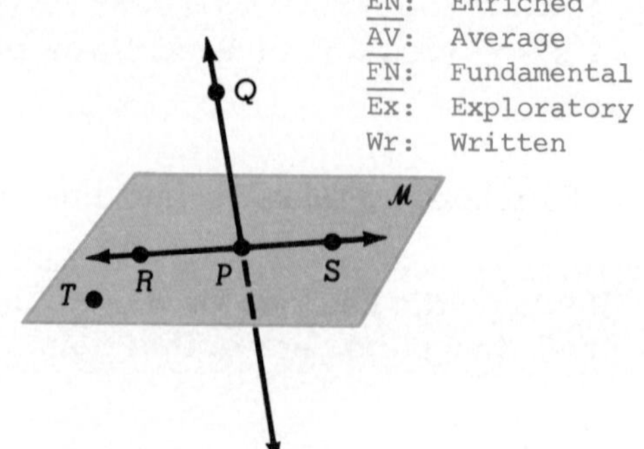

Exercises 1–10

1. Post. 1-1 2. Post. 1-5 3. Post. 1-4 4. Post. 1-3 5. Post. 1-4 6. Post. 1-1
7. Post. 1-1 8. Post. 1-2 9. Post. 1-6 10. Post. 1-6

Written **In the figure P, Q, and R are collinear. Points P and S lie in plane $\mathcal{M}$. Points R and T lie in plane $\mathcal{N}$. Determine whether each of the following statements is *true* or *false*.** FN: Ex: 1-10, Wr: 1-21 odds; pp. 12-13, Wr: 2-36 evens

1. P, Q, and R lie in plane $\mathcal{N}$.
2. P, Q, and R lie in plane $\mathcal{M}$.
3. $\overleftrightarrow{PS}$ does *not* lie in plane $\mathcal{M}$.
4. Q lies in plane $\mathcal{M}$.
5. P, Q, R, and S are coplanar.
6. Q does *not* lie in plane $\mathcal{M}$.
7. Q, R, and T are collinear.
8. P, Q, S, and T are coplanar.
9. Plane $\mathcal{M}$ and plane $\mathcal{N}$ intersect in $\overleftrightarrow{PR}$.
10. $\overleftrightarrow{QT}$ lies in plane $\mathcal{N}$.

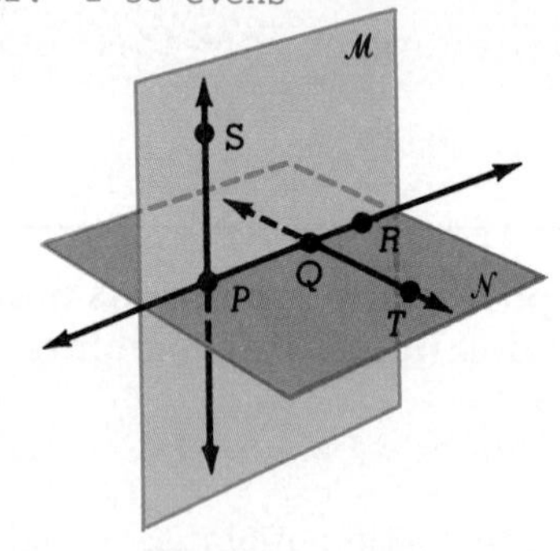

Exercises 1–10

The main emphasis of problems 11-18 is to reinforce the concept that three noncollinear points on a line, or a line and a point not on the line, determine a plane.

State the number of lines that can be drawn which contain the given sets of points taken two at a time.

11. two points
12. three collinear points
13. three noncollinear points
14. five points, *no* three of which are collinear
15. four points, three of which are collinear
16. the intersection of two planes
17. six points, *no* three of which are collinear
18. four points, *no* three of which are collinear

1. true 2. true 3. false 4. true 5. true 6. false 7. false 8. false 9. true
10. true 11. one 12. one 13. three 14. ten 15. four
16. one 17. fifteen 18. six

State the number of planes that can be drawn which contain the given sets of points taken three at a time.

19. three noncollinear points

20. three collinear points

21. four points, three of which are collinear

22. five points, no three of which are collinear

19. one 20. infinitely many 21. one if 3 noncollinear are taken; infinite if 3 collinear are taken 22. ten

Basic Functions

Some calculators differ in the functions they perform. Most calculators have the following keys and functions.

Key	Name	Function
+/−	Change Sign	changes the sign of the number
x^2	Square	calculates the square of the number
$\sqrt{x}$	Square Root	calculates the square root of the number
$1/x$	Reciprocal	calculates the reciprocal of the number

First enter the number and then press the appropriate key.

As we discuss calculators, we will assume that the evaluation of expressions is completed in the algebraic mode. That is, the algebraic order of operations holds when the calculator performs any sequence of operations.

Example **Evaluate $7 + 3 \div 5 + 5^2$.**

ENTER:	7	+	3	÷	5	+	5	x^2	=
DISPLAY:	7	7	3	3	5	7.6	5	25	32.6

The answer is 32.6.

If your calculator does *not* use the algebraic order of operations, your answer will be different. Read the manual for your calculator and adjust the order of entry accordingly.

Exercises **Use the calculator to compute each of the following.**

1. $6 \cdot 2 - 4 \cdot 2$ 4

2. $42 - 54 \div 6$ 33

3. $24 \div 6 - 3^2 \div 3$ 1

4. $6 \cdot 3 \div 9 - 1$ 1

5. $8 + 5^2 + 6 \div 3 - \sqrt{2}$

6. $13 - 4(17)^2 + \sqrt{0.978}$

7. Use the change sign key to evaluate $(^-91{,}651)(\sqrt{21{,}376}) \div {}^-12{,}878$. 1040.5238

8. Use the reciprocal key to evaluate $\frac{1}{101 + (75)(30)} + \sqrt{51}$. 7.1418538

5. 33.585786

6. -1142.0111

1–5 Theorems

Objectives: to recognize the five main parts of a proof; to identify the hypothesis and conclusion of a theorem

Sometimes photographs are misleading. In the following photograph, what are you led to believe?

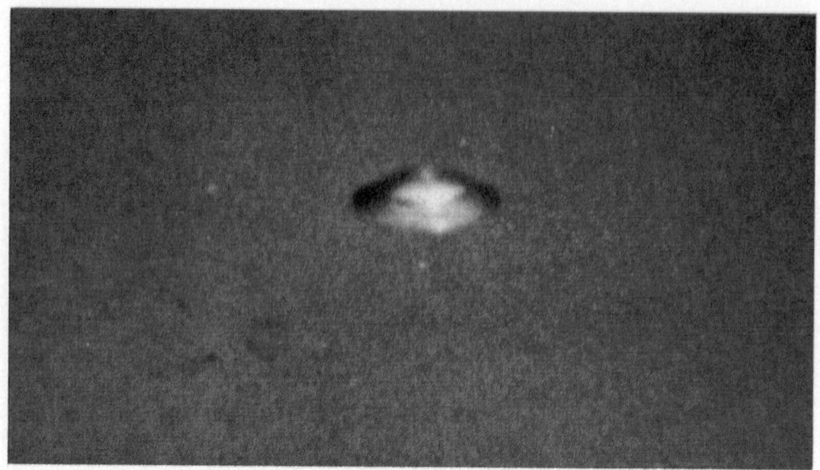

Are you convinced? Does this photograph prove there is life on other planets?

This figure shows a line ℓ and a point P *not* on the line. How many planes can contain both point P and line ℓ?

According to Postulate 1–3, a line contains at least two points. The points are labeled R and S. So, there are at least three points, P, R, and S, *not* on the same line.

According to Postulate 1–2 through any three points *not* on the same line there is exactly one plane.

According to Postulate 1–5, if two points lie in a plane, then the entire line containing them lies in that plane. So there is at least one plane containing P and ℓ.

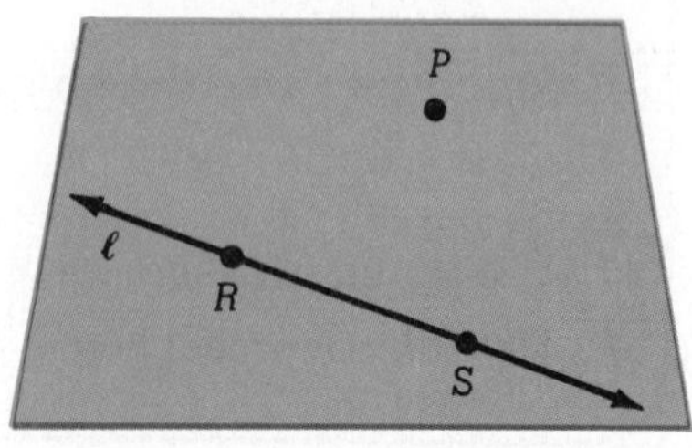

Physical models are most helpful in concept development.

Are you convinced?

Not everyone has the same idea of what is convincing. Some arguments are more convincing than others. Geometry uses a system of reasoning that many people find convincing.

In geometry, undefined terms, definitions, and postulates are taken for granted.

Undefined terms are basic terms from which other terms are defined.

Definitions are explanations of how words are to be used.

Postulates are statements that describe fundamental properties of the basic terms.

This information is not proven.

The information from undefined terms, definitions, and postulates is used to find new information, written as a **theorem.**

Theorems may be conditional or biconditional statements.

Theorems are statements that must be proven before accepted.

For example, the argument on the previous page leads to the following theorem. Theorems may be written in "if-then" or "if and only if" form.

If there is a line and a point *not* on the line, then there is exactly one plane that contains them. ***Theorem 1–1***

To prove a theorem, start with the *hypothesis.* Then use the information from postulates, definitions, and previously proven theorems to reach the *conclusion*.

Different postulates can lead to different conclusions.

Formal proofs have five main parts, namely, the *theorem,* the *given,* the *prove statement,* a *diagram,* and the *proof* with statements and reasons. Formal proofs can be written in the form below.

Theorem: Write out the theorem to be proven.

Given: Write the information given in the hypothesis of the theorem. Use the names for the terms from the diagram.

Prove: Write the conclusion of the theorem. Use the names from the diagram.

A diagram may be provided for the given statements. It should picture the information in the hypothesis of the theorem. Label the diagram with names to be used in the proof.

Proof:

STATEMENTS	REASONS
1. Write a list of numbered statements arranged in or- 2. der so that they lead to the conclusion. Each state- 3. ment must be justified by a reason.	1. Write a list of numbered reasons that go with the 2. statements on the left. Reasons used can be given 3. information, definitions, postulates, or theorems.

You cannot use the theorem itself or any subsequent theorem as a reason in a proof.

EN: Ex: 1-18, Wr: 2-14 evens; AV: Ex: 1-20, Wr: 1-23 odds; pp. 16-17, Wr: 6-22 evens; p. 17, Cal: 1-6

example

1 For Theorem 1–1, state the given. Then draw a diagram to illustrate the given.

Theorem 1–1 states, *if there is a line and a point not on the line, then there is exactly one plane that contains them.* The hypothesis, the part following *if,* states there is a line and a point *not* on the line. Name the line ℓ and the point P.

Given: P *not* on ℓ **Diagram:**

Names other than P and ℓ may be used.

1. the theorem, the given, the prove statement, a diagram, and the proof with statements and reasons
10. to show logically how the hypothesis leads to the conclusion

exercises

Exploratory **Answer the following about formal proofs.**

1. Name the five main parts of a proof.
2. What information is in the *given* statement? information in the hypothesis
3. What information is in the *prove* statement? information in the conclusion
4. What does the diagram illustrate? the diagram illustrates the hypothesis
5. Should a theorem be stated? Write yes or *no*. yes
6. Must a diagram be shown? Write yes or *no*. yes
7. Must the given be stated? yes
8. Must the *prove* statement be stated? yes
9. Name the headings for the two columns in a *proof.* statements, reasons
10. What is the purpose of the statements?
11. What is the purpose of the reasons? to justify each statement
12. What can be used as reasons? the given, postulates already stated, definitions already made, theorems already proved

State the hypothesis for each of the following theorems.

The answers to exercises 13-20 are underlined.

13. If <u>two lines intersect,</u> then exactly one plane contains both lines.
14. If <u>two lines intersect,</u> then they intersect in exactly one point.
15. If <u>a line and a plane intersect, and the plane does *not* contain the line,</u> then their intersection is a point.
16. If <u>four points are collinear,</u> then they are coplanar.

State the conclusion for the following theorems.

17. If three points are noncollinear, then <u>there is exactly one plane that contains them.</u>
18. If two points are in a plane, then <u>the line containing the two points is in the plane.</u>
19. If two distinct planes intersect, then <u>their intersection is a line.</u>
20. If four points are collinear, then <u>there is exactly one line that contains them.</u>

FN: Ex: 1-20, Wr: 1-13; pp. 16-17, Wr: 2-22 evens

Written **State the given and the prove statement for each of the following theorems. Use labels from a diagram you draw.** For answers to exercises 1-4, see the Teacher's Guide.

1. If two lines intersect, then exactly one plane contains both lines.
2. If two lines intersect, then they intersect in exactly one point.
3. If a line and a plane intersect, and the plane does *not* contain the line, then their intersection is a point.
4. If four points are collinear, then they are coplanar.

See student's work for exercises 5-14.

Draw and label a diagram to illustrate each of the following given statements.

5. **Given:** line ℓ and point P *not* on ℓ
6. **Given:** points A, B, and C *not* on the same line
7. **Given:** line $\boldsymbol{m}$ intersecting line $\boldsymbol{n}$
8. **Given:** line $\boldsymbol{m}$ contained in plane $\mathscr{P}$
9. **Given:** point R *not* in plane $\mathscr{M}$
10. **Given:** coplanar lines $\boldsymbol{m}$ and $\boldsymbol{n}$ point P on line $\boldsymbol{m}$

Draw and label a diagram to illustrate the hypothesis for each of the following theorems.

11. If three points are noncollinear, then there is exactly one plane that contains them.
12. If two points are in a plane, then the line containing the two points is in the plane.
13. If two distinct planes intersect, then their intersection is a line.
14. If four points are collinear, then there is exactly one line that contains them.

The following diagrams are taken from proofs. State the given for each diagram.
For answers to exercises 15-23, see the Teacher's Guide.

15.
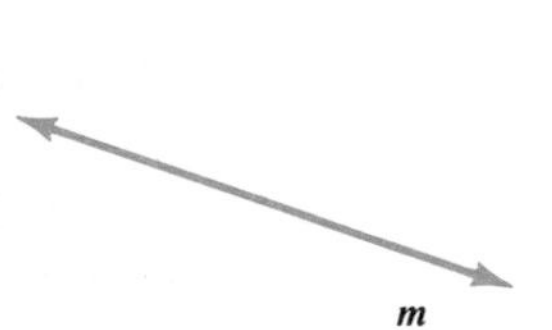

16.

17.
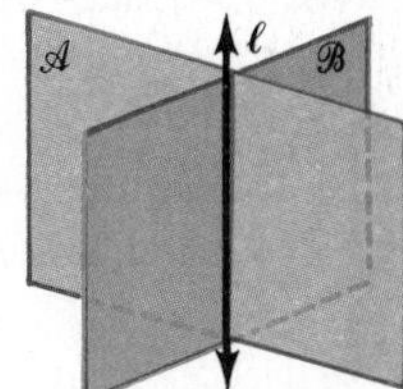

18.

19.
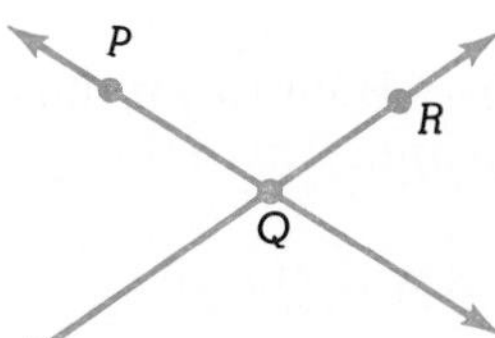

20.

21.
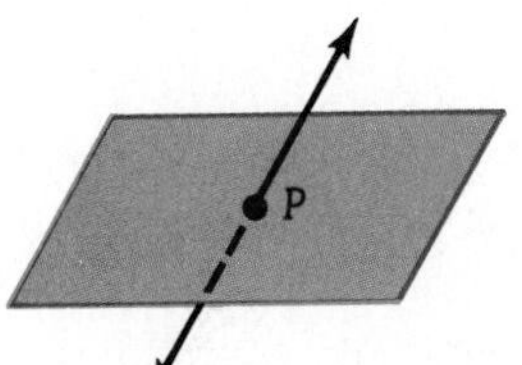

22.
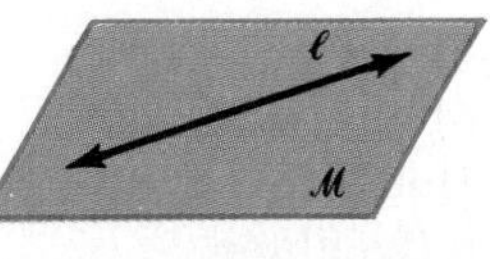

23.
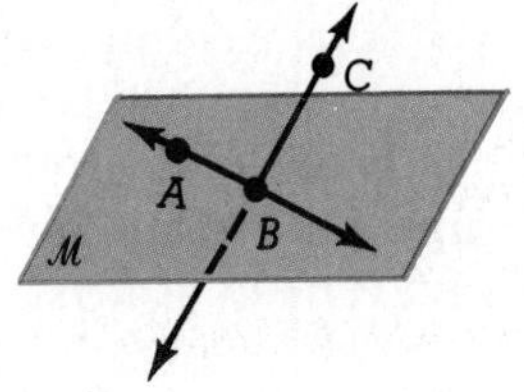

1–6 Writing Proofs

Objectives: to plan and develop formal proofs

A formal proof is a summary. It does *not* show the thinking and planning done to make a logical argument. The following suggestions will help you write a formal proof.

1. **Write out the theorem.**
2. **Draw a diagram.**
3. **Write the given and the prove statement.**
4. **Plan the proof.**
5. **Write the proof.**

Procedure for Writing Formal Proofs

Theorem: If there is a line and a point *not* on the line, then there is at least one plane that contains them.

Write out the theorem.

This information helps students define the problem.

Draw a diagram.

Diagrams help students see possible relationships.

Given: line ℓ and point P *not* on ℓ
Prove: At least one plane contains ℓ and P.

Write the given and the prove statement.

Review the definitions, postulates, and theorems already proven that relate to the theorem.

Plan the proof.

Postulate 1–2: Through any three points *not* on the same line, there is exactly one plane.
Postulate 1–3: A line contains at least two points.
Postulate 1–5: If two points lie in a plane, then the entire line containing those points lies in that plane.

Arrange the ideas in logical order. Start with the given and end with the prove statement.

line ℓ and point P *not* on ℓ
ℓ contains 2 points, say R and S.
There are 3 noncollinear points, namely R, S, and P.
Exactly one plane contains R, S, and P.
R and S lie in a plane, so ℓ lies in the plane.
ℓ and P lie in at least one plane.

List the statements with the reasons.

Write the proof.

This example can be used as a basis for discussion of formal proofs.

example 1 **Write a formal proof for the following theorem.**

Theorem: If there is a line and a point *not* on the line, then there is at least one plane that contains them.

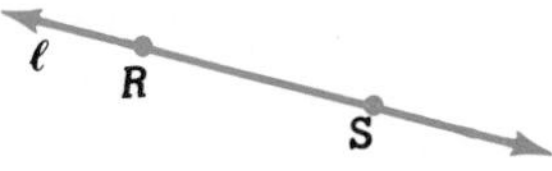

Given: line ℓ and point P *not* on ℓ

Prove: At least one plane contains ℓ and P.

Proof:

STATEMENTS	REASONS
1. line ℓ and point P *not* on ℓ	**1.** Given
2. points R and S on ℓ	**2.** Postulate 1–3: A line contains at least two points.
3. P, S, and R are noncollinear.	**3.** Definition of Noncollinear Points
4. Exactly one plane contains R, S, and P.	**4.** Postulate 1–2: Through any three points *not* on the same line there is exactly one plane.
5. At least one plane contains ℓ and P.	**5.** Postulate 1–5: If two points lie in a plane, then the entire line containing those two points lies in that plane.

The following theorem relates lines and planes.

If two lines intersect, then exactly one plane contains both lines. ***Theorem 1–2***

This example can be used to discuss planning a proof.

2 **Plan a proof to show that at least one plane contains two intersecting lines.**

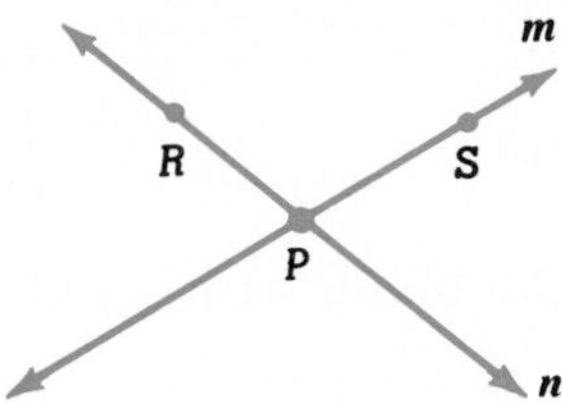

This plan assumes that P, R, and S are noncollinear.

The lines ***m*** and ***n*** intersect in P. Thus, by Postulate 1–3, ***m*** and ***n*** both contain two points. By Postulate 1–3, there are three points, namely P, R, and S. Then, by Postulate 1–2, exactly one plane contains P, R, and S. Finally, Postulate 1–5 says that the plane contains both ***m*** and ***n***.

EN: Ex: 1-3, Wr: 1-23 odds, p. 26, TG: 1-4; AV: Ex: 1-11 odds, Wr: 1-23 odds; p. 21, Wr: 4-22 evens
TG: refers to Topics in Geometry exercises

exercises

Exploratory **Name the postulates or theorems you have learned that have the same hypothesis as each of the following theorems. If you have *not* learned any, write *none*.**

1. If two lines intersect, then exactly one plane contains both lines.
2. If two planes intersect, then their intersection contains at least two points.
3. A plane contains at least three lines.
4. If two lines intersect, then their intersection contains one point.
5. Through any three points *not* on the same line, there are exactly three lines.
6. Through four collinear points, there is exactly one line.

7–12. For each of the theorems in exercises **1–6,** name the postulates or theorems you have learned that have the same conclusion. If you have *not* learned any, write *none.*

1. Theorem 1-2 2. Post. 1-6 3. Post. 1-4 4. Theorem 1-2 5. Post. 1-2 6. none
7. Theorem 1-2 8. none 9. none 10. none 11. none 12. Post. 1-1

FN: Ex: 1-12, Wr: 1-23 odds; p. 21 Wr: 1-23 odds

Written **For each of the following, fill in the blank with a reason. Use a definition, a postulate, or a proven theorem.**

1. S and Q are points. — Given
   There is exactly one line through S and Q. — ______ Post. 1-1
2. Q and R are points. — Given
   There is exactly one line containing Q and R. — ______ Post. 1-1
3. Q, S, and R are noncollinear points. — Given
   There is exactly one plane containing Q, S, and R. — ______ Post. 1-2
4. P, Q, and R are noncollinear. — Given
   There is only one plane containing P, Q, and R. — ______ Post. 1-2
5. Q and R lie in $\mathscr{L}$. — Given
   $\overleftrightarrow{QR}$ lies in $\mathscr{L}$. — ______ Post. 1-5
6. P is *not* on m. — Given
   There is only one plane containing P and m. — ______ Theorem 1-1
7. S is *not* on m. — Given
   Exactly one plane contains S and m. — ______ Theorem 1-1
8. S, P, and Q lie on ℓ. — Given
   S, P, and Q are collinear. — ______ definition of collinear points
9. S and R lie on m. — Postulate 1–1
   P does *not* lie on m. — Given
   S, R, and P are noncollinear. — ______ definition of noncollinear points
10. P does *not* lie on ℓ. — Given
    A and B lie on ℓ. — Given
    A, B, and P are coplanar. — ______ Theorem 1-1; Post. 1-2; definition of coplanar points

For each of the following, fill in the blank with a statement that follows from the stated reason.

11. ℓ and m intersect. — Given
    ______ Exactly one plane contains ℓ and m. — Theorem 1–2: If two lines intersect, then exactly one plane contains both lines.
12. P, Q, and R are noncollinear. — Given
    ______ There is exactly one plane through P, Q and R. — Postulate 1–2: Through any three points *not* on the same line, there is exactly one plane.

13. $\mathcal{M}$ and $\mathcal{N}$ intersect.	Given
The intersection of $\mathcal{M}$ and $\mathcal{N}$ is a line.	Postulate 1–6: If two planes intersect, then their intersection is a line.
14. $\mathcal{L}$ is a plane.	Given
P, Q, and R are noncollinear points.	Postulate 1–4: A plane contains at least three points *not* on the same line.
15. ℓ is a line.	Given
ℓ contains at least 2 points.	Postulate 1–3: A line contains at least two points.
16. *P* and *Q* are two points.	Given
There is exactly one line through P and Q.	Postulate 1–1: Through any two points there is exactly one line.
17. ℓ is a line and *P* is a point *not* on ℓ.	Given
Exactly one plane contains ℓ and P.	Theorem 1–1: If there is a line and a point *not* on the line, then there is exactly one plane that contains them.
18. *R* and *S* lie in $\mathcal{R}$.	Given
$\overleftrightarrow{RS}$ lies in $\mathcal{R}$.	Postulate 1–5: If two points lie in a plane, then the entire line containing those two points lies in that plane.

For each of the following theorems, name the given, the prove statement, and draw a diagram you would use in a formal proof. For answers to exercises 19-22, see the Teacher's Guide.

19. If two planes intersect, then their intersection contains at least two points.

20. If two lines intersect, then at least one plane contains both lines.

21. Two intersecting lines contain at least three points.

22. A plane contains at least three lines.

23. Complete the reasons for the incomplete proof that follows.

Theorem: If two planes intersect, then their intersection contains at least two points.

Given: $\mathcal{M}$ and $\mathcal{N}$ intersect.

Prove: The intersection of $\mathcal{M}$ and $\mathcal{N}$ contains points *A* and *B*.

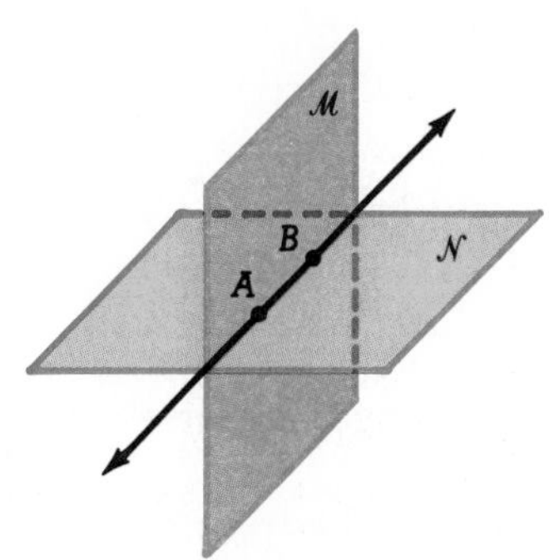

Proof:

STATEMENTS	REASONS
1. $\mathcal{M}$ and $\mathcal{N}$ intersect.	1. Given
2. The intersection of $\mathcal{M}$ and $\mathcal{N}$ is line ℓ.	2. Post. 1-6
3. Line ℓ contains points *A* and *B*.	3. Post. 1-3

topics in geometry

Finite Geometry

Point, line, and *plane* are undefined terms of geometry. The postulates of geometry describe the fundamental properties of these terms. *Different* geometries can be made by changing the undefined terms and postulates.

A miniature geometry can be created by changing the interpretation of *point, line,* and *plane.*

Postulate 1 For every two points, there is exactly one line that contains them.

Postulate 2 If a line contains two distinct points of a plane, it is contained in the plane.

Postulate 3 For any three points, there is at least one plane containing them. For any three non-collinear points, there is exactly one plane containing them.

Postulate 4 If two distinct planes intersect, then their intersection is a line.

Postulate 5 Every line contains at least two points, every plane contains at least three noncollinear points, and space contains exactly four noncoplanar points.

The following three-dimensional figure is one model for the miniature geometry.

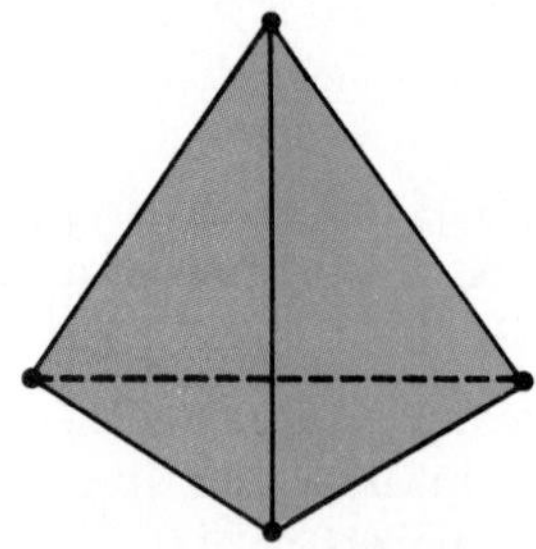

Each dot represents a point.
Each edge represents a line.
Each surface represents a plane.

Check this model against each postulate.

Using Postulates 1–5, the following theorems can be proven.

Theorem 1 If two lines intersect, the intersection contains exactly one point.

Theorem 2 A line and a point not on that line are contained in exactly one plane.

Theorem 3 Every line contains exactly two points.

Theorem 4 Every plane contains exactly three points.

Theorem 5 Every plane contains exactly three lines.

Exercises **Answer each of the following.**

1. How many points are in the geometry?
2. How many lines are in the geometry?
3. How many planes are in the geometry?
4. Name the postulates or theorems that justify the conclusions of Theorem 5.

1. 4 via postulate 5 2. 6 via postulate 5 and Theorem 3 3. 4 via postulate 5 and Theorem 4 4. Theorem 4, Post. 5, Post. 1

1–7 Inverses and Contrapositives

Objective: to write inverses and contrapositives of conditional statements

A statement formed by denying another statement is called a **negation.**

SUN	MON	TUE	WED	THU	FRI	SAT
		1	2	3	4	5
6	7	8	9	10	11	12
13	14	15	16	17	18	19
20	21	22	23	24	25	26
27	28	29	30			

Sentence Today is Sunday.

Negation Today is *not* Sunday.

Sentence Three points are noncollinear.

Negation Three points are collinear.

If a statement is true, then its negation is false. If a statement is false, then its negation is true.

A statement and its negation cannot both be true, nor can they both be false at the same time.

The negation of a statement may be written several ways. Some times a statement may *appear* to be the negation of another, when it is *not*.

example

1 **Name which statements are negations of the following statement.**

The point is on the line.

a. No point is on the line.
b. The point is *not* on the line.
c. The line is *not* the point.
d. The line does *not* contain the point.
e. The point is *not* the line.

Only **b** and **d** are negations of the given statement.

Given a conditional statement, its **inverse** can be formed by *negating* both the hypothesis and conclusion.

Statement If a figure is a square, then the figure is a rectangle.

Inverse If a figure is *not* a square, then the figure is *not* a rectangle.

As the example shows, the inverse of a true statement may *not* be true. A figure may *not* be a square but could be a rectangle.

Conditional statements also have **contrapositives.** A contrapositive statement is formed by interchanging the hypothesis and conclusion, and negating both.

Statement	If a figure is a square, then the figure is a rectangle.
Contrapositive	If a figure is *not* a rectangle, then the figure is *not* a square.

The contrapositive of a true statement is *always* a true statement. The contrapositive of a false statement is *always* a false statement.

example

2 Write the inverse and contrapositive of the following true statement. Determine whether or *not* they are true.

If two points lie in a plane, then the entire line containing the points lies in that plane.

Inverse If two points do *not* lie in a plane, then the entire line containing the points does *not* lie in the plane.

In this case, the inverse is true. Note points A and B on the figure.

Contrapositive If one entire line containing two points does *not* lie in a plane, then the two points do *not* both lie in the plane.

The contrapositive of a true statement is *always* true.

EN: Ex: 1-11 odds, Wr: 2-42 evens; AV: Ex: 1-11 odds; Wr: 1-41 odd; pp. 24-5, Wr: 2-77 evens

exercises

For answers to exercises 1-12, see the Teacher's Guide.

Exploratory **State the negation for each of the following.**

1. A figure is a triangle.
2. Two points lie in a plane.
3. Three points are collinear.
4. A figure is a polygon.
5. $\mathcal{M}$ intersects $\mathcal{N}$.
6. $\overleftrightarrow{AB}$ does *not* intersect $\mathcal{M}$.
7. ℓ does *not* lie in $\mathcal{M}$.
8. ℓ intersects t.
9. P, Q, and R are noncoplanar.
10. A, B, and C are noncollinear.
11. Two points lie in different planes.
12. Two lines are in distinct planes.

FN: Ex: 1-12, Wr: 1-42; pp. 24-25, Wr: 2-22 evens

Written **Determine whether or *not* each sentence is a negation of the given sentence. Write *yes* or *no*.**

$^{-}1$ is a real number.

1. yes if limited to the complex number system, otherwise no

1. $^{-}1$ is an imaginary number.

2. $^{-}1$ is really a number. no

3. 1 is a real number. no

4. $^{-}1$ is *not* really a number. no

5. $^{-}1$ is *not* a real number. yes

6. $^{-}1$ is a rational number. no

A triangle has four sides.

7. A triangle has three sides. no

8. A triangle does *not* have sides. no

9. A triangle has *no* sides. no

10. A triangle does *not* have four sides. yes

11. Four triangles have sides. no

12. A triangle has foresight. no

Tomorrow it will rain.

13. It will *not* rain tomorrow. yes

14. Tomorrow it won't rain. yes

15. Tomorrow the sun will shine. no

16. It will *not* rain today. no

17. Tomorrow it will *not* rain. yes

18. Today it will rain. no

A and B are on a line.

19. A and B are in a plane. no

20. A and B are *not* on a line. yes

21. A and B are *not* in a plane. no

22. A and B exist. no

23. A and B are points. no

24. A and B do *not* exist. no

For answers to exercises 25-42, see the Teacher's Guide.

Write the inverse and the contrapositive for each of the following statements.

25. If it rains, then the grass gets wet.

26. If $3x = 12$, then $x = 4$.

27. If you live in Texas, then you are an American.

28. If you ride a bicycle, then you have strong legs.

29. If two lines are perpendicular, then the two lines intersect.

30. If a triangle has a right angle, then it is a right triangle.

31. If n is even, then n^2 is even.

32. If a number is rational, then it is real.

33. If an animal is a chimpanzee, then it is a mammal.

34. If you practice hard, then you will make the team.

35. Parallel lines do *not* intersect.

36. A square is *not* a triangle.

37. A square is a rectangle.

38. Integers are real numbers.

39. $x < 0$ implies $5x > 6x$.

40. $2n + 1 = 5$ implies $n = 2$.

For exercises 35-40, students can write the inverse and contrapositive in "if-then" form.

For each of the following, write the inverse, converse, and contrapositive of the statement.

41. If today is Friday, then it is *not* Sunday.

42. If you want a job, then learn how a computer works.

Vocabulary

See the Teacher's Guide for suggestions on how to use Vocabulary and Chapter Summary.

points (1)
lines (1)
plane (1)
intersect (2)
undefined terms (5)
collinear points (5)
coplanar points (5)
noncollinear points (6)
noncoplanar points (8)
conditional statements (10)
if-then form (10)
hypothesis (11)
conclusion (11)
converse (11)
if and only if form (12)
biconditional statements (12)
postulates (14)
theorems (18)
formal proofs (19)
negation (27)
inverse (27)
contrapositive (28)

Chapter Summary

1. Points have *no* dimensions. (1)

2. Lines extend indefinitely and have *no* thickness or width. (1)

3. A plane extends indefinitely in all directions and has *no* thickness. (1)

4. Two lines, or lines and planes, intersect if they have points in common. (2)

5. Guidelines for a Definition: (5)
   1. Name the term being defined.
   2. Use only undefined terms or previously defined terms.
   3. Identify the set to which the term belongs.
   4. State the properties which distinguish the term from others in its set.
   5. Make it reversible.
   6. Make it concise.

6. All conditional statements can be written in *if-then* form and may be true or false. (10)

7. The converse of a conditional statement is formed by interchanging the hypothesis and conclusion. (11)

8. Postulate 1–1: Through any two points there is exactly one line. (14)

9. Postulate 1–2: Through any three points *not* on the same line there is exactly one plane. (14)

10. Postulate 1–3: A line contains at least two points. (15)

11. Postulate 1–4: A plane contains at least three points *not* on the same line. (15)

12. Postulate 1–5: If two points lie in a plane, then the entire line containing those two points lies in that plane. (15)

13. Postulate 1–6: If two planes intersect, then their intersection is a line. (15)

14. Theorem 1–1: If there is a line and a point *not* on the line, then there is exactly one plane that contains them. (19)

15. Formal proofs have five main parts, namely, the *theorem*, the *given*, the *prove* statement, a *diagram*, and the *proof* with statements and reasons. (19)

16. Procedure for Writing Formal Proofs: (22)
    1. Write out the theorem.
    2. Draw a diagram.
    3. Write the given and the prove statement.
    4. Plan the proof.
    5. Write the proof.

17. Theorem 1–2: If two lines intersect, then exactly one plane contains both lines. (23)

18. The inverse of a conditional statement is formed by negating both the hypothesis and conclusion. (27)

19. The contrapositive of a conditional statement is formed by interchanging the hypothesis and conclusion, and negating both. (28)

Chapter Review

See the Teacher's Guide for suggestions on how to use the Chapter Review.

1–1 Draw and label a diagram to show each of the following. See student's work.

1. ℓ intersects $\mathcal{M}$ at A.
2. A and B lie on ℓ, but C does *not*.
3. P does *not* lie on $\boldsymbol{m}$.
4. P does *not* lie in $\mathcal{M}$.

1–2 Answer each of the following. For answers to exercises 5-12, see the Teacher's Guide.

5. Noncoplanar points are points that are *not* coplanar. Write a good definition for noncoplanar points without using the word coplanar.
6. They do *not* intersect is *not* a good definition. Explain why.

1–3 Rewrite each of the following conditional statements in if-then form. Identify the hypothesis and the conclusion.

7. An angle is a right angle when it has a degree measure of 90.
8. A triangle is isosceles if it has at least two sides with the same length.

9–10. Write the converse for each statement in exercises **7** and **8**.

Rewrite each of the following biconditional statements in *if and only if* form.

11. Skew lines are lines which are *not* coplanar.
12. Concurrent lines are lines which have only one point in common.

1–4 Answer each of the following.

13. Suppose a set of points consists of a plane and a line *not* in the plane. State the minimum number of points in the set. 13. 4, If the line intersects the plane, then 3 points determine the plane plus 1 point outside the plane can be paired with one of the 3 points of the plane to determine the line. Thus 3 + 1 = 4.

14. Suppose two different planes both contain A and B. Describe the intersection of the planes. $\overleftrightarrow{AB}$

1–5 Draw and label a diagram to illustrate each of the following given statements.

15. **Given:** ℓ and $\mathscr{A}$ do *not* intersect.
16. **Given:** A, B, and C are noncollinear.
17. **Given:** p and q intersect at A.
18. **Given:** $\mathscr{L}$ and m intersect at R.

For exercises 15-18, see student's work.

1–6 Use the proof below to answer the questions that follow.

Theorem: If there is a line and a point *not* on the line, then there is at least one plane that contains them.

Given: ℓ and point P *not* on ℓ

Prove: At least one plane contains ℓ and P.

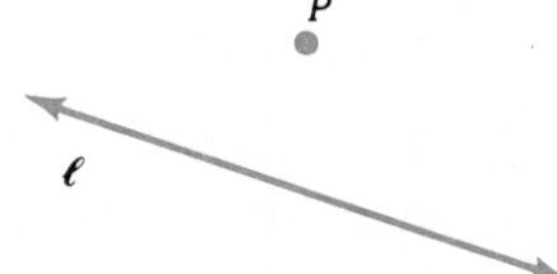

Proof:

STATEMENTS	REASONS
1. ℓ and point P *not* on ℓ.	1. Given
2. R and S on ℓ.	2. Postulate 1–3: A line contains at least two points.
3. P, S, and R are noncollinear.	3. Definition of Noncollinear Points
4. At least one plane contains R, S, and P.	4. ______
5. ______	5. Postulate 1–5: If two points lie in a plane, then the entire line containing those two points lies in that plane.

19. Complete reason **4** in the above proof. Post. 1-2

20. Complete statement **5** in the above proof. At least one plane contains ℓ and P.

For answers to exercises 21-25, see the Teacher's Guide.

1–7 Write the inverse and contrapositive for each of the following statements.

21. If it is green, then it is *not* yellow.
22. When the sun shines, the sky is blue.
23. If $2x = 8$, then $x = 4$.
24. If two points exist, then a line exists.

25. Write the inverse, converse, and contrapositive of the statement. "If the month is May, then it is *not* June." Determine whether the statements are true or false. Assume the original statement to be true.

See the Teacher's Guide for suggestions on how to use the Chapter Test.

Chapter Test

Draw and label a diagram to illustrate each of the following. For exercises 1-6, see student's work.

1. P lies in $\mathcal{M}$.
2. P, Q, and R are coplanar.
3. ℓ and m intersect at S.
4. p intersects $\mathcal{M}$ at A.
5. $\mathcal{L}$ does *not* contain A or B.
6. $\mathcal{M}$ and $\mathcal{N}$ intersect.

For answers to exercises 7-20, see the Teacher's Guide.

Rewrite each of the following conditional statements in if-then form. Identify the hypothesis and conclusion.

7. You are 16 years old only if you can drive a car.
8. When a number is an integer, it is a real number.
9. A triangle is equilateral, when it has three sides with the same measure.
10. An angle is *not* obtuse, if it is a right angle.

Write the converse for each of the following statements.

11. Statement in exercise **7**
12. Statement in exercise **8**
13. Statement in exercise **9**
14. Statement in exercise **10**

Write the inverse and the contrapositive for each of the following statements.

15. If two lines intersect, then they are *not* parallel.
16. If it snows, then the ground is white.
17. If points are collinear, then they lie on the same line.
18. If you ride a bicycle, then you have strong legs.

Write the given, the prove statement, and draw a diagram for each of the following.

19. If two lines intersect, then at least one plane contains both lines.
20. Two intersecting lines contain at least three points.

chapter 2 Measure

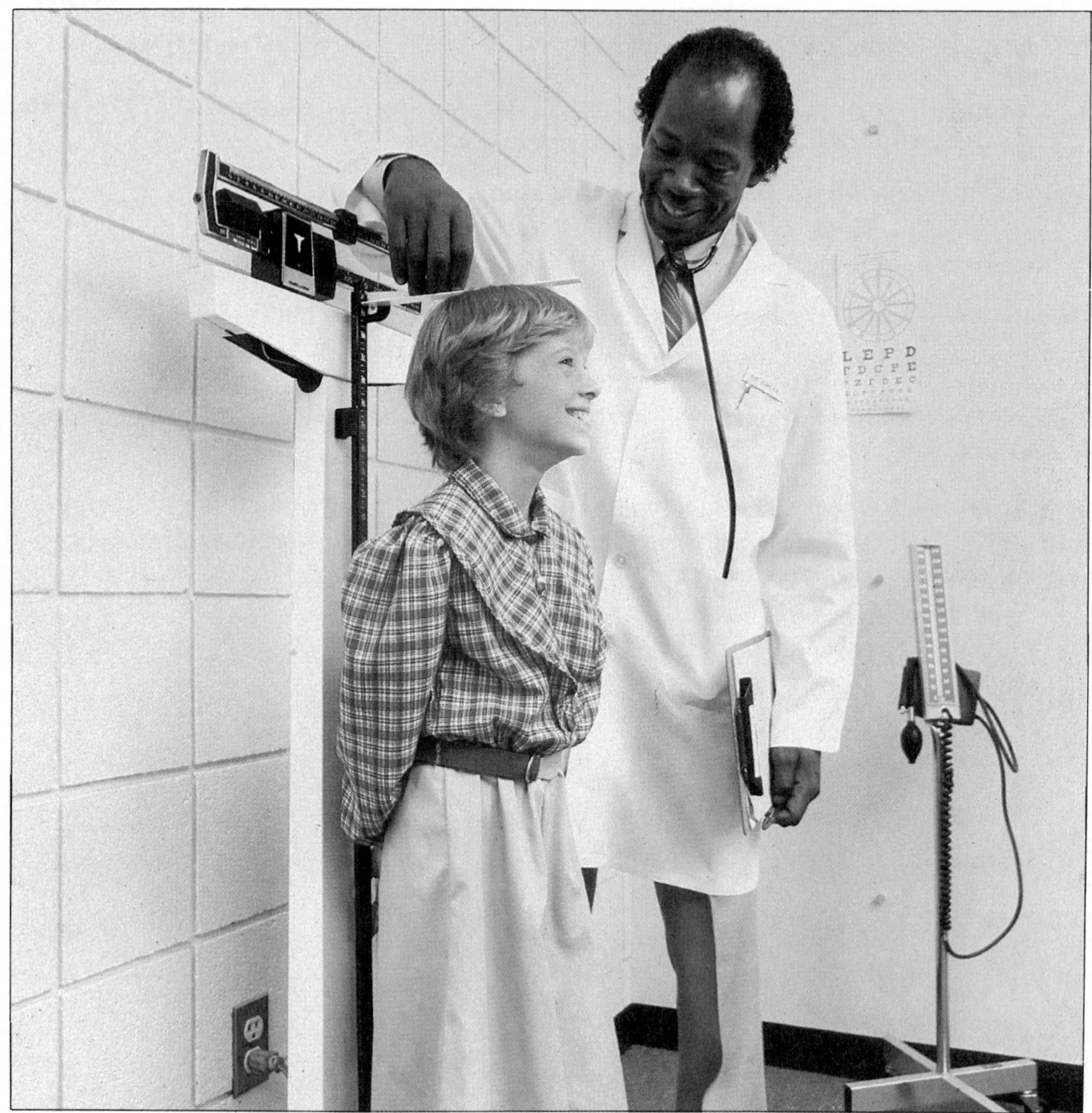

Measurement is important in many occupations. Don Whittaker is a nurse. He is measuring the height of a patient.

Objectives: to state the coordinates of points on the number line, to convert fractions to decimals, and vice versa

2–1 Number Lines

A point has *no* size or shape. However, it does have a position. Numbers can be used to name the positions of different points on a line.

The following figure is a **number line.** Some points on the line and their corresponding numbers are shown. These numbers are called **whole numbers.**

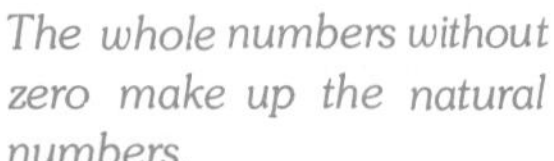

The whole numbers without zero make up the natural numbers.

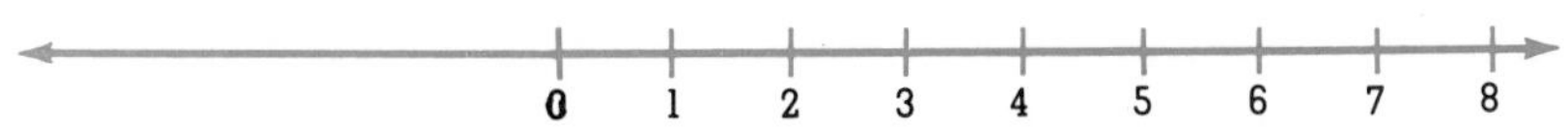

Negative numbers usually are used to name points to the left of zero. The following number line shows the **integers.** Notice that each positive integer can be paired with a negative integer, which is its opposite.

Remind students that the numbers continue indefinitely in both the positive and negative directions.

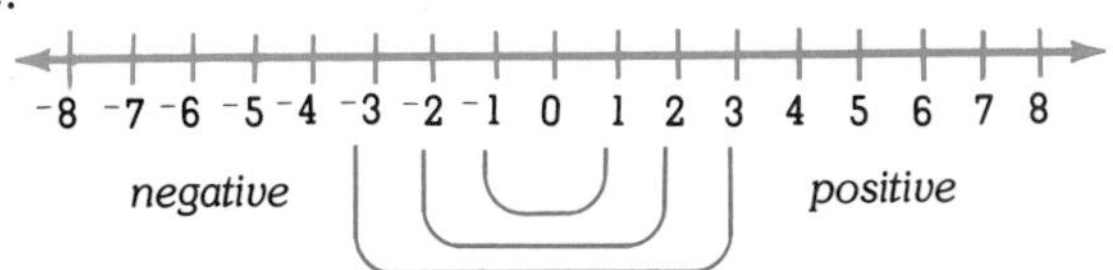

Many numbers can be expressed in the form $\frac{a}{b}$, where a and b denote integers and b is *not* zero. Any number of this type is called a **rational number.** The following number line shows some rational numbers.

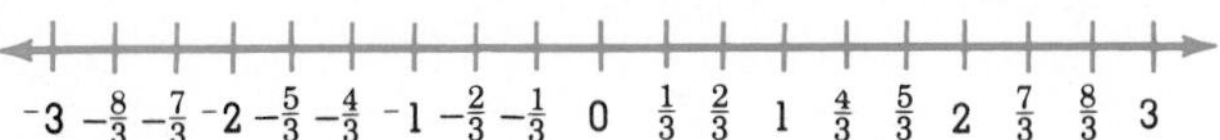

Every rational number can be written in decimal form as well as in fractional form. To change a fraction to a decimal, divide the numerator by the denominator.

1 Change $\frac{5}{8}$ to a decimal.

```
   0.625
8)5.000
  4 8
    20
    16
     40
     40
      0  ← remainder
```

The decimal form of $\frac{5}{8}$ is 0.625.

Notice that the division process in Example **1** stops or terminates when a remainder of 0 occurs. The resulting decimal quotient in these cases is called a **terminating decimal.**

A decimal in which a digit or a group of digits repeat is called a **repeating decimal.**

To terminate, the denominator must have factors of 2 and/or 5.

example

2 Change $\frac{1}{3}$ to a decimal.

$$\begin{array}{r} 0.333\ldots \\ 3\overline{)1.000} \\ \underline{9} \\ 10 \\ \underline{9} \\ 10 \\ \underline{9} \\ 1 \end{array}$$

← *remainder*

Notice that the same remainder, 1, repeats. Thus, the same quotient digit, 3, repeats.

The decimal form of $\frac{1}{3}$ is 0.333. . .

Point out that a fraction such as $2\frac{3}{4}$ changes to 2.75 in decimal form.

A repeating decimal can be indicated by placing a *bar* over the digit or digits that repeat. Thus, 0.333 . . . can be written as $0.\overline{3}$.

You can change a three-digit repeating decimal to a fraction by the following method.

example

3 Change $0.\overline{345}$ to a fraction.

Let $x = 0.\overline{345}$ — *By definition $0.\overline{345}$ means 0.345345. . .*

Multiply both sides by 1000. — *Why is 1000 chosen?*

$$\begin{aligned} 1000\,x &= 345.\overline{345} \\ x &= 0.\overline{345} \\ \hline 999\,x &= 345 \end{aligned}$$

Subtract the original equation.

$$\frac{999}{999}x = \frac{345}{999}$$

Divide both sides by 999.

$$x = \frac{345}{999}$$

Change $\frac{345}{999}$ to simplest form.

$$x = \frac{115}{333}$$

The fractional form of $0.\overline{345}$ is $\frac{115}{333}$.

Some decimals are nonterminating and nonrepeating. For example, the decimal name for π is nonterminating and nonrepeating. Nonterminating, nonrepeating decimals represent **irrational numbers.** The following is the decimal approximation for π to 26 decimal places.

Ask students whether or not 1.020020002 . . . is irrational.

$$\pi \text{ is } 3.14159265358979323846264338 \ldots$$

Taken together, the rational numbers and irrational numbers make up the **real numbers.** Each point on a number line can be named by a real number.

Unless otherwise stated, the word number *means real number.*

Each real number corresponds to exactly one point on a number line. Each point on a number line corresponds to exactly one real number.

Postulate 2–1 Number Line Postulate

The number associated with a point on a number line is called the **coordinate** of the point. On the number line below, the coordinate of A is $^-7$. The coordinate of B is 2.

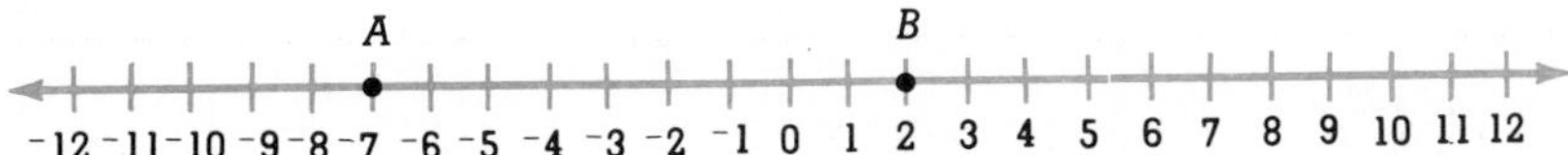

exercises

EN: Wr: 1-35 odds, 37-52; AV: Ex: 1-23 odds, Wr: 1-42

Exploratory **State the coordinate of each of the following points on the number lines below.**

1. H 1	2. F -1	3. B -8	4. E -2
5. G 0	6. A -10	7. J 5	8. K 7
9. C -6	10. I 3	11. D -4	12. L 9

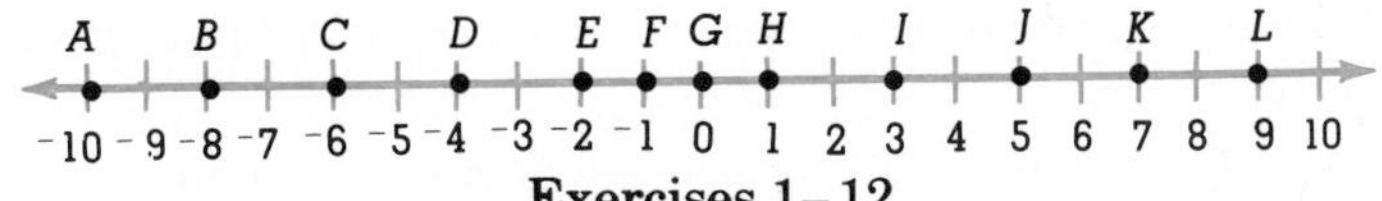

Exercises 1–12

13. T	14. S	15. Q	16. V
17. P	18. R	19. X	20. W
21. M	22. N	23. Y	24. Z

13. $\frac{2}{3}$ 14. $\frac{1}{3}$ 15. $-\frac{4}{3}$ 16. 1 17. -3 18. $-\frac{2}{3}$ 19. $\frac{7}{3}$ 20. $\frac{5}{3}$ 21. $-\frac{1}{3}$ 22. $-\frac{5}{3}$ 23. 0 24. $-\frac{7}{3}$

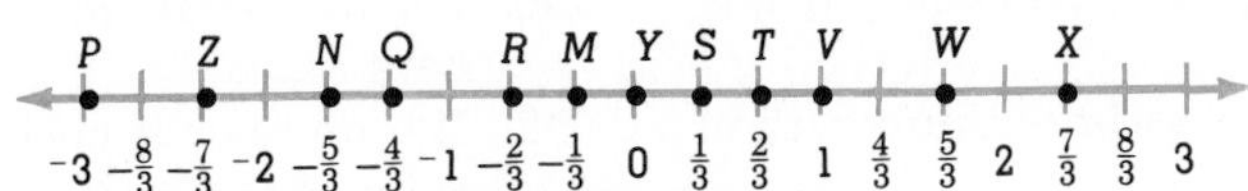

Exercises 13–14

FN: Ex: 1-24, Wr: 1-51 odds

Written **Change each fraction to decimal form.**

1. $\frac{3}{10}$ 0.3
2. $\frac{1}{4}$ 0.25
3. $-\frac{4}{5}$ -0.8
4. $\frac{7}{8}$ 0.875
5. $-\frac{3}{4}$ -0.75
6. $\frac{5}{8}$ 0.625
7. $\frac{2}{3}$ $0.\overline{6}$
8. $-\frac{3}{7}$ $-0.\overline{428571}$
9. $\frac{4}{12}$ $0.\overline{3}$
10. $-\frac{5}{6}$ $-0.8\overline{3}$
11. $\frac{4}{9}$ $0.\overline{4}$
12. $\frac{1}{12}$ $0.08\overline{3}$

Change each mixed numeral to decimal form.

13. $1\frac{1}{5}$ 1.2
14. $3\frac{3}{4}$ 3.75
15. $^-2\frac{7}{10}$ -2.7
16. $^-4\frac{3}{8}$ -4.375
17. $2\frac{2}{3}$ $2.\overline{6}$
18. $^-2\frac{1}{6}$ $-2.1\overline{6}$
19. $^-7\frac{1}{7}$ $-7.\overline{142857}$
20. $5\frac{2}{9}$ $5.\overline{2}$
21. $3 + \left(-\frac{2}{3}\right)$ $2.\overline{3}$
22. $^-5 + \frac{3}{8}$ -4.625
23. $^-2 + \frac{1}{9}$ $-1.\overline{8}$
24. $6 + \left(-\frac{4}{5}\right)$ 5.2

Change each repeating decimal to a fraction in simplest form.

25. $0.\overline{7}$ 7/9
26. $0.\overline{23}$ 23/99
27. $0.\overline{5}$ 5/9
28. $0.3\overline{27}$ 18/55
29. $0.\overline{524}$ 524/999
30. $0.\overline{231}$ 77/333
31. $1.\overline{2}$ 11/9
32. $4.2\overline{6}$ 64/15
33. $2.\overline{36}$ 26/11
34. $6.\overline{02}$ 596/99
35. $1.\overline{26}$ 125/99
36. $1.\overline{162}$ 43/37

Complete the following chart. Write yes or no.

	Number	$\frac{\pi}{2}$	$^-13$	0.07	$^-11\frac{2}{3}$	$0.6\overline{6}$	π	6.9	$\frac{5}{4}$	$1.7\overline{421}$	0
37.	Natural Number	No	No	No	No	No	No	No	No	No	No
38.	Whole Number	No	No	No	No	No	No	No	No	No	Yes
39.	Integer	No	Yes	No	No	No	No	No	No	No	Yes
40.	Rational Number	No	Yes	Yes	Yes	Yes	No	Yes	Yes	Yes	Yes
41.	Irrational Number	Yes	No	No	No	No	Yes	No	No	No	No
42.	Real Number	Yes	Yes	Yes	Yes	Yes	Yes	Yes	Yes	Yes	Yes

Determine whether each statement is *true* or *false*. If it is false, give an example that supports your answer.

43. All whole numbers are integers. True.

44. When a number is an integer, it is a whole number.
44. False. -5 is an integer but not a whole number.

45. No whole numbers are natural numbers.
False. 2 is a natural number and a whole number.

46. A number is a real number if it is a rational number. False. π is a real number but not a rational number.

47. If a number is *not* a real number, then it is *not* an irrational number. True.

48. When a number is a whole number, then it is a rational number. True

49. A number is a rational number if it is a natural number.

50. No irrational numbers are whole numbers. True.

51. If a number is *not* a natural number, then it is a rational number. False. π is not a natural number and is not a rational number.

52. If a number is positive, then it is a natural number. False. $\frac{1}{2}$ is positive and not a natural number.

49. False. $\frac{1}{2}$ is a rational number but not a natural number.

Objective: to find absolute value, to find the distance between two points

2–2 Distance

Many different rulers may be used to make measurements. The Ruler Postulate states this assumption.

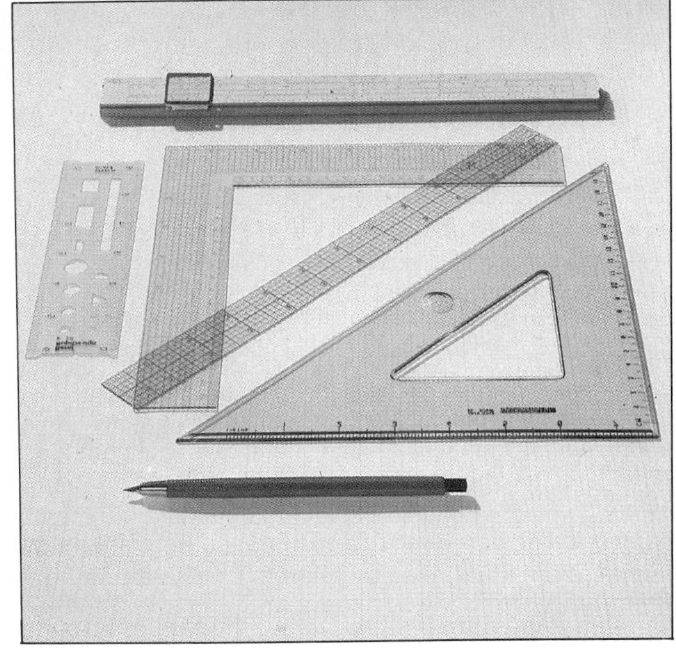

The positive number chosen by the Ruler Postulate determines the unit of measure.

A measurement always has two parts: a number and a unit.

The points on any line can be paired with the real numbers so that, given any two points *P* and *Q* on the line, *P* corresponds to zero, and *Q* corresponds to a positive number.

Postulate 2–2
Ruler Postulate

When a measurement is made, a number called the **measure** is associated with a unit, called the **unit of measure.**

A line that has a specific ordered assignment of numbers to points is called a number line.

Suppose you measure the width of a window, first using 1 inch as the unit and then using 1 centimeter as the unit. Although the width of the window remains the same, the measures, units, and measurements differ.

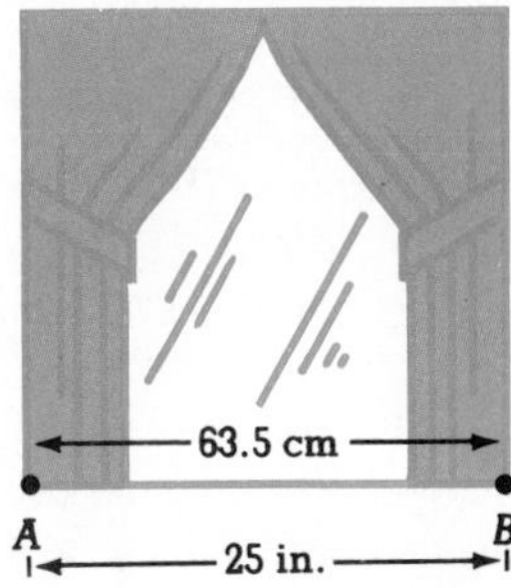

The window is 25 inches wide.

The measure is 25.
The unit of measure is 1 inch.
The measurement is 25 inches.

The window is 63.5 centimeters wide.

The measure is 63.5.
The unit of measure is 1 centimeter.
The measurement is 63.5 centimeters.

Given a certain unit of measure, the measure of the distance between two points is unique.

Emphasize that the measure is a unique positive number.

For any two points on a line and a given unit of measure, there is a unique positive number called the measure of the distance between the two points.

Postulate 2–3 Distance Postulate

The unit of measure is not always stated. If no units are stated, you can assume that the same unit is used for all measurements.

Suppose you want to find the measure of the distance between A and B on the number line below.

On a number line, the markings are placed at equal intervals apart.

A B

−6 −5 −4 −3 −2 −1 0 1 2 3 4 5 6

To find the measure of the distance, first identify the coordinates of A and B. Then, find the absolute value of the difference of the coordinates.

Use the Exploratory Exercises to help review absolute value.

$$|5 - 1| = |4| = 4 \qquad \text{or} \qquad |1 - 5| = |{}^{-}4| = 4$$

The measure of the distance between A and B is 4. To indicate this measure, write AB. Thus, in the example above, $AB = 4$.

example

1 Find *CD*, *CB*, *AB*, and *AC*.

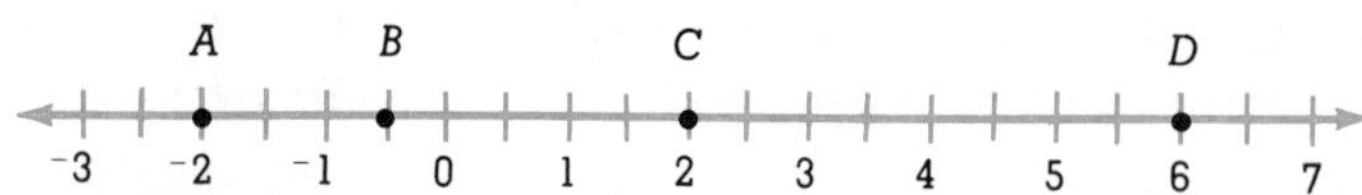

The markings are placed at equal intervals.

$$CD = |6 - 2| = |4| \text{ or } 4$$

$$CB = \left|-\tfrac{1}{2} - 2\right| = \left|{}^{-}2\tfrac{1}{2}\right| \text{ or } 2\tfrac{1}{2}$$

$$AB = \left|-\tfrac{1}{2} - {}^{-}2\right| = \left|1\tfrac{1}{2}\right| \text{ or } 1\tfrac{1}{2}$$

$$AC = |2 - {}^{-}2| = |4| \text{ or } 4$$

Since $CD = DC$, either $|2 - 6|$ or $|6 - 2|$ can be used to find CD. List the other ways to find CB, AB, and AC.

example

2 **Find *PQ*, *QR*, *PS*, and *RS*.**

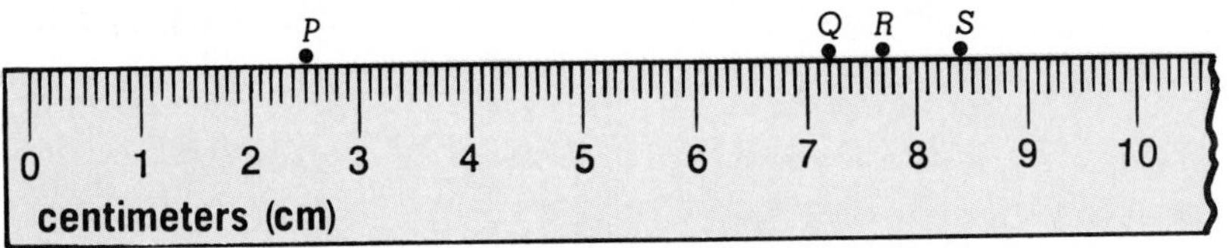

$PQ = |7.2 - 2.5|$
$= |4.7|$ or 4.7

$QR = |7.7 - 7.2|$
$= |0.5|$ or 0.5

$PS = |8.4 - 2.5|$
$= |5.9|$ or 5.9

$RS = |8.4 - 7.7|$
$= |0.7|$ or 0.7

The symbol RR represents the distance from point R to point R. Thus, $RR = 0$. For example, if the coordinate of R is 5, then RR = |5 - 5| or 0.

exercises

EN: Ex: 1-8, 26-40 evens, Wr: 6-60 evens; AV: Ex: 2-40 evens, Wr: 1-65 odds; p. 38, Wr: 43-52

Exploratory **State the absolute value for each of the following.**

1. 12 12
2. $^-33$ 33
3. 30 30
4. 90 90
5. $^-15$ 15
6. 17 17
7. 11 11
8. $^-7$ 7
9. $^-3$ 3
10. $^-61$ 61
11. 89 89
12. 39 39
13. $^-44$ 44
14. 97 97
15. $^-52$ 52
16. $^-58$ 58
17. $^-2.3$ 2.3
18. $7\frac{1}{2}$ $7\frac{1}{2}$
19. $-\frac{3}{4}$ $\frac{3}{4}$
20. $^-0.88$ 0.88
21. $^-12\frac{7}{8}$ $12\frac{7}{8}$
22. $^-0.01$ 0.01
23. 10.02 10.02
24. $\frac{1}{4}$ $\frac{1}{4}$

Identify each of the following statements as true or false.

25. $AB = 3$ True
26. $BA = {}^-3$ False
27. $CD = DC$ True
28. $BB = 0$ True
29. $CA = BD$ False
30. $CD = {}^-2$ False
31. $BA = AD$ True
32. $AC = CA$ True

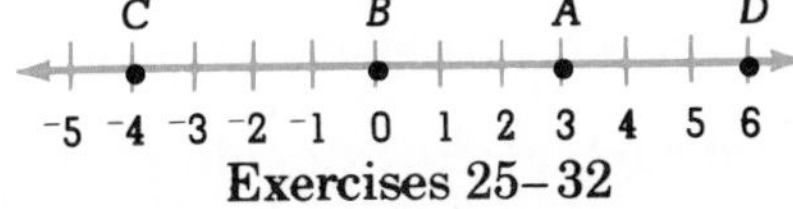

Exercises 25–32

33. $QR = \left|\frac{5}{2} - \frac{3}{2}\right|$ False
34. $RQ = \left|-\frac{3}{2} - \frac{5}{2}\right|$ True
35. $ST = \left|0 - \frac{3}{2}\right|$ True
36. $RT = -\left|\frac{3}{2} - \left(-\frac{3}{2}\right)\right|$ False
37. $^-ST = {}^-SR$ True
38. $SQ = -\frac{5}{2}$ False
39. $TQ = 2$ False
40. $QT = 1$ True

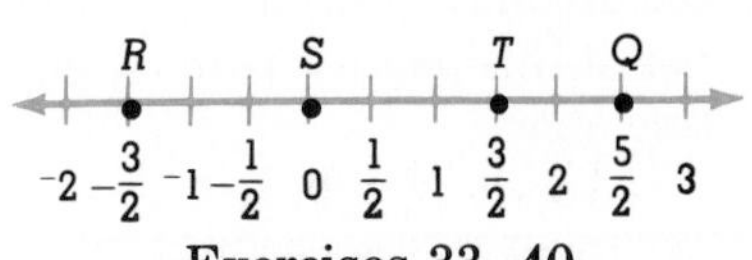

Exercises 33–40

FN: Ex: 1-40, Wr: 1-57 odds; p. 38, Wr: 2-50 evens

Written **Find each difference.**

1. $28 - 19$ 9
2. $4 - 7$ -3
3. $0 - 12$ -12
4. $24 - 42$ -18
5. $^-27 - 42$ -69
6. $^-59 - 38$ -97
7. $^-77 - 76$ -153
8. $^-99 - 29$ -128
9. $^-6 - {}^-17$ 11
10. $^-17 - {}^-23$ 6
11. $^-115 - {}^-28$ -87
12. $^-9 - {}^-12$ 3
13. $^-78 - {}^-19$ -59
14. $0 - {}^-35$ 35
15. $^-41 - {}^-36$ -5

Find each value.

16. $|2 - {}^-2|$ 4
17. $|{}^-2 - {}^-5|$ 3
18. $|0 - {}^-6|$ 6
19. $|5 - {}^-4|$ 9
20. $|3.6 - 9.2|$ 5.6
21. $|{}^-5.4 - 7.8|$ 13.2
22. $|7.7 - {}^-7.2|$ 14.9
23. $\left|{}^-5\frac{1}{4} - {}^-2\frac{1}{2}\right|$ $2\frac{3}{4}$
24. $\left|9\frac{3}{5} - {}^-6\right|$ $15\frac{3}{5}$
25. $\left|9 - {}^-2\frac{3}{4}\right|$ $11\frac{3}{4}$
26. $\left|6\frac{1}{3} - 8\frac{2}{3}\right|$ $2\frac{1}{3}$
27. $\left|{}^-2\frac{2}{3} - 2\frac{1}{6}\right|$ $4\frac{5}{6}$

Use the number line below to find each measure.

28. *AB* 5/6
29. *CD* 1/3
30. *DA* 2
31. *AE* 3 2/3
32. *BE* 2 5/6
33. *BC* 5/6
34. *AC* 1 2/3
35. *BD* 1 1/6
36. *AA* 0
37. *EC* 2
38. *ED* 1 2/3
39. *AD* 2
40. *CC* 0
41. *DC* 1/3
42. *CA* 1 2/3

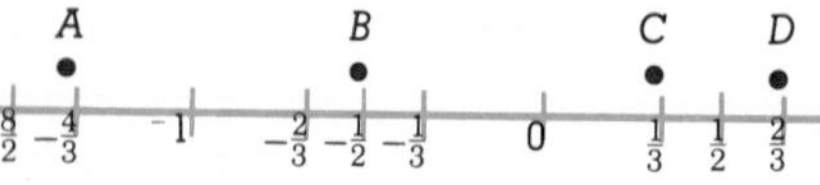
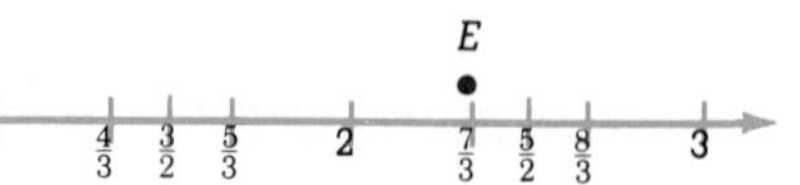

Use the ruler to find each measure.

43. *PQ* 0.3
44. *RS* 0.4
45. *SP* 1.1
46. *PT* 2.6
47. *QT* 2.3
48. *QR* 0.4
49. *PR* 0.7
50. *QS* 0.8
51. *SS* 0
52. *TR* 1.9
53. *TS* 1.5
54. *PS* 1.1
55. *RR* 0
56. *SR* 0.4
57. *RP* 0.7

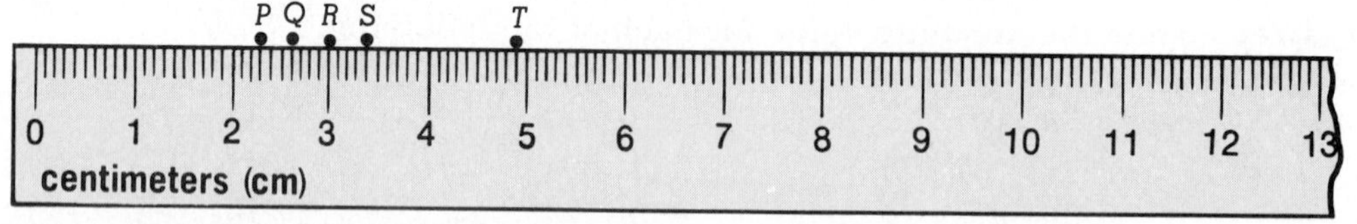

Given a number line marked in units, answer each of the following.

58. Beginning at coordinate $^-3$, move to the left 2 units then to the right 6 units. What is the coordinate of the new position? 1
59. Beginning at coordinate 8, move to the right 6 units then to the left 10 units. What is the coordinate of the new position? 4
60. Beginning at coordinate $^-9$, move to coordinate 5, then to coordinate $^-1$. What is the total distance you have traveled? 20
61. Beginning at coordinate 3, move to coordinate $^-7$, then to coordinate 2. What is the total distance you have traveled? 19

62-64. See student's work.

Find each of the following measurements using either an inch or centimeter ruler.

62. the length of the binding of this book
63. the length of your pencil
64. the distance from the lower left hand corner of this page to point *E* on the number line above
65. the length of the part of the number line above from arrow to arrow

65. approximately 15.5 cm or $6\frac{1}{16}$ inches

Percents — algebra review

Exercises **Solve each of the following.**

1. 15% of 80 is 12.
2. 112% of 500 is 560.
3. 81% of 32 is 25.92.
4. 98% of 140 is 137.2.
5. 2.5% of 84 is 2.1.
6. 10 is 20% of 50.
7. 37 is 12.5% of 296.
8. 18 is 30% of 60.
9. 55 is 62.5% of 88.
10. 8 is 20% of 40.
11. 16 is 40% of 40.
12. 17 is 25% of 68.

History of Computers

One of the first computing instruments was the abacus, which originated more than 5,000 years ago. The abacus uses several rows of beads to represent numbers. Each row stands for a place-value position, and the arrangement of beads in a row stands for a digit. The abacus is still used in some parts of the Middle and Far East.

The earliest mechanical calculating devices date to the beginning of the 1600's. These devices used gears, wheels, cranks, and levers to input data. In 1642, the French scientist-philosopher Blaise Pascal built a successful digital calculating machine to help him with calculations for his father's business accounts. Pascal's device carried out its computations by a process of integer counting. The machine used a mechanical gear system to add and subtract numbers, with as many as eight columns of digits.

In 1835 the English inventor Charles Babbage developed the "Analytical Engine." This device was able to combine arithmetic processes with decisions based on its own computations. It consisted of two basic components. The first component was a storage unit, with a memory device consisting of groups of 50 counter wheels that could store 1,000 figures of 50 digits each. The second component was the mill, an arithmetic desk-calculator section.

Many of Babbage's ideas were used by the U.S. statistician, Herman Hollerith. Hollerith designed a machine used to tabulate the 1890 United States census. His machine used punched cards and electric relays.

As a result of Hollerith's machine, the data for the 1890 census was classified and counted in one-third the time it had taken with the handwritten tally sheets used in the 1880 census.

During World War II, the U.S. Army needed to find a way to rapidly calculate firing and bombing targets. The Army sent a young mathematician, Herman H. Goldstine, to work with two engineers, John Mauchly and J. P. Eckert, at the Moore School of Engineering at the University of Pennsylvania. They developed a computer called ENIAC (Electronic Numerical Integrator And Computer) that used vacuum tubes instead of relays. Then, in the late 1950's and early 1960's, computers were developed that used transistors. These computers were faster, smaller, and more reliable than earlier models. Since the 1960's, computers have become much more miniaturized. Now, the circuits for an entire computer can be printed on chips, which will fit on your fingertip.

Objectives: to recognize properties of segments, to recognize the relationships of betweeneness

2–3 Segments and midpoints

Look at the figure at the right. Point Q is between P and R. Points $W, X, Y,$ and Z are *not* between P and R. In geometry, **between** is defined in the following way.

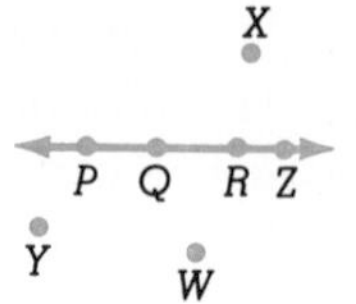

Unless stated otherwise, betweenness and collinearity of points may be assumed if they are given in a diagram.

Emphasize this assumption regarding points on a diagram.

A point Q is between points P and R if and only if each of the following conditions hold.
1. P, Q, and R are collinear
2. $PQ + QR = PR$.

Definition of Between

Emphasize that the two conditions must be satisfied

example

1 Show that Z is *not* between P and R in the figure below.

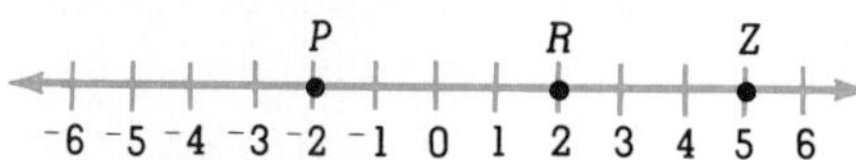

$$PZ + ZR \stackrel{?}{=} PR$$
$$|{}^-2 - 5| + |5 - 2| \stackrel{?}{=} |{}^-2 - 2|$$
$$7 + 3 \stackrel{?}{=} 4$$
$$10 \neq 4$$

Thus, $PZ + ZR \neq PR$.

Since the three points do *not* satisfy condition 2 of the definition of between, Z is *not* between P and R.

Emphasize that $\overline{AB}$ refers to the segment and that AB refers to the measure of the segment.

The part of the line below that includes points A and B and all the points between them is called a **segment.** Points A and B are called the *endpoints* of the segment.

Segment AB can be written $\overline{AB}$ or $\overline{BA}$.

The *length* of a segment is the distance between the two endpoints of the segment. The **midpoint** of a segment separates it into two segments of equal length.

Remind students that there are two requirements for a point to be a midpoint.

A point M is the midpoint of a segment, $\overline{PQ}$, if and only if M is between P and Q, and $PM = MQ$.

Definition of Midpoint

For extra practice show that -4 names the midpoint of the segment with endpoints -7 and -1; also show that 1 names the midpoint of the segment with endpoints 0 and 2.

example

2 Show that M is the midpoint of $\overline{PQ}$.

P M Q

$^-7$ $^-6$ $^-5$ $^-4$ $^-3$ $^-2$ $^-1$ 0 1 2 3 4 5 6 7

There are two conditions to be met.

1. Show that M is between P and Q.
   Assume from the figure that all three points are collinear.

$$PM + MQ \stackrel{?}{=} PQ$$
$$|^-5 - ^-1| + |^-1 - 3| \stackrel{?}{=} |^-5 - 3|$$
$$|^-4| + |^-4| \stackrel{?}{=} |^-8|$$
$$8 = 8$$

2. Show that $PM = MQ$.

$$PM \stackrel{?}{=} MQ$$
$$|^-5 - ^-1| \stackrel{?}{=} |^-1 - 3|$$
$$|^-4| \stackrel{?}{=} |^-4|$$
$$4 = 4$$

Since both conditions are met, M is the midpoint of $\overline{PQ}$.

Because distance is defined as unique, the midpoint of a segment is unique.

If a segment is given, then it has exactly one midpoint.

Theorem 2–1

AR: refers to Algebra Review Exercises

exercises

EN: Wr: 1-41 odds; AV: Ex: 1-10, Wr: 1-41 odds; p. 42, AR: 1-12

Exploratory **Use the number line below to state the coordinates of the endpoints for each of the following segments.**

1. $\overline{CD}$ C = -1, D = 0 **2.** $\overline{BF}$ B = -4, F = 6 **3.** $\overline{AG}$ A = -8, G = 9 **4.** $\overline{EB}$ E = 3, B = -4

5. $\overline{BA}$ B = -4, A = -8 **6.** $\overline{CG}$ C = -1, G = 9 **7.** $\overline{FE}$ F = 6, E = 3 **8.** $\overline{GA}$ G = 9, A = -8

9. $\overline{AD}$ A = -8, D = 0 **10.** $\overline{BE}$ B = -4, E = 3 **11.** $\overline{CF}$ C = -1, F = 6 **12.** $\overline{FG}$ F = 6, G = 9

13. $\overline{FA}$ F = 6, A = -8 **14.** $\overline{CB}$ C = -1, B = -4 **15.** $\overline{BD}$ B = -4, D = 0 **16.** $\overline{AE}$ A = -8, E = 3

17. $\overline{EF}$ E = 3, F = 6 **18.** $\overline{CE}$ C = -1, E = 3 **19.** $\overline{BG}$ B = -4, G = 9 **20.** $\overline{EG}$ E = 3, G = 9

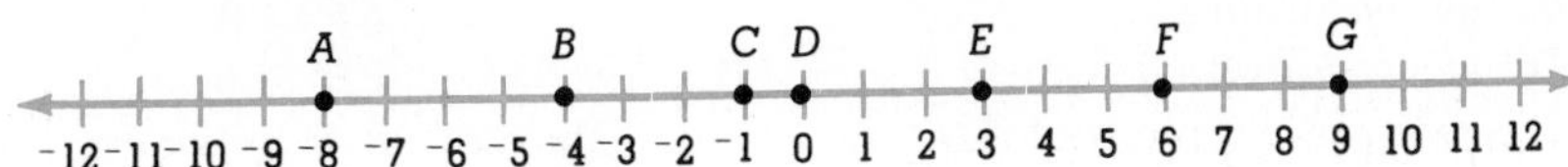

FN: Ex: 1-20, Wr.: 1-38; pp. 41-2, Wr: 2-56 evens, 59-65 odds; p. 42, AR: 1-12

Written Use the number line below to find the length of each of the following segments.

1. $\overline{CD}$ 1
2. $\overline{BF}$ 10
3. $\overline{AG}$ 17
4. $\overline{EB}$ 7
5. $\overline{BA}$ 4
6. $\overline{CG}$ 10
7. $\overline{FE}$ 3
8. $\overline{GA}$ 17
9. $\overline{AD}$ 8
10. $\overline{BE}$ 7
11. $\overline{CF}$ 7
12. $\overline{FG}$ 3
13. $\overline{FA}$ 14
14. $\overline{CB}$ 3
15. $\overline{BD}$ 4
16. $\overline{AE}$ 11
17. $\overline{EF}$ 3
18. $\overline{CE}$ 4
19. $\overline{BG}$ 13
20. $\overline{EG}$ 6

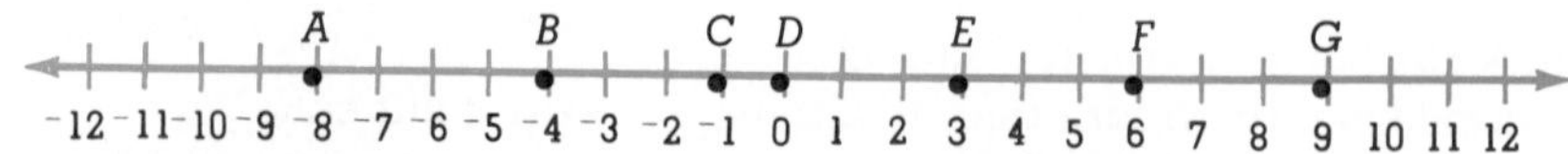

For answers to exercises 21-42, see the Teacher's Guide.

Use the number line below to answer each of the following.

21. Show that T is *not* between R and S.
22. Show that Q is *not* between V and R.
23. Show that N is *not* the midpoint of $\overline{PS}$.
24. Show that R is *not* the midpoint of $\overline{PS}$.
25. Show that Q is the midpoint of $\overline{PS}$.
26. Show that S is the midpoint of $\overline{QV}$.
27. Find the coordinate of the midpoint of $\overline{PT}$.
28. Find the coordinate of the midpoint of $\overline{NS}$.
29. Show that $NP + PQ = NQ$.
30. Show that $QT - QS = ST$.
31. Show that $RV - ST = RS + TV$.
32. Show that $QR + RS + ST = QT$.
33. Find the coordinate of the midpoint of $\overline{NT}$.
34. Show that $QR + RS = ST + TV$.

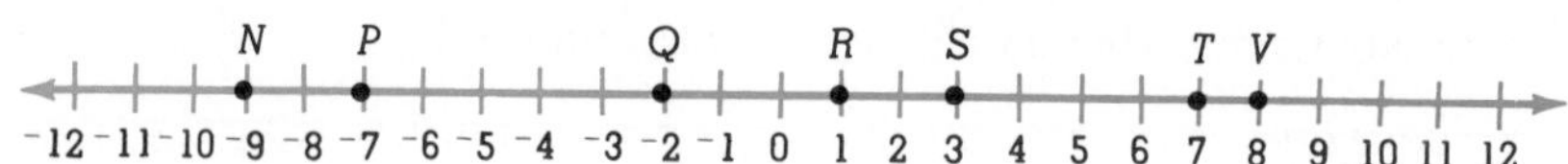

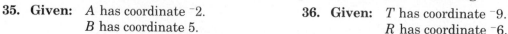

For each of the following, draw a diagram to illustrate the given. Then list definitions, postulates, or theorems that could be used to prove each of the following.

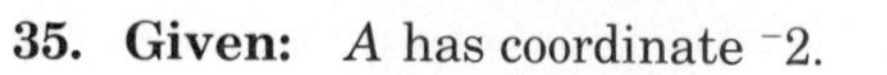

35. **Given:** A has coordinate $^{-}2$.
B has coordinate 5.
M has coordinate 1.5.
M is between A and B.
Prove: M is the midpoint of $\overline{AB}$.

36. **Given:** T has coordinate $^{-}9$.
R has coordinate $^{-}6$.
S has coordinate $^{-}3$.
R is between T and S.
Prove: R is the midpoint of $\overline{TS}$.

37. **Given:** A, B, and C are collinear.
$AB = 3$
$AC = 5$
$BC = 2$
Prove: B is between A and C.

38. **Given:** P, Q, and R are collinear.
$RQ = 6.5$
$PQ = 2.3$
Q is between P and R.
Prove: $PR = 8.8$

39. **Given:** N is the midpoint of $\overline{AB}$.
$AB = 4.5$
Prove: $NB = 2.25$

40. **Given:** M is the midpoint of $\overline{PQ}$.
$MQ = 7\frac{1}{2}$
Prove: $PM = 7\frac{1}{2}$

41. **Given:** A has coordinate $^{-}3$.
B has coordinate 0.
C has coordinate 2.
D has coordinate 3.
Prove: C is *not* the midpoint of $\overline{AD}$.

42. **Given:** E, F, and H are collinear.
$EH = 14$
$EF = 8$
$FH = 6$
Prove: F is between E and H.

Answer each of the following. X = 1 or X = -11   X = 8 or X = -2

43. The coordinate of B is $^-5$ and $AB = 6$. Find the possible coordinates of A.

44. The coordinate of P is 3 and $PQ = 5$. Find the possible coordinates of Q.

45. The coordinate of B is $^-5$ and $AB = 6$. Find the possible coordinates of the midpoint of $\overline{AB}$. M = -8

46. The coordinate of P is 3 and $PQ = 5$. Find the possible coordinates of the midpoint of $\overline{PQ}$. $M = \frac{1}{2}$

47. The coordinate of X is $^-7$ and the coordinate of the midpoint of $\overline{XY}$ is $^-1$. Find the coordinate of Y. 5

48. The coordinate of X is $-\frac{13}{5}$ and the coordinate of Y is $\frac{3\pi}{4}$. Find the coordinate of the midpoint of XY. $M = \frac{3}{8}\pi - \frac{13}{10}$

Challenge Draw a figure that satisfies the given conditions. See student's work.

1. a. $DE = EF$
b. E is *not* the midpoint of $\overline{DF}$.

2. a. Points V, W, X, Y, and Z are collinear.
b. $WY = YX$
c. V is between Y and Z.
d. X is next to V.
e. V is *not* between X and Z.

Length in the Metric System — excursions in geometry

The most widely used system of measurement is the **metric system.** It is a decimal system, which means that the units increase or decrease in size by multiples of ten.

Each kind of measurement has a basic unit. Prefixes are attached to the unit to define larger and smaller units. For example, the standard unit of length is the meter. Other commonly used units of length are kilometer, centimeter, and millimeter. This system is formally known as Systèmе International d'Unités and is abbreviated SI.

Prefix	Pronunciation	Symbol	Number of units
kilo	KIHL oh	k	1,000 (one thousand)
hecto	HEHK toh	h	100 (one hundred)
deka	DEHK uh	da	10 (ten)
deci	DEHS uh	d	0.1 (one-tenth)
centi	SEHN tuh	c	0.01 (one-hundredth)
milli	MIHL uh	m	0.001 (one-thousandth)

You may want students to convert measurements within the metric system.

The unit kilometer comes from *kilo* and *meter*. Thus, one kilometer is one thousand meters. Thirty-four kilometers is thirty-four thousand meters.

1. yes 2. no 3. no 4. no 5. yes 6. yes 7. no 8. no 9. no 10. no 11. no 12. yes

Exercises Are the measurements equivalent?

1. 450 cm, 4.5 m **2.** 7.2 m, 7200 cm **3.** 200 m, 2 cm **4.** 54 mm, 0.54 cm
5. 925 mm, 92.5 cm **6.** 4.1 cm, 41 mm **7.** 36.2 km, 3620 m **8.** 1.94 km, 194 m
9. 56 km, 0.56 m **10.** 14 m, 140 cm **11.** 6.8 mm, 68 cm **12.** 9.2 mm, 0.92 cm

Objectives: to recognize properties of real numbers, to apply formal proofs to equation solving

2–4 Properties of the Real Number System

Some classes may need a thorough review of these properties.

In arithmetic you have assumed the following properties of equality.

For any number a, $a = a$.

Postulate 2–4 Reflexive Property of Equality

For any numbers a and b, if $a = b$, then $b = a$.

Postulate 2–5 Symmetric Property of Equality

For any numbers a, b, and c, if $a = b$ and $b = c$, then $a = c$.

Postulate 2–6 Transitive Property of Equality

These properties can be applied to measures since measures are real numbers.

example

1 Prove for P, Q, R, and T in that order on a line, if $PQ = QR$ and $PQ = RT$, then $RT = QR$.

Given: $PQ = QR$
$PQ = RT$
Prove: $RT = QR$

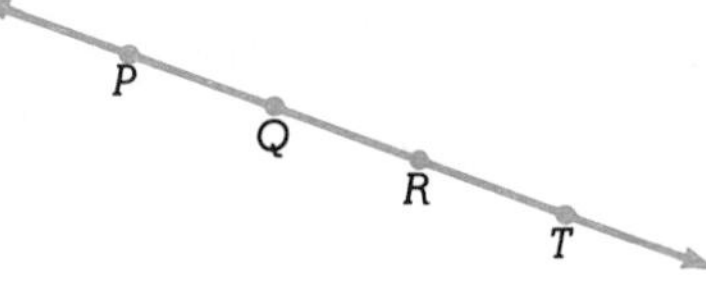

Proof:

STATEMENTS	REASONS
1. $PQ = RT$	1. Given
2. $RT = PQ$	2. Postulate 2–5: Symmetric Property of Equality
3. $PQ = QR$	3. Given
4. $RT = QR$	4. Postulate 2–6: Transitive Property of Equality

In longer geometric proofs, statements having the reflexive, symmetric, and transitive properties as reasons may be combined.

The following properties of equality are used to solve equations.

For any numbers a, b, and c, if $a = b$, then $a + c = b + c$ and $a - c = b - c$.

Postulate 2–7 Addition and Subtraction Properties of Equality

For any numbers a, b, and c, if $a = b$, then $a \cdot c = b \cdot c$ and if c is *not* zero, then $\frac{a}{c} = \frac{b}{c}$.

Postulate 2–8 Multiplication and Division Properties of Equality

For any numbers a and b, if $a = b$, then a may be replaced by b.

Postulate 2–9 Substitution Property of Equality

The chart below summarizes properties of addition and multiplication of real numbers.

For any numbers a, b, and c			
Property	**Addition**	**Multiplication**	
Commutative	$a + b = b + a$	$a \cdot b = b \cdot a$	*Postulate 2–10*
Associative	$(a + b) + c = a + (b + c)$	$(a \cdot b) \cdot c = a \cdot (b \cdot c)$	*Postulate 2–11*
Identity	$a + 0 = a = 0 + a$	$a \cdot 1 = a = 1 \cdot a$	*Postulate 2–12*
Inverse	$a + {}^{-}a = 0 = {}^{-}a + a$	If a is *not* zero, then $a \cdot \frac{1}{a} = 1 = \frac{1}{a} \cdot a$.	*Postulate 2–13*
Distributive Property of Multiplication over Addition: $a(b + c) = ab + ac$ and $(b + c)a = ba + ca$			*Postulate 2–14*

A review of operations with signed numbers can be most helpful.

example

2 **Prove that if $5x - 7 = 23$, then $x = 6$.**

Given: $5x - 7 = 23$

Prove: $x = 6$

Proof:

STATEMENTS	REASONS
1. $5x - 7 = 23$	**1.** Given
2. $5x - 7 + 7 = 23 + 7$	**2.** Postulate 2–7: Addition Property of Equality
3. $5x + 0 = 30$ *Notice that $5x - 7 + 7$ can be grouped as $5x + (^{-}7 + 7)$.*	**3.** Postulate 2–11: Associative Property of Addition, Postulate 2–13: Inverse Property of Addition, and Postulate 2–9: Substitution Property of Equality
4. $5x = 30$	**4.** Postulate 2–12: Identity Property of Addition
5. $\frac{5x}{5} = \frac{30}{5}$	**5.** Postulate 2–8: Division Property of Equality
6. $1x = \frac{30}{5}$	**6.** Postulate 2–13: Inverse Property of Multiplication
7. $x = 6$	**7.** Postulate 2–9: Substitution Property of Equality and Postulate 2–12: Identity Property of Multiplication

When referring to algebraic properties, postulate numbers may be omitted. Notice in the following proof that some steps contain more than one statement or reason.

example

3 Prove that if $6(a + 5) + 10a = {}^-2$, then $a = {}^-2$.

Several proofs of this type should be done to improve skills in step-by-step reasoning.

Given: $6(a + 5) + 10a = {}^-2$
Prove: $a = {}^-2$
Proof:

STATEMENTS	REASONS
1. $6(a + 5) + 10a = {}^-2$	**1.** Given
2. $6a + 30 + 10a = {}^-2$	**2.** Distributive Property of Multiplication over Addition
3. $16a + 30 = {}^-2$	**3.** Commutative and Associative Properties of Equality, Distributive Property of Multiplication over Addition, and Substitution Property of Equality
4. $16a = {}^-32$	**4.** Addition and Substitution Properties of Equality
5. $\frac{16a}{16} = \frac{{}^-32}{16}$	**5.** Division Property of Equality
6. $1a = -\frac{32}{16}$	**6.** Inverse Property of Multiplication
7. $a = -2$	**7.** Substitution Property of Equality

The Substitution Property of Equality often is called Substitution.

E: refers to Excursions in Geometry Exercises

EN: Ex: 1-19 odds, Wr: 1-6; pp. 46-7, Wr: 36-48 evens; p. 47, Ch: 1, 2;

exercises

AV: Ex: 1-20, Wr: 1-3; pp. 46-7, Wr: 2-48 evens; p. 47, E: 1-12

Exploratory **State the property shown in each of the following.**

1. $3 + (2 + 3) = 3 + (2 + 3)$ Reflexive

2. $3 + (2 + 3) = 3 + 5$ Substitution

3. If $3 = 2 + 1$, then $2 + 1 = 3$. Symmetric

4. If $5 + 7 = 7 + 5$, then $7 + 5 = 5 + 7$. Symmetric

5. If $8 = 3 + 5$ and $3 + 5 = \sqrt{64}$, then $8 = \sqrt{64}$. Transitive

6. If $8 + 1 = 9$ and $9 = 3 + 6$, then $8 + 1 = 3 + 6$. Transitive

7. $12 = 12$ Reflexive

8. $9 + 2 = (6 + 3) + 2$ Substitution

9. If $2 + 2 = 4$, then $6 + (2 + 2) = 6 + 4$. Addition

10. If $8 = 6 + 2$ and $6 + 2 = 5 + 3$, then $8 = 5 + 3$. Transitive

11. $AB = AB$ Reflexive

12. If $PQ = RS$, then $RS = PQ$. Symmetric

13. If $AB = BC$ and $BC = CD$, then $AB = CD$. Transitive

14. If $PQ = RS$, then $PQ + TV = RS + TV$. Addition

15. If $AB = BC$, then $AB + EF = BC + EF$. Addition

16. $PQ = PQ$ Reflexive

17. If $AB = BC$, then $BC = AB$. Symmetric

18. If $PQ = QR$ and $QR = RS$, then $PQ = RS$. Transitive

19. If $AB = CD$, then $AB + TV = CD + TV$. Addition

20. If $PQ = QR$, then $PQ - RS = QR - RS$. Subtraction

FN: Ex: 1-20, Wr: 1-3; pp. 46-7, Wr: 39-47 odds; p. 47, E: 1-12

Written **State the missing reasons for each of the following proofs.**

1. Given: $9x + 4 = 2\frac{1}{2}$

Prove: $x = -\frac{1}{6}$

Proof:

STATEMENTS	REASONS
1. $9x + 4 = 2\frac{1}{2}$	1. Given
2. $9x + 4 - 4 = 2\frac{1}{2} - 4$	2. Subtraction
3. $9x + 0 = -\frac{3}{2}$	3. Associative Property of Addition, Inverse Property of Addition, Substitution
4. $9x = -\frac{3}{2}$	4. Identity Property of Addition
5. $\frac{1}{9} \cdot 9x = \frac{1}{9}\left(-\frac{3}{2}\right)$	5. Multiplication
6. $1x = -\frac{1}{6}$	6. Inverse Property of Multiplication, Substitution
7. $x = -\frac{1}{6}$	7. Identity Property of Multiplication

2. Given: $\frac{3}{4}x = \frac{1}{3}$

Prove: $x = \frac{4}{9}$

Proof:

STATEMENTS	REASONS
1. $\frac{3}{4}x = \frac{1}{3}$	1. Given
2. $\frac{4}{3} \cdot \frac{3}{4}x = \frac{4}{3} \cdot \frac{1}{3}$	2. Multiplication
3. $1x = \frac{4}{9}$	3. Inverse Property of Multiplication, Substitution
4. $x = \frac{4}{9}$	4. Identity Property of Multiplication

3. Given: $4 - 7x = 25$

Prove: $x = {}^-3$

Proof:

STATEMENTS	REASONS
1. $4 - 7x = 25$	1. Given
2. ${}^-4 + 4 - 7x = {}^-4 + 25$	2. Addition
3. $0 - 7x = 21$	3. Inverse Property of Addition, Substitution
4. ${}^-7x = 21$	4. Identity Property of Addition
5. $\frac{{}^-7x}{{}^-7} = \frac{21}{{}^-7}$	5. Division
6. $1x = \frac{21}{{}^-7}$	6. Inverse Property of Multiplication, Substitution
7. $x = {}^-3$	7. Identity Property of Multiplication, Substitution

4. **Given:** $AB = CD$
Prove: $AC = BD$

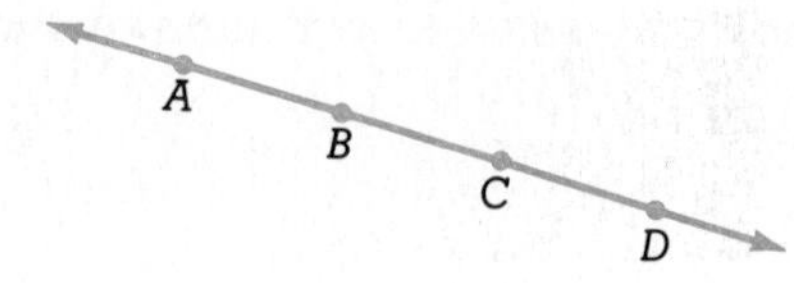

Proof:

STATEMENTS	REASONS
1. $AB = CD$	1. Given
2. $AB + BC = CD + BC$	2. Addition
3. $AC = BD$	3. Definition of Between, Substitution

5. **Given:** $PM = MS$
M is the midpoint of $\overline{PQ}$.
Prove: $MS = MQ$

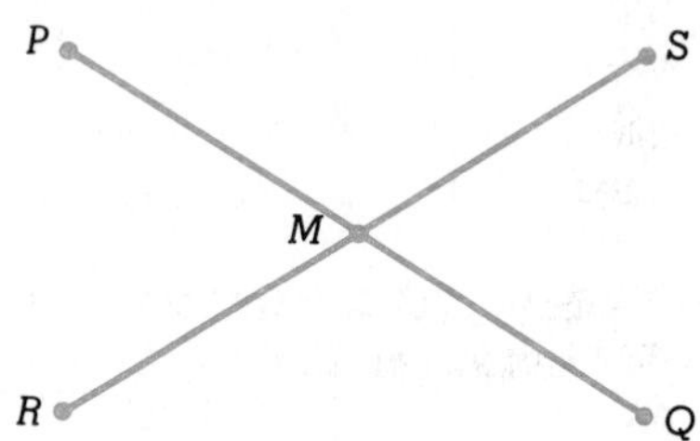

Proof:

STATEMENTS	REASONS
1. $PM = MS$	1. Given
2. M is the midpoint of $\overline{PQ}$.	2. Given
3. $PM = MQ$	3. Definition of Midpoint
4. $MQ = MS$	4. Substitution or Transitive and Symmetric
5. $MS = MQ$	5. Symmetric Property

6. **Given:** $MB = MQ$
M is between A and B.

Prove: $AB = AM + MQ$

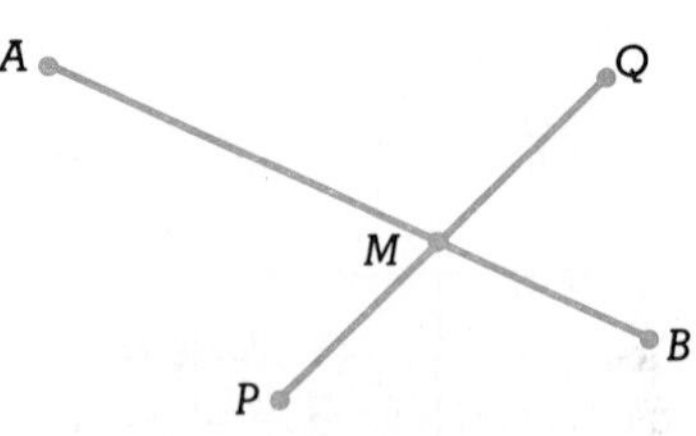

Proof:

STATEMENTS	REASONS
1. $MB = MQ$	1. Given
2. $AB = AM + MB$	2. Definition of Between
3. $AB = AM + MQ$	3. Substitution

careers — Carpet Installer

Vincent Carothers is a carpet installer. In order to cut and install carpeting, it is important for him to measure accurately. However, all measurements involve errors. Errors may occur because of human mistakes or flaws in the measuring instruments. To plan for these types of errors, Vincent estimates the **total probable error.** The total probable error is based upon the error in one measurement and the total number of measurements to be made.

Vincent uses the following formula.

$$T = E\sqrt{n}$$

T is the total probable error.
E is the error in one measurement.
n is the number of measurements.

Example Suppose Vincent uses a tape measure that is 0.005 centimeters shorter than the standard. To measure the length of a banquet room he uses the tape 16 times. A maximum error of 0.40 centimeters is allowed. Find the total probable error and tell whether or *not* it is within the maximum.

$$\begin{aligned} T &= E\sqrt{n} && \text{E is 0.005.} \\ &= (0.005)(\sqrt{16}) && \text{n is 16.} \\ &= (0.005)(4) \\ &= 0.02 \end{aligned}$$

The total probable error is 0.02 centimeters, which is within the 0.40 centimeter maximum.

Exercises For each of the following, find the total probable error and determine whether or *not* it is within the maximum.

1. A 100-foot long tape is 0.02 feet longer than standard. The tape will be used 49 times. A maximum error of 0.19 feet is allowed. T = 0.14 within the maximum
2. A worker makes consistent errors of 1.3 millimeters each time for 81 times. A maximum error of 15 millimeters is allowed. T = 11.7 within the maximum
3. One end of a tape is held 1.5 centimeters too low. This error occurs consistently 25 times. A maximum error of 4 centimeters is allowed. T = 7.5 not within the maximum
4. A tape measure is consistently held 2 feet too high. The tape is used 49 times. A maximum error of 5 feet is allowed. T = 14 not within the maximum
5. A machine makes consistent errors of 1.3 millimeters each time for 300 times. A maximum error of 15 millimeters is allowed. T ≈ 22.516 not within the maximum
6. A machine makes consistent errors of 0.4 millimeters each time for 5000 times. A maximum error of 30 millimeters is allowed. T ≈ 28.28 within the maximum

Objectives: to recognize theorems of congruency, to recognize congruency properties in the Midpoint and Bisector Theorems, to use congruence of segments in geometric proofs

2–5 Congruent Segments

$\overline{PQ}$ and $\overline{RS}$ below are congruent because they are both 4 units.

Two segments are congruent if and only if they have exactly the same length.

Definition of Congruent Segments

The symbol $\cong$ means *congruent* or *is congruent to*. In the example above, $\overline{PQ} \cong \overline{RS}$ means $\overline{PQ}$ is congruent to $\overline{RS}$.

Since congruence of segments is related to measure, the following theorems hold.

Point out the relationship between congruent segments and the measure of segments.

Congruence of segments is reflexive. ***Theorem 2–2***

Congruence of segments is symmetric. ***Theorem 2–3***

Congruence of segments is transitive. ***Theoerem 2–4***

The proofs of these theorems are all similar. The proof of Theorem 2–3 is shown below.

example

1 Prove that congruence of segments is symmetric.

Given: $\overline{PQ} \cong \overline{RS}$

Prove: $\overline{RS} \cong \overline{PQ}$

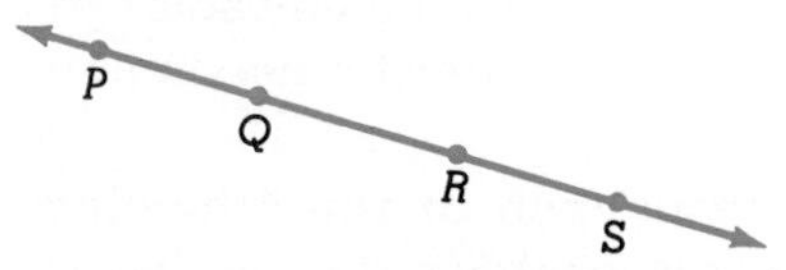

Proof:

STATEMENTS	REASONS
1. $\overline{PQ} \cong \overline{RS}$	1. Given
2. $PQ = RS$	2. Definition of Congruent Segments
3. $RS = PQ$	3. Postulate 2–5: Symmetric Property of Equality
4. $\overline{RS} \cong \overline{PQ}$	4. Definition of Congruent Segments

The proof of the following theorem shows that the midpoint of a segment separates the segment into two congruent segments.

If M is the midpoint of $\overline{PQ}$, then $\overline{PM} \cong \overline{MQ}$.

Theorem 2–5
Midpoint Theorem

example

2 Prove Theorem 2–5.

Given: M is the midpoint of $\overline{PQ}$.
Prove: $\overline{PM} \cong \overline{MQ}$

Proof:

STATEMENTS	REASONS
1. M is the midpoint of $\overline{PQ}$.	**1.** Given
2. $PM = MQ$	**2.** Definition of Midpoint
3. $\overline{PM} \cong \overline{MQ}$	**3.** Definition of Congruent Segments

If a segment, a line, or a plane intersects a segment at its midpoint, it is said to be a **segment bisector.**

$\overline{TM}$ is a bisector of $\overline{PQ}$.
$\overleftrightarrow{RM}$ is a bisector of $\overline{PQ}$.
$\mathcal{N}$ is a bisector of $\overline{PQ}$.

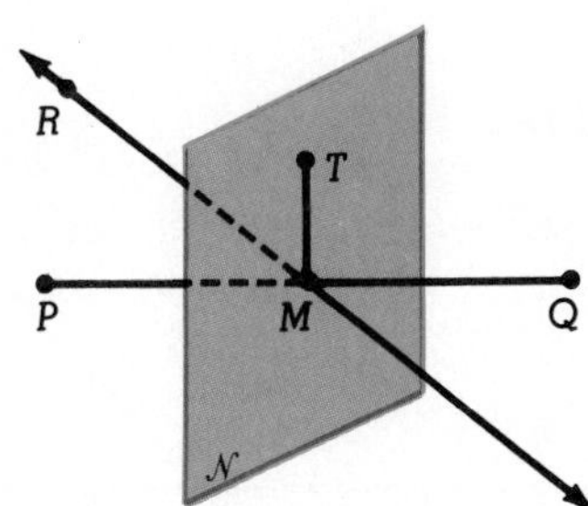

example

3 Prove that if $\overline{AB}$ bisects $\overline{CD}$ at M, then $CM = MD$.

Given: $\overline{AB}$ bisects $\overline{CD}$ at M.
Prove: $CM = MD$

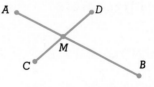

Encourage students to use drawings to help in forming proofs.

Proof:

STATEMENTS	REASONS
1. $\overline{AB}$ bisects $\overline{CD}$ at M.	**1.** Given
2. M is the midpoint of $\overline{CD}$.	**2.** Definition of Segment Bisector
3. $CM = MD$	**3.** Definition of Midpoint

If $\overline{PQ}$ is bisected at point M, then $\overline{PM} \cong \overline{MQ}$.	*Theorem 2–6* *Bisector Theorem*

exercises

EN: Ex: 1-7 odds, Wr: 1-24; p. 53, C: 2, 4, 6; AV: Ex: 1-8, Wr: 1-24; p. 53, C: 1-6

Exploratory **State the property shown in each of the following.**

1. $\overline{RS} \cong \overline{RS}$ reflexive
2. If $\overline{RS} \cong \overline{PQ}$ and $\overline{PQ} \cong \overline{TV}$, then $\overline{RS} \cong \overline{TV}$. transitive
3. If $\overline{PQ} \cong \overline{RS}$, then $\overline{RS} \cong \overline{PQ}$. symmetric
4. $\overline{PQ} \cong \overline{PQ}$ reflexive
5. If $\overline{AB} \cong \overline{CD}$ and $\overline{CD} \cong \overline{EF}$, then $\overline{AB} \cong \overline{EF}$. transitive
6. If $\overline{AB} \cong \overline{BC}$ and $\overline{BC} \cong \overline{CD}$, then $\overline{AB} \cong \overline{CD}$. transitive
7. If $\overline{RX} \cong \overline{PQ}$ and $\overline{PQ} \cong \overline{TR}$, then $\overline{RX} \cong \overline{TR}$. transitive
8. If $\overline{AB} \cong \overline{BC}$, then $\overline{BC} \cong \overline{AB}$. symmetric

FN: Ex: 1-8; Wr: 1-24; p. 52, Wr: 4-6; p. 53, C: 1-6

Written **Use the drawing below to identify each of the following statements as *true* or *false*.**

1. $\overline{PS}$ bisects $\overline{BC}$. True
2. D is the midpoint of $\overline{CE}$. False
3. $\overline{AB} \cong \overline{CD}$ True
4. $\overline{BQ} \cong \overline{CE}$ True
5. $\overline{AQ} \cong \overline{QD}$ True
6. $\overline{PR}$ bisects $\overline{AD}$. True
7. Q is the midpoint of $\overline{BC}$. True
8. $\overline{BC} \cong \overline{QE}$ True
9. $\overline{EC} \cong \overline{QC}$ True
10. $\overline{BQ} \cong \overline{QC}$ True

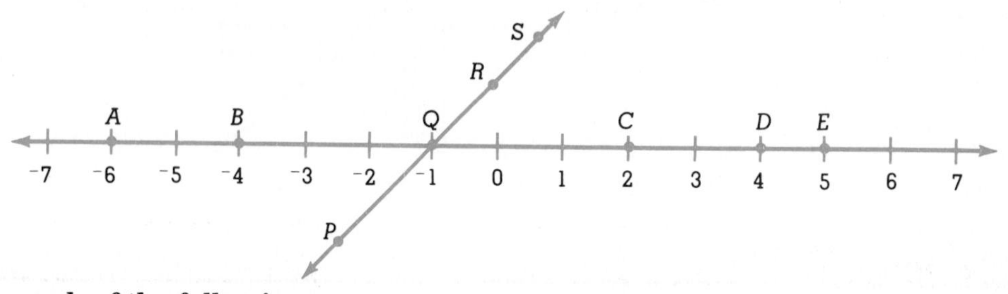

Answer each of the following. For answers to exercises 11-24, see the Teacher's Guide.

11. State the hypothesis of Theorem 2–5.
12. State the conclusion of Theorem 2–5.
13. Write the converse of Theorem 2–5.
14. Determine whether the converse of Theorem 2–5 is *true* or *false*. If false, give an example. See student's work.
15. State the hypothesis of Theorem 2–6.
16. Draw and label a diagram to illustrate the hypothesis of Theorem 2–6.
17. State the *given* for a proof of Theorem 2–6.
18. State the conclusion of Theorem 2–6.
19. State the *prove* statement for a proof of Theorem 2–6.
20. Give a definition for *bisects*.
21. Give a definition for *midpoint*.
22. Write a definition of midpoint based on congruence.
23. Give a plan for a proof of Theorem 2–6.
24. Write a formal proof for Theorem 2–6.

For answers to exercises 25-28, see the Teacher's Guide.

Prove each of the following statements.

25. Congruence of segments is reflexive.

26. Congruence of segments is transitive.

27. If M is between P and Q, and $\overline{PM} \cong \overline{MQ}$, then M is the midpoint of $\overline{PQ}$.

28. If $\overline{LP}$ bisects $\overline{RS}$ at M, then $\overline{RM} \cong \overline{MS}$.

Complete each proof.

29. **Given:** B is the midpoint of $\overline{AC}$.

Prove: $AB = \frac{1}{2}AC$

A B C

Proof:

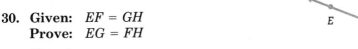

STATEMENTS	REASONS
1. B is the midpoint of $\overline{AC}$.	1. Given
2. $AB = BC$	2. Definition of Midpoint
3. $AB + BC = AC$	3. Definition of Between
4. $AB + AB = AC$	4. Substitution
5. $2AB = AC$	5. Distributive
6. $AB = \frac{1}{2}AC$	6. Multiplication, Inverse Prop. of Multiplication, Substitution, Identity Prop. of Multiplication

30. **Given:** $EF = GH$

Prove: $EG = FH$

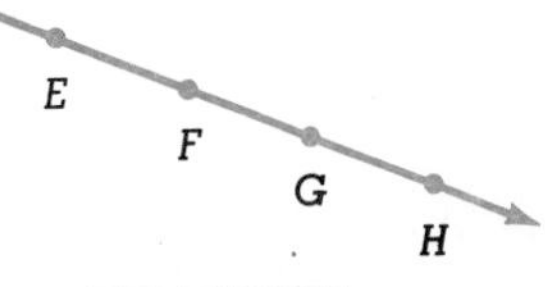

Proof:

STATEMENTS	REASONS
1. $EF = GH$	1. Given
2. $EF + FG = FG + GH$	2. Addition Prop. of Equality
3. $EG = EF + FG$	3. Definition of Between
4. $FH = FG + GH$	4. Definition of Between
5. $EG = FH$	5. Substitution

Significant Digits — excursions in geometry

All measurements are approximate. No matter how small the unit of measure, the exact measurement cannot be determined. The degree of accuracy of a measurement can be shown by the number of significant digits.

45.3 has three significant digits.

1.250 has four significant digits.

When leading zeros are used to show the position of the decimal point, they are not counted as significant digits. Zeros that only serve to locate decimal points are not significant.

0.071 has two significant digits.

Exercises **Determine how many significant digits are in each of the following.**

1. 19.5 3 **2.** 120.0 4 **3.** 0.006 1 **4.** 212.01 5 **5.** 0.090 2

6. 7.0 2 **7.** 0.040 2 **8.** 0.87 2 **9.** 5404 4 **10.** 191 3

The zero is significant since it implies the accuracy of the measurement.

Objectives: to use inequality symbols, to use inequality postulates in proofs

2–6 Properties of Inequalities

Segments may have the same length, but there are other possibilities.

A B A B A B

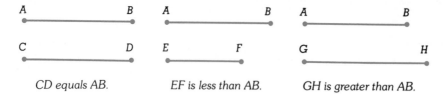

C D E F G H

CD equals AB. *EF is less than AB.* *GH is greater than AB.*

An equation or inequality can be used to describe each situation.

Remind students that $6 > 4$ is equivalent to $4 < 6$.

$CD = AB$ $EF < AB$ $GH > AB$

For any two numbers a and b, exactly one of the following statements is true.

Postulate 2–15
Comparison Property

$$a < b \qquad a = b \qquad a > b$$

The symbols $\neq$, $\leq$, and $\geq$ also can be used when comparing numbers. For example, $x \leq y$ means $x < y$ or $x = y$.

The symbol $\neq$ means $<$ or $>$. For many computers the symbol <> is used to mean $\neq$.

Operating with the same number on both sides of an inequality may or may *not* affect its truth value. The following properties state how the truth value is affected.

For any numbers a, b, and c:

1. If $a > b$, then $a + c > b + c$ and $a - c > b - c$.
2. If $a < b$, then $a + c < b + c$ and $a - c < b - c$.

Postulate 2–16
Addition and Subtraction Properties of Inequality

For any numbers a, b, and c:

1. If $c > 0$ and $a < b$, then $ac < bc$ and $\frac{a}{c} < \frac{b}{c}$.
2. If $c > 0$ and $a > b$, then $ac > bc$ and $\frac{a}{c} > \frac{b}{c}$.
3. If $c < 0$ and $a < b$, then $ac > bc$ and $\frac{a}{c} > \frac{b}{c}$.
4. If $c < 0$ and $a > b$, then $ac < bc$ and $\frac{a}{c} < \frac{b}{c}$.

Postulate 2–17
Multiplication and Division Properties of Inequality

Notice in 3 and 4 $c < 0$.

Emphasize that multiplying or dividing by a negative number reverses the inequality symbol.

For any numbers a, b, and c,

1. If $a < b$ and $b < c$, then $a < c$.

2. If $a > b$ and $b > c$, then $a > c$.

Postulate 2–18 Transitive Property of Inequality

examples

1 Prove that if $3x > 9x + 6$, then $x < ^-1$.

Given: $3x > 9x + 6$
Prove: $x < ^-1$

Proof:

STATEMENTS	REASONS
1. $3x > 9x + 6$	**1.** Given
2. $^-6x > 6$	**2.** Postulate 2–16: Subtraction Property of Inequality and Postulate 2–9: Substitution
3. $x < ^-1$	**3.** Postulate 2–17: Division Property of Inequality and Postulate 2–9: Substitution

2 Two segments, $\overline{PQ}$ and $\overline{RS}$, intersect at point T so that $\overline{RT}$ is congruent to $\overline{TQ}$. If PQ is greater than RS, prove that $PT > TS$.

Given: $\overline{RT} \cong \overline{TQ}$
$PQ > RS$
Prove: $PT > TS$

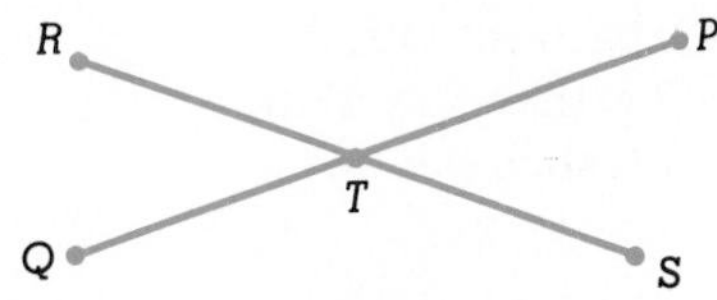

Proof:

STATEMENTS	REASONS
1. $PQ > RS$	**1.** Given
2. $RS = RT + TS$ $PQ = PT + TQ$	**2.** Definition of Between
3. $\overline{RT} \cong \overline{TQ}$	**3.** Given
4. $RT = TQ$	**4.** Definition of Congruent Segments
5. $PQ = PT + RT$	**5.** Postulate 2–9: Substitution Property of Equality
6. $PT + RT > RT + TS$	**6.** Postulate 2–9: Substitution Property of Equality
7. $PT > TS$	**7.** Postulate 2–16: Addition Property of Inequality and Postulate 2–9: Substitution of Equality

exercises

Exploratory **Replace each ■ with $<$, $>$, or $=$ to make each sentence true.**

1. 2 ■ 6 $<$
2. 7 ■ 15 $<$
3. 6 ■ 2 $>$
4. $^-5$ ■ $^-1$ $<$
5. $^-1$ ■ $^-6$ $>$
6. 0.01 ■ 0.001 $>$
7. $2 + 3$ ■ $4 + 1$ $=$
8. $3\frac{1}{2} + 1$ ■ $3\frac{1}{2}$ $>$
9. 1.25 ■ 1.253 $<$
10. $^-5 + 4$ ■ $2 + {}^-3$ $=$
11. $2\frac{1}{4} - 3$ ■ $2\frac{1}{4}$ $<$
12. $2\frac{1}{4} - 3$ ■ 3 $<$
13. $1\frac{7}{8}$ ■ $1\frac{3}{4}$ $>$
14. $^-2\frac{1}{2}$ ■ $^-2\frac{3}{4}$ $>$
15. $\frac{1}{2}$ ■ $\frac{3}{6}$ $=$

EN: Wr: 1-23 odds; p. 57, Wr: 25-30; p. 57, E: 1-10; AV: Ex: 1-15 odds, Wr: 1-23; p. 57, Wr: 25-30; p. 57, E: 1-10

Written **Use the number line below. Replace each ■ with $<$, $>$, or $=$ to make each sentence true.** FN: Ex; 1-15, Wr: 1-20; p. 57, Wr: 25-30; p. 57, E: 1-10

1. QR ■ ST $=$
2. PS ■ QV $<$
3. PQ ■ TV $>$
4. PS ■ RV $>$
5. RT ■ QS $=$
6. PV ■ RS $>$
7. PT ■ QV $>$
8. PR ■ RV $>$
9. PQ ■ QS $<$
10. RS ■ TV $<$
11. SV ■ PR $<$
12. PS ■ QT $<$

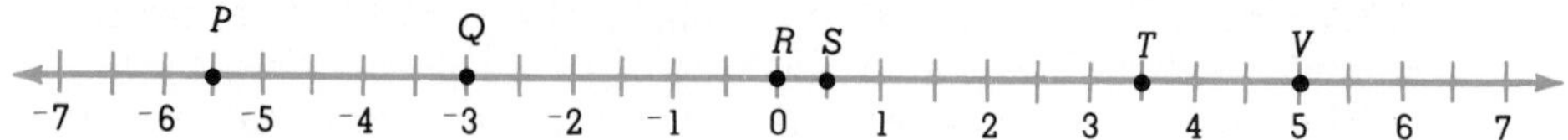

For answers to exercises 13-18, see the Teacher's Guide.

Prove each of the following statements.

13. If $3x + 7 > 43$, then $x > 12$.
14. If $2t - 9 < 21$, then $t < 15$.
15. If $11 - 5y < {}^-77$, then $y > 17.6$
16. If $8 - 3x < 44$, then $x > {}^-12$.
17. If $9(x + 2) < 72$, then $x < 6$.
18. If $5(5z - 3) > 60$, then $z > 3$.

19. Suppose P, Q, R, and S are collinear points with Q between P and R, and R between Q and S. Also, $\overline{PQ}$ is congruent to $\overline{RS}$, and QR is less than RS. Write an equation or inequality that relates PQ and QR. $QR < PQ$ or $PQ > QR$.

20. Suppose A, B, C, and D are collinear points with B between A and C, and C between B and D. Also, $\overline{AB}$ is congruent to $\overline{CD}$, and BC is greater than CD. Write an equation or inequality that relates BD and AC. $AC = BD$.

21. If $AB < CD$ and $CD < EF$, how are AB and EF related? $AB < EF$ by Transitive Prop.

22. If $PQ > RS$ and $RS > TV$, how are PQ and TV related? $PQ > TV$ by Transitive Prop.

23. Suppose A, B, and C are collinear points and $AB > AC$. Which of the following could *not* be true? b
    a. Point C is between A and B.
    b. Point B is between A and C.
    c. Point A is between B and C.

24. Suppose X, Y, and Z are collinear points and $XY = YZ$. Which of the following could be true? b
    a. Point X is between Y and Z.
    b. Point Y is between X and Z.
    c. Point Z is between X and Y.

Vocabulary

number line (35)
natural number (35)
whole number (35)
integer (35)
rational number (35)
terminating decimal (36)
repeating decimal (36)
irrational number (37)
real number (37)
coordinate (37)
measure (39)
unit of measure (39)
distance (40)
between (44)
segment (44)
endpoint (44)
length (44)
midpoint (44)
congruent segments (54)
segment bisector (55)

Chapter Summary

1. Numbers that can be written in the form $\frac{a}{b}$, where a and b are integers and b is *not* zero, are called *rational numbers*. Nonterminating, nonrepeating decimals represent *irrational numbers*. Taken together, the rational numbers and irrational numbers make up the *real numbers*. (35)
2. Number Line Postulate (Postulate 2–1): Each real number corresponds to exactly one point on a number line. Each point on a number line corresponds to exactly one real number. (37)
3. A number associated with a point on a number line is called the coordinate of the point. (37)
4. Ruler Postulate (Postulate 2–2): The points on any line can be paired with the real numbers so that, given any two points P and Q on the line, P corresponds to zero, and Q corresponds to a positive number. (39)
5. Distance Postulate (Postulate 2–3): For any two points on a line and a given unit of measure, there is a unique positive number called the measure of the distance between the two points. (40)
6. To find the measure of the distance between two points on a number line, find the absolute value of the difference of their coordinates. (40)
7. Definition of Between: A point Q is between points P and R if and only if each of the following conditions hold.
   1. P, Q, and R are collinear.
   2. $PQ + QR = PR$. (44)
8. Definition of Midpoint: A point M is the midpoint of a segment, $\overline{PQ}$, if and only if M is between P and Q, and $PM = MQ$. (44)
9. Theorem 2–1: If a segment is given, then it has exactly one midpoint. (45)

10. Properties of equality: (48)

	For any numbers a, b, and c	
Postulate 2–4	reflexive	$a = a$
Postulate 2–5	symmetric	If $a = b$, then $b = a$.
Postulate 2–6	transitive	If $a = b$ and $b = c$, then $a = c$.
Postulate 2–7	addition and subtraction	If $a = b$, then $a + c = b + c$, and $a - c = b - c$.
Postulate 2–8	multiplication and division	If $a = b$, then $a \cdot c = b \cdot c$, and if c is not zero, $\frac{a}{c} = \frac{b}{c}$.
Postulate 2–9	substitution	If $a = b$, then a may be replaced by b.

11. Properties of operations: (49)

	For any numbers a, b, and c		
	property	addition	multiplication
Postulate 2–10	commutative	$a + b = b + a$	$a \cdot b = b \cdot a$
Postulate 2–11	associative	$(a + b) + c = a + (b + c)$	$(a \cdot b) \cdot c = a \cdot (b \cdot c)$
Postulate 2–12	identity	$a + 0 = a = 0 + a$	$a \cdot 1 = a = 1 \cdot a$
Postulate 2–13	inverse	$a + {}^{-}a = 0 = {}^{-}a + a$	If a is not zero, then $a \cdot \frac{1}{a} = 1 = \frac{1}{a} \cdot a$.
Postulate 2–14	distributive property of multiplication over addition: $a(b + c) = ab + ac$ and $(b + c)a = ba + ca$		

12. Definition of Congruent Segments: Two segments are congruent segments if and only if they have exactly the same length. (54)

13. Theorem 2–2: Congruence of segments is reflexive. (54)

14. Theorem 2–3: Congruence of segments is symmetric. (54)

15. Theorem 2–4: Congruence of segments is transitive. (54)

16. Midpoint Theorem (Theorem 2–5): If M is the midpoint of $\overline{PQ}$, then $\overline{PM} \cong \overline{MQ}$. (54)

17. Bisector Theorem (Theorem 2–6): If $\overline{PQ}$ is bisected at point M, then $\overline{PM} \cong \overline{MQ}$. (56)

18. Properties of inequality: (58)

	For any numbers a, b, and c	
Postulate 2–15	comparison	$a < b$, or $a = b$, or $a > b$
Postulate 2–16	addition and subtraction	1. If $a > b$, then $a + c > b + c$ and $a - c > b - c$. 2. If $a < b$, then $a + c < b + c$ and $a - c < b - c$.
Postulate 2–17	multiplication and division	1. If $c > 0$ and $a < b$, then $ac < bc$ and $\frac{a}{c} < \frac{b}{c}$. 1. If $c > 0$ and $a > b$, then $ac > bc$ and $\frac{a}{c} > \frac{b}{c}$. 3. If $c < 0$ and $a < b$, then $ac > bc$ and $\frac{a}{c} > \frac{b}{c}$. 4. If $c < 0$ and $a > b$, then $ac < bc$ and $\frac{a}{c} < \frac{b}{c}$.
Postulate 2–18	transitive	1. If $a < b$ and $b < c$, then $a < c$. 2. If $a > b$ and $b > c$, then $a > c$.

Chapter Review

2–1 State the coordinates of each of the following points on the number line.

1. A $-1\frac{3}{4}$ **2.** B -1 **3.** C 0 **4.** D $1\frac{1}{2}$

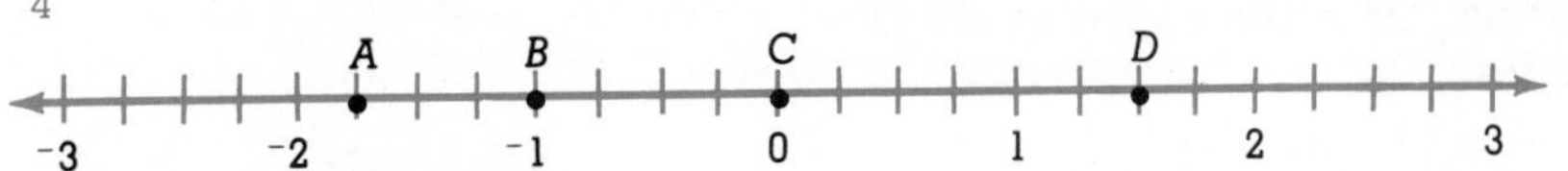

Change each fraction or mixed numeral to decimal form.

5. $\frac{7}{10}$ 0.7 **6.** $^{-}1\frac{2}{5}$ -1.4 **7.** $-\frac{2}{3}$ $-0.\overline{6}$ **8.** $2\frac{1}{6}$ $2.1\overline{6}$

Change each decimal to a fraction in simplest form.

9. $0.\overline{3}$ $\frac{1}{3}$ **10.** $1.\overline{4}$ $\frac{13}{9}$ **11.** $0.\overline{12}$ $\frac{4}{33}$ **12.** $6.2\overline{5}$ $\frac{563}{90}$

2–2 Use the number line below to find each measure.

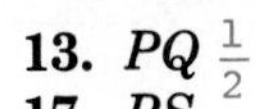

13. PQ $\frac{1}{2}$ **14.** QR $2\frac{1}{2}$ **15.** PT $4\frac{3}{4}$ **16.** SQ 3

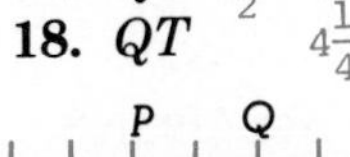

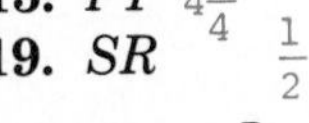

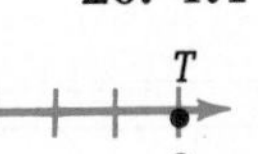

17. PS $3\frac{1}{2}$ **18.** QT $4\frac{1}{4}$ **19.** SR $\frac{1}{2}$ **20.** RT $1\frac{3}{4}$

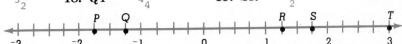

2–3 Use the number line below to answer each of the following .

21. Show that Q is between P and R.

22. Show that Q is *not* between R and T.

23. Show that S is *not* the midpoint of Q and T.

24. Show that R is the midpoint of P and T.

For answers to exercises 21-24, see the Teacher's Guide.

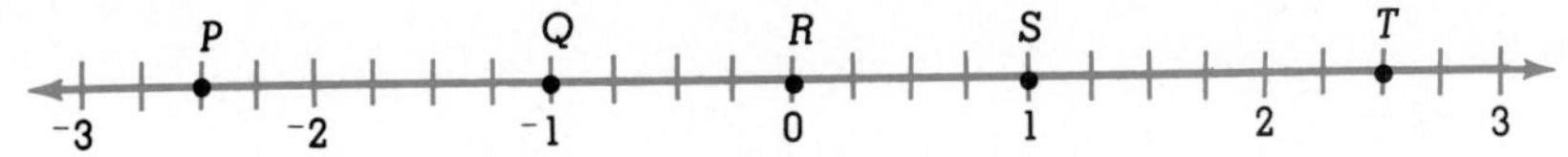

Complete the reasons for each of the following proofs.

2–4 **25. Given:** $3(6 - 4x) = 2 + 4x$
Prove: $x = 1$
Proof:

STATEMENTS	REASONS
1. $3(6 - 4x) = 2 + 4x$	1. Given
2. $18 - 12x = 2 + 4x$	2. Distributive , Substitution
3. $18 - 12x - 4x = 2 + 4x - 4x$	3. Subtraction
	Inverse Prop. of Addition ,
4. $18 - 12x - 4x = 2 + 0$	4. Associative Prop. of Addition , Substitution
5. $18 - 16x = 2$	5. Associative Prop. of Addition , Distributive
6. $^-18 + 18 - 16x = {}^-18 + 2$	6. Addition
7. $0 - 16x = {}^-16$	7. Inverse Prop. of Addition , Substitution
8. $^-16x = {}^-16$	8. Identity Prop. of Addition
9. $\frac{^-16x}{^-16} = \frac{^-16}{^-16}$	9. Division
10. $1x = 1$	10. Substitution , Inverse Prop. of Multiplication
11. $x = 1$	11. Identity Prop. of Multiplication
	Substitution , Identity Prop. of Addition

2–5 **26. Given:** M is between P and Q.
$\overline{PM} \cong \overline{MQ}$
Prove: M is the midpoint of $\overline{PQ}$.
Proof:

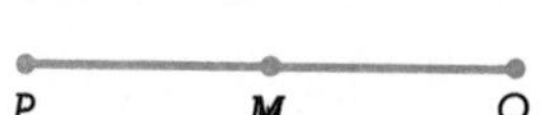

STATEMENTS	REASONS
1. M is between P and Q.	1. Given
2. $\overline{PM} \cong \overline{MQ}$	2. Given
3. $PM = MQ$	3. Definition of Congruent Segments
4. M is the midpoint of $\overline{PQ}$.	4. Definition of Midpoint

2–6 **27. Given:** $9(x + 2) < 72$
Prove: $x < 6$
Proof:

STATEMENTS	REASONS
1. $9(x + 2) < 72$	1. Given
2. $9x + 18 < 72$	2. Distributive , Substitution
3. $9x + 18 - 18 < 72 - 18$	3. Subtraction Prop. of Inequality
4. $9x + 0 < 54$	4. Substituion, Inverse Prop. of Addition
5. $9x < 54$	5. Identity Prop. of Addition
6. $\frac{9x}{9} < \frac{54}{9}$	6. Division Prop. of Inequality
7. $x < 6$	7. Inverse Prop. of Multiplication , Substitution ,
	Identity Prop. of Multiplication
	Associative Prop. of Addition

Chapter Test

Change each fraction or mixed numeral to decimal form.

1. $\frac{3}{100}$ 0.03
2. $-\frac{5}{8}$ -0.625
3. $^-3\frac{1}{3}$ $-3.\overline{3}$

Change each decimal to a fraction in simplest form.

4. $1.\overline{6}$ $\frac{5}{3}$
5. $0.0\overline{3}$ $\frac{1}{30}$
6. $1.\overline{45}$ $\frac{16}{11}$

Use the number line below for exercises 7–16.

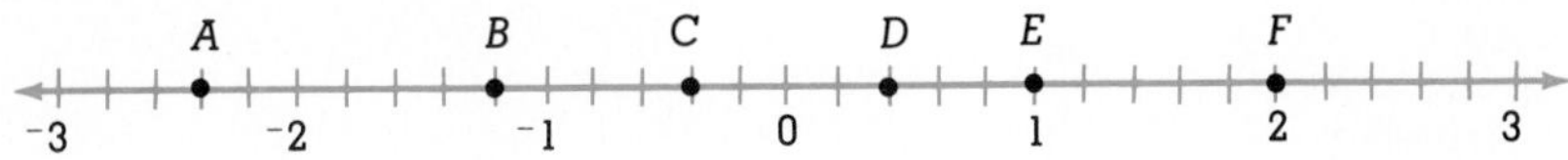

State the coordinate of each point.

7. B $-1\frac{1}{5}$
8. C $-\frac{2}{5}$
9. D $\frac{2}{5}$
10. F 2

Find each measure.

11. AC 2
12. BD $1\frac{3}{5}$
13. CF $2\frac{2}{5}$
14. AF $4\frac{2}{5}$
15. Show that B is between A and E.
16. Show that C is the midpoint of $\overline{BD}$.

For answers to exercises 15 and 16, see the Teacher's Guide.

17. Complete the reasons for the following proof.

Given: $6(9 - 2x) \geq 6 + 4x$
Prove: $x \leq 1$
Proof:

STATEMENTS	REASONS
1. $6(9 - 2x) \geq 6 + 4x$	1. Given
2. $54 - 12x \geq 6 + 4x$	2. Distributive, Substitution
3. $54 - 12x - 4x \geq 6 + 4x - 4x$	3. Subtraction Prop. of Inequality Associative Prop. of Addition, Distributive, Substitution
4. $54 - 16x \geq 6$	4. Inverse Prop. of Addition, Identity Prop. of Addition
5. $^-54 + 54 - 16x \geq {}^-54 + 2$	5. Addition Prop. of Inequality
6. $0 - 16x \geq {}^-48$	6. Inverse Prop. of Addition, Substitution
7. $^-16x \geq {}^-48$	7. Identity Prop. of Addition, Substitution
8. $\frac{^-16x}{^-16} \leq \frac{^-48}{^-16}$	8. Division Prop. of Inequality
9. $x \leq 3$	9. Inverse Prop. of Multiplication, Substitution

18. Complete the following proof. See the Teacher's Guide.

Given: P, M, and Q are collinear.
$PM + MQ = PQ$
$\overline{PM} \cong \overline{MQ}$
Prove: M is the midpoint of $\overline{PQ}$.

chapter

3 Angles and Perpendiculars

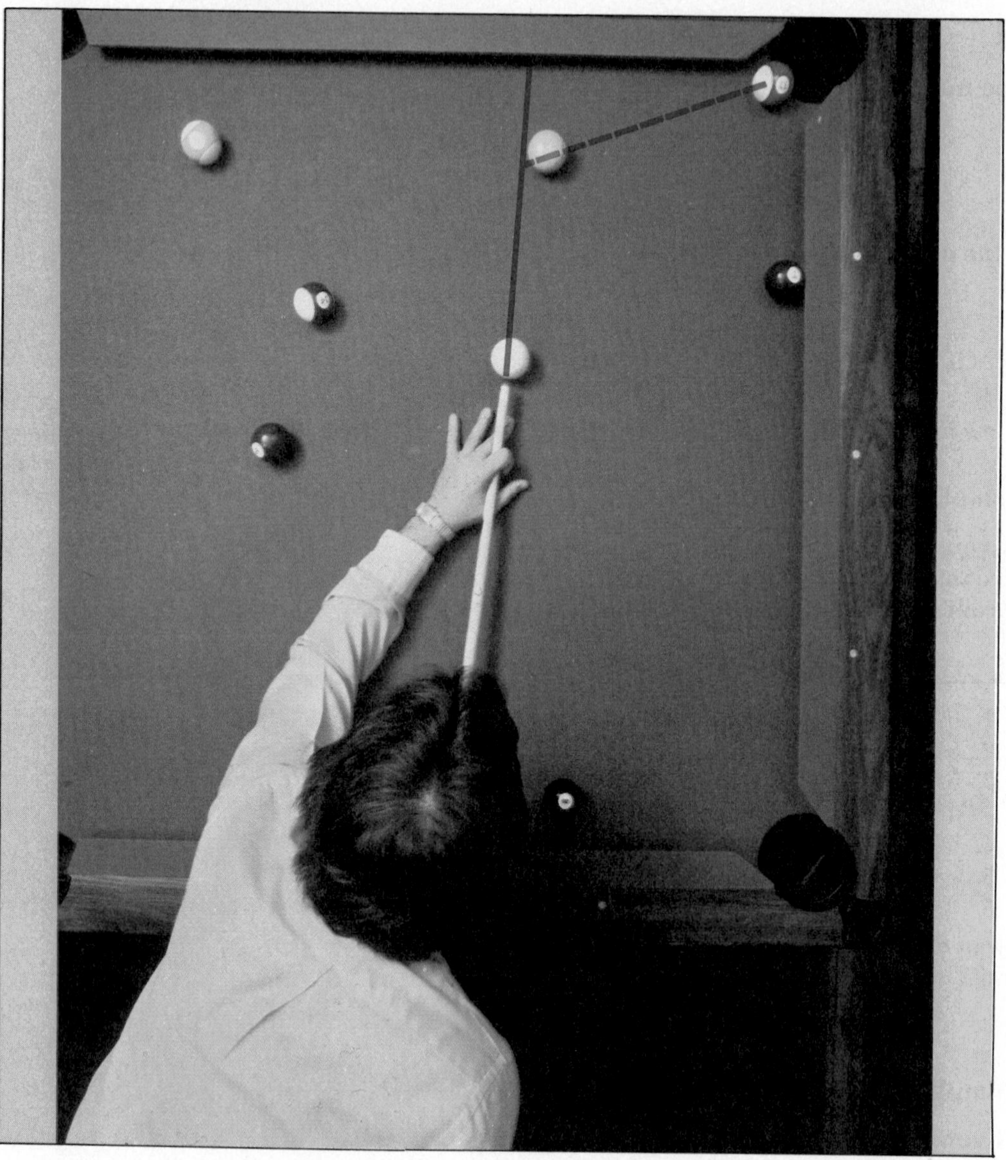

Many sports involve the use of angles. For example, the angles at which the balls are hit in billiards are very important.

3–1 Rays and Angles

Objectives: to name and identify the parts of an angle

A laser beam is a model of a ray. In geometry, a ray is a never ending straight path in one direction.

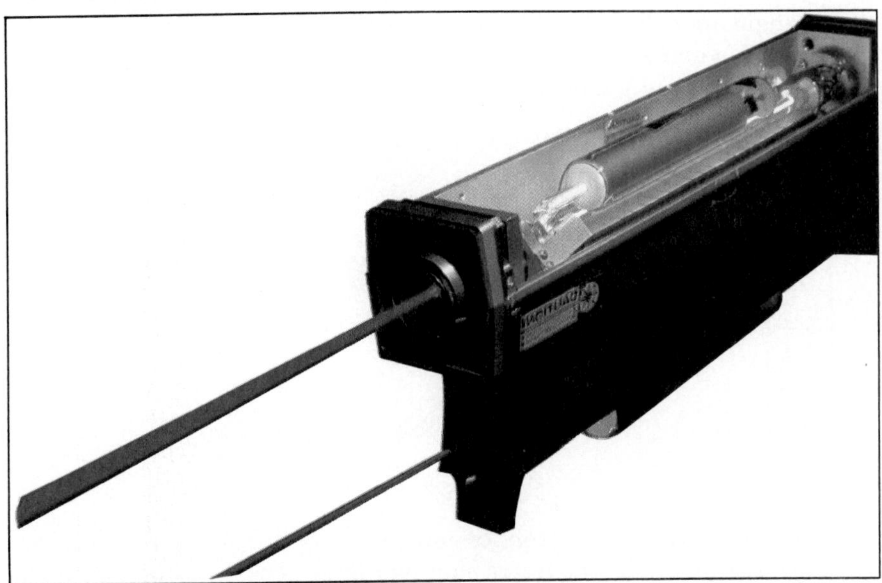

A ray is part of a line and it has one endpoint. To name a ray, name the endpoint first and then name any other point on the ray.

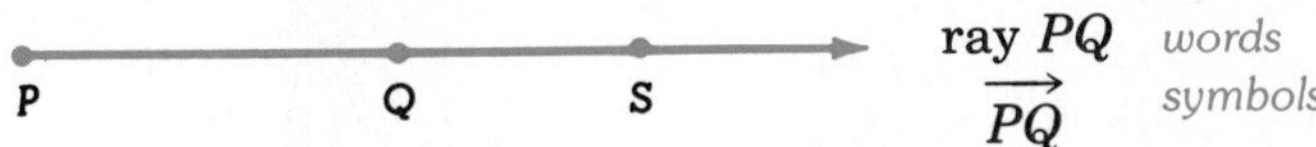

ray PQ *words*

$\overrightarrow{PQ}$ *symbols*

$\overrightarrow{PQ}$ is a ray if and only if it is the set of points $\overline{PQ}$ and all points S for which Q is between P and S.

Definition of Ray

Any point on a line determines two rays on that line. The point is the endpoint of the two rays that head in opposite directions.

Opposite rays have a common endpoint.

$\overrightarrow{PQ}$ and $\overrightarrow{PR}$ are **opposite rays.**

$\overrightarrow{PQ}$ and $\overrightarrow{PR}$ are opposite rays if and only if P is between Q and R.

Definition of Opposite Rays

A figure is an angle if and only if it consists of two noncollinear rays with a common endpoint.

Definition of Angle

The two rays that form an angle are called the **sides** of the angle. The common endpoint is called the **vertex** of the angle.

The pictures below can be described using angles.

The plural of vertex is vertices.

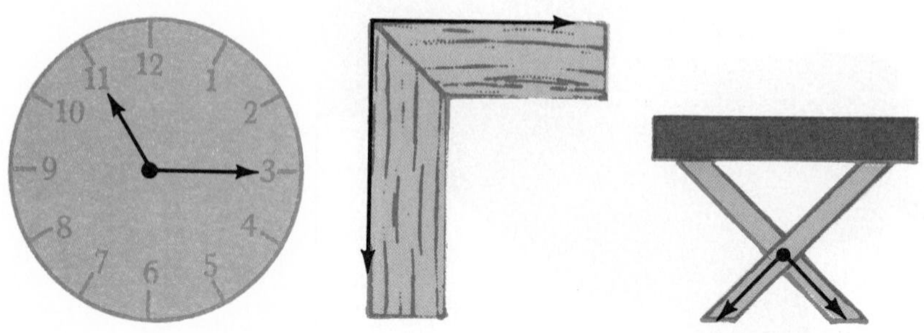

Angles can be named in several ways using letters or numbers. When three letters are used to name an angle, the letter naming the vertex is between the other two letters.

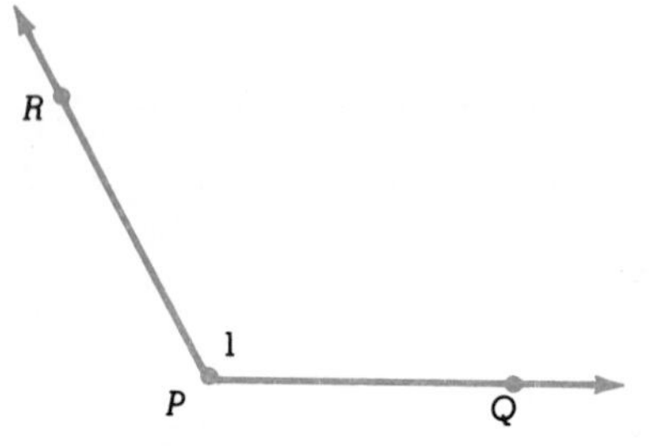

Words	**Symbols**
angle P	$\angle P$
angle RPQ	$\angle RPQ$
angle QPR	$\angle QPR$
angle 1	$\angle 1$

Use Example 1 to show that a single letter may be inadequate for naming an angle.

1 **Draw two angles which have a common side. Label the angles and name the common side.**

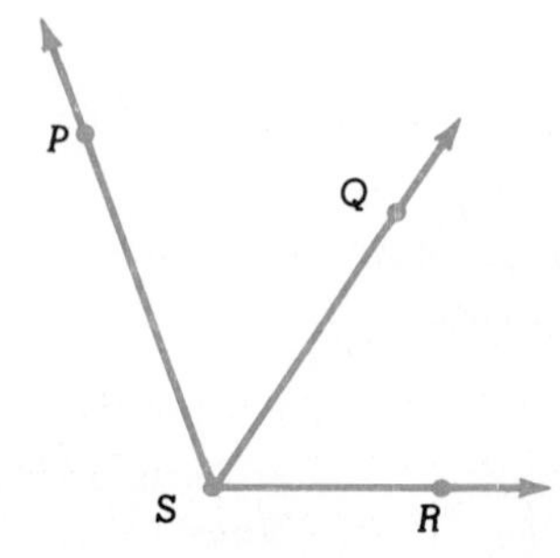

$\angle PSQ$ and $\angle QSR$ have side $\overrightarrow{SQ}$ in common.

An angle separates a plane into three distinct parts. The parts are the **interior** of the angle, the **exterior** of the angle, and the angle itself.

Neither the interior nor the exterior of an angle contains the angle.

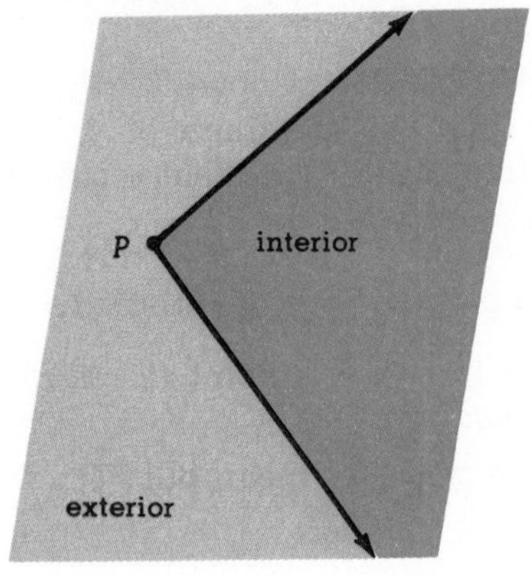

Any point in the green part of the plane is in the interior of $\angle P$. Any point in the yellow part of the plane is in the exterior of $\angle P$. The angle itself is shown in black.

A point is in the interior of an angle if it is between any two points, one on each side of the angle. Neither of these points is the vertex of the angle. In the diagram at the right, R is in the interior of $\angle P$.

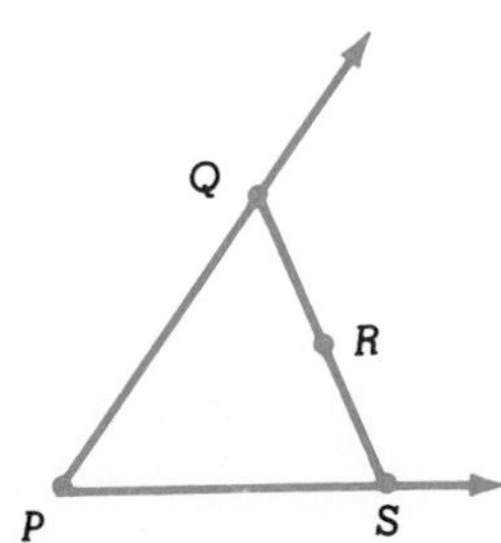

exercises

EN: Wr: 2-30 evens; AV: Ex: 1-15 odds, Wr: 1-29 odds; FN: Ex: 1-16, Wr: 1-29 odds

Exploratory **Determine whether each of the following is *true* or *false*.**

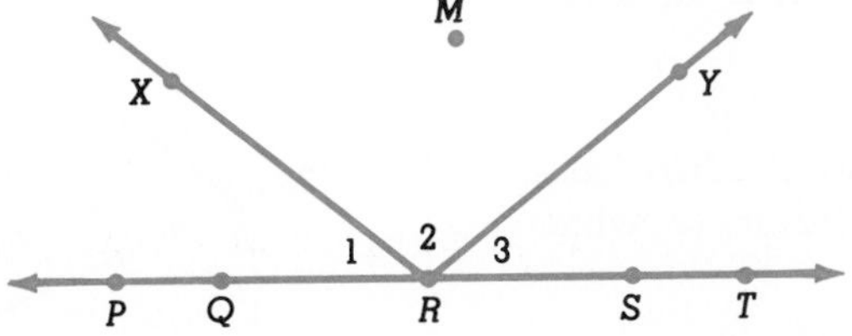

1. $\overrightarrow{RT}$ and $\overrightarrow{RS}$ name the same ray. true
2. $\overrightarrow{QT}$ and $\overrightarrow{TQ}$ name the same ray. false
3. T is the endpoint of $\overrightarrow{RT}$. false
4. S is the endpoint of $\overrightarrow{RS}$. false
5. $\overrightarrow{QS}$ and $\overrightarrow{QP}$ have the same endpoint. true
6. $\overrightarrow{RT}$ and $\overrightarrow{RQ}$ have the same endpoint. true
7. R lies on $\overrightarrow{SQ}$. true
8. S lies on $\overrightarrow{RQ}$. false
9. $\overrightarrow{RT}$ and $\overrightarrow{QP}$ are opposite rays. false
10. $\overrightarrow{SR}$ and $\overrightarrow{ST}$ are opposite rays. true
11. $\angle PRX$ and $\angle XRP$ name the same angle. true
12. $\angle YRS$ and $\angle 3$ name the same angle. true
13. S is in the interior of $\angle QRX$. false
14. M is in the interior of $\angle YRX$. true
15. R is the vertex of $\angle 3$. true
16. R is the vertex of $\angle 1$. true

Written **Answer each question.**

6. positive real numbers

1. How many endpoints does a ray have? one
2. What point is the endpoint of $\overrightarrow{PR}$? P
3. What is the intersection of two opposite rays? a point
4. If two rays have the same endpoint, are they opposite rays? not necessarily
5. Suppose $\overrightarrow{PQ}$ and $\overrightarrow{PR}$ are opposite rays on a number line. The coordinate of P is 0. The coordinate of R is 10. Is the coordinate of Q positive or negative? negative
6. Suppose $\overrightarrow{AB}$ and $\overrightarrow{AC}$ are opposite rays on a number line. The coordinate of A is 0. The coordinate of C is $^{-}4$. What is the set of possible coordinates for B?

For exercises 7-10, see student's work.

For each of the following, draw $\overrightarrow{PQ}$ and $\overrightarrow{RS}$ so that the given conditions are satisfied.

7. $\overrightarrow{PQ}$ and $\overrightarrow{RS}$ intersect, but $\overline{PQ}$ and $\overline{RS}$ do *not* intersect.
8. $\overrightarrow{PQ}$ and $\overrightarrow{RS}$ intersect at point P, but $\overline{PQ}$ and $\overline{RS}$ do *not* intersect.
9. $\overrightarrow{PQ}$ and $\overrightarrow{RS}$ intersect at point Q, but $\overline{PQ}$ and $\overline{RS}$ do *not* intersect.
10. P, Q, R, and S are collinear, but $\overrightarrow{PQ}$ and $\overrightarrow{RS}$ do *not* intersect.

Use the figures to answer each of the following.

11. Give another name for $\angle 1$. $\angle$ SQP or $\angle$ PQS
12. Name the vertex of $\angle TQR$. Q
13. Name the vertex of $\angle 3$. Q
14. Name the sides of $\angle PQT$. $\overrightarrow{QP}$, $\overrightarrow{QT}$
15. Name the sides of $\angle 2$. $\overrightarrow{QS}$, $\overrightarrow{QT}$
16. Name the common side of $\angle 1$ and $\angle 2$. $\overrightarrow{QS}$
17. Name all angles with $\overrightarrow{QV}$ as a side.
18. Name a point that lies on $\angle 4$. V, Q, or R
19. Name a point in the interior of $\angle TQR$. V
20. Name a point in the exterior of $\angle 2$. P, V, or R

$\angle$ PQV, $\angle$ SQV, $\angle$ TQV or $\angle$ 3, $\angle$ VQR or $\angle$ 4

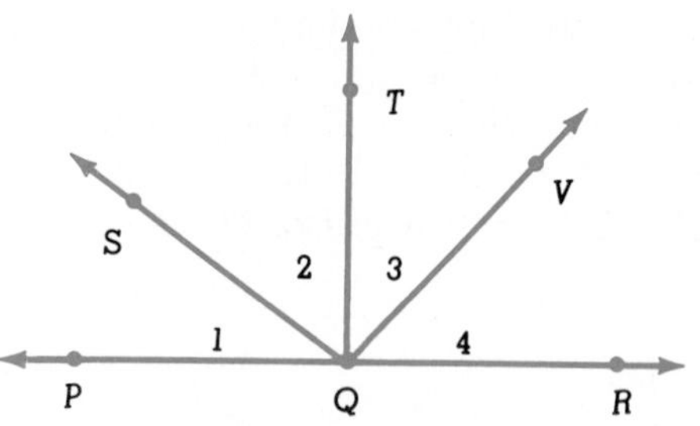

Exercises 11–20

21. Name the angles with point B as their vertex. $\angle$ ABD, $\angle$ DBC, $\angle$ ABC
22. What is another name for $\angle BAD$?
23. The interiors of $\angle ABD$ and $\angle DBC$ are both common to the interior of what angle? $\angle$ ABC
24. Name a pair of opposite rays. $\overrightarrow{DA}$, $\overrightarrow{DC}$

$\angle$ DAB, $\angle$ CAB, $\angle$ BAC

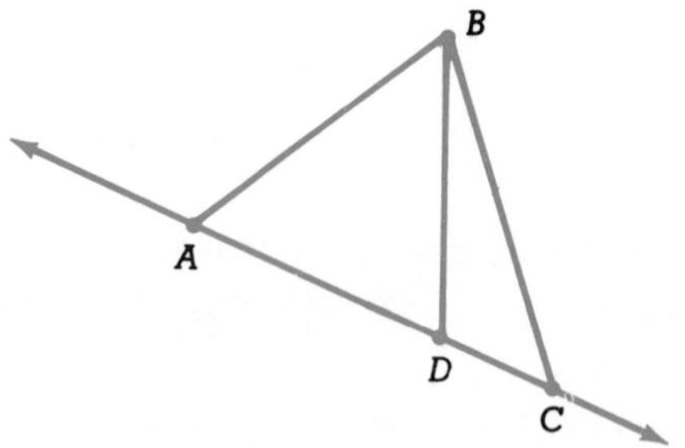

Exercises 21–24

For exercises 25-30, see student's work.

For each of the following, draw two angles so that the given conditions are satisfied.

25. Two angles intersect in a point.
26. Two angles intersect in a segment.
27. Two angles intersect in a ray.
28. Two angles intersect in two points.
29. Two angles intersect in four points.
30. The vertex of one angle lies in the interior of the other angle and vice versa.

3–2 Measuring Angles

Objective: to measure angles with a protractor

Angles are often measured in units called **degrees.**

Other units of measure for angles include the radian and the grad.

For every angle there is a unique positive number between 0 and 180 called the degree measure of the angle.

Postulate 3–1
Angle Measure Postulate

A **protractor** is used to find the *degree measure* of a given angle.

Place the center point of the protractor on the vertex of the angle. Line up the mark labeled 0 on either scale with one side of the angle. Then read the scale where it falls on the other side of the angle.

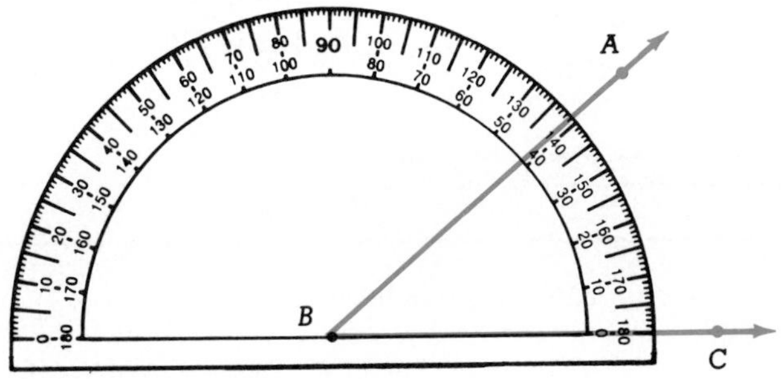

The degree measure of angle ABC is 40. words

$m\angle ABC = 40$ symbols

A line separates a plane into two regions called **half planes.** In the figure at the right, $\overleftrightarrow{QT}$ separates the plane into two half planes and is called the **edge** of each half plane. The ray QT is the side of two angles, each measuring 40 degrees (40°). The Protractor Postulate guarantees that in each half plane, there is only one 40° angle having $\overrightarrow{QT}$ as a side. The edge is not part of either half plane.

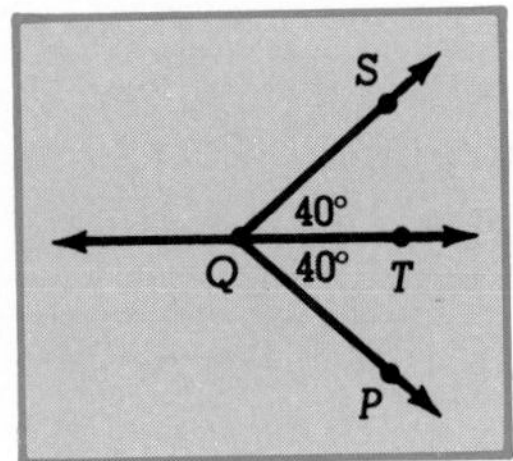

Given a ray on the edge of a half plane, for every positive number *r* between 0 and 180 there is exactly one ray in the half plane such that the degree measure of the angle formed by the two rays is *r*.

Postulate 3–2
Protractor Postulate

Together, the Angle Measure Postulate and the Protractor Postulate establish a one-to-one correspondence between angles and the real numbers between 0 and 180.

examples

1 **Find the degree measure for each numbered angle.**

Measure each angle with a protractor.

$m\angle 1 = 30$ $m\angle 2 = 95$
$m\angle 3 = 18$ $m\angle 4 = 37$

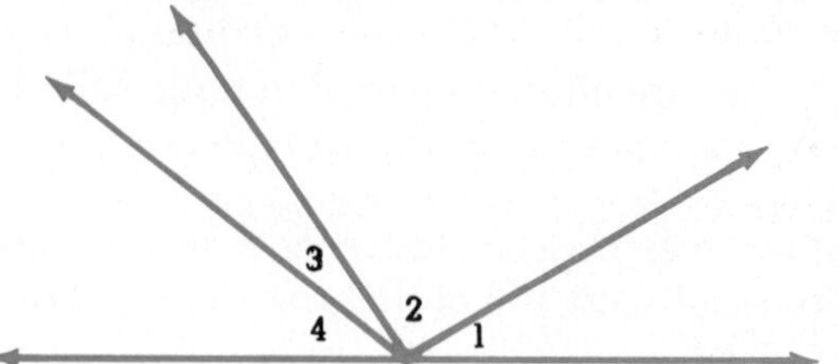

2 **Use a protractor to draw an angle having a degree measure of 65.**

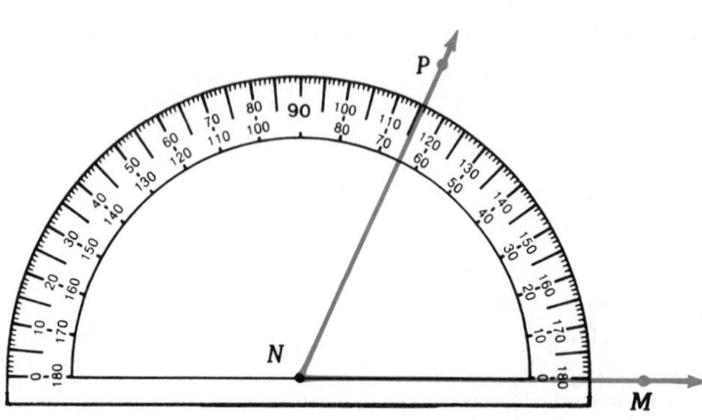

1. Draw $\overrightarrow{NM}$.
2. Place the center point of the protractor on N and line up the mark labeled zero with the ray.
3. Locate and draw point P at the mark labeled 65.
4. Draw $\overrightarrow{NP}$.

In the diagram, $\angle PQR$ and $\angle SQV$ are congruent angles because they both have a degree measure of 50.

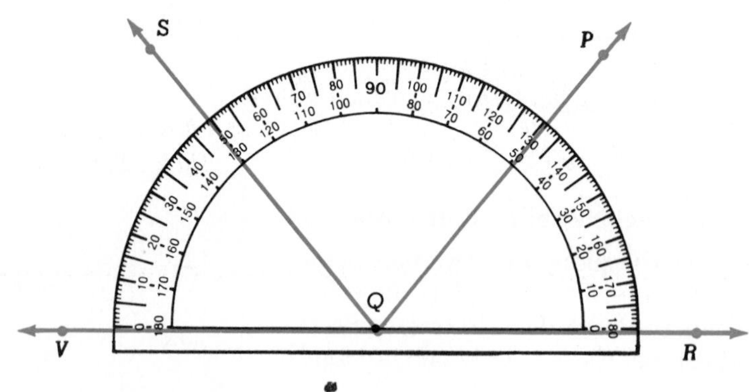

Angle PQR is congruent to angle SQV. *words*

$\angle PQR \cong \angle SQV$ *symbols*

Two angles are congruent if and only if they have the same measurement.

Definition of Congruent Angles

Congruence of angles is related to equality of numbers. Therefore, the following theorem can be stated.

Students prove Theorem 3-1 in Written exercises 27-29 on page 75.

Congruence of angles is reflexive, symmetric, and transitive.

Theorem 3–1

Have students state this theorem in if-then form using angle notation.

The parts of this theorem parallel the theorems about congruence of segments.

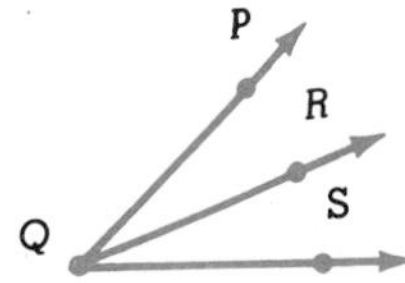

In the figure at the right, $\angle PQR$ and $\angle RQS$ are adjacent angles.

Angle PQS and angle RQS are not adjacent angles.

Two angles in the same plane are adjacent if and only if they have a common side and a common vertex, but no interior points in common

Definition of Adjacent Angles

Measures of adjacent angles can be added to find measures of other angles. For example, $m\angle PQS$ is 110 and $m\angle PQR + m\angle RQS$ is 80 + 30 or 110.

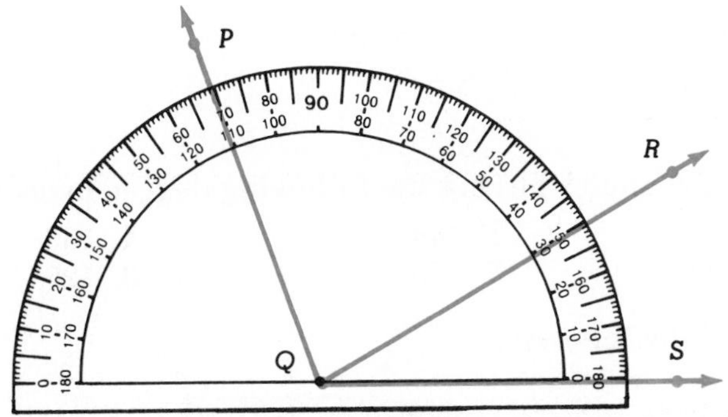

If R is in the interior of $\angle PQS$, then $m\angle PQR + m\angle RQS = m\angle PQS$.

Postulate 3–3 Angle Addition Postulate

Compare this postulate to the Definition of Between on page 44.

example

3 In the figure, $m\angle PTR = 130$ and $m\angle PTQ = 40$. Find $m\angle QTR$.

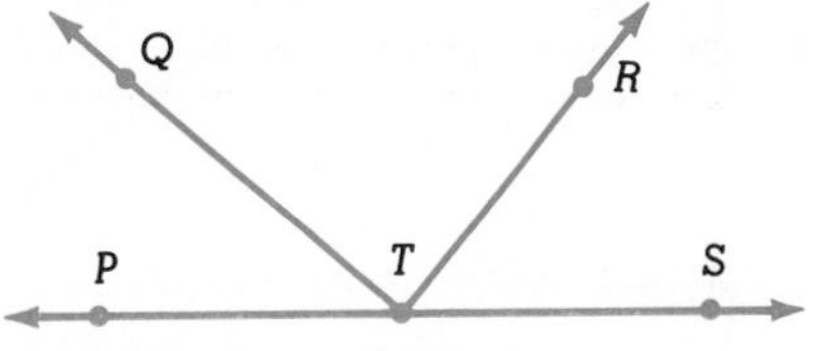

$m\angle PTQ + m\angle QTR = m\angle PTR$	Angle Addition Postulate
$40 + m\angle QTR = 130$	Substitution
$m\angle QTR = 90$	Subtraction Property of Equality

exercises

EN: Wr: 2-34 evens; AV: Ex: 1-15 odds, Wr: 1-35 odds; p. 70, Wr: 8, 10, 26, 28, 30

Exploratory **Find the degree measure for each of the following.**

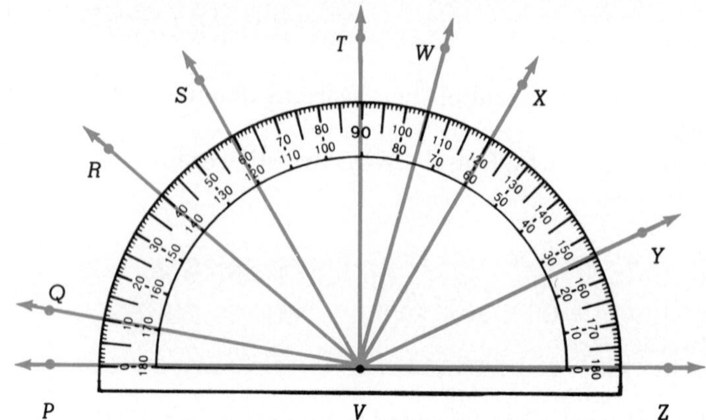

1. $\angle QVZ$ 170
2. $\angle RVZ$ 140
3. $\angle SVZ$ 120
4. $\angle TVZ$ 90
5. $\angle WVZ$ 75
6. $\angle XVZ$ 60
7. $\angle YVZ$ 25
8. $\angle RVY$ 115
9. $\angle QVT$ 80
10. $\angle QVP$ 10
11. $\angle SVP$ 60
12. $\angle SVX$ 60
13. $\angle TVY$ 65
14. $\angle WVX$ 15
15. $\angle RVW$ 65
16. $\angle SVY$ 95

FN: 1-15 odds, Wr: 1, 5, 9, 13, 17, 21, 25, 29, 33; p. 70, Wr: 8-30 evens For exercises 1-8, see student's work.

Written **Use a protractor to draw angles having the following degree measures.**

1. 45
2. 60
3. 144
4. 135
5. 75
6. 29
7. 179
8. 120

Use the figure to complete each of the following.

9. $m\angle OPS = m\angle OPT +$ <u>m ∠TPS</u>
10. $m\angle SRQ =$ <u>m ∠ SRP</u> + <u>m ∠PRQ</u>
11. $m\angle TPQ - m\angle SPR =$ <u>m ∠TPS + m ∠RPQ</u>
12. <u>m ∠ OPR</u> $- m\angle SPR = m\angle OPS$
13. $m\angle TPQ =$ <u>m ∠ TPS</u> + <u>m ∠ SPR</u> + <u>m ∠ RPQ</u>

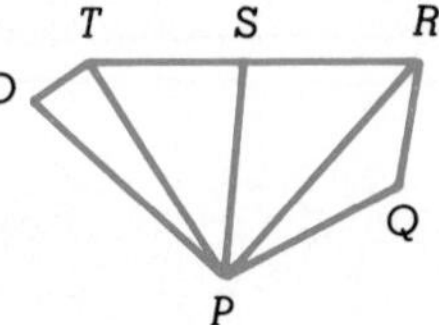

Exercises 9–13

Use the information given in each of the following to find the value of x.

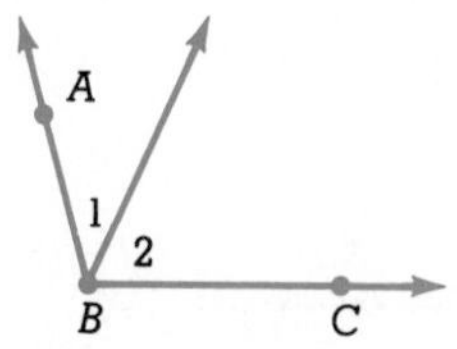

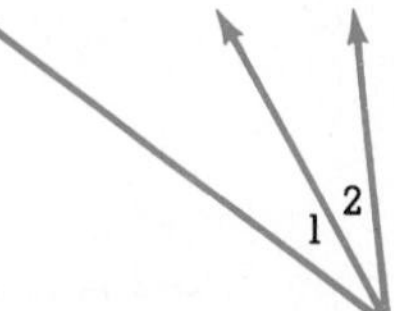

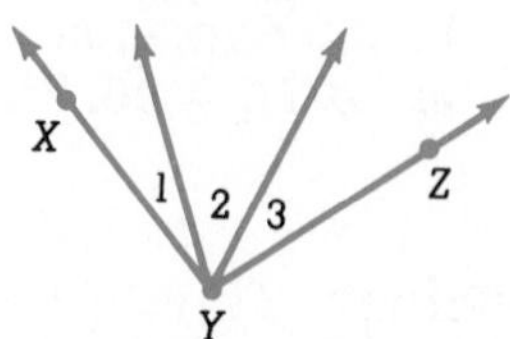

14. $m\angle 1 = 3x$
$m\angle 2 = 5x$
$m\angle ABC = 105$ $x = 13\frac{1}{8}$

15. $m\angle 1 = 2x + y$
$m\angle 2 = y + 40$
$\angle 1 \cong \angle 2$ $x = 20$

16. $m\angle 1 = 3x + 6$
$m\angle 2 = 2x + 18$
$m\angle 3 = 7x + 6$
$m\angle XYZ = 18x$ $x = 5$

Determine whether each of the following is *true* or *false*.

17. $\angle A \cong \angle A$ true

18. If $\angle A \cong \angle B$, then $m\angle A = m\angle B$. true

19. If $\angle B \cong \angle C$ and $\angle C \cong \angle A$, then $\angle B \cong \angle A$. true

20. If $\angle P \cong \angle Q$ and $m\angle P = 30$, then $m\angle Q = 30$. true

21. If $m\angle ABC = 50$ and $m\angle CBD = 50$, then $\angle ABC \cong \angle CBD$. true

22. Angle congruence is transitive. true

23. If $\angle BMA \cong \angle XYZ$, then $\angle XYZ \cong \angle BMA$. true

24. Angle congruence is reflexive. true

25. If $\angle A \cong \angle P$ and $\angle P \cong \angle Z$ and $m\angle A = 40$, then $m\angle Z = 80$. false

26. Angle congruence is *not* symmetric. false

For answers to exercises 27-29, see Teacher's Guide.

27. Prove that angle congruence is reflexive.

28. Prove that angle congruence is symmetric.

29. Prove that angle congruence is transitive.

Students should not use a protractor for exercises 30-35.

The figure contains lines ℓ, m, and n. The sum of the degree measures for all of the angles in the figure is 360. If $\angle 1 \cong \angle 5$, $\angle 6 \cong \angle 2$, $\angle 2 \cong \angle 3$, $\angle 1 \cong \angle 4$, $m\angle 7 = m\angle 3 + m\angle 4$, and $m\angle 3 = 30$, find the degree measures for each of the following angles.

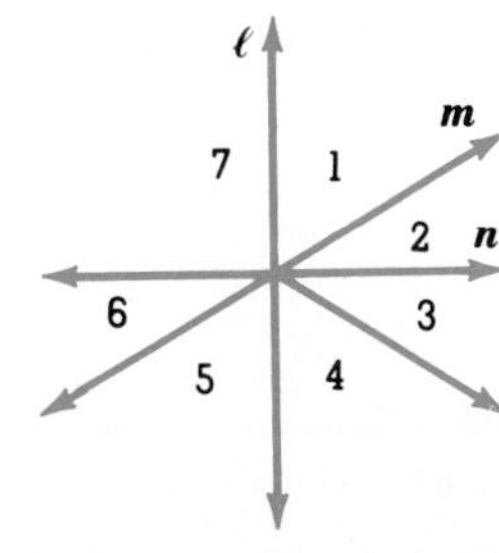

30. $\angle 2$ 30

31. $\angle 6$ 30

32. $\angle 4$ 60

33. $\angle 1$ 60

34. $\angle 5$ 60

35. $\angle 7$ 90

Radian Measure

excursions in geometry

One unit of angle measure is the degree. Another common unit of angle measure is the radian. This unit is defined using a circle.

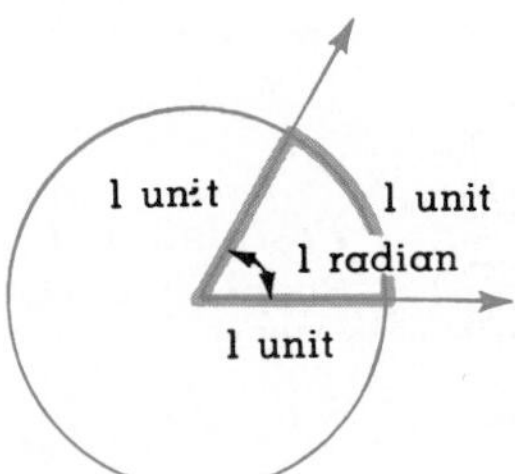

Cut a piece of string that is the same length as the radius of a circle. Lay the string along the edge of the circle and mark the endpoints of the string on the circle. The angle formed by drawing two rays from the center of the circle through each point measures 1 radian.

Exercises **If a circle has a 1 unit radius, then the distance around the circle is 2π units. Use this information to solve each problem.**

1. Find the radian measure of a right angle. $\frac{\pi}{2}$ radians

2. If the degree measures of two angles totals 180, find their total radian measure. π radians

3–3 Pairs of Angles

Objective: to determine if a pair of angles are complementary or supplementary

Pairs of angles can be related by the sum of their measures.

Two angles are supplementary if and only if the sum of their degree measures is 180.

Definition of Supplementary Angles

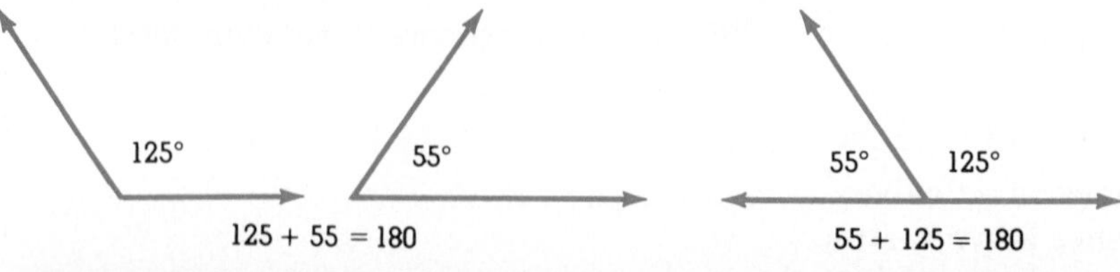

$125 + 55 = 180$ $55 + 125 = 180$

Each angle is called a supplement of the other.

Two angles are complementary if and only if the sum of their degree measures is 90.

Definition of Complementary Angles

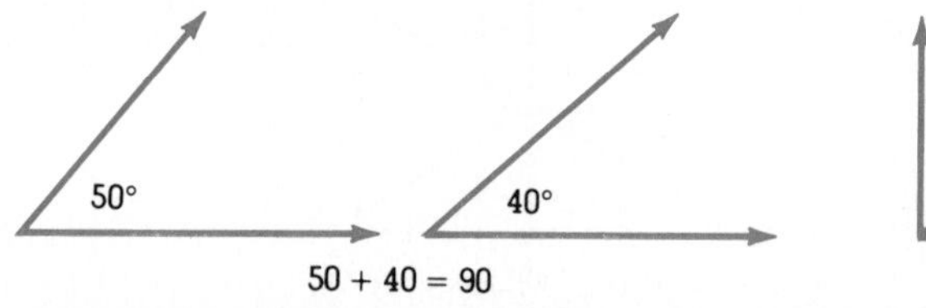

$50 + 40 = 90$

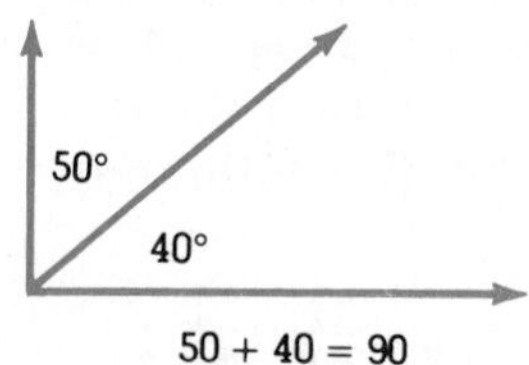

$50 + 40 = 90$

Each angle is called a complement of the other.

Two angles form a linear pair if and only if they are adjacent and their noncommon sides are opposite rays.

Definition of Linear Pair

Note that the Definition of Linear Pair and related theorems can be used in situations involving 180^{0} angles.

In the figure at the right, $\angle 1$ and $\angle 2$ are a linear pair because they are adjacent and $\overrightarrow{YX}$ and $\overrightarrow{YZ}$ are opposite rays.

If two angles form a linear pair, then they are supplementary angles.

Postulate 3–4 Supplement Postulate

Since linear pairs form supplementary angles, the sum of their degree measures is 180.

Suppose $\angle A$ is a supplement of $\angle B$. Also, suppose $\angle C$ is a supplement of $\angle B$. If $m\angle B = 40$, what can you say about $m\angle A$ and $m\angle C$? They both have a measure of 140.

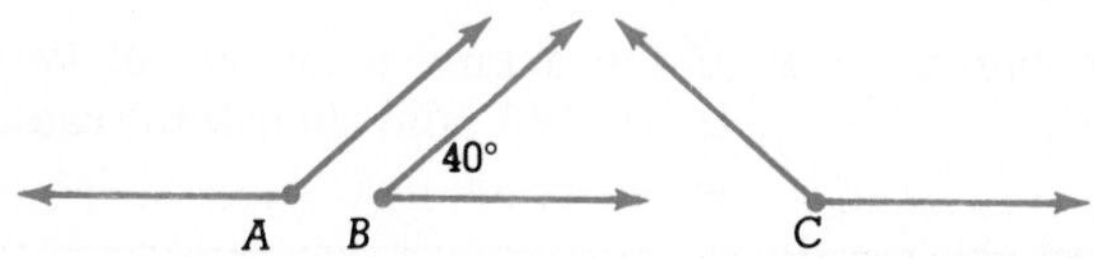

If two angles are supplementary to the same angle, then they are congruent. *Theorem 3–2*

examples

1 **Suppose $\angle A$ and $\angle B$ are supplementary to $\angle C$. If $m\angle C = 25$, find the degree measures of $\angle A$ and $\angle B$.**

$m\angle A + m\angle C = 180$	*Definition of Supplementary Angles*
$m\angle A + 25 = 180$	*Substitute 25 for m $\angle C$.*
$m\angle A = 180 - 25$ or 155	*Subtraction Property of Equality*
$m\angle B + m\angle C = 180$	*Definition of Supplementary Angles*
$m\angle B + 25 = 180$	*Substitute 25 for m $\angle C$.*
$m\angle B = 180 - 25$ or 155	*Subtraction Property of Equality*

$\angle A$ and $\angle B$ each have a degree measure of 155.

2 **Prove Theorem 3–2.**

Given: $\angle A$ is a supplement of $\angle B$.
$\angle C$ is a supplement of $\angle B$.

Prove: $\angle A \cong \angle C$

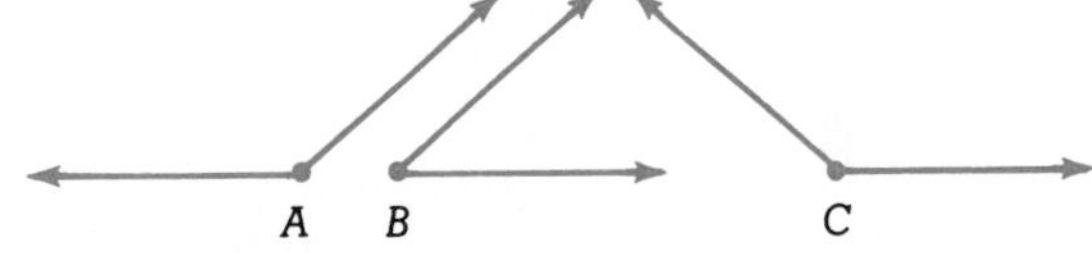

Proof:

STATEMENTS	REASONS
1. $\angle A$ is a supplement of $\angle B$. $\angle C$ is a supplement of $\angle B$.	1. Given
2. $m\angle A + m\angle B = 180$ $m\angle C + m\angle B = 180$	2. Definition of Supplementary Angles
3. $m\angle A + m\angle B = m\angle C + m\angle B$	3. Postulate 2–9: Substitution
4. $m\angle A = m\angle C$	4. Postulate 2–7: Subtraction Property of Equality
5. $\angle A \cong \angle C$	5. Definition of Congruent Angles

Suppose two angles are supplementary to congruent angles. The figure below shows two linear pairs. The 60 degree angles are congruent. What can you say about $\angle 1$ and $\angle 2$? They are congruent.

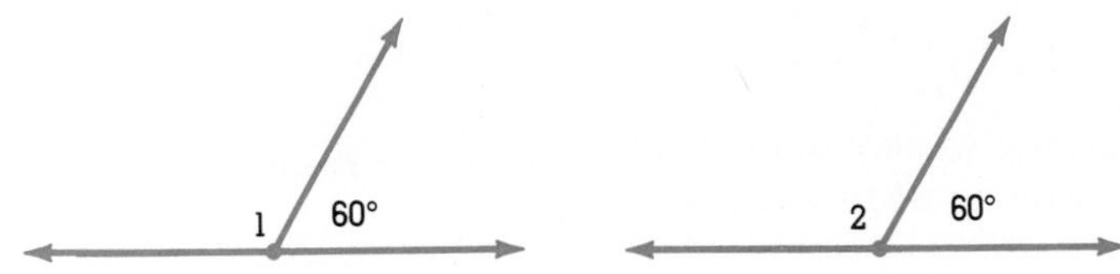

If two angles are supplementary to two congruent angles, then the two angles are congruent to each other. *Theorem 3–3*

example

3 **Prove Theorem 3–3.**

Given: $\angle A$ is a supplement of $\angle B$.
$\angle C$ is a supplement of $\angle D$.
$\angle B \cong \angle D$

Prove: $\angle A \cong \angle C$

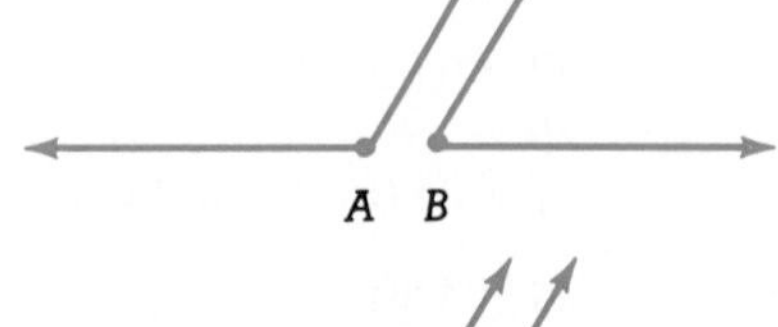

C D

Proof:

STATEMENTS	REASONS
1. $\angle A$ is a supplement of $\angle B$. $\angle C$ is a supplement of $\angle D$.	**1.** Given
2. $m\angle A + m\angle B = 180$ $m\angle C + m\angle D = 180$	**2.** Definition of Supplementary Angles
3. $m\angle A + m\angle B = m\angle C + m\angle D$	**3.** Postulate 2–9: Substitution
4. $\angle B \cong \angle D$	**4.** Given
5. $m\angle B = m\angle D$	**5.** Definition of Congruent Angles
6. $m\angle A + m\angle B = m\angle C + m\angle B$	**6.** Postulate 2–9: Substitution
7. $m\angle A = m\angle C$	**7.** Postulate 2–7: Subtraction Property of Equality
8. $\angle A \cong \angle C$	**8.** Definition of Congruent Angles

Theorems similar to those about supplementary angles can be proven for complementary angles. Students prove Theorems 3-4 and 3-5 in Written exercises 15 and 16, page 79.

If two angles are complementary to the same angle, then they are congruent to each other. *Theorem 3–4*

If two angles are complementary to two congruent angles, then the two angles are congruent to each other. *Theorem 3–5*

EN: Wr: 2-16 evens; AV: Ex: 1-7 odds; Wr: 3, 6, 9, 12, 15; pp. 74-75, Wr: 2, 8, 14, 20, 26, 32

exercises

For answers to exercises 1-8, see the Teacher's Guide.

Exploratory **Use the following theorem to answer exercises 1–8.**

If two sides of adjacent angles lie on a line, then the angles are supplementary.

1. State the hypothesis of the theorem.
2. Draw and label a diagram to illustrate the hypothesis of the theorem.
3. State the given that goes with your diagram for a proof of the theorem.
4. State the conclusion of the theorem.
5. State the prove statement that goes with your diagram for a proof of the theorem.
6. Give another name for two adjacent angles that lie on a line.
7. State the theorem or postulate from this lesson that is about adjacent angles and lines.
8. Given a plan for a proof of the theorem.

FN: Ex: 1-8, Wr: 1-15 odds; pp. 74-75 Wr: 3, 7, 11, 15, 19, 23, 27, 31, 35

Written **In the figure, the following pairs of angles are complementary: $\angle 1$ and $\angle 2$, $\angle 3$ and $\angle 4$, $\angle 5$ and $\angle 6$, $\angle 7$ and $\angle 8$. If $m\angle 1 = 45$, $m\angle 3 = 30$, $\angle 5 \cong \angle 6$, and $m\angle 8 = 10$, find the degree measure for each of the following.**

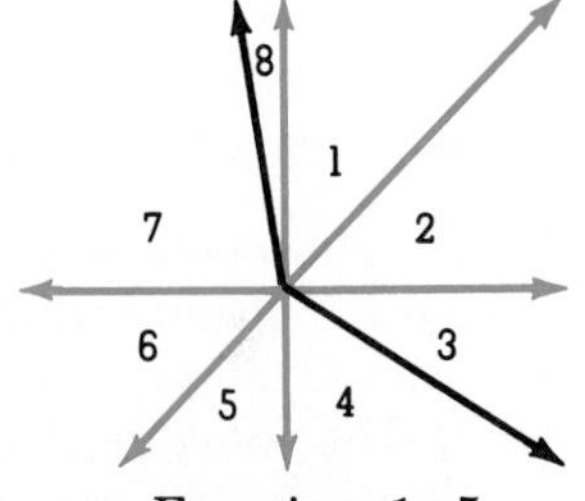

Exercises 1–5

1. $\angle 2$ 45
2. $\angle 4$ 60
3. $\angle 7$ 80
4. $\angle 6$ 45
5. $\angle 5$ 45

In the figure $\angle QVR \cong \angle RVS$, $m\angle PVQ = 72$, $m\angle TVS = 70$, and $\overrightarrow{VP}$ and $\overrightarrow{VT}$ are opposite rays.

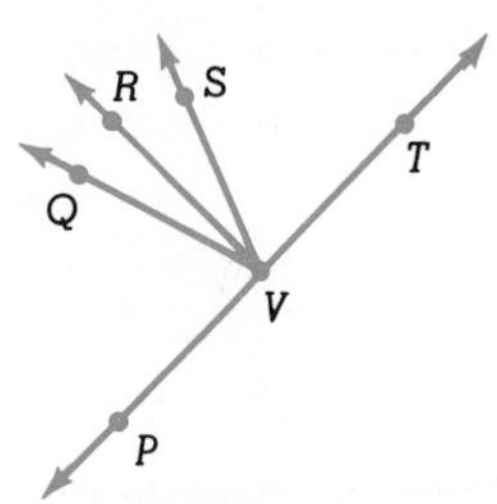

Exercises 6–11

6. Find $m\angle QVS$. 38
7. Find $m\angle QVR$. 19
8. Find $m\angle PVR$. 91
9. Find $m\angle TVR$. 89
10. Find $m\angle PVS$. 110
11. Find $m\angle TVQ$. 108
12. The measure of an angle is one-third the measure of its supplement. Find the measure of the angle. 45
13. The measure of an angle is one-fourth the measure of its complement. Find the measure of the angle. 18

For answers to exercises 14-16, see the Teacher's Guide.

14. Complete the statements and reasons for the following proof.

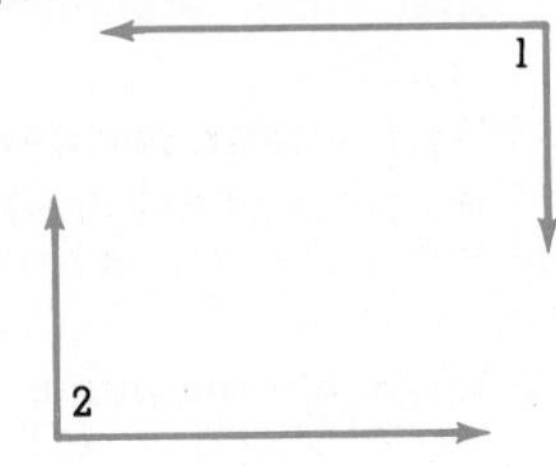

Theorem: If two angles are congruent and supplementary, then they each have a degree measure of 90.

Given: $\angle 1 \cong \angle 2$
$\angle 1$ and $\angle 2$ are supplementary.

Prove: $m\angle 1 = m\angle 2 = 90$

15. Prove Theorem 3–4.
16. Prove Theorem 3–5.

topics in geometry

Flow Proofs

One way to present a proof is to write it in flow proof form. The following example is a flow proof for Theorem 3–2.

Given: $\angle A$ is a supplement of $\angle B$.
$\angle C$ is a supplement of $\angle B$.
Prove: $\angle A \cong \angle C$

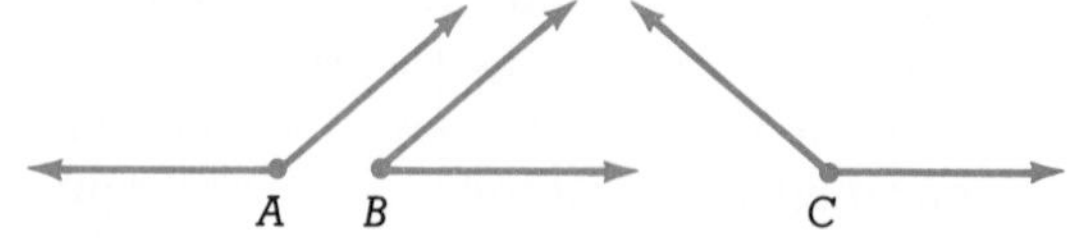

Flow Proof:

$\underline{\angle A \text{ is supplement of } \angle B.} \xrightarrow{1} m\angle A + m\angle B = 180$ } 2
$\underline{\angle C \text{ is supplement of } \angle B.} \xrightarrow{1} m\angle C + m\angle B = 180$ } $\to m\angle A + m\angle B = m\angle C + m\angle B \xrightarrow{3}$

$\xrightarrow{3} m\angle A = m\angle C \xrightarrow{4} \angle A \cong \angle C$

1. Definition of Supplementary Angles
2. Substitution
3. Subtraction Property of Equality
4. Definition of Congruent Angles

A flow proof organizes a series of statements in logical order, starting with given statements which are underlined. The arrows show the order the statements should follow.

The numbers above the arrows refer to the reasons that allow the statements to be made. The reasons are written below the proof. For example, if $\angle A$ is the supplement of $\angle B$, then the definition of supplementary angles implies that $m\angle A + m\angle B = 180$.

Exercises

Answer the questions below about the following flow proof.

Given: $\angle A$ is a supplement of $\angle B$.
$\angle C$ is a supplement of $\angle D$.
$\angle B \cong \angle D$
Prove: $\angle A \cong \angle C$

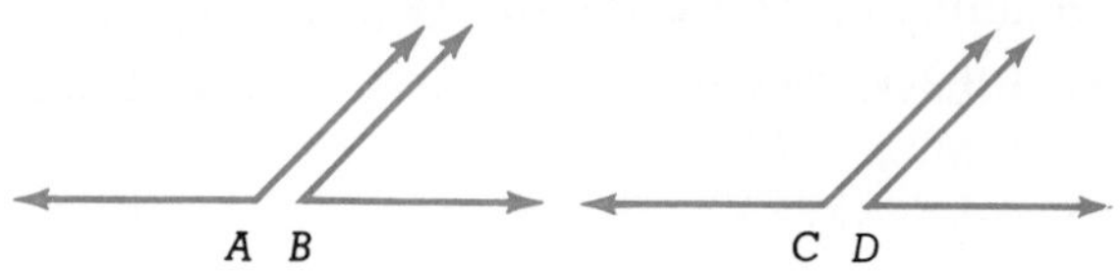

Flow Proof:

6. Both statements are justified by Substitution.

$\underline{\angle A \text{ is supplement of } \angle B.} \xrightarrow{1} m\angle A + m\angle B = 180$ } 2
$\underline{\angle C \text{ is supplement of } \angle D.} \xrightarrow{1} m\angle C + m\angle D = 180$ } $\to m\angle A + m\angle B = m\angle C + m\angle D$ } 2
$\underline{\angle B \cong \angle D} \xrightarrow{3} m\angle B = m\angle D$

$\xrightarrow{2} m\angle A + m\angle B = m\angle C + m\angle B \xrightarrow{4} m\angle A = m\angle C \xrightarrow{3} \angle A \cong \angle C$

1. Draw the symbol that is used to show that one statement follows from another. $\to$
2. Draw the symbol used to show that two or more statements imply another. $\mapsto$
3. Write the statements that imply $m\angle A + m\angle B = m\angle C + m\angle B$.
   3. $m\angle A + m\angle B = 180$, $m\angle C + m\angle B = 180$
4. Write the reason for arrow 1. Definition of Supplementary Angles
5. Write the reason for arrow 2. Substitution
6. Why do two arrows have a 2 above them?
7. Write the reason for arrow 3. Definition of Congruent Angles
8. Why do two arrows have a 3 above them? Both statements are justified by Definition of Congruent Angles.
9. Write the reason for arrow 4. Subtraction Property of Equality
10. Write a flow proof for Theorem 3–4. See the Teacher's Guide.

3–4 Right Angles

Objectives: to classify angles according to their measure, to use properties of angles in proofs

Angles can be classified according to their measures.

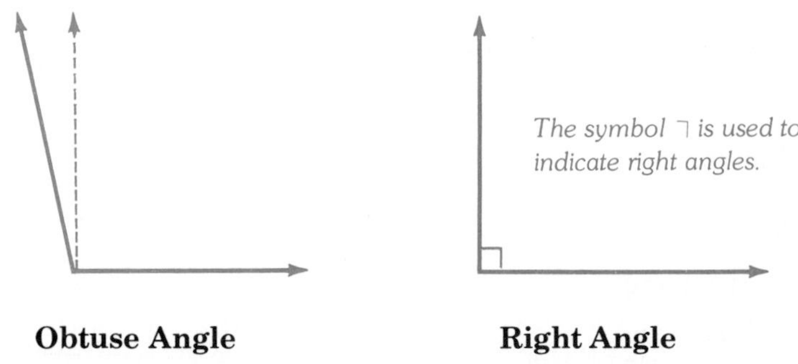

The symbol ⌝ is used to indicate right angles.

Acute Angle

A right angle is an angle whose degree measure is 90. An acute angle is one whose degree measure is less than 90. An obtuse angle is one whose degree measure is greater than 90.

Definition of Right, Acute, and Obtuse Angles

All right angles are congruent because they have the same measure.

If two angles are right angles, then the angles are congruent.

Theorem 3–6

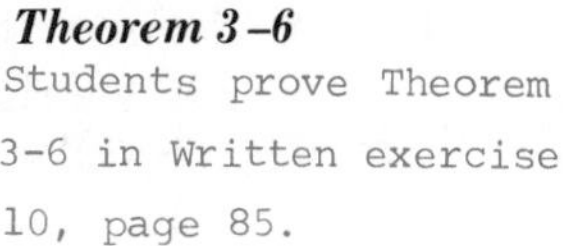
Students prove Theorem 3-6 in Written exercise 10, page 85.

Suppose two angles form a linear pair and one of them is a right angle. In the figure at the right, $\angle 1$ is a right angle.

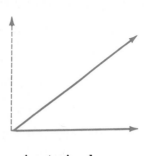

$m\angle 1 + m\angle 2 = 180$	*The angles in a linear pair are supplementary.*
$m\angle 1 = 90$	*$\angle 1$ is a right angle.*
$90 + m\angle 2 = 180$	*Substitution*
$m\angle 2 = 90$	*Subtraction Property of Equality*

This reasoning shows that $\angle 2$ is also a right angle.

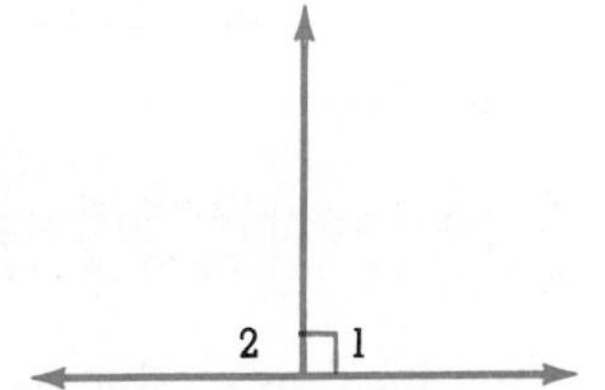

If one angle in a linear pair is a right angle, then the other angle is also a right angle.

Theorem 3–7

Students prove Theorem 3-7 in Written exercise 9, page 85.

To prove the following theorem, use substitution and the fact that congruent angles have the same measure.

Students prove Theorem 3-8 in Written exercise 2, page 84.

If two angles are congruent and supplementary, then each angle is a right angle.

Theorem 3–8

The proof of the following theorem is based on Theorem 3–7.

If two intersecting lines form one right angle, then they form four right angles.

Theorem 3–9

example

1 Prove Theorem 3–9.

Given: Two intersecting lines forming ∠1, ∠2, ∠3, and ∠4. ∠1 is a right angle.

Prove: ∠2, ∠3, and ∠4 are right angles.

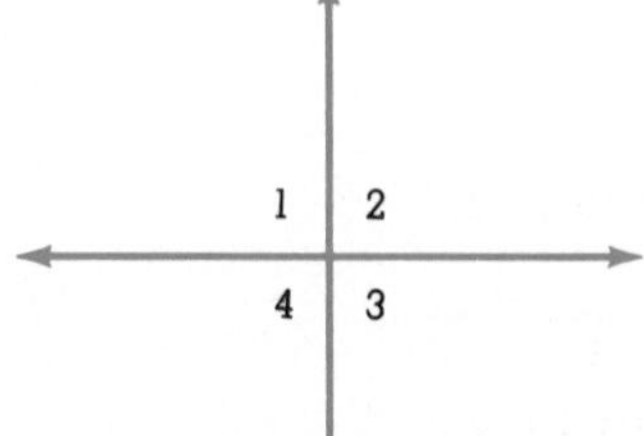

Proof:

STATEMENTS	REASONS
1. Two intersecting lines forming ∠1, ∠2, ∠3, and ∠4.	**1.** Given
2. ∠1 and ∠2 form a linear pair. ∠1 and ∠1 form a linear pair.	**2.** Definition of Linear Pair
3. ∠1 is a right angle.	**3.** Given
4. ∠2 is a right angle. ∠4 is a right angle.	**4.** Theorem 3–7: If one angle in a linear pair is a right angle, then the other angle is also a right angle.
5. ∠3 and ∠4 form a linear pair.	**5.** Definition of Linear Pair
6. ∠3 is a right angle.	**6.** Theorem 3–7

Two angles are vertical if and only if they are two nonadjacent angles formed by two intersecting lines.

Definition of Vertical Angles

In the figure, the angles with red interiors are vertical angles and the angles with blue interiors are vertical angles. Notice that an angle with a red interior and an angle with a blue interior form a linear pair.

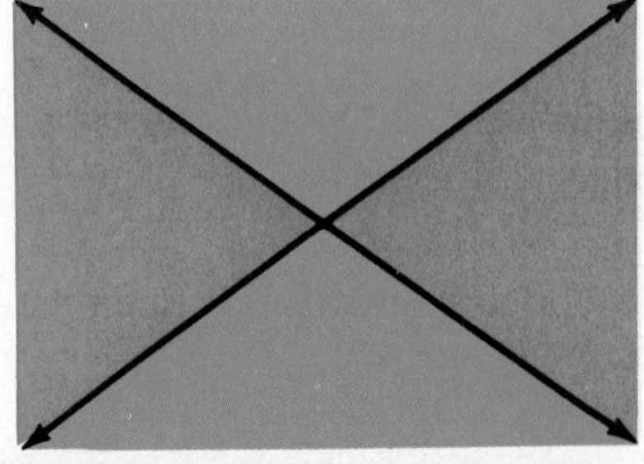

Students prove Theorem 3-10 in Written exercise 1, page 83.

If two angles are vertical, then they are congruent.

Theorem 3–10

exercises

EN: Wr: 2-10 evens; AV: Ex: 1-17 odds, Wr: 1-9 odds; p. 79, Wr: 2, 8, 10, 14, 16

Exploratory **Classify angles with each of the following degree measures as either acute, right, or obtuse, or none of these.**

1. 61 acute **2.** 174 obtuse **3.** 31 acute **4.** 260 none of these

5. 96 obtuse **6.** 3 acute **7.** 90 right **8.** 105 obtuse

9. 89 acute **10.** 0 none of these **11.** 180 none of these **12.** 94 obtuse

For answers to exercises 13-18, see the Teacher's Guide.

State the hypothesis and conclusion for a proof of each of the following theorems.

13. An angle with a degree measure of 90 and a right angle are congruent.

14. If two angles are vertical angles, then the angles are congruent.

15. If two angles are right angles, then the angles are supplementary.

16. If two angles are congruent and supplementary, then each angle is a right angle.

17. If one angle in a linear pair is a right angle, then the other angle also is a right angle.

18. If two angles are right angles, then the angles are congruent.

FN: Ex: 1-18, Wr: 1-6; p. 79, Wr: 2, 8, 10, 14, 16

Written **Complete the reasons for each of the following proofs.**

1. Theorem 3–10: If two angles are vertical, then they are congruent.

Given: $\angle 1$ and $\angle 2$ are vertical angles.

Prove: $\angle 1 \cong \angle 2$

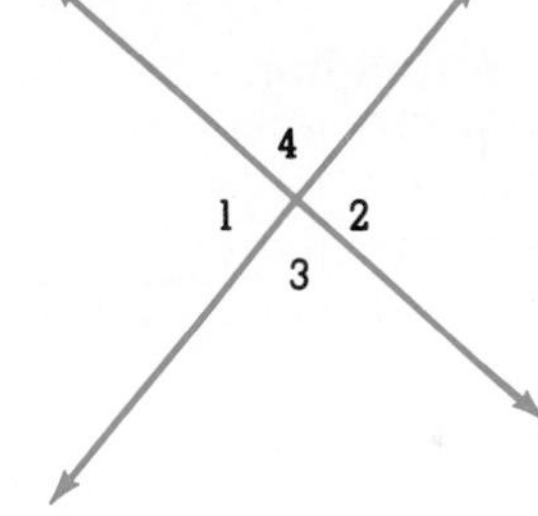

Proof:

STATEMENTS	REASONS
1. $\angle 1$ and $\angle 2$ are vertical angles.	**1.** Given
2. $\angle 1$ and $\angle 4$ form a linear pair. $\angle 2$ and $\angle 4$ form a linear pair.	**2.** Definition of Linear Pair
3. $\angle 1$ and $\angle 4$ are supplementary. $\angle 2$ and $\angle 4$ are supplementary.	**3.** Supplement Postulate
4. $\angle 1 \cong \angle 2$	**4.** Theorem 3-2

2. Theorem 3–8: If two angles are congruent and supplementary, then each angle is a right angle.

Given: $\angle 1 \cong \angle 2$
$\angle 1$ and $\angle 2$ are supplementary.

Prove: $\angle 1$ is a right angle.
$\angle 2$ is a right angle.

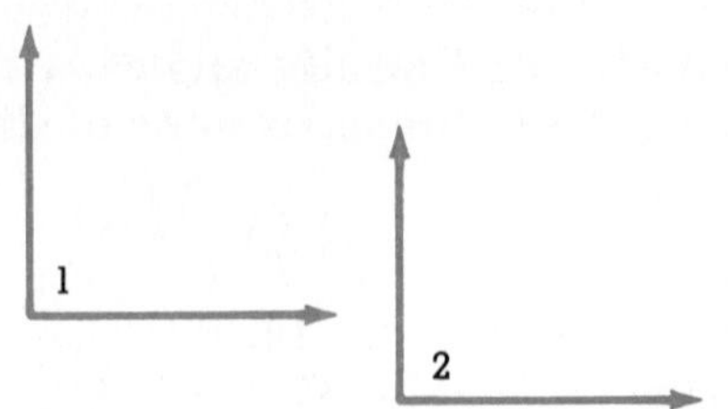

Proof:

STATEMENTS	REASONS
1. $\angle 1$ and $\angle 2$ are supplementary.	1. Given
2. $m\angle 1 + m\angle 2 = 180$	2. Definition of Supplementary Angles
3. $\angle 1 \cong \angle 2$	3. Given
4. $m\angle 1 = m\angle 2$	4. Definition of Congruent Angles
5. $m\angle 1 + m\angle 1 = 180$	5. Substitution
6. $2(m\angle 1) = 180$	6. Identity Property of Multiplication, Distributive, Substitution
7. $m\angle 1 = 90$	7. Division Property of Equality
8. $m\angle 2 = 90$	8. Symmetric Property of Equality, Substitution or Transitive Property of Equality
9. $\angle 1$ is a right angle. $\angle 2$ is a right angle.	9. Definition of Right Angle

Prove each of the following. For answers to exercises 3-10, see the Teacher's Guide.

3. **Given:** $\angle 2 \cong \angle 6$
Prove: $\angle 3 \cong \angle 7$

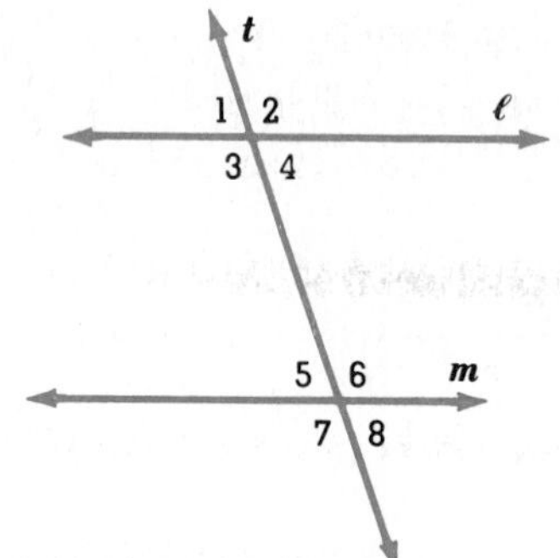

Exercise 3

4. **Given:** $\angle 2$ and $\angle 3$ are supplementary.
$\angle 2 \cong \angle 3$
Prove: $\angle 5$ and $\angle 7$ are right angles.

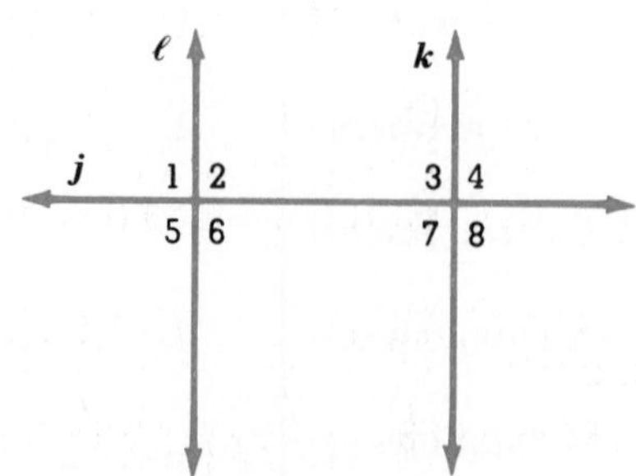

Exercise 4

5. **Given:** $\angle A$ and $\angle C$ are complementary.
$\angle 1 \cong \angle C$
$\angle 2 \cong \angle A$

Prove: $\angle ABC$ is a right angle.

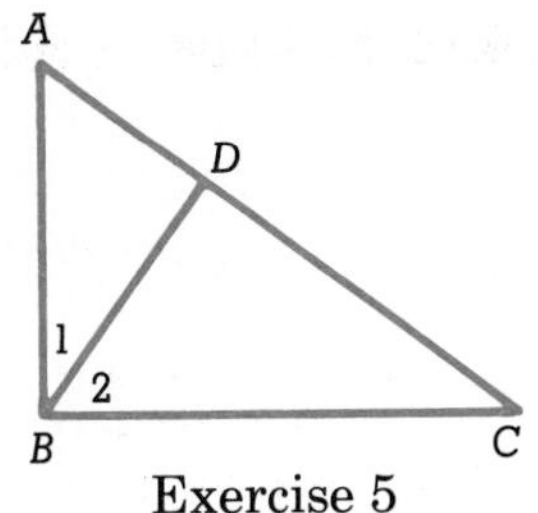

Exercise 5

6. **Given:** $\angle 2$ and $\angle 3$ are complementary.

Prove: $\angle 1$ and $\angle 4$ are complementary.

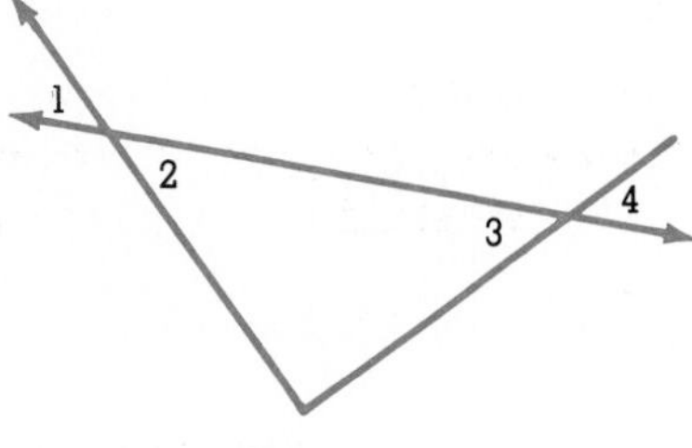

Exercise 6

7. An angle with a degree measure of 90 and a right angle are congruent.
8. If two angles are right angles, then the angles are supplementary.
9. If one angle in a linear pair is a right angle, then the other angle is also a right angle.
10. If two angles are right angles, then the angles are congruent.

Memory

The memory feature of a calculator can be used to store intermediate results or to store a value to be used repeatedly in a computation.

Many calculators have a store key, STO, and a recall key, RCL. The store key stores the number displayed in the memory. The recall key retrieves the stored number from the memory to the display.

Example: Evaluate $\frac{10.3}{^{-}6.5 + 2.8}$.

Enter:	6.5	+/−	+	2.8	=	STO	10.3	÷	RCL 	=	
Display:	6.5	−6.5		2.8	−3.7		10.3		−3.7	−2.7837838	

Exercises Use the memory on your calculator to evaluate each of the following.

1. $\frac{6}{7.5 - 6.3}$ 5
2. $\frac{(5)(3) + 8}{6 - (5)(6)}$ - .9583333
3. $\frac{(^{-}67.6)(3.1)}{^{-}10.2 + 2}$ 25.556098
4. $\frac{9 - (7)(6) \div 3}{^{-}15 - (^{-}16)}$ -5
5. $\frac{13.6 - (5.9)(2)}{(7.3)(6.5)}$ .0379347
6. $\frac{9 + (7.6)(11.1)}{(^{-}13)(1.2) - 6.1}$

6. -4.3023041

3–5 Perpendiculars

Objectives: to recognize and use properties and theorems of perpendicular lines

The weather vane provides an example of perpendicular lines. The north-south line is perpendicular to the east-west line.

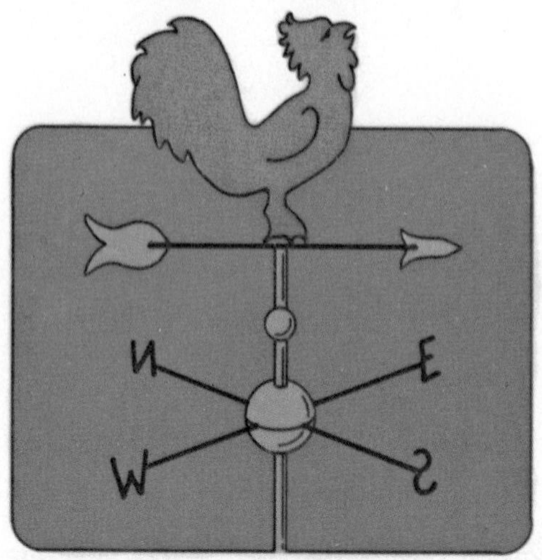

Two lines are perpendicular if and only if they intersect to form a right angle.

Definition of Perpendicular Lines

The symbol $\perp$ means *is perpendicular to*. In the figure below, the two lines are perpendicular.

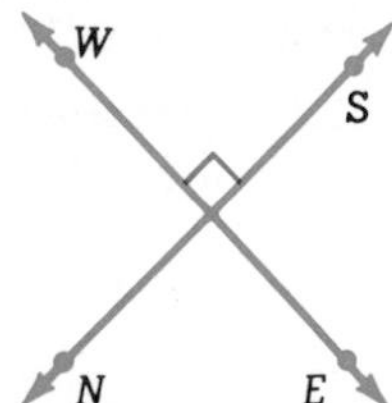

$\overleftrightarrow{NS}$ *is perpendicular to* $\overleftrightarrow{EW}$. *words*

$\overleftrightarrow{NS} \perp \overleftrightarrow{EW}$ *symbols*

Parts of lines are perpendicular to each other if they intersect and if the lines containing them are perpendicular. For example, a ray can be perpendicular to a segment. In the figure below, $\overrightarrow{RS} \perp \overline{PQ}$.

The same term, perpendicular, and the same symbol, $\perp$, are used for lines, segments, and rays.

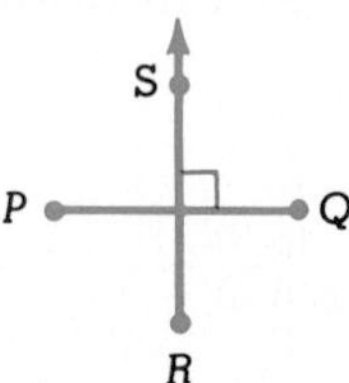

Recall that when two intersecting lines form one right angle, they form four right angles. This information leads to the theorem that follows.

If two lines are perpendicular, then they form four right angles.

Theorem 3–11

Have students draw a diagram to illustrate that several lines may be perpendicular to a given line, as well as other characteristics stated.

A given line may have many lines perpendicular to it. In a plane, through any given point on the line, there is exactly one line perpendicular to the given line. In space, there may be infinitely many lines perpendicular to the given line through the given point.

There is one line perpendicular for each plane that contains the given line.

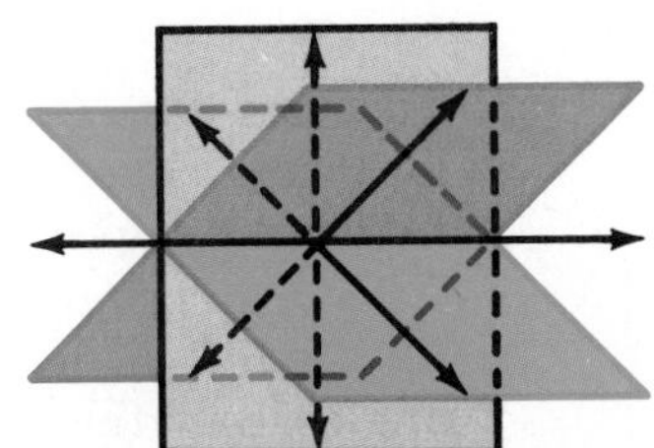

If a point is on a line in a given plane, then there is exactly one line in that plane perpendicular to the given line.

Theorem 3–12

Exactly one means at least one and no more than one.

Theorems 3–13 and 3–14 are converses of one another. Thus, one test for perpendicular lines is congruent adjacent angles.

If two lines are perpendicular, then they form congruent adjacent angles.

Theorem 3–13

If two intersecting lines form congruent adjacent angles, then they are perpendicular.

Theorem 3–14

example

1 Prove Theorem 3–13.

Given: $\overleftrightarrow{PQ} \perp \overleftrightarrow{QR}$

Prove: $\angle PQR \cong \angle RQS$
$\angle PQR \cong \angle PQT$
$\angle TQS \cong \angle RQS$
$\angle TQS \cong \angle PQT$

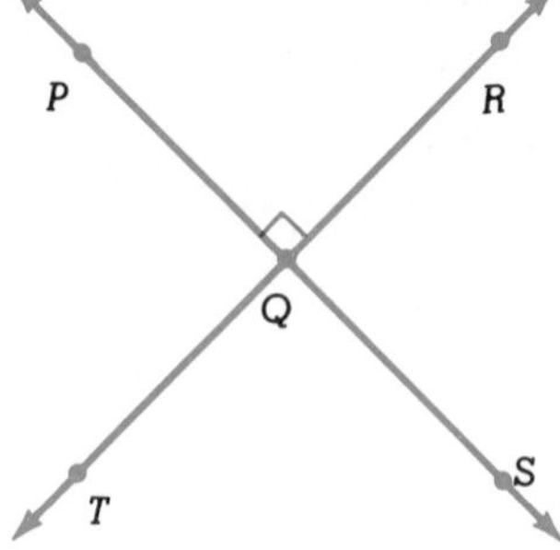

Proof:

STATEMENTS	REASONS
1. $\overleftrightarrow{PQ} \perp \overleftrightarrow{QR}$	1. Given
2. $\overleftrightarrow{PQ}$ and $\overleftrightarrow{QR}$ form a right angle.	2. Definition of Perpendicular Lines
3. $\overleftrightarrow{PQ}$ and $\overleftrightarrow{QR}$ form four right angles, $\angle PQR$, $\angle RQS$, $\angle SQT$, and $\angle TQP$.	3. Theorem 3–9: If two intersecting lines form one right angle, then they form four right angles.
4. $\angle PQR \cong \angle RQS$ $\angle PQR \cong \angle PQT$ $\angle TQS \cong \angle RQS$ $\angle TQS \cong \angle PQT$	4. Theorem 3–6: If two angles are right angles, then the angles are congruent.

EN: Wr: 1-5; AV: Ex: 1-19 odds; Wr: 1, 4, 5; p. 85, Wr: 8, 10

exercises

Exploratory **In the figure, $\overleftrightarrow{AB} \perp \overleftrightarrow{FE}$, $\overleftrightarrow{AE} \perp \overleftrightarrow{GC}$, and C is the midpoint of $\overline{AE}$. Determine whether each of the following is *true* or *false*.**

1. $\overleftrightarrow{BV} \perp \overleftrightarrow{VB}$ false
2. $\overleftrightarrow{GV} \perp \overleftrightarrow{AE}$ true
3. $m\angle 1 + m\angle 2 = 90$ true
4. $\overline{AC} \cong \overline{CE}$ true
5. $\overline{AC} \perp \overleftrightarrow{GC}$ true
6. $m\angle BVE = 90$ true
7. $\angle 3 \cong \angle 4$ true
8. $m\angle 3 + m\angle 4 = 180$ true
9. $m\angle AVF = 90$ true
10. $\overleftrightarrow{VB} \perp \overline{VA}$ false
11. $m\angle 4 = m\angle 1 + m\angle 2$ true
12. $\angle 2$ and $\angle 6$ are complementary. true
13. $\angle FVB$ and $\angle 4$ are complementary. false
14. $\angle GVA$ is a right angle. false
15. $\angle 6 \cong \angle 1$ true
16. $\overrightarrow{AE} \perp \overleftrightarrow{FV}$ false
17. $m\angle 1 + m\angle 6 = 90$ true
18. $\angle 4 \cong \angle 1$ false
19. $\angle 6$ and $\angle 3$ are supplementary. false
20. $\angle AVE$ and $\angle BVF$ are supplementary. true

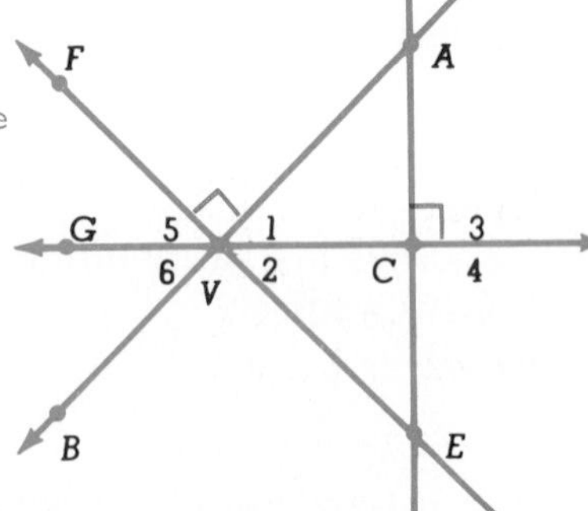

FN: Ex: 1-20, Wr: 1, 5; p. 85, Wr: 7, 9

Written 1. Complete the reasons for the following proof.

Theorem: If two intersecting lines form two congruent adjacent angles, then they are perpendicular.

Given: ℓ and m intersect.
$\angle 1 \cong \angle 2$

Prove: $\ell \perp m$

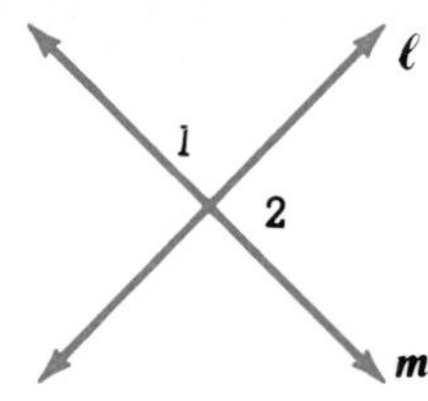

Proof:

STATEMENTS	REASONS
1. $\angle 1$ and $\angle 2$ form a linear pair.	1. Definition of Linear Pair
2. $\angle 1$ and $\angle 2$ are supplementary.	2. Postulate 3-4
3. $m\angle 1 + m\angle 2 = 180$	3. Definition of Supplemetary Angles
4. $\angle 1 \cong \angle 2$	4. Given
5. $m\angle 1 = m\angle 2$	5. Definition of Congruent Angles
6. $m\angle 1 + m\angle 1 = 180$	6. Postulate 2-9
7. $2(m\angle 1) = 180$	7. Postulate 2-12, Postulate 2-14, Postulate 2-9
8. $m\angle 1 = 90$	8. Postulate 2-8
9. $\angle 1$ is a right angle.	9. Definition of Right Angle
10. $\ell \perp m$	10. Definition of Perpendicular Lines

Prove each of the following. For answers to exercises 2-5, see the Teacher's Guide.

2. Theorem 3–11

3. If the noncommon sides of two adjacent acute angles are perpendicular, then the angles are complementary.

4. **Given:** $\angle YXZ$ and $\angle YZX$ are complementary.
$\angle 1 \cong \angle YZX$
$\angle 2 \cong \angle YXZ$

Prove: $\overleftrightarrow{XY} \perp \overleftrightarrow{YZ}$

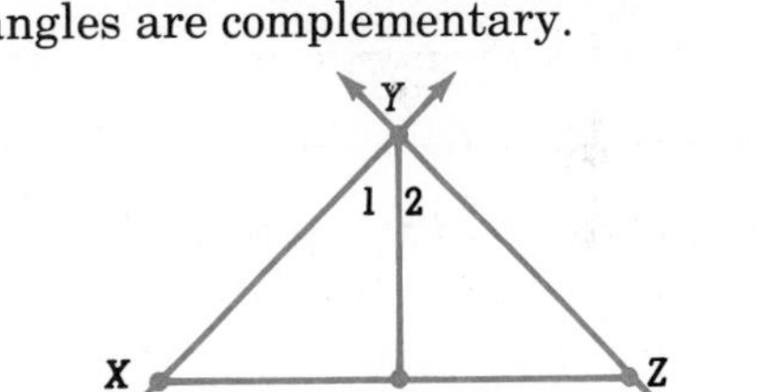

Exercise 4

5. **Given:** $\overline{AB} \perp \overline{AD}$
$\overline{BC} \perp \overline{CD}$
$\angle 2 \cong \angle 4$

Prove: $\angle 1 \cong \angle 3$

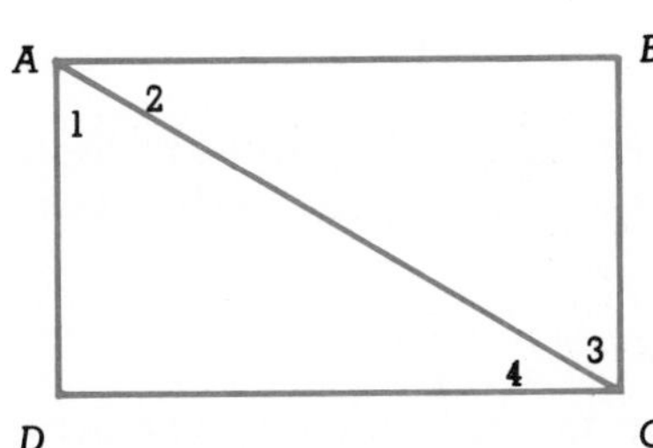

Exercise 5

Objectives: to recognize and use properties of perpendicular planes

3–6 Perpendicular Planes

A line is perpendicular to a plane if and only if the given line is perpendicular to every line in the plane that intersects it.

Definition of a Line Perpendicular to a Plane

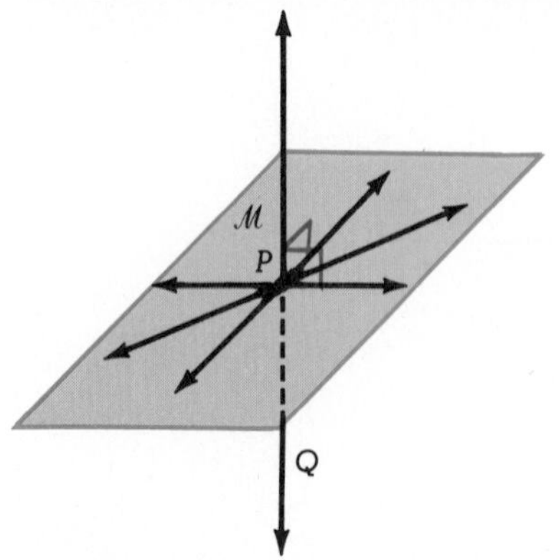

$\overleftrightarrow{PQ} \perp \mathcal{M}$ because it is perpendicular to every line in $\mathcal{M}$ that intersects $\overleftrightarrow{PQ}$. Parts of lines are perpendicular to a plane if and only if they intersect the plane and are contained on a line that is perpendicular to the plane. For example, $\overline{PQ} \perp \mathcal{M}$.

A plane is perpendicular to a line if and only if every line in the plane that intersects the given line is perpendicular to it.

Definition of a Plane Perpendicular to a Line

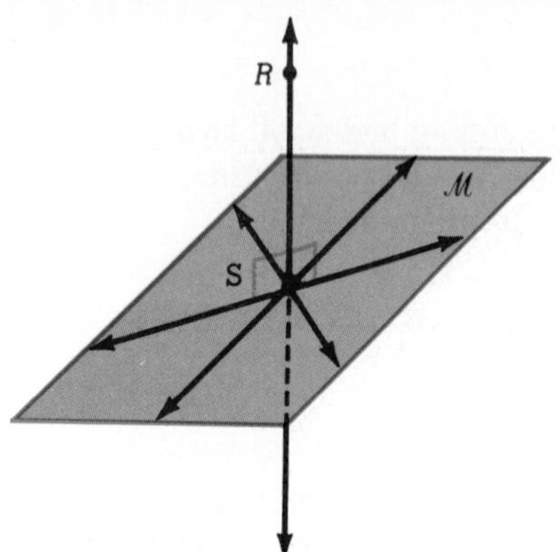

$\mathcal{M}$ is perpendicular to $\overleftrightarrow{RS}$.

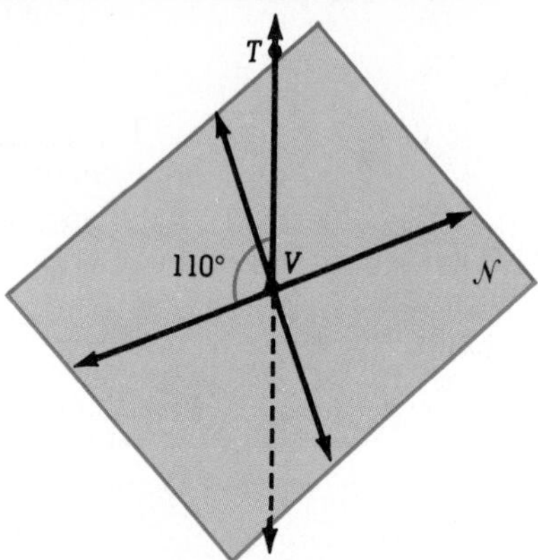

$\mathcal{N}$ is not perpendicular to $\overleftrightarrow{TV}$.

If a line is perpendicular to two intersecting lines at their point of intersection, then it is perpendicular to the plane that contains the two lines.

Theorem 3–15

Just as lines can be perpendicular to lines, planes can be perpendicular to planes. Most walls meet at right angles and provide a model for perpendicular planes.

Two planes are perpendicular if and only if any line in one of them that is perpendicular to their line of intersection is also perpendicular to the other plane.

Definition of Perpendicular Planes

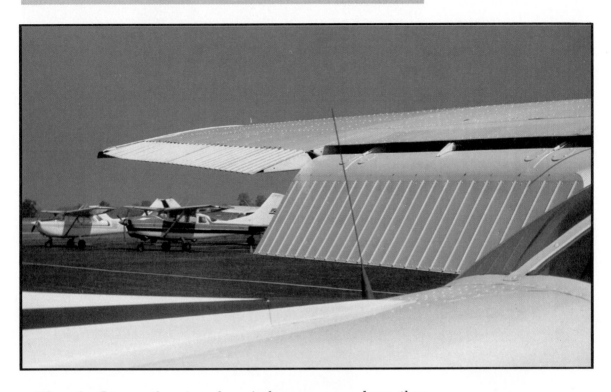

When the flaps on the wing of an airplane are up or down, they form an angle with the wing. Considered in cross section, this situation can be described using an angle. Considered in space, this situation can be described using another geometric figure called a **dihedral angle.**

Fold a sheet of paper once. The result is a model of a dihedral angle.

An angle is dihedral if and only if it consists of two noncoplanar half planes with a common edge.

Definition of Dihedral Angle

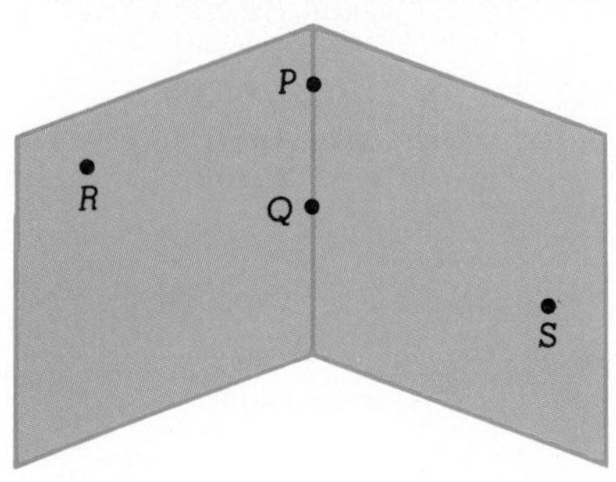

Each half plane in a dihedral angle is called a **face.** A dihedral angle is usually named by its edge and a point on each face. For example, the dihedral angle at the left is $\angle R\text{-}\overleftrightarrow{PQ}\text{-}S$.

It may be useful to have students construct models of dihedral angles.

example

1 **Name all eight dihedral angles.**

angles formed by bottom edges	angles formed by side edges
$\angle T\text{-}\overleftrightarrow{PQ}\text{-}S$	$\angle S\text{-}\overleftrightarrow{TP}\text{-}Q$
$\angle T\text{-}\overleftrightarrow{QR}\text{-}S$	$\angle P\text{-}\overleftrightarrow{TQ}\text{-}R$
$\angle T\text{-}\overleftrightarrow{SR}\text{-}Q$	$\angle Q\text{-}\overleftrightarrow{TR}\text{-}S$
$\angle T\text{-}\overleftrightarrow{SP}\text{-}Q$	$\angle R\text{-}\overleftrightarrow{TS}\text{-}P$

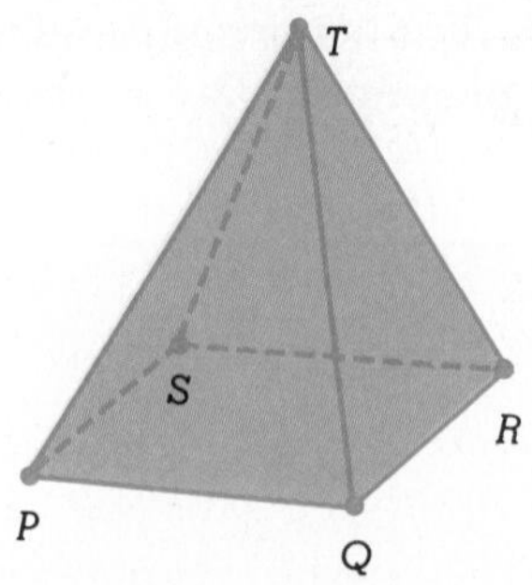

The cross section of a dihedral angle is an angle. Geometrically, the cross section is the intersection of a plane and the dihedral angle. The plane intersects the edge of the dihedral angle in a single point. The following figures show two different cross sections.

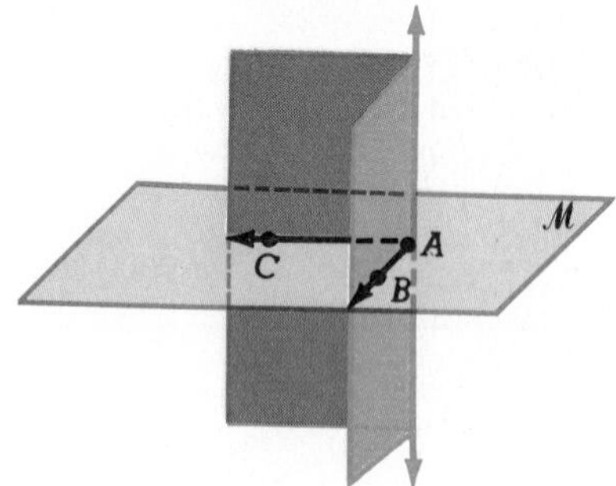

ℳ is perpendicular to the edge of this dihedral angle.

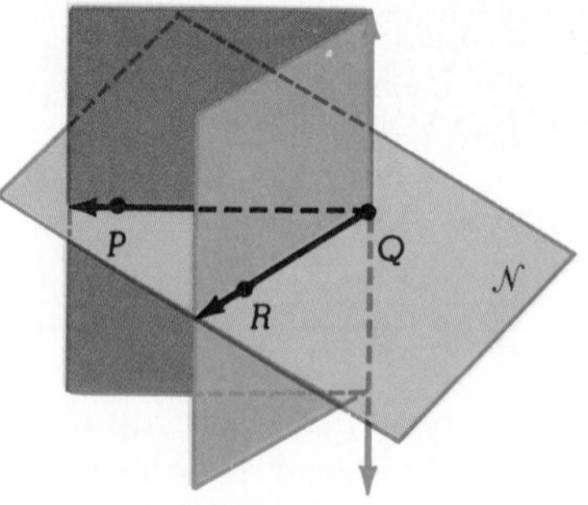

𝒩 is not perpendicular to the edge of this dihedral angle.

A **plane angle** of a dihedral angle is the intersection of the dihedral angle and a plane perpendicular to its edge. All the plane angles of a given dihedral angle have the same measure. Thus, the measure of a dihedral angle is defined to be the measure of any of its plane angles.

$\angle BAC$ is a plane angle.
$\angle RQP$ is not a plane angle.

A dihedral angle is a right dihedral angle if and only if its plane angles are right angles.

Definition of Right Dihedral Angle

Just as perpendicular lines form right angles, perpendicular planes form right dihedral angles.

Two planes are perpendicular if and only if they intersect to form a right dihedral angle.

Theorem 3–16

EN: Wr: 2-16 evens; AV: Ex: 1-9 odds, Wr: 1-15 odds; p. 89, Wr: 3

exercises

Exploratory **In the figure, $\overline{PQ} \perp \overline{QR}$, $\overline{PQ} \perp \overline{QS}$, and $\overline{QS} \perp \overline{QR}$.**

1. Name the dihedral angle with edge $\overleftrightarrow{PQ}$. ∠ S - $\overleftrightarrow{PQ}$ - R
2. Name the dihedral angle with edge $\overleftrightarrow{QS}$.
3. Name the dihedral angle with edge $\overleftrightarrow{QR}$.
4. Name the dihedral angle with edge $\overleftrightarrow{PS}$.
5. Name the dihedral angle with edge $\overleftrightarrow{SR}$.
6. Name the dihedral angle with edge $\overleftrightarrow{PR}$.
7. Name a plane angle for $\angle P\text{-}\overleftrightarrow{SQ}\text{-}R$. ∠ PQR
8. Name a plane angle for $\angle S\text{-}\overleftrightarrow{PQ}\text{-}R$. ∠ SQR
9. Name a plane angle for $\angle P\text{-}\overleftrightarrow{QR}\text{-}S$. ∠ PQS

2. ∠P - $\overleftrightarrow{QS}$ - R 3. ∠P - $\overleftrightarrow{QR}$ - S 4. ∠R - $\overleftrightarrow{PS}$ - Q 5. ∠P - $\overleftrightarrow{SR}$ - Q 6. ∠S - $\overleftrightarrow{PR}$ - Q

FN: Ex: 1-9, Wr: 1-11; p. 89, Wr: 3, 4

Written **In the figure at the right, $\mathscr{M} \perp \mathscr{L}$ and $\mathscr{L} \perp \mathscr{N}$.**

1. Name two dihedral angles. ∠ S - $\overleftrightarrow{RQ}$ - Z ∠ Y - $\overleftrightarrow{XT}$ - W
2. Name a plane angle for $\angle S\text{-}\overleftrightarrow{YQ}\text{-}Z$. ∠ SRX
3. Name a plane angle for $\angle R\text{-}\overleftrightarrow{XZ}\text{-}W$. ∠ QTV
4. $\overline{SR} \perp \overline{RX}$. Write *yes* or *no*. yes
5. $\overline{PQ} \perp \overline{QT}$. Write *yes* or *no*. yes
6. $\overline{RX} \perp \overline{TV}$. Write *yes* or *no*. no
7. $\overline{QT} \perp \overline{XW}$. Write *yes* or *no*. no

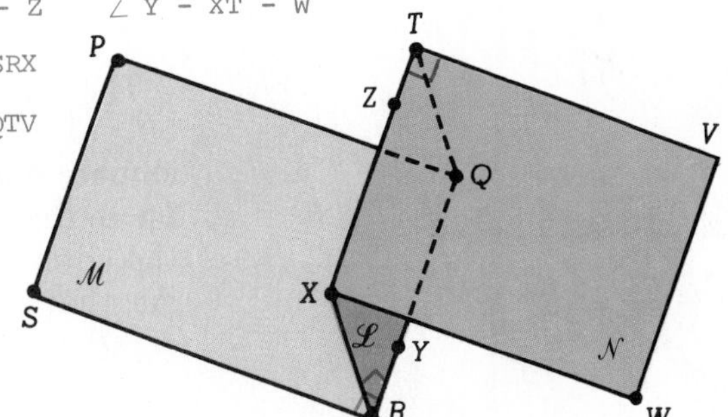

For answers to exercises 8-12, see student's work.

Draw a diagram to show each of the following.

8. Three dihedral angles with a common edge.
9. Two intersecting planes forming four right dihedral angles.
10. A dihedral angle with three plane angles shown.
11. A line intersecting both faces of a dihedral angle at different points.
12. Two dihedral angles that intersect in one line.

Answer each of the following. For answers to exercises 13-16, see the Teacher's Guide.

13. State a given, a prove statement, and draw a diagram for Theorem 3–15.
14. Prove that if a line is perpendicular to a plane, then any plane containing that line is perpendicular to the plane.
15. Prove that if two planes are perpendicular, then they intersect to form four right dihedral angles.
16. Prove that if two planes intersect to form a right dihedral angle, then the planes are perpendicular.

careers

Rescuer

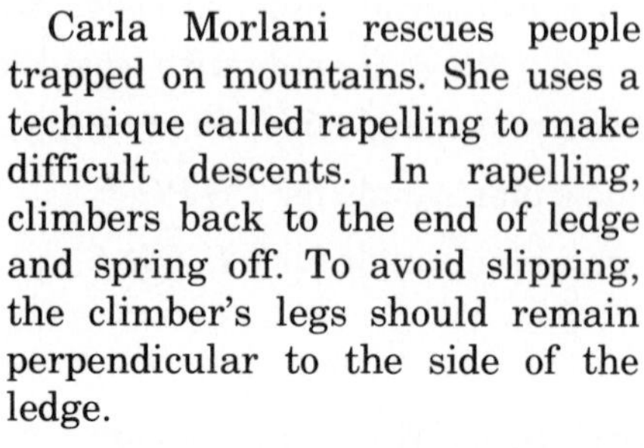

Carla Morlani rescues people trapped on mountains. She uses a technique called rapelling to make difficult descents. In rapelling, climbers back to the end of ledge and spring off. To avoid slipping, the climber's legs should remain perpendicular to the side of the ledge.

The ledge at the right is 50° off the vertical. The climber must be perpendicular to the ledge. By instinct, the climber moves to an angle that is the complement of 50°.

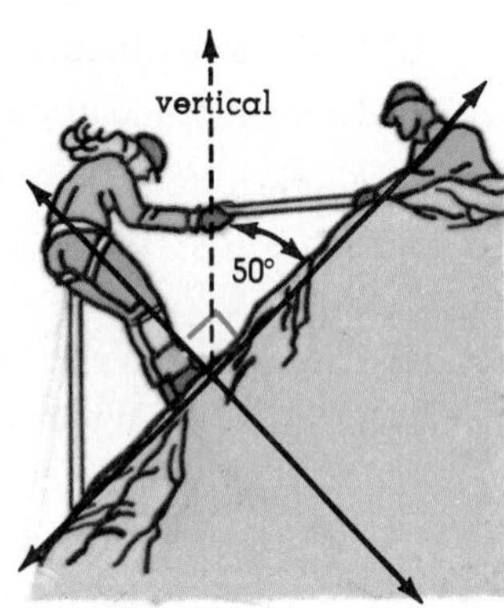

The degree measure of an angle plus the degree measure of its complement is 90. Find the complement of 50°.

$$\begin{aligned} \text{complement of } 50° + 50° &= 90° \\ &= 90° - 50° \\ &= 40° \end{aligned}$$

The complement of 50° is 40°.
The climber's angle measures 40°.

Exercises For each of the following ledge angles, find the climber's angle.

1. 65° 25° **2.** 16° 74° **3.** 47° 43°
4. 23° 67° **5.** 18° 72° **6.** 36° 54°

Vocabulary

ray (67)
opposite rays (67)
angle (68)
sides of angle (68)
vertex of angle (68)
interior of angle (69)
exterior of angle (69)
degrees (71)
protractor (71)
half plane (71)
edge of half plane (71)
congruent angles (72)
adjacent angles (73)
supplementary angles (76)
complementary angles (76)
linear pair (76)
right angle (81)
acute angle (81)
obtuse angle (81)
vertical angles (82)
perpendicular lines (86)
line perpendicular to a plane (89)
plane perpendicular to a line (89)
perpendicular planes (90)
dihedral angle (90)
face of dihedral angle (90)
plane angle (91)
right dihedral angle (91)

Chapter Summary

1. Definition of Ray: $\overrightarrow{PQ}$ is a ray if and only if it is the set of points $\overline{PQ}$ and all points S for which Q is between P and S. (67)
2. Definition of Angle: A figure is an angle if and only if it consists of two noncollinear rays with a common endpoint. (68)
3. Angle Measure Postulate (Postulate 3–1): For every angle there is a unique positive number between 0 and 180 called the degree measure of the angle. (71)
4. Protractor Postulate (Postulate 3–2): Given a ray on the edge of a half plane, for every positive number r between 0 and 180 there is exactly one ray in the half plane such that the degree measure of the angle formed by the two rays is r. (71)
5. Definition of Congruent Angles: Two angles are congruent if and only if they have the same measure. (72)
6. Theorem 3–1: Congruence of angles is reflexive, symmetric, and transitive. (73)
7. Definition of Adjacent Angles: Two angles in the same plane are adjacent if and only if they have a common side and a common vertex, but no points in the interior of one angle are in the interior of the other. (73)
8. Angle Addition Postulate (Postulate 3–3): If R is in the interior of $\angle PQS$, then $m\angle PQR + m\angle RQS = m\angle PQS$. (73)
9. Definition of Supplementary Angles: Two angles are supplementary if and only if the sum of their degree measures is 180. (76)
10. Definition of Complementary Angles: Two angles are complementary if and only if the sum of their degree measures is 90. (76)

11. Definition of Linear Pair: Two angles form a linear pair if and only if they are adjacent and their noncommon sides are opposite rays. (76)
12. Supplement Postulate (Postulate 3–4): If two angles form a linear pair, then they are supplementary angles. (76)
13. Theorem 3–2: If two angles are supplementary to the same angle, then they are congruent. (77)
14. Theorem 3–3: If two angles are supplementary to two congruent angles, then the two angles are congruent to each other. (78)
15. Theorem 3–4: If two angles are complementary to the same angle, then they are congruent to each other. (78)
16. Theorem 3–5: If two angles are complementary to two congruent angles, then the two angles are congruent to each other. (78)
17. Definition of Right, Acute, and Obtuse Angles: A right angle is an angle whose degree measure is 90. An acute angle is an angle whose degree measure is less than 90. An obtuse angle is an angle whose degree measure is greater than 90. (81)
18. Theorem 3–6: If two angles are right angles, then the angles are congruent. (81)
19. Theorem 3–7: If one angle in a linear pair is a right angle, then the other angle is also a right angle. (81)
20. Theorem 3–8: If two angles are congruent and supplementary, then each angle is a right angle. (81)
21. Theorem 3–9: If two intersecting lines form one right angle, then they form four right angles. (82)
22. Definition of Vertical Angles: Two angles are vertical if and only if they are two nonadjacent angles formed by two intersecting lines. (82)
23. Theorem 3–10: If two angles are vertical, then they are congruent. (82)
24. Definition of Perpendicular Lines: Two lines are perpendicular if and only if they intersect to form a right angle. (86)
25. Theorem 3–11: If two lines are perpendicular, then they form four right angles. (87)
26. Theorem 3–12: If a point is on a line in a given plane, then there is exactly one line in that plane perpendicular to the given line. (87)
27. Theorem 3–13: If two lines are perpendicular, then they form congruent adjacent angles. (87)
28. Theorem 3–14: If two intersecting lines form congruent adjacent angles, then they are perpendicular. (87)
29. Definition of a Line Perpendicular to a Plane: A line is perpendicular to a plane if and only if the given line is perpendicular to every line in the plane that intersects it. (90)
30. Definition of a Plane Perpendicular to a Line: A plane is perpendicular to a line if and only if every line in the plane that intersects the given line is perpendicular to it. (90)
31. Theorem 3–15: If a line is perpendicular to two intersecting lines at their point of intersection, then it is perpendicular to the plane that contains the two lines. (90)

32. Definition of Perpendicular Planes: Two planes are perpendicular if and only if any line in one of them that is perpendicular to their line of intersection is also perpendicular to the other plane. (91)
33. Definition of Dihedral Angle: An angle is dihedral if and only if it consists of two noncoplanar half planes with a common edge. (91)
34. Definition of Right Dihedral Angle: A dihedral angle is a right dihedral angle if and only if its plane angles are right angles. (92)
35. Theorem 3–16: Two planes are perpendicular if and only if they intersect to form a right dihedral angle. (92)

Chapter Review

3–1 In the figure, *P, Q, R,* and *S* are collinear.

1. Name the vertex of $\angle 4$. Q
2. Name the sides of $\angle 4$. $\overrightarrow{QP}$, $\overrightarrow{QV}$
3. Name a point in the interior of $\angle 3$. T
4. Name a point in the exterior of $\angle 3$. P
5. Name a pair of opposite rays.
6. Write another name for $\angle 2$.
7. Name a common side for $\angle 1$ and $\angle 2$. $\overrightarrow{RT}$
8. Name a pair of adjacent angles. $\angle 3$ and $\angle 4$ or $\angle 1$ and $\angle 2$

3–2 In the figure at the right, $m\angle QTS = 132$, $m\angle STR = 37$, and $\overrightarrow{TP}$ and $\overrightarrow{TS}$ are opposite rays.

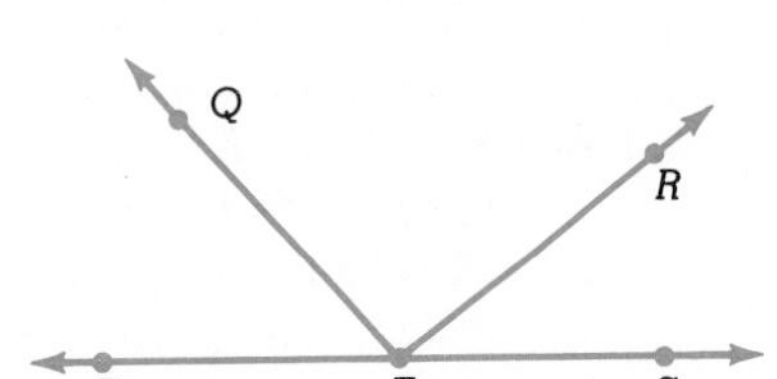

9. Find $m\angle RTQ$. 95
10. Find $m\angle QTP$. 48

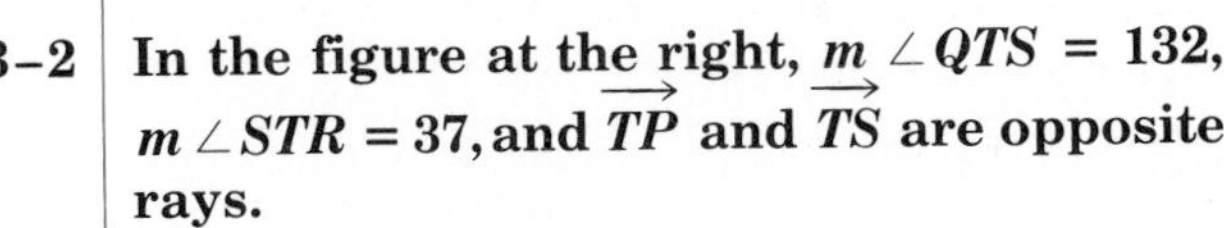

5. $\overrightarrow{QP}$ and $\overrightarrow{QR}$ or $\overrightarrow{RQ}$ and $\overrightarrow{RS}$

6. $\angle PRT$ or $\angle QRT$ or $\angle TRP$ or $\angle TRQ$

Determine whether each of the following is *true* or *false*.

11. If $\angle XYZ \cong \angle JKL$, then $\angle JKL \cong \angle XYZ$. true
12. If $m\angle ABC = 35$ and $\angle ABC \cong \angle RST$, then $m\angle RST = 35$. true
13. If $m\angle 1 = m\angle 2$ and $m\angle 2 = m\angle 3$ and $m\angle 3 = 85$, then $m\angle 1 = 95$. false

3–3 **In the figure, $m\angle RPS = 21$, $m\angle TPV = 65$, $\angle RPS \cong \angle SPT$, and $\overleftrightarrow{QV}$ and $\overleftrightarrow{WS}$ intersect at P. Find the degree measure for each of the following.**

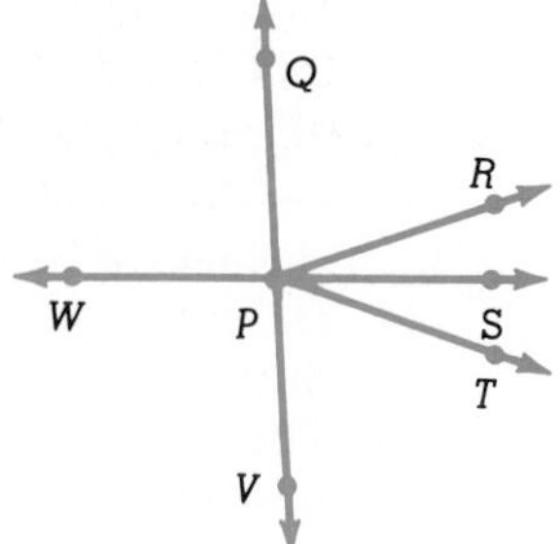

Exercises 14–17

14. $\angle TPS$ 21
15. $\angle WPV$ 94
16. $\angle QPW$ 86
17. $\angle RPQ$ 73
18. Prove that if two angles are congruent and complementary, then they each have a degree measure of 45.

For answers to exercises 18-22, see the Teacher's Guide.

3–4 **Prove each of the following.**

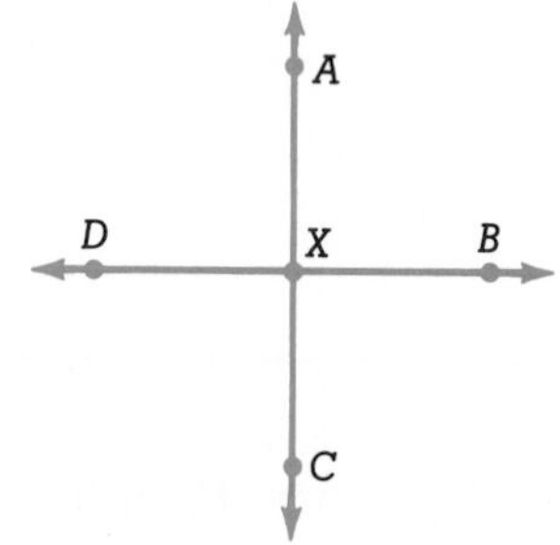

Exercises 19–20

19. **Given:** $\angle AXB$ is a right angle.
$\angle AXD \cong \angle AXB$
Prove: $\angle AXD$ is a right angle.
20. **Given:** $\angle AXB$ and $\angle DXC$ are supplementary.
Prove: $\angle AXD$ and $\angle BXC$ are supplementary.

3–5 **Prove each of the following.**

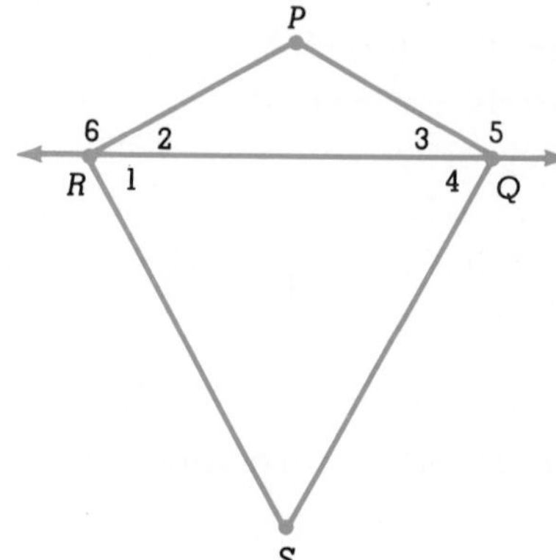

Exercises 21–22

21. **Given:** $\overline{PR} \perp \overline{RS}$
$\angle 2 \cong \angle 3$
$\angle 1 \cong \angle 4$
Prove: $\overline{PQ} \perp \overline{QS}$
22. **Given:** $\overline{PR} \perp \overline{RS}$
$\overline{PQ} \perp \overline{QS}$
$\angle 1 \cong \angle 4$
Prove: $\angle 6 \cong \angle 5$

3–6 **In the figure, $\overline{BC} \perp \overline{BE}$ and $\overline{AB} \perp \overline{BE}$. Answer each of the following.**

23. Name two dihedral angles.
24. Name a plane angle for $\angle D\text{-}\overleftrightarrow{BE}\text{-}A$. $\angle$ ABC or $\angle$ DEF

23. two of: $\angle A - \overleftrightarrow{BE} - C$, $\angle C - \overleftrightarrow{AF} - B$, $\angle A - \overleftrightarrow{CD} - B$, $\angle B - \overleftrightarrow{AC} - D$, $\angle F - \overleftrightarrow{AB} - C$, $\angle A - \overleftrightarrow{BC} - E$, $\angle F - \overleftrightarrow{ED} - B$, $\angle C - \overleftrightarrow{FD} - E$, $\angle A - \overleftrightarrow{EF} - D$

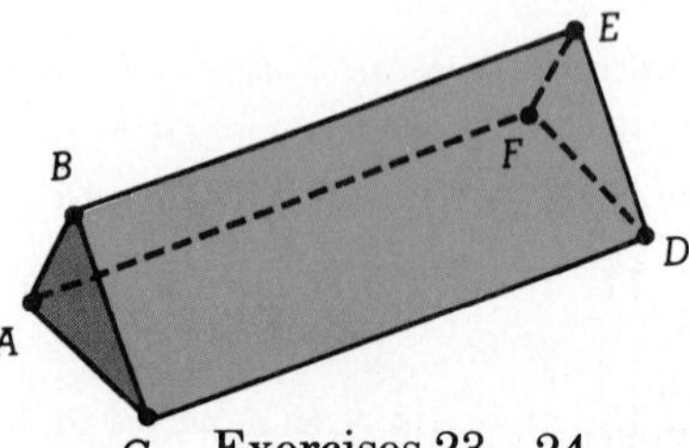

Exercises 23–24

Chapter Test

Determine whether each of the following is *true* or *false*.

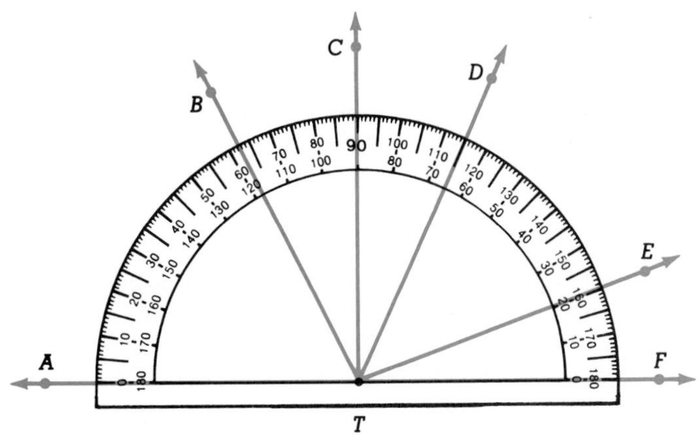

Exercises 1–14

1. $\overrightarrow{TA}$ and $\overrightarrow{TF}$ form opposite rays. true
2. $\overrightarrow{CT}$ is a side of $\angle FTC$. false
3. D is in the interior of $\angle BTC$. false
4. D is in the exterior of $\angle FTE$. true
5. $\overrightarrow{CT} \perp \overleftrightarrow{AF}$ true
6. $\angle BTC \cong \angle DTC$ true
7. $\angle FTD$ and $\angle DTC$ are complementary. true
8. $\angle ATB$ and $\angle BTF$ are complementary.
9. $\angle ATB$ and $\angle BTF$ form a linear pair. true
10. $\angle BTD$ and $\angle FTE$ are adjacent angles.
11. $m\angle ATB = m\angle DTE + m\angle FTE$ false
12. $m\angle BTD = m\angle CTB + m\angle DTC$ true
13. $\angle CTE$ is an acute angle. true
14. $\angle ETC$ is an obtuse angle. false

8. false

10. false

In the figure, $\mathscr{A} \perp \mathscr{B}$ and $\mathscr{B} \perp \mathscr{C}$.

15. Name a dihedral angle with edge $\overleftrightarrow{SR}$. $\angle$ P - $\overleftrightarrow{SR}$ - W
16. Name the faces of $\angle Y\text{-}\overleftrightarrow{VX}\text{-}S$. C and B
17. Find $m\angle TVZ$. 90
18. Name a plane angle for $\angle P\text{-}\overleftrightarrow{TR}\text{-}W$. $\angle$ NTV
19. If the supplement of an angle is three times the complement of an angle, what is the measure of the angle? 45

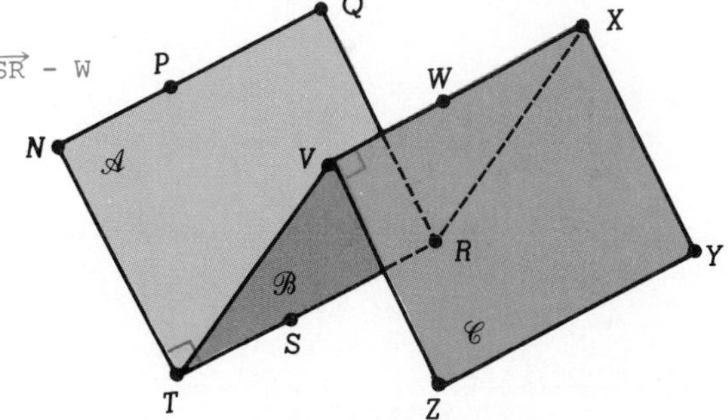

Exercises 15–18

For answers to exercises 20-23, see the Teacher's Guide.

Prove each of the following statements.

20. If two angles are vertical and one angle is a right angle, then the other is also a right angle.
21. If two adjacent angles are congruent and supplementary, then their common side is perpendicular to the other two sides.
22. If two intersecting lines form two congruent adjacent angles, then they are perpendicular.
23. If the angles in a linear pair are congruent, then the common side is perpendicular to the other two sides.

cumulative review

For answers to exercises 1-2, see student's work.

Draw and label a diagram to show each of the following.

1. $\overleftrightarrow{EF}$ and $\overleftrightarrow{GH}$ intersect at T.
2. Plane $\mathcal{M}$ contains $\overleftrightarrow{TS}$ and C.

Write each conditional statement in *if-then* form.

3. A rhombus is a quadrilateral.
   3. If a figure is a rhombus, then it is a quadrilateral.
4. Skew lines do *not* intersect.
   4. If two lines are skew, then they do not intersect.

Write the converse of each of the following in *if-then* form.

5. Every line contains at least three points.
   5. If a figure contains at least three points, then the figure is a line.
6. Two points are on a plane only if they are in the plane. If two points are in the plane, then they are on a plane.

Write the inverse and contrapositive of each of the following statements.

7. If a figure is a square, then it is a polygon.
   If a figure is not a square, it is not a polygon.
   If a figure is not a polygon, it is not a square.
8. If points lie in the same plane then they are coplanar. If points do not lie in the same plane, they are not coplanar. If points are not coplanar, they do not lie in the same plane.

Change each fraction to decimal form.

9. $\frac{4}{5}$ 0.8
10. $-\frac{17}{20}$ -0.85
11. $\frac{19}{3}$ $6.\overline{3}$

Change each decimal to fractional form.

12. $0.\overline{8}$ $\frac{8}{9}$
13. $0.4\overline{5}$ $\frac{41}{90}$
14. $0.0\overline{25}$ $\frac{5}{198}$

Use the number line below to find each measure.

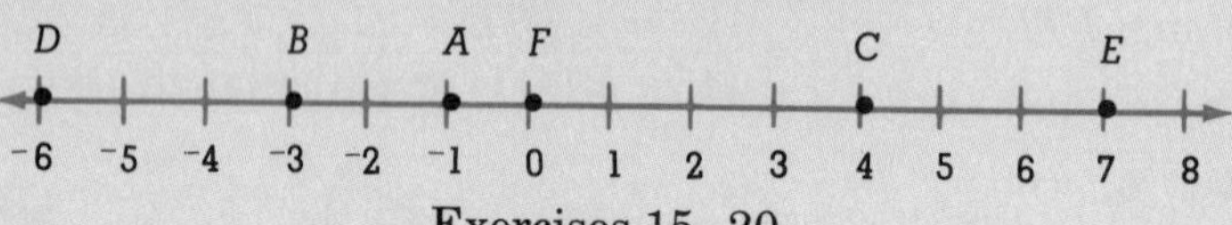

Exercises 15–20

15. FD 6
16. CE 3
17. CB 7
18. DF 6
19. AD 5
20. BE 10

21. Complete the reasons for the following proof.

Given: $2x + 8 = ^-6$
Prove: $x = ^-7$
Proof:

STATEMENTS	REASONS
1. $2x + 8 = ^-6$	1. Given
2. $2x + 8 + ^-8 = ^-6 + ^-8$	2. Postulate 2-7
3. $2x + 0 = ^-14$	3. Postulates 2-11, 2-13, and 2-9
4. $2x = ^-14$	4. Postulate 2-12
5. $\frac{2x}{2} = -\frac{14}{2}$	5. Postulate 2-8
6. $1x = ^-7$	6. Postulates 2-11, 2-13, and 2-9
7. $x = ^-7$	7. Postulates 2-12 and 2-9

22. Complete the reasons for the following proof.

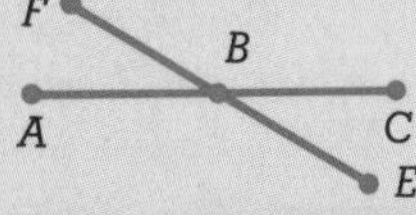

Given: $\overline{AB} \cong \overline{BC}$

Prove: $\overline{FE}$ bisects $\overline{AC}$.

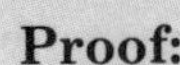

Proof:

STATEMENTS	REASONS
1. $\overline{AB} \cong \overline{BC}$	1. Given
2. $AB = BC$	2. Definition of Congruent Segments
3. B is the midpoint of $\overline{AC}$.	3. Definition of Midpoint
4. $\overline{FE}$ bisects $\overline{AC}$.	4. Definition of Segment Bisector

Use the figure below for exercises 23–28.

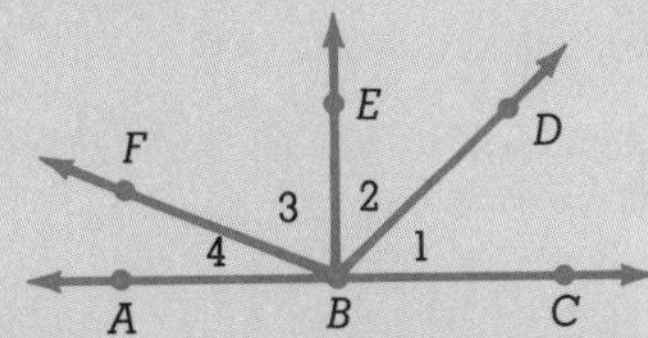

23. $\angle 2$ and $\angle$ EBD name the same angle.

24. The vertex of $\angle 3$ is B.

25. Two names for $\angle 1$ are $\angle$ DBC and $\angle$ CBD.

26. The sides of $\angle 4$ are $\overrightarrow{BA}$ and $\overrightarrow{BF}$.

27. Two points in the interior of $\angle FBC$ are E and D.

28. Two points exterior to $\angle EBA$ are D and C.

29. Complete the reasons for the following proof.

Given: $\angle A$ is a complement of $\angle B$.
$\angle C$ is a complement of $\angle B$.

Prove: $\angle A \cong \angle C$

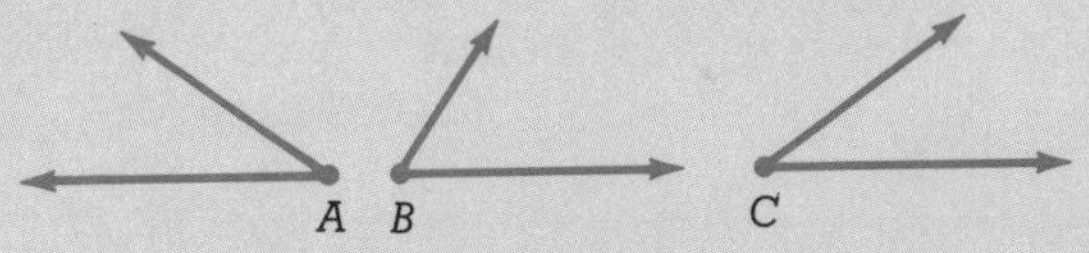

Proof:

STATEMENTS	REASONS
1. $\angle A$ is a complement of $\angle B$. $\angle C$ is a complement of $\angle B$.	1. Given
2. $m\angle A + m\angle B = 90$; $m\angle C + m\angle B = 90$	2. Definition of Complementary Angles
3. $m\angle A + m\angle B = m\angle C + m\angle B$	3. Postulate 2-9
4. $m\angle A = m\angle C$	4. Postulates 2-7, 2-11, 2-13, 2-12, and 2-9
5. $\angle A \cong \angle C$	5. Definition of Congruent Angles

Draw a figure, state the given and the prove statement for each of the following.

30. If two lines intersect so one pair of vertical angles are supplementary, then the other pair of vertical angles are supplementary. For answers to exercises 30-31, see the Teacher's Guide.

31. If two angles in a linear pair are congruent, then the common side of the angles is perpendicular to the other two sides.

chapter 4 Congruent Triangles

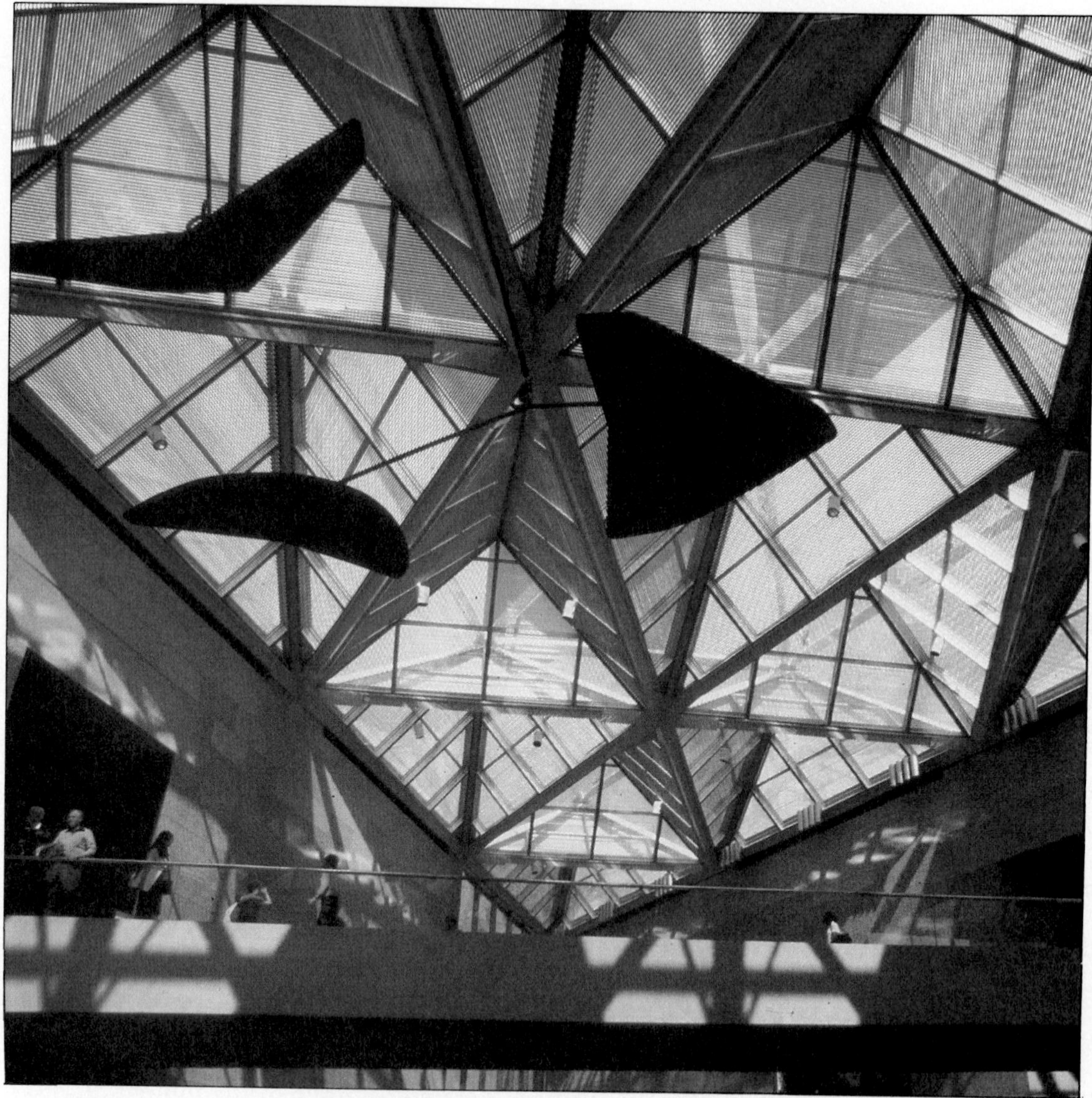

The building in the photograph above is constructed using many triangles that have the same size and shape. These triangles are called congruent triangles.

4–1 Triangles

Objective: to identify the parts of a triangle

Because of their rigid form, triangles are used in the construction of many structures. Notice the triangles in the photograph below. One is marked.

To demonstrate the rigidity of the triangular form, have students construct triangles, squares, and other shapes with straws having a string running through them. In this way, students see that squares and other shapes are easily deformed, but that triangles maintain their form.

Three noncollinear segments connected at their endpoints form a triangle. The segments are **sides** of the triangle. The endpoints are **vertices** of the triangle. An angle is formed at each vertex.

Vertices is the plural of vertex.

Triangle ABC, written $\triangle ABC$, has the following parts.

sides	vertices	angles
$\overline{AB}$	A	$\angle BAC$ or $\angle A$
$\overline{BC}$	B	$\angle ABC$ or $\angle B$
$\overline{CA}$	C	$\angle BCA$ or $\angle C$

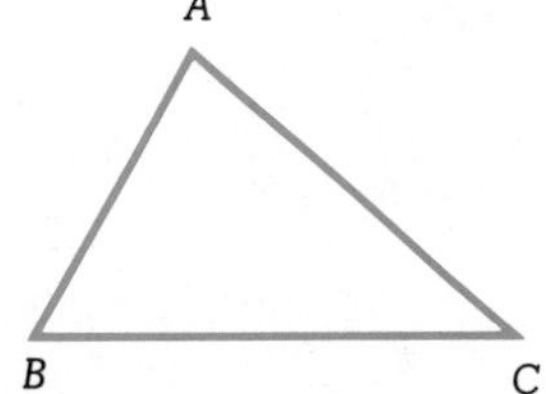

A triangle is a figure formed by three noncollinear segments called sides. Each endpoint of a side is an endpoint of exactly one other side.

Definition of Triangle

Triangles can be classified according to their angles.

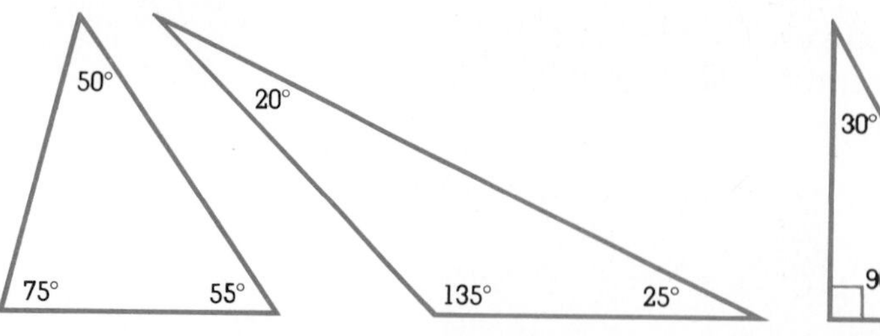

In an **acute triangle,** all the angles are acute.

In an **obtuse triangle,** one angle is obtuse.

In a **right triangle,** there is one right angle.

When all the angles of a triangle are congruent, the triangle is **equiangular.**

Triangles can also be classified according to the number of congruent sides.

Marks on the sides of triangles are used to indicate congruent sides.

Show that an obtuse triangle or a right triangle may also be isosceles.

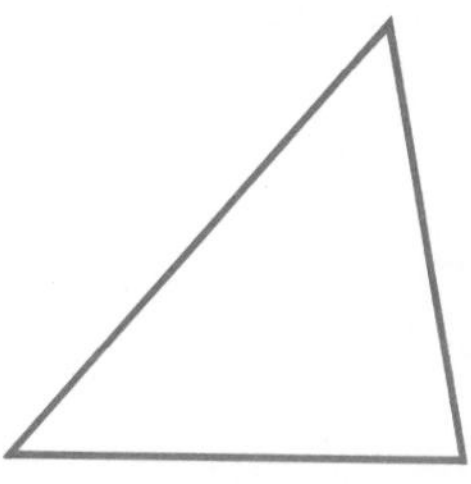

No two sides of a **scalene triangle** are congruent.

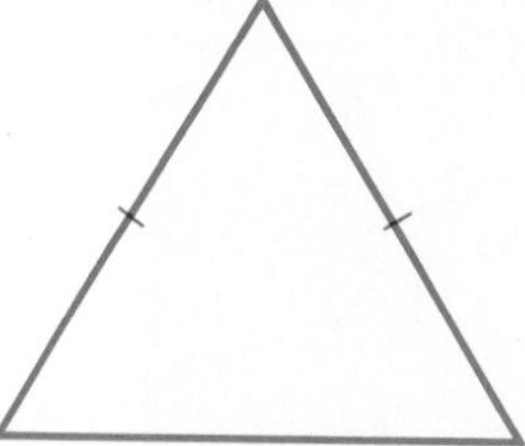

At least two sides of an **isosceles triangle** are congruent.

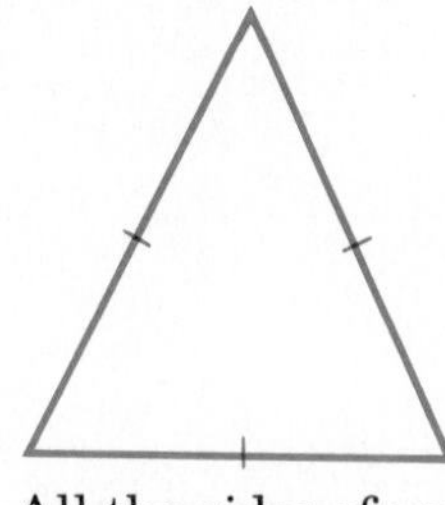

All the sides of an **equilateral triangle** are congruent.

Point out to students that all equilateral triangles are isosceles, but not all isosceles triangles are equilateral.

Notice that an equilateral triangle is also isosceles.

example

1 Suppose $\triangle PQR$ is an isosceles right triangle as shown. Solve for x and find the measure of each side.

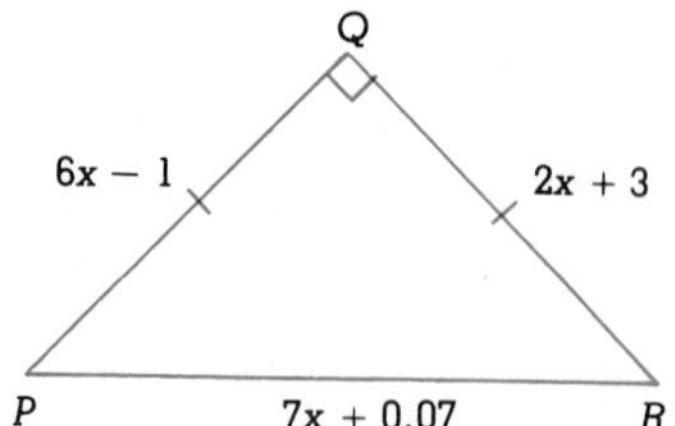

$\overline{PQ} \cong \overline{QR}$	*Given*
$PQ = QR$	*Definition of Congruent Segments*
$6x - 1 = 2x + 3$	*Substitution*
$4x - 1 = 3$	*Subtract 2x from both sides.*
$4x = 4$	*Add 1 to both sides.*
$x = 1$	*Divide both sides by 4.*

$PQ = 6x - 1$
$= 6(1) - 1$
$= 5$

$QR = 2x + 3$
$= 2(1) + 3$
$= 5$

$PR = 7x + 0.07$
$= 7(1) + 0.07$
$= 7.07$

A triangle separates a plane into three parts. The parts are the **interior,** the **exterior,** and the triangle itself.

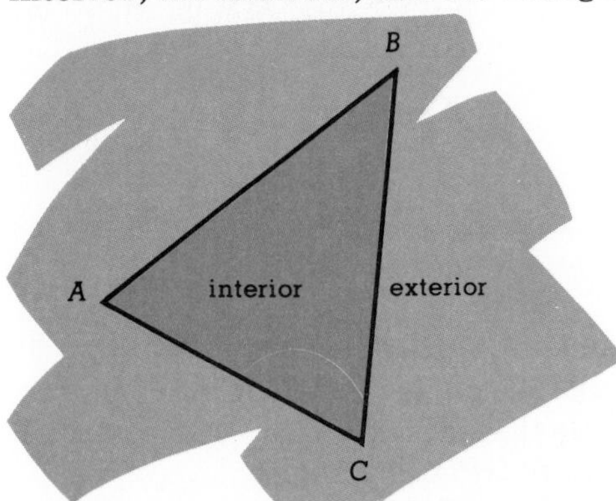

Any point in the green part of the plane is in the *interior* of $\triangle ABC$. Any point in the blue part of the plane is in the *exterior* of $\triangle ABC$. Any point on the segments in black is *on* $\triangle ABC$.

exercises

EN: Wr: 2-34 evens; AV: Ex: 1-21 odds, Wr: 1-33 odds; FN: Ex: 1-22, Wr: 1-33 odds

Exploratory **Classify each triangle as acute, obtuse, or right.**

1.

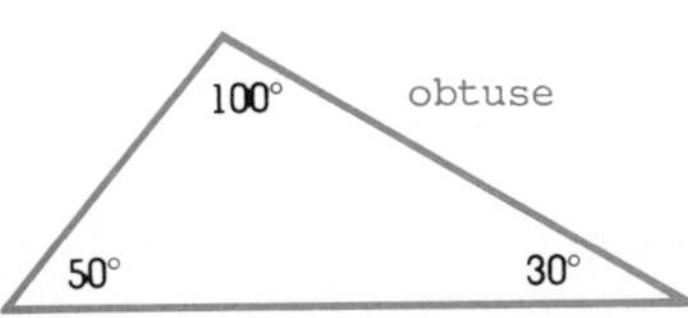

2.

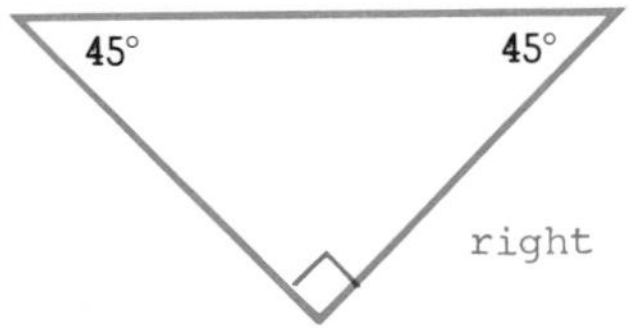

3.

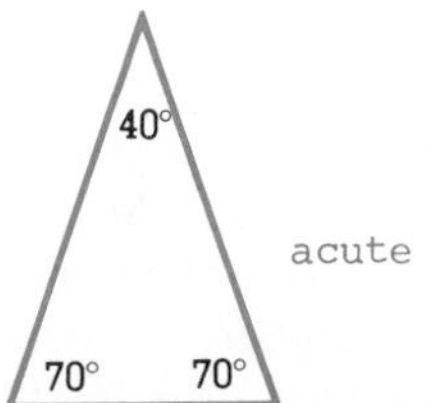

4.

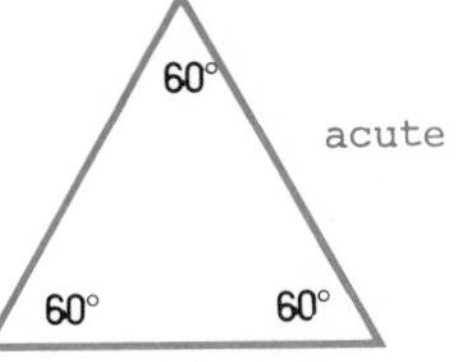

5.

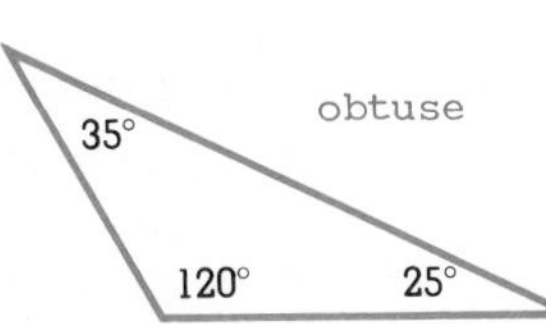

6.

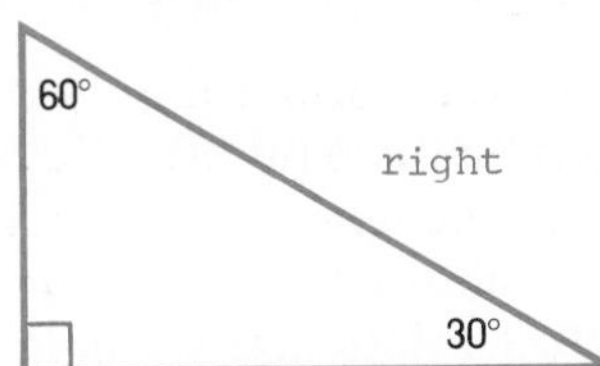

Classify each triangle as scalene, isosceles, or equilateral.

7.

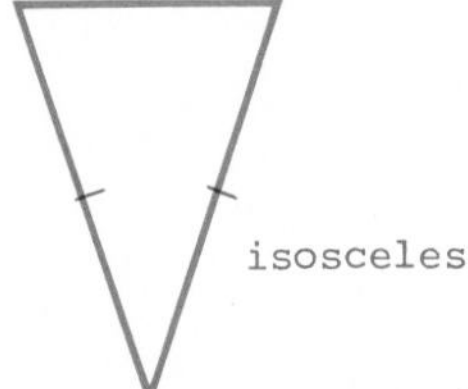

8.

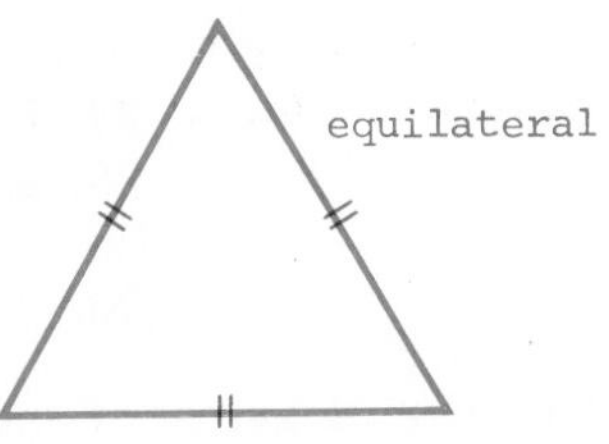

9.

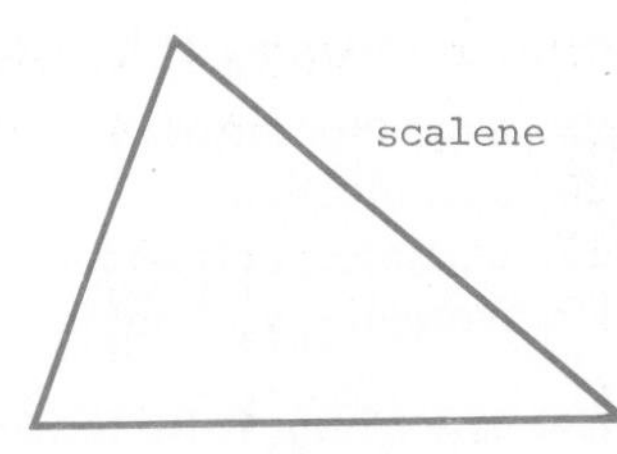

10.

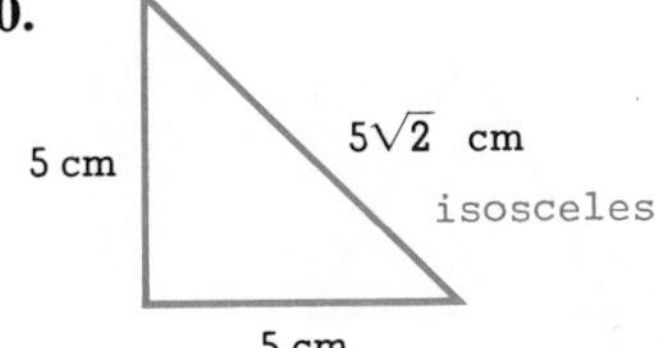

11.

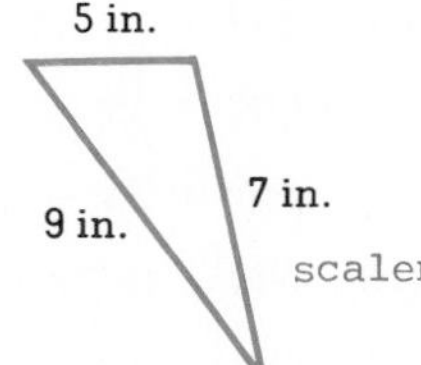

12.

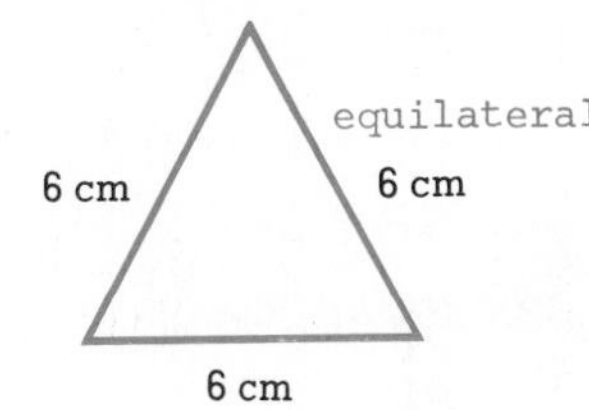

Use $\triangle DEF$ and $\triangle PQR$ to answer each of the following.

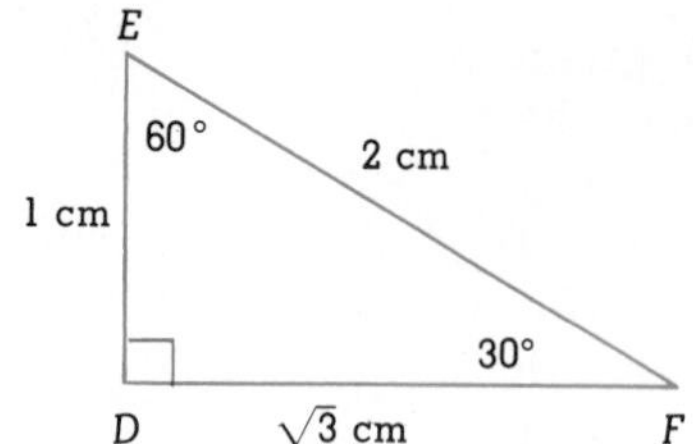

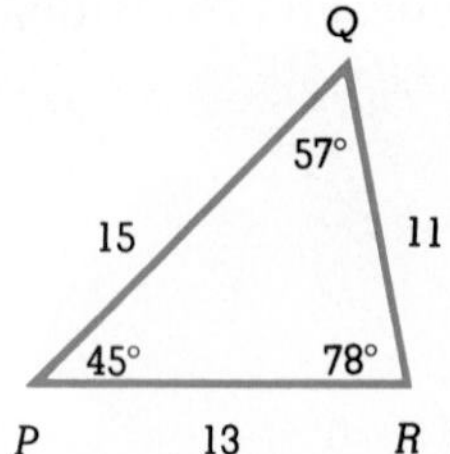

13. Name the vertices of $\triangle DEF$. E, D, F
14. Name the vertices of $\triangle PQR$. P, Q, R
15. Name the angles of $\triangle DEF$. ∠ DEF, ∠ EFD, ∠ EDF
16. Name the angles of $\triangle PQR$. ∠ PQR, ∠ QRP, ∠ QPR
17. Name the sides of $\triangle DEF$. $\overline{EF}$, $\overline{FD}$, $\overline{ED}$
18. Name the sides of $\triangle PQR$. $\overline{QP}$, $\overline{QR}$, $\overline{PR}$
19. Classify $\triangle DEF$ by angles. right
20. Classify $\triangle PQR$ by angles. acute
21. Classify $\triangle DEF$ by sides. scalene
22. Classify $\triangle PQR$ by sides. scalene

Written **The following figure contains eight triangles.**

1–8. Name each triangle. 1-8. △PST, △PQT, △QRT, △RST, △PRS, △PQS, △PQR, △QRS

9. Name the vertices of $\triangle STR$. S, T, R
10. Name the sides of $\triangle STR$. $\overline{ST}$, $\overline{TR}$, $\overline{SR}$
11. Name the angles of $\triangle STR$. ∠ STR, ∠ TRS, ∠ TSR
12. Name the vertices of $\triangle QSR$. Q, S, R
13. Name the sides of $\triangle QSR$. $\overline{QS}$, $\overline{SR}$, $\overline{QR}$
14. Name the angles of $\triangle QSR$. ∠ QSR, ∠ SRQ, ∠ RQS

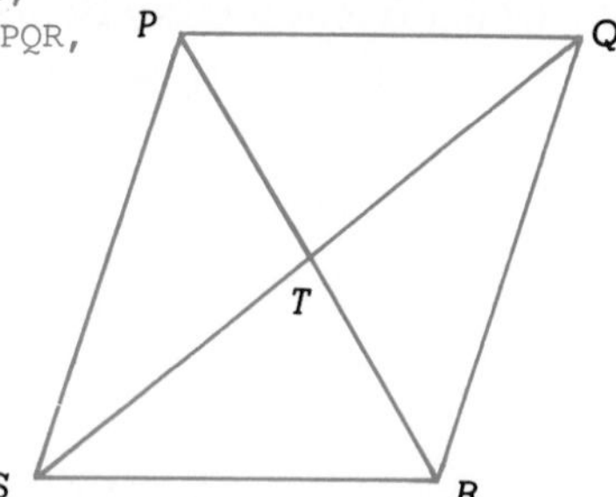

Give an if and only if definition for each of the following. For answers to exercises 15-22, see the Teacher's Guide.

15. triangle
16. right triangle
17. obtuse triangle
18. acute triangle
19. equiangular triangle
20. equilateral triangle
21. isosceles triangle
22. scalene triangle

For each of the following, draw a triangle that satisfies the given conditions. If *no* such triangle exists, write none. 23-28. See student's work.

23. isosceles, right
24. isosceles, acute
25. scalene, acute
26. scalene, obtuse
27. isosceles, obtuse
28. scalene, right
29. isosceles, scalene none
30. equilateral, obtuse none

Use the given information to find the measure of each side of $\triangle PQR$.

31. $PQ = 3x - 20$ PQ = 34
    $QR = x + 16$ QR = 34
    $RP = 2x - 2$ RP = 34
32. $PQ = x + 8$ PQ = 35 QR = 35 RP = 35
    $QR = \frac{1}{3}x + 26$
    $RP = 2x - 19$
33. $PQ = \frac{1}{2}x + 9$
    $PR = 2x - 21$
    PQ = 19 PR = 19 QR = 19
34. $PQ = 0.7x - 20$
    $QR = 0.5x - 12$
    PQ = 8 QR = 8 PR = 8

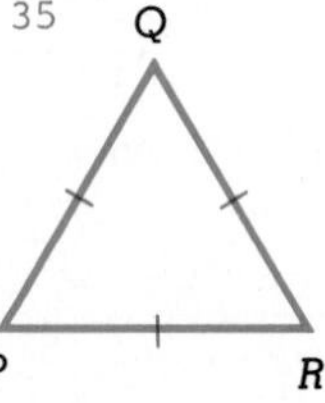

Objective: to use the Angle Sum Theorem and other properties of angles of triangles in proofs and for solving problems

4–2 Angle Measures

The figure at the right shows a piece of paper cut in the shape of a triangle.

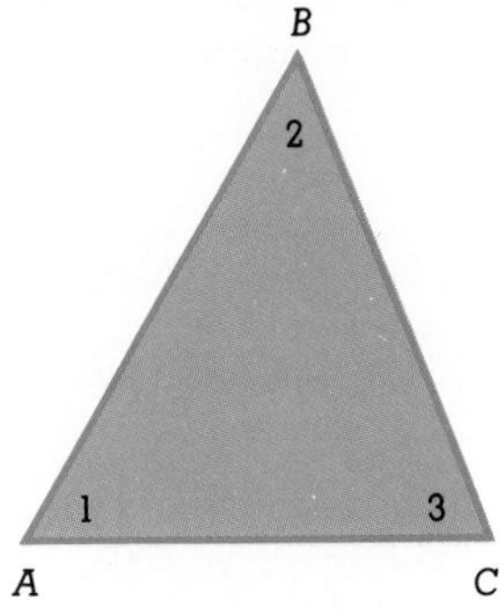

The paper is folded so that point B lies on $\overline{AC}$.

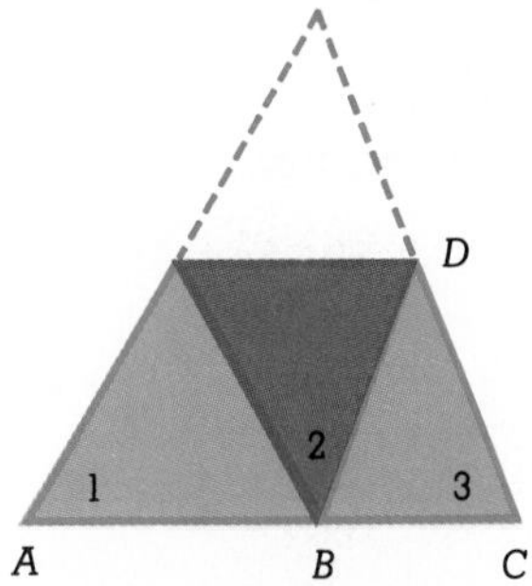

The paper is folded in two more places, so that $\angle 1$ and $\angle 3$ are positioned at point B.

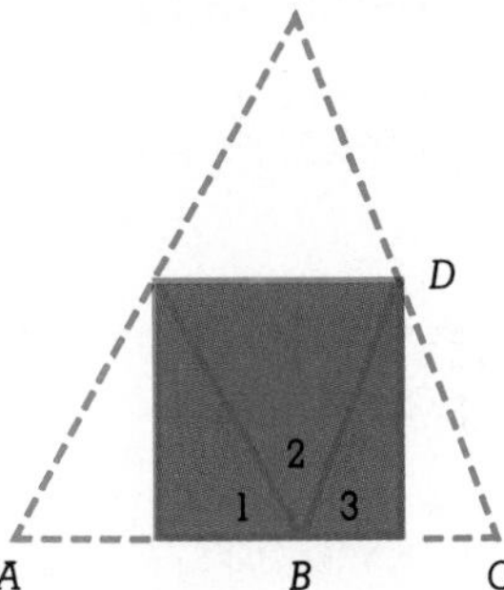

Notice that $\angle ABD$ and $\angle 3$ form a linear pair. Therefore, $m\angle ABD + m\angle 3 = 180$. Since $m\angle 1 + m\angle 2 = m\angle ABD$, by substitution it is also true that

$$m\angle 1 + m\angle 2 + m\angle 3 = 180.$$

Students may also confirm this by drawing arbitrary triangles and measuring the angles with a protractor.

Any triangular piece of paper can be folded in the same way as shown above. Many experiments such as this one suggest the following theorem.

The sum of the degree measures of the angles of a triangle is 180.

Theorem 4–1
Angle Sum Theorem

Theorem 4-1 is proved on page 188.

Since all the angles of an equiangular triangle are congruent, they have the same measure. Thus, each angle has a degree measure of 180 ÷ 3 or 60.

If a triangle is equiangular, then the degree measure of each angle is 60.

Theorem 4–2

Students prove Theorem 4-2 in Written exercise 11.

If you know the measure of two angles of a triangle, you can find the measure of the third angle.

Have students write an equation that represents this idea.

examples

1 **In the triangle at the right, $\angle R$ is a right angle, and $m\angle P = 30$. Find $m\angle Q$.**

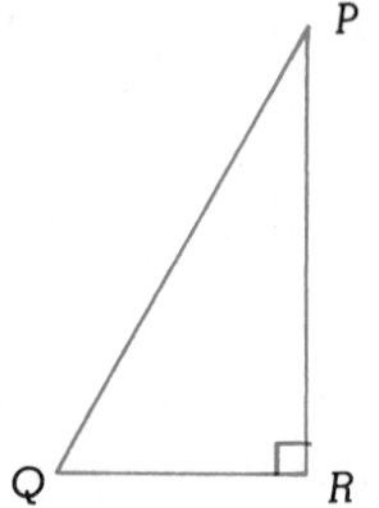

$m\angle P + m\angle Q + m\angle R = 180$	*Theorem 4–1*
$30 + m\angle Q + 90 = 180$	*Substitution*
$m\angle Q = 60$	*Subtraction Property of Equality*

2 **In the diagram at the right, $m\angle A = 60$, $m\angle D = 30$, and $m\angle E = 85$. Find $m\angle B$.**

$m\angle D + m\angle E + m\angle DCE = 180$	*Theorem 4–1*
$30 + 85 + m\angle DCE = 180$	*Substitution*
$m\angle DCE = 65$	*Subtraction Property of Equality*
$m\angle ACB = 65$	*$\angle DCE$ and $\angle ACB$ are vertical angles.*
$m\angle A + m\angle B + m\angle ACB = 180$	*Theorem 4–1*
$60 + m\angle B + 65 = 180$	*Substitution*
$m\angle B = 55$	*Subtraction Property of Equality*

The triangle in Example 1 is a right triangle. Notice that the degree measures of the other two angles total 90. The following theorem states this property for all right triangles.

If a triangle is a right triangle, then the acute angles are complementary.

Theorem 4–3

Students prove Theorem 4-3 in Written exercise 12.

exercises

EN: Wr: 2-20 evens, Ch ; AV: Ex: 1-17 odds, Wr: 1-17 odds; p. 106, Wr: 24-34 evens; p. 111, C: 1-4

Exploratory **Use the figure below to answer each of the following.**

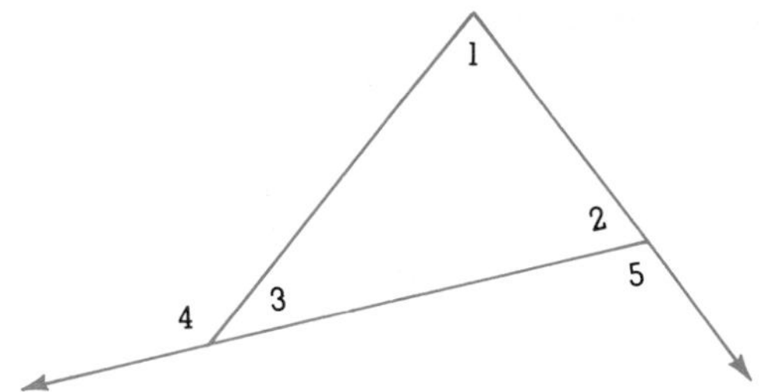

1. Find $m\angle 1$ if $m\angle 2 = 40$ and $m\angle 3 = 55$. 85
2. Find $m\angle 1$ if $m\angle 2 = 60$ and $m\angle 3 = 60$. 60
3. Find $m\angle 1$ if $m\angle 2 = 27$ and $m\angle 3 = 72$. 81
4. Find $m\angle 1$ if $m\angle 2 = 45$ and $m\angle 3 = 45$. 90
5. Find $m\angle 1$ if $m\angle 2 = 81$ and $m\angle 3 = 74$. 25
6. Find $m\angle 1$ if $m\angle 2 = 86$ and $m\angle 3 = 30$. 64
7. Find $m\angle 2$ if $m\angle 1 = 45$ and $m\angle 4 = 105$. 60
8. Find $m\angle 2$ if $m\angle 1 = 59$ and $m\angle 4 = 108$. 49
9. Find $m\angle 2$ if $m\angle 1 = 56$ and $m\angle 4 = 112$. 56
10. Find $m\angle 2$ if $m\angle 1 = 58$ and $m\angle 4 = 125$. 67
11. Find $m\angle 2$ if $m\angle 1 = 47$ and $m\angle 4 = 132$. 85
12. Find $m\angle 2$ if $m\angle 1 = 44$ and $m\angle 4 = 121$. 77
13. Find $m\angle 3$ if $m\angle 1 = 45$ and $m\angle 5 = 98$. 53
14. Find $m\angle 3$ if $m\angle 1 = 42$ and $m\angle 5 = 117$. 75
15. Find $m\angle 3$ if $m\angle 1 = 73$ and $m\angle 5 = 139$. 66
16. Find $m\angle 3$ if $m\angle 1 = 40$ and $m\angle 5 = 123$. 83
17. Find $m\angle 3$ if $m\angle 1 = 60$ and $m\angle 5 = 114$. 54
18. Find $m\angle 3$ if $m\angle 1 = 67$ and $m\angle 5 = 101$. 34

FN: Ex: 1-17 odds, Wr: 1-17 odds; p. 106, Wr: 2-14, 24-34 evens; p. 111, C: 1-4

Written **Use the figure below to answer each of the following.**

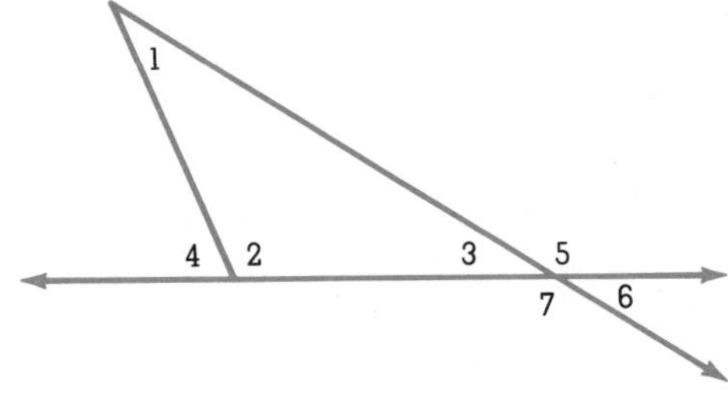

1. $m\angle 5 = 150$ 2. $m\angle 6 = 30$ 3. $m\angle 2 = 180 - x - y$ 4. $m\angle 7 = 4x$

1. Find $m\angle 5$ if $m\angle 1 = 40$ and $m\angle 2 = 110$.
2. Find $m\angle 6$ if $m\angle 1 = 55$ and $m\angle 2 = 95$.
3. Find $m\angle 2$ if $m\angle 1 = x$ and $m\angle 3 = y$.
4. Find $m\angle 7$ if $m\angle 1 = x$ and $m\angle 2 = 3x$.
5. Find $m\angle 1$ if $m\angle 2 = a$ and $m\angle 6 = 35$. $m\angle 1 = 145 - a$
6. Find $m\angle 4$ if $m\angle 1 = 2x + 8$ and $m\angle 3 = x + 5$. $m\angle 4 = 3x + 13$
7. Find $m\angle 3$ if $m\angle 1 = 3x$ and $m\angle 4 = 5x + 2$. $m\angle 3 = 2x + 2$
8. Find $m\angle 1$ if $m\angle 2 = 6x + 11$ and $m\angle 6 = 2x + 8$. $m\angle 1 = 161 - 8x$

Answer each of the following. For answers to exercises 9-10, see the Teacher's Guide.

9. Can a triangle have two right angles? no Write *yes* or *no*, then explain your answer.
10. Can a triangle have two obtuse angles? no Write *yes* or *no*, then explain your answer.

For answers to exercises 11-12, see the Teacher's Guide.

11. Prove Theorem 4–2.

12. Prove Theorem 4–3.

In the figure, $\overline{AB} \perp \overline{BC}$, $\overline{CD} \perp \overline{BC}$, $m\angle BEC = 125$, $m\angle A = x$, and $\angle ABE \cong \angle DCE$. Find the degree measure of each of the following.

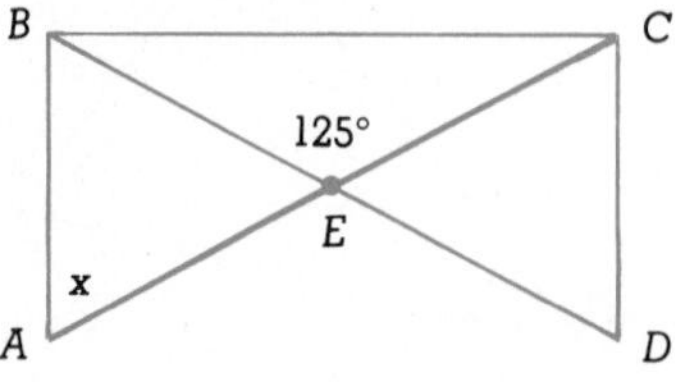

13. $\angle AEB$ $m\angle AEB = 55$

14. $\angle EBC$ $m\angle EBC = 27\frac{1}{2}$

15. $\angle CED$ $m\angle CED = 55$

16. $\angle ECD$ $m\angle ECD = 62\frac{1}{2}$

17. $\angle ECB$ $m\angle ECB = 27\frac{1}{2}$

18. $\angle ABE$ $m\angle ABE = 62\frac{1}{2}$

For answers to exercises 19-21, see the Teacher's Guide.

19. In the figure, $\angle Q$ and $\angle T$ are right angles. Prove $m\angle P = m\angle S$.

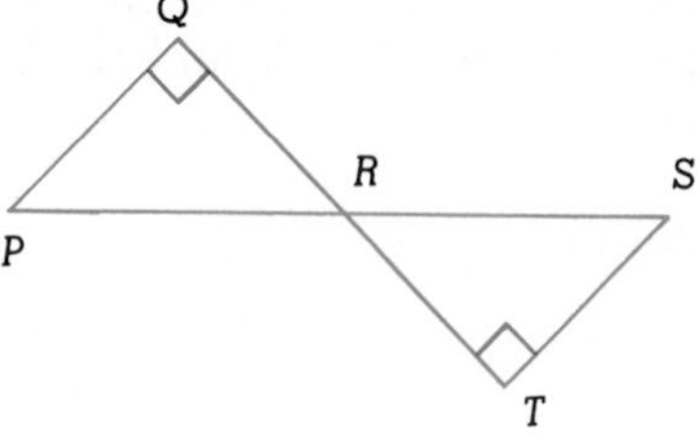

20. In the figure, $\angle P$ and $\angle T$ are right angles. Also, $m\angle QRS = 70$ and $m\angle SRT = 55$. Prove $m\angle Q = m\angle S$.

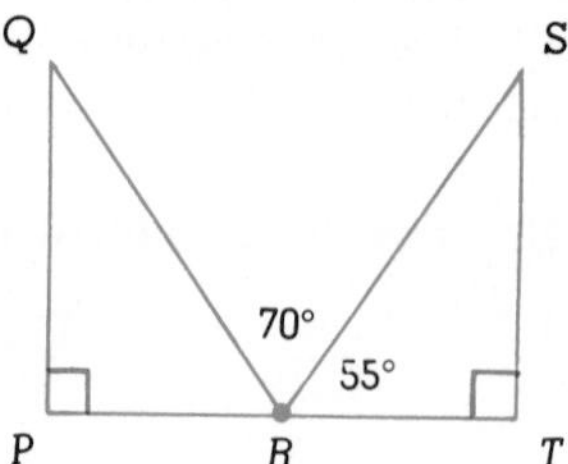

21. Prove that if a triangle is equiangular, then its angles are congruent to each other.

Challenge

Use the figure to find $m\angle 1 + m\angle 2 + m\angle 3$. $m\angle 1 + m\angle 2 + m\angle 3 = 360$

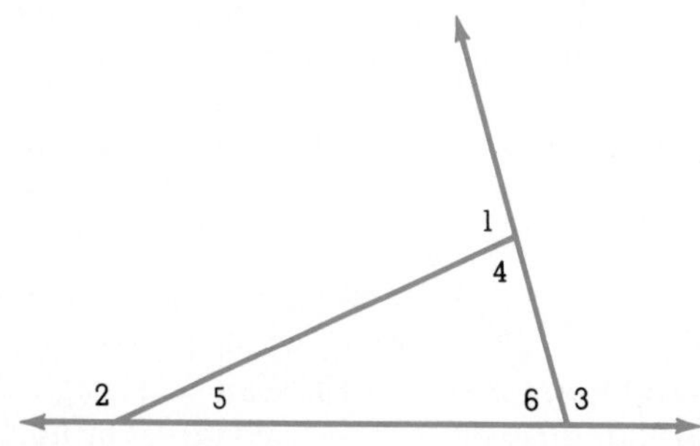

careers — Navigator

Denise Williams is a navigator for an airline. She uses degree measure to specify the direction a plane is moving. To find the course or bearing of the plane, she measures the angle formed between due north and the plane's line of motion.

Since there are 360 degrees in a complete revolution, bearings are written using three digit numerals between 000 and 359 inclusive.

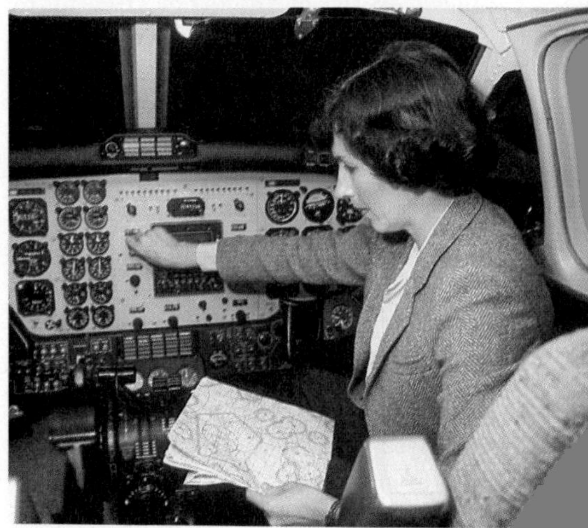

Why isn't there a bearing of 360?

Study the three flight paths below.

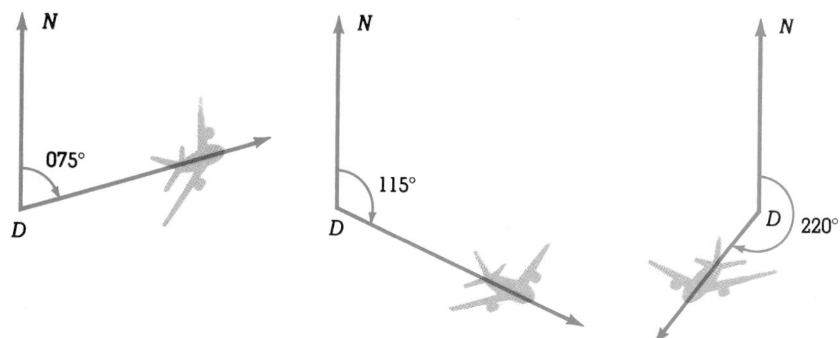

N stands for North.
D stands for departure point.

The bearing of the first plane is 075° and the bearing of the second plane is 115°. Notice that the angle is always measured clockwise from the north.

Exercises Answer each of the following.

1. What is the bearing of a plane departing an airport and flying due east? 090°
2. What is the bearing of a plane departing an airport and flying 45° north of west? 315°
3. Draw a diagram that depicts a plane with a bearing of 060°.
4. Draw a diagram that depicts a plane with a bearing of 180°.

For answers to exercises 3-4, see student's work.

Objectives: to identify congruent triangles, to name corresponding parts of congruent triangles, to label correspondence of congruent triangles correctly

4–3 Congruence

Suppose a rectangular piece of paper is cut along a straight line from one corner to the opposite corner. Two triangular pieces are formed. The edges of each piece form a triangle. When one piece is placed on top of the other they match exactly. What must be true about the parts of the two triangles? The corresponding parts are congruent.

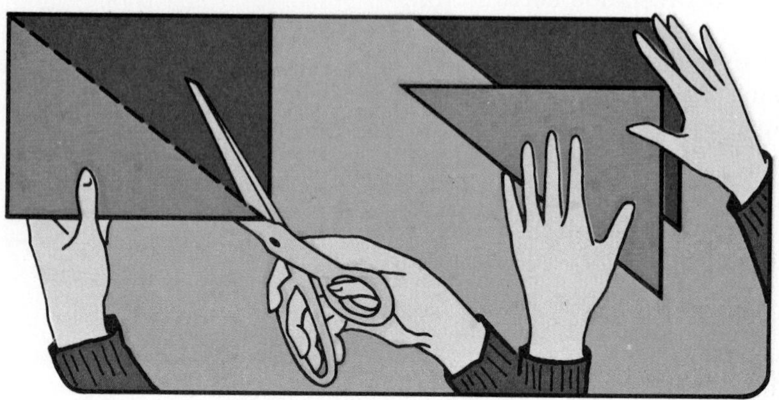

The two triangles below represent the pieces cut from the paper. Corresponding parts of the triangles can be used to describe how the papers fit together.

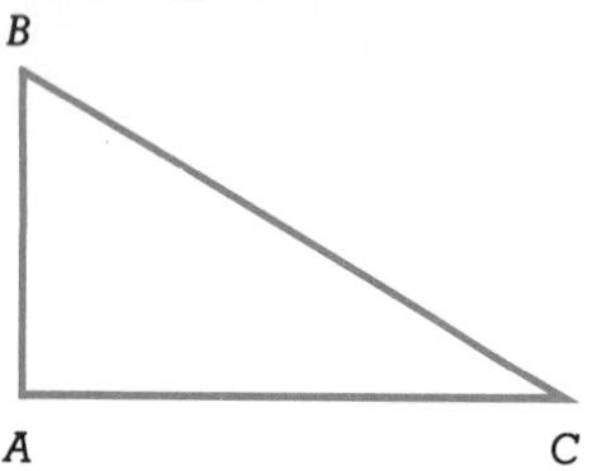

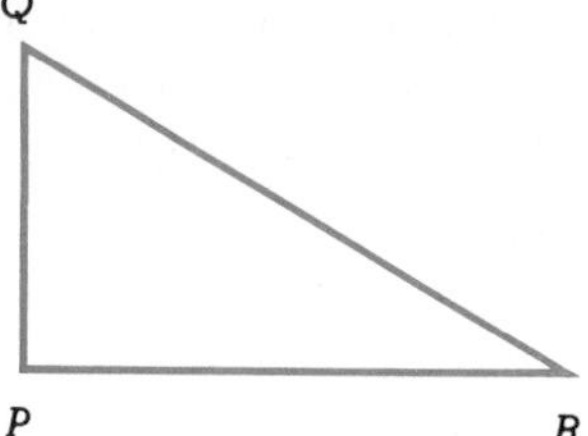

Corresponding angles describe matching the corners of the pieces of paper.

$\angle A$ corresponds to $\angle P$.
$\angle B$ corresponds to $\angle Q$.
$\angle C$ corresponds to $\angle R$.

It is important that students understand the meaning of corresponding parts.

Corresponding sides describe matching the edges of the pieces of paper.

$\overline{AB}$ corresponds to $\overline{PQ}$.
$\overline{BC}$ corresponds to $\overline{QR}$.
$\overline{CA}$ corresponds to $\overline{RP}$.

The matching parts of the papers fit exactly. Therefore, the corresponding parts of the triangles are congruent and the two triangles are called **congruent triangles.** Triangles that have the same size and shape are congruent.

Two triangles are congruent if and only if there is a correspondence such that their corresponding parts are congruent.

Definition of Congruent Triangles (CPCTC)

The abbreviation CPCTC means Corresponding Parts of Congruent Triangles are Congruent.

Special marks are used to show that certain parts of figures are congruent. Notice how marks are used on the triangles below.

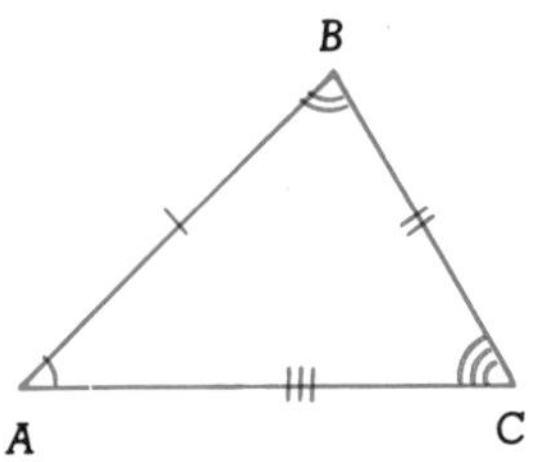

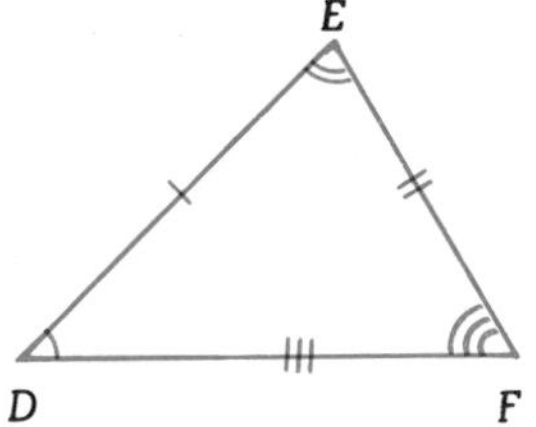

corresponding angles	corresponding sides
$\angle A \cong \angle D$	$\overline{AB} \cong \overline{DE}$
$\angle B \cong \angle E$	$\overline{BC} \cong \overline{EF}$
$\angle C \cong \angle F$	$\overline{CA} \cong \overline{FD}$

The two triangles above are congruent because they have six congruent corresponding parts. To indicate the congruence, write $\triangle ABC \cong \triangle DEF$. The order of letters indicates the correspondence. The first vertices, A and D, correspond, likewise, the second vertices, B and E, and the third vertices, C and F.

If two triangles are congruent, then the corresponding parts are congruent. Often, a geometric problem involves showing that parts of a figure are congruent. One method is to show that the parts are corresponding parts of congruent triangles. Thus, it is important to recognize corresponding parts of congruent triangles.

In the above figure, $\triangle ABC \cong \triangle DEF$ but $\triangle ABC \not\cong \triangle EDF$. Emphasize the correct order of letters when naming congruent triangles.

example

1 **Suppose $\triangle PQS \cong \triangle RQS$. What angle in $\triangle PQS$ is congruent to $\angle R$ in $\triangle RQS$? Which side of $\triangle PQS$ is congruent to $\overline{QS}$ in $\triangle RQS$?**

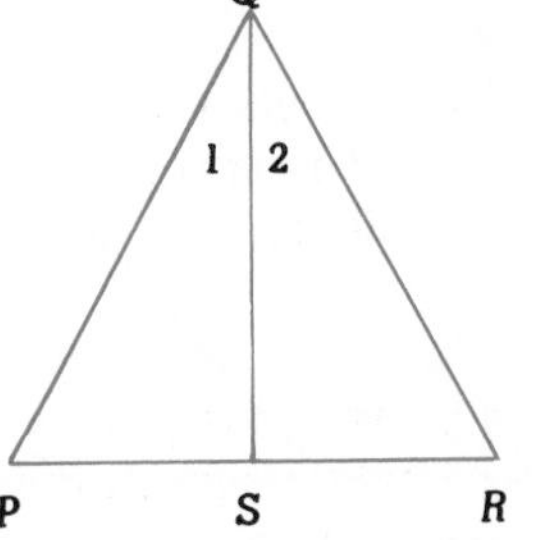

$\angle P$ is congruent to $\angle R$.
$\overline{QS}$ is congruent to $\overline{QS}$.

Since congruence of segments and angles is reflexive, symmetric, and transitive, so is congruence of triangles.

Congruence of triangles is reflexive, symmetric, and transitive. *Theorem 4–4*

Students prove Theorem 4-4 in Written exercises 29-31.

EN: Wr: 2-28 evens, 29-31; p. 111, C: 1-4; AV: Ex: 1-17 odds, Wr: 1-27 odds; p. 110, Wr: 19, 20

exercises

FN: Ex: 1-18, Wr: 1-27 odds; p. 109, Wr: 6, 8, 10, 14, 19

Exploratory **Suppose $\triangle PQR \cong \triangle STV$. For each of the following, name the corresponding part.**

1. $\angle P$ ∠ S
2. $\angle Q$ ∠ T
3. $\angle R$ ∠ V
4. $\angle S$ ∠ P
5. $\angle T$ ∠ Q
6. $\angle V$ ∠ R
7. $\overline{PQ}$ $\overline{ST}$
8. $\overline{QR}$ $\overline{TV}$
9. $\overline{RP}$ $\overline{VS}$
10. $\overline{ST}$ $\overline{PQ}$
11. $\overline{TV}$ $\overline{QR}$
12. $\overline{VS}$ $\overline{RP}$

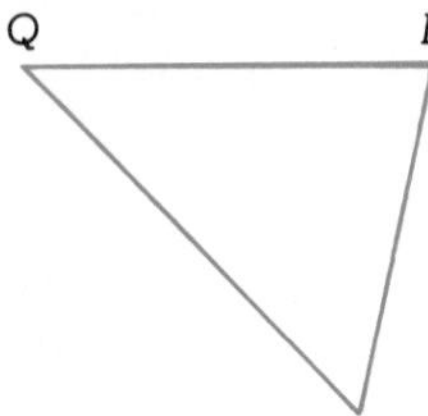

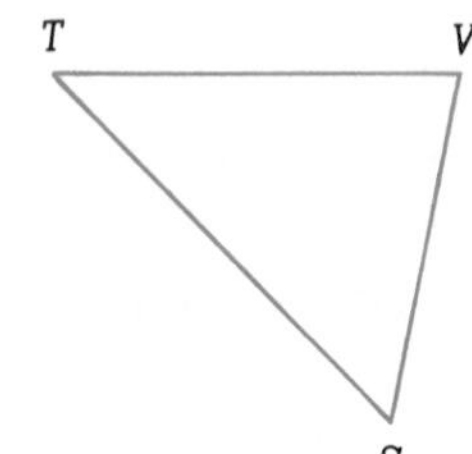

Use the drawings below to find a triangle to complete each congruence statement.

13. $\triangle ABC \cong$ ■ △ TSU

14. $\triangle GIH \cong$ ■ △ JKH

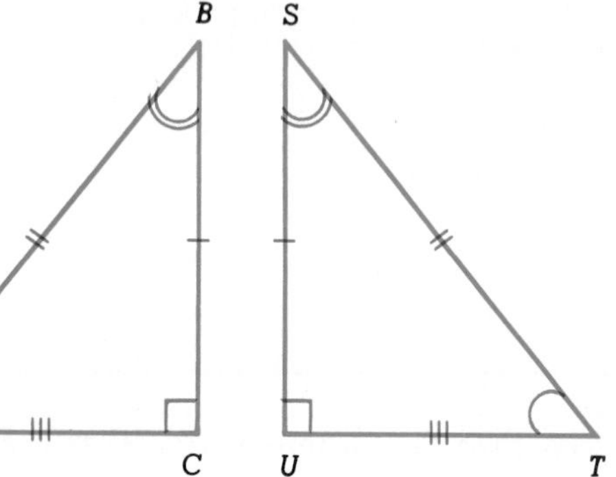

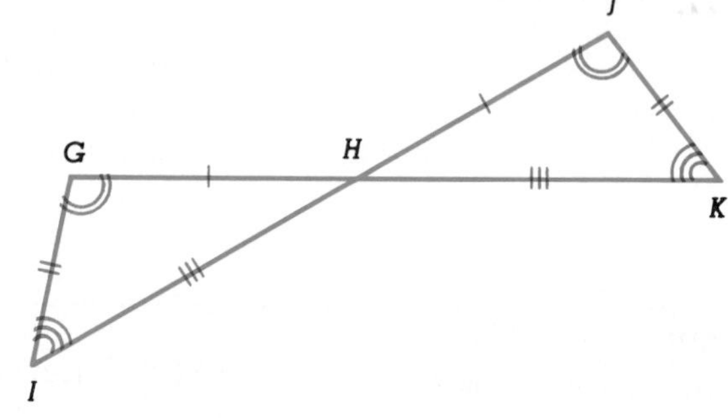

15. $\triangle WVZ \cong$ ■ △ XYZ

16. $\triangle RST \cong$ ■ △ XYW

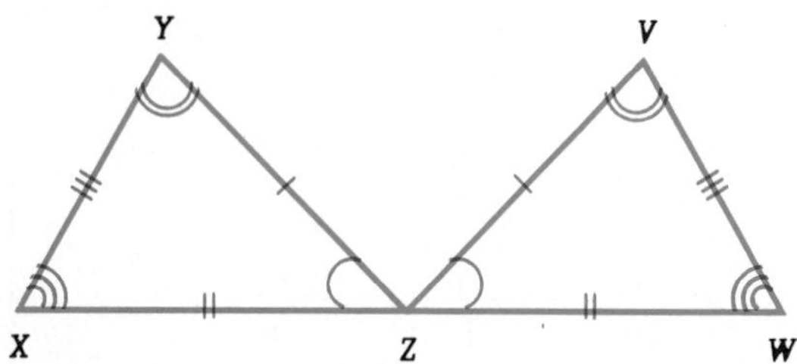

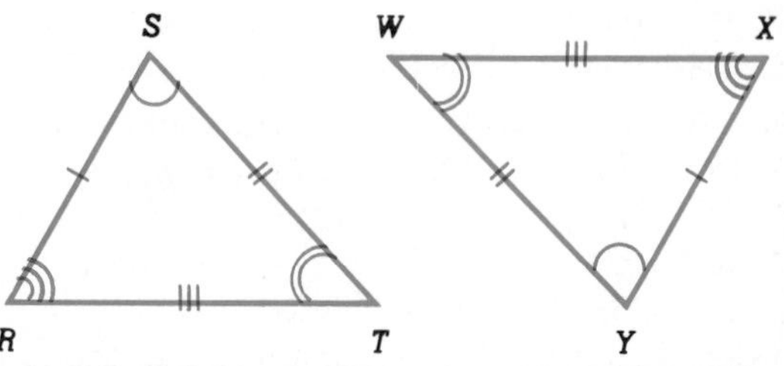

Answer each of the following.

17. Suppose $\triangle ABC \cong \triangle FGH$. List the pairs of angles and sides that are congruent. $\angle A$, $\angle F$; $\angle B$, $\angle G$; $\angle C$, $\angle H$; $\overline{AB}$, $\overline{FG}$; $\overline{BC}$, $\overline{GH}$; $\overline{AC}$, $\overline{FH}$

18. List the information needed to show that $\triangle YZX \cong \triangle RPS$. $\angle Y \cong \angle R$; $\angle Z \cong \angle P$; $\angle X \cong \angle S$; $\overline{YZ} \cong \overline{RP}$; $\overline{ZX} \cong \overline{PS}$; $\overline{YX} \cong \overline{RS}$

Written **Determine whether each of the following statements is correct. Write *yes* or *no*.**

1. $\triangle ABC \cong \triangle BDC$ no
2. $\triangle CAB \cong \triangle CDB$ yes
3. $\triangle CBA \cong \triangle DCB$ no
4. $\triangle BAC \cong \triangle BDC$ yes
5. $\triangle ABC \cong \triangle DBC$ yes
6. $\triangle DBC \cong \triangle BCA$ no

Exercises 1-18 can be used to emphasize the correct order of letters in naming congruent triangles.

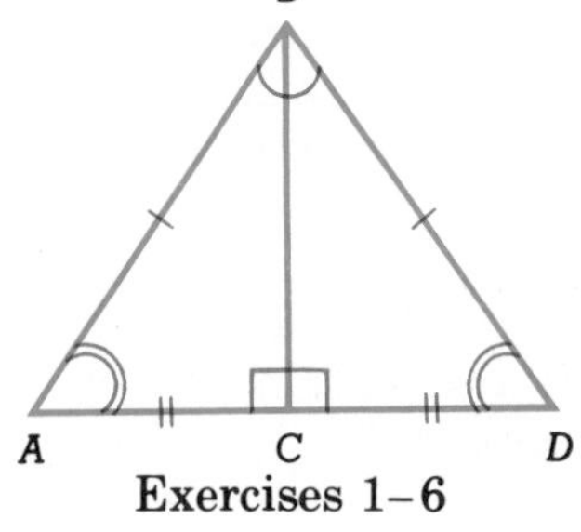

Exercises 1–6

7. $\triangle GHI \cong \triangle HGF$ yes
8. $\triangle GFH \cong \triangle GIH$ no
9. $\triangle FGH \cong \triangle IHG$ yes
10. $\triangle FHG \cong \triangle HGI$ no
11. $\triangle GHF \cong \triangle HGI$ yes
12. $\triangle GFH \cong \triangle HIG$ yes

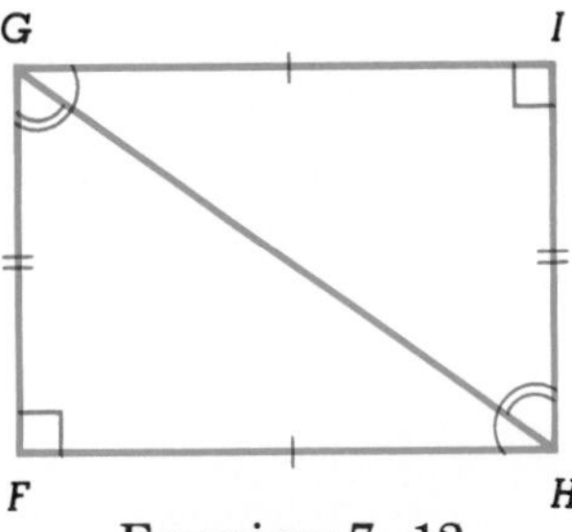

Exercises 7–12

13. $\triangle ZYX \cong \triangle YZA$ yes
14. $\triangle YZA \cong \triangle ZYX$ yes
15. $\triangle YZA \cong \triangle YZX$ no
16. $\triangle ZYX \cong \triangle ZYA$ no
17. $\triangle XYZ \cong \triangle AZY$ yes
18. $\triangle ZAY \cong \triangle ZXY$ no

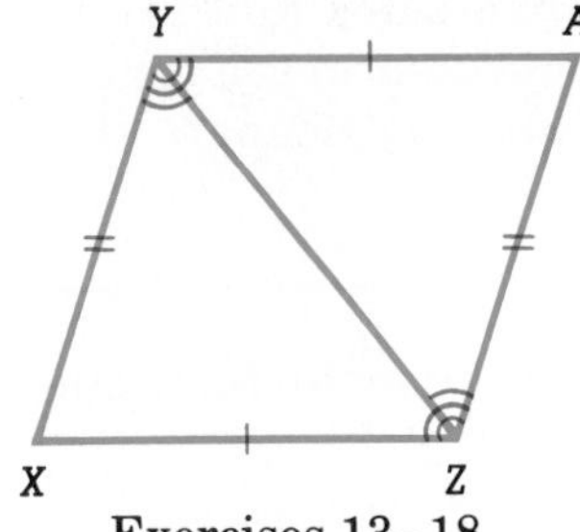

Exercises 13–18

Suppose $\triangle PQR \cong \triangle STR$. Answer each of the following.

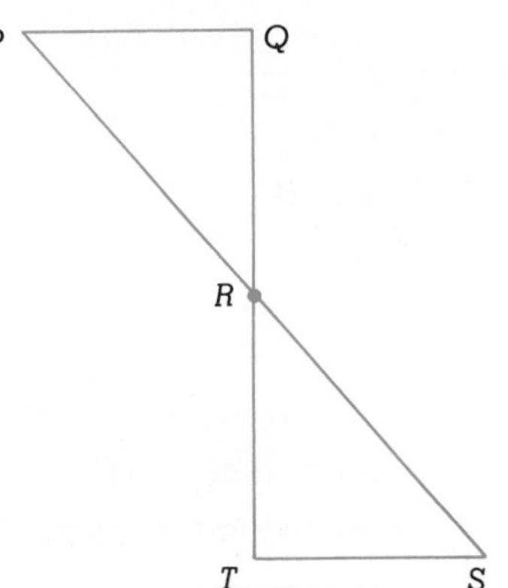

19. Which angle in $\triangle PQR$ corresponds to $\angle T$ in $\triangle STR$? $\angle Q$
20. Which angle in $\triangle STR$ corresponds to $\angle P$ in $\triangle PQR$? $\angle S$
21. Which side of $\triangle PQR$ corresponds to $\overline{RS}$ in $\triangle STR$? $\overline{RP}$
22. Which side of $\triangle PQR$ corresponds to $\overline{TS}$ in $\triangle STR$? $\overline{QP}$
23. Which side of $\triangle STR$ corresponds to $\overline{QR}$ in $\triangle PQR$? $\overline{TR}$
24. Which side of $\triangle STR$ corresponds to $\overline{RP}$ in $\triangle PQR$? $\overline{RS}$
25. Is $\triangle QPR \cong \triangle TRS$? Write *yes* or *no*. no
26. Is $\triangle RQP \cong \triangle RTS$? Write *yes* or *no*. yes
27. Is $\triangle RST \cong \triangle RQP$? Write *yes* or *no*. no
28. Is $\triangle TSR \cong \triangle PQR$? Write *yes* or *no*. no

29–31. Prove the three parts of Theorem 4–4.

For answers to exercises 29-31, see the Teacher's Guide.

4–4 Tests for Congruence

Objective: to use the SSS, SAS, and ASA tests for congruence

To show that two triangles are congruent, it is not necessary to show all six congruent corresponding parts. For example, suppose straws are used to make a model of a triangle. Start with three straws, each having a certain length. Fasten the straws together at the ends. There is only one way to put the straws together to form a triangle.

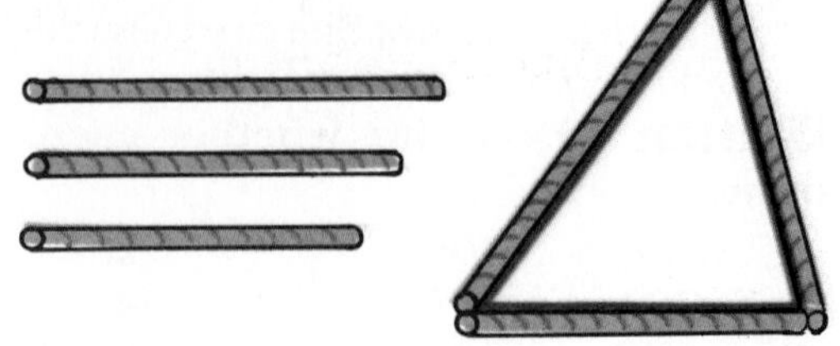

If each side of one triangle is congruent to the corresponding side of another triangle, then the triangles are congruent.

Postulate 4–1
SSS
The abbreviation SSS stands for side-side-side.

Suppose two straws are glued together to form a certain angle. There is only one length for the third straw that can be used to make a triangle. The two straws and the included angle they form completely determine the triangle.

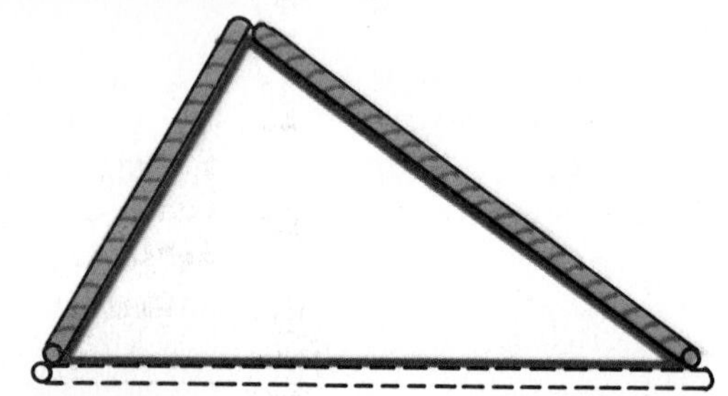

If two sides and the included angle of one triangle are congruent to the corresponding sides and included angle of another triangle, then the triangles are congruent.

Postulate 4–2
SAS
The abbreviation SAS stands for side-angle-side.

Discuss the meaning of included angle using visual examples.

example

1 Use the figure below to determine whether or *not* $\overline{AB} \cong \overline{CD}$.

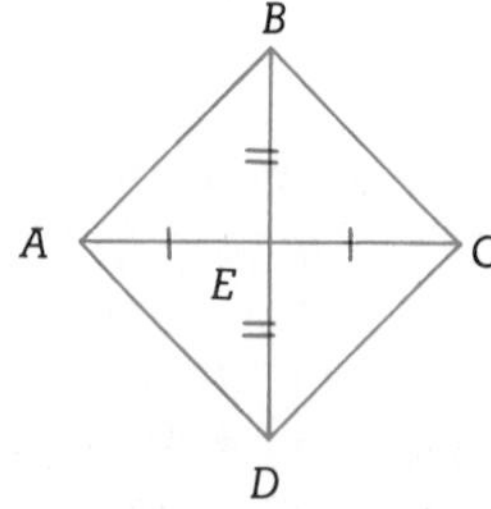

The marks on the figure show $\overline{AE} \cong \overline{CE}$ and $\overline{BE} \cong \overline{DE}$. Since vertical angles are congruent, $\angle AEB \cong \angle CED$. Thus, $\triangle AEB \cong \triangle CED$ by SAS. Since $\overline{AB}$ and $\overline{CD}$ are corresponding parts of congruent triangles *(CPCTC)*, it is true that $\overline{AB} \cong \overline{CD}$.

example

2 Prove the following.

Given: $\overline{PQ} \cong \overline{PS}$
$\overline{QR} \cong \overline{SR}$

Prove: $\angle 1 \cong \angle 2$

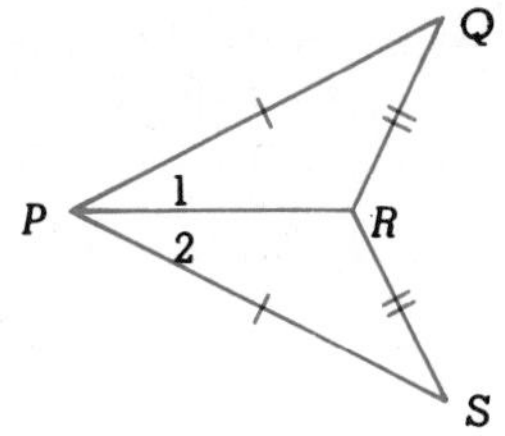

Proof:

STATEMENTS	REASONS
1. $\overline{PQ} \cong \overline{PS}$, $\overline{QR} \cong \overline{SR}$	**1.** Given
2. $\overline{PR} \cong \overline{PR}$	**2.** Theorem 2–2: Congruence of segments is reflexive.
3. $\triangle PQR \cong \triangle PSR$	**3.** Postulate 4–1: SSS
4. $\angle 1 \cong \angle 2$	**4.** Definition of Congruent Triangles *CPCTC*

In the triangle at the right, $\overline{AB}$ is included between $\angle A$ and $\angle B$.

The abbreviation ASA stands for angle-side-angle.

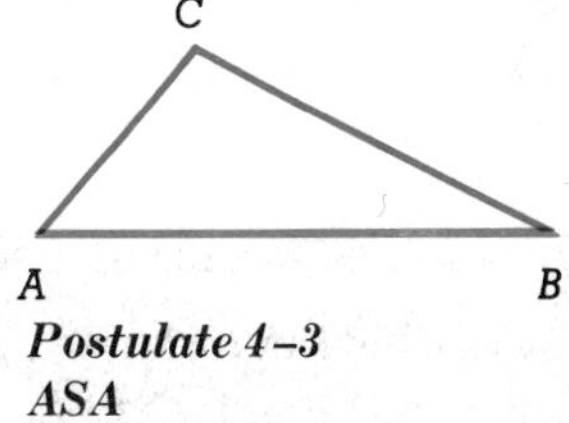

If two angles and the included side of one triangle are congruent to the corresponding angles and included side of another triangle, then the triangles are congruent.

Postulate 4–3
ASA

Discuss the meaning of included side using visual examples.

3 Prove the following.

Given: $\angle Q$ and $\angle S$ are right angles.
$\overline{QR} \cong \overline{SR}$

Prove: $\angle P \cong \angle T$

Proof:

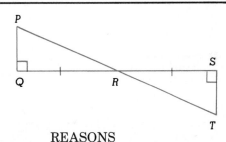

STATEMENTS	REASONS
1. $\angle Q$ and $\angle S$ are right angles.	**1.** Given
2. $\angle Q \cong \angle S$	**2.** Theorem 3–6: If two angles are right angles, then the angles are congruent.
3. $\overline{QR} \cong \overline{SR}$	**3.** Given
4. $\angle PRQ \cong \angle TRS$	**4.** Theorem 3–10: If two angles are vertical, then they are congruent.
5. $\triangle PRQ \cong \triangle TRS$	**5.** Postulate 4–3: ASA
6. $\angle P \cong \angle T$	**6.** Definition of Congruent Triangles *CPCTC*

EN: Ex: 1-9, Wr: 2-30 evens, Ch: 1-4; AV: Ex: 1-15 odds, Wr: 1-29 odds; p. 115, Wr: 20-28 evens, 29-31

exercises

Exploratory **Are the following pairs of triangles congruent? State *yes* or *no*. If *yes*, state whether by SSS, SAS, or ASA.**

1.

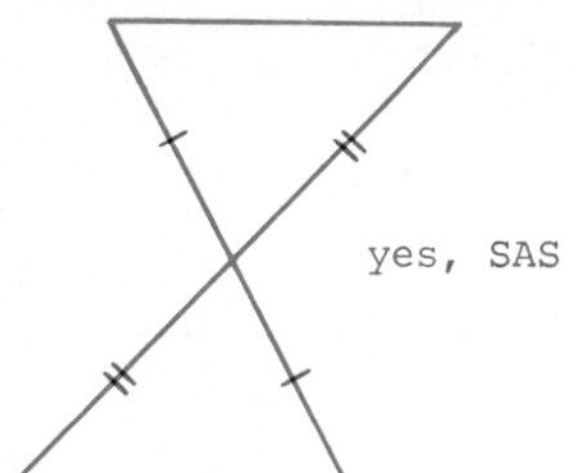

2.

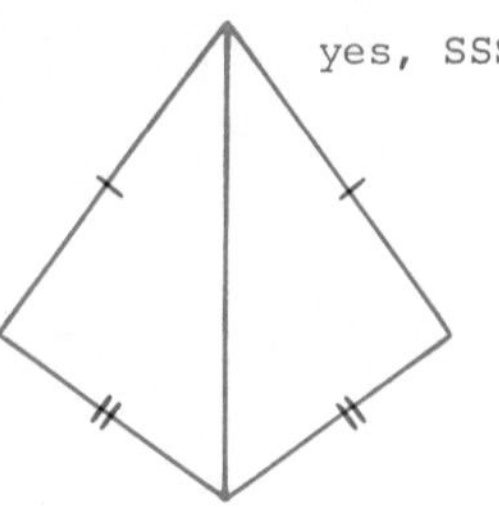

3.

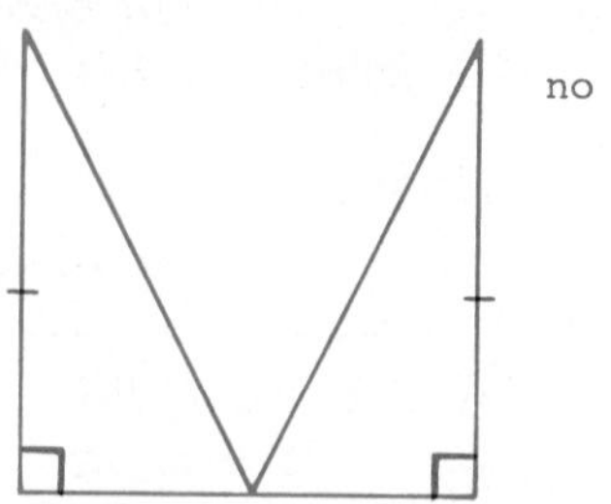

4.

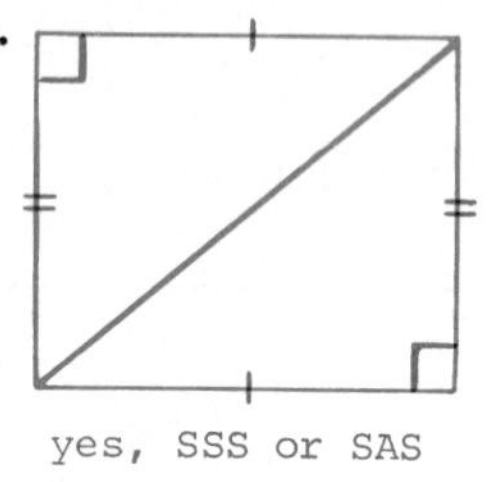

5.

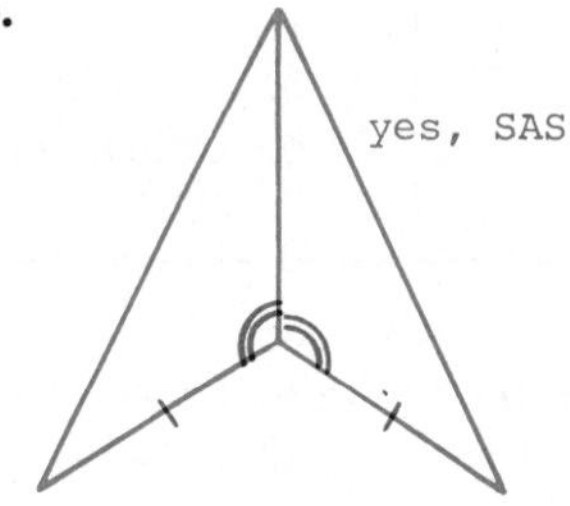

6.

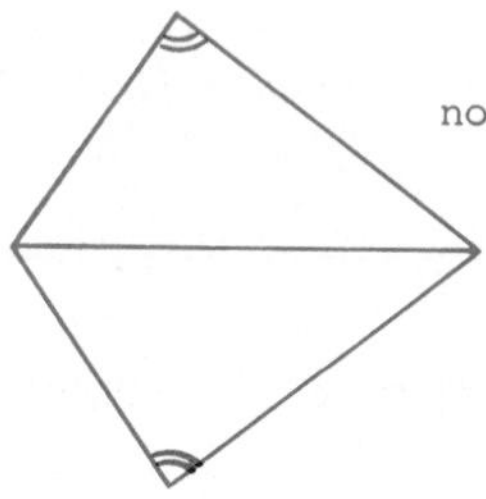

7.

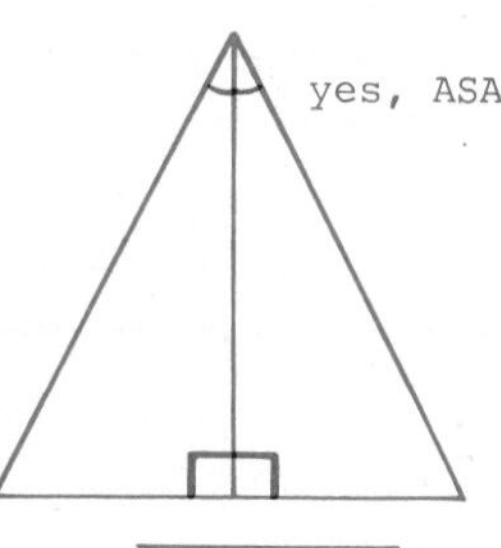

8.

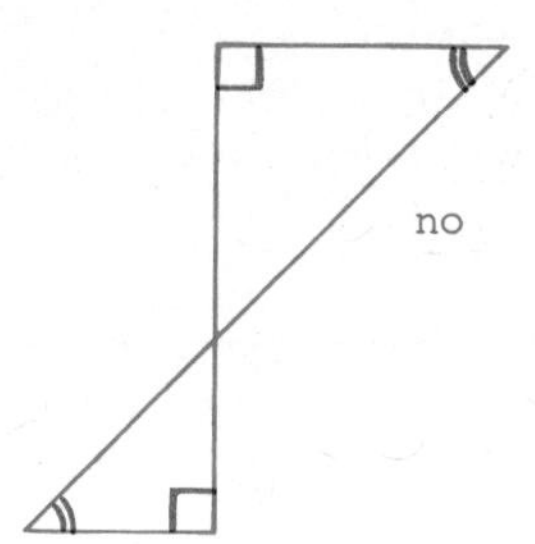

9.

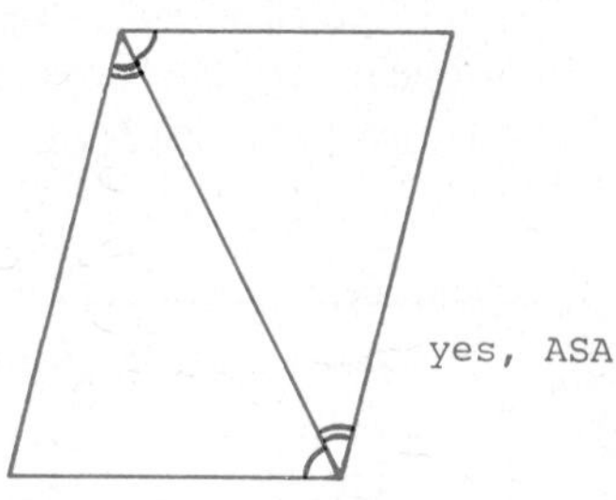

10.

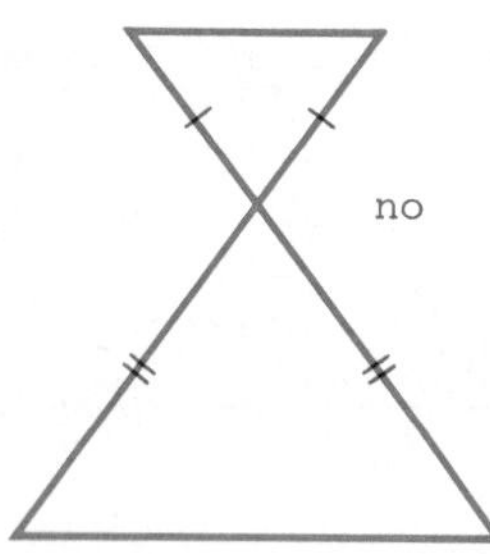

11.

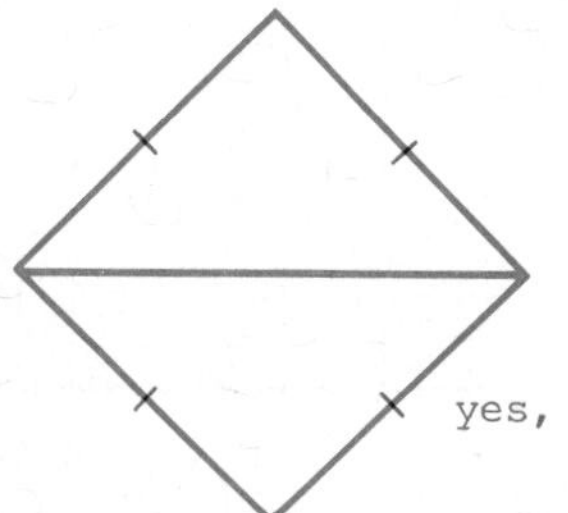

12.

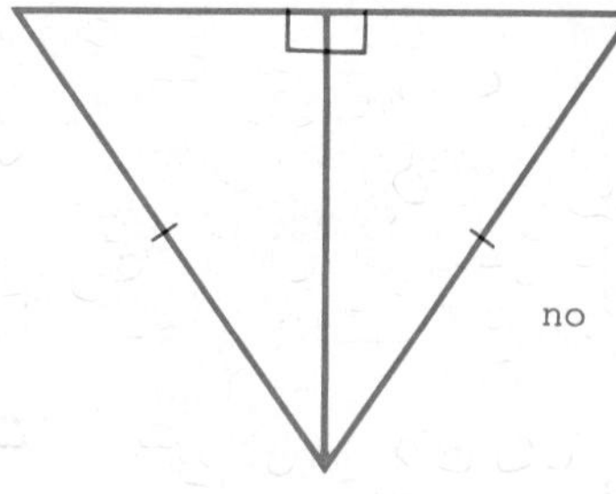

13.

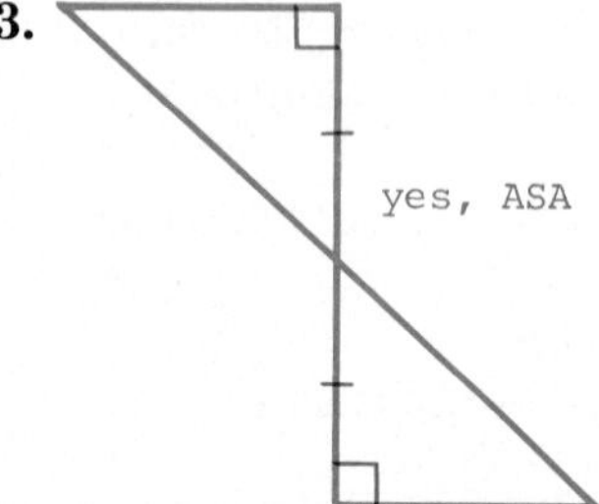

14.

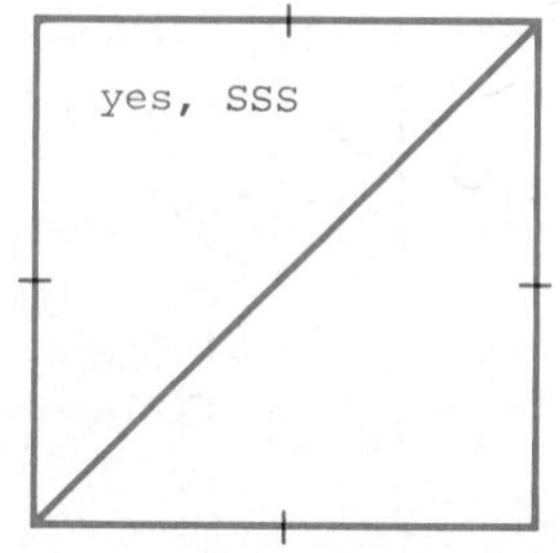

15.

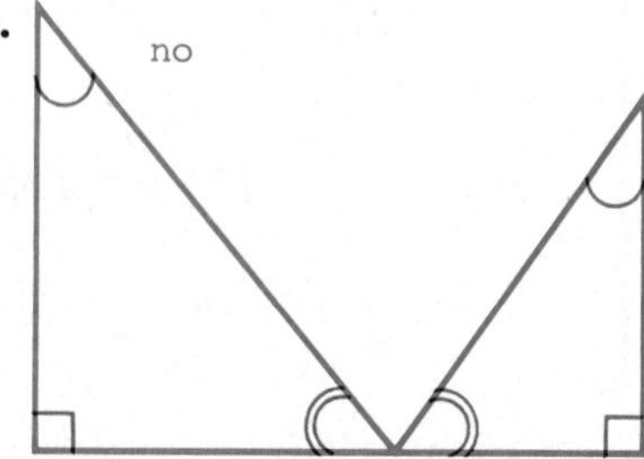

FN: Ex: 1-15, Wr: 1-29 odds; p. 114, Wr: 4, 8, 12, 16, 20, 24, 28

Written **Prove each of the following.**

For answers to exercises 1-10, see the Teacher's Guide.

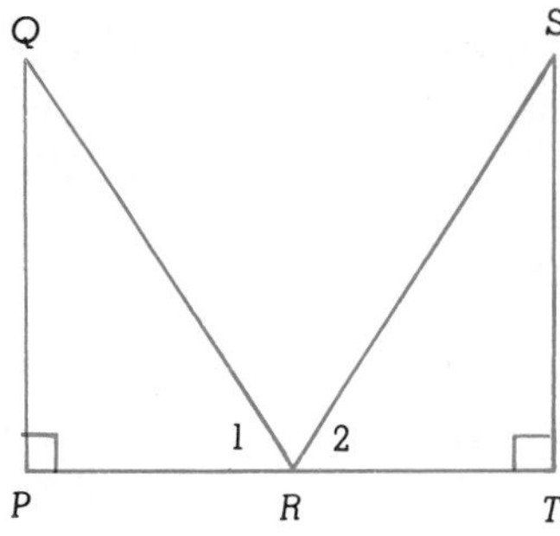

Exercises 1–3

1. **Given:** $\angle 1 \cong \angle 2$
   $\angle P$ and $\angle T$ are right angles.
   R is the midpoint of $\overline{PT}$.
   Prove: $\overline{QP} \cong \overline{ST}$.

2. **Given:** $\overline{QP} \cong \overline{ST}$
   $\angle P$ and $\angle T$ are right angles.
   R is the midpoint of $\overline{PT}$.
   Prove: $\overline{QR} \cong \overline{SR}$

3. **Given:** $\angle 1 \cong \angle 2$
   $\angle P$ and $\angle T$ are right angles.
   $\overline{QR} \cong \overline{SR}$
   Prove: $\overline{PR} \cong \overline{TR}$

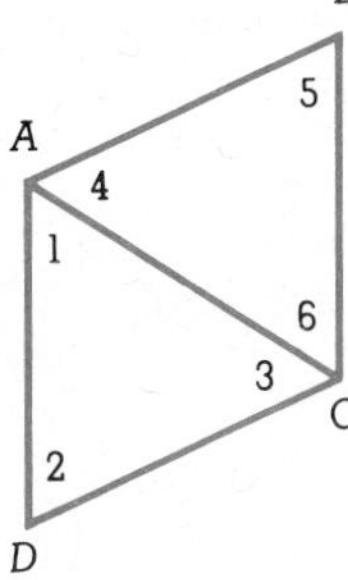

Exercises 4–6

4. **Given:** $\overline{AD} \cong \overline{CB}$
   $\overline{DC} \cong \overline{BA}$
   Prove: $\angle 2 \cong \angle 5$

5. **Given:** $\angle 1 \cong \angle 6$
   $\angle 3 \cong \angle 4$
   Prove: $\overline{AD} \cong \overline{CB}$

6. **Given:** $\angle 3 \cong \angle 4$
   $\overline{DC} \cong \overline{BA}$
   Prove: $\angle 1 \cong \angle 6$

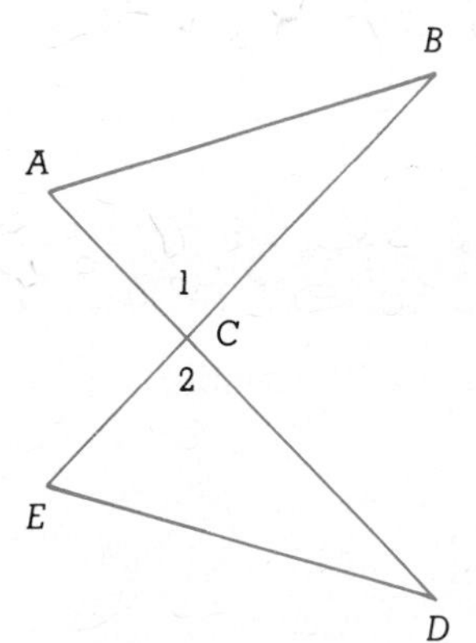

Exercises 7–10

7. **Given:** $\overline{AC} \cong \overline{EC}$
   $\angle A \cong \angle E$
   Prove: $\overline{AB} \cong \overline{ED}$

8. **Given:** $\overline{AC} \cong \overline{EC}$
   $\angle A \cong \angle E$
   Prove: $\overline{BC} \cong \overline{DC}$

9. **Given:** $\overline{AC} \cong \overline{EC}$
   $\overline{BC} \cong \overline{DC}$
   Prove: $\angle A \cong \angle E$

10. **Given:** $\overline{AC} \cong \overline{EC}$
    $\overline{BC} \cong \overline{DC}$
    Prove: $\angle B \cong \angle D$

20. ∠5, Definition of Linear Pair, the Supplement Postulate
21. ∠6, Definition of Linear Pair, the Supplement Postulate

Using the figure, fill in the blanks to make true statements. Give a reason for each answer.

11. $\angle QVP \cong$ ■ ∠SVT, Theorem 3-10
12. $\triangle PVQ \cong$ ■ △TVS, SAS
13. $\overline{PQ} \cong$ ■
14. $\angle 3 \cong$ ■ ∠4, CPCTC
15. $\overline{QT} \cong$ ■
16. $\triangle PQT \cong$ ■ △TSP, SAS
17. $\angle 2 \cong$ ■ ∠1, CPCTC
18. $\overline{TR} \cong$ ■ $\overline{PR}$, CPCTC, SAS
19. $\overline{QR} \cong$ ■ $\overline{SR}$, Given
20. $\angle 5 \cong$ ■
21. $\angle 4$ and ■ are supplementary.
22. $\angle 3$ and ■ are supplementary. ∠6, Theorem 3-3
23. $\triangle QRT \cong$ ■ △SRP, SSS or SAS
24. $\angle RTQ \cong$ ■ ∠RPS, CPCTC
25. $\angle QVS \cong$ ■ ∠PVT, Theorem 3-10
26. $\triangle PVT$ is an ■ triangle. isosceles, Def. of Isos. △
27. $VQ =$ ■ VS, Given
28. $\triangle PRT$ is an ■ triangle. isosceles, Definition of Isosceles Triangle

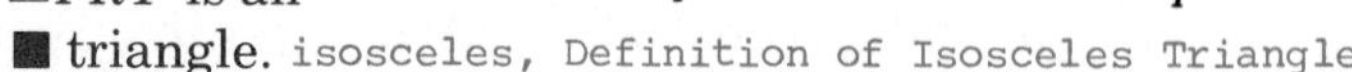

29. If $m\angle 1 = 30$, then $m\angle PVT =$ ■. m∠PVT = 120
30. If $m\angle 3 = 95$, then $m\angle 6 =$ ■. m∠6 = 85

For reasons to exercises 29-30, see the Teacher's Guide.

13. $\overline{TS}$, CPCTC (Note that CPCTC will be used for Corresponding Parts of Congruent Triangles are Congruent.)
15. $\overline{SP}$, Postulate 2-2, Postulate 2-7, Postulate 3-3

Challenge **Use the figures and information given below to answer each problem.**

Given: $\overline{AB} \cong \overline{XY}$
$\angle A \cong \angle X$
$\overline{AC} \cong \overline{XP}$
$\angle ABC \cong \angle XYZ$

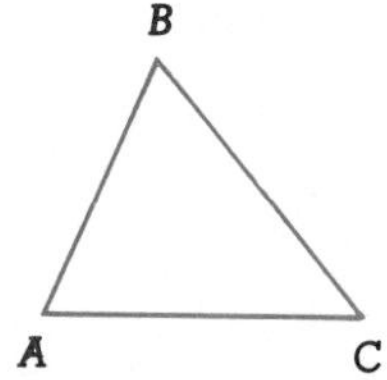

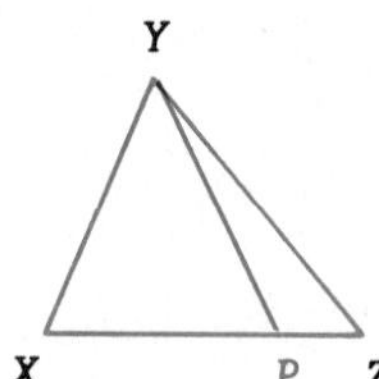

For answers to exercises 1-2, see the Teacher's Guide.

1. Prove that $\triangle ABC \cong \triangle XYP$.
2. Prove that $\angle ABC \cong \angle XYP$.
3. How are $\angle XYP$ and $\angle XYZ$ related? (Hint: Use the results of exercise **2.**) They are congruent.
4. How is the figure at the right misleading? P and Z represent the same point.

Seeing Patterns — excursions in geometry

Look at the sequence of figures below. Then, draw the figure that comes next.
Look at the right half of each figure which is a numeral. The next figure is

    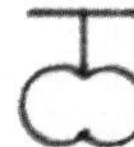   

4–5 More Tests for Congruence

Objectives: to use AAA test for congruence, to recognize correct tests for congruent triangles

To show two triangles congruent, at least three congruent pairs of corresponding parts are needed. Can any three pairs of congruent corresponding parts be used? Three tests already have been postulated, SSS, SAS, and ASA. Another test follows directly from these. No.

If two angles and a nonincluded side of one triangle are congruent to the corresponding angles and nonincluded side of another triangle, then the triangles are congruent.

Theorem 4–5
AAS
The abbreviation AAS stands for angle-angle-side.

example

1 Prove Theorem 4–5.

Given: $\angle P \cong \angle A$
$\angle Q \cong \angle B$
$\overline{QR} \cong \overline{BC}$

Prove: $\triangle PQR \cong \triangle ABC$

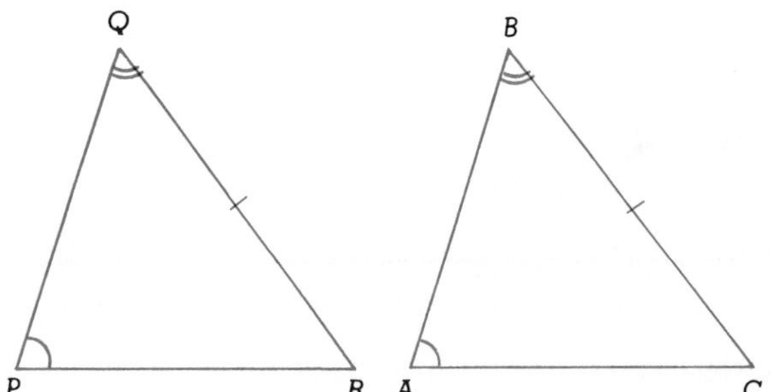

Proof:

STATEMENTS	REASONS
1. $m\angle P + m\angle Q + m\angle R = 180$ $m\angle A + m\angle B + m\angle C = 180$	1. Theorem 4–1: Angle Sum Theorem
2. $\angle P \cong \angle A$ $\angle Q \cong \angle B$	2. Given
3. $m\angle P = m\angle A$ $m\angle Q = m\angle B$	3. Definition of Congruent Angles
4. $m\angle P + m\angle Q + m\angle R = m\angle P + m\angle Q + m\angle C$	4. Postulate 2–9: Substitution
5. $m\angle R = m\angle C$	5. Postulate 2–7: Subtraction Property of Equality
6. $\angle R \cong \angle C$	6. Definition of Congruent Angles
7. $\overline{QR} \cong \overline{BC}$	7. Given
8. $\triangle PQR \cong \triangle ABC$	8. Postulate 4–3: ASA *Use steps 2, 6, and 7.*

example

2 Prove the following.

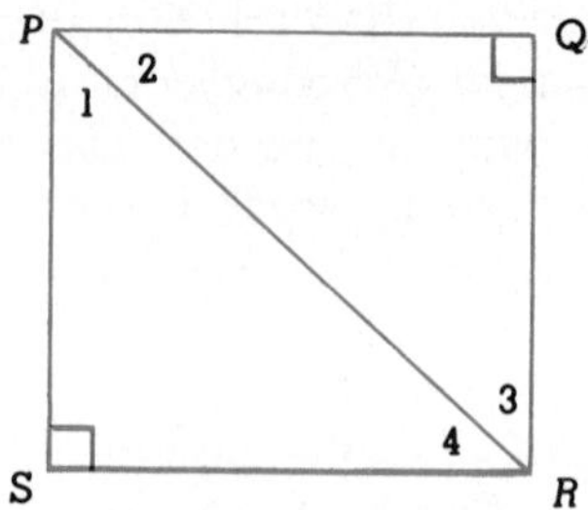

Given: $\angle Q$ and $\angle S$ are right angles.
$\angle 1 \cong \angle 3$

Prove: $\triangle PQR \cong \triangle RSP$

Proof:

STATEMENTS	REASONS
1. $\angle Q$ and $\angle S$ are right angles.	1. Given
2. $\angle Q \cong \angle S$	2. Theorem 3–6: If two angles are right angles, then the angles are congruent.
3. $\angle 1 \cong \angle 3$	3. Given
4. $\overline{PR} \cong \overline{PR}$	4. Theorem 2–2: Congruence of segments is reflexive.
5. $\triangle PQR \cong \triangle RSP$	5. Theorem 4–5: AAS *Use steps 2, 3, and 4.*

Suppose you are given measurements for two sides and a nonincluded angle of a triangle. The measurements of the sides are 7.3 cm and 5 cm. The angle measures 40°. Is this enough information to determine only one triangle?

No, two different triangles can be drawn using the given information. There is *not* enough information to know which is desired.

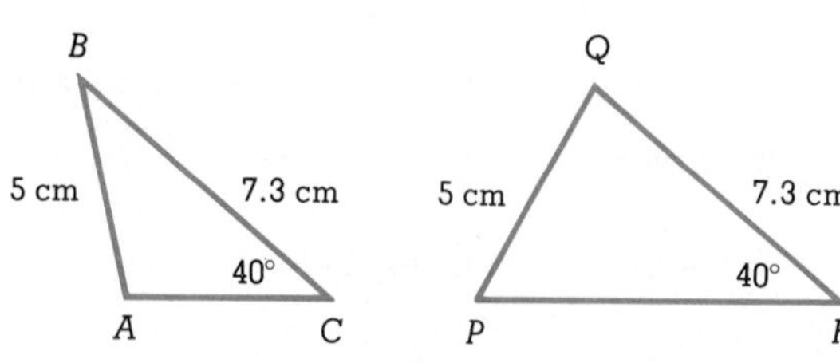

Two sides and a nonincluded angle of $\triangle ABC$ are congruent to two corresponding sides and a nonincluded angle of $\triangle PQR$. The two triangles are *not* congruent. Thus, side-side-angle or SSA is not a test for congruent triangles.

Is angle-angle-angle or AAA a test for congruent triangles? No.

exercises

EN: Wr: 2-14 evens; AV: Ex: 1-11 odds, Wr: 1-11 odds, AR: 1-6; p. 119, Wr: 2-30 evens

Exploratory Use the marks shown to determine whether or *not* each pair of triangles is congruent. If the triangles are congruent, state the postulate or theorem used. If there is *not* enough information, then state "not enough information".

FN: Ex: 1-12, Wr: 1-11 odds, AR: 1-12; p. 119, Wr: 2-30 evens

1. 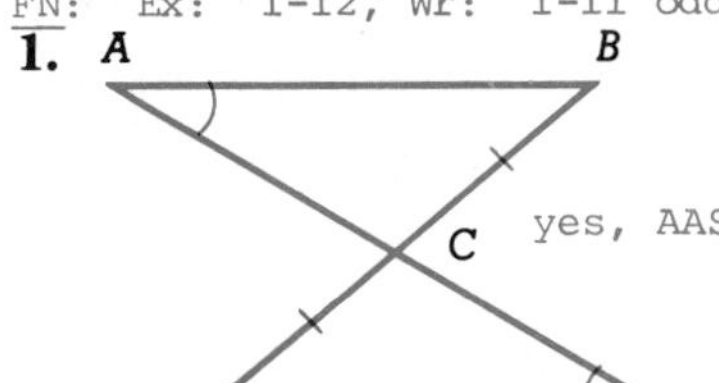

2. 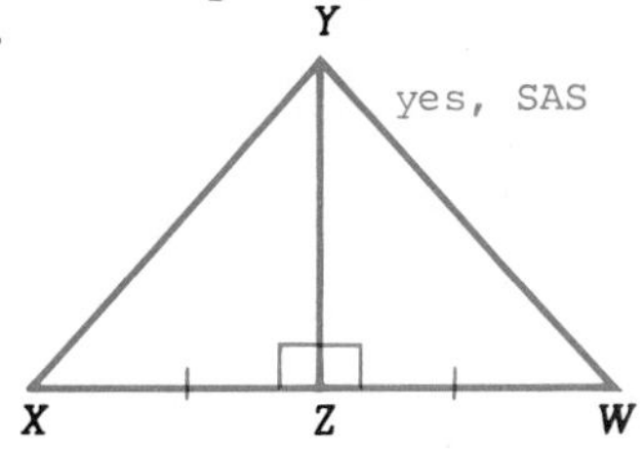

3. 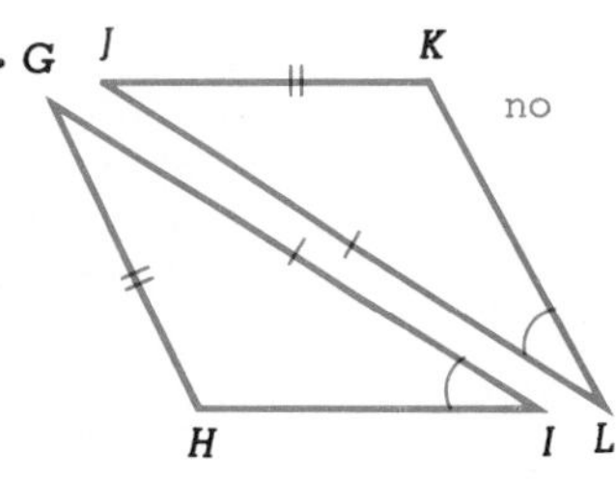

4. 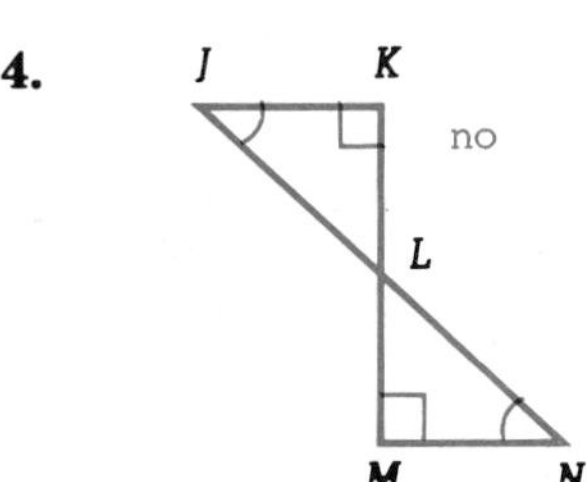

5. 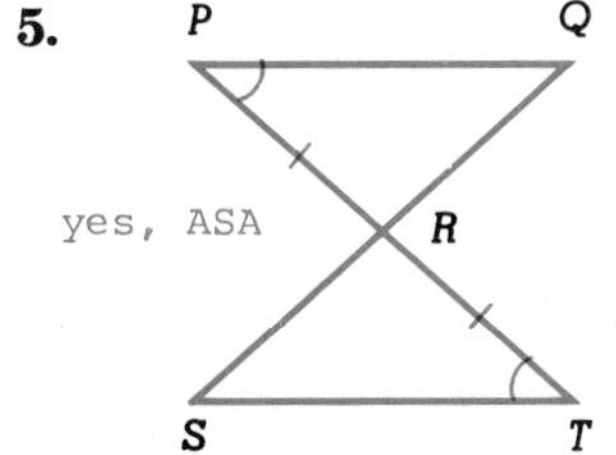

6. 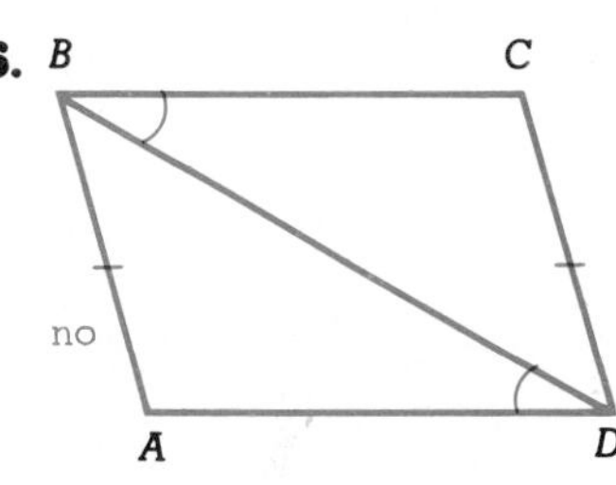

7. 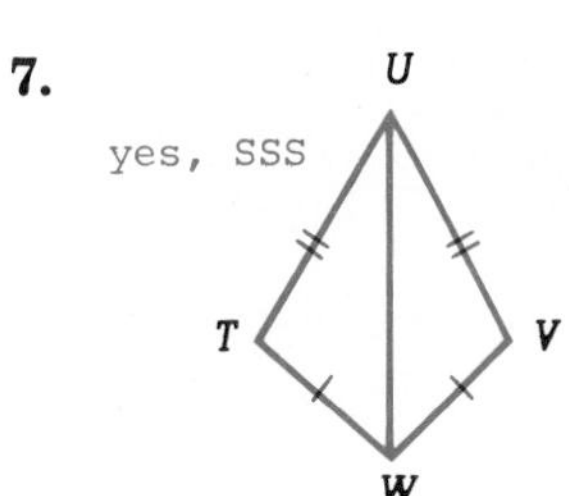

8. 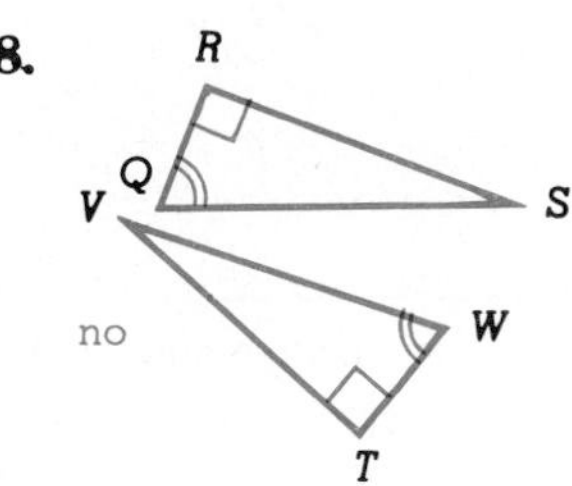

9. 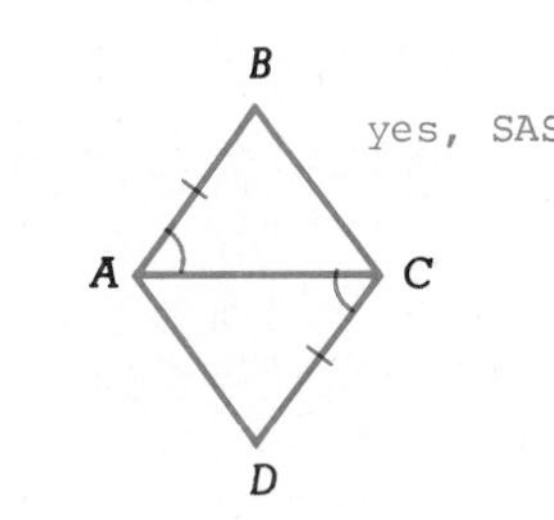

10. 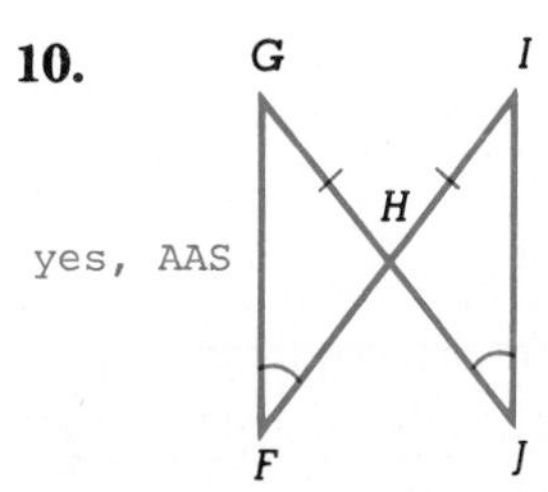

11. 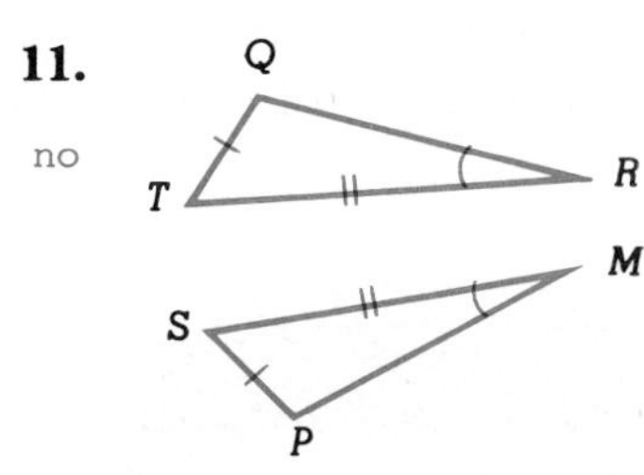

12. 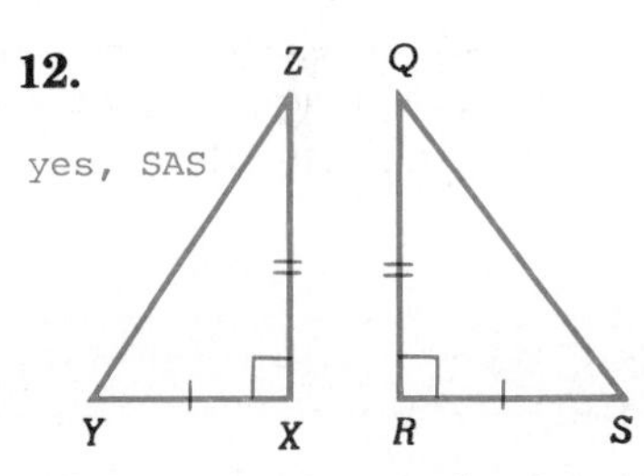

Written Prove each of the following. For answers to exercises 1-12, see the Teacher's Guide.

1. **Given:** $\overline{BC} \cong \overline{DC}$, $\angle A \cong \angle E$, $\angle 1 \cong \angle 2$
   Prove: $\overline{AC} \cong \overline{EC}$

2. **Given:** $\overline{BC} \cong \overline{DC}$, $\angle A \cong \angle E$, $\angle 1 \cong \angle 2$
   Prove: $\overline{AB} \cong \overline{ED}$

3. **Given:** $\angle A \cong \angle E$, $\angle 1 \cong \angle 2$, $\overline{AC} \cong \overline{EC}$
   Prove: $\angle B \cong \angle D$

4. **Given:** $\overline{AC} \cong \overline{EC}$, $\angle 1 \cong \angle 2$, $\overline{BC} \cong \overline{DC}$
   Prove: $\angle B \cong \angle D$

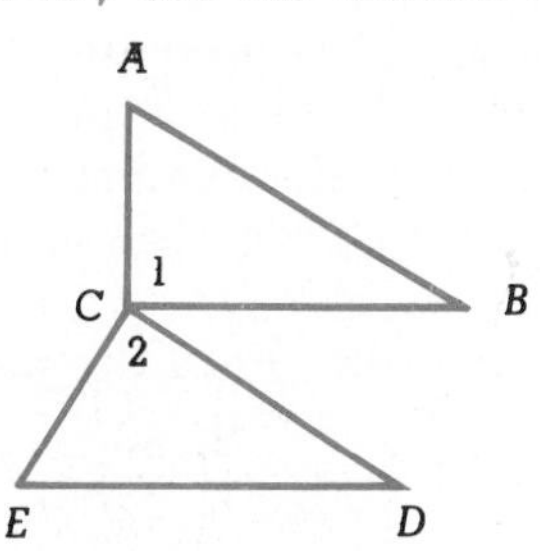

Exercises 1–4

5. **Given:** $\angle A \cong \angle C$
$\angle 1 \cong \angle 2$
Prove: $\overline{BD}$ bisects $\overline{AC}$.

6. **Given:** $\angle A \cong \angle C$
$\overline{BD} \perp \overline{AC}$
Prove: $\overline{AB} \cong \overline{CB}$

7. **Given:** $\overline{AB} \cong \overline{CB}$
$\overline{BD}$ bisects $\overline{AC}$.
Prove: $\angle A \cong \angle C$

8. **Given:** $\angle 1 \cong \angle 2$
$\angle 3$ and $\angle 4$ are right angles.
Prove: $\overline{AD} \cong \overline{CD}$

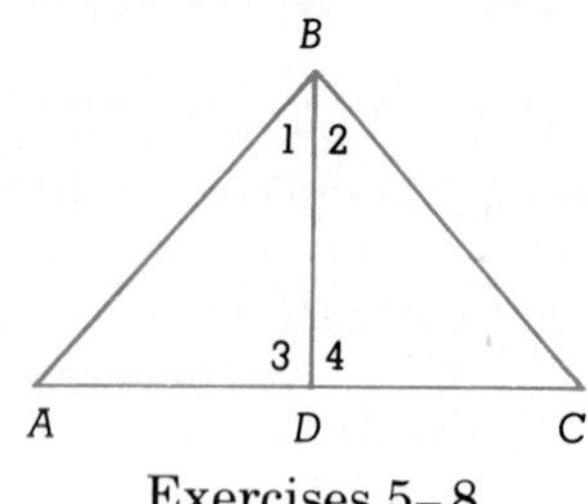

Exercises 5–8

9. **Given:** J is the midpoint of $\overline{GK}$.
$\angle H$ and $\angle L$ are right angles.
Prove: $\overline{HG} \cong \overline{LK}$

10. **Given:** J is the midpoint of $\overline{HL}$.
$\angle G \cong \angle K$
Prove: $\angle H \cong \angle L$

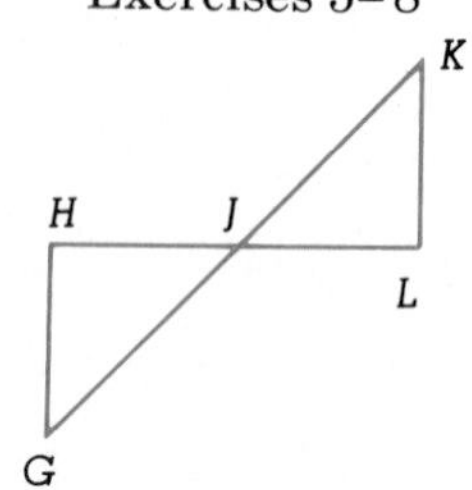

Exercises 9 and 10

11. **Given:** $\overline{SP}$ and $\overline{SR}$ are in $\mathcal{M}$.
$\overline{QS} \perp \mathcal{M}$
$\angle P \cong \angle R$
Prove: $\overline{QP} \cong \overline{QR}$

12. **Given:** $\overline{SP}$ and $\overline{SR}$ are in $\mathcal{M}$.
$\overline{QS} \perp \mathcal{M}$
$\angle P \cong \angle R$
Prove: $\overline{PS} \cong \overline{RS}$

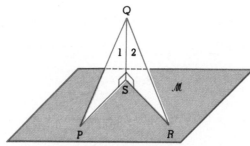

Exercises 11 and 12

13. Draw two triangles that are *not* congruent, but for which SSA holds. Indicate all measurements. See student's work.
14. Draw two triangles that are *not* congruent, but for which AAA holds. Indicate all measurements. See student's work.

Prime Factorization — algebra review

A **prime number** is an integer, greater than 1, whose only positive factors are 1 and itself. A **composite number** is any positive integer, except 1, that is not prime. A composite number can always be expressed as a product of prime factors. Expressing a composite number in this way is called **a prime factorization.**

The prime factorization of 60 is $2 \cdot 2 \cdot 3 \cdot 5$ or $2^2 \cdot 3 \cdot 5$.

Exercises **Find the prime factorization of each of the following.**

1. 8 2^3
2. 36 $2^2 \cdot 3^2$
3. 40 $2^3 \cdot 5$
4. 65 $5 \cdot 13$
5. 54 $2 \cdot 3^3$
6. 63 $3^2 \cdot 7$
7. 72 $2^3 \cdot 3^2$
8. 120 $2^3 \cdot 3 \cdot 5$
9. 155 $5 \cdot 31$
10. 216 $2^3 \cdot 3^3$
11. 280 $2^3 \cdot 5 \cdot 7$
12. 340 $2^2 \cdot 5 \cdot 17$

4–6 Medians, Altitudes, and Bisectors

Objective: to use medians, altitudes, and bisectors in proofs involving congruent triangles

Every triangle has three **medians** and three **altitudes.** They are defined in the following way.

A segment is a median of a triangle if and only if its endpoints are a vertex of the triangle and the midpoint of the side opposite the vertex.

Definition of Median of a Triangle

A segment is an altitude of a triangle if and only if the following conditions hold.
1. **Its endpoints are a vertex of a triangle and a point on the line containing the opposite side.**
2. **It is perpendicular to the line containing the opposite side.**

Definition of Altitude of a Triangle

If an altitude is also a median, then it is called a **perpendicular bisector** of the opposite side.

Be sure students understand the distinction between a median and an altitude.

For each of the triangles below, the altitude and median from one vertex are shown.

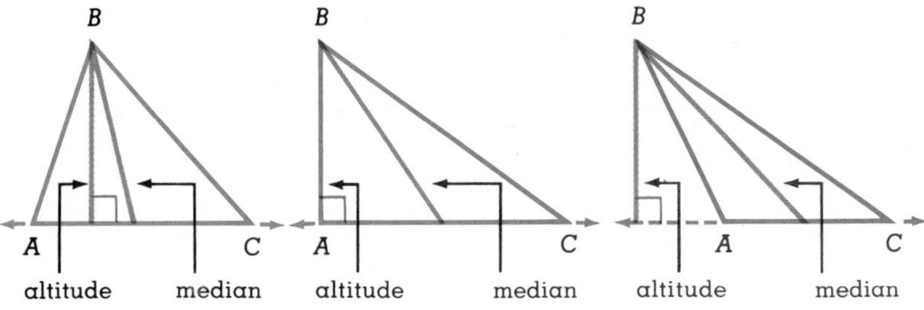

example

1 Prove the following.

Given: $\overline{AB} \cong \overline{CB}$
$\overline{BD}$ is a median of $\triangle ABC$.

Prove: $\angle ABD \cong \angle CBD$

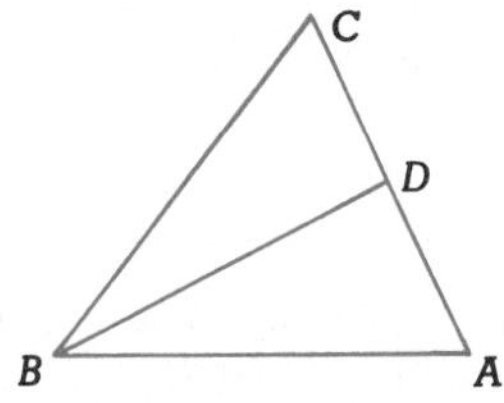

Proof:

STATEMENTS	REASONS
1. $\overline{BD}$ is a median of $\triangle ABC$.	1. Given
2. D is a midpoint of $\overline{AC}$.	2. Definition of Median of a Triangle
3. $\overline{AD} \cong \overline{CD}$	3. Theorem 2–5: Midpoint Theorem
4. $\overline{AB} \cong \overline{CB}$	4. Given
5. $\overline{BD} \cong \overline{BD}$	5. Theorem 2–2: Congruence of segments is reflexive.
6. $\triangle ABD \cong \triangle CBD$	6. Postulate 4–1: SSS *Use steps 3, 4, and 5.*
7. $\angle ABD \cong \angle CBD$	7. Definition of Congruent Triangles *CPCTC*

In the figure at the right, $\angle PQS \cong \angle RQS$. Since $\overrightarrow{QS}$ and the sides of $\angle PQR$ form two congruent angles, $\overrightarrow{QS}$ is called the **bisector** of $\angle PQR$.

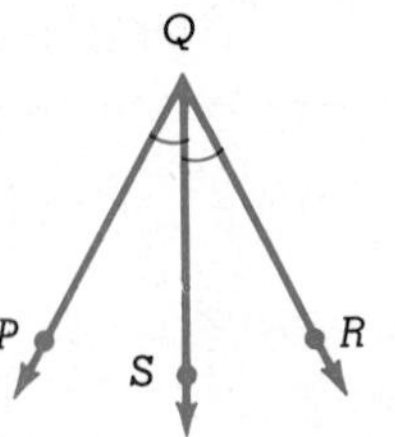

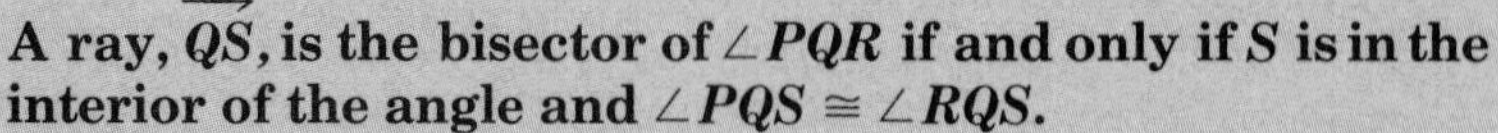
A ray, $\overrightarrow{QS}$, is the bisector of $\angle PQR$ if and only if S is in the interior of the angle and $\angle PQS \cong \angle RQS$.

Definition of Angle Bisector

By using the Angle Measure Postulate and the Protractor Postulate, you can prove that an angle has *exactly one* bisector.

In the figure at the right, $\overrightarrow{CD}$ bisects $\angle ACB$. Notice that $\overline{CD}$ is contained in $\overrightarrow{CD}$ which bisects $\angle ACB$. Therefore, $\overline{CD}$ is also called an angle bisector of $\triangle ABC$.

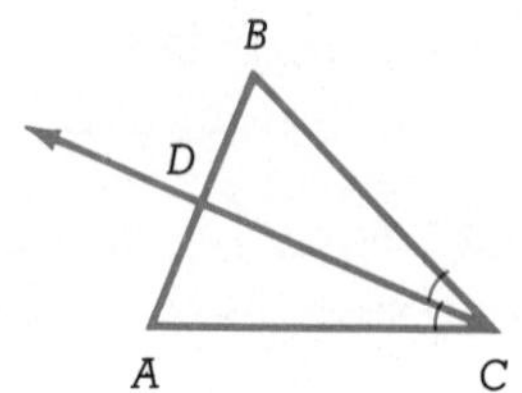

How many angle bisectors does a triangle have?

A segment is an angle bisector of a triangle if and only if it is contained in the bisector of one of the angles of the triangle and its endpoints are on the triangle.

Definition of Angle Bisector of a Triangle

example

2 Prove the following.

Given: $\overline{PR}$ bisects $\angle QPS$.
$\overline{PR} \perp \overline{QS}$

Prove: $\triangle PQS$ is isosceles.

Note that $\overline{PR}$ bisects the angle because $\overline{PR}$ is contained in $\overrightarrow{PR}$.

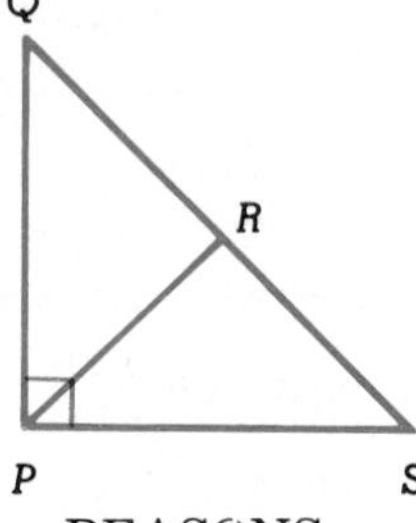

Proof:

STATEMENTS	REASONS
1. $\overline{PR}$ bisects $\angle QPS$.	**1.** Given
2. $\angle QPR \cong \angle SPR$	**2.** Definition of Angle Bisector
3. $\overline{PR} \perp \overline{QS}$	**3.** Given
4. $\angle QRP$ and $\angle SRP$ are right angles.	**4.** Definition of Perpendicular Lines
5. $\angle QPR \cong \angle SRP$	**5.** Theorem 3–6: If two angles are right angles, then the angles are congruent.
6. $\overline{PR} \cong \overline{PR}$	**6.** Theorem 2–2: Congruence of segments is reflexive.
7. $\triangle PQR \cong \triangle PSR$	**7.** Postulate 4–3: ASA *Use steps 2, 5, and 6.*
8. $\overline{QP} \cong \overline{SP}$	**8.** Definition of Congruent Triangles *CPCTC*
9. $\triangle PQS$ is isosceles.	**9.** Definition of Isosceles Triangle

exercises

EN: Wr: 2-20 evens, Ch: 1-5; AV: Ex: 1-11 odds, Wr: 1-19 odds; p. 123, Wr: 2-14 evens

Exploratory **In the figure at the right, $\overline{AC}$ bisects $\angle BAD$, and $\overline{CE}$ bisects $\angle ACD$. Also, $\overline{AB}$ is an altitude of $\triangle ABD$, and $\overline{CE}$ is an altitude of $\triangle ACD$. Find the degree measure for each of the following.**

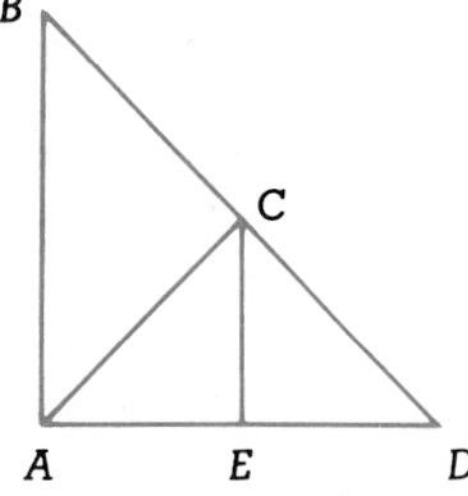

1. $\angle BAD$ 90
2. $\angle CEA$ 90
3. $\angle CED$ 90
4. $\angle BAC$ 45
5. $\angle CAE$ 45
6. $\angle ACE$ 45
7. $\angle DCE$ 45
8. $\angle ECD$ 45
9. $\angle CDE$ 45
10. $\angle DCA$ 90
11. $\angle ACB$ 90
12. $\angle CBA$ 45

FN: Ex: 1-12, Wr: 1-17 odds; p. 123, Wr: 2-12 evens

For answers to exercises 1-10, see student's work.

Written **Draw diagrams to illustrate each of the following.**

1. $\overline{PS}$ is an altitude of $\triangle PQR$, and S is between Q and R.
2. $\overline{PS}$ is a median of $\triangle PQR$, and S is between Q and R.
3. $\overrightarrow{SQ}$ bisects $\angle PSR$.
4. $\overline{HL}$ is an angle bisector of $\triangle HJK$.
5. $\overline{BD}$ is a median of $\triangle ABC$, and bisects $\angle ABC$.
6. $\overline{EC}$ is an altitude of $\triangle ABC$ and bisects $\angle BCA$.
7. $\angle PVR$ and $\angle TVR$ form a linear pair. $\overrightarrow{VQ}$ bisects $\angle PVR$, and $\overrightarrow{VS}$ bisects $\angle TVR$.
8. $\overrightarrow{AP}$ bisects $\angle MLR$ and $\angle NLQ$.
9. $\triangle ABC$ is a right triangle with altitude $\overline{BC}$ and median $\overline{BD}$.
10. $\overline{PT}$ and $\overline{RS}$ are medians of $\triangle PQR$ and intersect at V.

Prove each of the following. For answers to exercises 11-20, see the Teacher's Guide.

11. **Given:** $\overline{AB}$ is an altitude of $\triangle ABD$.
$\overline{CD}$ is an altitude of $\triangle BCD$.
$\overline{BC} \cong \overline{AD}$, $\overline{CD} \cong \overline{AD}$
$\overline{AB} \cong \overline{CD}$
Prove: $\overline{BD}$ bisects $\angle ABC$.

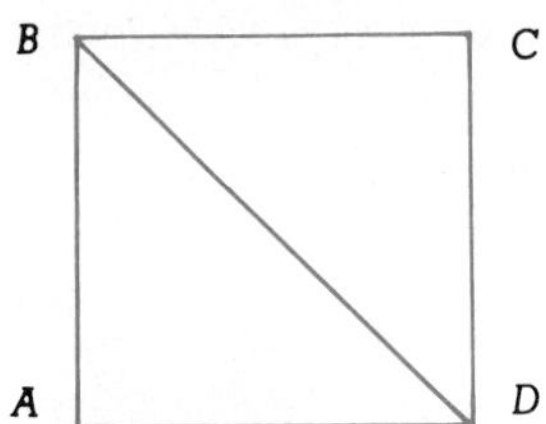

12. **Given:** $\overline{PR}$ is an altitude of $\triangle PQR$.
R is the midpoint of $\overline{PS}$.
R is the midpoint of $\overline{QT}$.
Prove: $\overline{RS}$ is an altitude of $\triangle RST$.

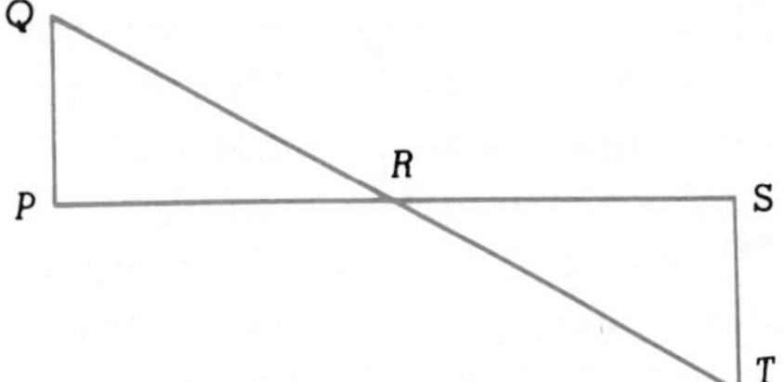

13. The median from the vertex angle of an isosceles triangle bisects the vertex angle.
14. The median from the vertex angle of an isosceles triangle is an altitude of the triangle.
15. If a median of a triangle is also an altitude, then the triangle is isosceles.
16. If a median of a triangle is also an altitude, then it is an angle bisector of the triangle.

17. If $\overline{BD}$ bisects $\angle ABC$, $\overline{DE}$ is an altitude of $\triangle ADB$, and $\overline{DF}$ is an altitude of $\triangle CDB$, then $\overline{DE} \cong \overline{DF}$.

18. Corresponding medians of congruent triangles are congruent.

19. The medians drawn to the congruent sides of an isosceles triangle are congruent.

20. If an angle and its bisector are given, then the bisector is the only bisector of the given angle.

For answers to exercises 1-5, see the Teacher's Guide and see student's work.

Challenge **Draw several examples to answer each of the following questions.**

1. If one median of a triangle is also an altitude, what is true about the triangle?
2. If one altitude of a triangle is also an angle bisector, what is true about the triangle?
3. If one endpoint of an altitude of a triangle does not lie on the triangle, what is true about the triangle?
4. If two medians are also altitudes, what is true about the triangle?
5. Can you make any conclusions about the intersection of the medians, altitudes, or angle bisectors in different types of triangles?

Input Equipment

computers

Before information can be entered into the computer, it must be changed from a form that you understand to a form that the computer "understands". This is the purpose of the input device.

For many years, the "key punch" machine was the input device used almost exclusively. This device is still in use today. Input data is typed on cards in the form of punched holes. A card reader is used to "read" these punched holes and transmit them, in electronic form, to the computer.

Perhaps the most common input device today is the computer terminal. When you type on the keyboard of a computer terminal, in most cases the key that you press sends an electronic pulse to the computer.

Two other input devices are graphic tablets and light pens. Both of these devices allow you to "write" an answer. The computer can then interpret your response.

Objectives: to use properties of isosceles and equilateral triangles in proofs, to use auxiliary segments in proofs

4–7 Isosceles Triangles

Some proofs include geometric figures that are *not* given in the theorem. Often, these figures are lines or parts of lines. They are included on the diagram in color. The proof of the following theorem uses an **auxiliary** segment.

If two sides of a triangle are congruent, then the angles opposite those sides are congruent.

Theorem 4–6 Isosceles Triangle Theorem

1 Prove Theorem 4–6.

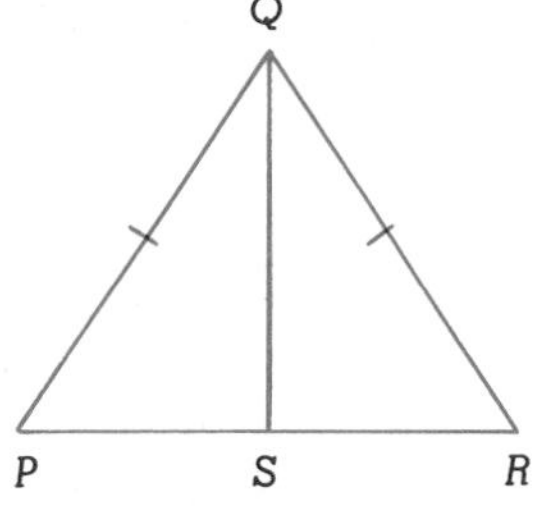

Given: $\triangle PQR$
$\overline{PQ} \cong \overline{RQ}$

Prove: $\angle P \cong \angle R$

Proof:

STATEMENTS	REASONS
1. Call S the midpoint of $\overline{PR}$, and draw $\overline{QS}$.	1. Theorem 2–1: If a segment is given, then it has exactly one midpoint, and Postulate 1–1: Through any two points, there is exactly one line.
2. $\overline{PS} \cong \overline{RS}$	2. Theorem 2–5: Midpoint Theorem
3. $\overline{PQ} \cong \overline{RQ}$	3. Given
4. $\overline{QS} \cong \overline{QS}$	4. Theorem 2–2: Congruence of segments is reflexive.
5. $\triangle PQS \cong \triangle RQS$	5. Postulate 4–1: SSS *Use steps 2, 3, and 4.*
6. $\angle P \cong \angle R$	6. Definition of Congruent Triangles *CPCTC*

The proofs of the following theorems are based on the Isosceles Triangle Theorem.

If a triangle is equilateral, then the triangle is equiangular.

Theorem 4–7

If a triangle is equilateral, then each angle has a degree measure of 60.

Theorem 4–8

Students prove Theorems 4-7 and 4-8 in Written exercises 21-22.

It is not necessary to introduce an auxiliary figure unless it is useful for proving the given theorem. The segment in the proof of Theorem 4–6 is useful because it helps form two triangles. The proof is based on showing these two triangles are congruent.

The proof of the following theorem also uses an auxiliary segment.

If two angles of a triangle are congruent, then the sides opposite those angles are congruent. *Theorem 4–9*

Students prove Theorem 4-9 in Written exercise 23.

According to Theorem 4–7 and the following theorem, a triangle is equilateral if and only if it is equiangular.

If a triangle is equiangular, then the triangle is equilateral. *Theorem 4–10*

examples

2 Plan a proof for Theorem 4–9.

Draw the bisector of $\angle PQR$ and let T be the point where the bisector intersects $\overline{PR}$. Show $\triangle PQT \cong \triangle RQT$ by AAS. Then, $\overline{PQ} \cong \overline{RQ}$ because they are corresponding parts of congruent triangles.

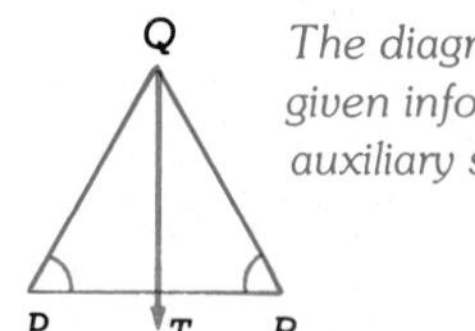

The diagram shows the given information and auxiliary segment.

3 Prove Theorem 4–10.

Given: $\triangle PQR$ is equiangular.
Prove: $\triangle PQR$ is equilateral.

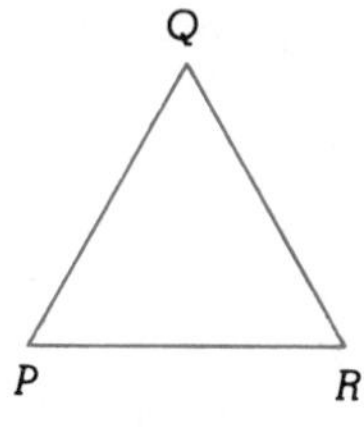

Proof:

STATEMENTS	REASONS
1. $\triangle PQR$ is equiangular.	1. Given
2. $\angle P \cong \angle Q$ $\angle Q \cong \angle R$ $\angle R \cong \angle P$	2. Definition of Equiangular Triangle
3. $\overline{QR} \cong \overline{PR}$ $\overline{RP} \cong \overline{QP}$ $\overline{PQ} \cong \overline{RQ}$ *Notice that $\overline{PR}$ and $\overline{RP}$ name the same segment. Similarly, $\overline{QP}$ and $\overline{PQ}$ name the same segment.*	3. Theorem 4–9: If two angles of a triangle are congruent, then the sides opposite those angles are congruent.
4. $\triangle PQR$ is equilateral.	4. Definition of Equilateral Triangle

exercises

EN: Ex: 1-4, Wr: 2-22 evens; AV: Ex: 1-9 odds, Wr: 1-19 odds; p. 127, Wr: 2-20 evens

Exploratory **For each of the following will the auxiliary figure be helpful for the proof? State *yes* or *no*.**

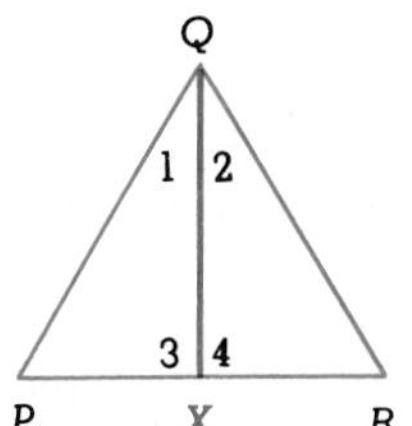

1. **Given:** $\overline{PQ} \cong \overline{QR}$
   Prove: $\angle P \cong \angle R$
   Draw $\overline{QX}$ so it bisects $\angle PQR$. yes
2. **Given:** $\overline{PQ} \cong \overline{QR}$
   Prove: $\angle P \cong \angle R$
   Draw $\overline{QX}$ so it bisects $\overline{PR}$. yes
3. **Given:** $\overline{PQ} \cong \overline{QR}$
   Prove: $\angle P \cong \angle R$
   Draw $\overline{QX}$ perpendicular to $\overline{PR}$. no
4. **Given:** $\overline{PQ} \cong \overline{QR}$
   Prove: $\angle P \cong \angle R$
   Draw X, the midpoint of $\overline{PR}$. yes
5. **Given:** $\overline{PQ} \cong \overline{PR}$
   Prove: $\angle Q \cong \angle R$
   Draw $\overline{QX}$ so it bisects $\angle PQR$. no
6. **Given:** $\angle P \cong \angle R$
   Prove: $\overline{PQ} \cong \overline{RQ}$
   Draw $\overline{QX}$ perpendicular to $\overline{PR}$. yes
7. **Given:** $\angle P \cong \angle R$
   Prove: $\overline{PQ} \cong \overline{RQ}$
   Draw $\overline{QX}$ so it bisects $\angle PQR$. yes
8. **Given:** $\angle R \cong \angle P$
   Prove: $\overline{QR} \cong \overline{QP}$
   Draw X, the midpoint of $\overline{PR}$. no
9. **Given:** $\angle P \cong \angle Q$
   Prove: $\overline{PQ} \cong \overline{PR}$
   Draw median $\overline{QX}$. no

FN: Ex: 1-9, Wr: 1-19 odds; p. 127, Wr: 2-18 evens

Written **Answer each of the following.** See student's work for 1, 2, 4, 5, 7, and 8.

1. Draw $\triangle ABC$ so that $\overline{AD} \perp \overline{BC}$, but $\overline{BD}$ and $\overline{DC}$ are *not* congruent.
2. Draw $\triangle ABC$, so that $\overline{BD} \cong \overline{DC}$, but $\overline{AD}$ is *not* perpendicular to $\overline{BC}$.
3. Suppose $\overline{AD}$ is the perpendicular bisector of $\overline{BC}$ in $\triangle ABC$. Classify the triangle as scalene, isosceles, or equilateral. isosceles
4. Draw $\triangle ABC$ so that $\overline{AD}$ bisects $\angle BAC$, but $\overline{BD}$ and $\overline{DC}$ are *not* congruent.
5. Draw $\triangle ABC$ so that $\overline{BD} \cong \overline{DC}$, but $\overline{AD}$ does *not* bisect $\angle BAC$.
6. Suppose $\overline{AD}$ bisects both $\angle BAC$ and $\overline{BC}$ in $\triangle ABC$. Classify the triangle as scalene, isosceles, or equilateral. isosceles
7. Draw $\triangle ABC$ so that $\overline{AD}$ bisects $\angle BAC$, but $\overline{AD}$ is *not* perpendicular to $\overline{BC}$.
8. Draw $\triangle ABC$ so that $\overline{AD} \perp \overline{BC}$, but $\overline{AD}$ does *not* bisect $\angle BAC$.
9. Suppose $\overline{AD}$ bisects $\angle BAC$ and $\overline{AD} \perp \overline{BD}$ in $\triangle ABC$. Classify the triangle as scalene, isosceles, or equilateral. isosceles

Before you introduce an auxiliary figure, be sure it exists and it is *not* a special case. For each of the following, determine whether or *not* you can introduce the figure in $\triangle PQR$. Write *yes* or *no*. If your answer is *no*, explain.

Sample **Let $\overline{PX}$ bisect $\angle P$ where X is the midpoint of $\overline{QR}$.**

No. Every angle has exactly one bisector, it may *not* necessarily intersect the opposite side of the triangle at its midpoint.

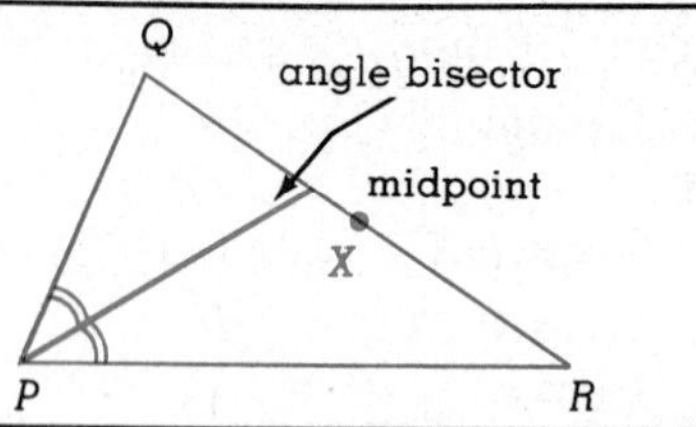

For reasons to exercises 10-15, see the Teacher's Guide.

10. Let $\overline{QX}$ bisect $\angle Q$ where X is between P and R. yes
11. Let $\overline{RX}$ be the perpendicular bisector of $\overline{PQ}$. no
12. Let $\overline{RV}$ bisect $\angle R$ and $\overline{PQ}$. no
13. Let M be the midpoint of $\overline{QR}$. Draw $\overline{PM}$. yes
14. Let $\overline{XY}$ bisect $\overline{QP}$ and $\overline{PR}$, where X is on $\overline{QP}$ and Y is on $\overline{PR}$. yes
15. Let $\overline{XY}$ be perpendicular to $\overline{QP}$ and $\overline{PR}$, where X is on $\overline{QP}$ and Y is on $\overline{PR}$. no

For answers to exercises 16-23, see the Teacher's Guide.

Prove each of the following.

16. **Given:** $\overline{PQ} \cong \overline{PS}$, $\overline{QR} \cong \overline{SR}$
    Prove: $\angle Q \cong \angle S$

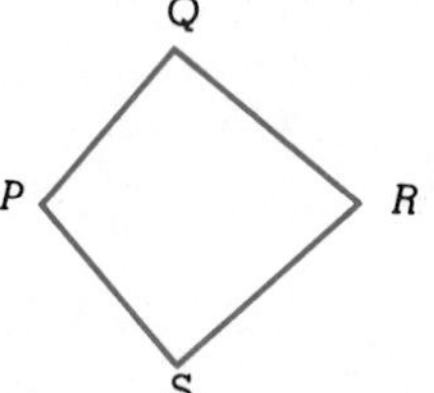

17. **Given:** $\overline{AB} \cong \overline{BC}$
    Prove: $\angle 3 \cong \angle 4$

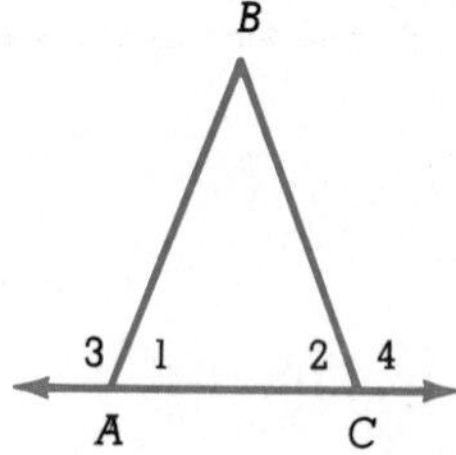

18. **Given:** $\overline{PQ} \cong \overline{RS}$, $\overline{PS} \cong \overline{RQ}$
    Prove: $\angle P \cong \angle R$

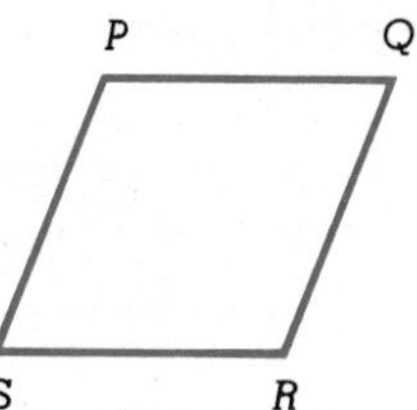

19. **Given:** $\overline{ZT} \cong \overline{ZR}$, $\overline{TX} \cong \overline{RY}$
    Prove: $\angle 5 \cong \angle 7$

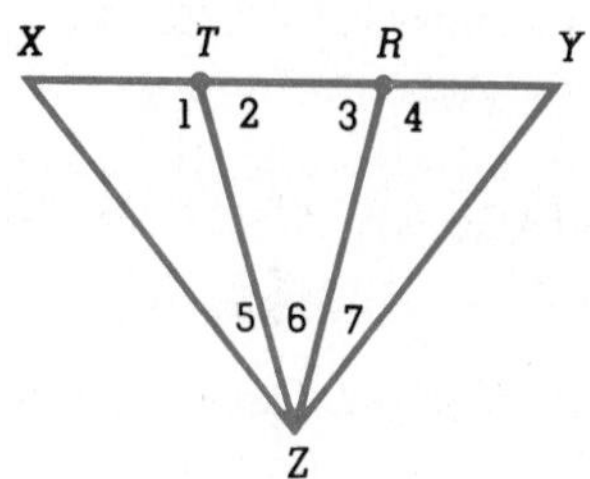

20. **Given:** $\overline{AB} \cong \overline{CB}$, $\overline{AD} \cong \overline{CD}$
    Prove: $\angle A \cong \angle C$

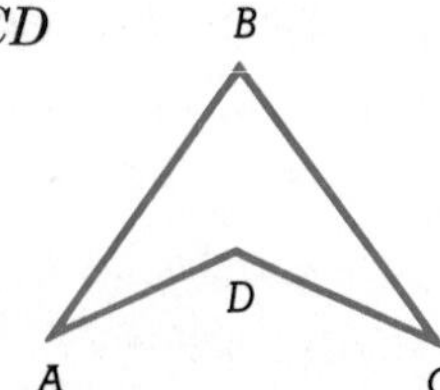

21. Theorem 4–7
22. Theorem 4–8
23. Theorem 4–9

Objective: to recognize and use tests for congruence of right triangles in proofs

4–8 Right Triangles

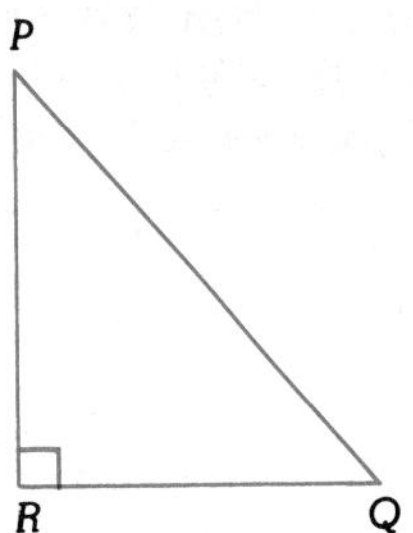

In a right triangle, the side opposite the right angle is called the **hypotenuse.** The other two sides are called the **legs.** The hypotenuse of $\triangle PQR$ is $\overline{PQ}$. The legs are $\overline{PR}$ and $\overline{RQ}$.

All right angles are congruent. Thus, any two right triangles always have one pair of angles congruent. The following theorems state ways to prove that two right triangles are congruent.

If the hypotenuse and an acute angle of one right triangle are congruent to the corresponding hypotenuse and acute angle of another right triangle, then the triangles are congruent.

Theorem 4–11 HA

If the legs of one right triangle are congruent to the corresponding legs of another right triangle, then the triangles are congruent.

Theorem 4–12 LL

Students prove Theorems 4-11 and 4-12 in Written exercises 9-10.

example

1 Prove the following.

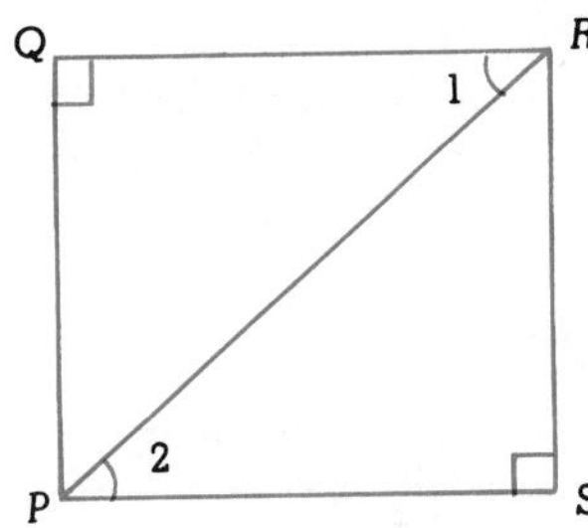

Given: $\angle Q$ and $\angle S$ are right angles.
$\angle 1 \cong \angle 2$

Prove: $\triangle PQR \cong \triangle RSP$

Proof:

STATEMENTS	REASONS
1. $\angle Q$ and $\angle S$ are right angles.	1. Given
2. $\triangle PQR$ and $\triangle RSP$ are right triangles.	2. Definition of Right Triangles
3. $\angle 1 \cong \angle 2$	3. Given
4. $\overline{PR} \cong \overline{PR}$	4. Theorem 2–2: Congruence of segments is reflexive.
5. $\triangle PQR \cong \triangle RSP$	5. Theorem 4–11: HA

Suppose one leg and an acute angle of one right triangle are congruent to the corresponding leg and acute angle of another right triangle. Are the triangles congruent? There are two different cases to consider.

CASE 1: The legs are included between the acute angle and the right angles.

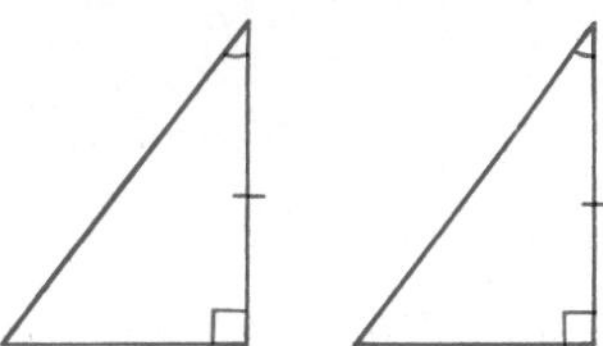

CASE 2: The legs are *not* included between the acute angle and the right angles.

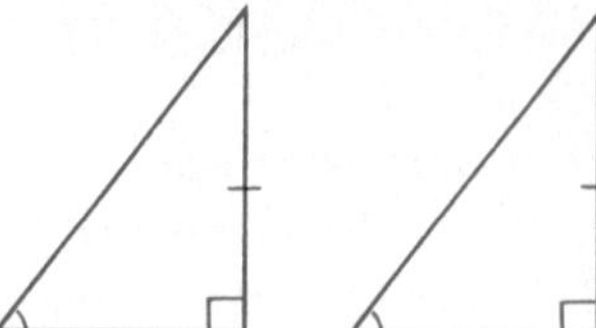

In the first case, the triangles are congruent by ASA. In the second case, the triangles are congruent by AAS.

Students prove Theorem 4-13 in Written exercise 11.

If one leg and an acute angle of one right triangle are congruent to the corresponding leg and acute angle of another right triangle, then the triangles are congruent.

Theorem 4–13
LA

example

2 **Prove the following.**

Given: $\overline{BE} \perp \overline{AD}$
C is the midpoint of $\overline{AD}$.
$\angle B \cong \angle E$

Prove: $\overline{AB} \cong \overline{DE}$

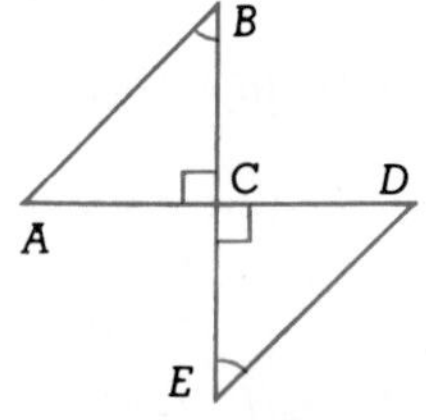

Proof:

STATEMENTS	REASONS
1. $\overline{BE} \perp \overline{AD}$	1. Given
2. $\angle BCA$ and $\angle DCE$ are right angles.	2. Theorem 3–11: If two lines are perpendicular, then they form four right angles.
3. $\triangle BCA$ and $\triangle ECD$ are right triangles.	3. Definition of Right Triangles
4. C is the midpoint of $\overline{AD}$.	4. Given
5. $\overline{AC} \cong \overline{DC}$	5. Theorem 2–5: Midpoint Theorem
6. $\angle B \cong \angle E$	6. Given
7. $\triangle BCA \cong \triangle ECD$	7. Theorem 4–13: LA *Use steps 5 and 6.*
8. $\overline{AB} \cong \overline{DE}$	8. Definition of Congruent Triangles *CPCTC*

Viewed from the side, a ladder leaning against a building forms a right triangle. If a ladder is placed against a building so it reaches a certain window, then the foot of the ladder touches the ground at a certain spot. What conclusion can you make about any other ladder of the same length placed in the same position? It forms a congruent triangle.

> **If the hypotenuse and a leg of one right triangle are congruent to the corresponding sides of another right triangle, then the triangles are congruent.**

Postulate 4–4
HL

exercises

EN: Ex: 1-3, Wr: 2-10 evens; AV: Ex: 1-5 odds, Wr: 1-9 odds; p. 131, Wr: 2-22 evens

Exploratory Use the marks shown to determine whether or *not* each pair of triangles is congruent. If the triangles are congruent, state the postulate or theorem you used. If there is *not* enough information, then state "not enough information."

1.

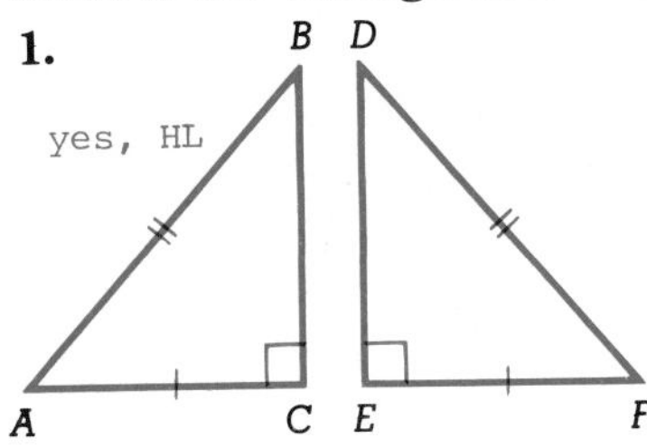

2.

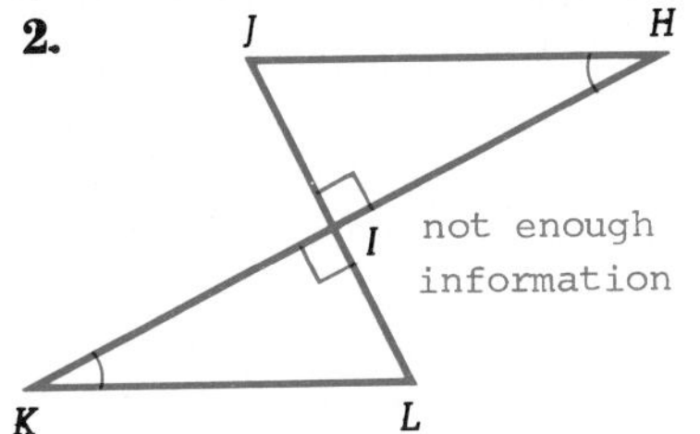

3.

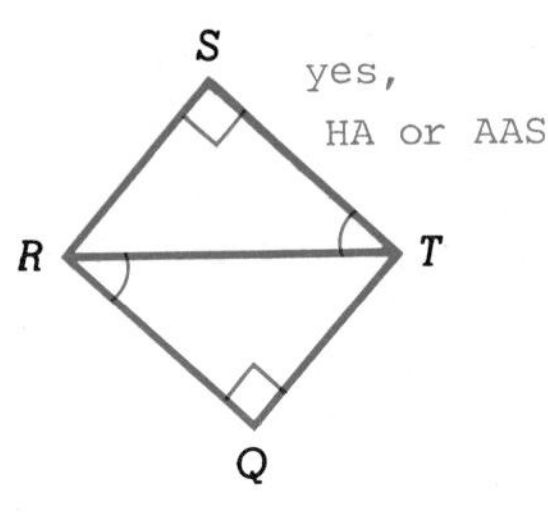

4.

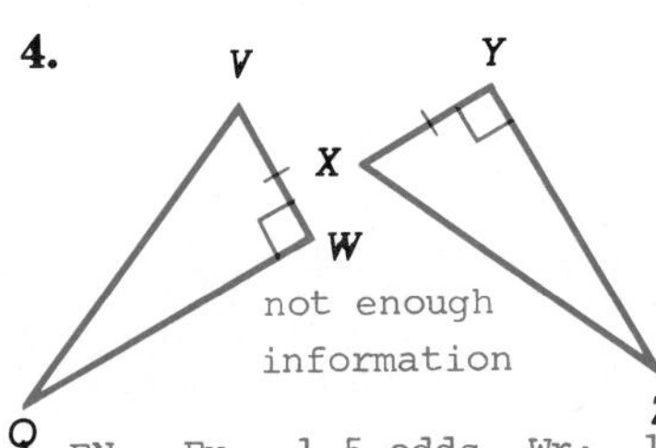

5.

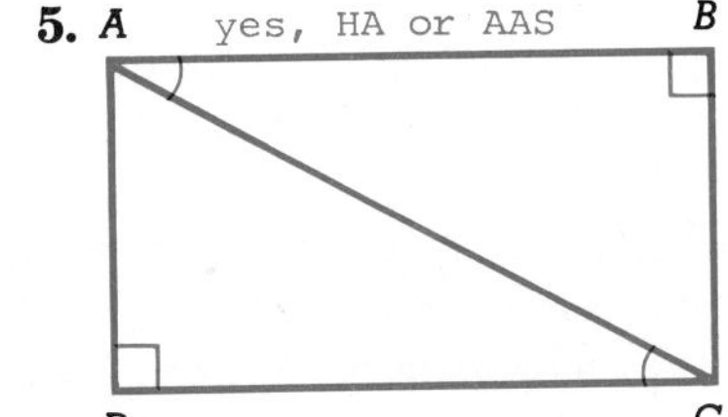

6.

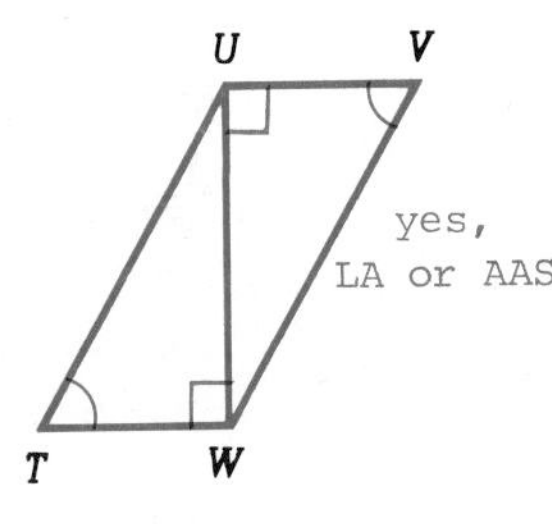

FN: Ex: 1-5 odds, Wr: 1-9 odds; p. 131, Wr: 2-20 evens

Written Prove each of the following.

For answers to exercises 1-11, see the Teacher's Guide.

1. **Given:** $\angle Q$ and $\angle S$ are right angles. $\angle 1 \cong \angle 2$
   Prove: $\overline{QP} \cong \overline{SR}$
2. **Given:** $\angle Q$ and $\angle S$ are right angles. $\angle 1 \cong \angle 2$
   Prove: $\overline{QR} \cong \overline{SP}$
3. **Given:** $\angle Q$ and $\angle S$ are right angles. $\overline{QP} \cong \overline{SR}$
   Prove: $\overline{QR} \cong \overline{SP}$
4. **Given:** $\angle Q$ and $\angle S$ are right angles. $\overline{QP} \cong \overline{SR}$
   Prove: $\angle 4 \cong \angle 3$

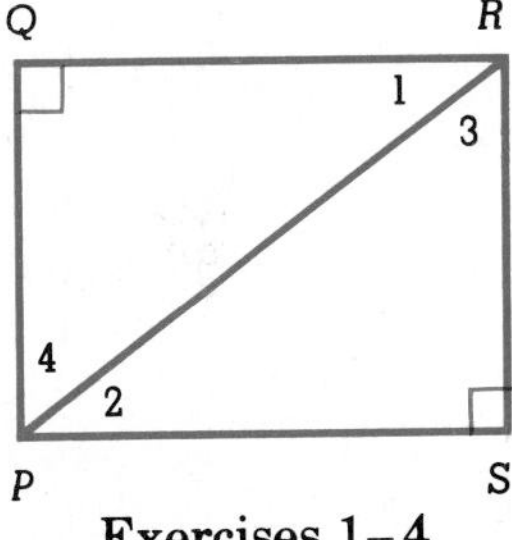

Exercises 1–4

5. **Given:** $\overline{BA} \perp \overline{AE}$, $\overline{DE} \perp \overline{AE}$, C is the midpoint of $\overline{AE}$. $\angle ABC \cong \angle EDC$
   Prove: $\angle 1 \cong \angle 2$
6. **Given:** $\overline{AC} \cong \overline{EC}$, $\angle 3 \cong \angle 4$, $\angle A$ and $\angle E$ are right angles.
   Prove: $\angle 1 \cong \angle 2$
7. **Given:** $\overline{BD} \perp \overline{XC}$, X is the midpoint of $\overline{BD}$.
   Prove: $\angle 3 \cong \angle 4$
8. **Given:** $\overline{CB} \cong \overline{CD}$, $\angle 5 \cong \angle 6$
   Prove: $\triangle BXC \cong \triangle DXC$

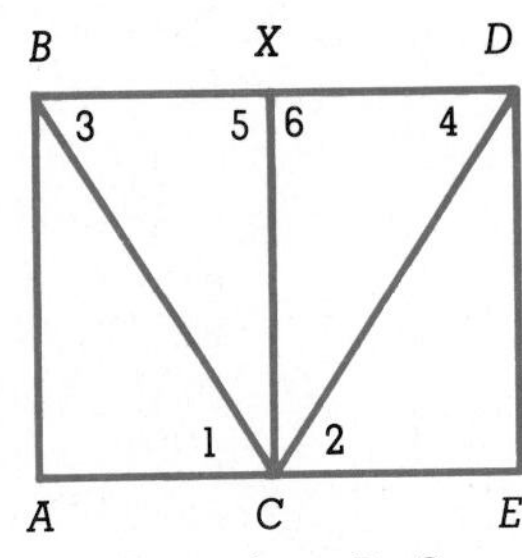

Exercises 5–8

9. Theorem 4–11
10. Theorem 4–12
11. Theorem 4–13

Vocabulary

triangle (103)
sides (103)
vertices (103)
acute triangle (104)
obtuse triangle (104)
right triangle (104)
equiangular triangle (104)
scalene triangle (104)
isosceles triangle (104)
equilateral triangle (104)
interior (105)
exterior (105)
congruent triangles (112)
SSS (116)
SAS (116)
ASA (117)
AAS (121)
median (125)
altitude (125)
perpendicular bisector (125)
angle bisector (126)
auxiliary figure (129)
hypotenuse (133)
legs (133)
HA (133)
LL (133)
LA (134)
HL (135)

Chapter Summary

1. Definition of Triangle: A triangle is a figure formed by three noncollinear segments called sides. Each endpoint of a side is an endpoint of exactly one other side. (103)
2. Angle Sum Theorem (Theorem 4–1): The sum of the degree measures of the angles of a triangle is 180. (107)
3. Theorem 4–2: If a triangle is equiangular, then the degree measure of each angle is 60. (108)
4. Theorem 4–3: If a triangle is a right triangle, then the acute angles are complementary. (108)
5. Definition of Congruent Triangles: Two triangles are congruent if and only if there is a correspondence such that their corresponding parts are congruent. (113)
6. Theorem 4–4: Congruence of Triangles is reflexive, symmetric, and transitive. (114)
7. SSS (Postulate 4–1): If each side of one triangle is congruent to the corresponding side of another triangle, then the triangles are congruent. (116)
8. SAS (Postulate 4–2): If two sides and the included angle of one triangle are congruent to the corresponding sides and included angle of another triangle, then the triangles are congruent. (116)
9. ASA (Postulate 4–3): If two angles and the included side of one triangle are congruent to the corresponding angles and included side of another triangle, then the triangles are congruent. (117)
10. AAS (Theorem 4–5): If two angles and a nonincluded side of one triangle are congruent to the corresponding angles and nonincluded side of another triangle, then the triangles are congruent. (121)
11. Definition of Median of a Triangle: A segment is a median of a triangle if and only if its endpoints are a vertex of the triangle and the midpoint of the opposite side. (125)

12. Definition of Altitude of a Triangle: A segment is an altitude of a triangle if and only if the following conditions hold.
    1. Its endpoints are a vertex of a triangle and a point on the line containing the opposite side.
    2. It is perpendicular to the line containing the opposite side. (125)
13. Definition of Angle Bisector: A ray, $\overrightarrow{QS}$, is the bisector of $\angle PQR$ if and only if S is in the interior of the angle and $\angle PQS \cong \angle RQS$. (126)
14. Isosceles Triangle Theorem (Theorem 4–6): If two sides of a triangle are congruent, then the angles opposite those sides are congruent. (129)
15. Theorem 4–7: If a triangle is equilateral, then the triangle is equiangular. (129)
16. Theorem 4–8: If a triangle is equilateral, then each angle has a degree measure of 60. (129)
17. Theorem 4–9: If two angles of a triangle are congruent, then the sides opposite those angles are congruent. (130)
18. Theorem 4–10: If a triangle is equiangular, then the triangle is equilateral. (130)
19. HA (Theorem 4–11): If the hypotenuse and an acute angle of one right triangle are congruent to the corresponding hypotenuse and acute angle of another right triangle, then the triangles are congruent. (133)
20. LL (Theorem 4–12): If the legs of one right triangle are congruent to the corresponding legs of another right triangle, then the triangles are congruent. (133)
21. LA (Theorem 4–13): If one leg and an acute angle of one right triangle are congruent to the corresponding leg and acute angle of another right triangle, then the triangles are congruent. (134)
22. HL (Postulate 4–4): If the hypotenuse and a leg of one right triangle are congruent to the corresponding hypotenuse and leg of another right triangle, then the triangles are congruent. (135)

Chapter Review

4–1 Use the figure at the right to answer each of the following.

1. Name the triangle. $\triangle$ TVW
2. Name the sides of the triangle. $\overline{TV}$, $\overline{WV}$, $\overline{TW}$
3. Name the angles of the triangle. $\angle$ T, $\angle$ V, $\angle$ W
4. Suppose the triangle is equilateral. Solve for x and find the measure of each side. TV = 8, WV = 8, TW = 8

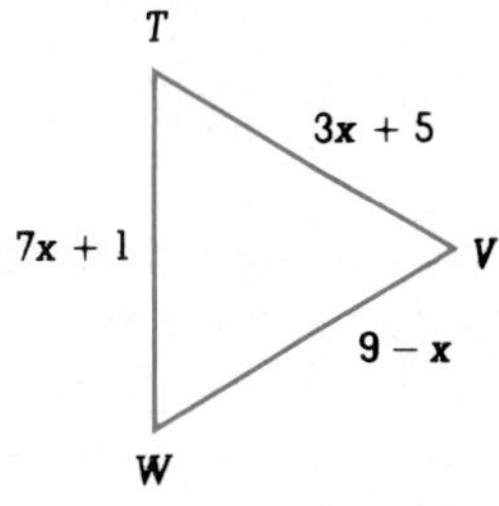

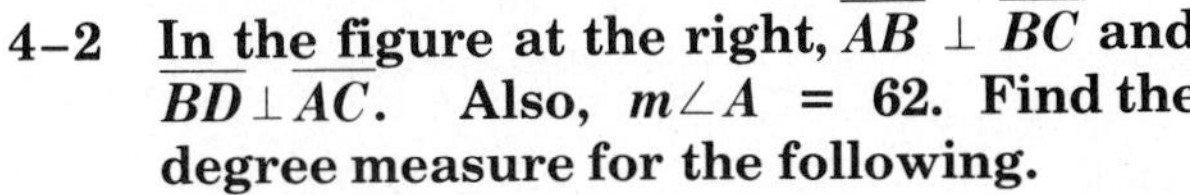
4–2 In the figure at the right, $\overline{AB} \perp \overline{BC}$ and $\overline{BD} \perp \overline{AC}$. Also, $m\angle A = 62$. Find the degree measure for the following.

5. $\angle ABD$ 28
6. $\angle ABC$ 90
7. $\angle DBC$ 62
8. $\angle BCD$ 28

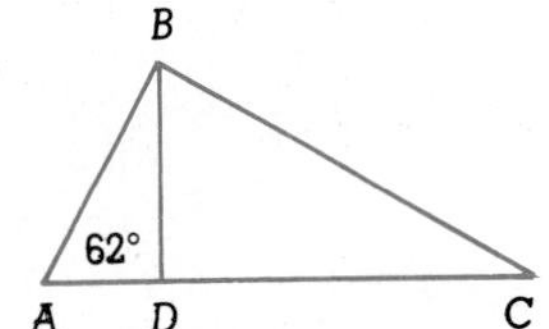

4–3 In the figure at the right, suppose $\triangle PQS \cong \triangle RQS$. Name the part of $\triangle RQS$ that is congruent to the part of $\triangle PQS$ given below.

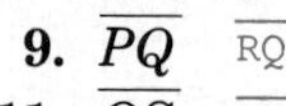

9. $\overline{PQ}$ $\overline{RQ}$
10. $\angle P$ $\angle R$
11. $\overline{QS}$ $\overline{QS}$
12. $\angle 1$ $\angle 2$
13. $\overline{SP}$ $\overline{SR}$
14. $\angle PSQ$ $\angle RSQ$

For answers to exercises 15-22, see the Teacher's Guide.

4–4 Use the figure at the right to prove each of the following.

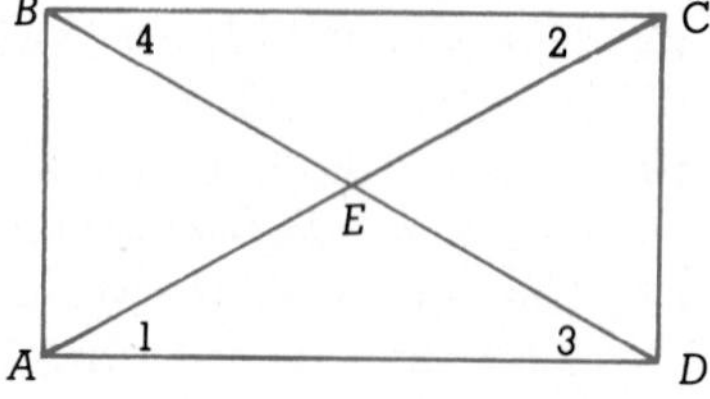

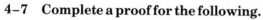

15. **Given:** $\overline{AC}$ and $\overline{BD}$ bisect each other.
    Prove: $\overline{AB} \cong \overline{DC}$
16. **Given:** E is the midpoint of $\overline{AC}$.
    $\angle 1 \cong \angle 2$
    Prove: $\angle 3 \cong \angle 4$

4–5 Use the figure at the right to prove each of the following.

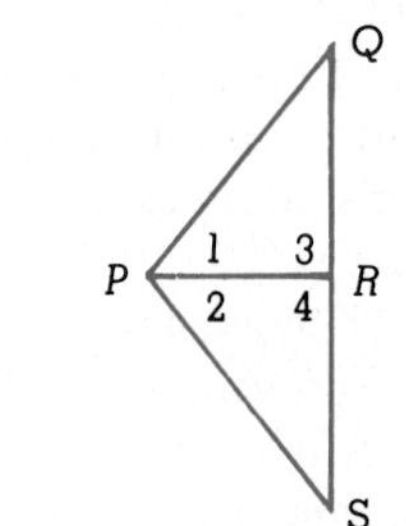

17. **Given:** $\overline{PR} \perp \overline{QS}$
    $\angle Q \cong \angle S$
    Prove: R is the midpoint of $\overline{QS}$.
18. **Given:** $\overline{PQ} \cong \overline{PS}$
    $\overline{PR}$ bisects $\overline{QS}$.
    Prove: $\angle 1 \cong \angle 2$

4–6 Use the figure at the right to prove each of the following.

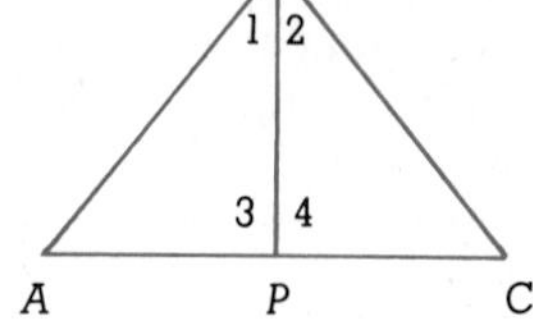

19. **Given:** $\overline{AB} \cong \overline{CB}$
    $\overline{BP}$ bisects $\angle ABC$.
    Prove: $\overline{BP}$ is a median of $\triangle ABC$.
20. **Given:** $\overline{BC} \cong \overline{BA}$
    $\overline{BP}$ is a median of $\triangle ABC$.
    Prove: $\overline{BP}$ is an altitude of $\triangle ABC$.

4–7 Complete a proof for the following.

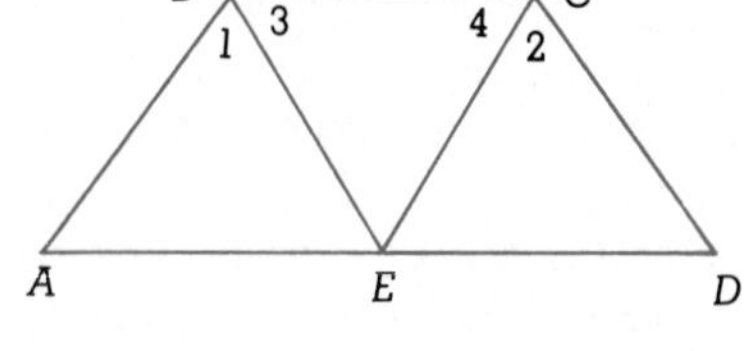

21. **Given:** $\angle A \cong \angle D$
    $\overline{AB} \cong \overline{DC}$
    E is the midpoint of $\overline{AD}$.
    Prove: $\angle 3 \cong \angle 4$.

4–8 22. **Given:** $\angle A$ and $\angle C$ are right angles.
    $\angle 2 \cong \angle 4$
    Prove: $\overline{AB} \cong \overline{DC}$

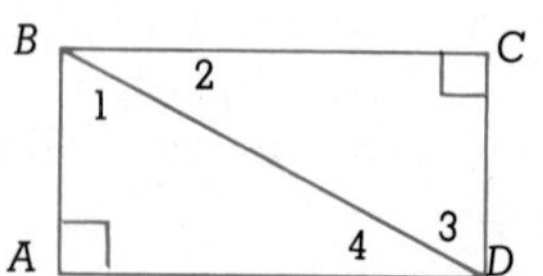

Chapter Test

Use the figure to answer each of the following.

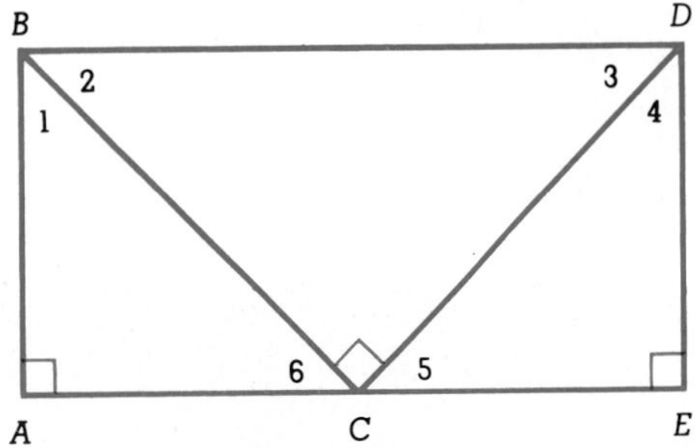

Exercises 1–5

1. Name the triangle with A as one vertex. $\triangle$ ABC
2. Name the right angle in $\triangle DCE$. $\angle$ E
3. Suppose $\triangle BAC \cong \triangle CED$. Name the part of $\triangle CED$ that is congruent to $\angle 1$. $\angle 5$
4. Suppose $\triangle BCD$ is isosceles, with $\overline{BC} \cong \overline{DC}$. If $BC = 2x - 5$ and $DC = x + 3$, find the value of x. x = 8
5. Suppose C is the midpoint of $\overline{AE}$, $\overline{BC}$ is congruent to $\overline{DC}$, and $\angle BDE$ is a right angle. If $m\angle 4 = 57$, find $m\angle 6$. $m\angle 6 = 33$

Determine whether or *not* each of the following represents a test for congruent triangles. Write yes or *no*.

6. HA yes
7. SSS yes
8. AA no
9. ASA yes
10. HL yes
11. AAA no
12. AAS yes
13. SSA no
14. LA yes
15. LL yes

For answers to exercises 16-18, see the Teacher's Guide.

Prove each of the following.

16. **Given:** $\triangle ABC$ is equilateral.
$\angle 1 \cong \angle 6$
$\angle 2 \cong \angle 3$
$\angle 4 \cong \angle 5$
Prove: $\overline{AD} \cong \overline{CD}$

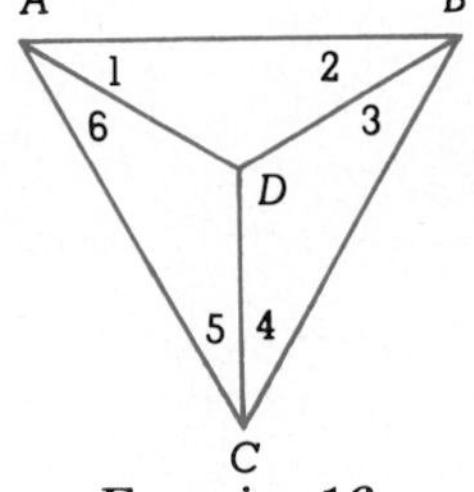

Exercise 16

17. **Given:** $\angle L$ and $\angle N$ are right angles.
$\overline{LP} \cong \overline{NM}$
Prove: $\overline{LM} \cong \overline{NP}$

18. **Given:** $\angle L$ and $\angle N$ are right angles.
$\overline{LM} \cong \overline{NP}$
Prove: $\angle LMN$ is a right angle.

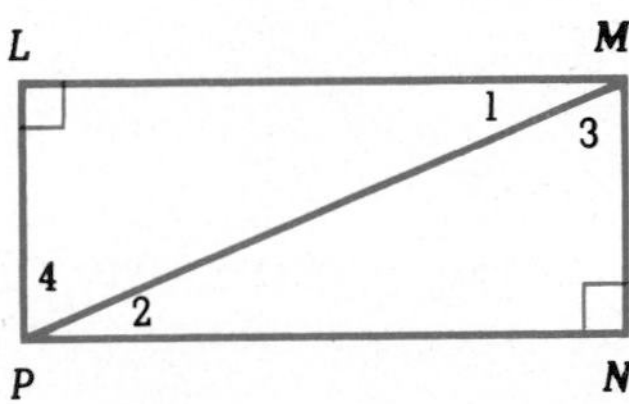

Exercises 17 and 18

chapter 5 Triangle Inequalities

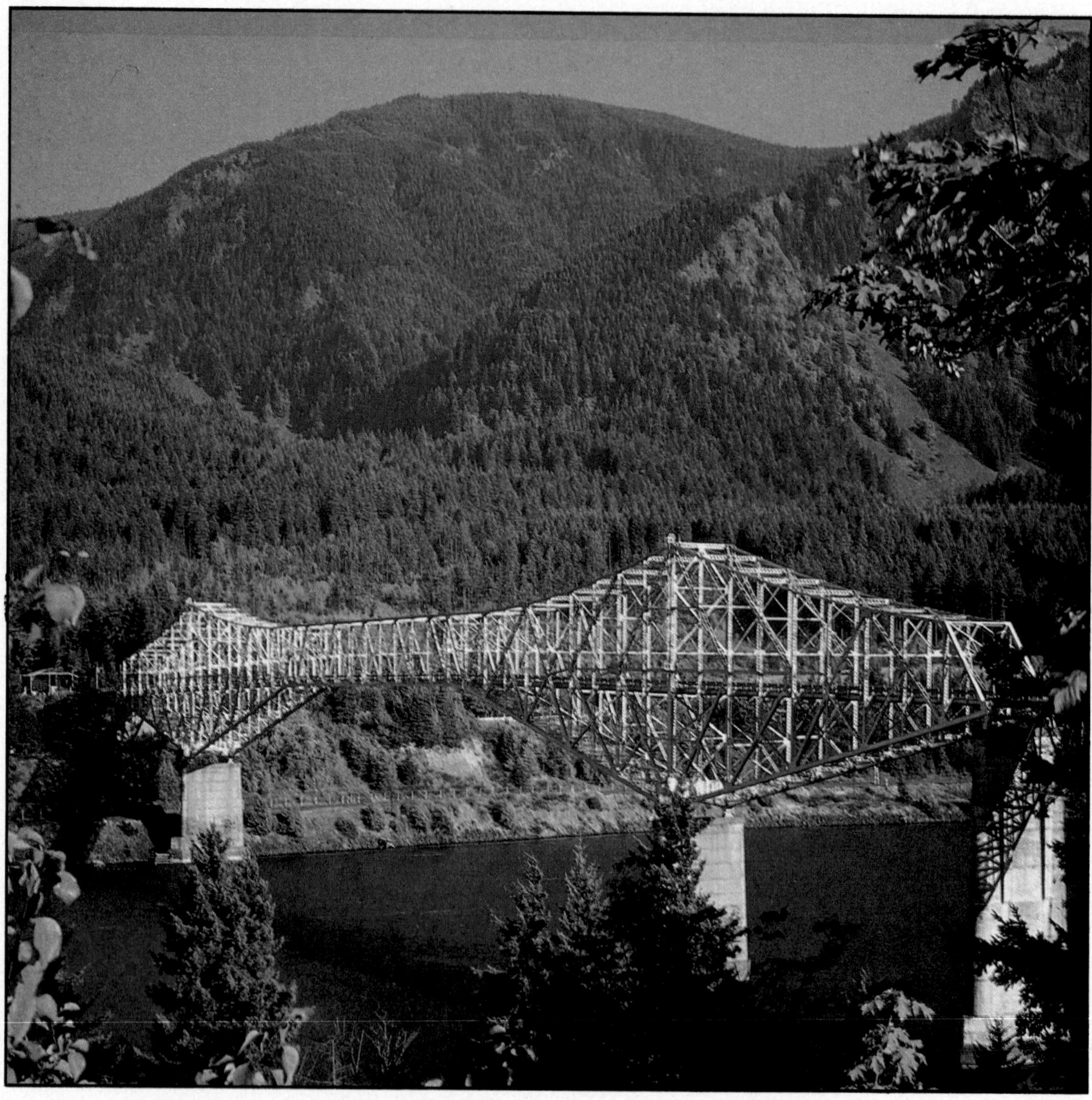

Many structures use triangular shapes. Triangles can be used to compare distances or to determine the shortest path from one point to another.

Objectives: to write inequalities relating the interior and exterior angles of triangles, to use inequality and exterior angle theorems in proofs

5–1 Exterior Angles

In the figure below, $\angle 1$ is an **exterior angle** of $\triangle PQR$.

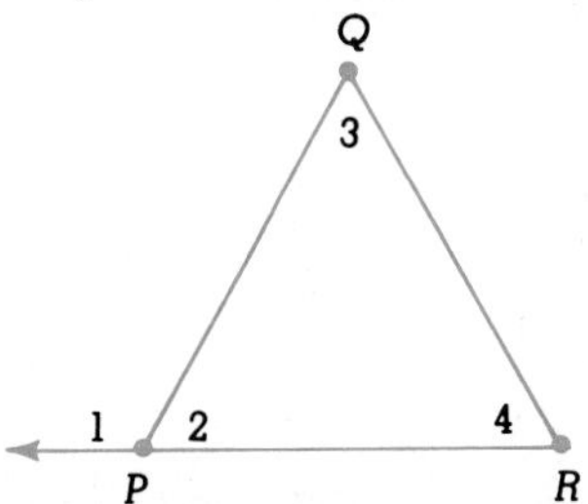

An angle is an exterior angle of a triangle if and only if it forms a linear pair with one of the angles of the triangle.

Definition of Exterior Angle of a Triangle

Notice that $\angle 1$ and $\angle 2$ are adjacent angles and form a linear pair. The other angles of the triangle are not adjacent to $\angle 1$. These two angles, $\angle 3$ and $\angle 4$, are called **remote interior angles** with respect to $\angle 1$.

An exterior angle is not vertical to an angle of a triangle.

There are two exterior angles at each vertex. $\angle 1$ and $\angle 5$ are the exterior angles at vertex P. There are a total of six exterior angles for a given triangle.

Be aware that some students may want to associate exterior angles of a triangle with the concept of vertical angles.

Exterior Angle	Remote Interior Angles
$\angle 1$	$\angle Q$ and $\angle R$
$\angle 5$	$\angle Q$ and $\angle R$
$\angle 6$	$\angle P$ and $\angle R$
$\angle 7$	$\angle P$ and $\angle R$
$\angle 8$	$\angle P$ and $\angle Q$
$\angle 9$	$\angle P$ and $\angle Q$

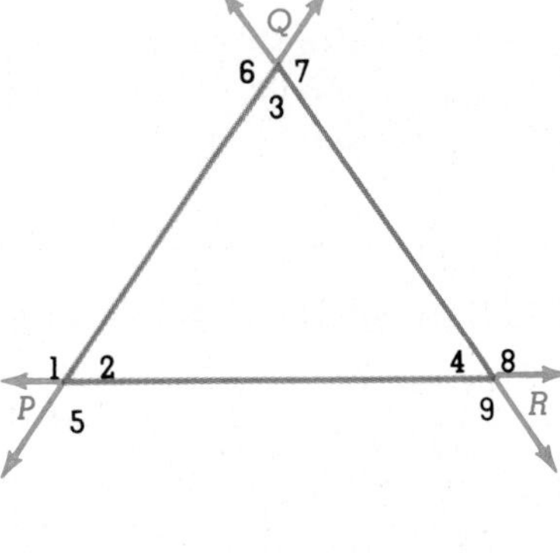

By Postulate 3–4, the angles in a linear pair are supplementary. Thus, the measure of an exterior angle of a triangle is related to the measures of the remote interior angles.

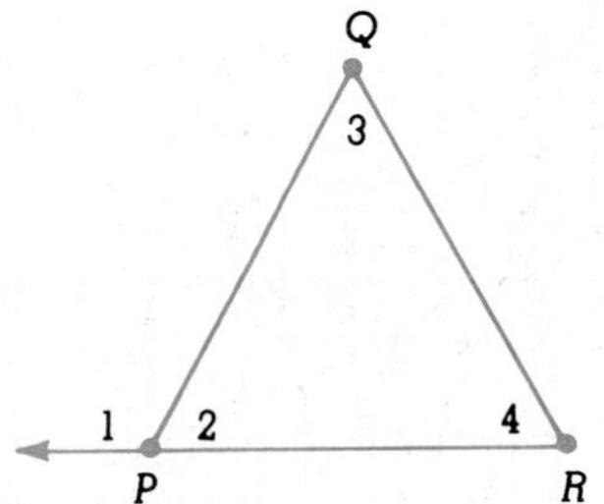

$m\angle 1 + m\angle 2 = 180$	*The angles in a linear pair are supplementary.*
$m\angle 2 + m\angle 3 + m\angle 4 = 180$	*Angle Sum Theorem*
$m\angle 1 + m\angle 2 = m\angle 2 + m\angle 3 + m\angle 4$	*Substitution*
$m\angle 1 = m\angle 3 + m\angle 4$	*Subtraction Property of Equality*

If an angle is an exterior angle of a triangle, then its measure is equal to the sum of the measures of the two remote interior angles.

Theorem 5–1
Exterior Angle Theorem

Students prove Theorem 5-1 in Written exercise 19.

example

1 **Use the information from the figure to find values for x, y, and z.**

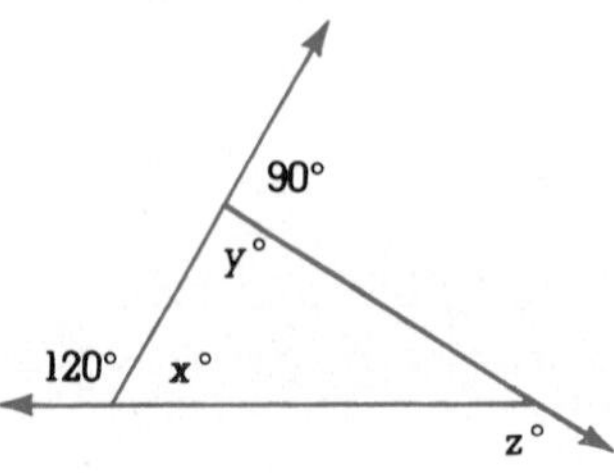

$$120 + x = 180 \qquad 90 + y = 180 \qquad z = x + y$$
$$x = 60 \qquad y = 90 \qquad = 60 + 90$$
$$= 150$$

This lesson provides the opportunity to review concepts of inequalities as dictated by class needs.

The following theorem is a direct result of the inequality properties. It is useful in proofs involving inequalities.

The Inequality Theorem could be used as a definition for inequality.

For any numbers a and b, $a > b$ if and only if there is a positive number c such that $a = b + c$.

Theorem 5–2
Inequality Theorem

Both parts of Theorem 5-2 are proved in Written exercises 20-21.

example

2 **Write an inequality that relates only x and y if $y + 10 = x + 19$.**

$$y + 10 = x + 19$$
$$y + 10 - 10 = x + 19 - 10$$
$$y = x + 9$$

Therefore, $y > x$.

The Inequality Theorem leads to the following theorem concerning triangles and the measures of their angles.

If an angle is an exterior angle of a triangle, then its measure is greater than the measure of either remote interior angle.

Theorem 5–3

 This theorem also can be proved indirectly (see Chapter 6).

example

3 Prove Theorem 5–3.

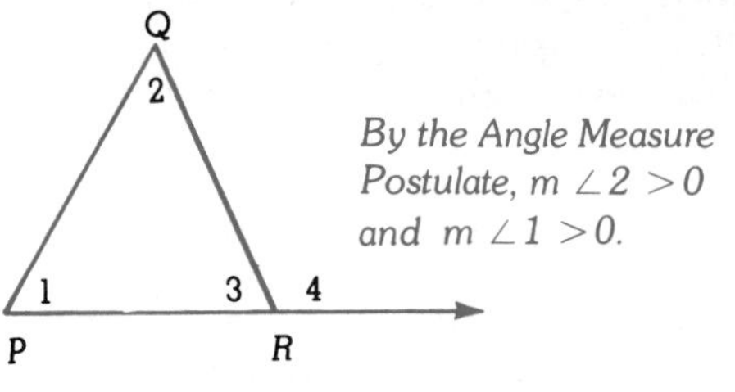

By the Angle Measure Postulate, $m\angle 2 > 0$ and $m\angle 1 > 0$.

Given: $\angle 4$ is an exterior angle of $\triangle PQR$.
Prove: $m\angle 4 > m\angle 1$
$m\angle 4 > m\angle 2$

Proof:

STATEMENTS	REASONS
1. $\angle 4$ is an exterior angle of $\triangle PQR$.	1. Given
2. $m\angle 4 = m\angle 1 + m\angle 2$	2. Theorem 5–1: Exterior Angle Theorem
3. $m\angle 4 > m\angle 1$ $m\angle 4 > m\angle 2$	3. Theorem 5–2: Inequality Theorem

Show students how the statements in step 3 follow from the Inequality Theorem.

EN: Ex: 1, 3, 9, 11, 17, 23, Wr: 2-22 evens; AV: Ex: 1-21 odds, Wr: 1-23 odds;

exercises

FN: Ex: 1-24, Wr: 1-23 odds

Exploratory **For each of the following write an inequality that relates only *x* and *y*.**

1. $x = 45 + y$ x > y
2. $x - y = 25$ x > y
3. $180 - x = 53 - y$ x > y
4. $75 - y = 180 - x$ x > y
5. $x + 30 = y$ x < y
6. $60 + 45 + x = 180 + y$ x > y
7. $46 + x + 89 = 91 + y$ x < y
8. $y + 85 = x$ x > y

For each of the following, write an inequality that relates only $m\angle 1$ and $m\angle 2$.

9. $m\angle 1 = 180 + m\angle 2$ m∠1 > m∠2
10. $m\angle 1 = 46 + m\angle 2$ m∠1 > m∠2
11. $55 + m\angle 1 = m\angle 2$ m∠1 < m∠2
12. $25 + 30 + m\angle 1 = m\angle 2$ m∠1 < m∠2
13. $180 - m\angle 1 = 55 + 70 - m\angle 2$ m∠1 > m∠2
14. $180 + m\angle 1 - 91 = m\angle 2 - 46$ m∠1 < m∠2
15. $m\angle 1 = m\angle 2 + m\angle 3 + m\angle 4$ m∠1 > m∠2
16. $m\angle 1 + m\angle 3 = m\angle 2 - m\angle 4$ m∠2 > m∠1

For each of the following, find the value of *x*.

17. x = 33

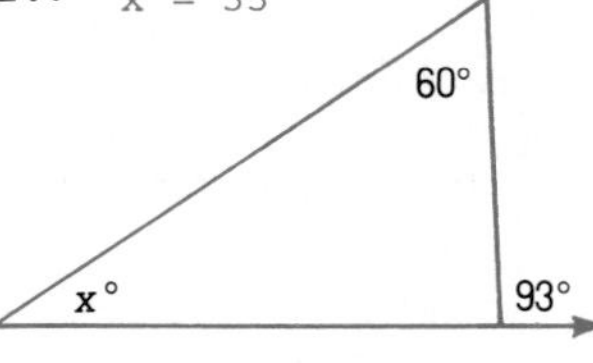

18. x = 79

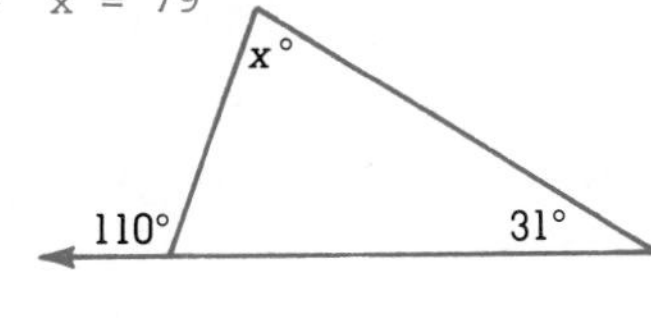

19. x = 30

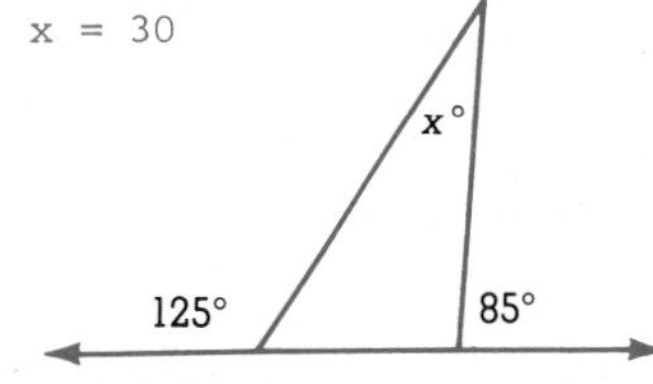

20. x = 50

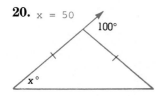

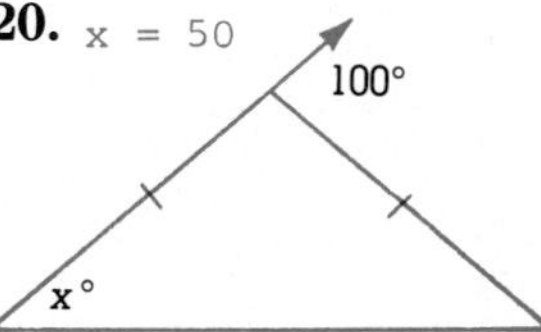

21. x = 120

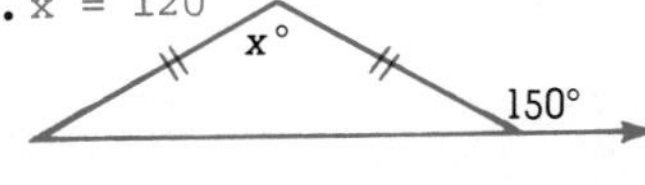

22. x = 114

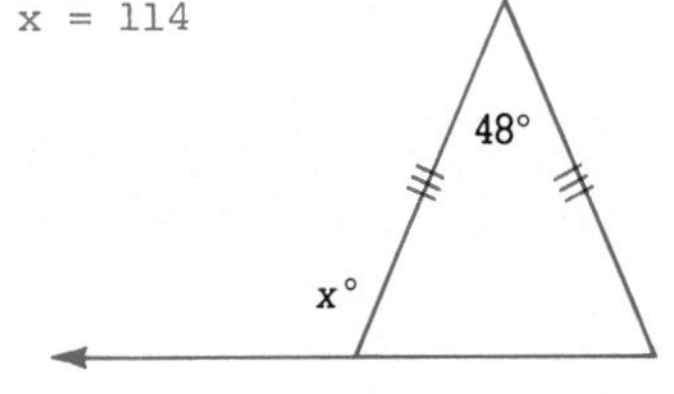

23. x = 53

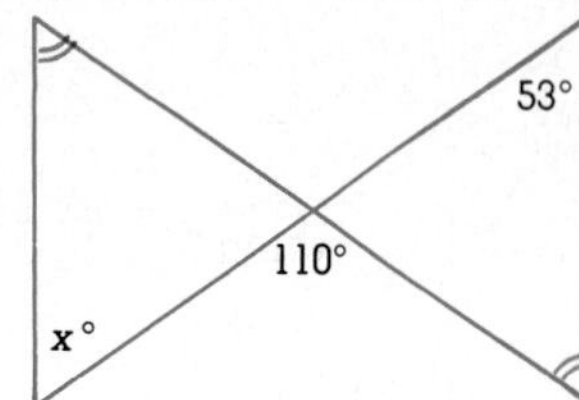

24. x = 60

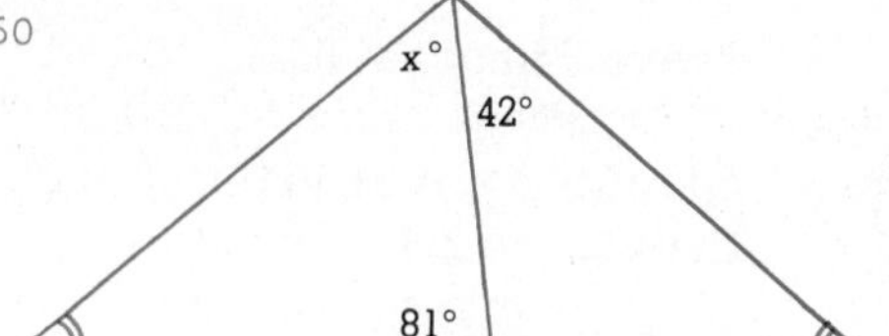

Written **Use the information given in the figure to find the value of each of the following.**

1. x	40	**2.** y	80
3. z	100	**4.** w	80
5. t	20	**6.** s	120
7. v	30	**8.** r	30

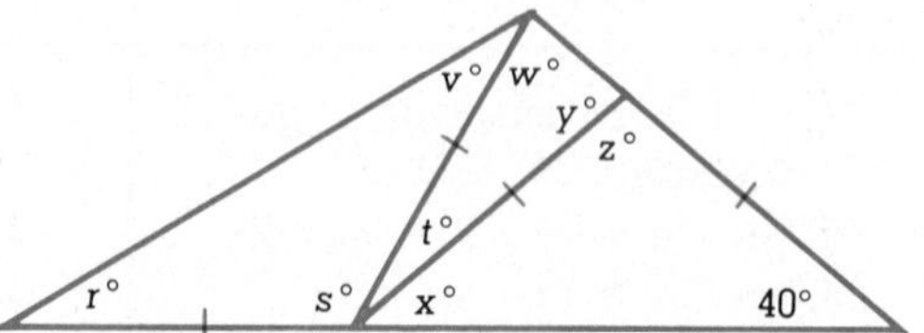

Use the information given in the figure to find the value of each of the following.

9. x	55	**10.** z	125
11. y	70	**12.** w	25
13. t	125	**14.** v	30

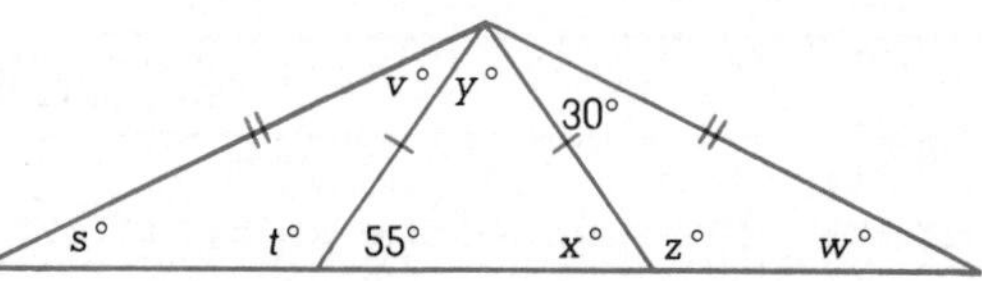

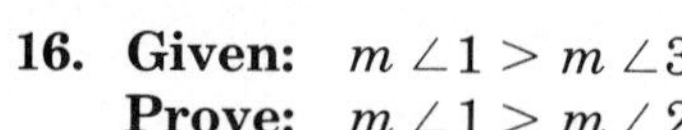

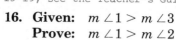

Prove the following. For answers to exercises 15-19, see the Teacher's Guide.

15. Given: $\angle 1 \cong \angle 2$
Prove: $\triangle PQR$ is isosceles.

16. Given: $m\angle 1 > m\angle 3$
Prove: $m\angle 1 > m\angle 2$

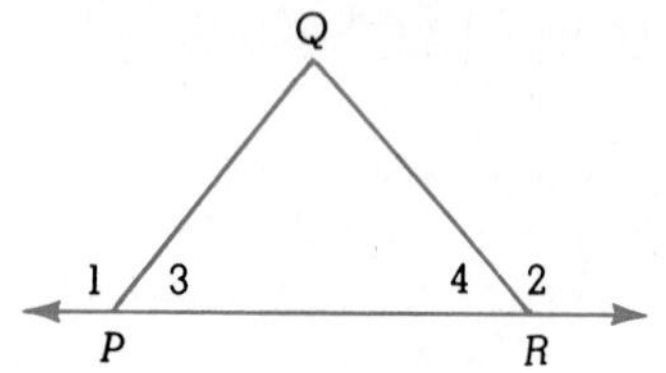

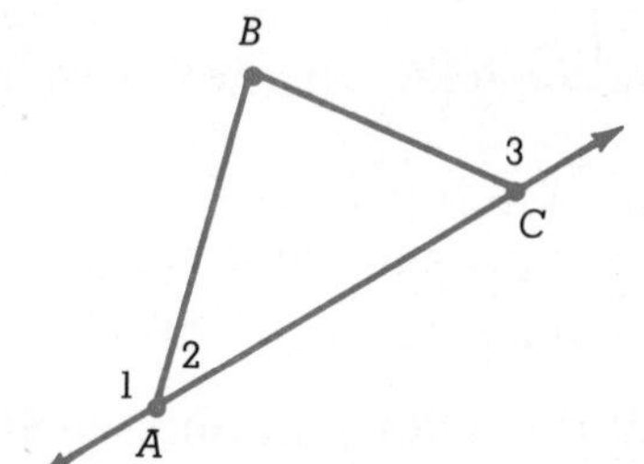

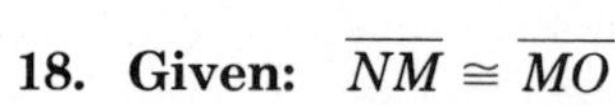

17. Given: P, Q and N are collinear.
Prove: $m\angle 1 > m\angle 3$

18. Given: $\overline{NM} \cong \overline{MO}$
N, O, and K are collinear.
N, M, and L are collinear.
Prove: $m\angle 1 > m\angle 2$

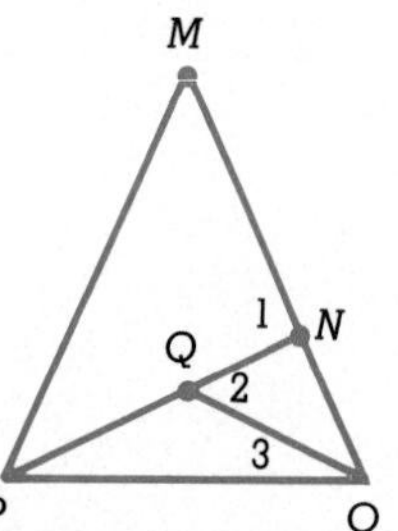

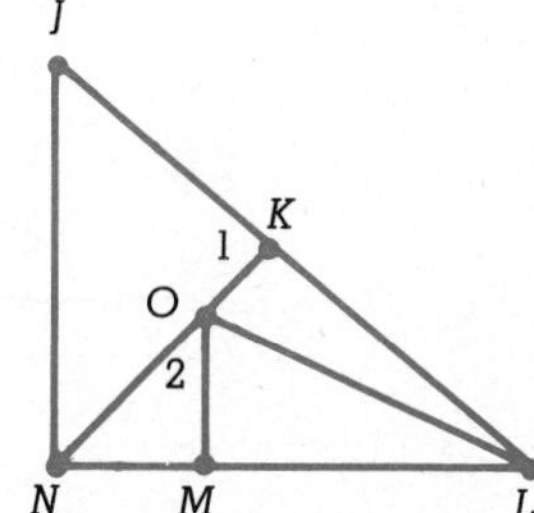

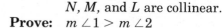

19. Prove Theorem 5–1.

20. Supply the reasons for the following proof.

Theorem: For any numbers a and b, if there is a positive number c such that $a = b + c$, then $a > b$.

Given: $c > 0$ and $a = b + c$
Prove: $a > b$ Exercises 20-21 together illustrate a proof of Theorem 5-2.

Proof:

STATEMENTS	REASONS
1. $c > 0$ and $a = b + c$	1. Given
2. $a - b = c$	2. Subtraction Property of Equality
3. $a - b > 0$	3. Substitution
4. $a > b$	4. Addition Property of Inequality

21. Supply the reasons for the following proof.

Theorem: For any numbers a and b, if $a > b$, then there is a positive number c such that $a = b + c$.

Given: $a > b$
Prove: There is a c such that $c > 0$, and $a = b + c$, namely c is $a - b$.

Proof: Point out that statements of steps 2 and 7 together prove the theorem.

STATEMENTS	REASONS
1. $a > b$	1. Given
2. $a - b > 0$	2. Subtraction Property of Inequality
3. $a = a + 0$	3. Identity Property of Addition
4. $a = a + (b - b)$	4. Inverse Property of Addition, Substitution
5. $a = (a + b) - b$	5. Associative Property of Addition
6. $a = (b + a) - b$	6. Commutative Property of Addition
7. $a = b + (a - b)$	7. Associative Property of Addition

Prove each of the following. For answers to exercises 22-23, see the Teacher's Guide.

22. Given: $b = x + c$
Prove: $y > x$

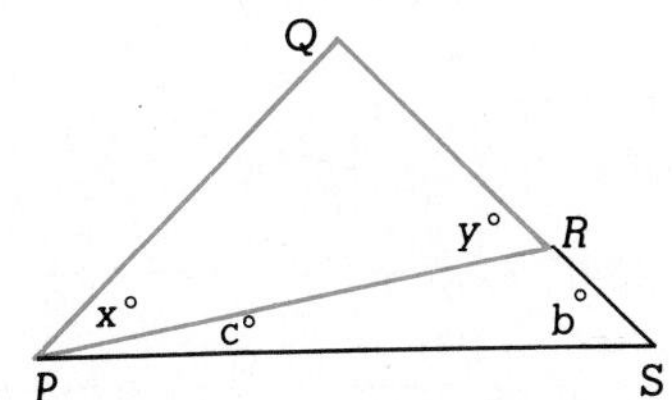

23. Given: $\overline{PQ} \cong \overline{PS}$
Prove: $m \angle SQR > m \angle 2$

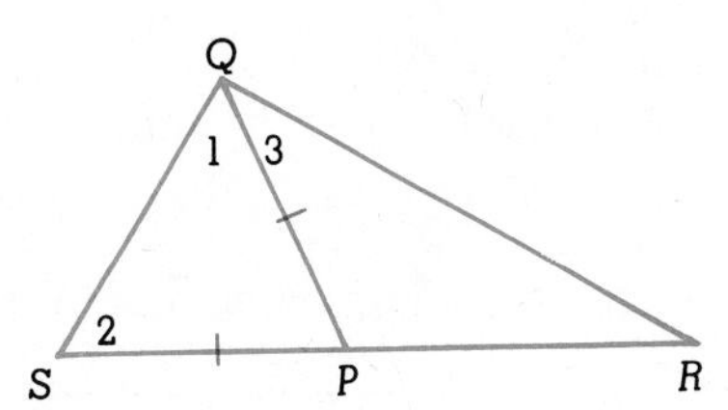

5–2 Using Diagrams

Objectives: to recognize information which can and cannot be assumed from a diagram, to effectively use diagrams in writing proofs

Diagrams help state given information. They may be used to show any of the following.

Existence

When points, lines, rays, angles, triangles, and so on appear on a figure, you may *assume* they exist.

These assumptions shorten the number of steps to a proof.

Relative Position

When points appear on a line or part of a line, you may *assume* they are collinear. Also, you may *assume* betweenness with respect to points on a line, and location with respect to half-planes, interiors, and exteriors. Adjacent angles and linear pairs are shown in figures, too.

Intersection

When lines, rays, or segments appear to intersect, you may *assume* that they do intersect.

Note that a strictly logical proof does not depend on a diagram. Such proofs use postulates, definitions, and previously defined theorems.

Diagrams are marked to give further information about congruence and measure. Such information normally is written in the given statements, if the diagram is with a proof.

DO *NOT* ASSUME *ANY* OF THE FOLLOWING UNLESS A FIGURE IS MARKED.

congruence
equality of measure
inequality of measure
bisectors or midpoints
perpendiculars or right angles
specific measures

The properties listed must be given or proven.

example

1 Which of the following statements can be assumed from the appearance of the figure?

1. V is between Q and T.
2. $\overline{PR}$ bisects $\angle QPS$.
3. $\overline{PT} \cong \overline{TS}$
4. $\overline{PR}$ bisects $\overline{QS}$.
5. $\overline{QR} \cong \overline{RS}$
6. $\overline{QT} \perp \overline{PS}$
7. $\angle QRV$ is a right angle.
8. $\angle ATP$ and $\angle QTS$ form a linear pair.

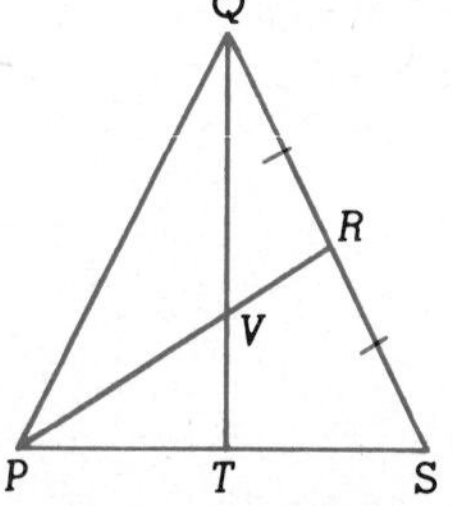

The statements **1, 4, 5,** and **8** can be assumed.

Often, a geometric proof shows that parts of a figure are congruent. One method of proving parts congruent is to show they are corresponding parts of congruent triangles. Thus, the problem becomes one of locating two triangles that contain the parts and then proving that the triangles are congruent. For example, consider the following.

Given: $\overline{RP} \cong \overline{RT}$
$\overline{RQ} \cong \overline{RS}$
Prove: $\overline{PS} \cong \overline{TQ}$

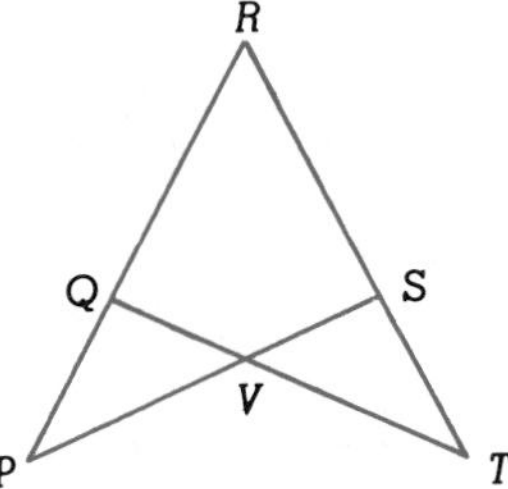

Altogether there are four triangles in the figure. To see the overlapping triangles in the diagram, it is helpful to outline the separate triangles in different colors.

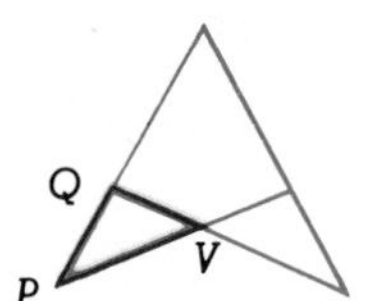

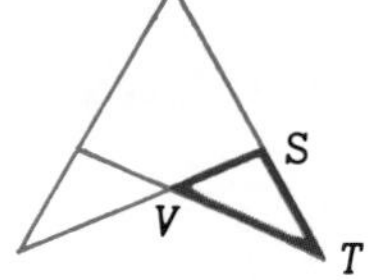

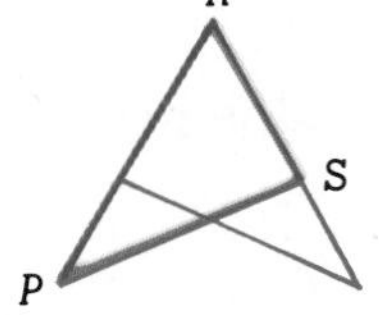

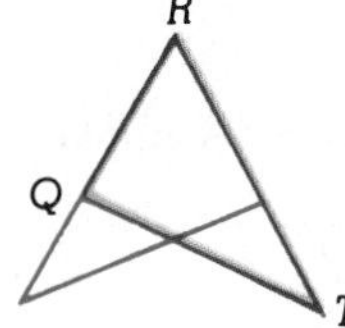

These concepts can be reinforced with the use of paper cutouts and/or chalkboard diagrams.

Another way to see the triangles is to draw them separately. Keep in mind the given statements and the assumptions that can be made from the original diagram.

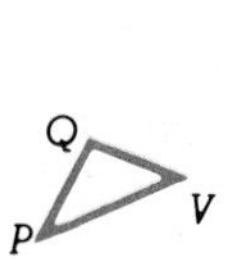

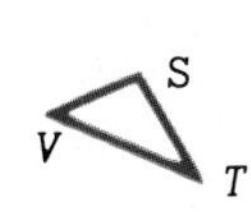

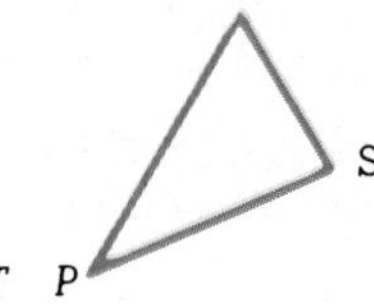

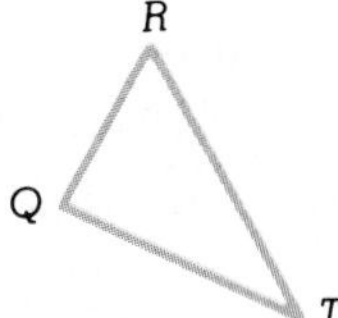

When redrawing triangles make sure they are labeled correctly and in the same position.

Two overlapping triangles, $\triangle PSR$ and $\triangle TQR$, contain the corresponding parts $\overline{PS}$ and $\overline{TQ}$.

To complete the proof, show that $\triangle PSR \cong \triangle TQR$ by using SAS. Then, conclude $\overline{PS} \cong \overline{TQ}$ since they are corresponding parts of congruent triangles.

CPCTC

examples

2 **Name two triangles that can be used to prove the following.**

Given: $\overline{QP} \perp \overline{PT}$
$\overline{ST} \perp \overline{PT}$
$\angle Q \cong \angle S$
Prove: $\overline{PR} \cong \overline{TR}$

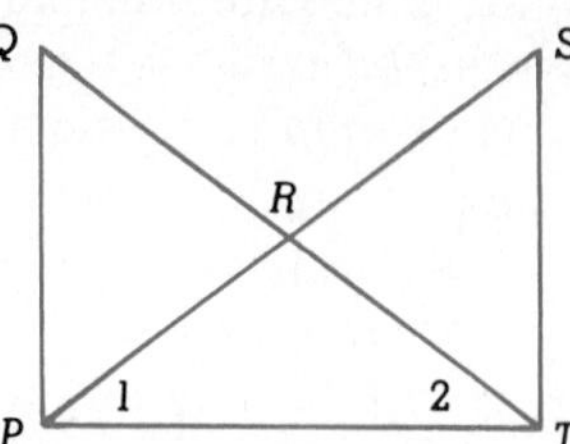

One way of completing the proof is to first show $\angle 1$ and $\angle 2$ are corresponding parts of congruent triangles and then use the converse of the Isosceles Triangle Theorem.

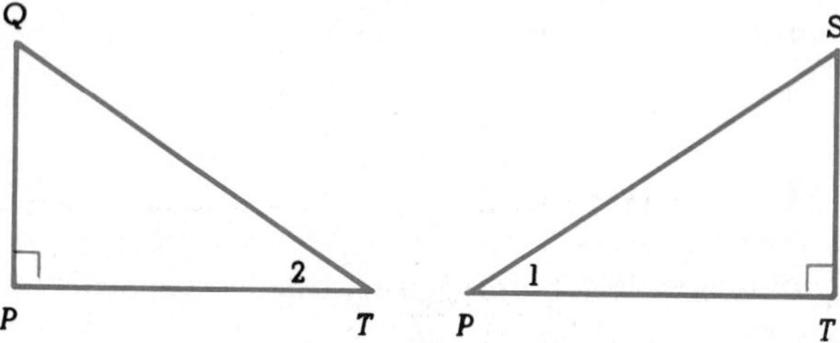

$\triangle TQP$ and $\triangle PST$ are right triangles that are congruent by LA. $\triangle TQP$ contains $\angle 2$ and $\triangle PST$ contains $\angle 1$.

3 **Name two triangles that can be used in proving the following.**

Given: $\overline{PQ} \cong \overline{SQ}$
Prove: $m\angle 2 > m\angle 1$

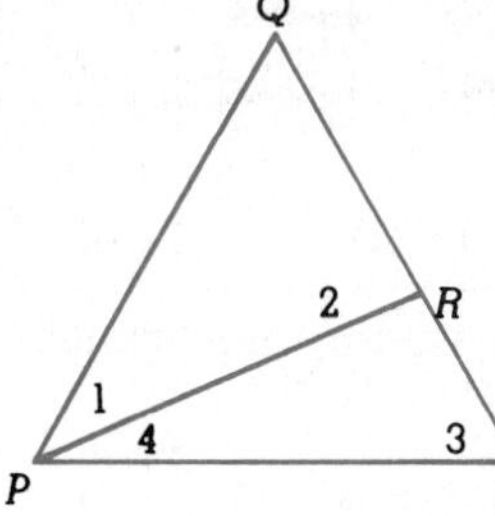

$\triangle PQS$ is a triangle that can be used to prove $m\angle 3 = m\angle 1 + m\angle 4$ since $\overline{PQ} \cong \overline{SQ}$.

$\triangle PRS$ is the triangle that can be used to prove $m\angle 2 = m\angle 4 + m\angle 3$ by using an exterior angle and remote interior angles.

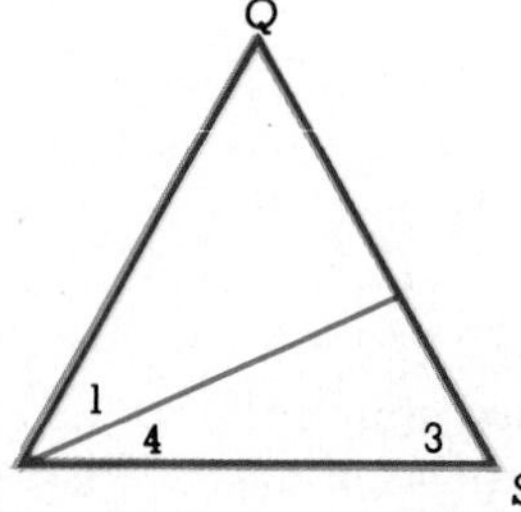

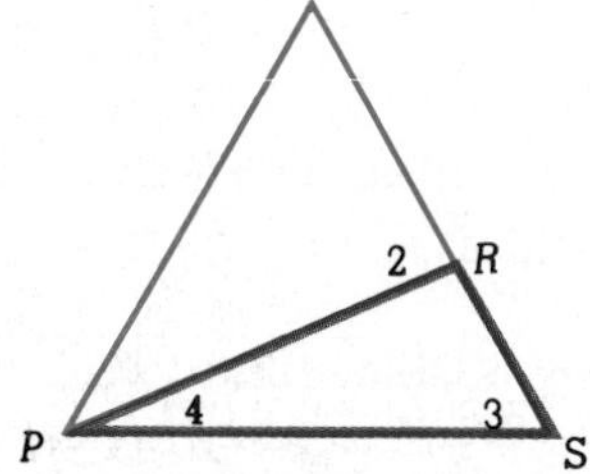

EN: Ex: 2-26 evens, Wr: 14-28 evens; AV: Ex: 1-27 odds, Wr: 1-27 odds;
pp. 144-145, Wr: 16-22 evens

exercises

Exploratory **Determine whether or *not* each of the following may be assumed from a diagram.**

1. adjacent angles yes
2. existence of a point yes
3. congruent segments no
4. perpendicular lines no
5. equality of distance measure no
6. intersection of rays yes
7. existence of a ray yes
8. perpendicular rays no
9. existence of a triangle yes
10. collinearity of segments yes
11. linear pair yes
12. vertical angles yes
13. intersection of lines yes
14. perpendicular segments no
15. right angles no

Using the figure, determine whether or *not* the following statements can be assumed.

16. $\angle PST$ and $\angle RST$ form a linear pair. yes
17. $\overline{QR} \perp \overline{PV}$ no
18. $RV + VQ = RQ$ yes
19. T is between P and V. yes
20. $\angle SPT$ and $\angle VQT$ are congruent. no
21. $\overline{PS} \cong \overline{QV}$ no
22. $\overline{PT} \cong \overline{QT}$ yes
23. $PV = TV + PT$ yes
24. $\angle QVT$ is a right angle. no
25. $\angle PTS$ is adjacent to $\angle STV$. yes
26. $\overline{PV}$ bisects $\overline{QS}$. no
27. T is the midpoint of $\overline{PV}$. no

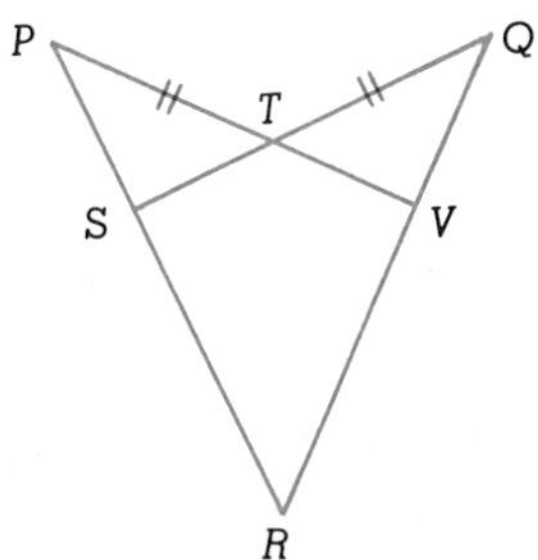

FN: Ex: 1-27, Wr: 1-26; pp. 144-145, Wr: 10-20 evens; p. 151, C: 1-6

Written **Determine whether or *not* each of the following can be assumed from a diagram. If the answer is sometimes, draw diagrams to show when it can be assumed and when it cannot be assumed.**

1. angle bisectors sometimes
2. existence of a line yes
3. betweenness of points yes
4. equality of angle measure sometimes
5. intersection of a line and a ray yes
6. inequality of distance measure sometimes
7. collinearity of points yes
8. congruent triangles sometimes
9. congruent angles sometimes
10. existence of segments yes
11. bisector of segments sometimes
12. existence of an angle yes

Using the figure, answer each of the following.

13. Which angles can be assumed to be congruent? $\angle 9$, $\angle 8$ and $\angle 8$, $\angle 7$
14. Can we assume $m\angle 7 + m\angle 6 = 180$? yes
15. Which sides can be assumed to be congruent? $\overline{BE}$, $\overline{CE}$
16. Can we assume A, E, and D are collinear? yes
17. Can we assume $m\angle 2 = m\angle 4$? no
18. Can we assume B, C, and D exist? yes
19. Can we assume F is in the interior of $\triangle BEC$? no
20. Can we assume F is in the interior of $\triangle ABD$? yes

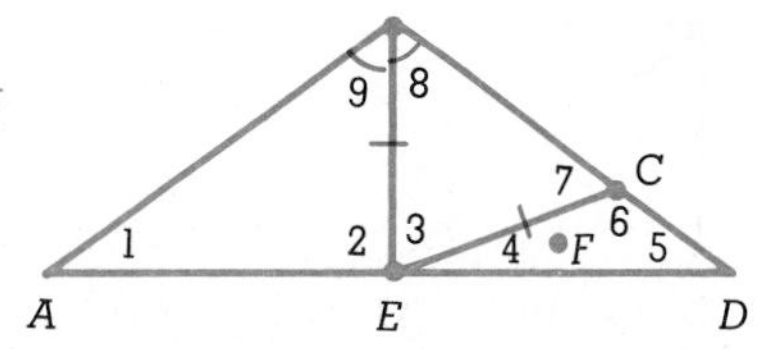

21. △ ABC, △ ACE, △ CDE, △ ABE, △ ADE

24. △ WXZ, △ TXZ, △ TYZ, △ XYZ, △ WXY

Name all the triangles contained in each of the following figures.

21.

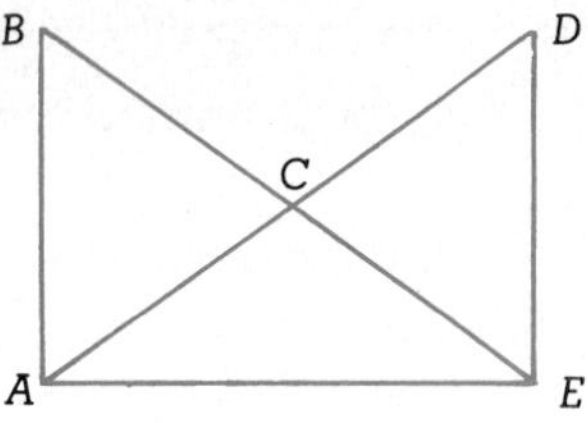

22.

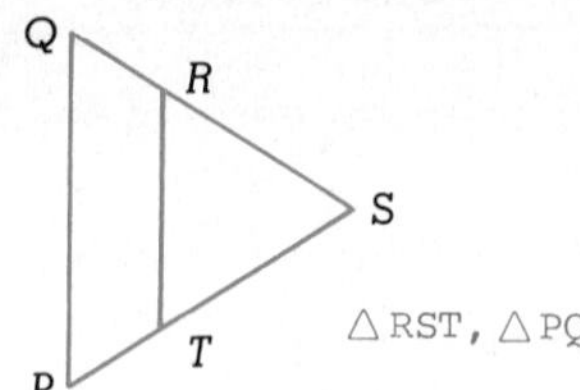

△ RST, △ PQS

23.

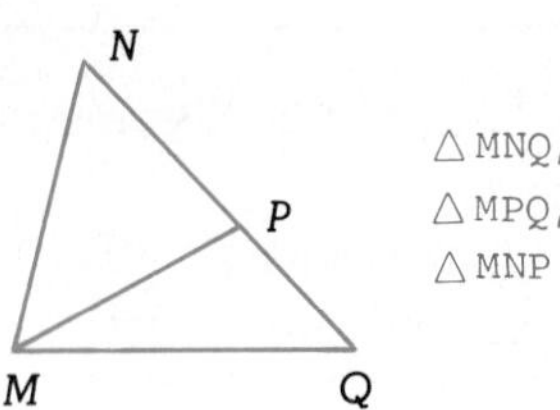

△ MNQ,
△ MPQ,
△ MNP

24.

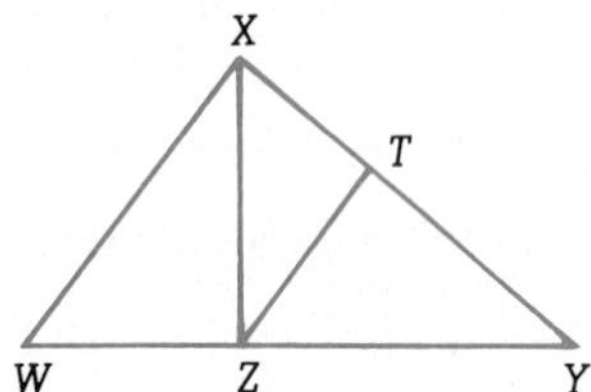

25.

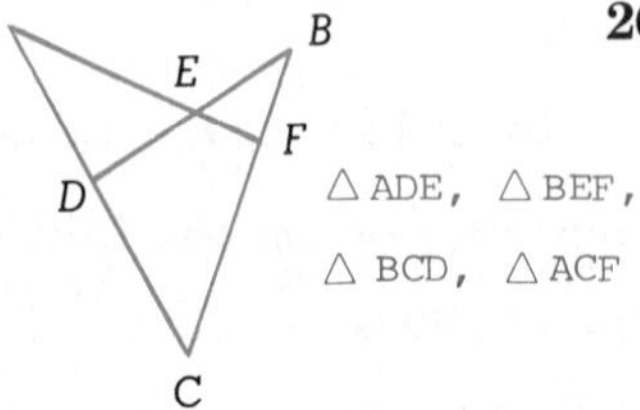

△ ADE, △ BEF,
△ BCD, △ ACF

26.

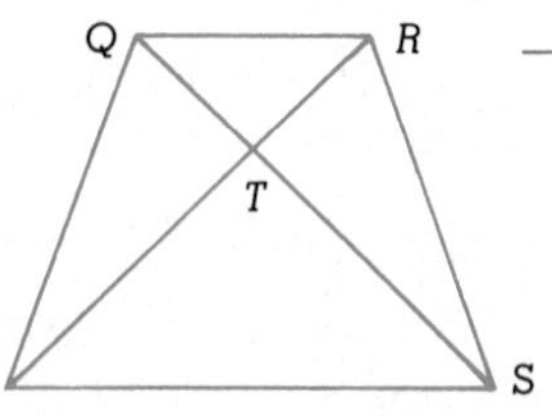

27. Identify the triangles used in Reasons **2** and **4** of the following proof.

Step 2: △ QSR
Step 4: △ QPS

Given: $\overline{QS} \cong \overline{QR}$
Prove: $m\angle 3 > m\angle 1$

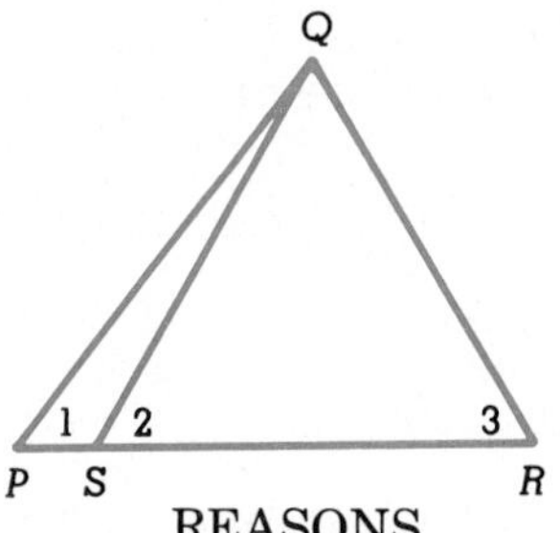

Proof:

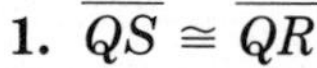

STATEMENTS	REASONS
1. $\overline{QS} \cong \overline{QR}$	**1.** Given
2. $\angle 3 \cong \angle 2$	**2.** Theorem 4–6: Isosceles Triangle Theorem
3. $m\angle 3 = m\angle 2$	**3.** Definition of Congruent Angles
4. $m\angle 2 > m\angle 1$	**4.** Theorem 5–3: If an angle is an exterior angle of a triangle, then its measure is greater than the measure of either remote interior angle.
5. $m\angle 3 > m\angle 1$	**5.** Postulate 2–9: Substitution

Prove each of the following. For answers to exercises 28-29, see the Teacher's Guide.

28. Given: $\overline{PM} \cong \overline{QO}$
$\angle MPQ \cong \angle OQP$
Prove: $\overline{PN} \cong \overline{QN}$

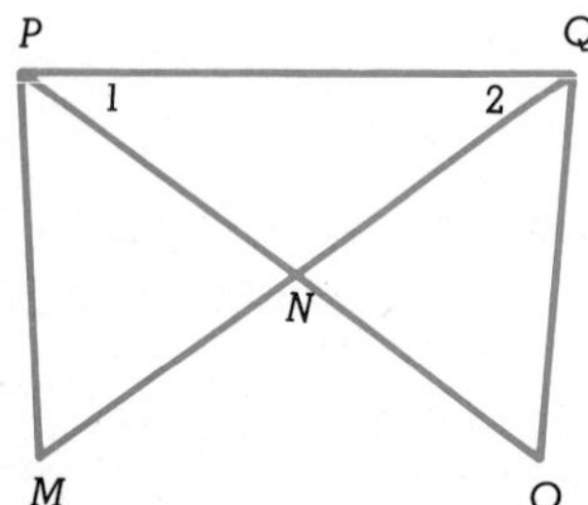

29. Given: $\overline{XW} \perp \overline{WZ}$, $\overline{YZ} \perp \overline{WZ}$
$\overline{XW} \cong \overline{YZ}$
Prove: $\overline{XP} \cong \overline{YP}$

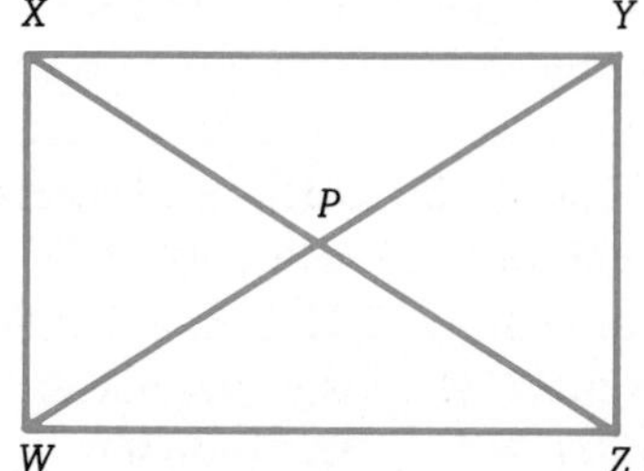

26. △ QRT, △ PST, △ QPT, △ RST, △ QSP, △ RPS, △ PQR, △ SRQ

careers

Architect

Martha Johnson is an architect. She designs a building so that it is attractive, safe, and functional. Martha considers the needs of the persons who will use the building. These needs include being warm in the winter and cool in the summer. For heating and cooling, she can use solar collectors. These devices collect energy from the sun. The outer structure of the building is designed to catch the sun's rays. Some collectors are tilted at a fixed angle to the sun. Other collectors move to follow the sun.

The fixed angle for a collector is determined from local latitude.

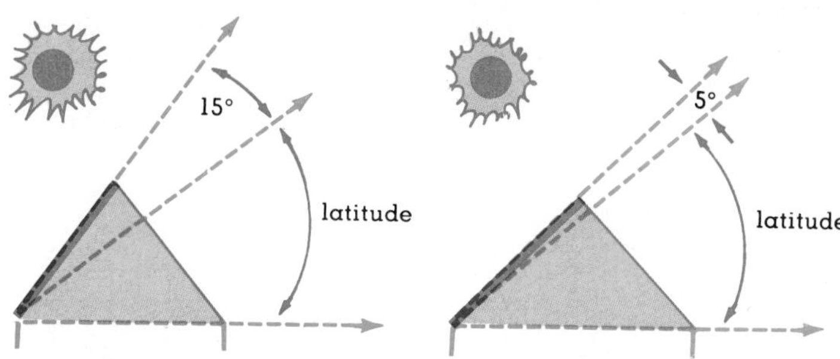

Albany, New York has a latitude of 42°. The collector heating angle and the heating and cooling angle are determined in the following way.

As a project, you may have students investigate this and other energy-saving techniques and the role of mathematics in energy.

heating angle = *latitude* + 15°
= 42° + 15°
= 57°

heating and cooling angle = *latitude* + 5°
= 42° + 5°
= 47°

Exercises Find the heating angle and the heating and cooling angle for the following locations with the given latitude.

1. Amarillo, Texas 35° 50°, 40°
2. Atlantic City, N.J. 39° 54°, 44°
3. Anchorage, Alaska 61° 76°, 66°
4. Austin, Nevada 39° 54°, 44°
5. Atlanta, Georgia 33° 48°, 38°
6. Baker, Oregon 44° 59°, 49°

Objectives: to recognize relationships between sides and angles of triangles and to use these relationships in proofs, to use theorems regarding the distance between a point and line in proofs

5–3 Sides and Angles

If two sides of a triangle are *not* congruent, then the angles opposite those sides are *not* congruent. The following diagram suggests how the sides and angles are related.

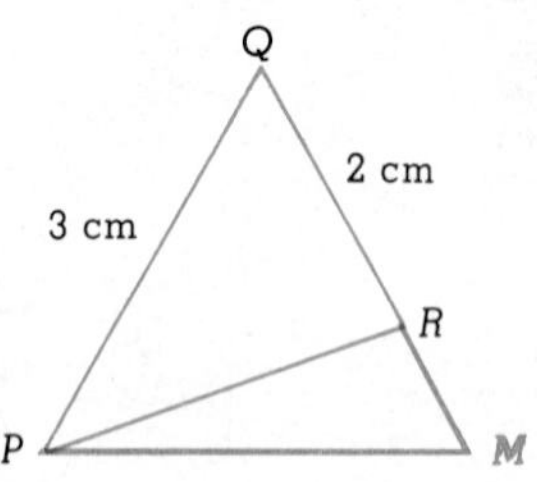

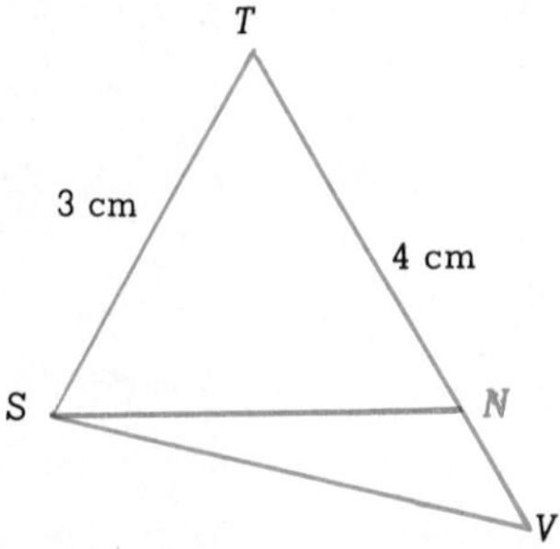

To help students make angle comparisons, $\triangle PQM$ and $\triangle STV$ are isosceles.

$PQ > RQ$
$m\angle QRP > m\angle QPR$

$ST < VT$
$m\angle TVS < m\angle TSV$

If the measures of two sides of a triangle are unequal, then the measures of the angles opposite those sides are unequal in the same order.

Theorem 5–4
The angle with the greater measure is opposite the side with the greater measure.

Theorem 5-4 is proved in Written exercise 1.

example

1 Plan a proof for Theorem 5–4.

Given: $\triangle PQR$
$PQ > RQ$
Prove: $m\angle 2 > m\angle 1$

Students may need help in identifying the triangles used and in finding the corresponding parts.

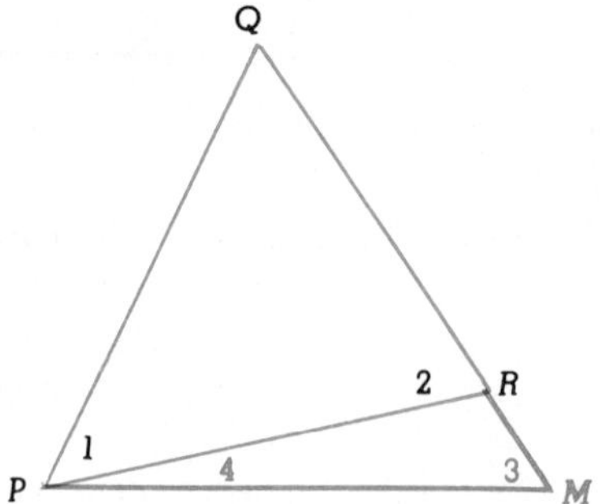

Extend $\overline{QR}$ to M so that $\overline{QM} \cong \overline{QP}$. The new triangle formed, $\triangle PQM$, is isosceles. Thus, the base angles are congruent. Using this information, show that $m\angle 1 + m\angle 4 = m\angle 3$.

Also, $m\angle 2 = m\angle 3 + m\angle 4$, since $\angle 2$ is an exterior angle of $\triangle PRM$. From substitution, conclude that $m\angle 2 = m\angle 1 + m\angle 4 + m\angle 4$. As a result, $m\angle 2 > m\angle 1$ by the Inequality Theorem. *By Postulate 3–1, $m\angle 4 + m\angle 4 > 0$.*

Suppose two angles of a triangle are not congruent. The figure shows such a situation. The sides opposite those angles can be related in exactly one of the following ways.

$m\angle P > m\angle R$
$QR \ ? \ QP$

$QR = QP$

If the two sides have equal measures, they are congruent. The triangle is isosceles and the two angles must be congruent, which is impossible.

$QR < QP$

According to Theorem 5–4, if two sides have unequal measures, then the measures of the angles opposite those sides are unequal in the same order. Thus, $m\angle P < m\angle R$, which is impossible.

$QR > QP$

The measures of the two sides must be related in this way, since the other two ways are impossible.

The reasoning leading to Theorem 5-5 is indirect. Students learn to write formal indirect proofs in Chapter 6.

If the measures of two angles of a triangle are unequal, then the measures of the sides opposite those angles are unequal in the same order.

Theorem 5–5
The side with the greater measure is opposite the angle with the greater

example

Illustrate Theorem 5-5 by drawing 25°-60°-95° and 30°-30°-120° triangles.

2 Prove that if a segment is the perpendicular segment from a point to a line, then it is the shortest segment.

Given: $\overline{PQ} \perp t$
$\overline{PR}$ is any other segment from P to t.
Prove: $PR > PQ$

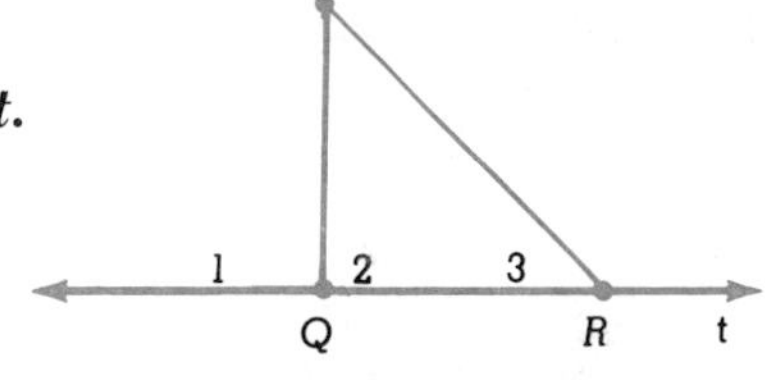

Proof:

STATEMENTS	REASONS
1. $\overline{PQ} \perp t$	**1.** Given
2. $\angle 1 \cong \angle 2$	**2.** Theorem 3–13: If two lines are perpendicular, then they form congruent adjacent angles.
3. $m\angle 1 = m\angle 2$	**3.** Definition of Congruent Angles
4. $m\angle 1 > m\angle 3$	**4.** Theorem 5–3: If an angle is an exterior angle of a triangle, then its measure is greater than the measure of either remote interior angle.
5. $m\angle 2 > m\angle 3$	**5.** Postulate 2–9: Substitution
6. $PR > PQ$	**6.** Theorem 5–5: If the measures of two angles of a triangle are unequal, then the measures of the sides opposite those angles are unequal in the same order.

The proofs of the following theorems are almost identical. One of the cases of Theorem 5–6 is proven in Example 2.

A physical model, such as a plumb line is helpful in illustrating these theorems.

A segment is the shortest segment from a point to a line if and only if it is the segment perpendicular to the line. *Theorem 5–6*

A segment is the shortest segment from a point to a plane if and only if it is the segment perpendicular to the plane. *Theorem 5–7*

EN: Ex: 1, 5, Wr: 2-8 evens; p. 151, C: 1-6; AV: Ex: 1-7 odds, Wr: 1-7 odds; p. 150, Wr: 22-28 evens; p. 151, C: 1-6

exercises

FN: Ex: 1-8, Wr: 1-7 odds; p. 150, Wr: 27-28; p. 155, EG: 1-6

Exploratory **For each of the following triangles, list the angles in order from the angle with the least measure to the angle with the greatest measure.**

1. ∠B, ∠A, ∠C

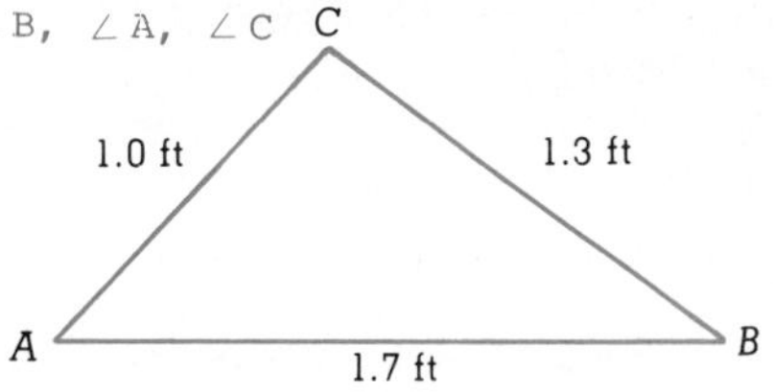

   C; A; B; 1.0 ft; 1.3 ft; 1.7 ft

2. ∠F, ∠E, ∠D

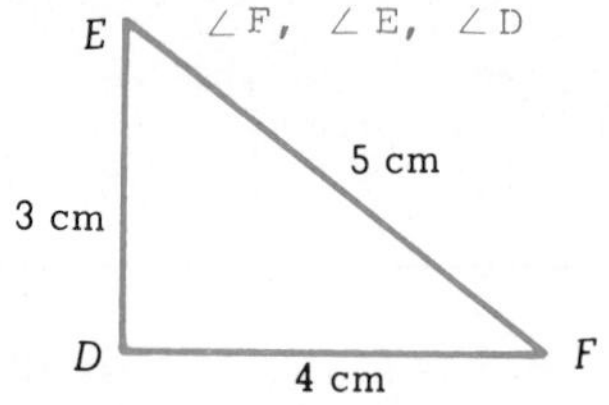

   E; D; F; 3 cm; 5 cm; 4 cm

3. ∠I, ∠G, ∠H

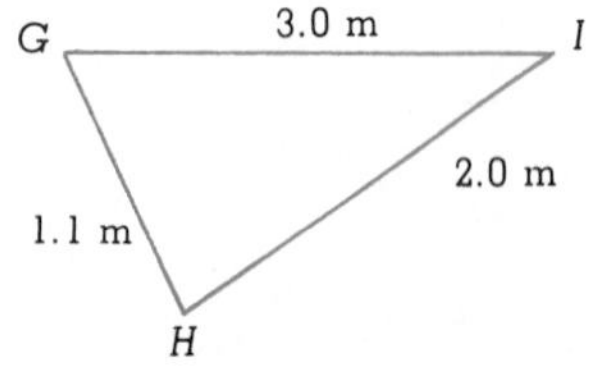

   G; I; H; 3.0 m; 2.0 m; 1.1 m

4. ∠M, ∠K, ∠L

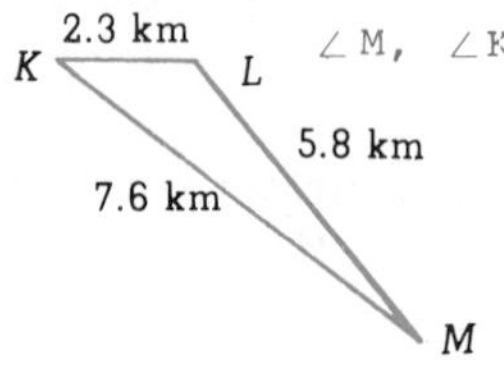

   K; L; M; 2.3 km; 5.8 km; 7.6 km

For each of the following triangles, list the sides in order from the side with the least measure to the side with the greatest measure.

5. $\overline{ML}$, $\overline{LN}$, $\overline{MN}$

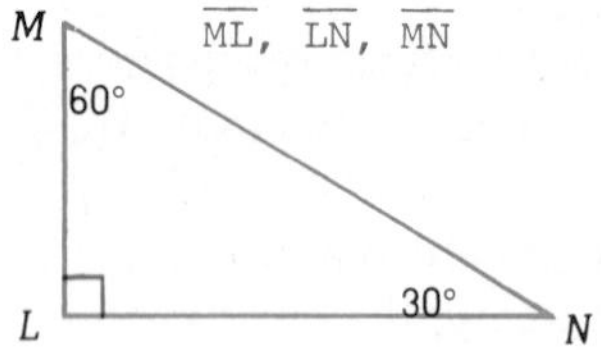

   M; L; N; 60°; 30°

6. $\overline{PR}$, $\overline{RQ}$, $\overline{PQ}$

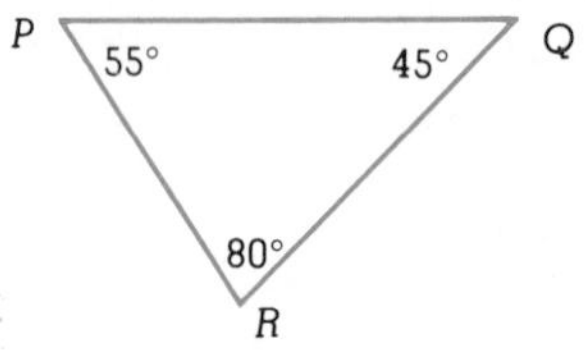

   P; Q; R; 55°; 45°; 80°

7. $\overline{ST}$, $\overline{TV}$, $\overline{SV}$

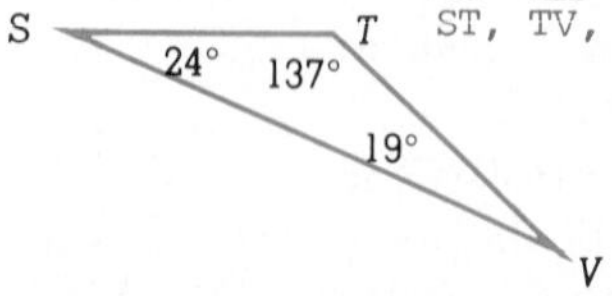

   S; T; V; 24°; 137°; 19°

8. $\overline{WX}$, $\overline{XY}$, $\overline{WY}$

   X; W; Y; 68°; 60°; 52°

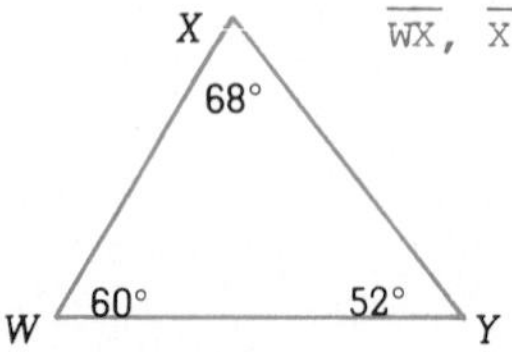

Written **Prove the following.** For answers to exercises 1-8, see the Teacher's Guide.

1. Theorem 5–4
2. Theorem 5–7

3. **Given:** $\triangle ABC$
$\angle A$ is a right angle.
Prove: $BC > BA$

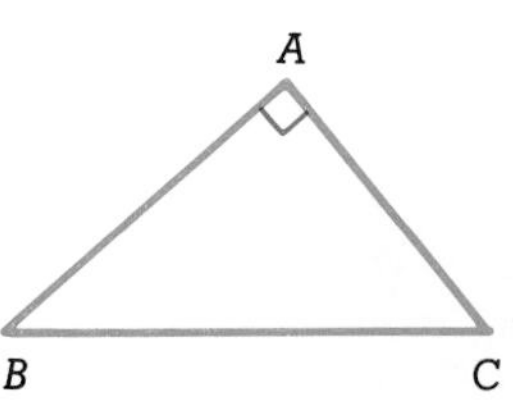

4. **Given:** $\triangle ABC$
$\angle A$ is a right angle.
Prove: $BC > AC$

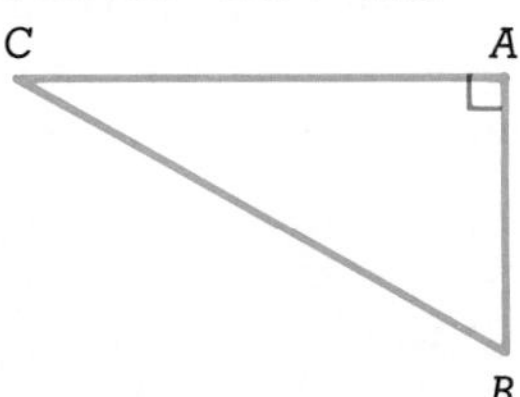

5. **Given:** $\triangle PQR$, $QR > QP$
$\overline{PR} \cong \overline{PQ}$
Prove: $QR > PR$

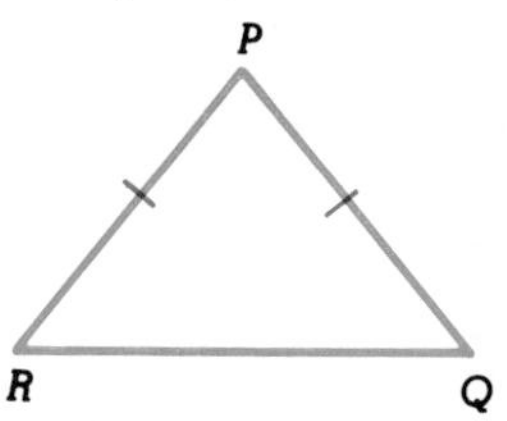

6. **Given:** $\triangle PQR$, $QR > QP$
$\overline{PR} \cong \overline{PQ}$
Prove: $m\angle P > m\angle Q$

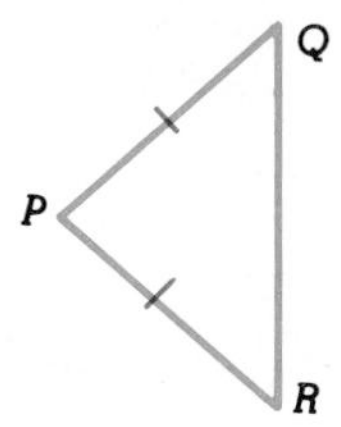

7. **Given:** $TE > AE$
$m\angle P > m\angle PAE$
Prove: $TE > PE$

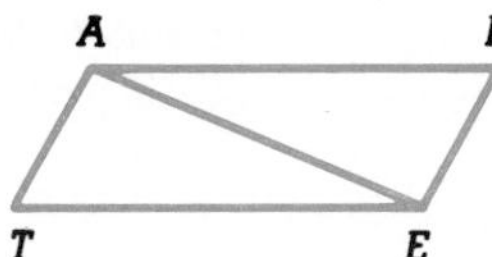

8. **Given:** $\overline{AC} \cong \overline{AE} \cong \overline{KE}$
Prove: $m\angle 1 > m\angle 2$

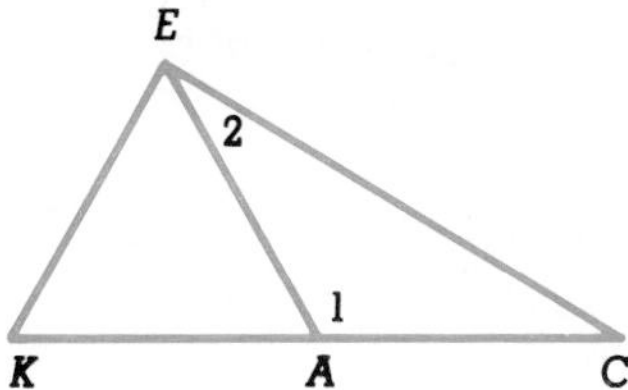

Closed Curves — excursions in geometry

The figure below can be traced so that, starting at one point, every other point is touched exactly once before reaching the starting point again. This figure is a **simple closed curve.**

Simple closed curves separate a plane into the inside, the outside, and the curve itself. One way to test whether a point is inside or outside is to first draw a segment from the given point to another point outside the curve. Then, count the number of times the segment crosses the curve. If the number is odd, the point is inside. If the number is even, the point is outside.

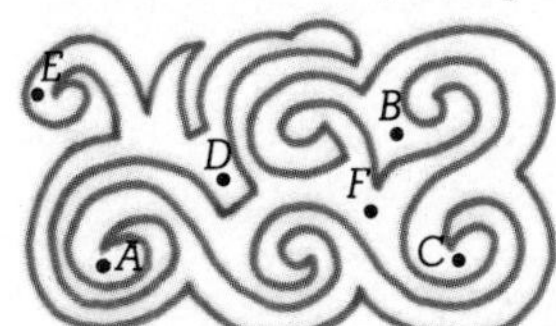

Exercises Determine whether the point given is inside or outside the curve.

1. A inside
2. B inside
3. C inside
4. D inside
5. E inside
6. F outside

5–4 The Triangle Inequality

Objective: to recognize and use the Triangle Inequality Theorem

You probably have heard that a straight line is the shortest distance between two points. According to this principle, which path in the picture should you take to go from point A to point B?

The following theorem applies the principle to triangles.

Emphasize that the Triangle Inequality Theorem concerns only a single triangle.

The sum of the measures of any two sides of a triangle is greater than the measure of the third side.

Theorem 5–8
Triangle Inequality
It must hold for all three cases.

According to the Triangle Inequality Theorem, certain sets of measures cannot be used to form a triangle.

example

1 Determine whether or not it is possible to draw a triangle with sides of 2 units, 3 units, and 6 units.

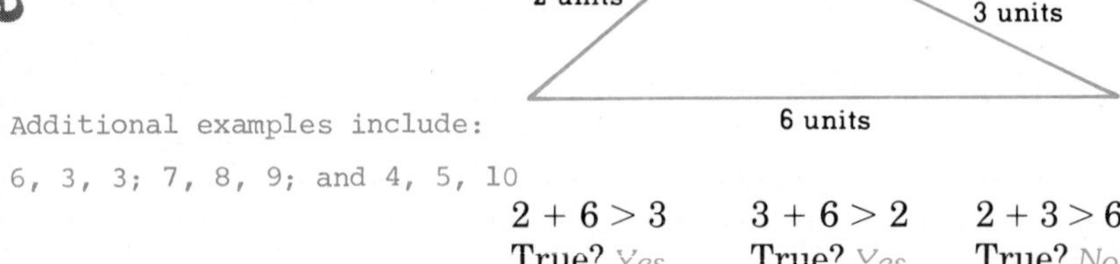

Additional examples include:

6, 3, 3; 7, 8, 9; and 4, 5, 10

$2 + 6 > 3$	$3 + 6 > 2$	$2 + 3 > 6$
True? *Yes*	True? *Yes*	True? *No*

The sum of the measures of any two sides must be greater than the measure of the third side.

No, it is *not* possible to draw a triangle with the given sides.

The proof of the Triangle Inequality Theorem uses an auxiliary segment.

example

2 Prove the Triangle Inequality Theorem.

Given: $\triangle PQR$
Prove: $PQ + PR > RQ$

Draw diagrams showing ∠ QPR as a right angle, and ∠ QPR as an acute angle.

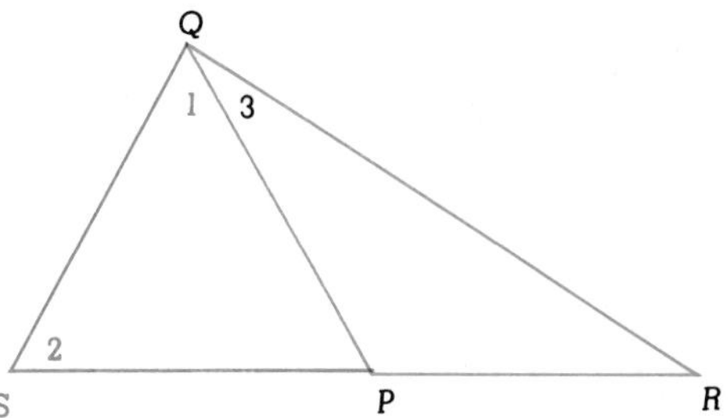

Proof:

STATEMENTS	REASONS
1. Draw $\overline{PS}$ so that P is between S and R and $PQ = PS$.	**1.** Postulate 2–2: Ruler Postulate
2. $PS + PR = RS$	**2.** Definition of Betweenness
3. $\overline{PQ} \cong \overline{PS}$	**3.** Definition of Congruent Segments
4. $\angle 1 \cong \angle 2$	**4.** Theorem 4–6: Isosceles Triangle Theorem
5. $m\angle 1 = m\angle 2$	**5.** Definition of Congruent Angles
6. $m\angle SQR = m\angle 1 + m\angle 3$	**6.** Postulate 3–3: Angle Addition Postulate
7. $m\angle SQR = m\angle 2 + m\angle 3$	**7.** Postulate 2–9: Substitution
8. $m\angle SQR > m\angle 2$	**8.** Theorem 5–2: Inequality Theorem
9. $RS > RQ$	**9.** Theorem 5–5: If the measure of two angles of a triangle are unequal, then the measures of the sides opposite those angles are unequal in the same order.
10. $PS + PR > RQ$	**10.** Postulate 2–9
11. $PQ + PR > RQ$	**11.** Postulate 2–9

EN: Wr: 2-14 evens; p. 159, Cal: 1-9; AV: Ex: 2-20 evens, Wr: 2-12 evens; p. 159, Cal: 1-5; pp. 154-5, Wr: 2-6 evens

exercises

FN: Ex: 1-20, Wr: 1-14 odds; p. 155, Wr: 4, 6, 8

Exploratory **For each of the following, determine whether or *not* it is possible to draw a triangle with sides of the given measures. Write *yes* or *no*.**

1. 1, 2, 3 no
2. 11, 12, 17 yes
3. 2.5, 6, 6.5 yes
4. 9, 40, 41 yes
5. 16, 12, 17 yes
6. 4.7, 9, 4.1 no
7. 2.2, 12, 14.3 no
8. 20, 48, 52 yes
9. 14, 15, 30 no
10. 2.3, 12, 12.2 yes
11. 215, 204, 7 no
12. 100, 100, 5 yes

Use the Triangle Inequality to complete the following table.

	first side measure	second side measure	third side measure must be	
			longer than	shorter than
13.	3	7	4	10
14.	6	10	4	16
15.	12	15	3	27
16.	1.19	2.34	1.15	3.53
17.	5.2	8.3	3.1	13.5
18.	13	19	6	32
19.	0.2	1.0	0.8	1.2
20.	1.7	1.8	0.1	3.5

Written **Two sides of a triangle are 14 centimeters and 15 centimeters in length. Determine whether or *not* each of the following can be the length of the third side.**

1. 5 centimeters yes
2. 17 centimeters yes
3. 9 centimeters yes
4. 16 centimeters yes
5. 29 centimeters no
6. 34 centimeters no

Prove each of the following. For answers to exercises 7-14, see the Teacher's Guide.

7. Given: $\angle ABC \cong \angle ACB$
Prove: $AD + AB > CD$

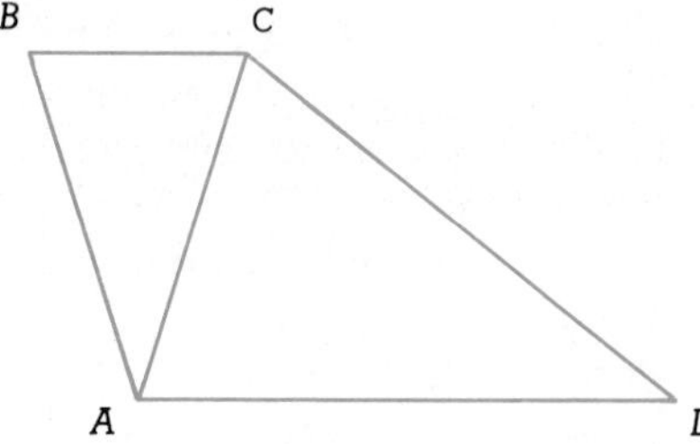

8. Given: $\triangle PTS \cong \triangle QRS$
Prove: $PR > QR$

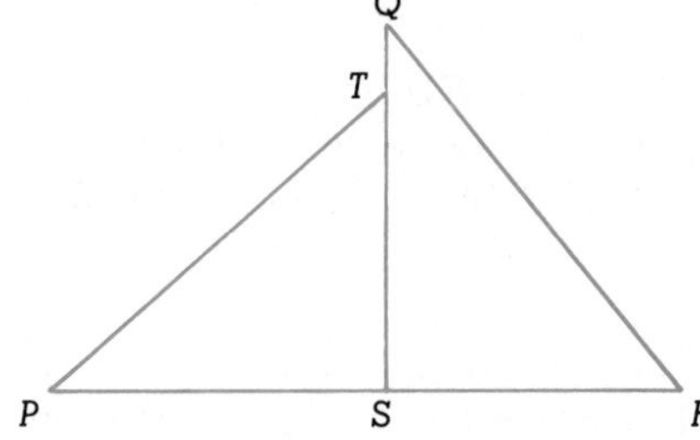

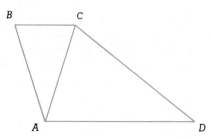

9. Given: $\overline{ED}$ bisects $\overline{AC}$.
$\overline{ED} \perp \overline{AC}$
Prove: $BC > BA$

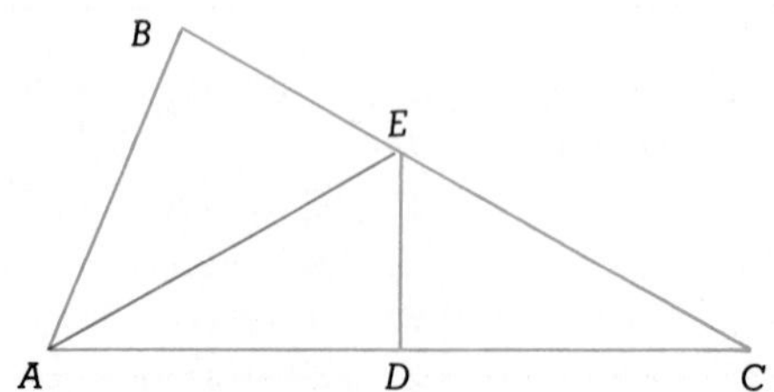

10. Given: $MN = MQ$
Prove: $OP + ON > PQ$

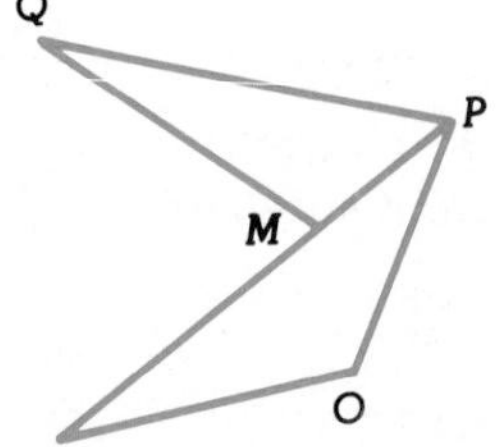

11. Given: $\triangle GRC$
$\overline{RA}$ is an altitude.
Prove: $RC > RA$

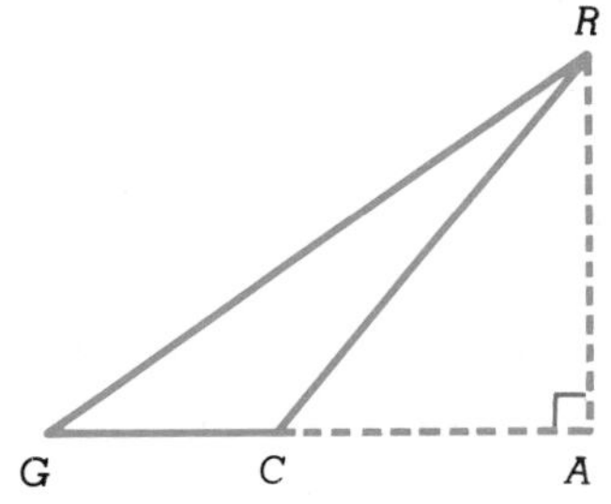

12. Given: $\triangle SKY$
Prove: $SK - KY < SY$

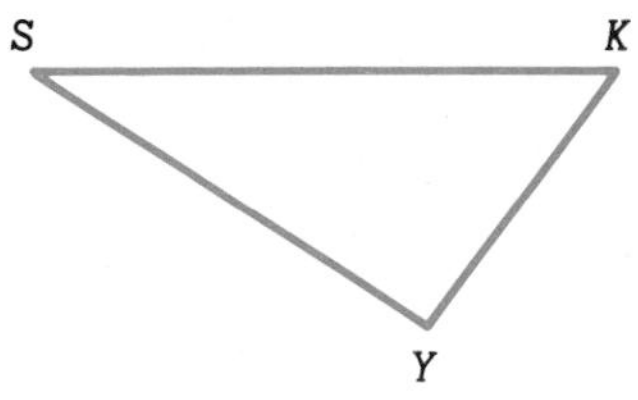

13. Given: $\triangle ABC$
$\overline{AD}$, $\overline{BE}$, and $\overline{CF}$ are altitudes.
Prove: $AB + BC + AC >$
$AD + BE + CF$

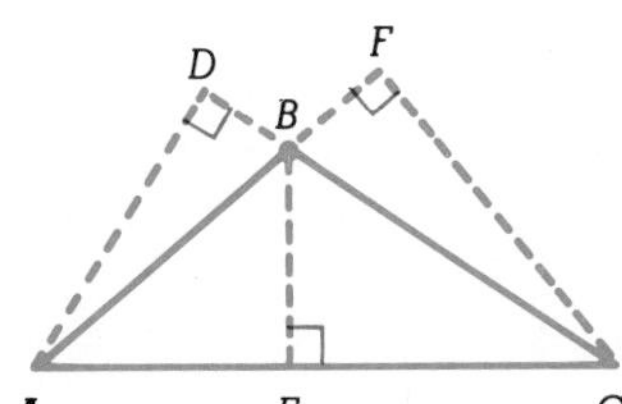

14. Given: $\triangle DAB$ and $\triangle DAC$
Prove: $DA + AB + BC + CD >$
$DB + CA$

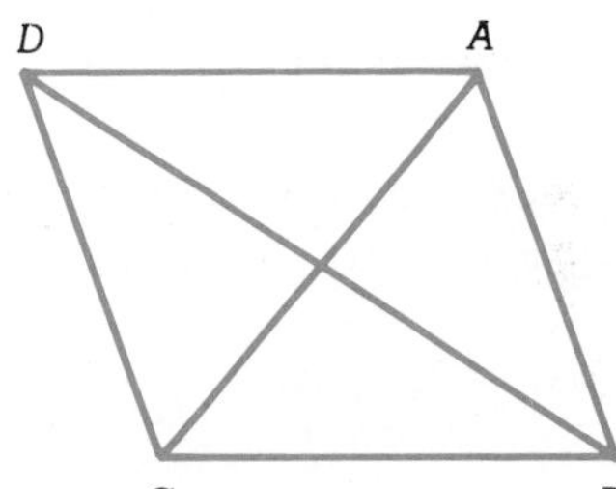

Powers

Some calculators have keys that can be used to find the powers of a number. The key, y^x, is read "y to the x power." To use the key, first enter y, press

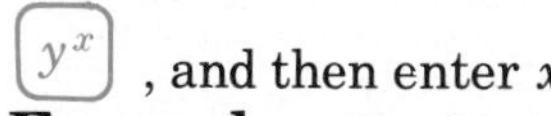

y^x, and then enter x.

Example: Evaluate 1.35^4.

Enter: 1.35 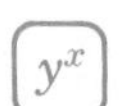 y^x 4 = $\quad y = 1.35,\ x = 4$

Display: 1.35 4 3.32150625

Exercises **Use the "y to the x power" key to find each of the following.**

1. $(4.1)^6$ 4750.1042
2. $(5.7)^4$ 1055.6001
3. $(2.2)^{1/4}$ 1.2178833
4. $(0.45)^{1/7}$ 0.89219324
5. $\left(\frac{15}{2}\right)^{3/4}$ 4.5320631
6. $\left(\frac{7}{5}\right)^{2/3}$ 1.2514649
7. $7^4 + 3^{1/2}$ 2402.732
8. $4 + 5^{1/2} + 3^3$ 33.236068
9. $8^{2/3} + 2^{3/2}$ 6.8284271

5–5 The Hinge Theorem

Objective: to recognize and use the Hinge Theorem and its converse

Drafting artists sometimes use compasses to compare lengths. If the angle of the compass is changed, the distance between the compass points changes.

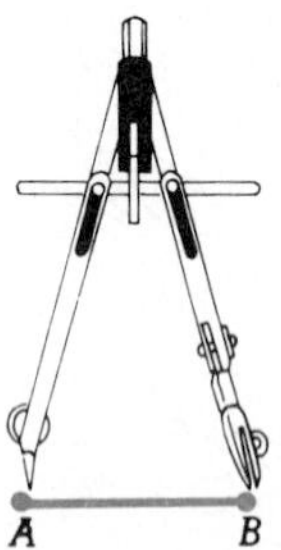

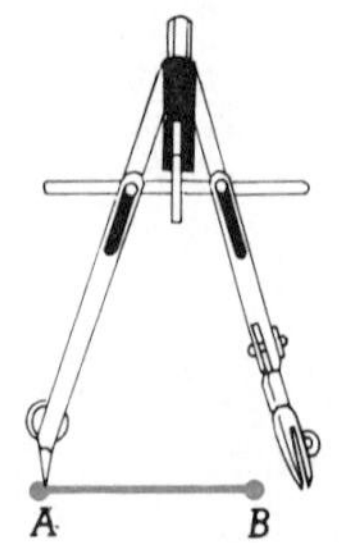

The angle between the parts of the compass is the included angle.

Compare a 2 cm - 30° - 3 cm triangle with a 2 cm - 60° - 3 cm triangle. The third sides are about 2.6 cm and 7 cm respectively.

The larger the angle of the compass, the longer the distance between its points. The smaller the angle of the compass, the shorter the distance between its points.

Theorem 5–9
Hinge Theorem

If two sides of one triangle are congruent to two sides of another triangle and the measures of the included angles are unequal, then the measures of the third sides are unequal in the same order.

Emphasize that the Hinge Theorem concerns two separate triangles.

In the following diagram, notice that $AB < CD$. If the compass is not changed after matching the points to A and B, then it will not match the points C and D. How do you change the angle of the compass so its points match C and D? The converse of the Hinge Theorem describes this situation.

A plan for a proof of the Hinge Theorem is in the Challenge on page 164.

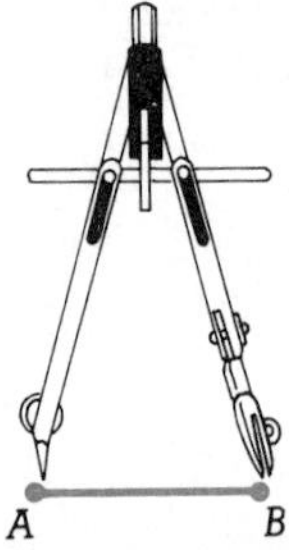

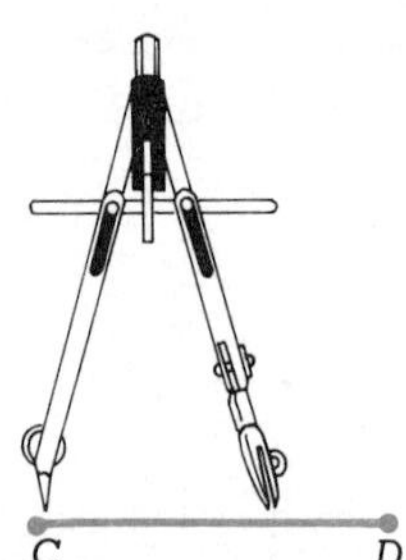

Theorem 5–10
Converse of the Hinge Theorem

If two sides of one triangle are congruent to two sides of another triangle and the measures of the third sides are unequal, then the measures of the angles included between the pairs of congruent sides are unequal in the same order.

The reasoning behind the converse of the Hinge Theorem is presented in exercises 13-14 on page 163.

examples

1 **Prove the following.**

Given: $\overline{AB} \cong \overline{CB}$
$m\angle 1 < m\angle 2$
Prove: $AD < CD$

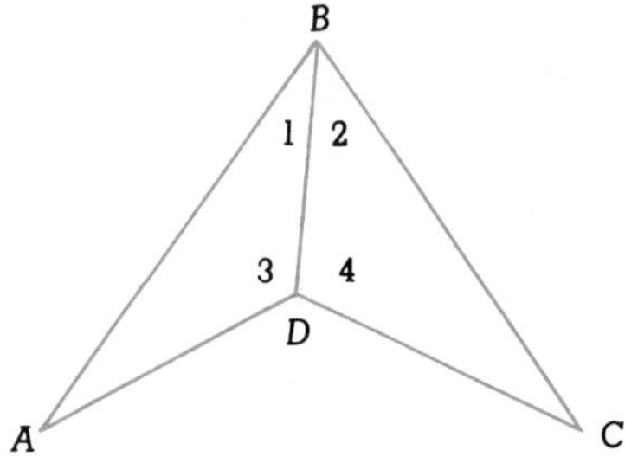

Proof:

STATEMENTS	REASONS
1. $\overline{AB} \cong \overline{CB}$	1. Given
2. $\overline{BD} \cong \overline{BD}$	2. Theorem 2–2: Congruence of segments is reflexive.
3. $m\angle 1 < m\angle 2$	3. Given
4. $AD < CD$	4. Theorem 5–9: The Hinge Theorem

2 **In the figure below, $\triangle QTS$ has $\angle 1 \cong \angle 2$, $\overline{PQ} \cong \overline{SR}$, and $PT < QR$. Write an inequality to show how the measures of $\angle PQT$ and $\angle QSR$ are related.**

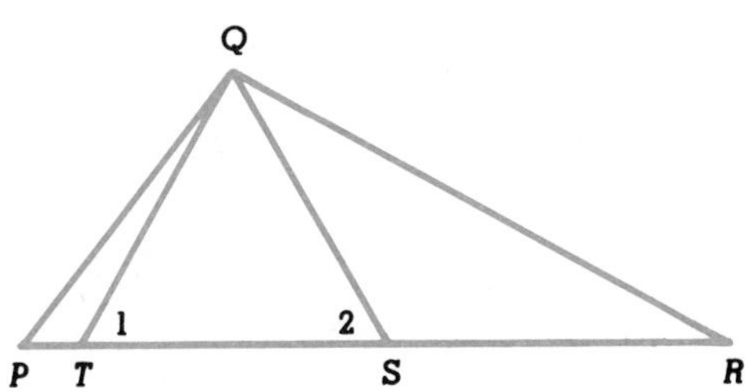

$\angle 1 \cong \angle 2$	Given
$\overline{QT} \cong \overline{QS}$	Theorem 4–9: Converse of Isosceles Triangle Theorem
$\overline{PQ} \cong \overline{SR}$	Given
$PT < QR$	Given

By the statements indicated in color, $\triangle PQT$ and $\triangle QSR$ satisfy the hypothesis of Theorem 5–10. Thus, the measures of the angles are related in the following way.

$$m\angle PQT < m\angle QSR$$

EN: Ex: 3-6, Wr: 2-14 evens; p. 164, Ch: 1-2, E: 1; p. 165, TG: 1-3; AV: Ex: 1-6, Wr: 1-11 odds; p. 164, E: 1; p. 159, Wr: 13-14

exercises

FN: Ex: 1-6, Wr: 1-13 odds; p. 158, Wr: 2-10 evens; p. 159, Ca: 1-3

Exploratory **Name the theorem that best describes each situation below.**

1. When a door opens, the measure of the distance between the edge of the door and the frame increases. Theorem 5-9

2. A pendulum swings in a triangular frame. The distances of the weight from the endpoints of the frame depend on the angles formed at the vertex of the frame. Theorem 5-9

3. To mark off a segment shorter than a given segment, match the points of a compass with the endpoints, then decrease the angle of the compass. Theorem 5-10

4. To mark off a segment longer than a given segment, match the points of a compass with the endpoints, then increase the angle of the compass. Theorem 5-10

5. If two noncongruent triangles have two sides of one congruent to two sides of the other, then the triangle with the included angle with the lesser measure has the shorter third side. Theorem 5-9

6. If two noncongruent triangles have two sides of one congruent to two sides of the other, then the triangle with the shorter third side has the included angle with the lesser measure. Theorem 5-10

Written **Write a proof for each of the following.** For answers to exercises 1-14, see the Teacher's Guide.

1. Given: $\overline{PQ} \cong \overline{SQ}$

Prove: $PR > SR$

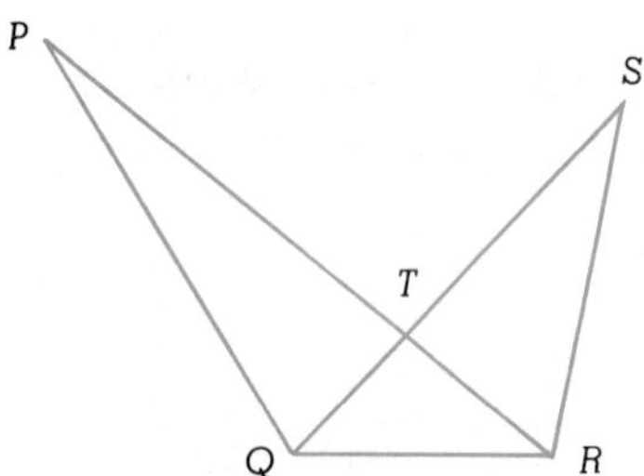

2. Given: $\overline{PQ} \cong \overline{RS}$

$QR < PS$

Prove: $m\angle 3 < m\angle 1$

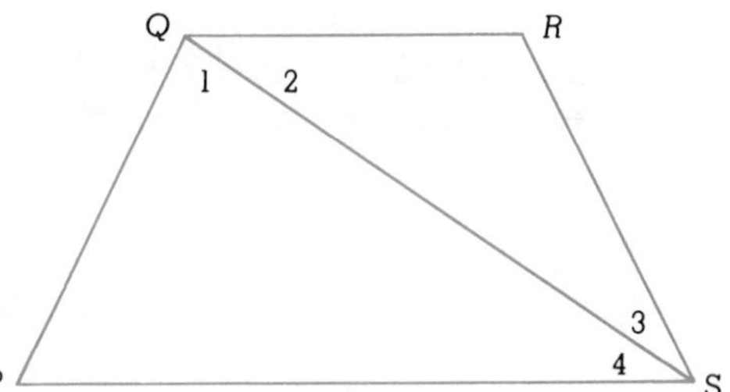

Prove each of the following.

3. Given: $\overline{AB} \cong \overline{BC}$

$m\angle 4 > m\angle 3$

Prove: $AD > CD$

4. Given: $\overline{AB} \cong \overline{BC}$

$AD > CD$

Prove: $m\angle 4 > m\angle 3$

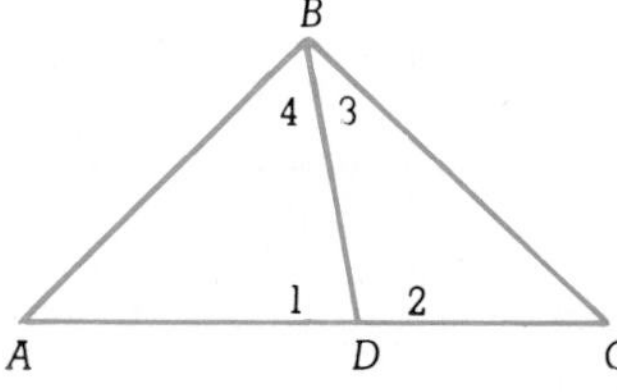

Exercises 3 and 4

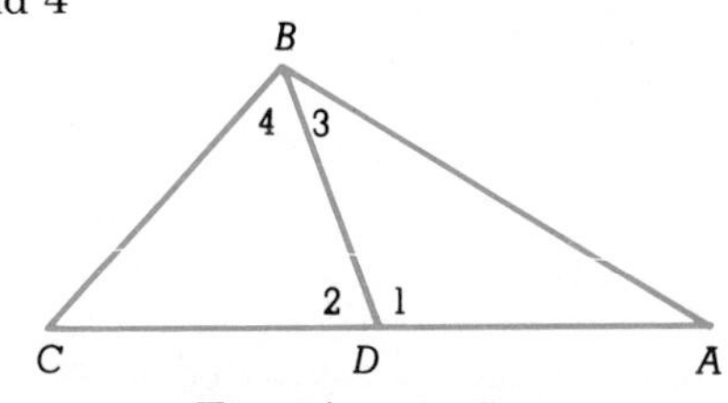

Exercises 5–7

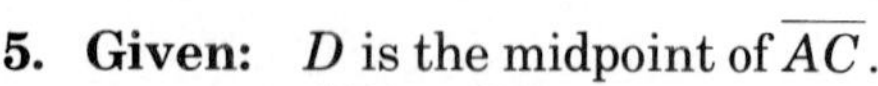

5. Given: D is the midpoint of $\overline{AC}$.

$AB > CB$

Prove: $m\angle 1 > m\angle 2$

6. Given: $\overline{BD}$ bisects $\overline{AC}$.

$AB > CB$

Prove: $m\angle 1 > m\angle 3$

7. Given: $\overline{BD}$ bisects $\overline{AC}$.

$AB > CB$

Prove: $m\angle 1 > m\angle A$

8. Given: $\overline{PR} \cong \overline{PQ}$
$SQ > SR$
Prove: $m\angle 1 < m\angle 2$

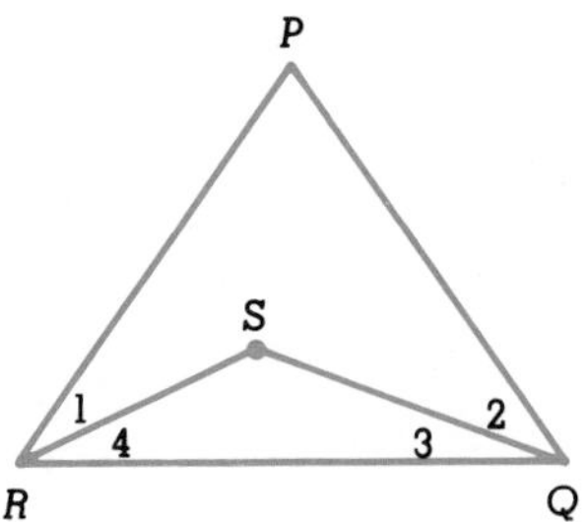

9. Given: $\triangle TER$
$\overline{TR} \cong \overline{EU}$
Prove: $TE > RU$

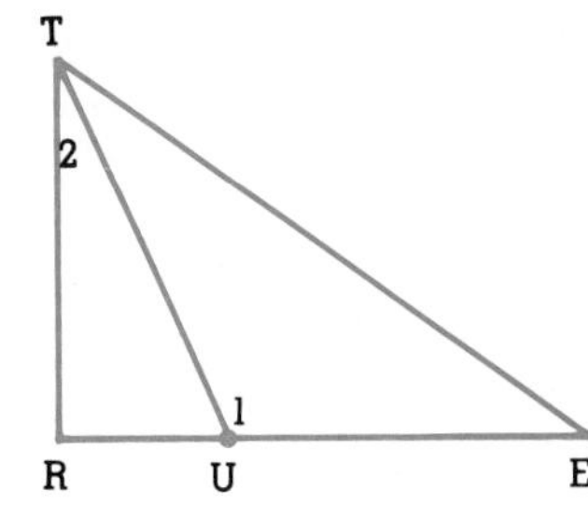

10. Given: $\triangle FCE$ with $\overline{AE}$ bisecting $\overline{FC}$
$m\angle CAE = 50$
Prove: $m\angle C > m\angle F$

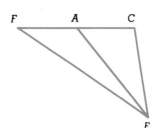

11. Given: $\overline{ER} \cong \overline{EC}$
$\overline{GE} \cong \overline{AE}$
$RA > RG$
$m\angle CEA > m\angle REA$
Prove: $CA > RG$

12. Given: $\overline{ER} \cong \overline{EC}$
$\overline{GE} \cong \overline{AE}$
$RA > RG$
$m\angle CEA > m\angle REA$
Prove: $m\angle CEA > m\angle GER$

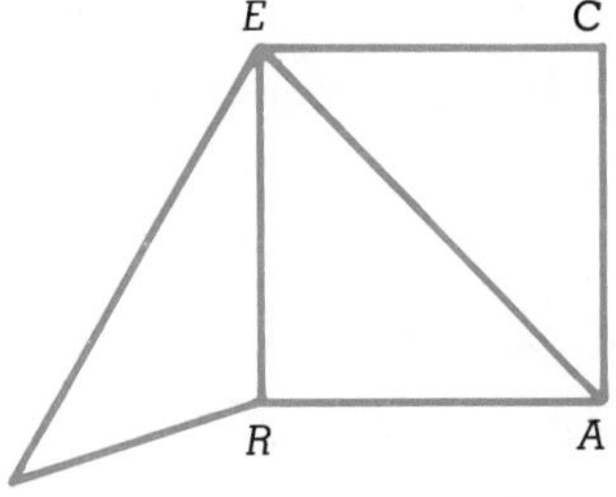

Exercises 11 and 12

Use the diagram and the given statements below for each of the following.

Given: $\overline{PQ} \cong \overline{AB}$
$\overline{PR} \cong \overline{AC}$
$QR > BC$

Exercises 13-14 provide reasoning behind the converse of the Hinge Theorem.

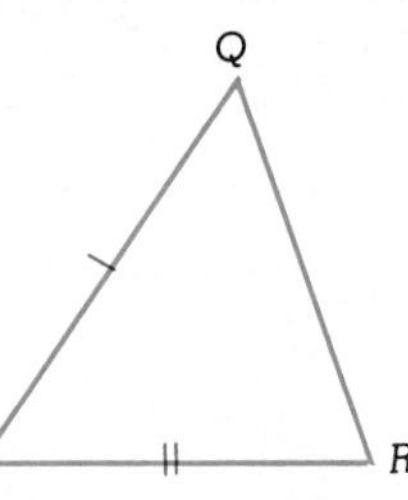

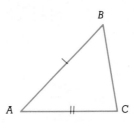

13. It is impossible for $\angle P$ and $\angle A$ to have the same measure. Show that assuming $m\angle P = m\angle A$, implies $QR = BC$, which contradicts $QR > BC$.

14. It is impossible for $m\angle P$ to be less than $m\angle A$. Show that assuming $m\angle P < m\angle A$, implies $QR < BC$, which contradicts $QR > BC$.

Challenge The following is a plan for a proof of the Hinge Theorem.

Given: $\triangle PQR$ and $\triangle ABC$
$\overline{PQ} \cong \overline{AB}$
$\overline{PR} \cong \overline{AC}$
$m\angle P > m\angle A$
Prove: $QR > BC$

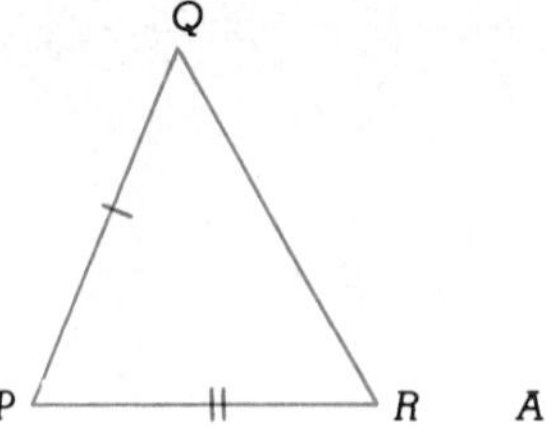

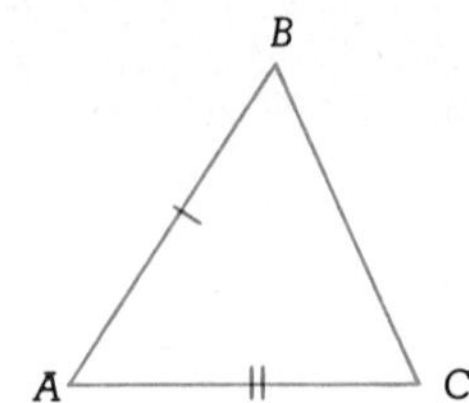

Plan for proof: On $\triangle PQR$ draw $\overrightarrow{PS}$ so that $\angle SPR \cong \angle BAC$ and $\overline{PS} \cong \overline{AB}$.

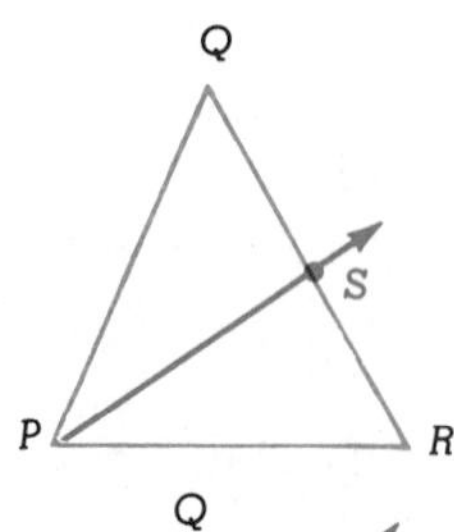

Case 1: S lies on $\overline{QR}$.
By SAS, show that $\triangle SPR \cong \triangle BAC$. Conclude $\overline{SR} \cong \overline{BC}$. Therefore, $QR = QS + SR$, since S is between Q and R. Thus $QR > SR$ and, by substitution, $QR > BC$.

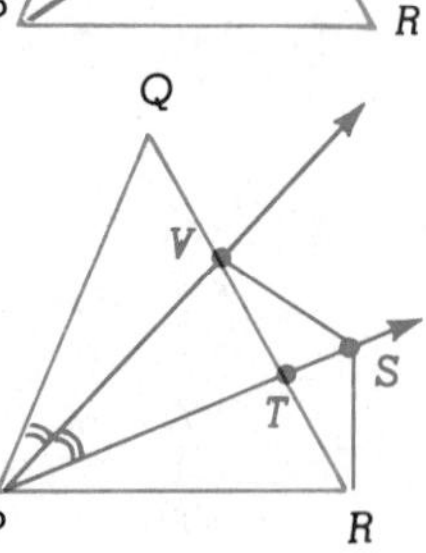

Case 2: S does *not* lie on $\overline{QR}$.
Let $\overrightarrow{PS}$ intersect $\overline{QR}$ at T and draw $\overrightarrow{PV}$ so that $\angle QPT$ is bisected and V lies on $\overline{QR}$. By SAS, show that $\triangle QPV \cong \triangle SPV$ and conclude $\overline{QV} \cong \overline{VS}$. The Triangle Inequality implies $VR + VS > SR$. Thus, by substitution, $VR + QV > SR$, or $QR > SR$. Next, use SAS to show $\triangle SPR \cong \triangle BAC$ and conclude $\overline{SR} \cong \overline{BC}$. Thus, using substitution, $QR > BC$.

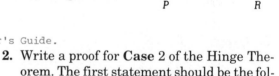

For answers to exercises 1-2, see the Teacher's Guide.

1. Write a proof for **Case** 1 of the Hinge Theorem. The first statement should be the following.
   On $\triangle PQR$, draw $\overrightarrow{PS}$ so that $\angle SPR \cong \angle BAC$, $\overline{PS} \cong \overline{AB}$, and S lies on $\overline{QR}$.

2. Write a proof for **Case** 2 of the Hinge Theorem. The first statement should be the following.
   On $\triangle PQR$, draw $\overrightarrow{PS}$ so that $\angle SPR \cong \angle BAC$ and $\overline{PS} \cong \overline{AB}$.
   Let T be the intersection of $\overrightarrow{PS}$ and $\overline{QR}$.

Triangles — excursions in geometry

How many triangles can you find in the figure below? 44 triangles

topics in geometry — Projective Geometry

Different forms of geometry can be used to help solve the problem of making maps of the earth. One geometry used is called **projective geometry.** Projective geometry can be used to copy the earth's surface onto several different forms of maps.

One way the earth can be drawn is by using a cylinder. Imagine placing a cylinder around the earth. Points are plotted from the sphere to the cylinder. What do you notice? Points near the equator are placed on the map with little change in their position. Points near the poles can have a great deal of distortion. The map is a flat drawing of a sphere.

Another type of map is drawn by using a cone. The cone is placed on one half of the sphere. Points are projected from the sphere to the cone. Where are the distances the most inaccurate? This type of map has less distortion than the cylindrical form. There is more surface closely aligned with its map.

A third type of map is drawn by using a plane. The points on the surface of the earth are projected onto a flat surface. Imagine placing a flashlight inside the earth. The light would shine through the surface and project an image on the plane. Is the distortion greater at the equator or at the poles?

All of the maps shown above are useful and are ways of drawing a map of a sphere on a flat surface.

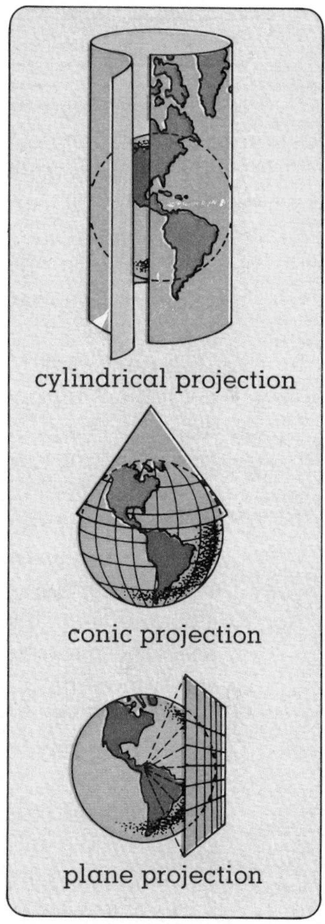

Exercises Answer the following questions.

1. Which type of map would most accurately plot the points of the North Pole? conic
2. Which type of map would a traveler use to travel from New York to London to Rome to New Delhi to Honolulu to Los Angeles to New York? cylindrical
3. Research other ways that maps are drawn. Compare the other mappings to the projections named above. See student's work.

Vocabulary

exterior angle (141)
remote interior angles (141)
Triangle Inequality (156)
Hinge Theorem (160)

Chapter Summary

1. Exterior Angle Theorem (Theorem 5–1): If an angle is an exterior angle of a triangle, then its measure is equal to the sum of the measures of the two remote interior angles. (142)
2. Inequality Theorem (Theorem 5–2): For any numbers a and b, $a > b$ if and only if there is a positive number c such that $a = b + c$. (142)
3. Theorem 5–3: If an angle is an exterior angle of a triangle, then its measure is greater than the measure of either remote interior angle. (142)
4. Diagrams may be used to show the existence of figures, the relative position of figures, or intersections. (146)
5. To see overlapping triangles in a diagram, it is helpful to outline each triangle in a color or to draw each triangle separately in the same position. (147)
6. Theorem 5–4: If the measures of two sides of a triangle are unequal, then the measure of the angles opposite those sides are unequal in the same order. (152)
7. Theorem 5–5: If the measures of two angles of a triangle are unequal, then the measures of the sides opposite those angles are unequal in the same order. (153)
8. Theorem 5–6: A segment is the shortest segment from a point to a line if and only if it is the segment perpendicular to the line. (154)
9. Theorem 5–7: A segment is the shortest segment from a point to a plane if and only if it is the segment perpendicular to the plane. (154)
10. Triangle Inequality Theorem (Theorem 5–8): The sum of the measures of any two sides of a triangle is greater than the measure of the third side. (156)
11. Hinge Theorem (Theorem 5–9): If two sides of one triangle are congruent to two sides of another triangle and the measures of the included angles are unequal, then the measures of the third sides are unequal in the same order. (160)
12. Converse of the Hinge Theorem (Theorem 5–10): If two sides of one triangle are congruent to two sides of another triangle and the measures of the third sides are unequal, then the measures of the angles included between the pairs of congruent sides are unequal in the same order. (160)

Chapter Review

5–1 For each of the following write an inequality that relates only *PQ* and *PR*.

1. $PQ + QR = PR$ PQ < PR
2. $PR - PQ = QR$ PR > PQ
3. $4 + PQ - PR = 10$ PQ > PR
4. $PQ - PR = 25$ PQ > PR

Use the information given in the figure to find the value for each of the following.

5. x 120
6. y 30
7. z 30
8. v 60
9. w 60
10. r 55
11. s 55
12. t 65

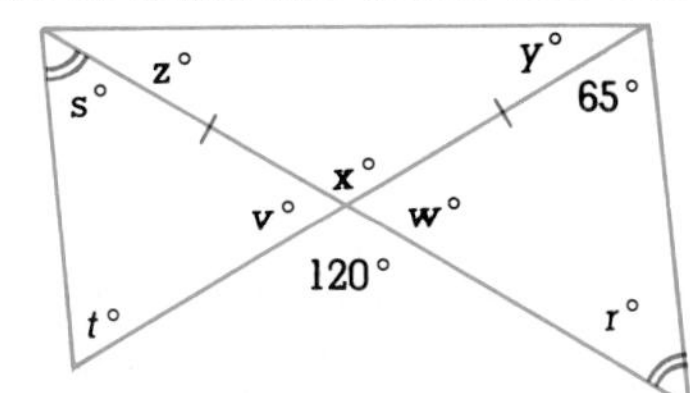

5–2 Determine if the following statements can be assumed from the appearance of the figure. Write *yes* or *no*.

13. E is between A and D. yes
14. $\overline{BD}$ bisects $\overline{EC}$. no
15. $\overline{BF} \cong \overline{CF}$ no
16. $\overline{EA} \cong \overline{DA}$ no
17. $\overline{EA} \cong \overline{ED}$ yes
18. $\angle BED$ is a right angle. no

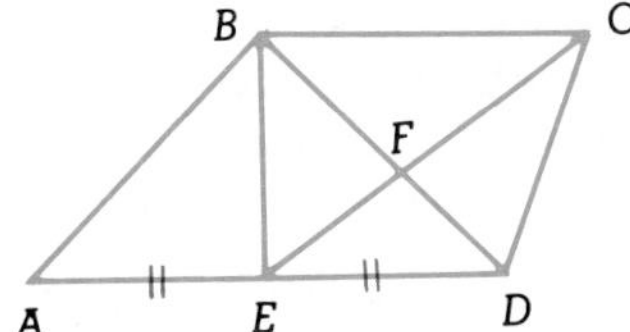

Name all the triangles in each of the following figures.

19. △CDF, △CDG, △DFG, △DEG, △EFG

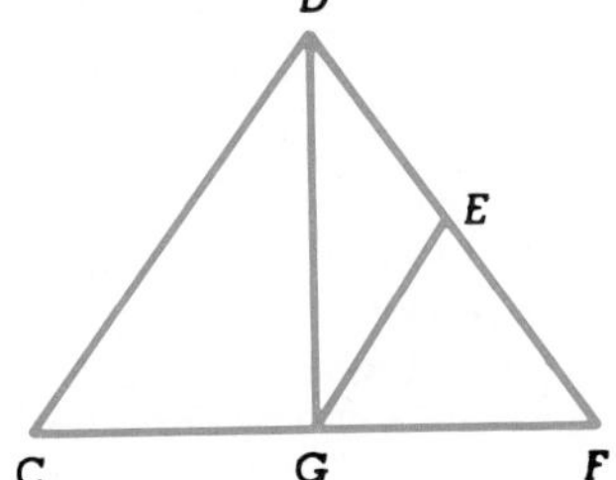

20. △ABD, △ADF, △ABF, △ABC, △BCE, △BCD, △CDE

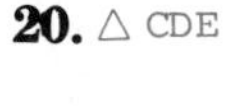

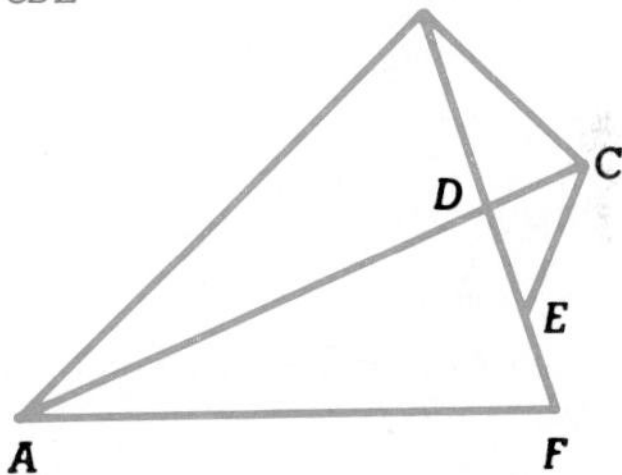

5–3 For each of the following triangles, list the sides from least to greatest and list the angles from least to greatest.

21.

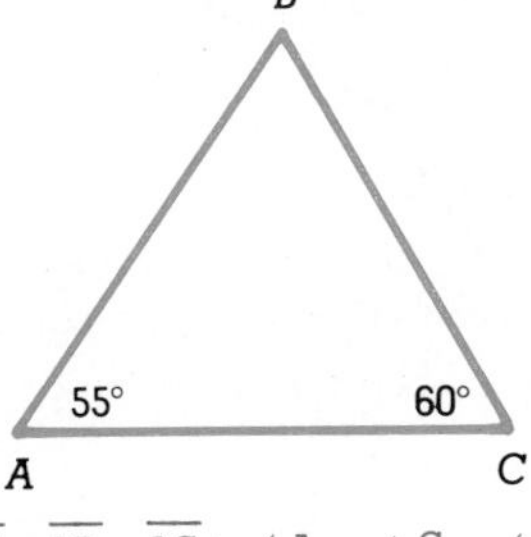

$\overline{BC}$, $\overline{AB}$, $\overline{AC}$; $\angle A$, $\angle C$, $\angle B$

22.

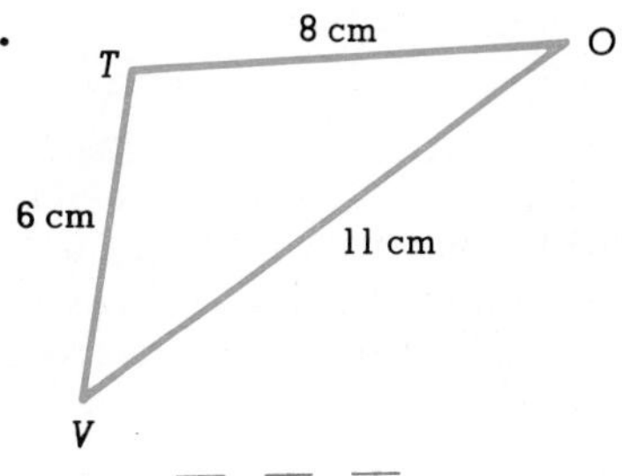

$\overline{TV}$, $\overline{TO}$, $\overline{VO}$; $\angle O$, $\angle V$, $\angle T$

For answers to exercises 23-24, see the Teacher's Guide.

23. Given: $\overline{AK} \cong \overline{AC}$
Prove: $m\angle 1 > m\angle 2$

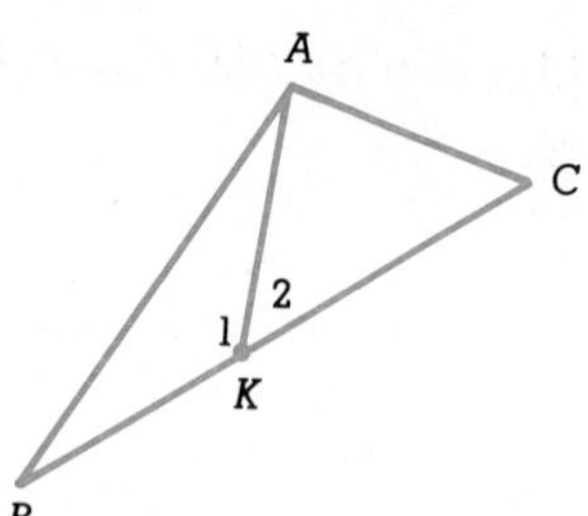

24. Given: $\triangle APE$ is equilateral.
Prove: $PQ > QA$

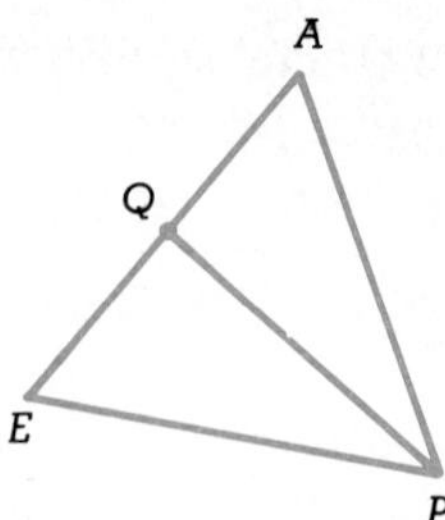

5–4 Two sides of a triangle measure 23 feet and 7 feet. Determine whether or *not* each of the following can be a measurement for the third side.

25. 45 feet no
26. 29 feet yes
27. 9 feet no
28. 37 feet no
29. 27 feet yes
30. 24 feet yes

Use the Triangle Inequality Theorem to complete each of the following.

31. If a triangle has two sides measuring 7 units and 9 units, then the measure of the third side is longer than __2__ units and shorter than __16__ units.

32. If a triangle has two sides measuring 5 units and 11 units, then the measure of the third side is longer than __6__ units and shorter than __16__ units.

For answers to exercises 33-35, see the Teacher's Guide.

33. Given: $\triangle XYZ$
Prove: $XY - YZ < XZ$

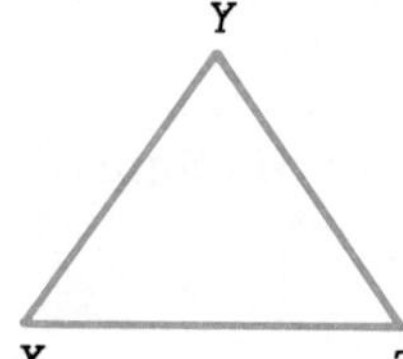

5–5 Write a proof for each of the following.

34. Given: $\overline{AB} \cong \overline{CB}$
$m\angle ABE > m\angle CBE$
Prove: $AE > CE$

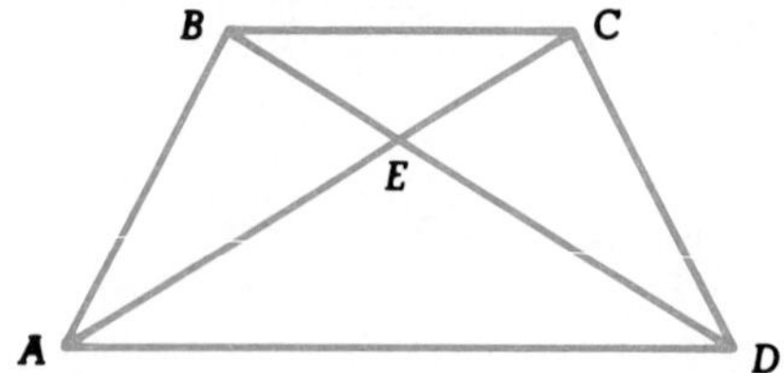

35. Given: $AD > BC$
Prove: $m\angle ABD > m\angle BAC$

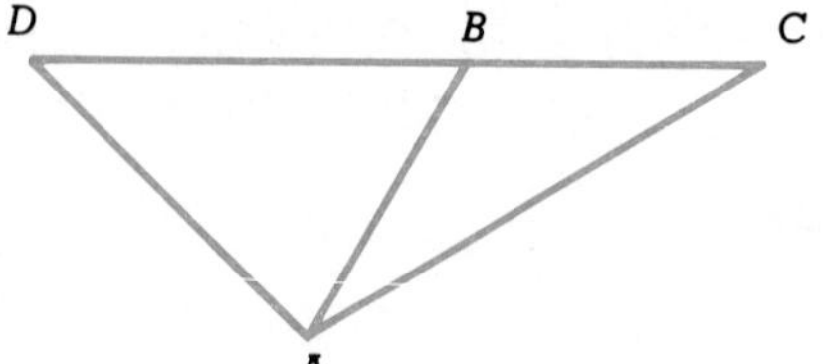

Chapter Test

For each of the following, suppose $\overline{PQ} \cong \overline{PV}$, $\overline{PR} \cong \overline{PT}$, $m\angle 9 = 60$, and $m\angle 4 = 20$. Find each measure.

1. $m\angle 7$ 90
2. $m\angle 8$ 90
3. $m\angle 3$ 30
4. $m\angle 6$ 60
5. $m\angle 2$ 30
6. $m\angle 5$ 120
7. $m\angle 10$ 120
8. $m\angle V$ 40
9. $m\angle Q$ 40
10. $m\angle 1$ 20

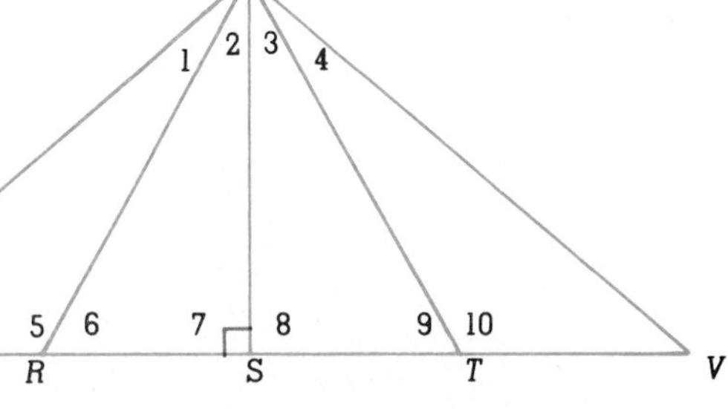

14. Definition of Right△ ; LL; or SAS

Name the postulates or theorems that justify each of the following statements.

11. The midpoint of $\overline{AC}$ is D.
12. $m\angle 5 = 90$
13. $\overline{BD} \cong \overline{BD}$ Theorem 2-2
14. $\triangle ABD \cong \triangle CBD$
15. $AB = CB$
16. $\angle 1 \cong \angle 2$ CPCTC

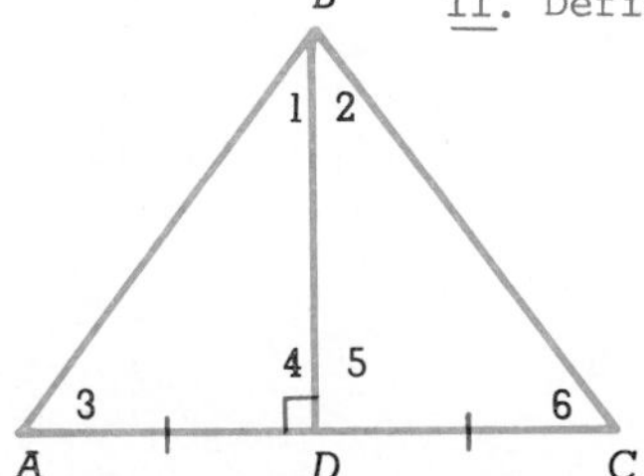

11. Definition of Midpoint

15. CPCTC; Definition of Congruent Segments

12. Theorem 3-11; Definition of Right Angle, Theorem 3-7, Theorem 3-9

Prove each of the following. For answers to exercises 17-20, see the Teacher's Guide.

17. Given: $m\angle 7 = 90$
Prove: $m\angle 5 > m\angle 4$

18. Given: $\overline{PR} \cong \overline{PT}$
$m\angle 2 > m\angle 3$
Prove: $RS > TS$

19. Given: $m\angle 8 = 90$
Prove: $PV > PT$

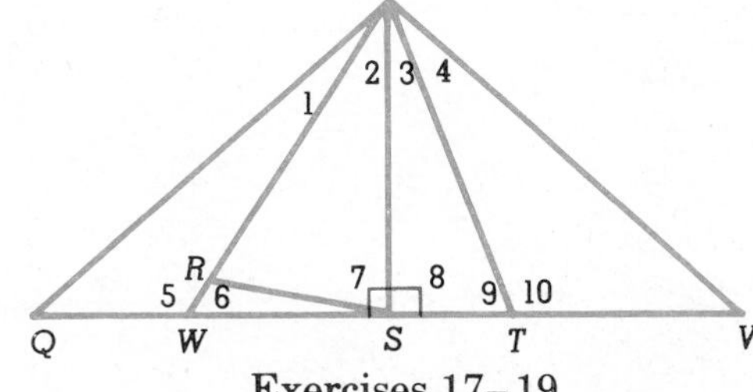

Exercises 17–19

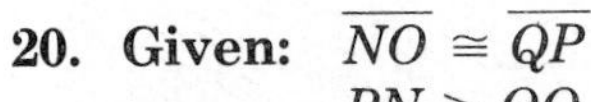

20. Given: $\overline{NO} \cong \overline{QP}$
$PN > OQ$
Prove: $MP > MO$

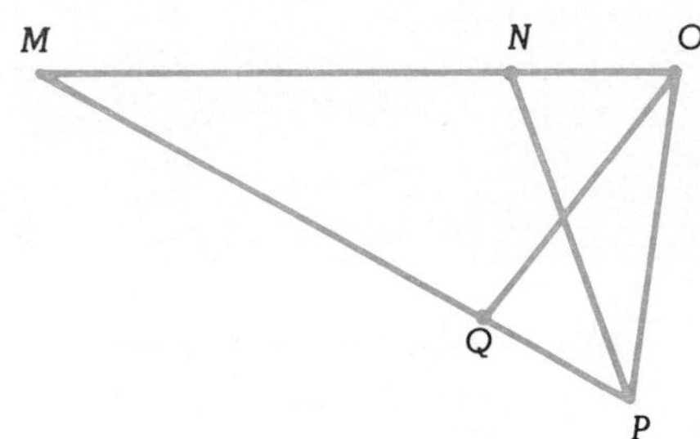

Exercise 20

chapter 6 Parallels

Many real-life phenomena may be described using parallel lines. Fences are stretched on parallel posts. Buildings have parallel boards. What parallel lines can you see in this photograph?

Rows of tulips

Objectives: to describe the possible relationships between two lines, to identify the relationship among pairs of angles formed by pairs of lines and a transversal

6–1 Parallels and Transversals

The sides of a road never meet. An optical illusion makes it appear as though they intersect.

In a plane, lines that never meet are called **parallel lines.**

Two lines are parallel if and only if they lie in the same plane and do not intersect.

Definition of Parallel Lines

The symbol, ∥, means **is parallel to.** In the figure below, the two lines are parallel.

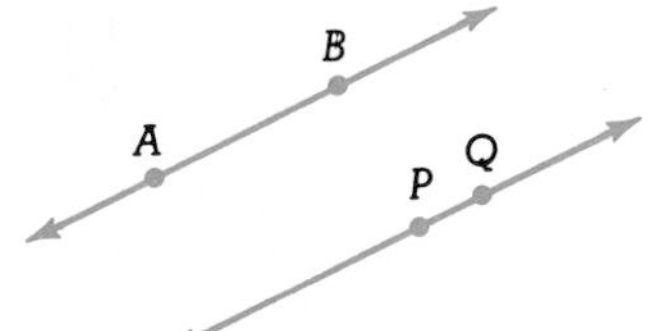

$\overleftrightarrow{AB} \parallel \overleftrightarrow{PQ}$ *symbols*

$\overleftrightarrow{AB}$ is parallel to $\overleftrightarrow{PQ}$. *words*

The same term, parallel, and the same notation, ∥, are used for lines, segments, rays, and planes.

Parts of lines are parallel to each other if the lines containing them are parallel. For example, a ray can be parallel to a segment. In the figure above, $\overrightarrow{AB} \parallel \overline{PQ}$. *What other combinations are possible?*

$\overline{AB} \parallel \overline{PQ}$, $\overrightarrow{AB} \parallel \overrightarrow{PQ}$, $\overline{AB} \parallel \overrightarrow{PQ}$, $\overleftrightarrow{AB} \parallel \overline{PQ}$, $\overleftrightarrow{AB} \parallel \overline{PQ}$, $\overline{AB} \parallel \overleftrightarrow{PQ}$, etc.

Some lines do not intersect and yet are not parallel. They are called **skew lines.**

Two lines are skew if and only if they do not intersect and are not in the same plane.

Definition of Skew Lines

Meter sticks can be used to illustrate skew lines.

Thus, there are three different ways that two lines can be positioned in space, intersecting, parallel, or skew.

example

1 In the figure below, name all pairs of lines that appear to be parallel. Then, name all pairs of lines that appear to be skew.

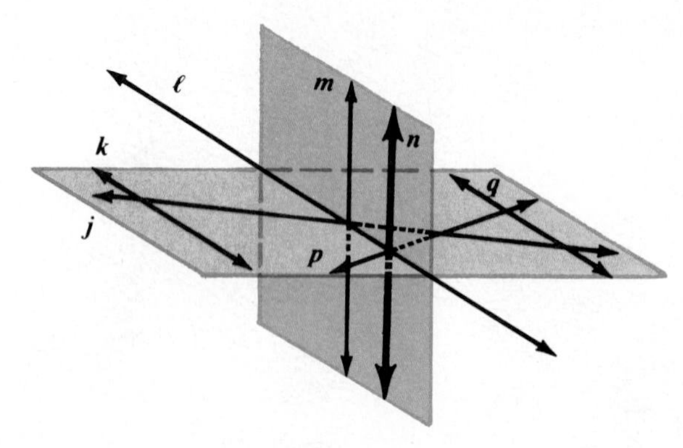

The pairs of parallel lines are as follows.

$k \parallel \ell$	$m \parallel n$
$k \parallel q$	$\ell \parallel q$

The pairs of skew lines are as follows.

k and ***m***	***p*** and ***m***
k and ***n***	***q*** and ***m***
j and ***n***	***q*** and ***n***

In a plane, a line is a transversal if and only if it intersects two other lines in two different points.

Definition of Transversal

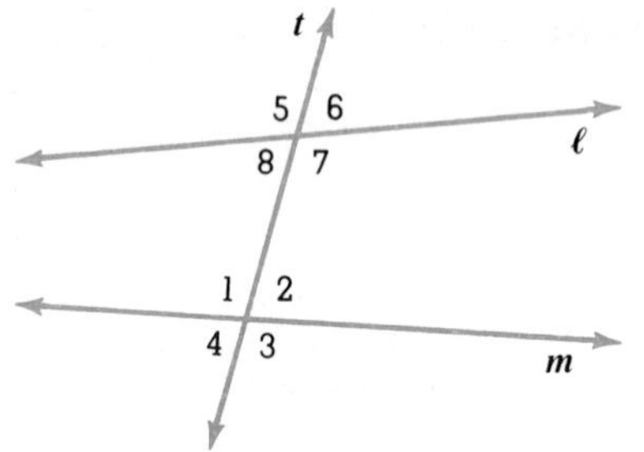

The transversal, ***t***, *intersects*, or *cuts*, lines ℓ and ***m***.

Eight angles are formed by the intersection of a transversal and two lines. Different names are used for various sets of these angles.

Interior Angles	$\angle 1, \angle 2, \angle 7, \angle 8$
Alternate Interior Angles	$\angle 1$ and $\angle 7$, $\angle 2$ and $\angle 8$
Exterior Angles	$\angle 3, \angle 4, \angle 5, \angle 6$
Alternate Exterior Angles	$\angle 6$ and $\angle 4$, $\angle 5$ and $\angle 3$
Corresponding Angles	$\angle 1$ and $\angle 5$, $\angle 2$ and $\angle 6$
	$\angle 3$ and $\angle 7$, $\angle 4$ and $\angle 8$
Consecutive Interior Angles	$\angle 7$ and $\angle 2$, $\angle 1$ and $\angle 8$

The theorems on the next page state how some of the pairs of angles are related.

If two lines are cut by a transversal and one pair of alternate interior angles are congruent, then the other pair of alternate interior angles also are congruent. *Theorem 6–1*

If two lines are cut by a transversal and one pair of corresponding angles are congruent, then all pairs of corresponding angles are congruent. *Theorem 6–2*

Students prove Theorem 6-2 in Written exercise 26.

example

2 Prove Theorem 6–1.

Note that linear pairs are assumed from the diagram.

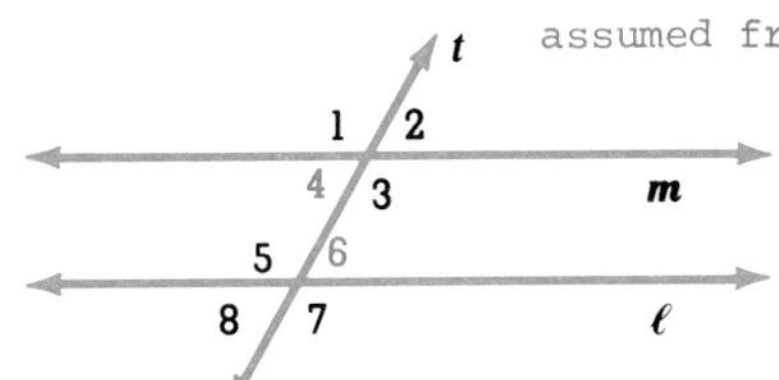

Given: $\angle 4 \cong \angle 6$
Prove: $\angle 3 \cong \angle 5$

Proof:

STATEMENTS	REASONS
1. $\angle 4$ and $\angle 3$ form a linear pair. $\angle 5$ and $\angle 6$ form a linear pair.	**1.** Given
2. $\angle 4$ and $\angle 3$ are supplementary. $\angle 5$ and $\angle 6$ are supplementary.	**2.** Postulate 3–4: Supplement Postulate
3. $\angle 4 \cong \angle 6$	**3.** Given
4. $\angle 3 \cong \angle 5$	**4.** Theorem 3–3: If two angles are supplementary to two congruent angles, then the two angles are congruent to each other.

EN: Ex: 15-22, Wr: 1-19 odds, 20-27; p. 175, Ch: 1-3; AV: Ex: 1-22, Wr: 1-27 odds; p. 175, AR: 1-12

exercises

FN: Ex: 1-22, Wr: 1-19; p. 175, AR: 1-12

Exploratory **Describe each of the following as intersecting, parallel, or skew lines.**

3. skew or parallel, (hopefully not intersecting)

1. rungs on a ladder parallel
2. railroad crossing sign intersecting
3. airline flight paths
4. rows of corn parallel
5. airport runways parallel or intersecting
6. electric power lines parallel or skew
7. lines on writing paper parallel
8. guitar strings parallel
9. spokes on a wheel intersecting or skew
10. artist's T-square intersecting
11. slats on blinds parallel
12. bowling alleys parallel
13. skis on a skier parallel, skew, or intersecting
14. columns on the front of a building parallel

Determine whether each of the following is *true* or *false*.

15. Two lines are parallel if they do not intersect. false
16. A line that intersects two skew lines is a transversal. false
17. If a line intersects two parallel lines, then it is a transversal. true
18. Skew lines are parallel. false
19. Alternate interior angles are on the same side of a transversal. false
20. It is possible for two parallel lines both to be parallel to a third line. true
21. Alternate exterior angles are on opposite sides of a transversal. true
22. A transversal can be perpendicular to two lines. true

Written **Using the diagram below, name the relationship between the following pairs of angles, given $m \parallel \ell$ and $n \parallel p$.**

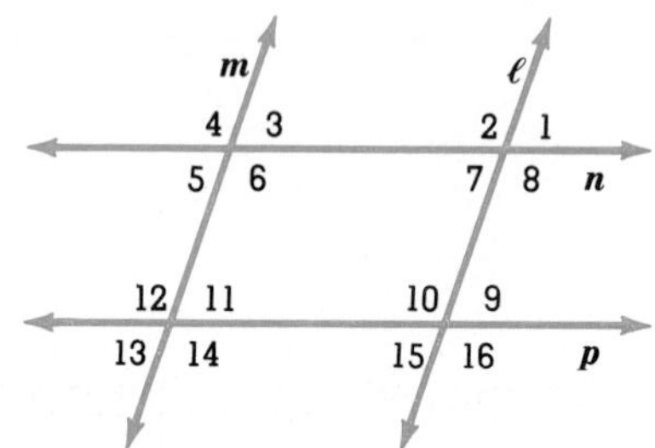

4. consecutive interior

1. ∠1 and ∠15 alt. exterior
2. ∠1 and ∠5 alt. exterior
3. ∠1 and ∠9 corresponding
4. ∠11 and ∠10
5. ∠12 and ∠6 alt. interior
6. ∠6 and ∠8 corresponding
7. ∠3 and ∠7 alt. interior
8. ∠14 and ∠10 alt. interior
9. ∠7 and ∠10 consecutive interior
10. ∠5 and ∠13 corresponding

Using the diagram below, name the relationship between the following pairs of angles.

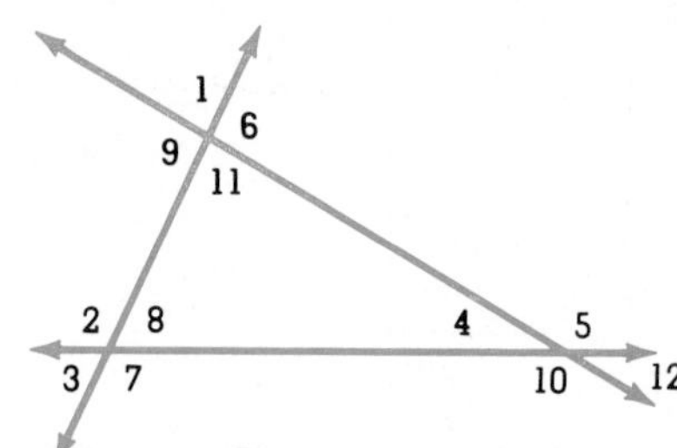

17. consecutive interior

14. consecutive interior

11. ∠1 and ∠2 corresponding
12. ∠11 and ∠5 alt. interior
13. ∠6 and ∠3 alt. exterior
14. ∠11 and ∠8
15. ∠7 and ∠4 alt. interior
16. ∠3 and ∠5 alt exterior
17. ∠11 and ∠4
18. ∠7 and ∠12 corresponding
19. Use the figure above. Copy and complete the following table.

angle	1	2	3	4	5	6	7	8	9	10	11	12
degree measure of angle	85	115	65	30	150	95	115	65	95	150	85	30

For answers to exercises 20-27, see the Teacher's Guide.

Write an if and only if definition for each of the following.

20. parallel line segments
21. parallel rays
22. alternate interior angles
23. corresponding angles
24. alternate exterior angles
25. consecutive interior angles

Prove each of the following.

26. Theorem 6–2
27. If two lines are cut by a transversal and one pair of consecutive interior angles is supplementary, then the other pair of consecutive interior angles is supplementary.

For answers to exercises 1-3, see the Teacher's Guide.

Challenge **For each of the following, write *yes* or *no*. Then, explain.**

1. Parallelism of lines is reflexive.
2. Parallelism of lines is symmetric.
3. Parallelism of lines is transitive.

Factoring — algebra review

The following checklist can be used to help you factor a given polynomial.

1. Check for the greatest common monomial factor.

2. Check for special products.
 a. If there are *two terms,* look for difference of squares, sum of cubes, difference of cubes.
 b. If there are *three terms,* look for perfect squares.

3. Try other factoring methods.
 a. If there are *three terms,* try the trinomial pattern.
 b. If there are *four or more terms,* try grouping.

Example **Factor $6a^2 + 27a - 15$.**

$6a^2 + 27a - 15 = 3(2a^2 + 9a - 5)$ *3 is the GCF.*
$= 3(2a - 1)(a + 5)$ *Use the trinomial pattern.*

Exercises **Factor.** For answers to exercises 1-12, see the Teacher's Guide.

1. $y^2 - 25$
2. $x^4 - y^4$
3. $x^2 - 7x + 10$
4. $r^3 + 6r^2s + 8rs^2$
5. $10m^2 + 19m + 6$
6. $21b^2 + 13b - 20$
7. $x^2 - 2xy + x - 2y$
8. $3a^2 + 12ab - 2a - 8b$
9. $^-b^2 + 8b + a^2 - 16$
10. $r^2 + 4rs + 4s^2 - 9y^2$
11. $3y^2 - 19y + 28$
12. $64a^3 - 1$

6–2 Indirect Proof

Objectives: to write the assumption used in an indirect proof, to write an indirect proof

Bill Hopkins was a unique teacher. He gave all multiple choice questions with only two choices, ***a*** and ***b***, on his quizzes. One of his students, Sandy Thomas, did a long range study of the quizzes. She developed the following statements about the answers to the quiz questions.

Statement **1**: If the fifth question is ***a***, then the first question is ***a***.
Statement **2**: If the first question is ***a***, then the second question is ***b***.
Statement **3**: If the fourth question is ***a***, then the second question is ***a***.

From these three statements, Sandy wanted to prove "If the fourth question is ***a***, then the fifth question is ***b***." She presented the following argument.

Assume: The fourth question is ***a*** and the fifth question is *not* ***b***.

Usually, indirect proofs are written in paragraph form.

Since the fifth question is *not* ***b***, it must be ***a***. The fifth question being ***a*** means the first question is ***a*** using Statement **1**. Therefore, the second question is ***b*** from Statement **2**. But, she knew the fourth question was ***a***. From Statement **3** she concluded the second question must be ***a***. But, the second question cannot be both ***a*** and ***b***. So a contradiction has been reached. Therefore, the original statement "The fourth question is ***a*** and the fifth question is *not* ***b***" must be false. That means Sandy's Theorem must be true.

Students may need several examples of indirect proofs in order to develop greater understanding of this concept.

This kind of reasoning is called **indirect reasoning.** It is based on a contradiction. A conditional statement where p is the hypothesis and q is the conclusion is true if the statement "p and *not* q" is false. We assume "p and *not* q" to be true and check to see if a contradiction is found.

In order to use this type of indirect reasoning, you must be able to state the assumption from the "if-then" statement.

example

1 State the assumption necessary to use indirect reasoning from the following "if-then" statement.

If you are 18 years old, then you qualify for a drivers license.

The assumption can be stated as follows.

You are 18 years old and you do *not* qualify for a drivers license.

example

2 **State the assumption necessary to use indirect reasoning from the following "if-then" statement.**

If two sides of a triangle are congruent, then the angles opposite those sides are congruent.

The assumption can be stated as follows.

Two sides of a triangle are congruent and the angles opposite those sides are *not* congruent.

Following is an example of indirect reasoning in geometry.

example

3 **Write an argument using indirect reasoning to prove the following statement.**

If a triangle is a right triangle, then it has no more than one right angle.

The assumption can be stated as follows.

A triangle is a right triangle and it has more than one right angle.

If two of the angles of the triangle are right angles, then the third angle must measure 0, because the sum of the degree measures of all three angles is 180. Thus, a contradiction is found since the degree measure of an angle must be greater than 0.

Therefore, if a triangle is a right triangle, then it has no more than one right angle.

Some students may need extra help in understanding contradictions in this type of proof.

If a triangle is a right triangle, then it has no more than one right angle.

Theoerem 6–3

You can use indirect reasoning in geometry proofs. Use the following steps to write an indirect proof.

1. **Make the assumption *p* and *not q*.**
2. **Show that the assumption leads to a contradiction.**
3. **State that "*p* and *not q*" is false.**
4. **Conclude that the statement to be proven is true.**

How to Write an Indirect Proof

The pairs of angles formed by a transversal and two parallel lines have many relationships that can be proven. The following theorem can be proven using indirect reasoning.

In a plane, if two lines are cut by a transversal so that a pair of alternate interior angles are congruent, then the two lines are parallel. *Theorem 6–4*

example

4 Prove Theorem 6–4.

Given: $\angle 1 \cong \angle 2$

Prove: $\ell \parallel m$

Proof:

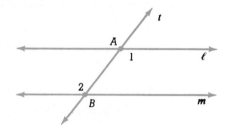

Step 1: Assume: $\angle 1 \cong \angle 2$ and ℓ and m are *not* parallel.

Step 2: Then, ℓ and m intersect, at point P. Now, $\angle 2$ is in the exterior of $\triangle BAP$. Thus, $m\angle 2 > m\angle 1$ because the measure of an exterior angle of a triangle is greater than the measure of either remote interior angle. But, $\angle 1 \cong \angle 2$ implies that $m\angle 1 = m\angle 2$. The Comparison Property has been contradicted. The measures of two angles cannot be both equal and unequal at the same time.

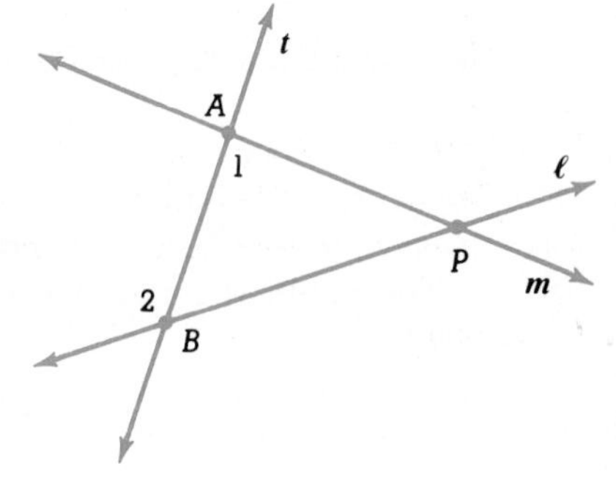

Step 3: The original assumption, $\angle 1 \cong \angle 2$ and ℓ and m are *not* parallel is false.

Step 4: Thus, $\ell \parallel m$.

EN: Ex: 2-12 evens, Wr: 1-10; AV: Ex: 1-12, Wr: 1-7; pp. 174-75, Wr: 2-26 evens

exercises

FN: Ex: 1-12, Wr: 1-7; p. 175, Wr: 20-25, 27; p. 180, E: 1-6

Exploratory **For each of the following, state the assumption you would use to start an indirect proof.** For answers to exercises 1-12, see the Teacher's Guide.

1. If the leaves of a plant are in groups of three, then the plant is poison ivy.
2. If a mushroom is red, then it is poisonous.
3. If the radio does *not* play well, then it is defective.
4. If the lamp will *not* turn on, then the light bulb is defective.

5. If two lines intersect, then they intersect in at least one point.
6. If a line *not* in a plane intersects the plane, then they intersect in no more than one point.
7. A right triangle has no more than two acute angles.
8. A triangle has at most one obtuse angle.
9. In a plane, if two lines are parallel to the same line, then they are parallel to each other.
10. If two lines *not* in the same plane do *not* intersect, then they are skew lines.
11. If the measure of two angles of a triangle are unequal, then the measures of the sides opposite those angles are unequal in the same order.
12. If two sides of one triangle are congruent to two sides of another triangle, but the lengths of the third sides are unequal, then the measures of the angles included between the pairs of congruent sides are unequal in the same order.

For answers to exercises 1-10, see the Teacher's Guide.

Written **Write the assumption that would be used to start an indirect proof.**

1. If two lines in the same plane are cut by a transversal so a pair of alternate exterior angles are congruent, then the two lines are parallel.
2. If two lines in the same plane are cut by a transversal so a pair of consecutive interior angles are supplementary, then the two lines are parallel.
3. If a plane and a line *not* in the plane intersect, then they intersect in no more than one point.
4. Given a line and a point *not* on the line, then there is no more than one plane that contains them.
5. If a transversal intersects two parallel lines, then both pairs of alternate interior angles formed are congruent.
6. If two lines intersect, then no more than one plane contains them.
7. Copy and complete the following indirect proof. Fill in the blanks where indicated.

Theorem: If a triangle is a right triangle, then it has no more than two acute angles.

Note that the triangle shown illustrates the assumption for the indirect proof.

Given: $\triangle ABC$ is a right triangle with right angle C.
Prove: $\triangle ABC$ has no more than two acute angles

Assumption for indirect proof: ____________________

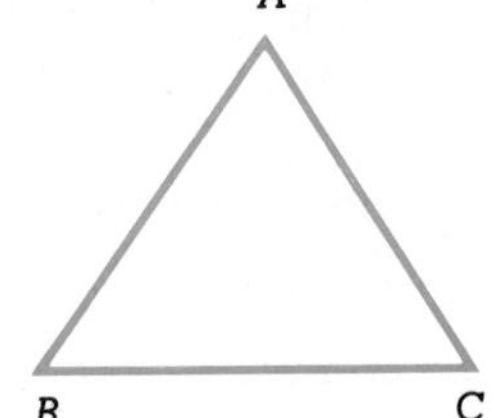

Triangle ABC has three acute angles, $\angle A$, $\angle B$, and $\angle C$. Why? (a) The degree measure of angle C is less than 90. Why? (b) But, triangle ABC is a right triangle with right angle C. Why? (c) Therefore, the degree measure of angle C is 90. Why? (d) But, the degree measure of angle C cannot be equal to 90 and less than 90 at the same time. Why? (e) Thus, triangle ABC has no more than two acute angles. Why? (f)

8. Copy and complete the following indirect proof. Fill in the blanks where indicated.

Theorem: If two lines intersect, then they intersect in no more than one point.

Given: lines ℓ and m intersect
Prove: lines ℓ and m intersect in no more than one point

Assumption for indirect proof: ____________________

Lines ℓ and m have two points in their intersection, P and Q. Why? (a) Both lines ℓ and m contain P and Q. Why? (b) But, through any two points, there is exactly one line. Why? (c) Thus, lines ℓ and m intersect in no more than one point. Why? (d)

Write an indirect proof for each of the following.

9. A triangle has at most one obtuse angle.

10. If a line *not* in a plane intersects the plane, then they intersect in no more than one point.

Classifying Ideas — excursions in geometry

A definition identifies the set to which the term being defined belongs, and states the properties which distinguish the term from others in its set. Satisfying these two requirements may involve the grouping or classifying of ideas.

The ideas included in the definition of an angle can be classified as follows.

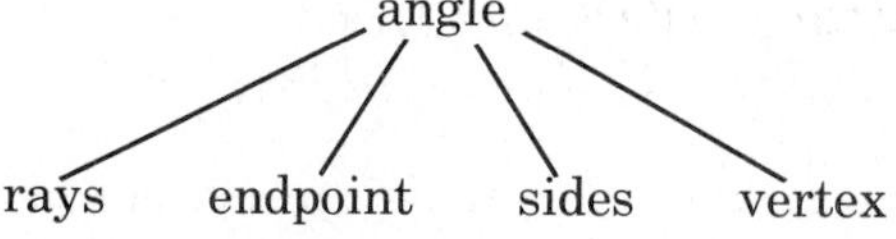

The word angle includes all the other ideas.

In exercises 1-6, the correct answer is underlined.

Exercises **Select the word in each group whose definition includes all the others.**

1. points
lines
<u>geometry</u>
planes

2. acute
<u>triangle</u>
obtuse
right

3. algebra
arithmetic
geometry
<u>mathematics</u>

4. <u>parallelogram</u>
rectangle
rhombus
square

5. vertex
side
angle
<u>triangle</u>

6. hexagon
octagon
<u>polygon</u>
pentagon

6–3 Testing for Parallel Lines

Objectives: to recognize and to use tests for parallel lines

Many copy machines have a series of sorting trays that hold the copies. Viewed from the side, they look like a row of parallel lines.

Notice that each tray is set at an angle. The angles all have the same degree measure. This situation suggests the following theorem for parallel lines.

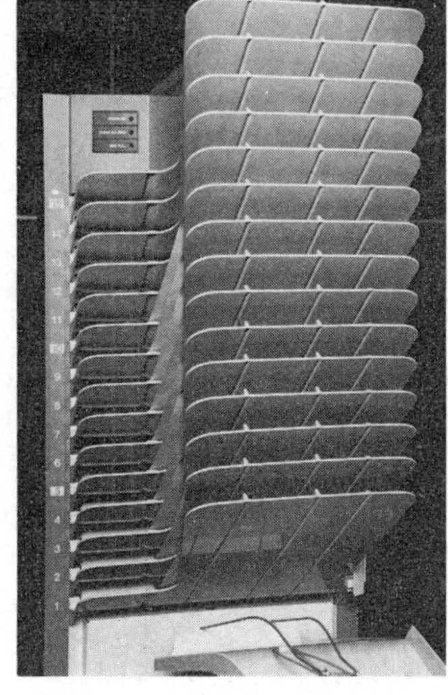

Remember a line is a transversal if it intersects two lines in two different points.

In a plane, if two lines are cut by a transversal so that a pair of corresponding angles are congruent, then the two lines are parallel.

Theorem 6–5

example

1 **Prove Theorem 6–5.**

Given: $\angle 1 \cong \angle 2$
Prove: $\ell \parallel m$

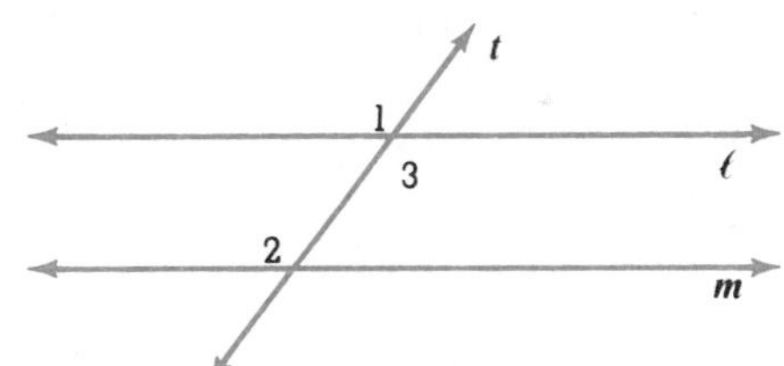

Proof:

STATEMENTS	REASONS
1. $\angle 1 \cong \angle 2$	**1.** Given
2. $\angle 3 \cong \angle 1$	**2.** Theorem 3–10: If two angles are vertical, then they are congruent.
3. $\angle 3 \cong \angle 2$	**3.** Theorem 3–1: Congruence of angles is reflexive, symmetric, and transitive.
4. $\ell \parallel m$	**4.** Theorem 6–4: In a plane, if two lines are cut by a transversal so that a pair of alternate interior angles are congruent, then the two lines are parallel.

Using Theorem 6–4 and 6–5 the following theorems can be proven.

In a plane, if two lines are cut by a transversal so that a pair of consecutive interior angles are supplementary, then the lines are parallel. *Theorem 6–6*

In a plane, if two lines are cut by a transversal so that a pair of alternate exterior angles are congruent, then the lines are parallel. *Theorem 6–7*

In a plane, if two lines are perpendicular to the same line, then the two lines are parallel. *Theorem 6–8*

Students prove Theorems 6-6 and 6-7 in Written exercises 10-11.

These theorems are tests for parallel lines. Example **2** shows how these tests are used to prove lines parallel.

example

2 **Prove the following.**

Given: $\overline{BD}$ and $\overline{EA}$ bisect each other.

Prove: $\overline{AB} \parallel \overline{ED}$

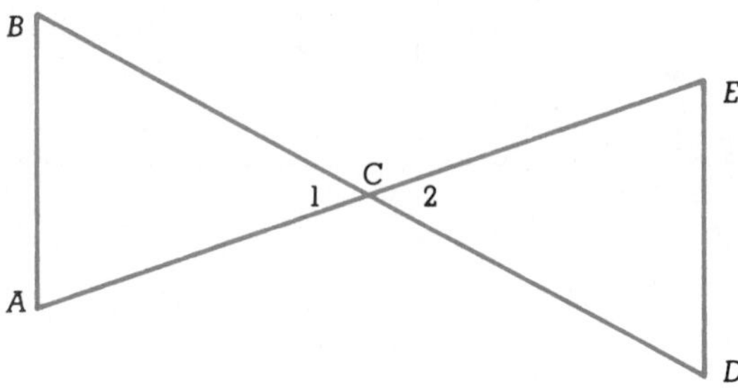

Proof:

STATEMENTS	REASONS
1. $\overline{BD}$ and $\overline{EA}$ bisect each other.	**1.** Given
2. $\overline{BC} \cong \overline{DC}$ $\overline{AC} \cong \overline{EC}$	**2.** Theorem 2–6: Bisector Theorem
3. $\angle 1 \cong \angle 2$	**3.** Theorem 3–10: If two angles are vertical, then they are congruent.
4. $\triangle BCA \cong \triangle DCE$	**4.** Postulate 4–2: SAS
5. $\angle A \cong \angle E$	**5.** Definition of Congruent Triangles CPCTC
6. $\overline{AB} \parallel \overline{ED}$	**6.** Theorem 6–4: In a plane, if two lines are cut by a transversal so that a pair of alternate interior angles are congruent, then the two lines are parallel.

example

3 Prove Theorem 6–8.

Given: $\ell \perp t$
$m \perp t$

Prove: $\ell \parallel m$

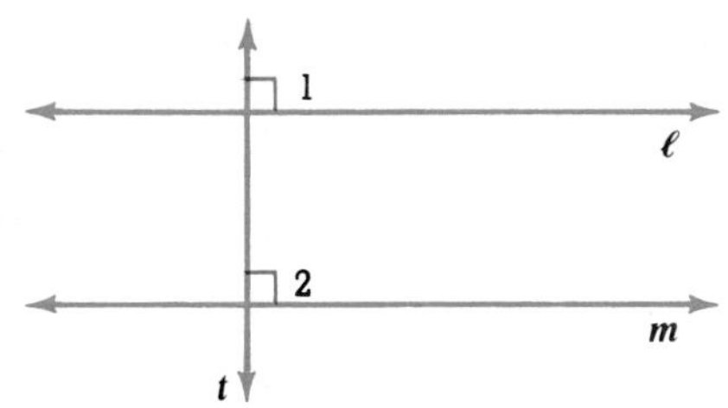

Proof:

STATEMENTS	REASONS
1. $\ell \perp t$, $m \perp t$	**1.** Given
2. $\angle 1$ is a right angle. $\angle 2$ is a right angle.	**2.** Theorem 3–11: If two lines are perpendicular, then they form four right angles.
3. $\angle 1 \cong \angle 2$	**3.** Theorem 3–6: If two angles are right angles, then the angles are congruent.
4. $\ell \parallel m$	**4.** Theorem 6–5: In a plane, if two lines are cut by a transversal so that a pair of corresponding angles are congruent, then the two lines are parallel.

EN: Ex: 7-9, Wr: 2-12 evens; p. 185, C: 1-3; AV: Ex: 1-9, Wr: 1-6; p. 180, Wr: 8-10,

exercises

E: 1-6; p. 185, C: 1-3

Exploratory **For each of the following, determine which theorem or theorems you would use to prove $\ell \parallel m$.** Answers may vary. Typical answers are given.

1. Theorem 3-10; Theorem 6-6

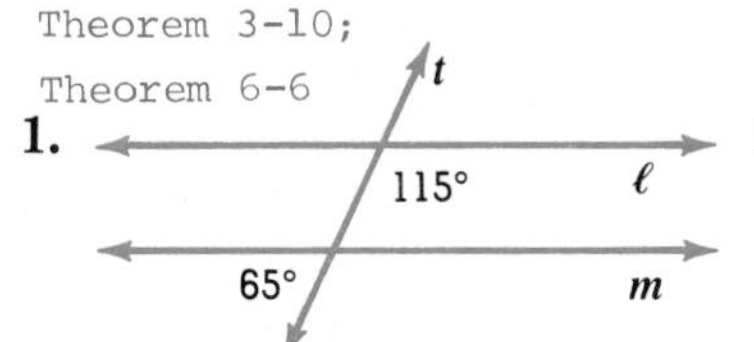

2. Theorem 6-5

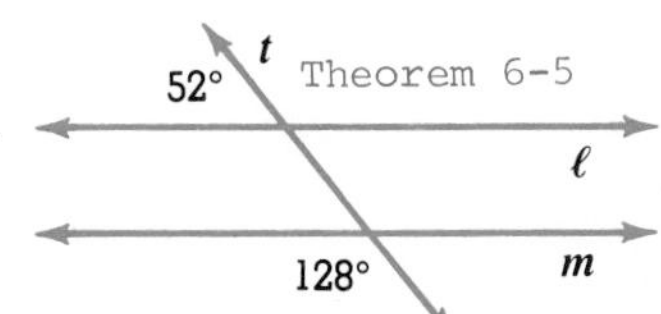

3. Theorem 6-8

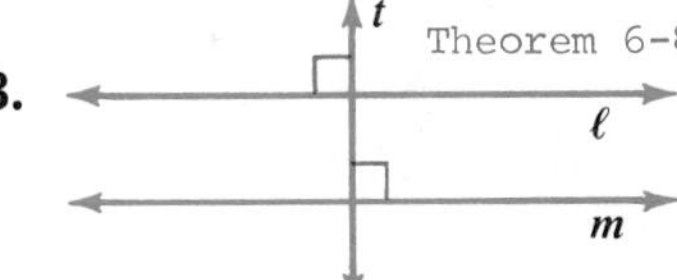

4. Theorem 6-7

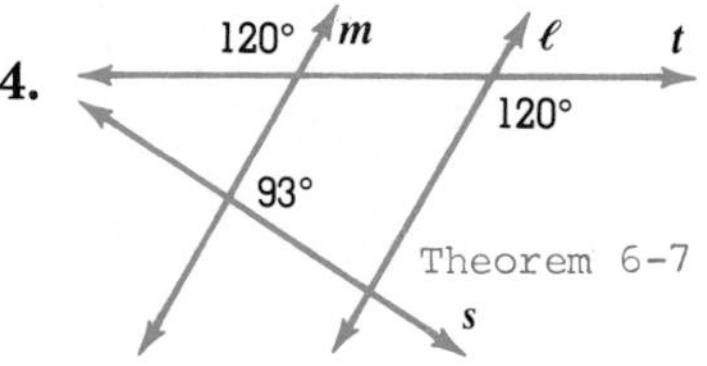

5. Theorem 6-4

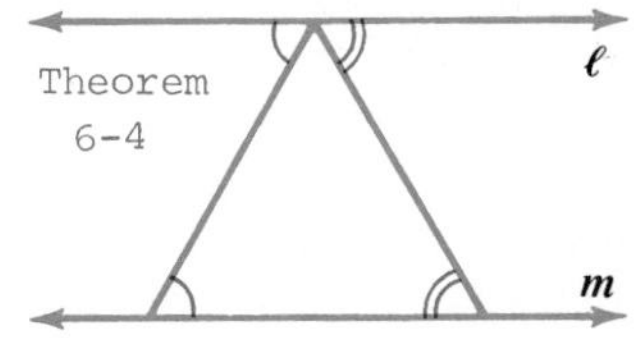

6. Theorem 6-7

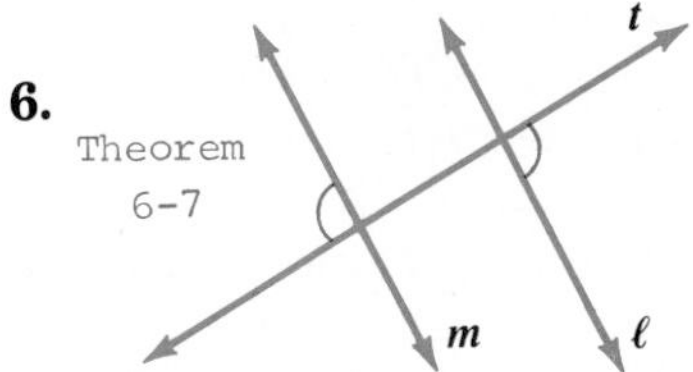

7. Theorem 6-5

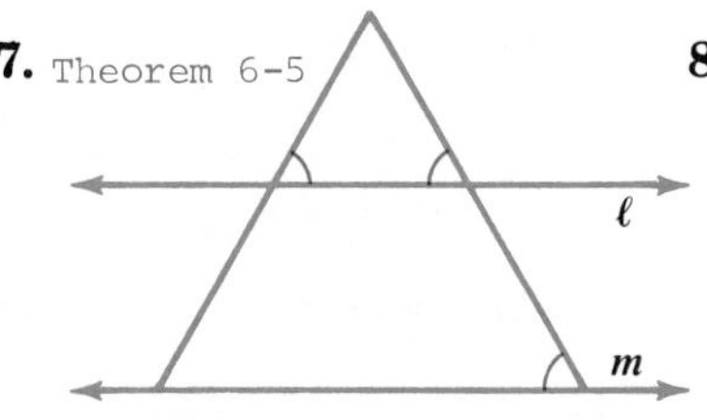

8. not possible

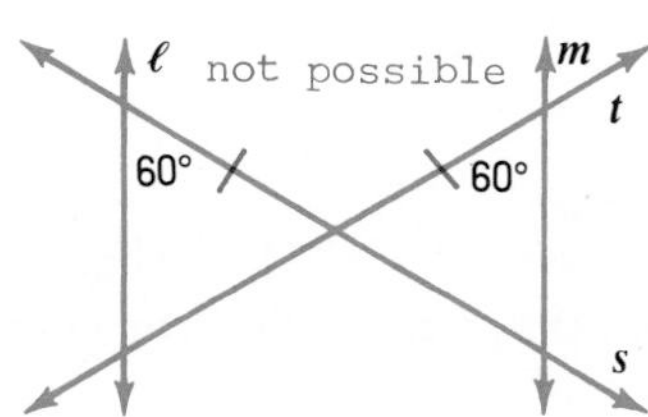

9. Theorem 6-6

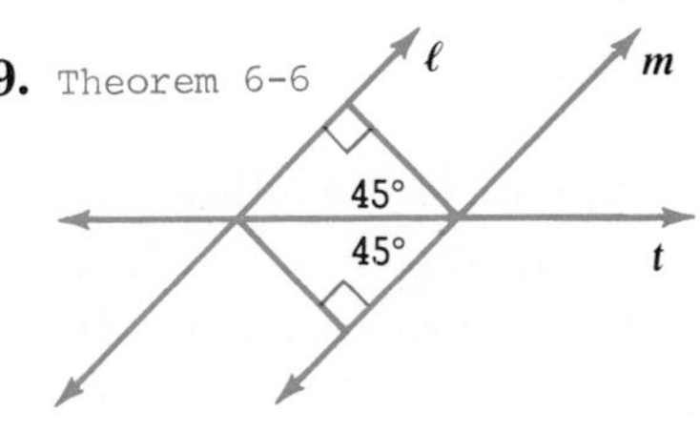

FN: Ex: 1-9, Wr: 1-6; p. 185, C: 1-3; p. 180, Wr: 8-10

For answers to exercises 1-12, see the Teacher's Guide.

Written **Prove each of the following.**

1. **Given:** $\angle R$ and $\angle S$ are supplementary.
   $\angle Q \cong \angle S$
   Prove: $\overline{QP} \parallel \overline{RS}$

2. **Given:** $\angle Q$ and $\angle R$ are supplementary.
   $\angle S \cong \angle Q$
   Prove: $\overline{QR} \parallel \overline{PS}$

Exercises 1 and 2

3. **Given:** $\angle 1 \cong \angle 3$
   $\overline{AD} \cong \overline{CB}$
   Prove: $\overline{DC} \cong \overline{BA}$

4. **Given:** $\overline{AD} \cong \overline{CB}$
   $\overline{DC} \cong \overline{BA}$
   Prove: $\overline{DC} \parallel \overline{AB}$

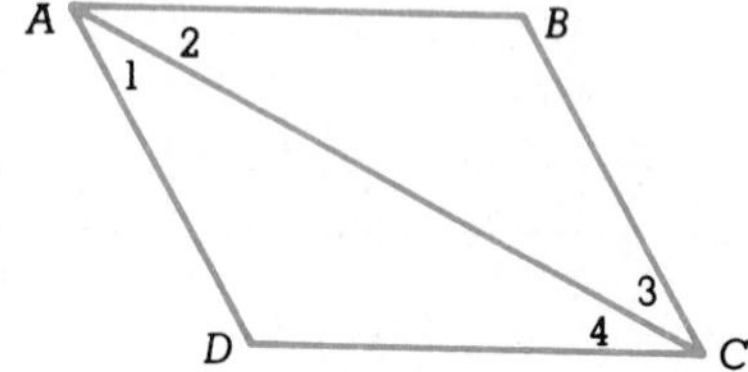

Exercises 3 and 4

5. **Given:** $\overline{MP} \cong \overline{MQ}$
   $\angle 1 \cong \angle N$
   Prove: $\overline{PQ} \parallel \overline{LN}$

6. **Given:** $\overline{MP} \cong \overline{MQ}$
   $\angle L$ and $\angle 4$ are supplementary.
   Prove: $\overline{PQ} \parallel \overline{LN}$

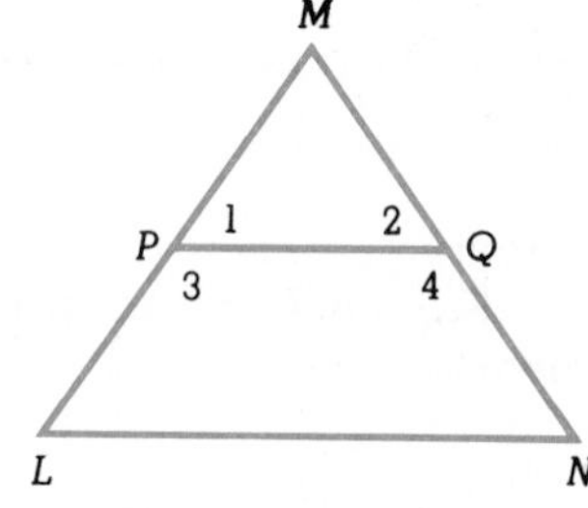

Exercises 5 and 6

7. **Given:** $\angle 1 \cong \angle 2$
   Prove: $\overline{BC} \parallel \overline{FE}$

8. **Given:** $\overline{AF} \perp \overline{AD}$
   $\overline{CD} \perp \overline{AD}$
   Prove: $\overline{AF} \parallel \overline{CD}$

9. **Given:** $\angle F$ and $\angle 2$ are complementary.
   $\angle C$ and $\angle 1$ are complementary.
   Prove: $\overline{AF} \parallel \overline{CD}$

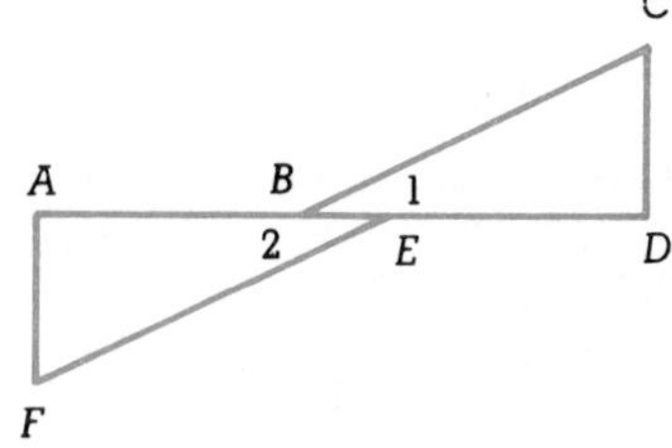

Exercises 7–9

Prove each of the following.

10. Theorem 6–6

11. Theorem 6–7

12. If two lines are cut by a transversal so a pair of corresponding angles are congruent, then the bisectors of those angles are parallel.

careers

Soil Scientist

Fran Williams is a soil scientist for Anderson Brothers' Farms. He helps plan land use, including preventing soil erosion and providing irrigation. Fran plans the location of parallel rows of pipelines to irrigate the fields such as the one pictured at the right.

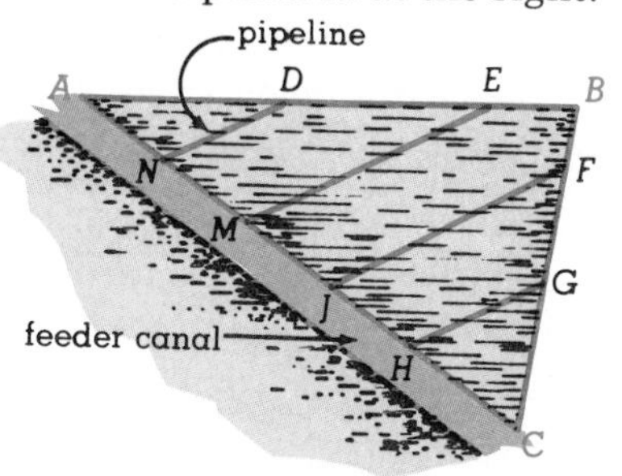

The pipes must be aligned at the correct angles to be parallel. For example, in the field pictured, suppose $m\angle C = 65$, $m\angle B = 80$, and pipeline $\overline{GH}$ is laid so that $m\angle GHC = 60$. Find the degree measure of $\angle AEM$.

$$\begin{aligned} m\angle A + m\angle B + m\angle C &= 180 \\ m\angle A + 80 + 65 &= 180 \\ m\angle A &= 35 \end{aligned}$$

$$\begin{aligned} \angle CME &\cong \angle CHG \\ m\angle CME &= m\angle CHG \\ m\angle CME &= 60 \end{aligned}$$

$$\begin{aligned} m\angle CME + m\angle AME &= 180 \\ 60 + m\angle AME &= 180 \\ m\angle AME &= 120 \\ m\angle A + m\angle AME + m\angle AEM &= 180 \\ 35 + 120 + m\angle AEM &= 180 \\ m\angle AEM &= 25 \end{aligned}$$

Exercises **For each of the following, find $m\angle AEK$.**

1. m∠AEK = 90 2. m∠AEK = 75 3. m∠AEK = 70

1.

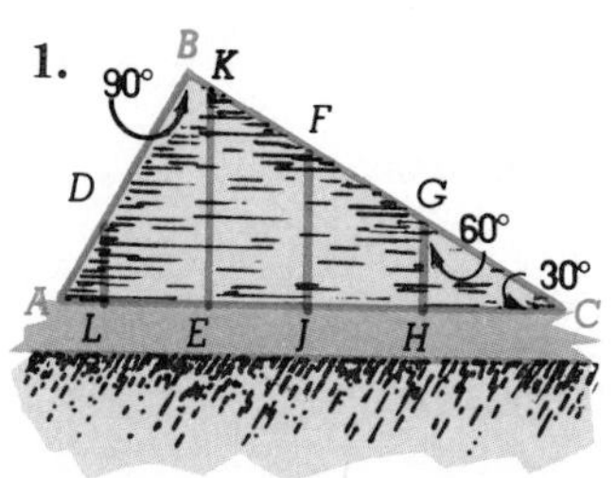

2.

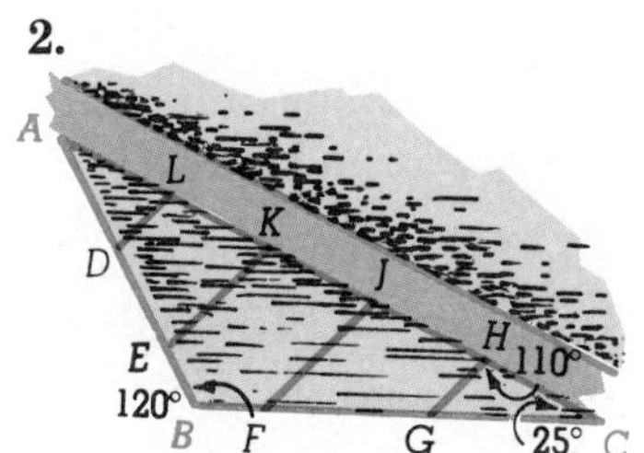

3.

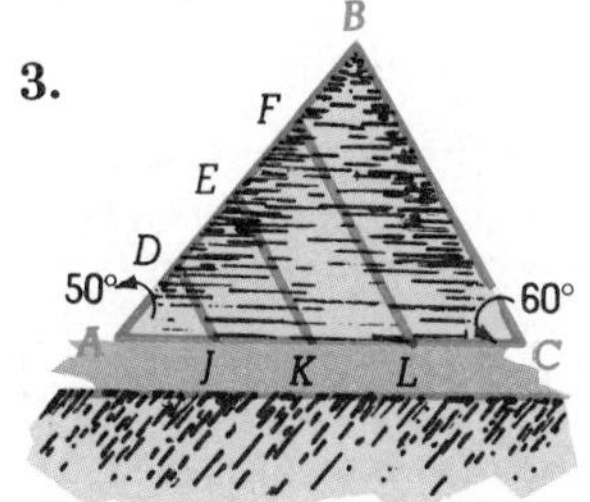

Objectives: to use properties of parallel lines to find measures of angles, to use the Parallel Postulate and related theorems in proofs

6–4 The Parallel Postulate

Around 300 B.C., Euclid developed a system for geometry similar to what is used today. He wrote five postulates. His first four postulates were very basic and simple. In contrast, the fifth postulate was more complex.

Many mathematicians throughout history thought Euclid's fifth postulate could be proven. They tried to prove it, without success.

The Parallel Postulate is one version of Euclid's fifth postulate.

This statement is called Playfair's Axiom after John Playfair's statement published in 1795.

If there is a line and a point *not* on the line, then there is exactly one line through the point that is parallel to the given line.

Postulate 6–1 Parallel Postulate

Notice that "exactly one" is used in the Parallel Postulate. Thus, the Parallel Postulate assumes two cases.

First, it states that at least one line can be drawn through a given point parallel to a given line.

Second, it states that no more than one line can be drawn parallel to a given line.

Other geometries have been developed based on the two cases stated. One geometry states that no line can be drawn parallel while another geometry states that more than one line can be drawn parallel.

In using the Parallel Postulate to prove statements about parallel lines, it is helpful to use indirect proofs.

If two parallel lines are cut by a transversal, then each pair of corresponding angles are congruent.

Theorem 6–9

If two parallel lines are cut by a transversal, then each pair of alternate interior angles are congruent.

Theorem 6–10

If two parallel lines are cut by a transversal, then each pair of consecutive interior angles are supplementary.

Theorem 6–11

If two parallel lines are cut by a transversal, then each pair of alternate exterior angles are congruent.

Theorem 6–12

Students prove Theorems 6-10, 6-11, and 6-12 in Written exercises 19, 20, and 21.

example

1 Prove Theorem 6–9.

Given: $\ell \parallel m$
Prove: $\angle 1 \cong \angle 2$
$\angle 3 \cong \angle 4$
$\angle 5 \cong \angle 6$
$\angle 7 \cong \angle 8$

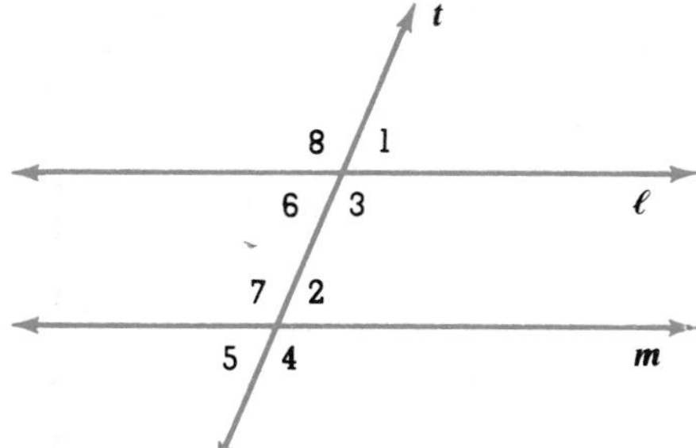

Proof:

Suppose $\angle 1$ is *not* congruent to $\angle 2$.

Draw $\overleftrightarrow{QP}$ so that $m\angle RQP = m\angle 2$. The Protractor Postulate justifies such a construction and guarantees that $\overleftrightarrow{QP}$ and ℓ are different lines. By the definition of congruent angles, $\angle RQP \cong \angle 2$. Thus, since they are corresponding angles, $\overleftrightarrow{QP} \parallel m$. But, $\ell \parallel m$. Since $\overleftrightarrow{QP}$ and ℓ are different lines, and both go through Q, the Parallel Postulate is contradicted.

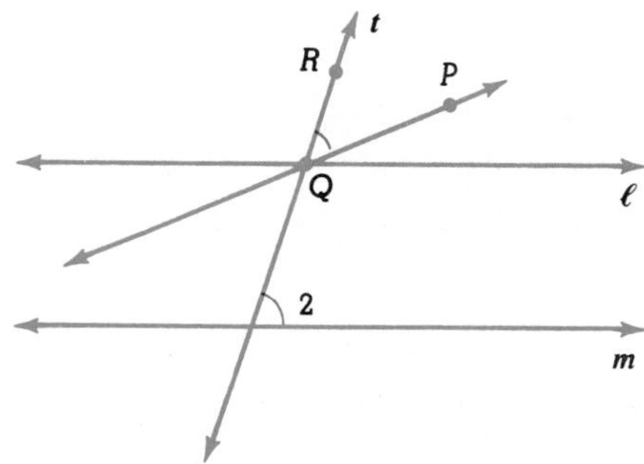

The original assumption is false.

Thus, $\angle 1 \cong \angle 2$.

If one pair of corresponding angles is congruent, then all pairs of corresponding angles are congruent. Since $\angle 1 \cong \angle 2$, all other pairs are congruent. Thus, $\angle 3 \cong \angle 4$, $\angle 5 \cong \angle 6$, and $\angle 7 \cong \angle 8$.

Many theorems of Euclidean geometry depend on the Parallel Postulate. These theorems will be used as reasons in many proofs.

The sum of the degree measures of the angles of a triangle was accepted to be 180 without proof in Chapter 4. Using the Parallel Postulate, we can now prove it.

example

2 **Prove that the sum of the degree measures of the angles of a triangle is 180.**

This is the Angle Sum Theorem, Theorem 4-1, p. 107.

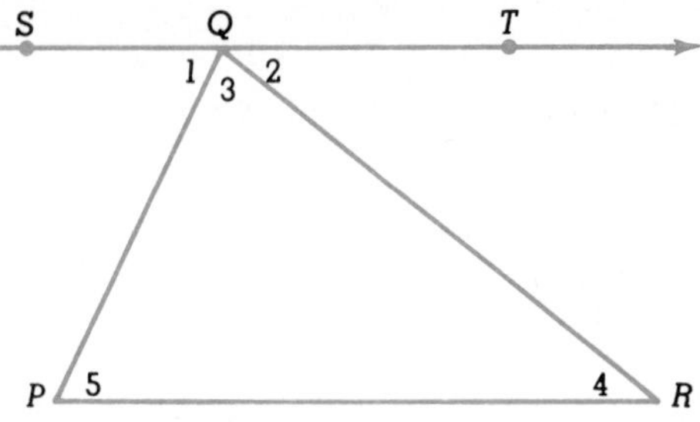

Given: $\triangle PQR$

Prove: $m\angle 5 + m\angle 4 + m\angle 3 = 180$

Proof:

STATEMENTS	REASONS
1. Draw $\overleftrightarrow{ST}$ through Q and parallel to $\overline{PR}$	**1.** Postulate 6–1: Parallel Postulate
2. $m\angle 1 + m\angle PQT = 180$	**2.** Postulate 3–4: If two angles form a linear pair, then they are supplementary.
3. $m\angle 2 + m\angle 3 = m\angle PQT$	**3.** Postulate 3–3: The Angle Addition Postulate
4. $m\angle 1 + m\angle 2 + m\angle 3 = 180$	**4.** Postulate 2–9: Substitution
5. $\angle 2 \cong \angle 4$, $\angle 1 \cong \angle 5$	**5.** Theorem 6–10: If two parallel lines are cut by a transversal, then each pair of alternate interior angles are congruent.
6. $m\angle 2 = m\angle 4$, $m\angle 1 = m\angle 5$	**6.** Definition of Congruent Angles
7. $m\angle 5 + m\angle 4 + m\angle 3 = 180$	**7.** Postulate 2–9: Substitution

EN: Wr: 2-10 evens, 11-22; p. 190, Ch: 1-2; AV: Ex: 1-6, Wr: 1-20; p. 184, Wr: 8-12 evens

exercises

For answers to exercises 1-4, see the Teacher's Guide.

Exploratory **Use the figure to answer each of the following. Assume $t \parallel s$ and $\ell \parallel m$.**

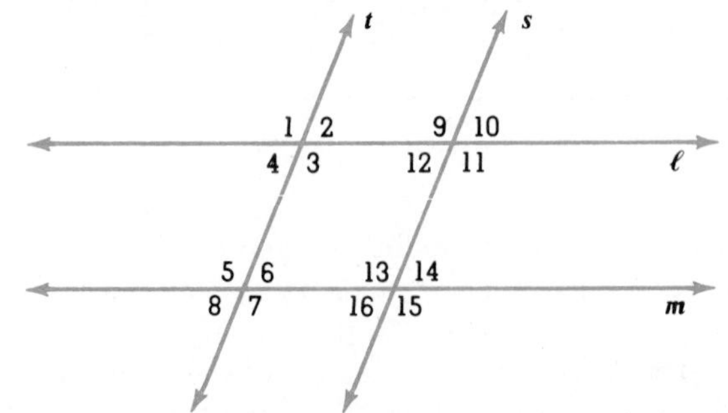

1. Name four pairs of congruent alternate interior angles and the transversals which form them.
2. Name four pairs of congruent corresponding angles and the transversals which form them.
3. Name four pairs of supplementary consecutive interior angles and the transversals which form them.
4. Name four pairs of congruent exterior angles and the transversals which form them.

FN: Ex: 1-6, Wr: 1-18; p. 184, Wr: 7-10

In the figure at the right, $\overline{ST} \parallel \overline{PR}$.

5. Name four pairs of congruent alternate interior angles. ∠1, ∠5 ∠2, ∠4 ∠TQP, ∠6 ∠SQR, ∠7
6. Name four pairs of supplementary consecutive interior angles. ∠1, ∠6 ∠2, ∠7 ∠TQP, ∠5 ∠SQR, ∠4

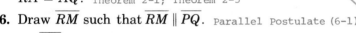

Written **Each of the following might be a statement in a formal proof. For each statement, name a postulate or theorem that justifies the statement.**

1. Draw $\overleftrightarrow{QT}$ so that $\overline{QT} \parallel \overline{PR}$. Parallel Postulate (6-1)
2. Draw $\overline{SV}$ so that $\overline{PR} \parallel \overline{SV}$. Parallel Postulate (6-1)
3. Draw $\overline{SV}$ so that $\angle QSV \cong \angle SPR$. Parallel Postulate (6-1) or Protractor Postulate (3-2)
4. Call W the midpoint of $\overline{PR}$. Theorem 2-1
5. On $\overline{RQ}$, call A the point such that $\overline{RA} \cong \overline{AQ}$. Theorem 2-1; Theorem 2-5
6. Draw $\overline{RM}$ such that $\overline{RM} \parallel \overline{PQ}$. Parallel Postulate (6-1)
7. On $\overline{RQ}$, call C the point such that $\overline{SC}$ bisects $\overline{RQ}$. Theorem 2-6: Bisector Theorem
8. On $\overline{PR}$, call D the point such that $\overline{SD} \parallel \overline{RQ}$. Parallel Postulate (6-1)
9. Draw $\overline{RS}$. Postulate 1-1
10. Draw $\overline{PF}$ so that $\angle SPF \cong \angle SQR$. Protractor Postulate (3-2) or Parallel Postulate (6-1)

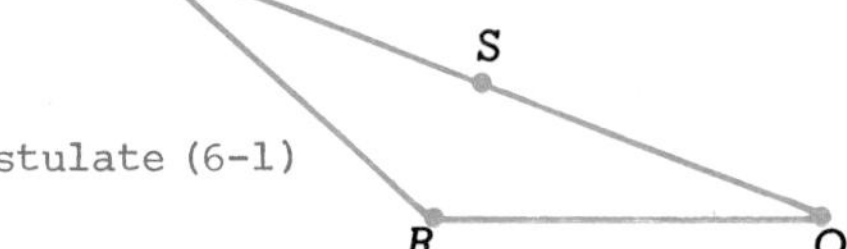

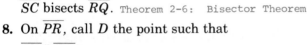

In the diagram at the right, $\overline{QR} \parallel \overline{TV}$. Find the degree measures for each of the following.

11. $m\angle 1$ 33
12. $m\angle 4$ 57
13. $m\angle 2$ 57
14. $m\angle 6$ 90
15. $m\angle 3$ 123
16. $m\angle 5$ 90
17. $m\angle 7$ 90
18. $m\angle Q$ 60

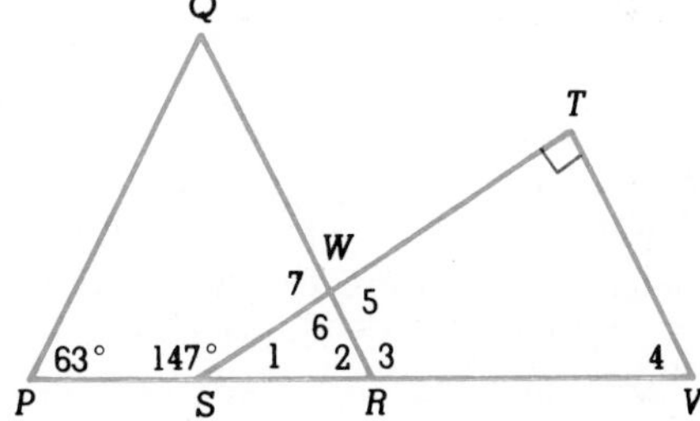

Prove each of the following. For answers to exercises 19-22, see the Teacher's Guide.

19. Theorem 6–10 by contradicting the Parallel Postulate.
20. Theorem 6–11 by contradicting the Parallel Postulate.
21. Theorem 6–12 by contradicting the Parallel Postulate.
22. If $\ell \parallel m$ and $m \parallel n$, then $\ell \parallel n$.

Challenge **Answer each of the following.**

1. In the diagram, $\overrightarrow{QT} \parallel \overrightarrow{RS}$, find $m\angle P + m\angle Q + m\angle R$.

   m ∠P + m∠Q + m ∠R = 360

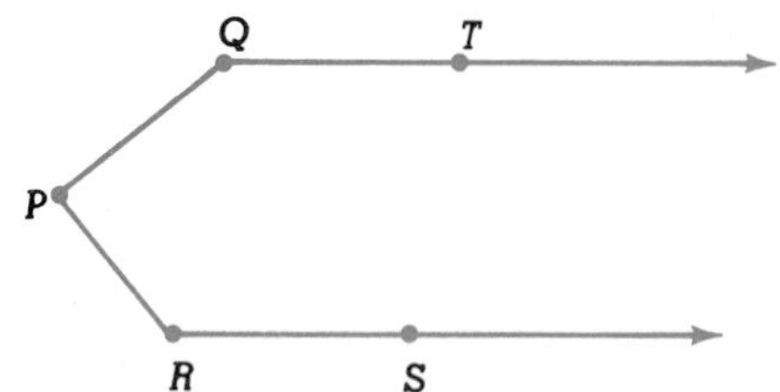

2. Use the diagram to find $m\angle D$. m ∠D = 108

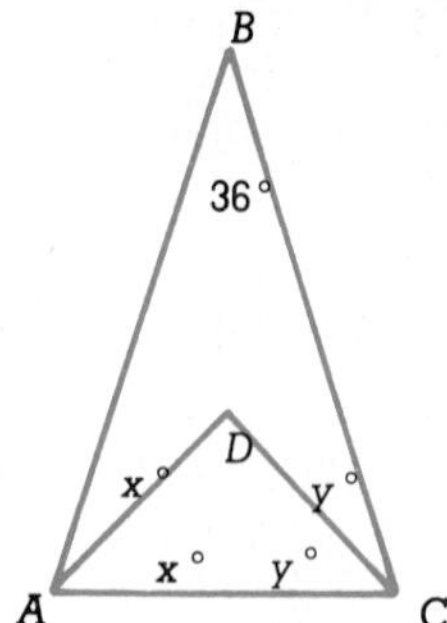

Computer Languages

computers

Before modern computer languages were developed and standardized, it was necessary to communicate with a computer in fundamental numeric code. The computer programmer had to reserve various addresses for locations of constants and variables, to manipulate them in prescribed ways and to store the results where needed. Such fundamental programs were written in what is referred to as "machine language." Machine language is inconvenient since it requires a complete knowledge of computers. Symbolic languages were developed to help the programmer. These languages make it possible to program computers in a relatively short time.

Many microcomputers use the computer language BASIC (*B*eginner's *A*ll-purpose *S*ymbolic *I*nstruction *C*ode). Special attention will be given to this language in the Appendix.

FORTRAN was developed early in the history of programming languages primarily for scientific use. It has had a wide usage, is quite standardized, and is still used extensively. FORTRAN's symbol expressions follow that of ordinary algebra quite carefully.

COBOL translates about 250 reserved words and phrases common to business English to instructions for the computer. The experienced COBOL programmer can easily follow any COBOL program since the design is quite carefully dictated.

Another programming language used is PASCAL. It is a structured language. The program is reduced to writing appropriate modules which are used by a main program. Since PASCAL is not an interactive language, it usually requires more careful and detailed programming than BASIC.

It is difficult to compare languages since each language has been developed for a different purpose. The preference of the programmer, the purpose of the program, and the available language for a computer determines the language to be used.

6–5 Using Parallels

Objectives: to recognize properties of parallel and perpendicular lines, to use properties of parallel and perpendicular lines in proofs

Viewed from the sides, the floors of a building represent parallel line segments. In most buildings, the outside walls are vertical. They are perpendicular to the ground floor. What angle do they form with each of the other floors? 90°

In a plane, if a line is perpendicular to one of two parallel lines, then it is perpendicular to the other.

Theorem 6–13

example

1 **Prove Theorem 6–13.**

Given: $t \perp m$
$\ell \parallel m$
Prove: $t \perp \ell$

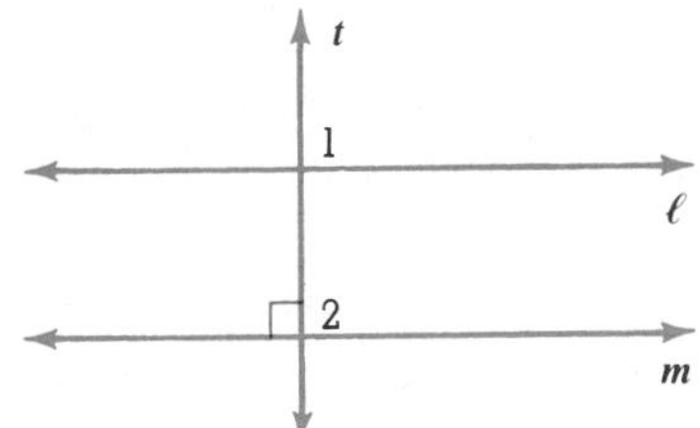

Proof:

STATEMENTS	REASONS
1. $t \perp m$	1. Given
2. $\angle 2$ is a right angle.	2. Theorem 3–11: If two lines are perpendicular, then they form four right angles.
3. $m\angle 2 = 90$	3. Definition of Right Angle
4. $\ell \parallel m$	4. Given
5. $\angle 1 \cong \angle 2$	5. Theorem 6–9: If two parallel lines are cut by a transversal, then each pair of corresponding angles are congruent.
6. $m\angle 1 = m\angle 2$	6. Definition of Congruent Angles
7. $m\angle 1 = 90$	7. Postulate 2–9: Substitution
8. $\angle 1$ is a right angle.	8. Definition of Right Angle
9. $t \perp \ell$	9. Definition of Perpendicular Lines

Many geometric figures have parallel segments. By using the properties of parallel lines, you can discover properties of the figures themselves.

examples

2 **In the figure at the right, opposite sides are parallel. How are the measures of the opposite sides related?**

They are equal.

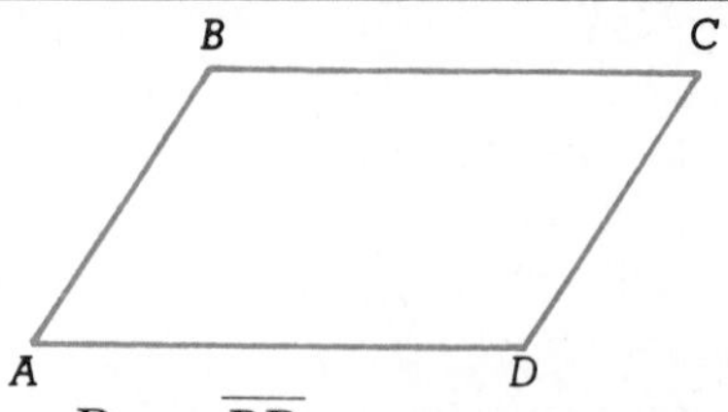

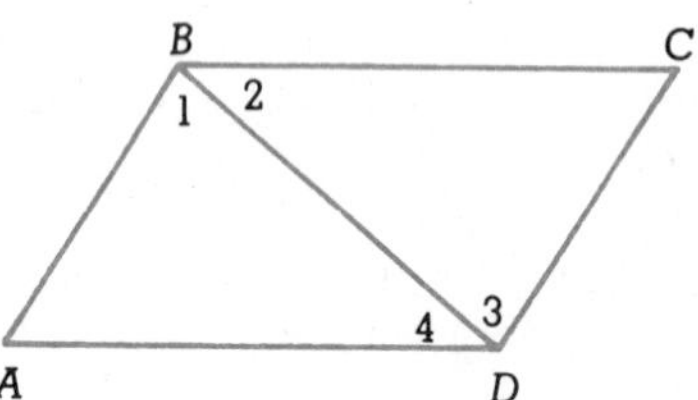

Draw $\overline{BD}$.
Since $\overline{BC} \parallel \overline{AD}$, you can show that $\angle 2 \cong \angle 4$. Similarly, since $\overline{AB} \parallel \overline{CD}$, you can show that $\angle 1 \cong \angle 3$. Finally, $\overline{BD} \cong \overline{DB}$. Thus, the two triangles formed are congruent. That is,

$$\triangle ABD \cong \triangle CDB.$$

The opposite sides of the figure are corresponding parts of congruent triangles and are congruent. Since congruent segments have the same measures, you can conclude the following.

$$AB = CD \text{ and } DA = BC$$

3 **Complete the following proof.**

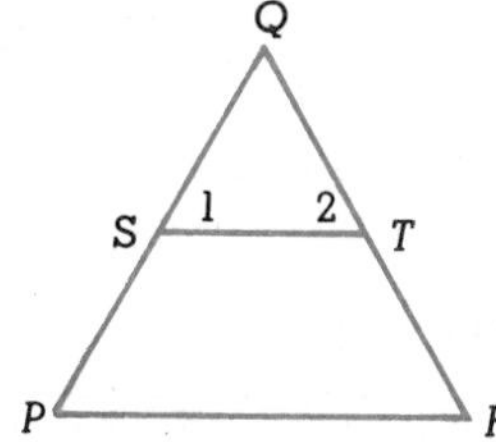

Given: $\overline{QS} \cong \overline{QT}$
$\overline{ST} \parallel \overline{PR}$

Prove: $\angle P \cong \angle R$

Proof:

STATEMENTS	REASONS
1. $\overline{QS} \cong \overline{QT}$	1. Given
2. $\angle 1 \cong \angle 2$	2. Theorem 4–6: Isosceles Triangle Theorem
3. $\overline{ST} \parallel \overline{PR}$	3. Given
4. $\angle P \cong \angle 1$ $\angle 2 \cong \angle R$	4. Theorem 6–9: If two parallel lines are cut by a transversal, then each pair of corresponding angles are congruent.
5. $\angle P \cong \angle R$	5. Theorem 3–1: Congruence of angles is reflexive, symmetric, and transitive.

EN: Ex: 2-22 evens, Wr: 2-12 evens; AV: Ex: 1-22, Wr: 1-11 odds; p. 189, Wr: 21-22

exercises

Exploratory **In the diagram, $m \parallel n$. For each of the following, state *yes* or *no*.**

1. $\angle 5 \cong \angle 2$ yes
2. $\angle 3 \cong \angle 8$ yes
3. $\angle 3 \cong \angle 4$ yes
4. $\angle 2 \cong \angle 6$ no
5. $\angle 4 \cong \angle 8$ yes
6. $m\angle 5 + m\angle 6 = m\angle 7$ yes
7. $m\angle 3 + m\angle 6 = m\angle 12$ no

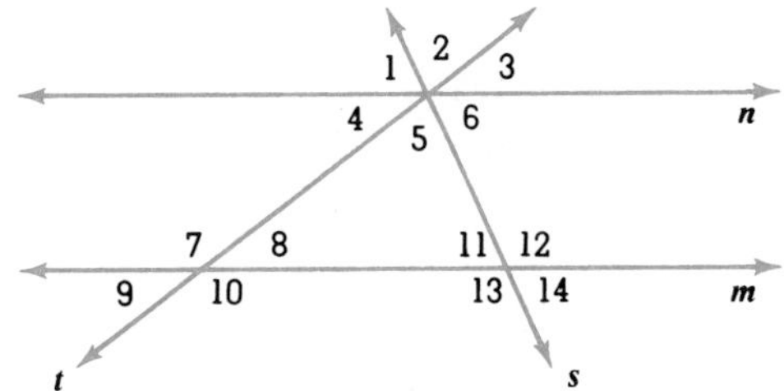

8. $\angle 4$ and $\angle 12$ are alternate interior angles. no
9. $\angle 2$ and $\angle 4$ are corresponding angles. no
10. $\angle 4$ and $\angle 7$ are supplementary angles. yes
11. $\angle 5$ and $\angle 11$ are supplementary angles. no

In the diagram, $\ell \parallel m$ and $r \parallel s$. For each of the following, state *yes* or *no*.

12. $\angle 2 \cong \angle 3$ yes
13. $\angle 1 \cong \angle 4$ yes
14. $\angle 7 \cong \angle 8$ yes
15. $\angle 6 \cong \angle 9$ yes
16. $m\angle 3 + m\angle 4 + m\angle 7 = 180$ yes
17. $m\angle 1 + m\angle 2 + m\angle 7 = 180$ yes
18. $\angle 5$ and $\angle 2$ are corresponding angles. no

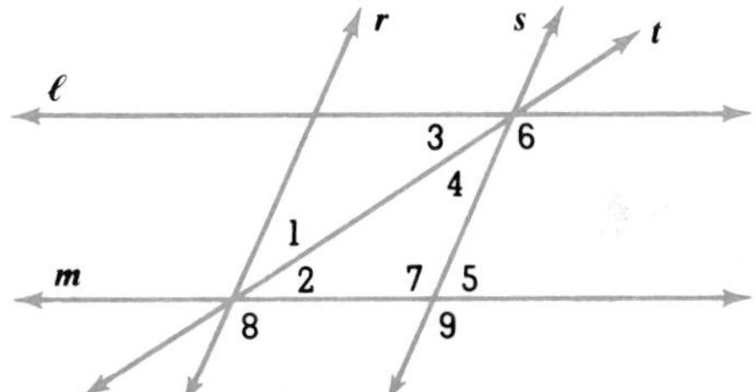

19. $\angle 7$ and $\angle 8$ are alternate interior angles. yes
20. $\angle 4$ and $\angle 7$ are supplementary angles. no
21. $\angle 6$ and $\angle 5$ are supplementary angles. yes
22. $\angle 3$ and $\angle 4$ are vertical angles. no

FN: Ex: 1-22, Wr: 1-11 odds; p. 189, Wr: 19-20

Written **Prove each of the following.** For answers to exercises 1-10, see the Teacher's Guide.

1. **Given:** $\overline{AB} \parallel \overline{CD}$
   $\overline{BC} \perp \overline{CD}$, $\overline{AB} \perp \overline{AD}$
   Prove: $\overline{BC} \parallel \overline{AD}$

2. **Given:** $\overline{BC} \parallel \overline{AD}$
   $\overline{CD} \perp \overline{BC}$
   $\overline{AB} \perp \overline{AD}$
   Prove: $\overline{AB} \parallel \overline{CD}$

Exercises 1 and 2

3. **Given:** $\overline{QS} \parallel \overline{PT}$
   $\angle T$ is a right angle.
   Prove: $\triangle RQS$ is a right triangle.

4. **Given:** $\overline{QS} \parallel \overline{PT}$
   $\angle T$ is a right angle.
   Prove: $\overline{RS} \perp \overline{QS}$

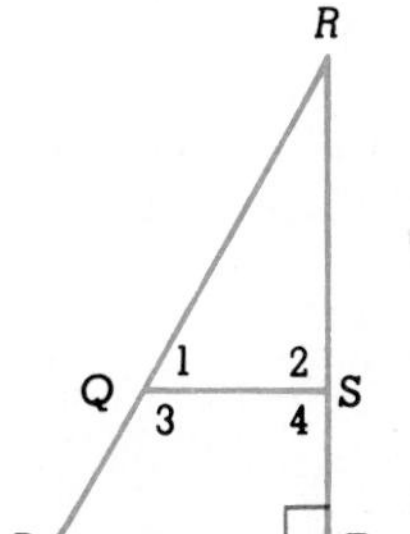

Exercises 3 and 4

5. **Given:** $\overline{BA} \parallel \overline{ED}$
$\overline{BA} \cong \overline{DE}$
Prove: $\overline{EC} \cong \overline{AC}$

6. **Given:** $\overline{BA} \parallel \overline{ED}$
C is the midpoint of $\overline{BD}$.
Prove: $\overline{EC} \cong \overline{AC}$

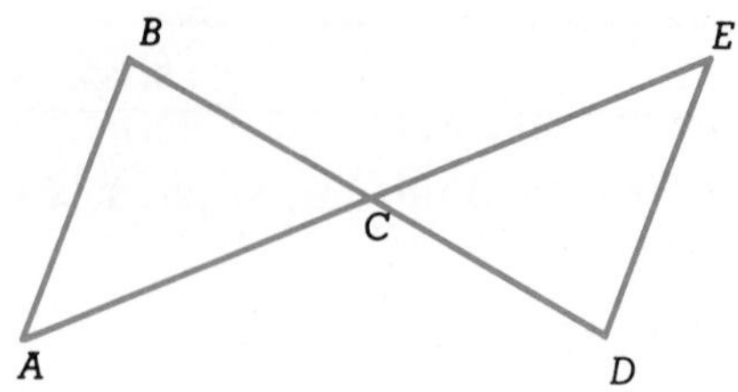

Exercises 5 and 6

7. **Given:** $\overline{QS} \parallel \overline{PT}$
$\triangle QRS$ is equilateral.
R is the midpoint of $\overline{PT}$.
Prove: $\overline{PQ} \cong \overline{TS}$

8. **Given:** $\overline{QS} \parallel \overline{PT}$
$\triangle QRS$ is equilateral.
R is the midpoint of $\overline{PT}$.
Prove: $\angle P \cong \angle T$

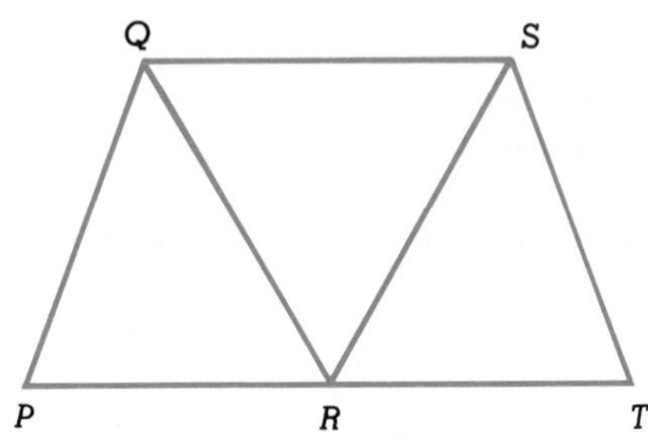

Exercises 7 and 8

9. **Given:** $\overline{BC} \parallel \overline{AE}$
$\angle 1 \cong \angle 2$
$\angle 3 \cong \angle 4$
Prove: $\overline{BD} \perp \overline{AD}$

10. **Given:** $\overline{AB} \parallel \overline{CE}$
$\overline{BD} \cong \overline{AD}$
Prove: $\angle BDC \cong \angle ADE$

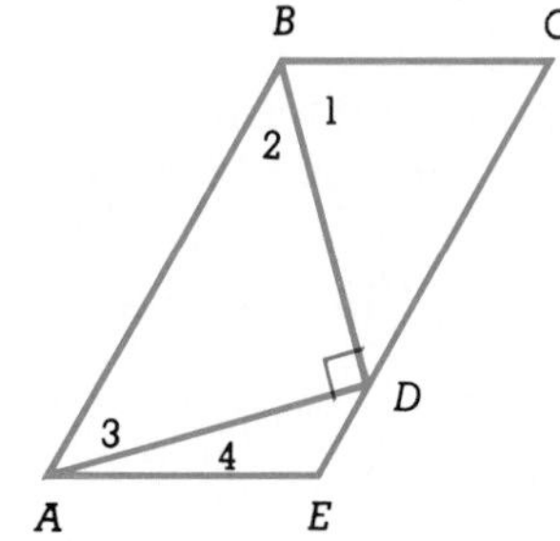

Exercises 9 and 10

In exercises 11-12, point out that the triangle and the T-square shown in the diagrams can be considered straightedges.

Drafting artists normally have two different triangles. For each of the following, name the degree measure of the angles the parallel lines form with the straightedge.

11. Triangle: 45, 135; T-square: 75, 105

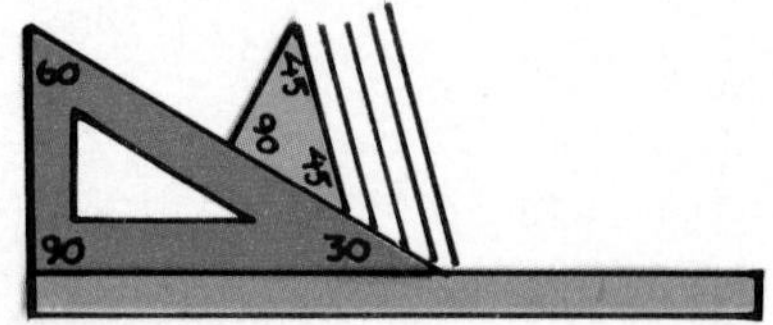

12. Triangle: 90, 90; T-square: 120, 60

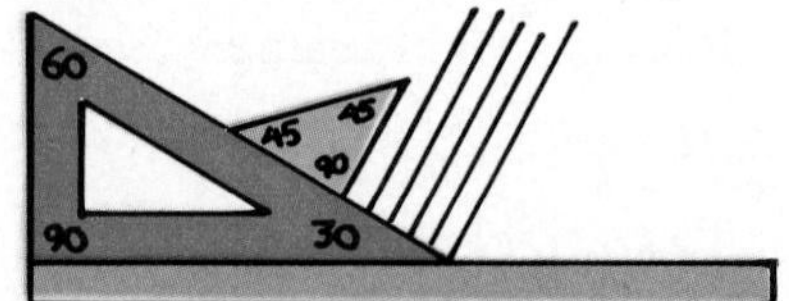

6–6 Distance

Objective: to recognize and use distance relationships between lines and between points and lines

Given a line and a point *not* on the line, it is possible to construct another line through the point and perpendicular to the given line. In fact, there is only one such line.

Given a line and a point *not* on the line, there is exactly one line through the point that is perpendicular to the given line.

Theorem 6–14

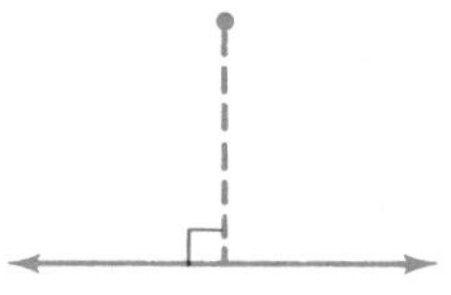

Because there is only one perpendicular segment between a point and a line, it can be used to define the distance from a point to a line.

The distance between a point and a line is the length of the segment perpendicular to the line from the point. The measure of the distance between a line and a point on the line is zero.

Definition of the Distance Between a Point and a Line

Can you talk about the distance between two lines? If the two lines are parallel, the answer is yes.

In a plane, two lines are parallel if and only if they are everywhere equidistant.

Theorem 6–15

Equidistant *means* at the same distance.

When weavers stretch yarn on a frame, they adjust the distance between strips of yarn both at the top and at the bottom of the frame. Then they know the strips of yarn are the same distance apart from top to bottom.

Knowing two lines are parallel, we can define the distance by using any point of one line and the other line.

The distance between two parallel lines is the distance between one of the lines and any point on the other line.

Definition of the Distance Between Parallel Lines

example

1 Prove Theorem 6–15.

Given: $\ell \parallel m$
Prove: $AC = DB$

A flow proof can be used to help students visualize the sequence of ideas.

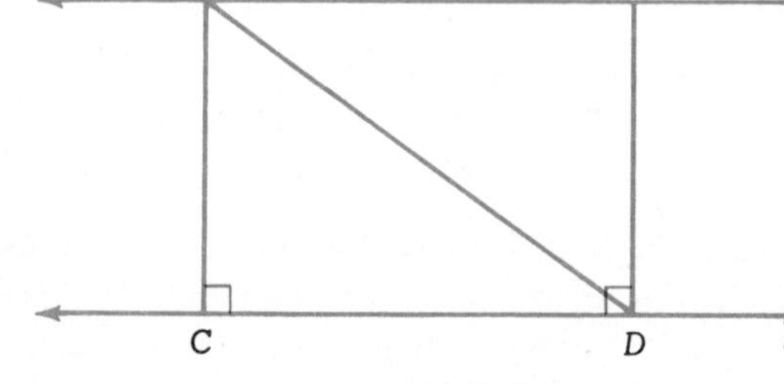

Proof:

STATEMENTS	REASONS
1. A and B lie on ℓ.	1. Postulate 1–3: A line contains at least two points.
2. $\overline{AC} \perp m$ $\overline{BD} \perp m$	2. Theorem 6–14: Given a line and a point *not* on a line, there is exactly one line through the point that is perpendicular to the given line.
3. $\ell \parallel m$	3. Given
4. $\overline{BD} \perp \ell$	4. Theorem 6–13: In a plane, if a line is perpendicular to one of two parallel lines, then it is perpendicular to the other.
5. $\angle ACD$ is a right angle. $\angle DBA$ is a right angle.	5. Theorem 3–11: If two lines are perpendicular, then they form four right angles.
6. Draw $\overline{AD}$.	6. Postulate 1–1: Through any two points, there is exactly one line.
7. $\triangle ACD$ is a right triangle. $\triangle DBA$ is a right triangle.	7. Definition of Right Triangle
8. $\angle BAD \cong \angle CDA$	8. Theorem 6–10: If two parallel lines are cut by a transversal, then each pair of alternate interior angles are congruent.
9. $\overline{AD} \cong \overline{AD}$	9. Theorem 2–2: Congruence of segments is reflexive.
10. $\triangle ACD \cong \triangle DBA$	10. Theorem 4–11: HA
11. $\overline{AC} \cong \overline{DB}$	11. Definition of Congruent Triangles CPCTC
12. $AC = DB$	12. Definition of Congruent Segments

EN: Ex: 1-6, Wr: 5-20; p. 199, E: 1-3, Ch: 1-4; AV: Ex: 1-6, Wr: 1-10, 19, 20; p. 199, Ch: 1-2; p. 194, Wr: 6-12 evens

exercises

Exploratory **Use the theorem to answer each of the following.** For answers to exercises 1-8, see the Teacher's Guide.

Given a line and a point *not* on the line there is exactly one line through the point that is perpendicular to the given line.

1. State the hypothesis of the theorem.
2. Draw and label a diagram to illustrate the hypothesis of the theorem.
3. State the given for a proof of the theorem.
4. State the conclusion of the theorem.
5. State the prove statement for a proof of the theorem.
6. The conclusion of the theorem contains the word exactly. Thus, the conclusion actually has two parts. State the two parts.

In a plane, two lines are parallel if and only if they are everywhere equidistant.

7. State the two parts of this theorem.
8. Draw and label a diagram to illustrate both parts of this theorem.

FN: Ex: 1-8, Wr: 1-18; pp. 193-4, Wr: 2-12 evens

Written **Use a protractor and the theorems from this chapter to determine whether or *not* the lines shown in color in each of the following are parallel. Write *yes* or *no*. Explain your answer.**

1. Yes, alt. interior ∠'s are ≅. 2. Yes, alt. interior ∠'s are ≅ after a transversal is drawn.

1.

2.

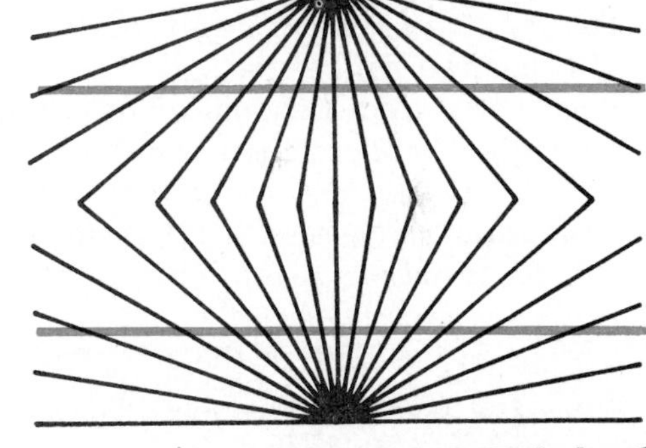

3.

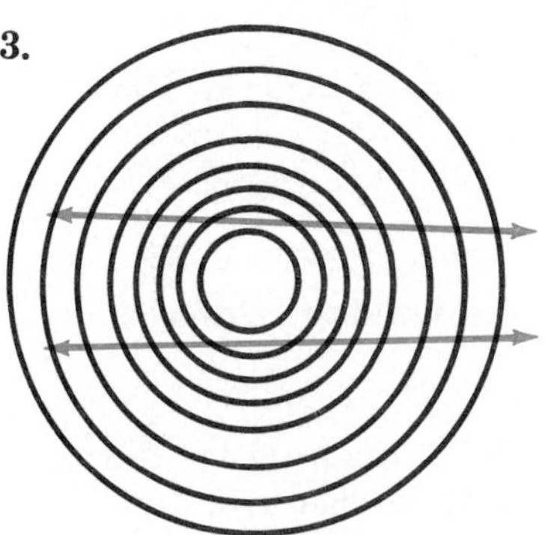

4.

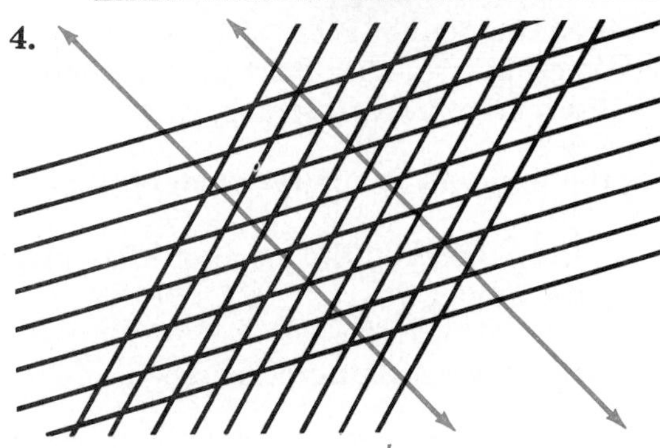

3. No, alt. interior ∠'s are not ≅ after a transversal is drawn.

4. Yes, alt. interior ∠'s are ≅.

Use the following proof of Theorem 6–14 to answer the questions.

Theorem: Given a line and a point *not* on the line, there is exactly one line through the point that is perpendicular to the given line.

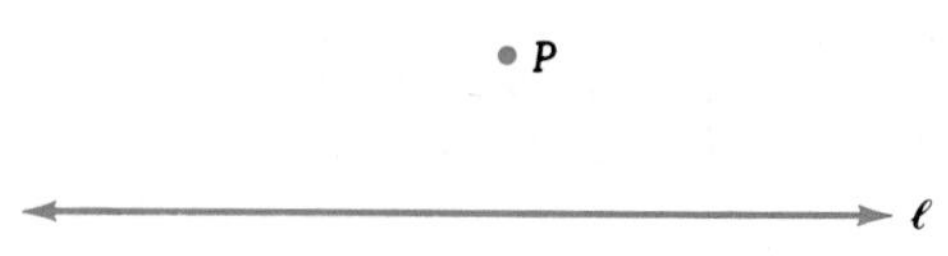

Given: ℓ and P *not* on ℓ

Prove: There is exactly one line through P that is perpendicular to ℓ.

Proof:

Part 1: Prove there is at least one perpendicular.

Through P draw m so that $m \parallel \ell$. Then, through P draw $\overleftrightarrow{PQ}$ so that $\overleftrightarrow{PQ} \perp m$. Therefore, $\overleftrightarrow{PQ} \perp \ell$.

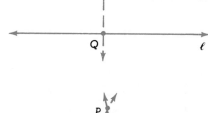

Part 2: Prove there is no more than one perpendicular.

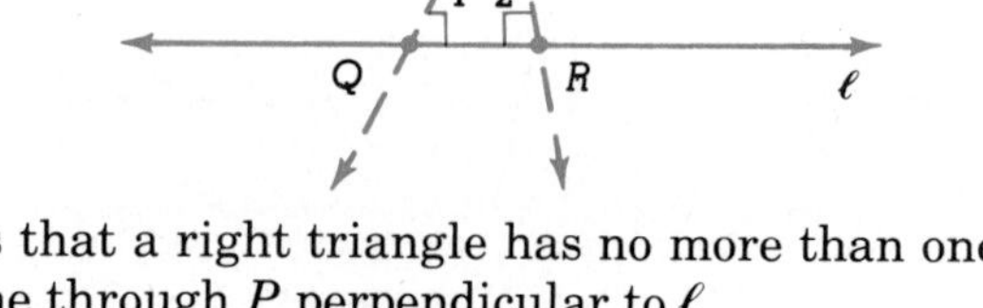

Suppose there is more than one perpendicular. Call $\overleftrightarrow{PQ}$ and $\overleftrightarrow{PR}$ two different lines through P and perpendicular to ℓ.

Then, $\angle 1$ and $\angle 2$ are right angles. Thus, $\triangle PQR$ has two right angles.

This is a contradiction, since Theorem 6–3 states that a right triangle has no more than one right angle. Therefore, there is no more than one line through P perpendicular to ℓ.

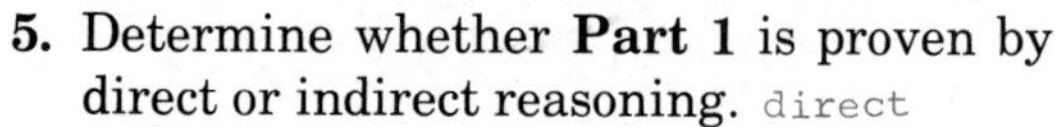

5. Determine whether **Part 1** is proven by direct or indirect reasoning. direct

6. State the postulate or theorem that justifies the **Part 1** statement. Through P draw m so that $m \parallel \ell$. Parallel Postulate 6-1

7. State the postulate or theorem that justifies the **Part 1** statement. Through P draw $\overleftrightarrow{PQ}$ so that $\overleftrightarrow{PQ} \perp m$. Theorem 3-12

8. State the postulate or theorem that justifies the **Part 1** statement, $\overleftrightarrow{PQ} \perp \ell$. Theorem 6-13

9. Determine whether **Part 2** is proven by direct or indirect reasoning. indirect

10. State the assumption made in **Part 2** of the proof. There is more than one perpendicular.

Use the theorem to answer each of the following.

If a point is on the bisector of an angle, then it is equidistant from the sides of the angle.

For answers to exercises 11-20, see the Teacher's Guide.

11. State the given for a proof of this theorem.

12. Draw and label a diagram to illustrate the hypothesis of the theorem.

13. Plan a proof of the theorem.

14. Write a proof for the theorem.

15. State the converse of the theorem.

16. Plan a proof for the converse of the theorem. Assume the point and the angle are coplanar.

17. Write a proof for the converse of the theorem.

18. Write an *if and only if* definition for the bisector of an angle, using "equidistant."

19. **Given:** $\angle 1$ and $\angle 2$ are right angles.
$\overline{AD} \parallel \overline{BC}$
Prove: $\overline{AD} \cong \overline{BC}$

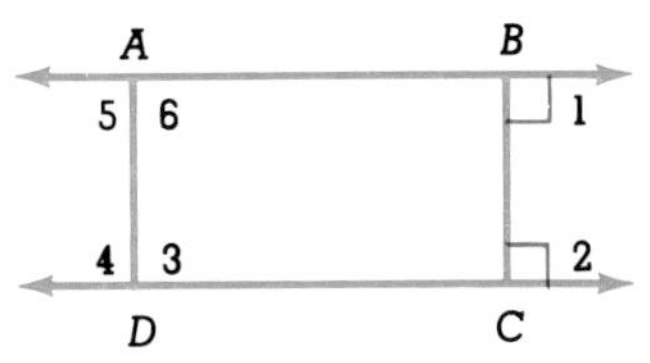

20. Juan is constructing a patio for his yard. He has the posts set as shown. In order to ensure $\overline{BA} \parallel \overline{CD}$, how far from A and C should D be located?

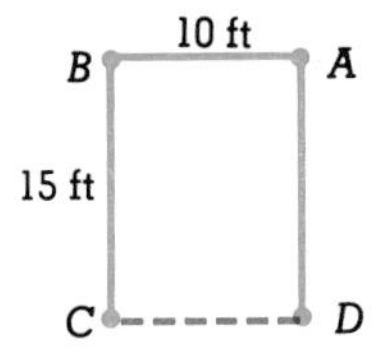

For answers to exercises 1-4, see the Teacher's Guide.

Challenge **Two planes, or a plane and a line, are parallel if and only if they do not intersect. Answer each of the following questions.**

1. If two lines lie in parallel planes, are the lines parallel? Write *yes* or *no*. Explain.

2. If a line is perpendicular to one of two parallel planes, is it perpendicular to the other? Write *yes* or *no*. Explain.

3. Explain how you would find the distance between two parallel planes.

4. Are parallel planes everywhere equidistant? Write *yes* or *no*. Explain.

Contradictions

excursions in geometry

Contradictory statements derived from an axiomatic system are called paradoxes. They indicate something is wrong with the axiomatic system. Several times in the history of mathematics the resolution of a paradox by changing an axiomatic system has led to the creation of new mathematics.

Find the contradiction in each of the following cases. For answers to exercises 1-3, see the Teacher's Guide.

1. Epimenides, the Cretan, stated that all Cretans are liars.

2. This statement is false.

3. Every library in Laputa lists the books in that library in a special book called a catalog. While some librarians list the catalog in the catalog, others do not. Gulliver, Chief Librarian of Laputa, decided to make a master catalog of all catalogs that do not list themselves. He expected to make a swift decision but found he was up in the air. Should or should *not* this new catalog list itself?

Vocabulary

parallel lines (171)
skew lines (171)
transversal (172)
interior angles (172)
alternate interior angles (172)
exterior angles (172)
alternate exterior angles (172)
corresponding angles (172)
consecutive interior angles (172)
indirect reasoning (176)
exactly one (186)
equidistant (195)

Chapter Summary

1. There are three different ways that two lines can be positioned in space, intersecting, parallel, or skew. (171)
2. Theorem 6–1: If two lines are cut by a transversal and one pair of alternate interior angles are congruent, then the other pair of alternate interior angles also are congruent. (173)
3. Theorem 6–2: If two lines are cut by a transversal and one pair of corresponding angles are congruent, then all pairs of corresponding angles are congruent. (173)
4. Theorem 6–3: If a triangle is a right triangle, then it has no more than one right angle. (177)
5. How to Write an Indirect Proof: (177)
    1. Make the assumption p and *not* q.
    2. Show that the assumption leads to a contradiction.
    3. State that "p and *not* q" is false.
    4. Conclude that the statement to be proven is true.
6. Theorem 6–4: In a plane, if two lines are cut by a transversal so that a pair of alternate interior angles are congruent, then the lines are parallel. (178)
7. Theorem 6–5: In a plane, if two lines are cut by a transversal so that a pair of corresponding angles are congruent, then the two lines are parallel. (181)
8. Theorem 6–6: In a plane, if two lines are cut by a transversal so that a pair of consecutive interior angles are supplementary, then the lines are parallel. (182)
9. Theorem 6–7: In a plane, if two lines are cut by a transversal so that a pair of alternate exterior angles are congruent, then the lines are parallel. (182)
10. Theorem 6–8: In a plane, if two lines are perpendicular to the same line, then the two lines are parallel. (182)
11. Parallel Postulate (Postulate 6–1): If there is a line and a point not on the line, then there is exactly one line through the point that is parallel to the given line. (186)

12. Theorem 6–9: If two parallel lines are cut by a transversal, then each pair of corresponding angles are congruent. (186)
13. Theorem 6–10: If two parallel lines are cut by a transversal, then each pair of alternate interior angles are congruent. (186)
14. Theorem 6–11: If two parallel lines are cut by a transversal, then each pair of consecutive interior angles are supplementary. (186)
15. Theorem 6–12: If two parallel lines are cut by a transversal, then each pair of alternate exterior angles are congruent. (186)
16. Theorem 6–13: In a plane, if a line is perpendicular to one of two parallel lines, then it is perpendicular to the other. (191)
17. Theorem 6–14: Given a line and a point not on the line, there is exactly one line through the point that is perpendicular to the given line. (195)
18. Definition of the Distance Between a Point and a Line: The distance between a point and a line is the length of the segment perpendicular to the line from the point. The measure of the distance between a line and a point on the line is zero. (195)
19. Theorem 6–15: In a plane, two lines are parallel if and only if they are everywhere equidistant. (195)
20. Definition of the Distance Between Parallel Lines: The distance between two parallel lines is the distance between one of the lines and any point on the other line. (196)

Chapter Review

6–1 Using the diagram at the right, find an example for each of the following.

1. Two parallel lines t, n
2. Two parallel rays
3. Two skew lines t, m
4. Two noncoplanar lines t, m
5. Two parallel lines and a transversal
6. Two coplanar lines that intersect

6. m, ℓ; t, ℓ; n, m; n, ℓ

5. t, n, ℓ ℓ is the transversal

2. any two of: $\overrightarrow{AR}$, $\overrightarrow{TS}$; $\overrightarrow{AR}$, $\overrightarrow{ST}$; $\overrightarrow{RQ}$, $\overrightarrow{TS}$; $\overrightarrow{RQ}$, $\overrightarrow{ST}$; $\overrightarrow{RA}$, $\overrightarrow{TS}$; $\overrightarrow{RA}$, $\overrightarrow{ST}$; $\overrightarrow{QA}$, $\overrightarrow{TS}$; $\overrightarrow{QA}$, $\overrightarrow{ST}$

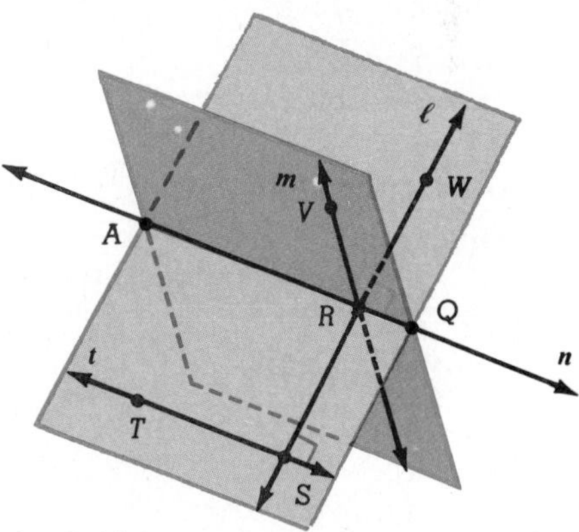

For answers to exercises 7-10, see the Teacher's Guide.

6–2 Prove each of the following by contradiction.

7. A triangle has no more than one right angle.
8. If a plane and a line *not* in the plane intersect, then they intersect in no more than one point.

6–3 Use the figure to prove each of the following.

9. **Given:** T is the midpoint of $\overline{QS}$ and $\overline{PR}$.
   Prove: $\overline{QP} \parallel \overline{RS}$
10. **Given:** $\triangle QPT \cong \triangle SRT$
    Prove: $\overline{QR} \parallel \overline{PS}$

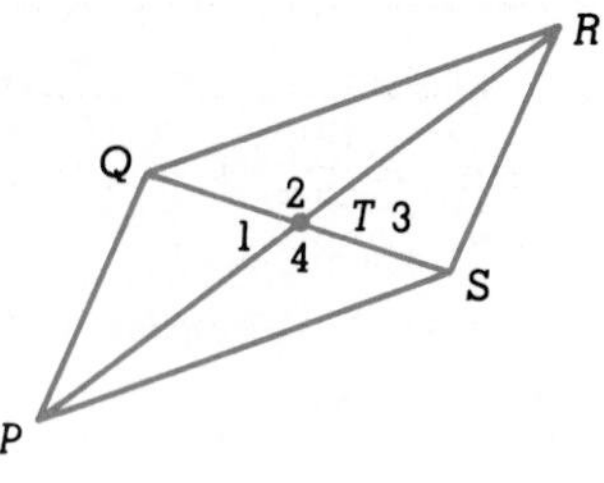

6–4 11. Complete Reasons 1 and 5 for the following proof.

Given: $\triangle PQR$
Prove: $m\angle 5 + m\angle 4 + m\angle 3 = 180$

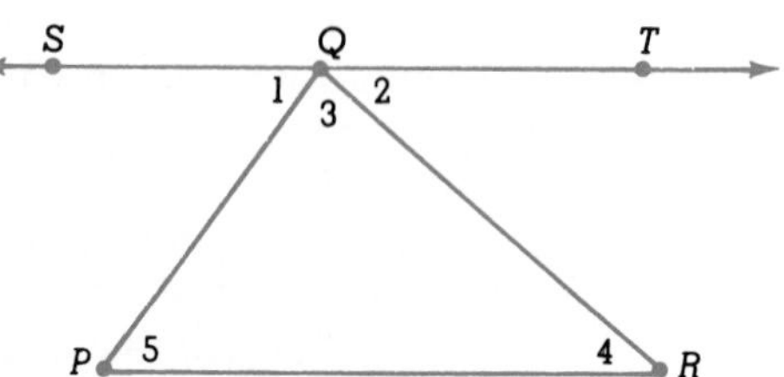

Proof:

STATEMENTS	REASONS
1. Draw $\overleftrightarrow{ST}$ through Q and parallel to $\overleftrightarrow{PR}$.	1. Parallel Postulate (6-1)
2. $m\angle 1 + m\angle PQT = 180$	2. Postulate 3–4: The angles in a linear pair are supplementary.
3. $m\angle 2 + m\angle 3 = m\angle PQT$	3. Postulate 3–3: The Angle Addition Postulate
4. $m\angle 1 + m\angle 2 + m\angle 3 = 180$	4. Postulate 2–9: Substitution
5. $\angle 2 \cong \angle 4$ $\angle 1 \cong \angle 5$	5. Theorem 6-10
6. $m\angle 2 = m\angle 4$ $m\angle 1 = m\angle 5$	6. Definition of Congruent Angles
7. $m\angle 5 + m\angle 4 + m\angle 3 = 180$	7. Postulate 2–9: Substitution

For answers to exercises 12-14, see the Teacher's Guide.

6–5 Use the figure to prove each of the following.

12. **Given:** $\overline{DE} \parallel \overline{AC}$
    E is the midpoint of $\overline{BC}$.
    $\overline{EF} \cong \overline{BE}$
    Prove: D is the midpoint of $\overline{AB}$.

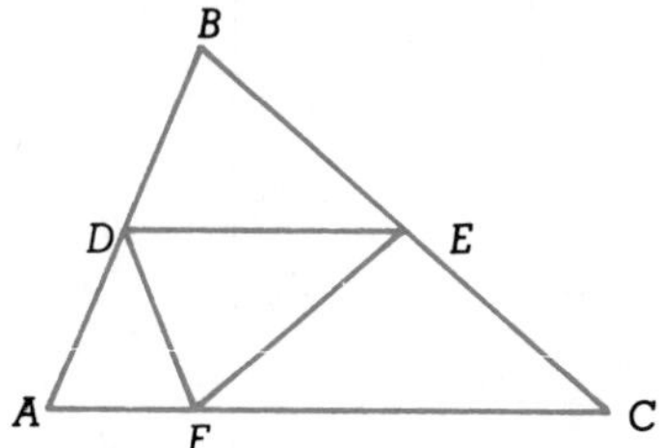

6–6 Prove each of the following.

13. In a plane, if two lines are everywhere equidistant, then the lines are parallel.

14. If two lines are parallel, then they are everywhere equidistant.

Chapter Test

Use the diagram to find an example for each of the following. For answers to exercises 1-12, see the Teacher's Guide.

1. Two parallel segments
2. Two parallel lines and a transversal
3. Two skew lines
4. Two coplanar lines that are *not* parallel
5. A ray and a segment that are *not* parallel
6. Two noncoplanar lines

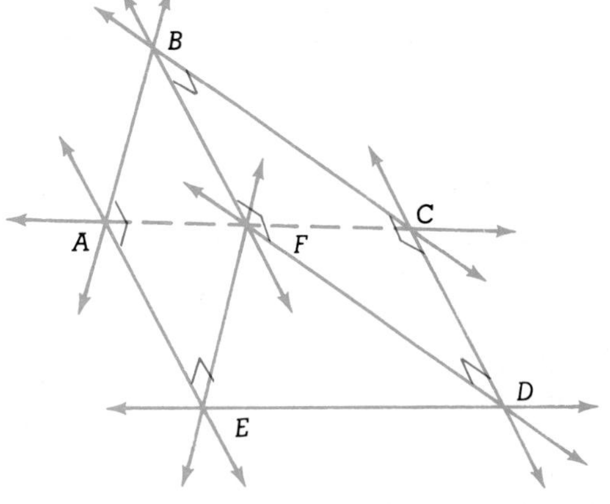

Prove each of the following by indirect reasoning.

7. If the measures of two angles of a triangle are unequal, then the measures of the sides opposite those angles are unequal in the same order.

8. In a plane, through a given point on a line, there is exactly one line perpendicular to the given line.

Prove each of the following.

9. **Given:** $\triangle ABC \cong \triangle DEF$
   Prove: $\overline{AB} \parallel \overline{DE}$

10. **Given:** $\overline{AB} \parallel \overline{DE}$
    $\triangle ABC$ is a right triangle.
    $\angle E$ is a right angle.
    $\angle B$ is a right angle.
    Prove: $\overline{BC} \parallel \overline{EF}$

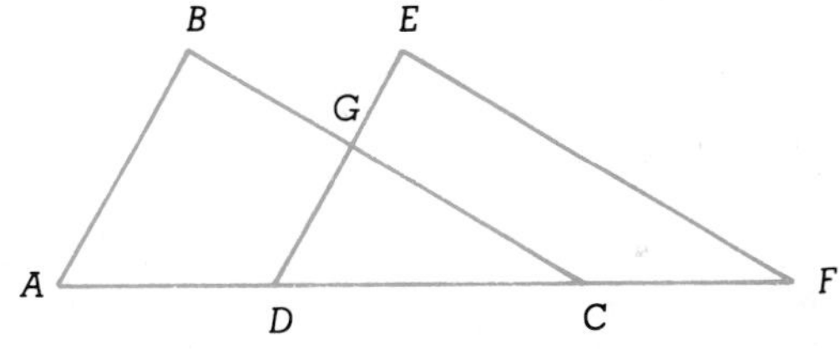

Exercises 9 and 10

11. **Given:** $\angle 2 \cong \angle 5$
    $\angle 1 \cong \angle 4$
    Prove: $\overrightarrow{AB} \parallel \overrightarrow{CG}$

12. **Given:** $\overrightarrow{AB} \parallel \overrightarrow{CG}$
    $\angle 2 \cong \angle 5$
    Prove: $\overrightarrow{AE} \parallel \overrightarrow{CB}$

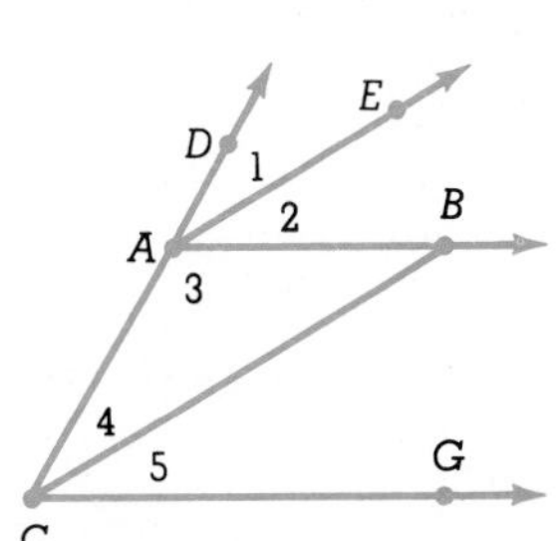

Exercises 11 and 12

cumulative review

Complete each of the following.

1. Points have __no__ dimensions.
2. A line contains at least __two__ point(s).
3. The inverse of a conditional statement is formed by __negating__ both the hypothesis and the conclusion.
4. A number associated with a point on a number line is called the __coordinate__ of the point.
5. To find the measure of the distance between two points on a number line, find the __absolute__ value of the difference of their coordinates.
6. If a segment is given, then it has exactly __one__ midpoint(s).
7. Two angles are ____ if and only if the sum of their degree measures is 180. supplementary
8. A __right__ angle is an angle whose degree measure is 90.
9. Two angles are __vertical__ if and only if they are two nonadjacent angles formed by two intersecting lines.
10. An angle is __dihedral__ if and only if it consists of two noncoplanar half planes with a common edge.

For answers to exercises 11-12, see the Teacher's Guide.

Prove each of the following.

11. **Given:** $\overline{DB} \perp \overline{AC}$
B is the midpoint of $\overline{AC}$.
Prove: $\overline{AD} \cong \overline{CD}$

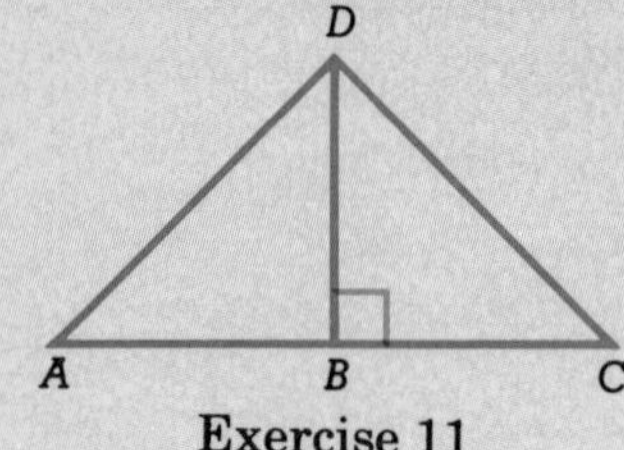

Exercise 11

12. **Given:** T is the midpoint of $\overline{SW}$.
$\overline{SW} \perp \overline{RS}$, $\overline{SW} \perp \overline{WV}$
Prove: $\triangle RST \cong \triangle VWT$

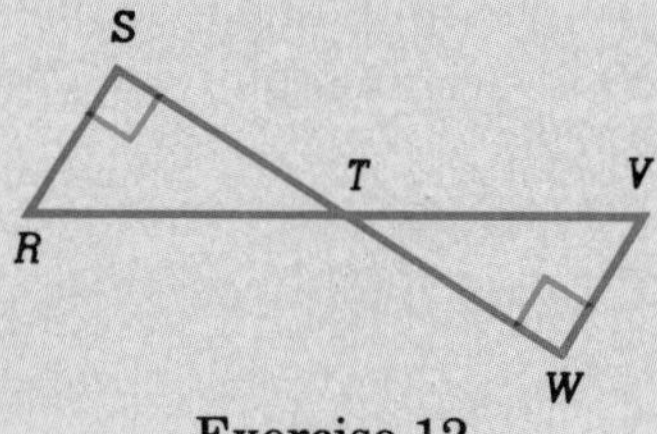

Exercise 12

Use the information given in the figure to find each of the following.

13. $m \angle 1$ 135
14. $m \angle 5$ 45
15. $m \angle 6$ 45
16. $m \angle 4$ 95
17. $m \angle 8$ 95
18. $m \angle 7$ 40
19. $m \angle 2$ 22.5
20. $m \angle 3$ 22.5

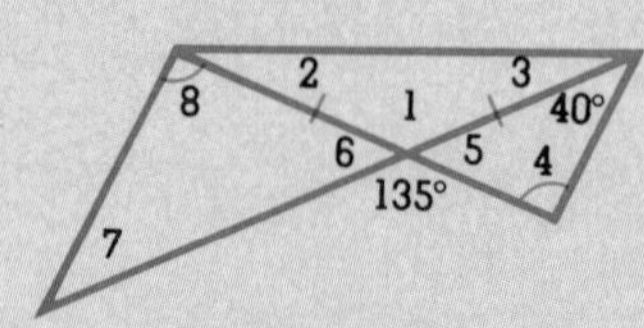

Exercises 13–20

Two sides of a triangle have measures 14 and 21 respectively. Determine whether or *not* each of the following can be a measure for the third side.

21. 5 no
22. 18 yes
23. 36 no
24. 31 yes
25. 8 yes
26. 20 yes

For answers to exercises 27-31, see the Teacher's Guide.

Using the diagram at the right, find an example for each of the following.

27. Two parallel lines
28. Two parallel rays
29. Two skew lines
30. Two noncoplanar lines
31. Two parallel lines and a transversal

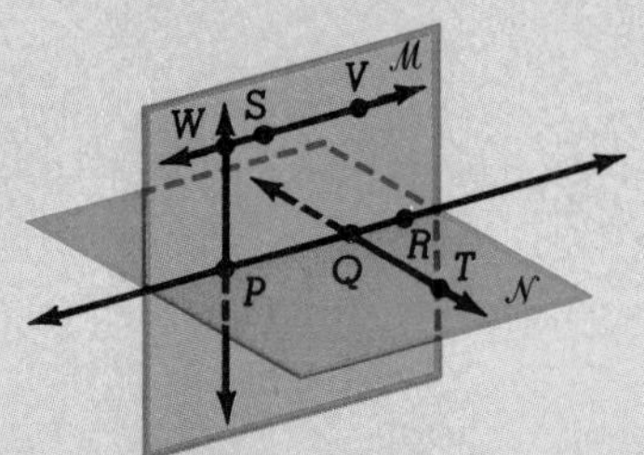

Exercises 27–31

For answers to exercises 32-35, see the Teacher's Guide.

Write the assumption that would be used to start an indirect proof.

32. If two angles are supplementary to two congruent angles, then the two angles are congruent to each other.

33. The acute angles of a right triangle are complementary.

Prove each of the following.

34. Given: $\overleftrightarrow{AB} \parallel \overleftrightarrow{DC}$
$\overleftrightarrow{AD} \parallel \overleftrightarrow{BC}$
$m\angle 6 = 110$
Prove: $m\angle 1 = 110$

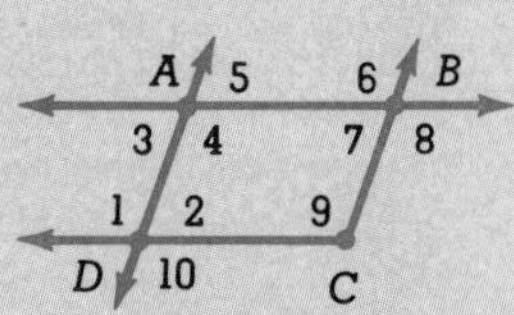

Exercise 34

35. Given: $\triangle BGD \cong \triangle GDF$
Prove: $\angle GCF$ and $\angle DFC$ are supplementary.

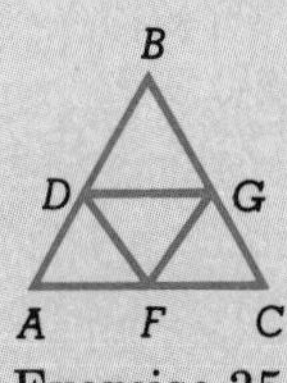

Exercise 35

Complete each of the following.

36. Reasoning based on a contradiction is called indirect reasoning.
37. Two lines are skew if and only if they do not intersect and are noncoplanar.
38. In a plane, a line is a ______ if and only if it intersects two other lines in two different points.
39. Alternate interior angles are congruent if they are formed by two parallel lines and a transversal.
40. The Parallel Postulate states " if there is a line and a point *not* on the line, then there is exactly one line through the point that is parallel to the given line."

38. transversal

chapter 7 Polygons

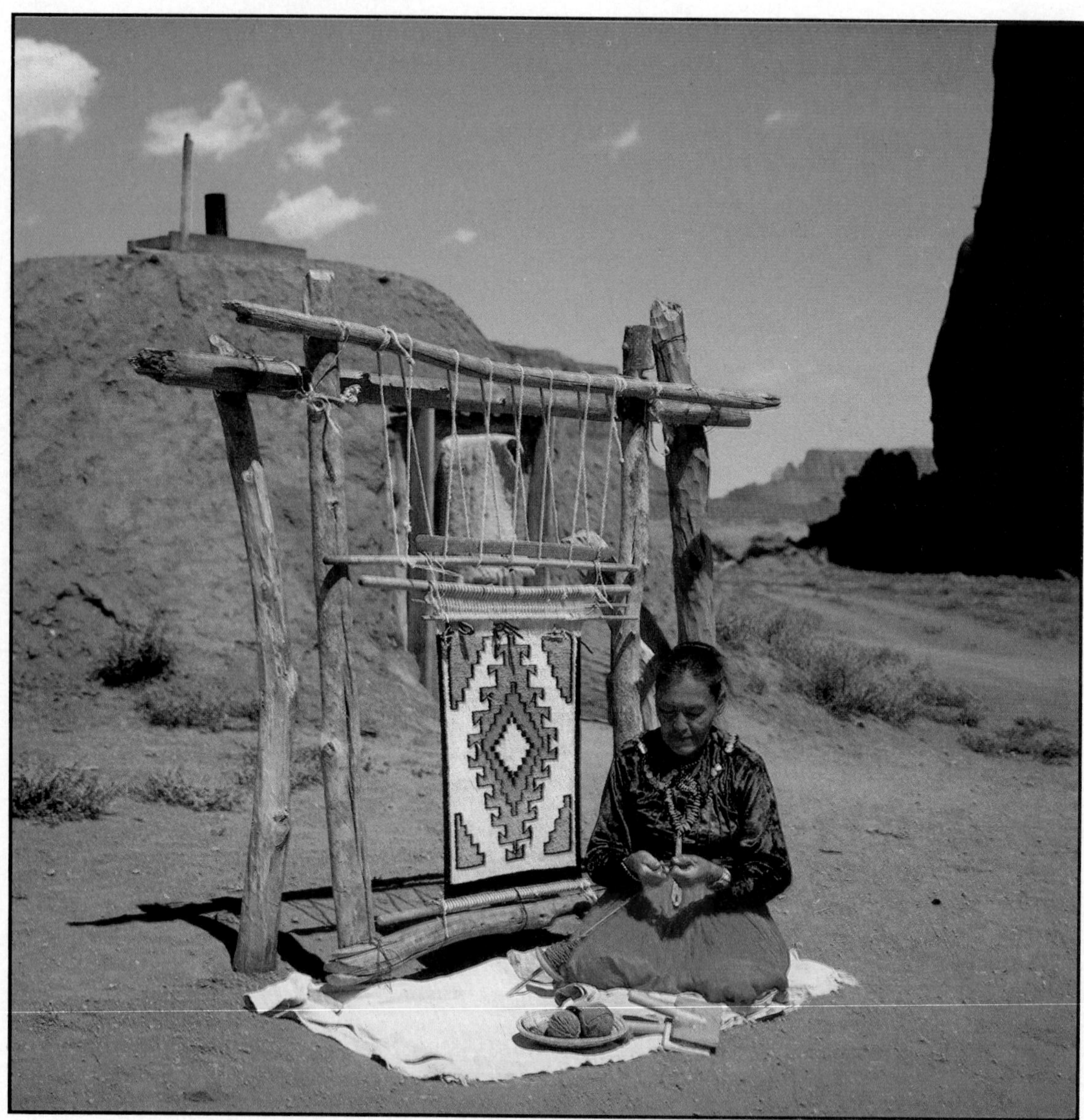

Designs in Native American weavings often contain polygonal shapes. The rug in this photograph was designed by a Navajo Indian.

Objectives: to recognize polygons, to name polygons by sides and by angles, to classify polygons in terms of convex, concave, regular, not regular, etc.

7–1 Classifying Polygons

The following figures are formed by connecting a series of points. Each figure is called a **polygon.**

The term polygon is derived from a Greek word meaning "many-angled."

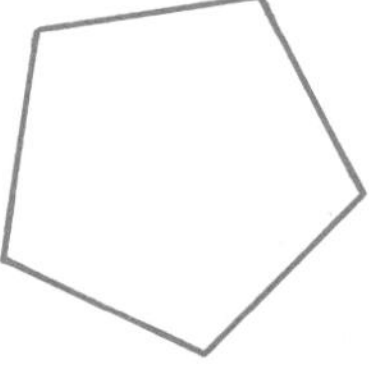

Definition of Polygon

A figure is a polygon if and only if it meets each of the following conditions.
1. **It is formed by three or more coplanar segments called sides.**
2. **Sides that have a common endpoint are noncollinear.**
3. **Each side intersects exactly two other sides, but only at their endpoints.**

If a figure fails to meet one or more of the above conditions, then it is not a polygon.

example

1 Explain why the figure at the right is *not* a polygon.

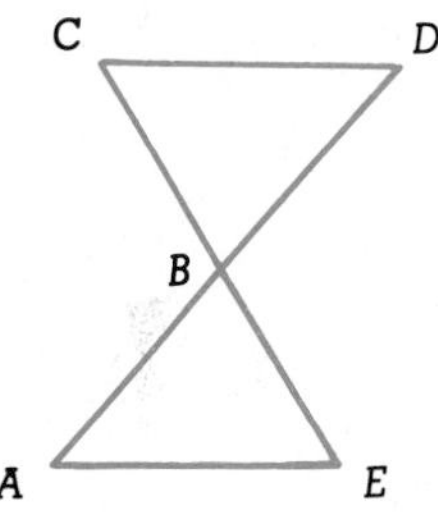

The figure fails to meet condition 2 because $\overline{AB}$ and $\overline{BD}$ have a common endpoint and are collinear. The figure also fails to meet condition 3 because $\overline{AB}$ intersects $\overline{BC}$, $\overline{BE}$, and $\overline{BD}$.

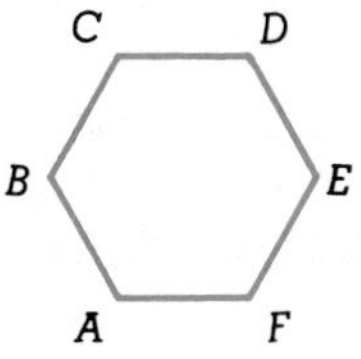

The endpoints of the sides of a polygon are the **vertices.** The vertices of the polygon at the right are A, B, C, D, E, and F. When referring to a polygon, the vertices are listed in consecutive order. For example, the polygon at the right can be referred to as *polygon ABCDEF*.

The sides of polygon $ABCDEF$ are $\overline{AB}$, $\overline{BC}$, $\overline{CD}$, $\overline{DE}$, $\overline{EF}$, and $\overline{FA}$. Two consecutive sides are $\overline{DE}$ and $\overline{EF}$.

Name two consecutive angles.

Polygons can be classified by the number of their sides. The chart at the right gives some common names for polygons.

In general, a polygon with n sides is called an ***n*-gon.** Thus, an octagon is also called an 8-gon. A polygon with 13 sides is called a 13-gon.

Number of Sides	Polygon
3	triangle
4	quadrilateral
5	pentagon
6	hexagon
7	heptagon
8	octagon
9	nonagon
10	decagon
12	dodecagon

Another way to classify polygons is as **convex** or **concave.** A polygon is convex if and only if any line containing a side of the polygon does *not* contain a point in the interior of the polygon. A polygon is concave if and only if it is *not* a convex polygon.

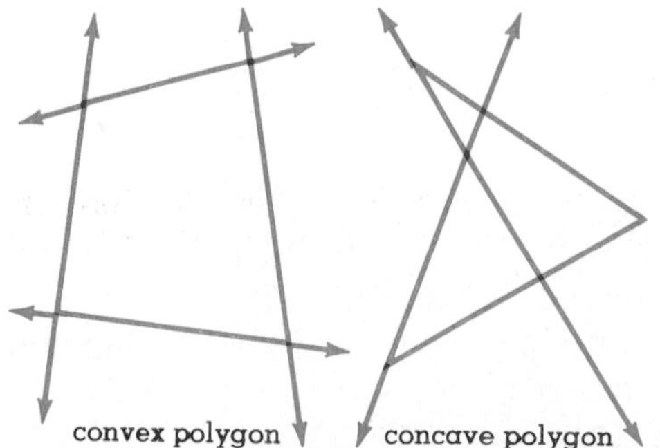

Another word for concave is nonconvex.

A polygon is regular if and only if it is a convex polygon with all sides congruent and all angles congruent.

Definition of Regular Polygon

The following figures are regular polygons.

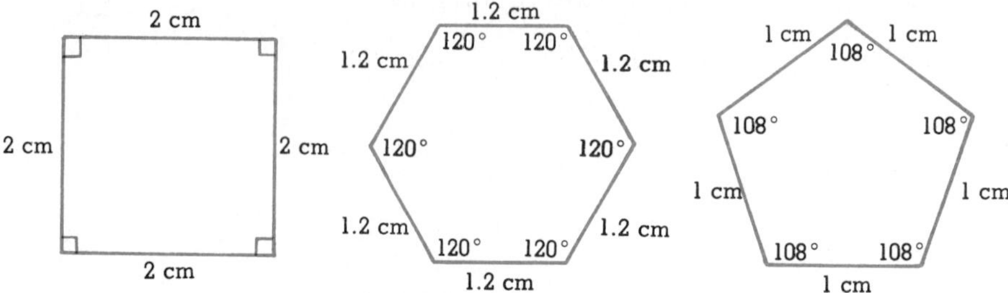

For a convex polygon to be a regular polygon, it must be *both* equilateral *and* equiangular. A polygon meeting one of these conditions but *not* the other is not a regular polygon.

Note that concave polygons cannot be regular by the second condition.

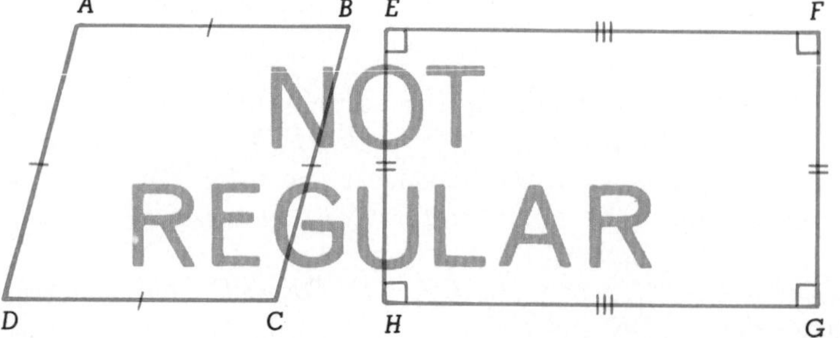

Polygon ABCD is equilateral but not equiangular.

Polygon EFGH is equiangular but not equilateral.

example

2 **Classify the following polygons by the number of sides, as convex or concave, and as regular or *not* regular.**

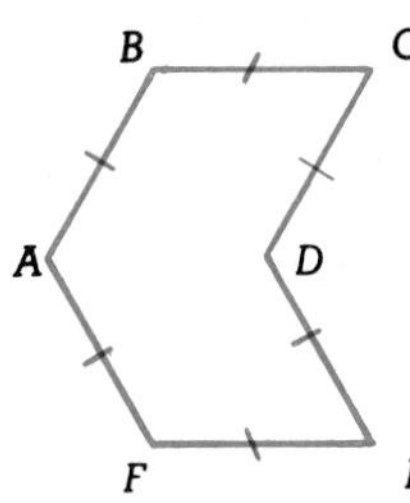

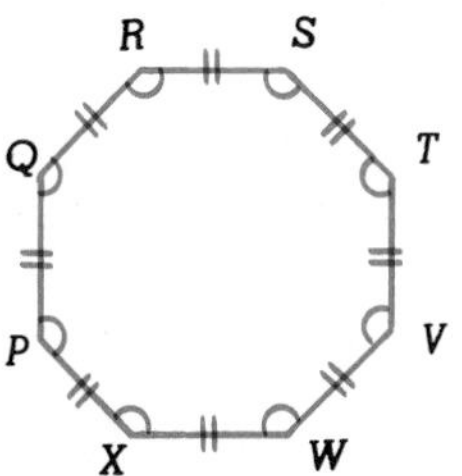

Polygon *ABCDEF* has 6 sides. It is a hexagon.

If $\overline{CD}$ is extended through *D*, it passes through the interior of the hexagon. Thus, the polygon is concave.

Since it is concave, it is *not* regular even though all its sides are congruent.

Remind students that all regular polygons are convex.

Polygon *PQRSTVWX* has 8 sides. It is an octagon.

No side of the octagon can be extended to pass through the interior. Thus, the polygon is convex.

All the sides are congruent and all the angles are congruent. Thus, it is regular.

EN: Wr: 5-28; AV: Ex: 1-9, Wr: 2-28 evens; FN: Ex: 1-9, Wr: 1-27 odds

exercises

Exploratory **Determine whether or *not* each of the following are polygons.**

1. no

2. yes

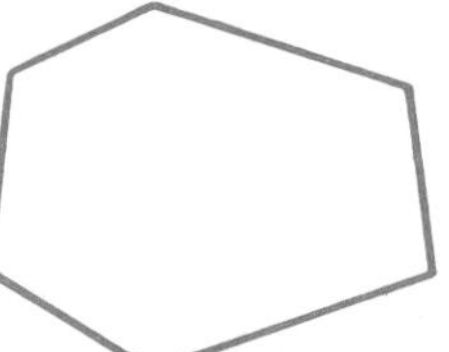

3. no

4. yes

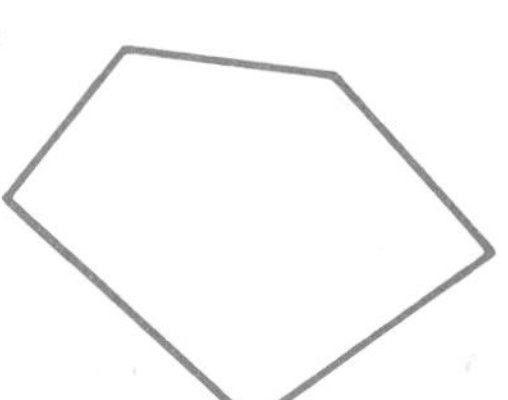

5. yes

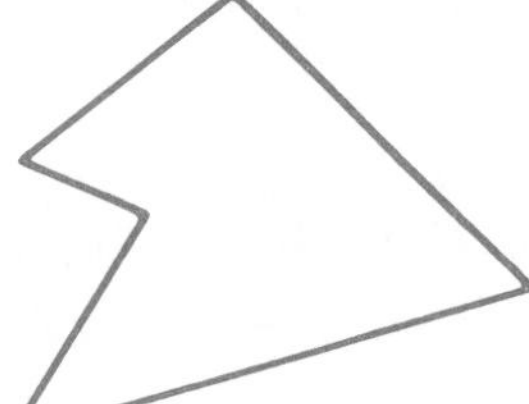

6. yes

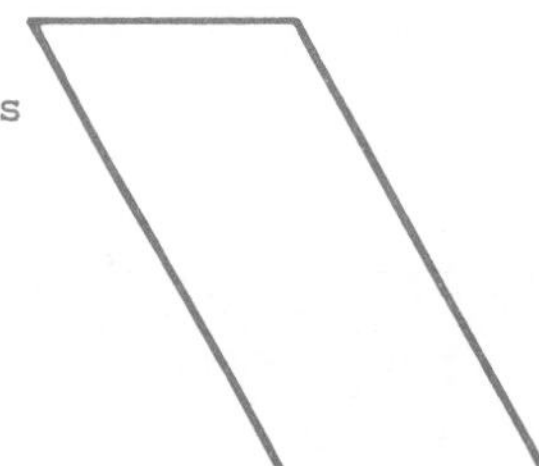

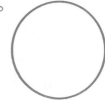

7. no

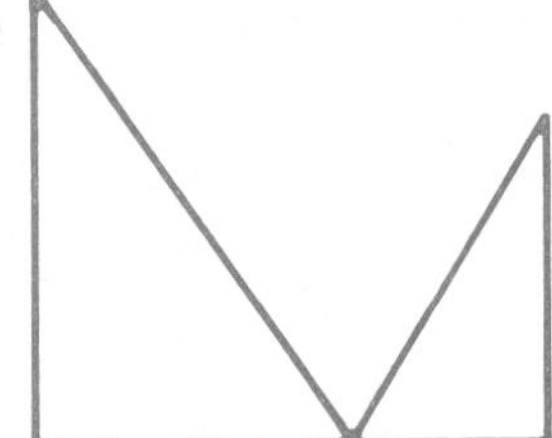

8. no

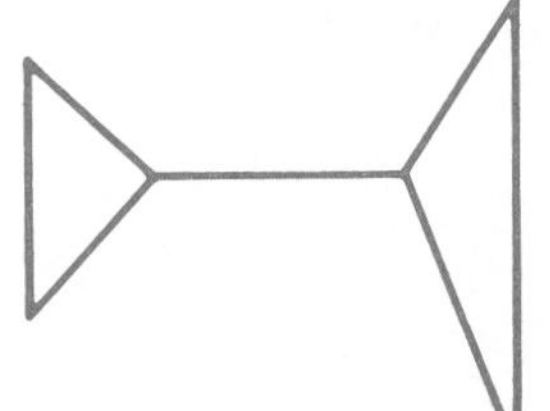

9. yes

Written **For each of the following, classify the polygon with the given number of sides.**

1. 3 triangle	**2.** 8 octagon	**3.** 10 decagon	**4.** 4 quadrilateral
5. 24 24-gon	**6.** 6 hexagon	**7.** n n-gon	**8.** x x-gon

Classify each of the following polygons by the number of sides. Then classify each polygon as *convex* or *concave*.

9. pentagon; convex

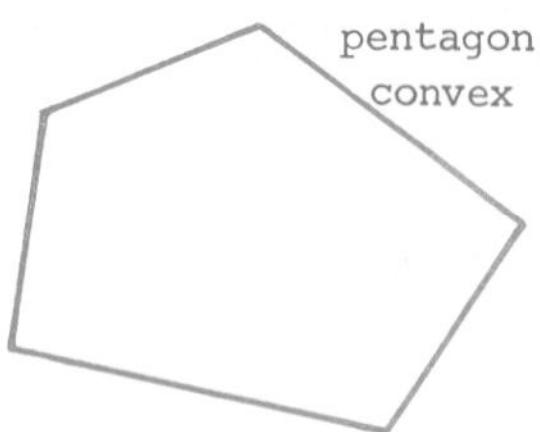

10. quadrilateral; concave

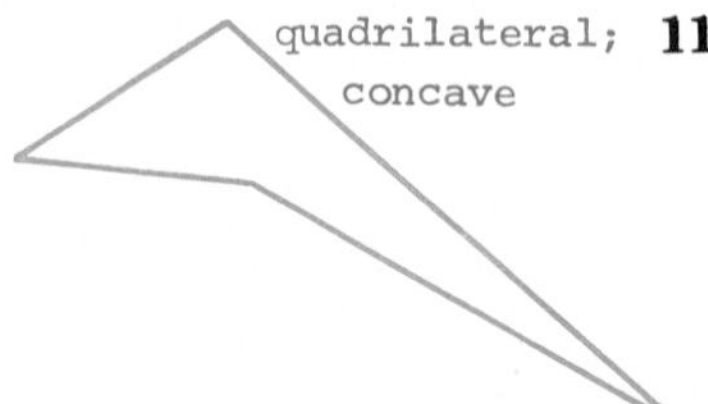

11. hexagon; convex

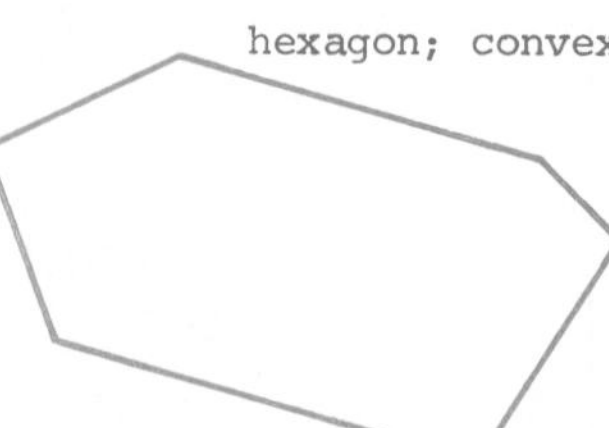

12. triangle; convex

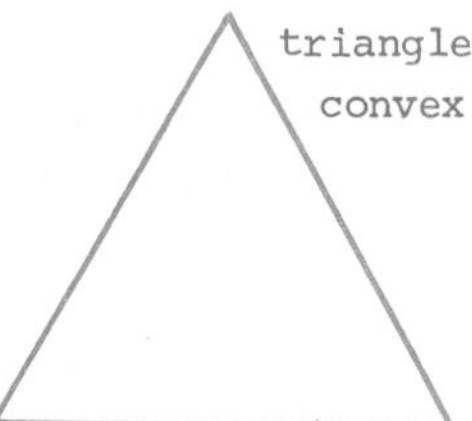

13. heptagon; concave

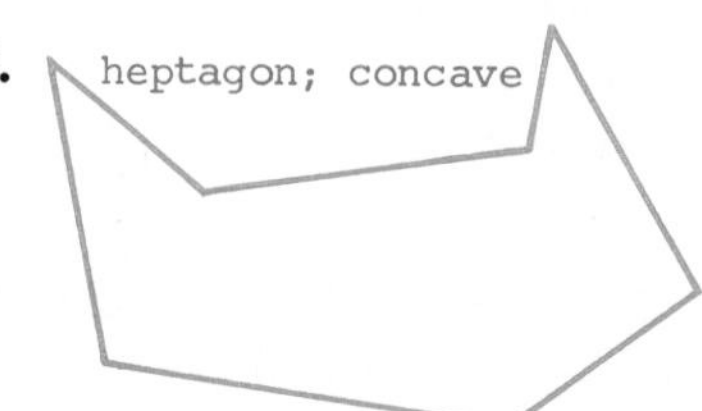

14. octagon; concave

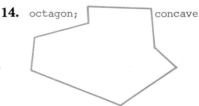

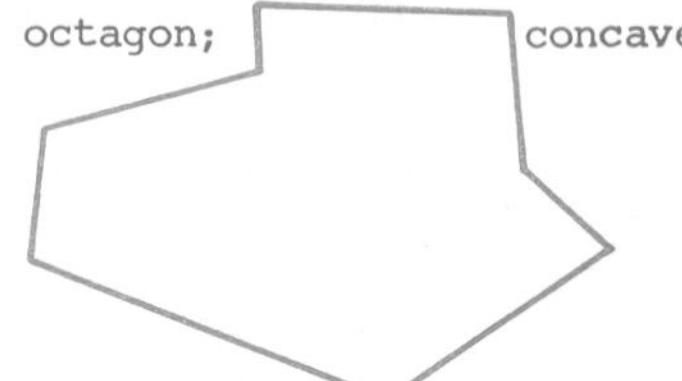

For answers to exercises 15-24, see the Teacher's Guide.

Use polygon *ABCDE* to answer each of the following.

15. Name the vertices of the polygon.
16. Name the angles of the polygon.
17. Name the sides of the polygon.
18. Classify the polygon by the number of sides.
19. Classify the polygon as convex or concave.
20. Classify the polygon as regular or not regular.
21. Name a pair of consecutive angles of the polygon.
22. Name a pair of consecutive sides of the polygon.

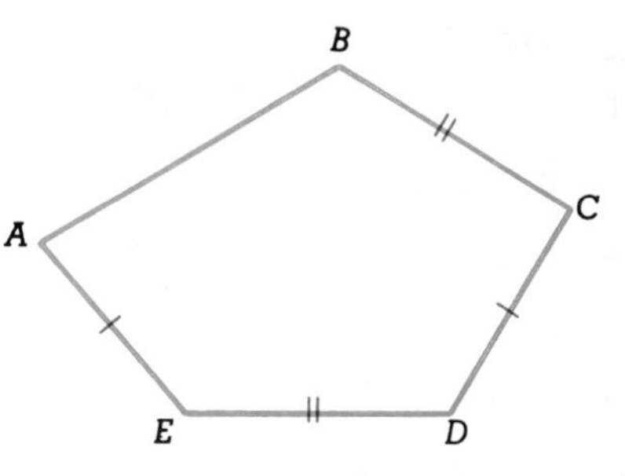

Exercises 15 – 22

Give an if and only if definition for each of the following.

23. a pair of consecutive angles of a polygon
24. a pair of consecutive sides of a polygon

25. Regular: it is both equiangular and equilateral. 26. Not regular: it is not equilateral.

Classify each of the following as *regular* or *not regular*. Then explain your answer.

25.

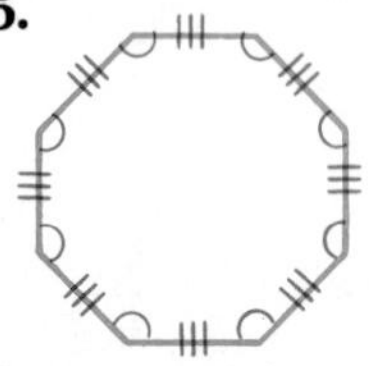

26.

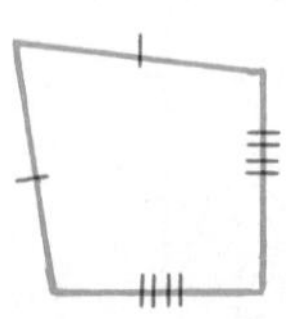

27.

28.

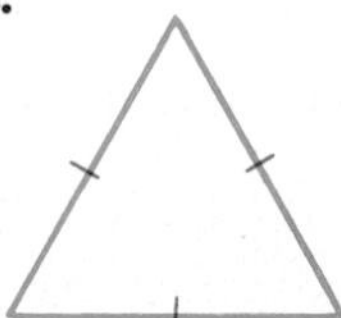

27. Not regular: it is not equiangular. 28. Regular: it is equilateral and by the Isosceles Triangle Theorem, also equiangular.

7–2 Angles of Polygons

Objectives: to find the sum of the degree measures of a polygon, to find the degree measure of one angle of a regular polygon, to find the degree measure of each interior and exterior angle of a regular polygon, to use problem-solving procedures

According to the Angle Sum Theorem, the sum of the degree measures of the angles of a triangle is 180. Is there a fixed sum for the degree measures of the angles of a convex quadrilateral or a convex pentagon? yes

A segment joining two nonconsecutive vertices of a convex polygon is called a **diagonal** of the polygon. In each of the following polygons, all possible diagonals from one vertex are shown.

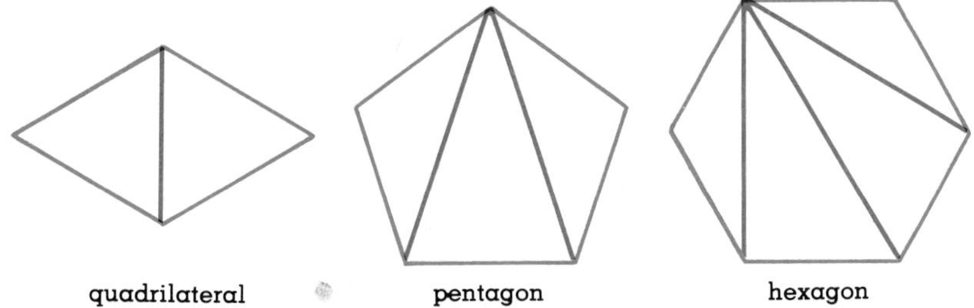

quadrilateral pentagon hexagon

Notice that in each case, the polygon is separated into triangles. The sum of the measures of the angles of each polygon can be found by adding the measures of the angles of the triangles.

Polygon	Number of Sides	Number of Triangles	Sum of Degree Measures of Angles
triangle	3	1	$(1 \cdot 180)$ or 180
quadrilateral	4	2	$(2 \cdot 180)$ or 360
pentagon	5	3	$(3 \cdot 180)$ or 540
hexagon	6	4	$(4 \cdot 180)$ or 720
heptagon	7	5	$(5 \cdot 180)$ or 900
octagon	8	6	$(6 \cdot 180)$ or 1080
nonagon	9	7	$(7 \cdot 180)$ or 1260
decagon	10	8	$(8 \cdot 180)$ or 1440
.	.	.	.
.	.	.	.
.	.	.	.
n-gon	n	$n - 2$	$(n - 2)180$

Have students draw diagonals in a concave polygon and note that some diagonals will lie in the interior.

These and many other examples suggest the following theorem.

This theorem can be proved by induction.

Theorem 7–1

If a convex polygon has n sides, and S is the sum of the degree measures of its angles, then $S = (n - 2)180$.

Remind students that $n \geq 3$.

examples

1 Find the sum of the degree measures of the angles of a hexagon.

$$\begin{aligned} S &= (n - 2)180 \\ &= (6 - 2)180 \quad \text{A hexagon has 6 sides.} \\ &= 4 \cdot 180 \\ &= 720 \end{aligned}$$

2 The degree measure of one angle of a regular polygon is 140. Find the number of sides.

Let n represent the number of sides. *Define a variable.*
A polygon has the same number of angles as it has sides. Since a regular polygon is equiangular, each of its angles has the same degree measure. From Theorem 7–1, the sum of the degree measures of the angles is $(n - 2)180$. Therefore, the following equation can be used to find the number of sides of a regular polygon.

$$\text{degree measure of one angle} = \frac{\text{sum of degree measures of angles}}{\text{number of angles}}$$ *Write an equation.*

$$140 = \frac{(n-2)180}{n}$$ *Solve the equation.*

$140n = (n - 2)180$ *Multiply by n.*

$140n = 180n - 360$ *Distributive Property*

$^{-}40n = {}^{-}360$ *Subtract 180n from both sides.*

$n = 9$ *Divide by $^{-}40$.*

$$140 = \frac{(n-2)180}{n}$$

$$140 \stackrel{?}{=} \frac{(9-2)180}{9}$$ *Check the solution.*

$$140 \stackrel{?}{=} \frac{1260}{9}$$

$$140 = 140$$

The polygon has 9 sides. *Answer the problem.*

1. Define a variable.
2. Write an equation.
3. Solve the equation.
4. Check the solution.
5. Answer the problem.

Problem Solving Procedure

Recall that an exterior angle of a triangle forms a linear pair with one of the interior angles of the triangle. In the figure at the right, $\angle 4$ is an exterior angle of $\triangle ABC$.

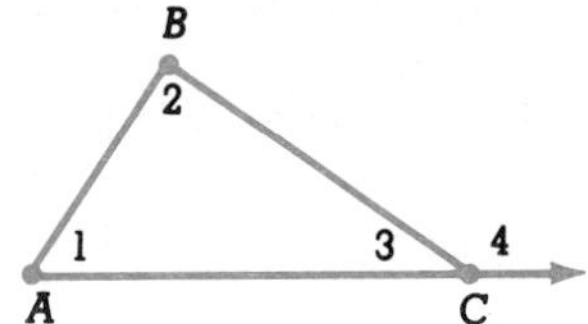

In general, a pair of **exterior angles** are formed at each vertex of any convex polygon. A pentagon, like the one at the right, has a total of 10 exterior angles.

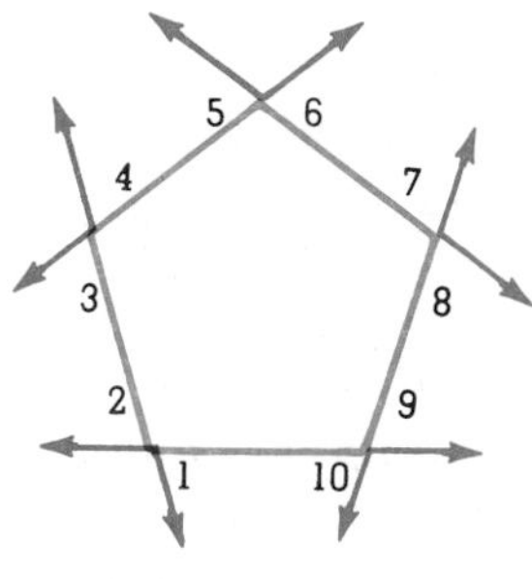

In the hexagon at the right, the sides are extended to form one exterior angle at each vertex. At each vertex, the interior angle of the hexagon and the exterior angle form a linear pair. Altogether, there are six linear pairs.

The total degree measures of these exterior angles can be found as follows.

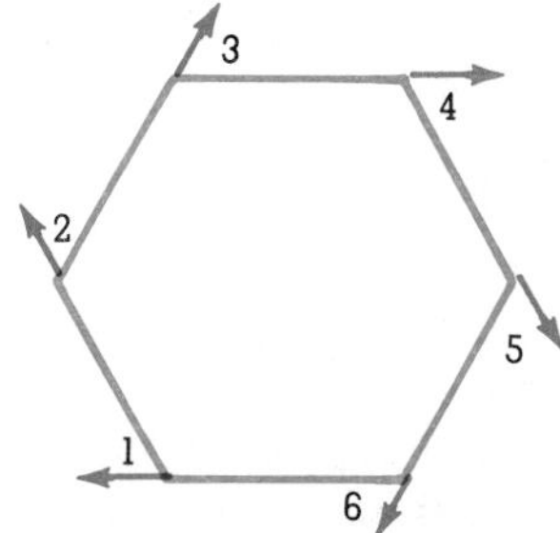

sum of measures of exterior angles	=	*sum of measures of linear pairs*	−	*sum of measures of interior angles*
	=	$6 \cdot 180$	−	$(6-2)180$
	=	1080	−	720
	=	360		

s = n • 180 - (n - 2) • 180
s = n • 180 - n • 180 + 360
s = 360

What sum would you find for an n-gon?

If a polygon is convex, then the sum of the degree measures of the exterior angles, one at each vertex, is 360. *Theorem 7–2*

EN: Ex: 9-11, Wr: 12-48 evens; p. 215, Cal: 1-12; AV: Ex: 1-11 odds, Wr: 1-37 odds; p. 215, Cal: 1-12

exercises

FN: Ex: 1-10, Wr: 1-37 odds; p. 215, Cal: 1-5; p. 210, Wr: 10-28 evens

Exploratory **For each of the following convex polygons, find the number of diagonals that can be drawn from one vertex. Then, find the number of triangles formed by these diagonals.**

1. triangle 0; 0
2. quadrilateral 1; 2
3. pentagon 2; 3
4. hexagon 3; 4
5. heptagon 4; 5
6. octagon 5; 6
7. nonagon 6; 7
8. decagon 7; 8
9. 15-gon 12; 13
10. n-gon n-3; n-2
11. Give an if and only if definition for an exterior angle of a convex polygon. See the Teacher's Guide.

Written **1–10.** For each of the convex polygons in exploratory exercises **1–10** find the total number of diagonals that can be formed. 1. 0 2. 2 3. 5 4. 9 5. 14 6. 20 7. 27 8. 35 9. 90 10. $\frac{n(n-3)}{2}$

Find the sum of the degree measures of the angles of a convex polygon for each number of sides given.

11. 17 2,700	**12.** 20 3,240	**13.** 12 1,800	**14.** 13 1,980
15. 59 10,260	**16.** 15 2,340	**17.** x $(x - 2)180$	**18.** t $(t - 2)180$

For each of the following, the degree measure of one angle of a regular polygon is given. Find the number of sides.

19. 150 12	**20.** 160 18	**21.** 120 6	**22.** 60 3
23. 165 24	**24.** 156 15	**25.** 144 10	**26.** 179 360

For each of the following, the number of sides of a regular polygon is given. Find the degree measure of each interior angle and each exterior angle.

27. 4 90, 90	**28.** 5 108, 72	**29.** 8 135, 45	**30.** 10 144, 36
31. 7 128.6, 51.4	**32.** 20 162, 18	**33.** d $\frac{180(d-2)}{d}, \frac{360}{d}$	**34.** x $\frac{180(x-2)}{x}, \frac{360}{x}$

Solve each problem.

35. The sum of the degree measures of the angles of a convex polygon is 3240. Find the number of sides. 20

36. The sum of the degree measures of the angles of a convex polygon is 1260. Find the number of sides. 9

37. The degree measure of one exterior angle of a regular polygon is 30. Find the number of sides. 12

38. The degree measure of one exterior angle of a regular polygon is 45. Find the number of sides. 8

39. Explain why the sum of the degree measures of the angles of a convex polygon cannot be less than 180. A triangle is the smallest polygon with 180° as the sum of the measures of the angles.

40. Two angles of a hexagon are congruent. Each of the other angles has a degree measure twice that of each of the first two angles. Find the degree measure of each angle. 72, 144

41. Two angles of a quadrilateral are congruent. Each of the other two angles has a degree measure three times that of each of the first two angles. Find the degree measure of each angle. 45, 135

42. Explain why the sum of the degree measures of the angles of a convex polygon cannot be 2070. $S = (n - 2)180$; $n = 13.5$; But the number of sides of a polygon must be a natural number.

Each of the following figures was formed by extending the sides of a regular polygon. Find the degree measure of the angles formed at each labeled vertex.

43. 36

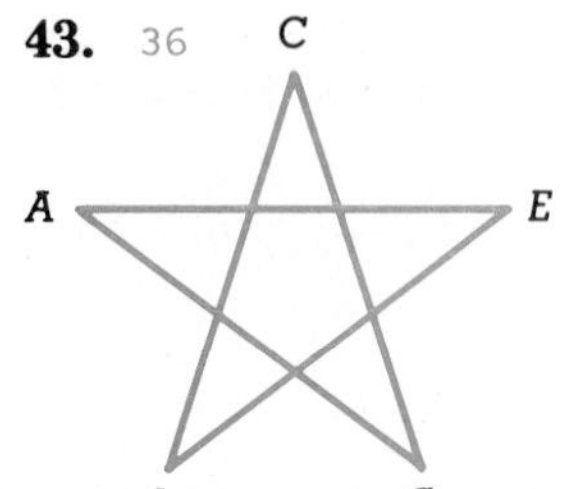

44. 60

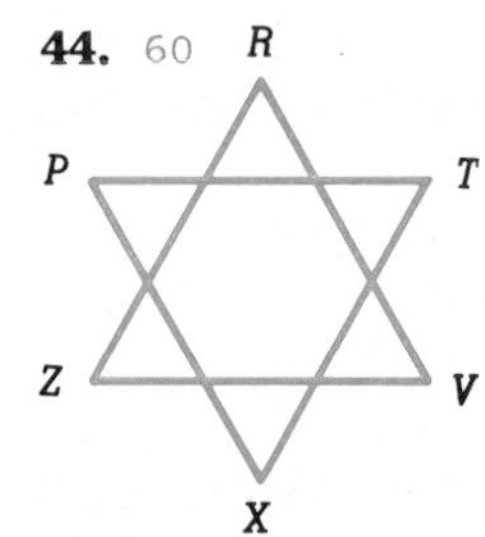

45. 90

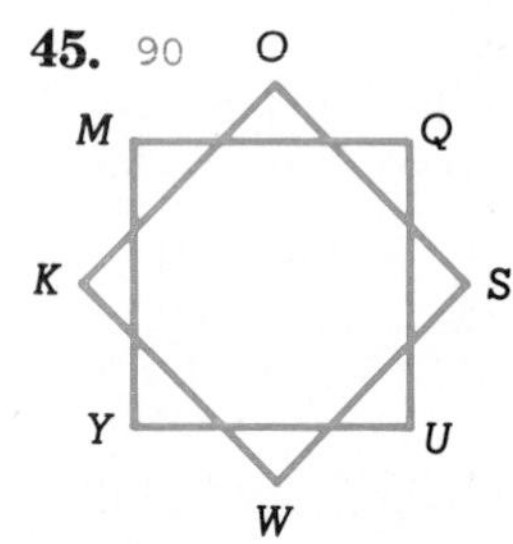

Write an algebraic proof for each of the following.

For answers to exercises 46-49, see the Teacher's Guide.

46. The sum of the degree measures of a regular pentagon is 540.

47. The sum of the degree measures of the exterior angles, one at each vertex, of a convex quadrilateral is 360.

48. The sum of the degree measures of the exterior angles, one at each vertex, of a convex n-gon is 360.

49. The sum of the degree measures of the exterior angles, two at each vertex, of a convex n-gon is 720.

Finding Roots

The calculator can be used to find the values of expressions such as $\sqrt{45}$, $\sqrt[3]{45}$, and $(\sqrt[3]{45})^9$.

To find the square root many calculators have a [√] key.

Example **Find $\sqrt{45}$.**

Enter: 45 [√x] [=]

Display: 45 6.7082039

To find values for the expressions $\sqrt[3]{45}$ and $(\sqrt[3]{45})^9$ a combination of keys is necessary. By using [INV] and [y^x] the value of a root can be found. The only restriction is that negative numbers not be used if the index is even.

Example **Find $\sqrt[3]{45}$ and $(\sqrt[3]{45})^9$.**

Enter: 45 [INV] [y^x] 3 [=]

Display: 45 3 3.5568933

Enter: 45 [INV] [y^x] 3 [y^x] 9 [=]

Display: 45 3 3.5568933 9 91124.999

Exercises **Find the value for each of the following.**

1. $\sqrt{145}$ 12.041595
2. $\sqrt[4]{125}$ 3.3437015
3. $\sqrt[3]{28}$ 3.036589
4. $(\sqrt[4]{3})^{16}$ 81
5. $(\sqrt[4]{74})^3$ 25.23038
6. $(\sqrt[4]{169})^2$ 13
7. $(\sqrt[7]{4})^2$ 1.4859943
8. $(\sqrt[4]{81})^5$ 243
9. $(\sqrt[3]{14})^3$ 14
10. $\sqrt[3]{5}$ 1.7099759
11. $(\sqrt[3]{625})^4$ 5343.6749
12. $(\sqrt[3]{9})^{\frac{2}{3}}$ 1.6294982

Objectives: to recognize and to use properties of parallelograms

7–3 Parallelograms

The edges of each piece of the stained glass window represent a special kind of quadrilateral. Notice that in each piece both pairs of opposite sides are parallel. The quadrilateral formed is called a **parallelogram.**

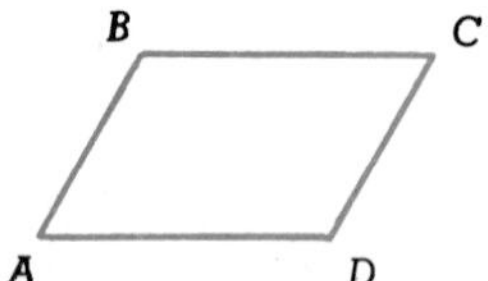

The figure is called *parallelogram ABCD* and written $\square ABCD$.

A quadrilateral is a parallelogram if and only if both pairs of opposite sides are parallel.

Definition of Parallelogram

The following theorem states an important characteristic of all parallelograms.

If a quadrilateral is a parallelogram, then a diagonal separates it into two congruent triangles.

Theorem 7–3

example

1 **Prove Theorem 7–3.**

Given: $\square ABCD$ with diagonal $\overline{BD}$

Prove: $\triangle ABD \cong \triangle CDB$

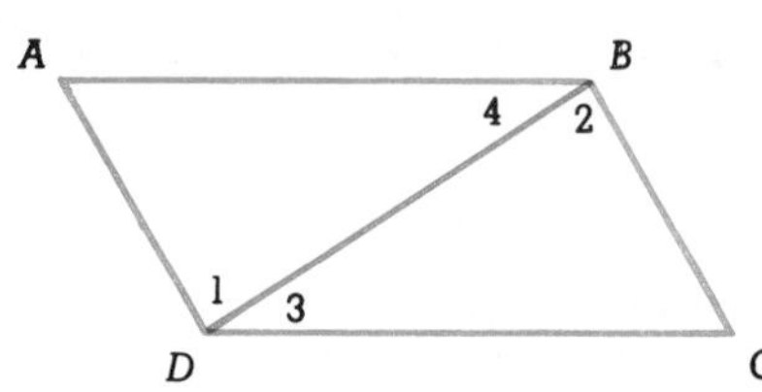

Proof:

STATEMENTS	REASONS
1. $\square ABCD$ with diagonal $\overline{BD}$	1. Given
2. $\overline{AB} \parallel \overline{DC}$ $\overline{AD} \parallel \overline{BC}$	2. Definition of Parallelogram
3. $\angle 1 \cong \angle 2$ $\angle 3 \cong \angle 4$	3. Theorem 6–9: If two parallel lines are cut by a transversal, then each pair of alternate interior angles is congruent.
4. $\overline{BD} \cong \overline{BD}$	4. Theorem 2–2: Congruence of line segments is reflexive.
5. $\triangle ABD \cong \triangle CDB$	5. Postulate 4–3: ASA

In the parallelogram at the right, $\angle R$ and $\angle T$ are **opposite angles.** Name another pair of opposite angles. $\angle Q$ and $\angle S$

One pair of **opposite sides** is $\overline{RS}$ and $\overline{QT}$. Name another pair of opposite sides. $\overline{RQ}$ and $\overline{ST}$

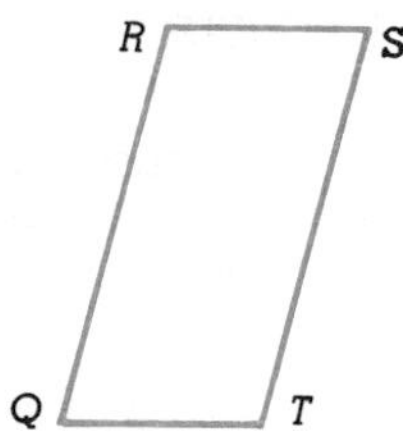

Students prove Theorems 7-4 and 7-5 in Written exercises 13-14.

If a quadrilateral is a parallelogram, then its opposite angles are congruent. *Theorem 7–4*

If a quadrilateral is a parallelogram, then its opposite sides are congruent. *Theorem 7–5*

The diagonals of a parallelogram intersect and four triangles are formed. Notice that $\triangle ABE$ and $\triangle CDE$ appear to be congruent. Also, $\triangle AED$ and $\triangle CEB$ appear to be congruent. The proof of the following theorem is based on these pairs of triangles.

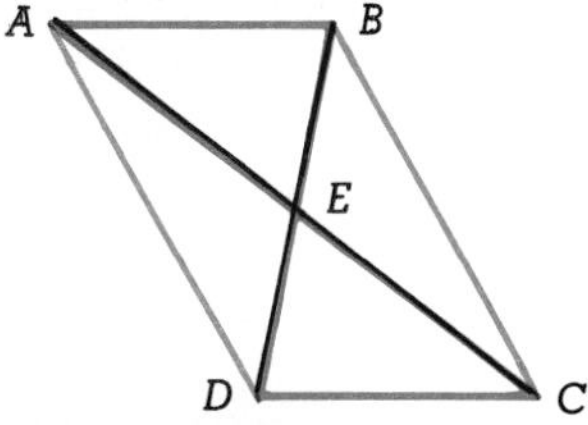

If a quadrilateral is a parallelogram, then its diagonals bisect each other. *Theorem 7–6*

example

2 **Prove Theorem 7–6.**

Given: $\square EFGH$ with diagonals $\overline{EG}$ and $\overline{FH}$

Prove: $\overline{ED} \cong \overline{GD}$

$\overline{DH} \cong \overline{DF}$

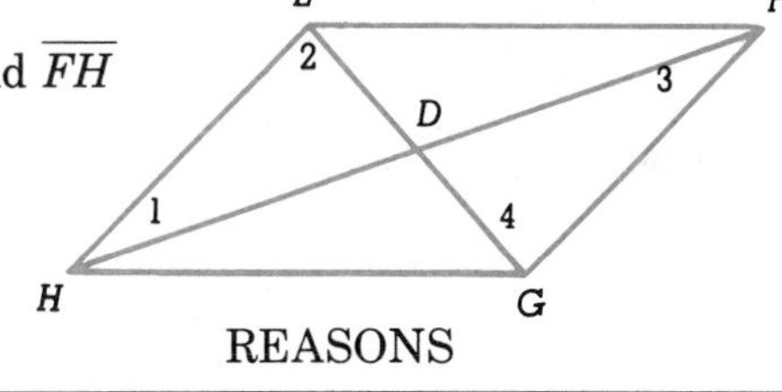

Proof:

STATEMENTS	REASONS
1. $\square EFGH$ with diagonals $\overline{EG}$ and $\overline{FH}$	1. Given
2. $\overline{FG} \cong \overline{HE}$	2. Theorem 7–5: If a quadrilateral is a parallelogram, then its opposite sides are congruent.
3. $\overline{FG} \parallel \overline{EH}$	3. Definition of Parallelogram
4. $\angle 1 \cong \angle 3$ $\angle 2 \cong \angle 4$	4. Theorem 6–9: If two parallel lines are cut by a transversal, then each pair of alternate interior angles is congruent.
5. $\triangle EDH \cong \triangle GDF$	5. Postulate 4–3: ASA
6. $\overline{ED} \cong \overline{GD}$ $\overline{DH} \cong \overline{DF}$	6. Definition of Congruent Triangles CPCTC

EN: Ex: 1-15 odds, Wr: 2-16 evens; p. 219, Ch: 1-2 E: 1-5;

exercises

AV: Ex: 2-16 evens, Wr: 1-17 odds; p. 219, E: 1-5; pp. 214-5, Wr: 38-48 evens

Exploratory **Determine whether or *not* each of the following statements must be true about the parallelogram at the right. State *yes* or *no*.**

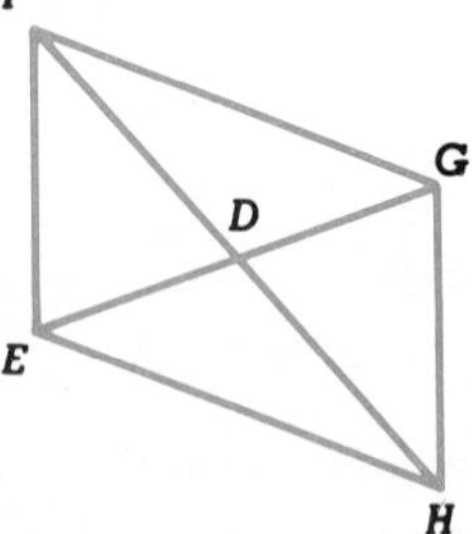

1. $\overline{FE} \parallel \overline{GH}$ yes
2. $\angle FGH \cong \angle FEH$ yes
3. $\angle FDE \cong \angle GDH$ yes
4. $\overline{EH} \parallel \overline{FG}$ yes
5. $\overline{GH} \cong \overline{FE}$ yes
6. $\overline{FD} \cong \overline{DG}$ no
7. $\overline{FD} \cong \overline{DE}$ no
8. $\overline{FD} \cong \overline{HD}$ yes

Determine whether or *not* each of the following statements must be true about the parallelogram at the right. State *yes* or *no*.

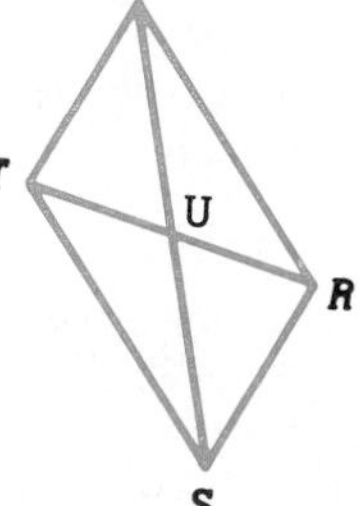

9. $\overline{QR} \cong \overline{QU}$ no
10. $\overline{QR} \cong \overline{TS}$ yes
11. $\triangle RUS \cong \triangle QUT$ no
12. $\triangle QST \cong \triangle SQR$ yes
13. U is the midpoint of $\overline{TR}$. yes
14. U is the midpoint of $\overline{QS}$. yes
15. $\triangle QUT \cong \triangle SUR$ yes
16. $\triangle QST \cong \triangle RTS$ no

($\triangle RUS \cong \triangle TUQ$)

FN: Ex: 1-16, Wr: 1-12; pp. 214-5, Wr: 2-46 evens

Written **For each of the following, use the parallelogram at the right and the given information to find the value of x.**

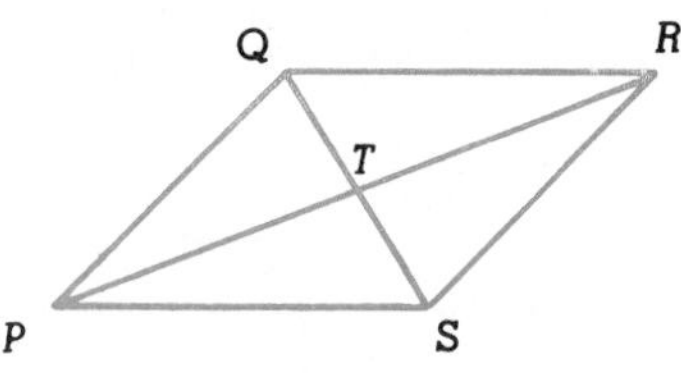

1. $QR = 16$
   $PS = x$ 16
2. $PT = 7$
   $PR = x$ 14
3. $QS = 2.4$
   $TQ = x$ 1.2
4. $RS = 3.9$
   $PQ = x$ 3.9
5. $RQ = 4x + 9$
   $PS = 7x - 6$ 5
6. $QP = 2x + 5$
   $SR = 3x$ 5
7. $TR = 3x - 10$
   $PR = 28$ 8
8. $QS = 2x + 7$
   $TS = 5x - 8$ $\frac{23}{8}$

For each of the following, use the parallelogram at the right and the given information to find the value of x.

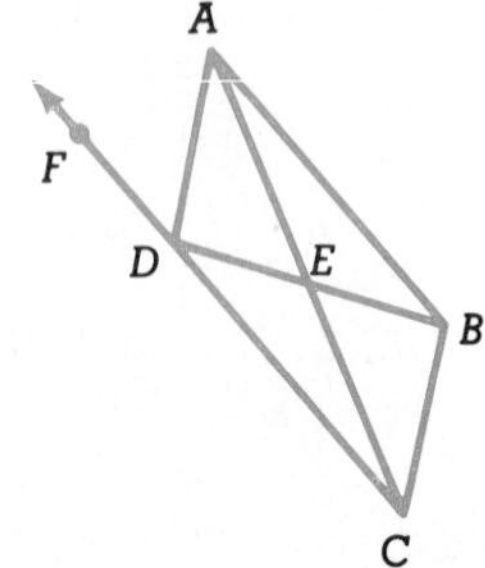

9. $m\angle AEB = 2x$
   $m\angle AED = x$ 60
10. $m\angle BDC = x$ 35
    $m\angle ADB = x + 40$
    $m\angle ABC = 110$
11. $m\angle BAE = x$ 25
    $m\angle EAD = x + 20$
    $m\angle BAD = 70$
12. $m\angle BCE = 45$
    $m\angle ECD = 25$
    $m\angle ADF = x$ 70

For answers to exercises 13-17, see the Teacher's Guide.

Complete a proof for each of the following.

13. Theorem 7–4

14. Theorem 7–5

15. Given: $\square HIJK$
Prove: $\angle HKJ$ is supplementary to $\angle IJK$.
Hint: Extend $\overline{KJ}$.

Exercise 15

16. Given: $\square ABCD$
$\overline{DE} \perp \overline{AC}$
$\overline{BF} \perp \overline{AC}$
Prove: $\overline{DE} \parallel \overline{BF}$

17. Given: $\square ABCD$
$\overline{DE} \perp \overline{AC}$
$\overline{BF} \perp \overline{AC}$
Prove: $\overline{DE} \cong \overline{BF}$

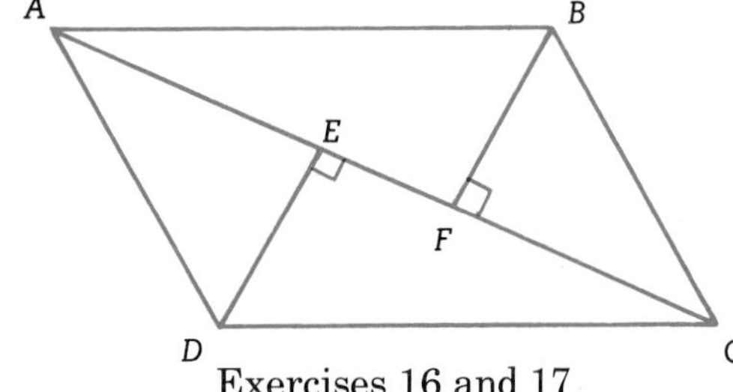

Exercises 16 and 17

For answers to exercises 1-2, see the Teacher's Guide.

Challenge **Complete a proof for each of the following.**

1. Given: $\square PQST$
$\overline{RP}$ bisects $\angle QPT$.
$\overline{VS}$ bisects $\angle QST$.
Prove: $\overline{RP} \parallel \overline{VS}$

2. Given: $\square PQST$
$\overline{RP}$ bisects $\angle QPT$.
$\overline{VS}$ bisects $\angle QST$.
Prove: $\overline{RP} \cong \overline{VS}$

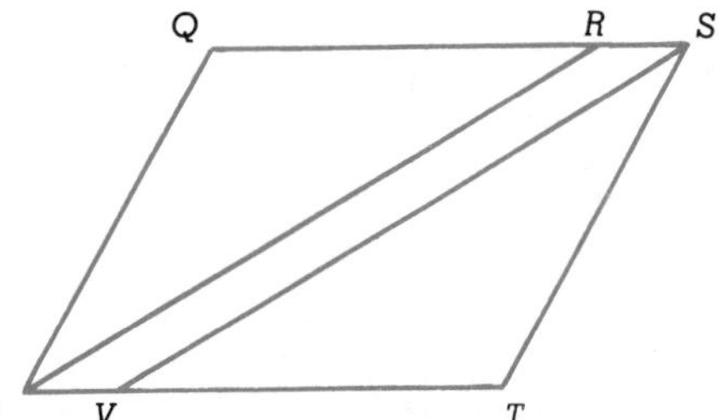

Loops **excursions in geometry**

Which of the following loops of string will make a knot when the ends are pulled tight?

yes no yes no yes

Objectives: to recognize conditions that determine if a polygon is a parallelogram, to use these tests for parallelograms in proofs

7–4 Tests for Parallelograms

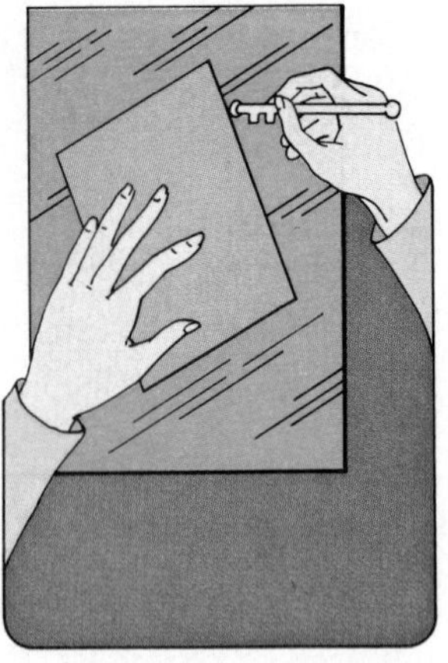

Hazel Thompson is cutting glass pieces in the shape of parallelograms. She must know how to be sure her cutting pattern is a parallelogram.

There are several tests for a parallelogram. Hazel is most likely to use the following.

If both pairs of opposite sides of a quadrilateral are congruent, then the quadrilateral is a parallelogram.

Theorem 7–7

example

1 Prove Theorem 7–7.

Given: $\overline{AB} \cong \overline{CD}$
$\overline{AD} \cong \overline{CB}$

Prove: Quadrilateral $ABCD$ is a parallelogram.

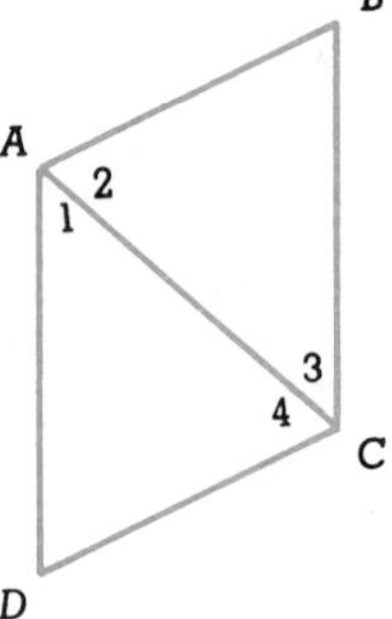

Proof:

STATEMENTS	REASONS
1. $\overline{AB} \cong \overline{CD}$ $\overline{AD} \cong \overline{CB}$	1. Given
2. $\overline{AC} \cong \overline{AC}$	2. Theorem 2–2: Congruence of line segments is reflexive.
3. $\triangle ABC \cong \triangle CDA$	3. Postulate 4–1: SSS
4. $\angle 2 \cong \angle 4$ $\angle 1 \cong \angle 3$	4. Definition of Congruent Triangles CPCTC
5. $\overline{AB} \parallel \overline{DC}$ $\overline{AD} \parallel \overline{BC}$	5. Theorem 6–5: In a plane, if two lines are cut by a transversal so that a pair of alternate interior angles are congruent, then the lines are parallel.
6. Quadrilateral $ABCD$ is a parallelogram.	6. Definition of Parallelogram

The proofs of Theorem 7–7 and Theorem 7–8 are very similar. They both use the triangles formed by the diagonals and sides of a given quadrilateral.

Students prove Theorem 7-8 in Written exercise 1.

If two sides of a quadrilateral are parallel and congruent, then the quadrilateral is a parallelogram.

Theorem 7–8

The following theorem is the converse of Theorem 7–6.

If the diagonals of a quadrilateral bisect each other, then the quadrilateral is a parallelogram.

Theorem 7–9

example

2 Prove Theorem 7–9.

Given: $\overline{BD}$ bisects $\overline{AC}$.
$\overline{AC}$ bisects $\overline{BD}$.

Prove: Quadrilateral $ABCD$ is a parallelogram.

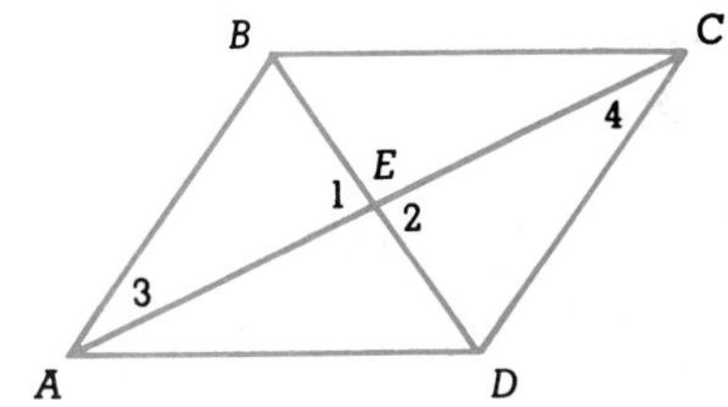

Proof:

STATEMENTS	REASONS
1. $\overline{BD}$ bisects $\overline{AC}$. $\overline{AC}$ bisects $\overline{BD}$.	1. Given
2. $\overline{AE} \cong \overline{CE}$ $\overline{BE} \cong \overline{DE}$	2. Theorem 2–6: Bisector Theorem
3. $\angle 1 \cong \angle 2$	3. Theorem 3–10: If two angles are vertical, then they are congruent.
4. $\triangle BEA \cong \triangle DEC$	4. Postulate 4–2: SAS
5. $\angle 3 \cong \angle 4$ $\overline{AB} \cong \overline{CD}$	5. Definition of Congruent Triangles CPCTC
6. $\overline{AB} \parallel \overline{CD}$	6. Theorem 6–5: In a plane, if two lines are cut by a transversal so that a pair of alternate interior angles are congruent, then the lines are parallel.
7. Quadrilateral $ABCD$ is a parallelogram.	7. Theorem 7–8: If two sides of a quadrilateral are parallel and congruent, then the quadrilateral is a parallelogram.

EN: Ex: 1-15 odds, Wr: 1-15 odds; AV: Ex: 1-15 odds, Wr: 1-10; pp. 218-9, Wr: 6-16 evens

exercises

FN: Ex: 1-16, Wr: 1-15 odds; p. 219, Wr: 13, 15, 17

Exploratory **Determine whether or *not* each of the following tests could be used to prove that a quadrilateral is a parallelogram. State *yes* or *no*.**

1. Both pairs of opposite sides are parallel. yes
2. Both pairs of opposite sides are congruent. yes
3. The quadrilateral is regular. yes
4. Pairs of consecutive sides are congruent. no
5. Pairs of consecutive angles are congruent. no
6. Both pairs of opposite angles are congruent. yes

For explanations to exercises 7-16, see the Teacher's Guide.

For each of the following given set of conditions, determine whether or *not* the quadrilateral must be a parallelogram. State *yes* or *no*. Then, explain.

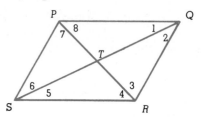

7. $\overline{RQ} \cong \overline{SP}$
   $\angle 2 \cong \angle 6$ yes
8. $\angle 2 \cong \angle 3$
   $\overline{QR} \cong \overline{PS}$ no
9. $QT = 5$
   $RT = 9$
   $PT = 5$
   $ST = 5$ no
10. $m\angle 1 = 60$
    $m\angle 2 = 70$
    $m\angle 5 = 60$
    $m\angle 6 = 70$ yes
11. $m\angle PQR = 71$
    $m\angle QPS = 109$
    $\angle PQR \cong \angle RSP$ yes
12. $QR = 8$
    $PQ = 8$
    $RS = 4$
    $SP = 4$ no

Exercises 7–12

13. E is the midpoint of $\overline{BD}$.
    E is the midpoint of $\overline{AC}$. yes
14. $\overline{AB} \cong \overline{BC}$
    $\overline{CD} \cong \overline{AD}$ no
15. $\triangle ABC \cong \triangle CDA$ yes
16. $\triangle ABE \cong \triangle CDE$ yes

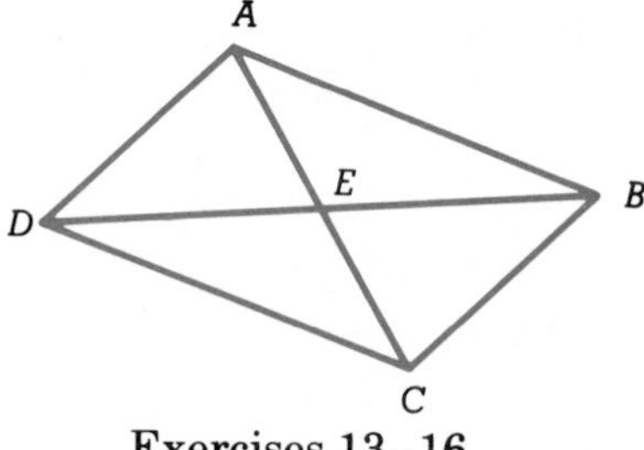

Exercises 13–16

For answers to exercises 1-15, see the Teacher's Guide.

Written **Prove each of the following.**

1. Theorem 7–8
2. If both pairs of opposite angles of a quadrilateral are congruent, then the quadrilateral is a parallelogram.
3. If one pair of opposite angles of a quadrilateral are congruent and one pair of opposite sides are parallel, then the quadrilateral is a parallelogram.
4. If quadrilateral $EFGH$ has $\angle G \cong \angle E$ and $\overline{FG} \cong \overline{GH} \cong \overline{HE}$, then the quadrilateral is parallelogram.
5. **Given:** $\overline{AE} \cong \overline{CE}$
   $\angle ECD \cong \angle EAB$
   Prove: Quadrilateral $ABCD$ is a parallelogram.
6. **Given:** $\overline{BA} \parallel \overline{CD}$
   $\angle DBC \cong \angle ADB$
   Prove: Quadrilateral $ABCD$ is a parallelogram.

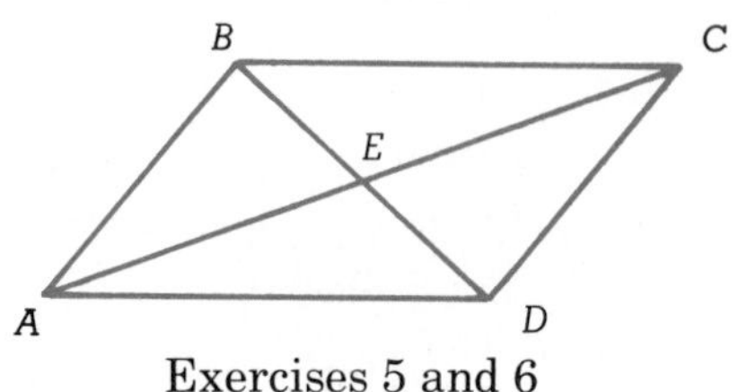

Exercises 5 and 6

7. **Given:** $\triangle PQR \cong \triangle STV$
$\overline{PR} \parallel \overline{VS}$
Prove: Quadrilateral $PRSV$ is a parallelogram.

8. **Given:** $\square PQST$
$\overline{QR} \cong \overline{TV}$
Prove: Quadrilateral $PRSV$ is a parallelogram.

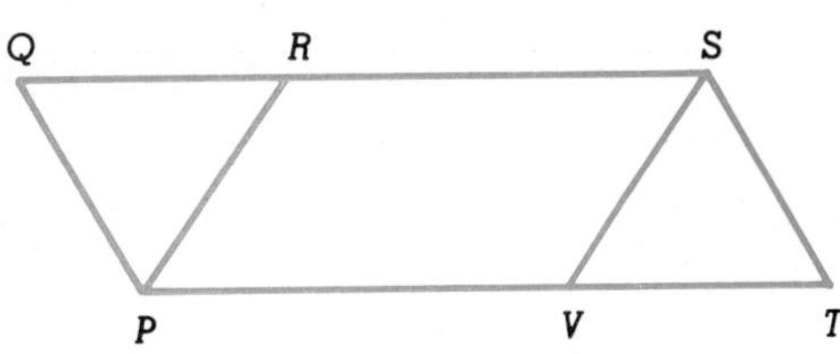

Exercises 7 and 8

9. **Given:** $\square ABCD$
E is the midpoint of $\overline{AB}$.
F is the midpoint of $\overline{BC}$.
G is the midpoint of $\overline{CD}$.
H is the midpoint of $\overline{DA}$.
Prove: Quadrilateral $EFGH$ is a parallelogram.

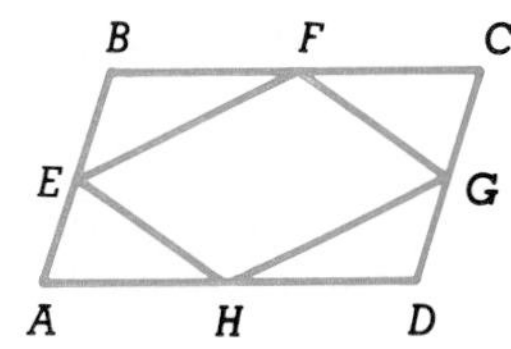

Exercise 9

10. **Given:** $\overline{AF} \cong \overline{CF}$
$\overline{BE} \cong \overline{GD}$
F is the midpoint of $\overline{EG}$.
Prove: Quadrilateral $ABCD$ is a parallelogram.

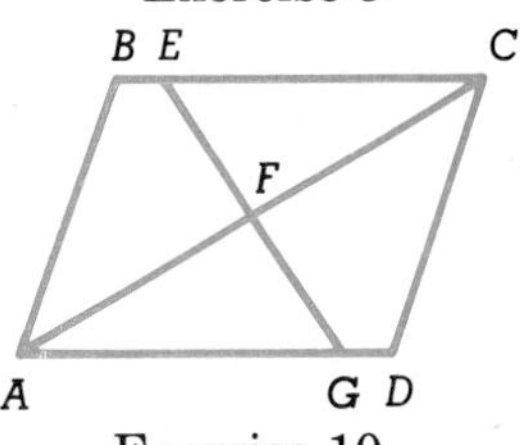

Exercise 10

11. **Given:** $\overline{AB} \cong \overline{BC}$
D is the midpoint of $\overline{CF}$.
D is the midpoint of $\overline{BE}$.
Prove: Quadrilateral $ABEF$ is a parallelogram.

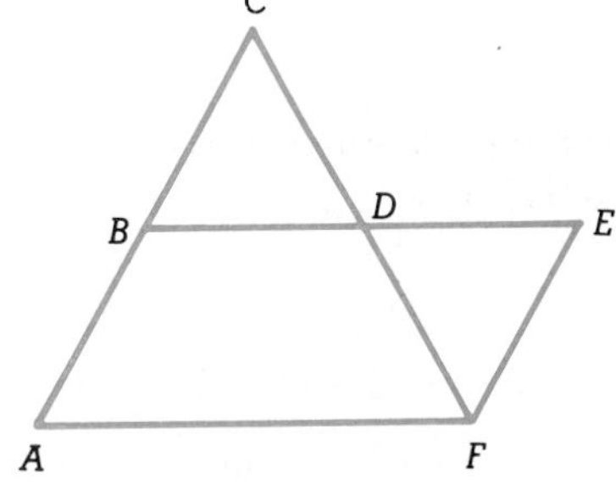

Exercise 11

12. **Given:** $\overline{FB} \perp \overline{AC}$
$\overline{FD} \perp \overline{CE}$
$\overline{FB} \perp \overline{FD}$
Prove: Quadrilateral $FBCD$ is a parallelogram.

13. **Given:** $\angle ABF \cong \angle EDF$
$\overline{FD} \parallel \overline{AC}$
Prove: Quadrilateral $FBCD$ is a parallelogram.

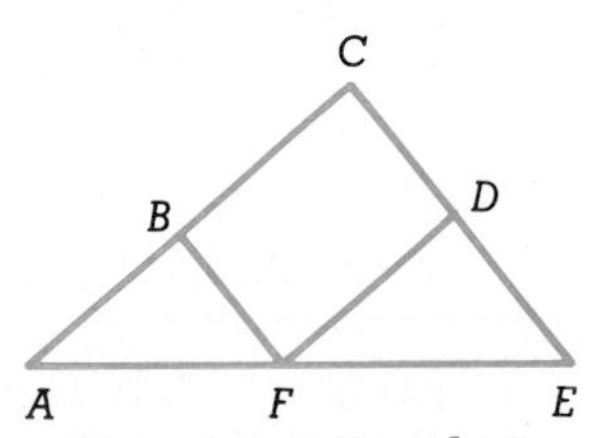

Exercises 12 and 13

14. **Given:** $\square ACEF$
$\angle G \cong \angle F$
$\overline{BG} \parallel \overline{CD}$
Prove: Quadrilateral $BCDG$ is a parallelogram.

15. **Given:** $\square BCDG$
$\angle E \cong \angle A$
$\overline{CE} \parallel \overline{AF}$
Prove: Quadrilateral $ACEF$ is a parallelogram.

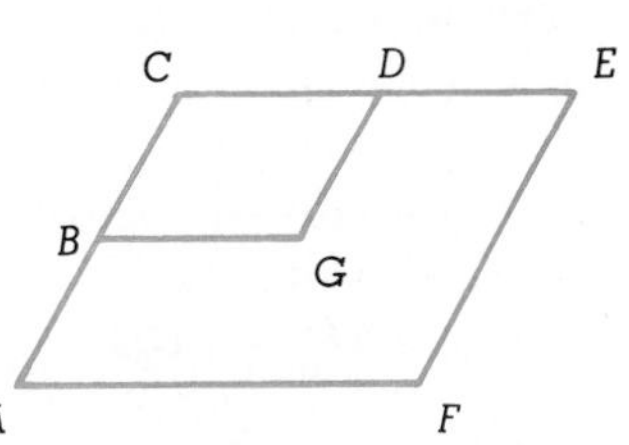

Exercises 14 and 15

7–5 Special Parallelograms

Objectives: to recognize properties of rectangles, rhombi, and squares, to use properties of these special parallelograms in proofs

The shapes of the figures below are examples of three special parallelograms. These parallelograms are classified by their sides and their angles.

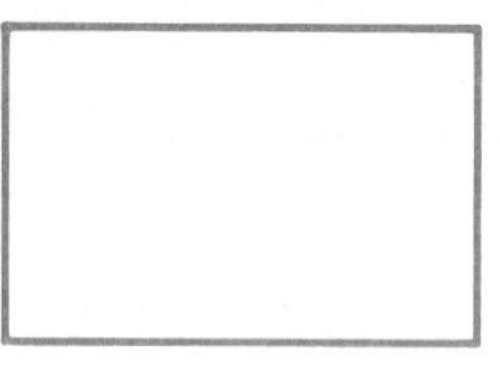

rectangle

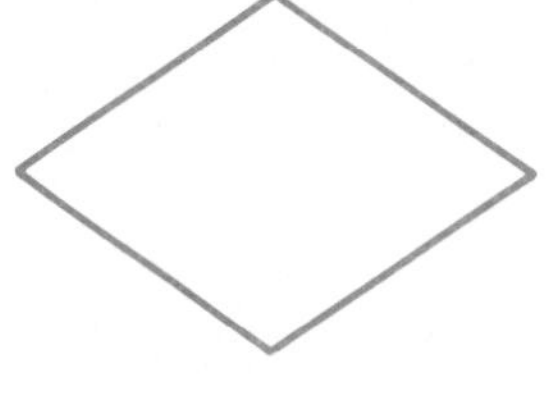

rhombus

square

A quadrilateral is a rectangle if and only if it is a parallelogram with four right angles.

Definition of Rectangle

Study rectangle $ABCD$ at the right. What appears to be true about diagonals $\overline{AC}$ and $\overline{BD}$? They appear to be congruent.

If a quadrilateral is a rectangle, then its diagonals are congruent.

Theorem 7–10

example

1 **Prove Theorem 7–10.**

Given: Rectangle $ABCD$ with diagonals $\overline{AC}$ and $\overline{BD}$.

Prove: $\overline{AC} \cong \overline{BD}$

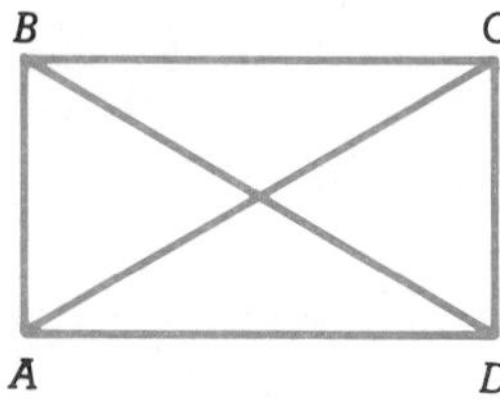

Proof:

STATEMENTS	REASONS
1. Rectangle $ABCD$ with diagonals $\overline{AC}$ and $\overline{BD}$	1. Given
2. $\overline{AB} \cong \overline{CD}$	2. Theorem 7–5: If a quadrilateral is a parallelogram, then its opposite sides are congruent.
3. $\angle BAD$ and $\angle CDA$ are right angles.	3. Definition of Rectangle
4. $\angle BAD \cong \angle CDA$	4. Theorem 3–6: If two angles are right angles, then the angles are congruent.
5. $\overline{AD} \cong \overline{AD}$	5. Theorem 2–2: Congruence of line segments is reflexive.

6. $\triangle BAD$ and $\triangle CDA$ are right triangles.	6. Definition of Right Triangle
7. $\triangle BAD \cong \triangle CDA$	7. Theorem 4–12: If the legs of one right triangle are congruent to the corresponding legs of another right triangle, then the triangles are congruent.
8. $\overline{BD} \cong \overline{CA}$	8. Definition of Congruent Triangles CPCTC

A quadrilateral is a rhombus if and only if it is a parallelogram with all four sides congruent.

Definition of Rhombus

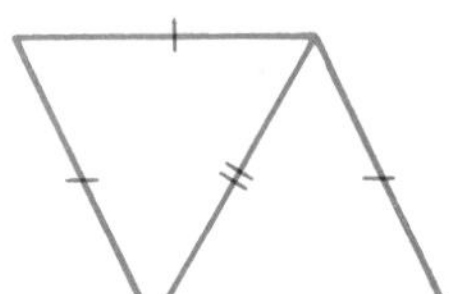

The plural forms of rhombus are "rhombuses" and "rhombi".

The diagonals of a rhombus *not* only bisect each other, but also bisect opposite angles of the rhombus. This property can be proven by showing pairs of triangles congruent.

If a quadrilateral is a rhombus, then each diagonal bisects a pair of opposite angles.

Theorem 7–11

example

2 **Prove Theorem 7–11.**

Given: Rhombus $QRST$ with diagonals $\overline{RT}$ and $\overline{QS}$

Prove: $\overline{QS}$ bisects $\angle RQT$ and $\angle RST$.
$\overline{RT}$ bisects $\angle QRS$ and $\angle STQ$.

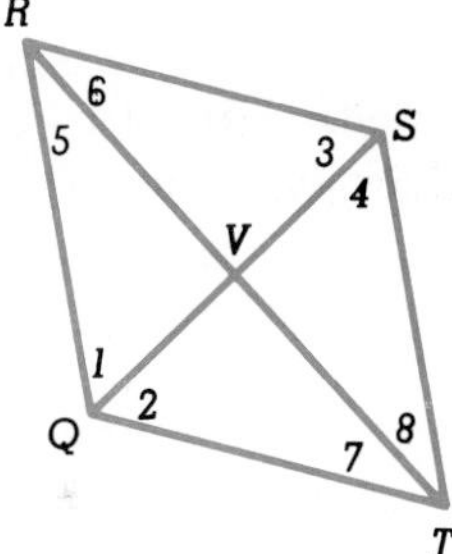

Proof:

STATEMENTS	REASONS
1. Rhombus $QRST$ with diagonals $\overline{RT}$ and $\overline{QS}$	1. Given
2. $\overline{QR} \cong \overline{QT}$, $\overline{SR} \cong \overline{ST}$ $\overline{QR} \cong \overline{SR}$, $\overline{QT} \cong \overline{ST}$	2. Definition of Rhombus
3. $\overline{QS} \cong \overline{QS}$, $\overline{RT} \cong \overline{RT}$	3. Theorem 2–2: Congruence of line segments is reflexive.
4. $\triangle QRS \cong \triangle QTS$ $\triangle TQR \cong \triangle TSR$	4. Postulate 4–1: SSS
5. $\angle 1 \cong \angle 2$, $\angle 3 \cong \angle 4$ $\angle 5 \cong \angle 6$, $\angle 7 \cong \angle 8$	5. Definition of Congruent Triangles CPCTC
6. $\overline{QS}$ bisects $\angle RQT$ and $\angle RST$. $\overline{RT}$ bisects $\angle QRS$ and $\angle STQ$.	6. Definition of Angle Bisector

Another property of the diagonals of a rhombus is that they intersect to form four right angles.

If a quadrilateral is a rhombus, then its diagonals are perpendicular.

Theorem 7–12

A rhombus may or may not be a rectangle. Also, a rectangle may or may not be a rhombus. A quadrilateral that is both a rectangle and a rhombus is called a **square.**

A quadrilateral is a square if and only if it is a rectangle and all four sides are congruent.

Definition of Square

EN: Wr: 1-6, 8-28 evens; p. 228, Ch: 1; p. 229, Ca: 1-4; AV: Ex: 1-8, Wr: 1-22; p. 229, Ca: 1-4; p. 223, Wr: 11, 13, 15

exercises

FN: Ex: 1-8, Wr: 1-23; p. 229, Ca: 1-4; p. 223, Wr: 8-14 evens

Exploratory **Name which quadrilaterals have each of the following properties.**

1. All angles are right angles.
2. The opposite sides are parallel.
3. The opposite sides are congruent.
4. The opposite angles are congruent.
5. All sides are congruent.
6. It is equiangular.
7. It is equilateral.
8. It is equiangular and equilateral.

For answers to exercises 1-8, see the Teacher's Guide.

Written **Copy and complete the following table by indicating whether the quadrilaterals have the indicated properties. Write *yes* or *no*.**

	Property	Parallelogram	Rectangle	Rhombus	Square
1.	The diagonals bisect each other.	√	√	√	√
2.	The diagonals are congruent.		√		√
3.	Each diagonal bisects a pair of opposite angles.			√	√
4.	The diagonals form two pairs of congruent triangles.	√	√	√	√
5.	The diagonals form four congruent triangles.			√	√
6.	The diagonals are perpendicular.			√	√

Use the rhombus and the given information to solve each problem.

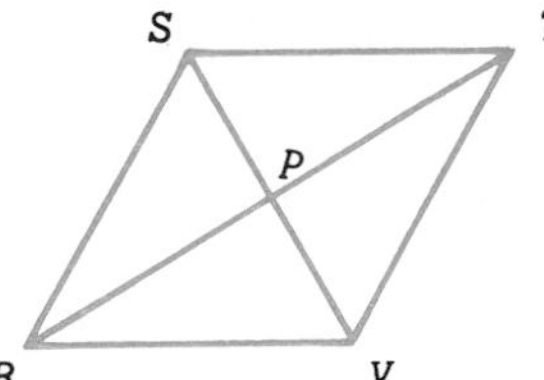

Exercises 7–12

7. $ST = 10\frac{7}{8}$ Find TV. $10\frac{7}{8}$
8. $ST = 12.3$ Find TV. 12.3
9. $SP = 52.1$ Find SV. 104.2
10. $SP = 22\frac{5}{8}$ Find SV. $45\frac{1}{4}$
11. $PT = 6\frac{3}{4}$ Find RT. $13\frac{1}{2}$
12. $PT = 7.6$ Find RT. 15.2

Use the rhombus and the given information to solve each problem.

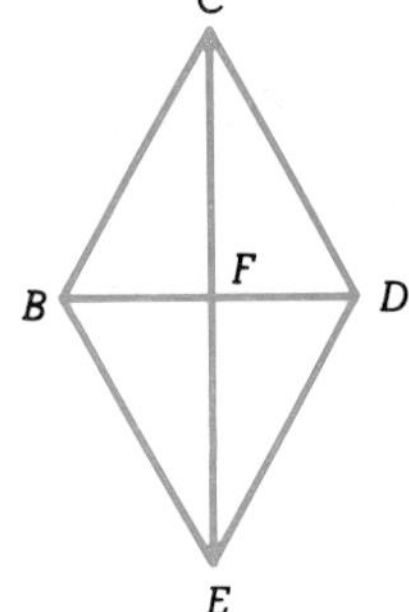

Exercises 13–20

13. $m\angle EBC = 112.6$ Find $m\angle EBD$. 56.3
14. $m\angle BCD = 75.0$ Find $m\angle BCE$. 37.5
15. $m\angle BDC = 25.9$ Find $m\angle EDC$. 51.8
16. $m\angle CDE = 123.4$ Find $m\angle DBC$. 61.7
17. Find $m\angle BFE$. 90
18. Find $m\angle DFC$. 90
19. $m\angle BEC = 2x + 10$
$m\angle CED = 5x - 20$
Find x. 10
20. $m\angle CBD = 2x + 24$
$m\angle EBD = x^2$
Find x. 6 or -4

For answers to exercises 21-28, see the Teacher's Guide.

Prove each of the following.

21. If a quadrilateral is a square, then its diagonals bisect each other.

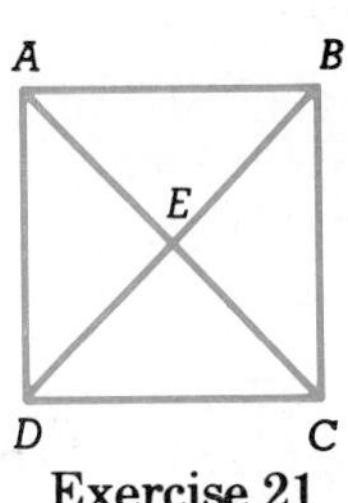

Exercise 21

22. If a quadrilateral is a square, then its diagonals are perpendicular.

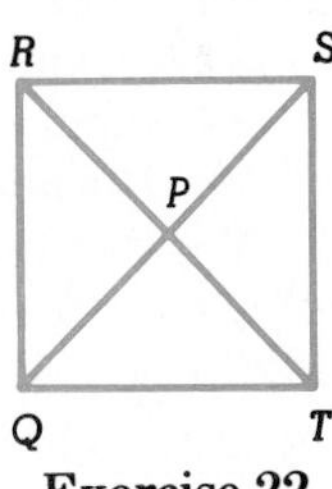

Exercise 22

23. If a parallelogram has one right angle, then it is a rectangle.

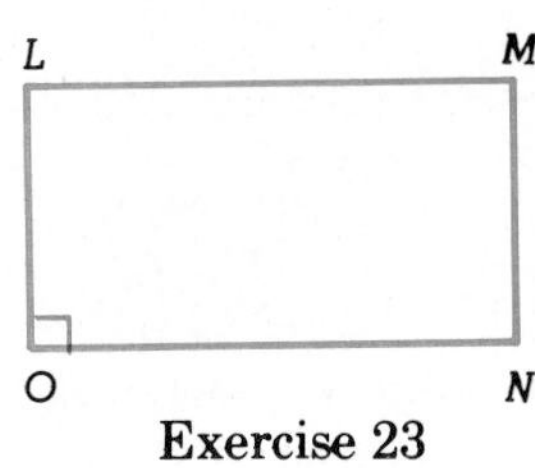

Exercise 23

24. If the diagonals of a parallelogram are perpendicular, then it is a rhombus.

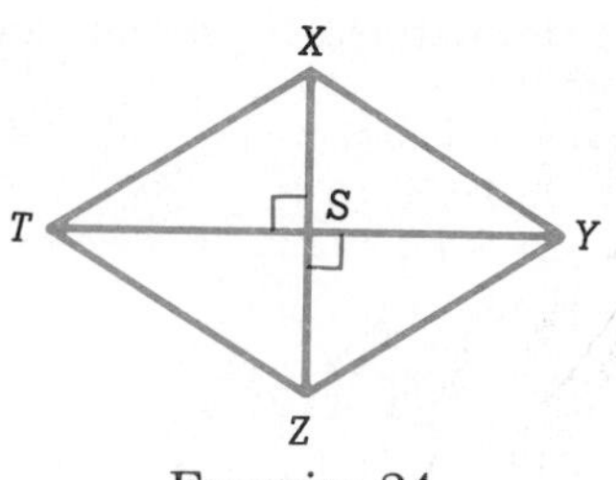

Exercise 24

25. If a parallelogram has two consecutive sides that are congruent, then it is a rhombus.

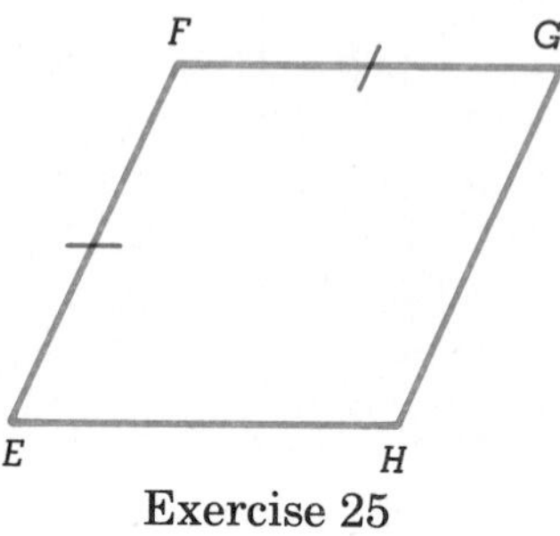

Exercise 25

26. Theorem 7–12

27. If the diagonals of a parallelogram bisect its angles, then it is a rhombus.

28. If the diagonals of a parallelogram are congruent, then it is a rectangle.

For answers to exercises 1-2, see the Teacher's Guide.

Challenge Prove each of the following.

1. **Given:** $PRTW$ is a square.
Q is the midpoint of $\overline{PR}$.
S is the midpoint of $\overline{RT}$.
V is the midpoint of $\overline{TW}$.
X is the midpoint of $\overline{PW}$.
Prove: $\overline{QV} \perp \overline{SX}$

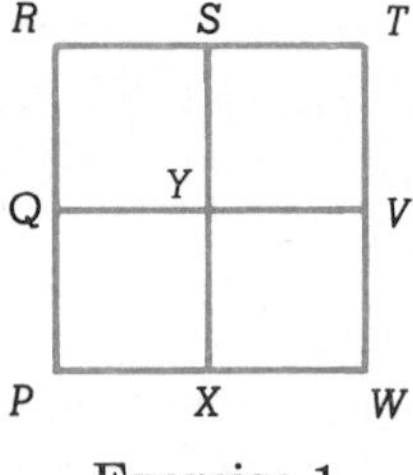

Exercise 1

2. **Given:** $\square ABCD$ is a rhombus.
$\overline{AF} \cong \overline{BG}$
$\overline{BG} \cong \overline{CH}$
$\overline{CH} \cong \overline{DE}$
$\overline{DE} \cong \overline{AF}$
Prove: Quadrilateral $EFGH$ is a parallelogram.

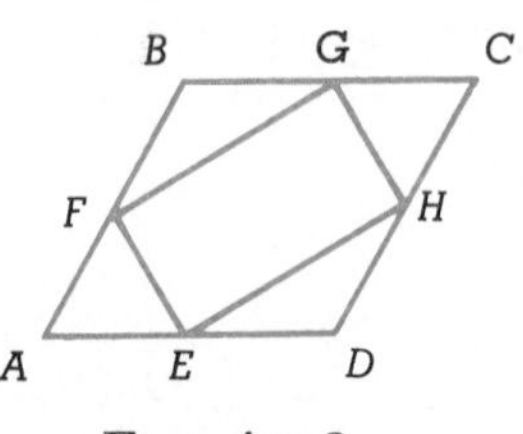

Exercise 2

careers **Mineralogist**

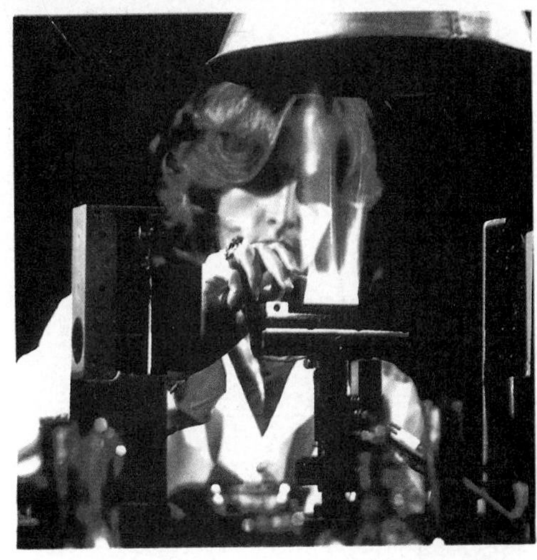

Kathy Seall is a mineralogist for B. T. Duvall Power Co. As a mineralogist she studies the various crystals found in nature. Crystals can be used to change sunshine into electric current.

In their original state, crystals are solids with flat surfaces. The flat surfaces, called faces, have different geometric shapes, depending on the type of crystal.

One way to classify crystals is by the number of faces, the shape of the faces, and the congruent faces. For example, alum crystals have eight faces, each of which is an equilateral triangle.

The photograph at the right shows wulfenite crystals. How many faces do you see? What are the shapes of each of the faces? Are any faces congruent? yes

Answers will vary.

The faces are polygons.

Exercises **For each of the following crystals, name the number of faces, the shape of the faces, and identify any congruent faces.**

1. borax 6; rectangles; opposite faces

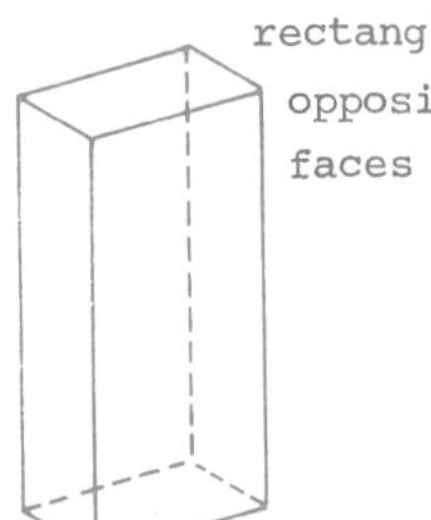

2. calcite 12; triangles; all faces

3. quartz 18; rectangles & triangles; all triangles

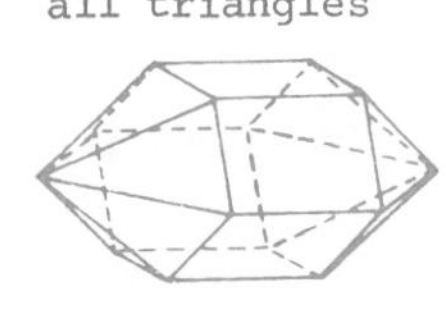

all rectangles

4. gypsum 10; rectangles & quadrilaterals; opposite faces

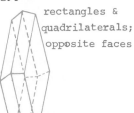

7–6 Trapezoids

Objectives: to recognize trapezoids, to recognize and to use properties of trapezoids in proofs and other problems

The design of the College Park Pyramids in Indianapolis is based on a quadrilateral called a **trapezoid.**

A quadrilateral is a trapezoid if and only if it has exactly one pair of parallel sides.

Definition of Trapezoid

The parallel sides of a trapezoid are called **bases.** The nonparallel sides of a trapezoid are called **legs.** If the legs are congruent, then the trapezoid is called an **isosceles trapezoid.** One pair of **base angles** is $\angle B$ and $\angle C$. Another pair of base angles is $\angle A$ and $\angle D$.

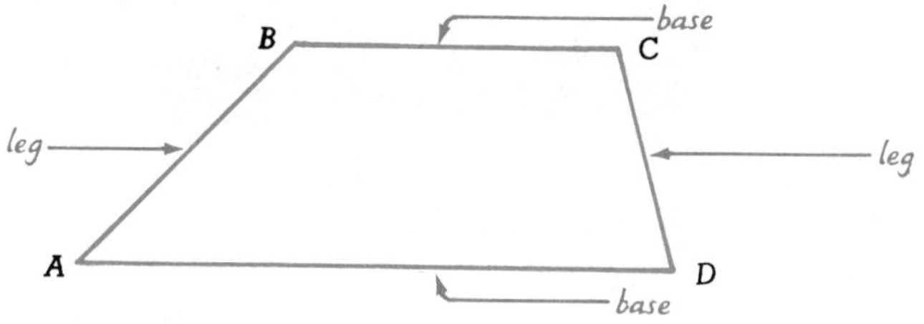

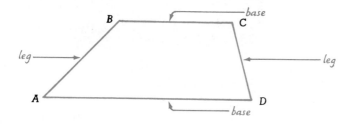

It is helpful to illustrate various examples of trapezoids in which the parallel sides are not always horizontal.

Isosceles trapezoids have special properties.

If a trapezoid is isosceles, then each pair of base angles is congruent.

Theorem 7–13

In the following example, one pair of base angles is proven to be congruent.

example

1 **Prove the following.**
Given: $\overline{PS} \parallel \overline{QR}$
$\overline{PQ} \cong \overline{SR}$
Prove: $\angle P \cong \angle S$

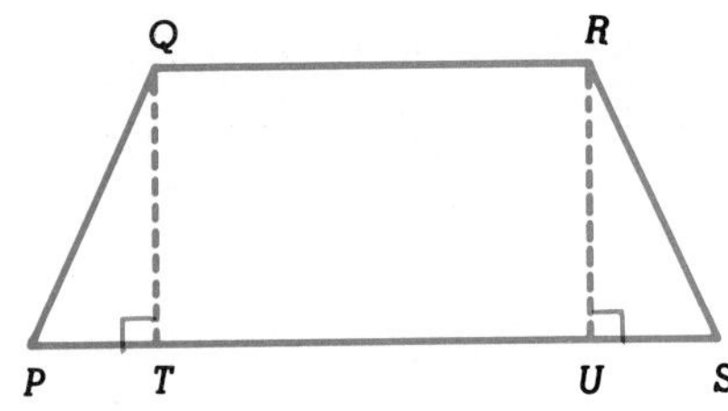

Proof:

STATEMENTS	REASONS
1. Draw $\overline{QT}$ perpendicular to $\overline{PS}$. Draw $\overline{RU}$ perpendicular to $\overline{PS}$.	1. Theorem 6–12: Given a line and a point not on the line, there is exactly one line through the point and perpendicular to the given line.
2. $\overline{PS} \parallel \overline{QR}$, $\overline{PQ} \cong \overline{SR}$	2. Given
3. $\overline{QT} \cong \overline{RU}$	3. Theorem 6–13: In a plane, two lines are parallel if and only if they are everywhere equidistant.
4. $\angle QTP$ and $\angle RUS$ are right angles.	4. Theorem 3–11: If two lines are perpendicular, then they form four right angles.
5. $\triangle QTP$ and $\triangle RUS$ are right triangles.	5. Definition of Right Triangle
6. $\triangle QTP \cong \triangle RUS$	6. Postulate 4–4: HL
7. $\angle P \cong \angle S$	7. Definition of Congruent Triangles CPCTC

Theorem 7–13 can be used to prove Theorem 7–14.

If a trapezoid is isosceles, then its diagonals are congruent.

Theorem 7–14

Students prove Theorem 7-14 in Written exercise 42.

In trapezoid $ACDF$ at the right, B is the midpoint of $\overline{AC}$ and E is the midpoint of $\overline{DF}$. Segment BE is called the **median** of the trapezoid.

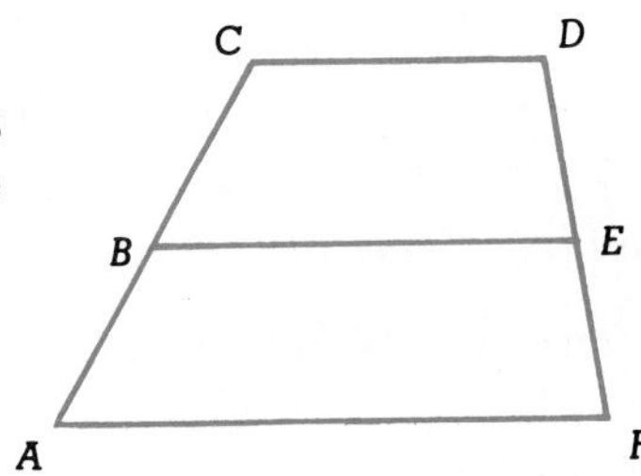

A line segment is the median of a trapezoid if and only if its endpoints are the midpoints of the legs of the trapezoid.

Definition of Median

The median of a trapezoid has the following property.

If a quadrilateral is a trapezoid, then the median is parallel to the bases, and its measure is one-half the sum of the measures of the bases.

Theorem 7–15

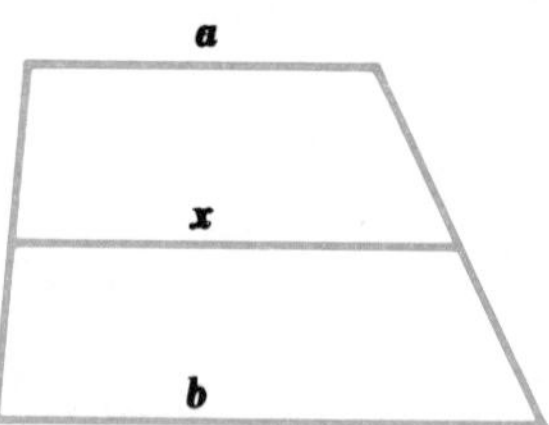

In general, if the measure of the short base of a trapezoid is represented by a, the measure of the long base is represented by b, and the measure of the median is represented by x, then the following is true.

$$\text{measure of median} = \frac{1}{2}(\text{measure of short base} + \text{measure of long base})$$

$$x = \frac{1}{2}(a + b)$$

example

2 **The bases of a trapezoid have lengths of 22 inches and 14 inches. Find the length of the median.**

$$x = \frac{1}{2}(a + b)$$
$$= \frac{1}{2}(14 + 22)$$
$$= \frac{1}{2}(36)$$
$$= 18$$

The median is 18 inches long.

EN: Ex: 1-11 odds, Wr: 10-42 evens; p. 235, TG: 1-3; AV: Ex: 1-12, Wr: 1-33 odds; p. 235, TG: 1-2; pp. 227-8, Wr: 23-25, 27

exercises

FN: Ex: 1-12, Wr: 1-35 odds; p. 228, Wr: 24-25

Exploratory **Determine whether or *not* it is possible for a trapezoid to have the following. State *yes* or *no*.**

1. a leg longer than either base yes
2. two congruent sides, but not be isosceles yes
3. three congruent sides yes
4. congruent bases no
5. congruent diagonals yes
6. bisecting diagonals no
7. one pair of opposite angles congruent no
8. two pairs of opposite sides parallel no
9. two right angles yes
10. two obtuse angles yes
11. three obtuse angles no
12. four acute angles no

13. The opposite angles of an isosceles trapezoid are supplementary. Explain why this is true. See the Teacher's Guide.

Written **For each of the following, the lengths of the bases of a trapezoid are given. Find the length of the median.**

1. 6 cm, 18 cm 12 cm
2. 4 in., 18 in. 11 in.
3. $3\frac{1}{4}$ ft, $2\frac{3}{4}$ ft 3 ft
4. $4\frac{1}{3}$ yd, $5\frac{1}{3}$ yd $4\frac{5}{6}$ yd
5. 9.6 mm, 4.4 mm 7 mm
6. 7.3 m, 2.5 m 4.9 m
7. 87.6 cm, 91.4 cm 89.5 cm
8. 14.3 mm, 32.1 mm 23.2 mm
9. $23\frac{1}{4}$ mi, $18\frac{1}{4}$ mi $20\frac{3}{4}$ mi
10. 6.0 km, 3.5 km 4.75 km
11. 54.1 m, 42.7 m 48.4 m
12. $33\frac{1}{3}$ ft, $12\frac{2}{3}$ ft 23 ft

The figure at the right is an isosceles trapezoid with bases $\overline{AD}$ and $\overline{BC}$. Use this figure and the information given to find the indicated measures.

13. $BD = 8.2$ Find AC. 8.2
14. $AB = 14.6$ Find CD. 14.6
15. $CD = 13.5$ Find AB. 13.5
16. $CA = 16.7$ Find BD. 16.7
17. $DB = 2y + 3$ $AC = 4y - 5$ Find DB and AC. DB = AC = 11
18. $DC = y^2$ $BA = 7y + 8$ Find DC and BA.
19. $AB = 16a - 12$ $CD = 8a + 8$ Find AB and CD. AB = CD = 28
20. $AC = 7a + 18$ $BD = a^2$ Find AC and BD.

18. DC = BA = 1 or 64
20. AC = BD = 4 or 81

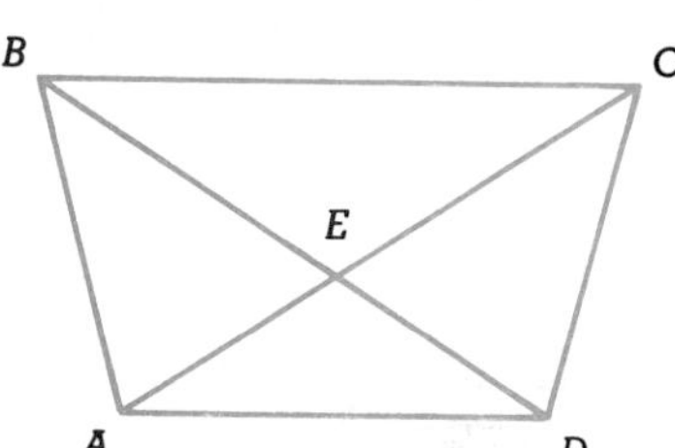

Exercises 13–20

The figure at the right is an isosceles trapezoid with bases $\overline{RS}$ and $\overline{TW}$. Use this figure and the information given to find the indicated measures.

21. $m\angle WSR = 115$ Find $m\angle TRS$. 115
22. $m\angle SWT = 60$ Find $m\angle RTW$. 60
23. $m\angle WSR = 132$ Find $m\angle SWT$. 48
24. $m\angle WTR = 53$ Find $m\angle SRT$. 127
25. $m\angle XSR = 25$ Find $m\angle XTW$. 25
26. $m\angle XSR = 32$ Find $m\angle XRS$. 32
27. $m\angle WRS = 27$ Find $m\angle STW$. 27
28. $m\angle WRS = 35$ Find $m\angle SXR$. 110
29. $m\angle SWR = 23$ Find $m\angle RTS$. 23
30. $m\angle STR = 21$ Find $m\angle RWS$. 21
31. $m\angle WXT = 126$ Find $m\angle XTW$. 27
32. $m\angle SXR = 131$ Find $m\angle RWT$. 24.5

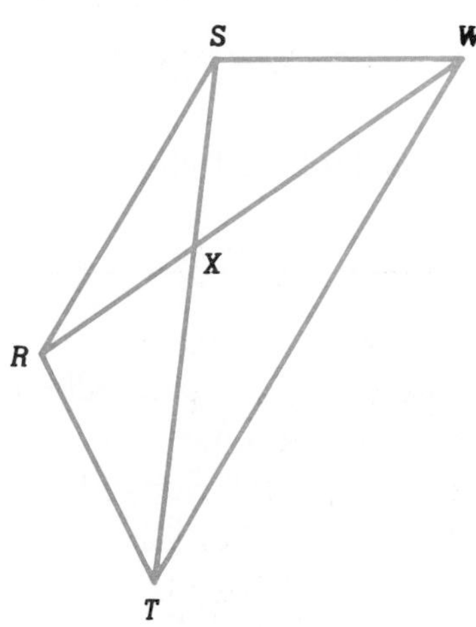

Exercises 21–32

For answers to exercises 33-43, see the Teacher's Guide.

33. Prove that if a trapezoid is isosceles, then its opposite angles are supplementary.

Prove each of the following.

34. **Given:** $\overline{LM} \parallel \overline{RN}$
$\overline{LR} \cong \overline{MN}$
$\overline{RP} \perp \overline{LM}$, $\overline{NQ} \perp \overline{LM}$
Prove: $\triangle LRP \cong \triangle MNQ$

35. **Given:** $\overline{LM} \parallel \overline{RN}$
$\overline{LR} \cong \overline{MN}$
$\overline{RP} \perp \overline{LM}$, $\overline{NQ} \perp \overline{LM}$
Prove: $\angle RLP \cong \angle NMQ$

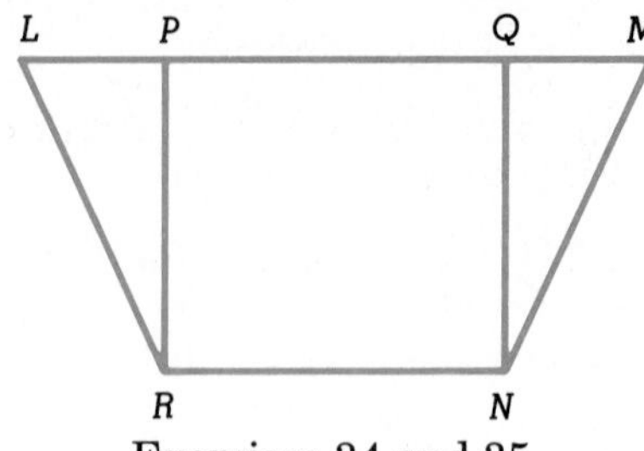

Exercises 34 and 35

Use the following information in exercises 36–39.

Given: $\overline{RT} \parallel \overline{PW}$
$\overline{TX} \parallel \overline{RP}$
Q is the midpoint of $\overline{PR}$.
V is the midpoint of $\overline{SW}$.

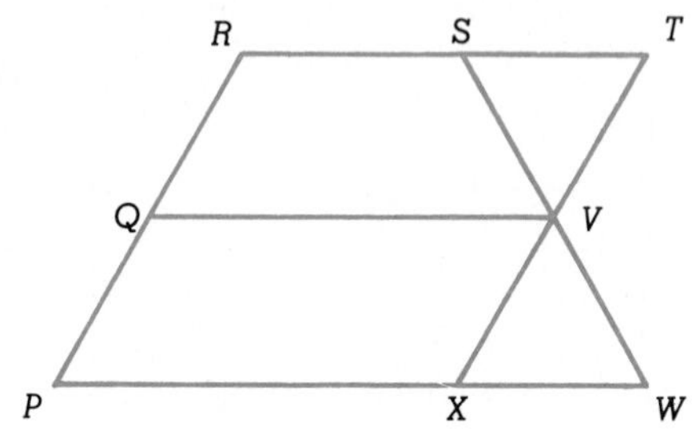

Exercises 36–39

36. **Prove:** V is the midpoint of $\overline{TX}$.
37. **Prove:** $\triangle SVT \cong \triangle WVX$
38. **Prove:** Quadrilateral $QRTV$ is a parallelogram.
39. **Prove:** $\overline{QV} \parallel \overline{PW}$

Prove each of the following.

40. **Given:** Trapezoid $RSPT$ is isosceles.
Prove: $\triangle RSQ$ is isosceles.

41. **Given:** $\triangle PQT$ is isosceles.
$\overline{TP} \parallel \overline{RS}$
Prove: Quadrilateral $RSPT$ is a trapezoid.

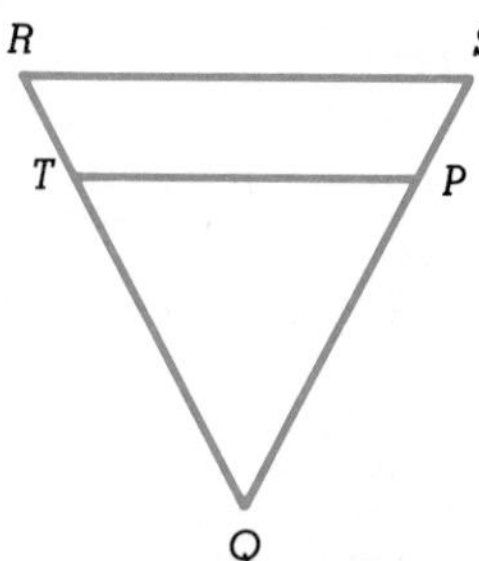

Exercises 40 and 41

42. Theorem 7–14

43. If the base angles of a trapezoid are congruent, then the trapezoid is isosceles.

topics in geometry ◦ Hyperbolic Geometry

One of the basic postulates of Euclidean geometry, the geometry that you are studying in this text, is the Parallel Postulate. This postulate is as follows: If there is a line and a point not on the line, then there is exactly one line through the point and parallel to the given line.

In the nineteenth century, consistent mathematical theories that contradicted Euclid's Parallel Postulate were discovered. One theory was called hyperbolic or Lobachevskian geometry. In Lobachevskian geometry, the Parallel Postulate is as follows: If there is a line and a point not on the line, then there are at least two lines through the point parallel to the given line.

Euclidean Parallel Postulate

P a

b

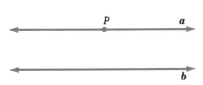

There is exactly one line ***a*** that contains point *P* and is parallel to line ***b***.

Lobachevskian Parallel Postulate

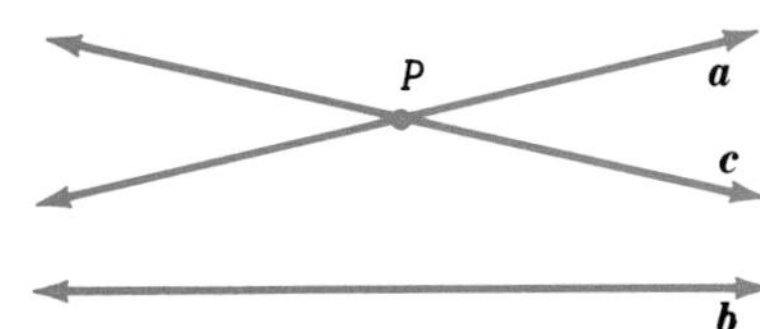

There are at least two lines, line ***a*** and line ***c***, that contain point *P* and are parallel to line ***b***.

The figure above that illustrates the Lobachevskian Parallel Postulate looks impossible. It appears that when lines ***a*** and ***c*** are extended they will intersect line ***b***. Try to imagine that space is infinite and that lines ***a*** and ***b*** extend forever. The lines could get closer and closer to each other but never intersect. Thus, in hyperbolic geometry, parallel lines never meet but the distance between them becomes less as they are further extended.

An important theorem of Euclidean geometry states: If a figure is a triangle, then the sum of the degree measures of the angles is 180. In hyperbolic geometry, the sum of the degree measures of the angles of a triangle is less than 180. As a triangle increases in area, the sum of the measures of its angles decreases. Thus, in hyperbolic geometry only triangles equal in area have the same sum of angle measures.

For answers to exercises 1-3, see the Teacher's Guide.

Exercises **Find a reference for hyperbolic geometry. Then, answer the questions.**

1. Find at least one other theorem of hyperbolic geometry that contradicts a theorem of Euclidean geometry.

2. Use a model for hyperbolic geometry and draw a quadrilateral. How does it differ from a quadrilateral in Euclidean geometry?

3. Write a brief biographical sketch of the life of either Nicholas Lobachevsky, Janos Bolyais, or Karl Friedrich Gauss.

7–7 Perimeter

Objectives: to find the perimeter of a polygon, to use the formulae for perimeters in problem solving

Julie Newton is a carpenter. The floor plan below shows a room she will panel on her next job.

You can assume the corners of the room in this floor plan are right angles.

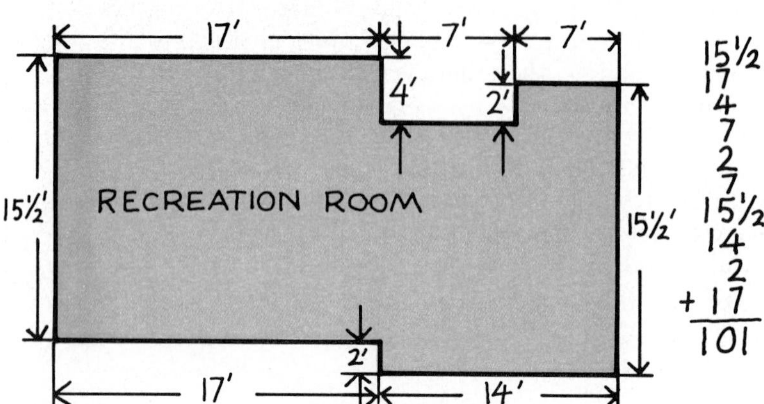

To determine the amount of molding she needs for ceiling trim, Ms. Newton first finds the **perimeter** of the room. She adds the measures for each side of the room. The perimeter is 101 feet.

The perimeter of a polygon is the total length of its sides.

The sum of the measures of the sides of a polygon is the measure of the perimeter of the polygon.

Definition of Perimeter

Each pair of opposite sides of a rectangle is congruent. Thus, only two measurements, the length and the width, are needed to find the perimeter of a rectangle.

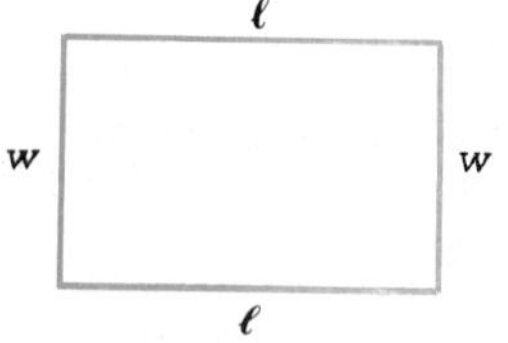

Let ℓ be the measure of the length.
Let w be the measure of the width.
Let P be the measure of the perimeter.

$P = \ell + w + \ell + w$	*Definition of Perimeter*
$= \ell + \ell + w + w$	*Commutative Property of Addition*
$= 2\ell + 2w$	*Substitution*
$= 2(\ell + w)$	*Distributive Property*

If a rectangle has a perimeter of P units, a length of ℓ units, and a width of w units, then $P = 2(\ell + w)$.

Theorem 7–16 Perimeter of Rectangle

example

1 Find the amount of wood molding needed around the floor of a rectangular room measuring 12.4 meters by 4.7 meters.

$$
\begin{aligned}
P &= 2(\ell + w) \\
&= 2(12.4 + 4.7) \\
&= 2(17.1) \\
&= 34.2
\end{aligned}
$$

The amount of wood molding needed is 34.2 meters.

Recall that all sides of a regular polygon are congruent. Therefore, to find the perimeter of a regular polygon the only information you need is the measure of one side and the number of sides of the polygon.

2 Find the perimeter of a regular polygon with 5 sides.

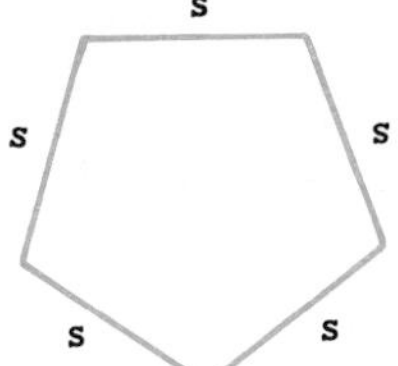

Let s stand for the measure of a side.
Let P stand for the measure of the perimeter.

$P = s + s + s + s + s$ — *Definition of Perimeter*
$\quad = 5s$ — *Substitution*

It can be helpful to show other examples similar to example 2 before presenting Theorem 7-17.

This, and many other examples, suggest the following theorem.

If a regular n-gon has a perimeter of P units and a side measures s units, then $P = ns$.

Theorem 7–17 Perimeter of Regular Polygon

The formal proof of this theorem uses mathematical induction.

example

3 The perimeter of a regular octagon is 32 feet. Find the length of each side.

$P = ns$
$32 = 8s$ — *Substitute 32 for P and 8 for n.*
$4 = s$ — *Solve for s.*

The length of each side is 4 feet.

EN: Ex: 8-10, Wr: 4-34 evens, 36-39; AV: Ex: 1-9 odds, Wr: 2-38 evens; pp. 233-4, Wr: 14, 20, 28, 32, 35, 37

exercises

FN: Ex: 1-10, Wr: 1-37 odds; pp. 233-4, Wr: 10, 12, 18, 20, 30, 32, 38, 39

Exploratory **Find the perimeter for each of the following floor plans. Assume all angles that appear to be right angles are right angles.**

1.

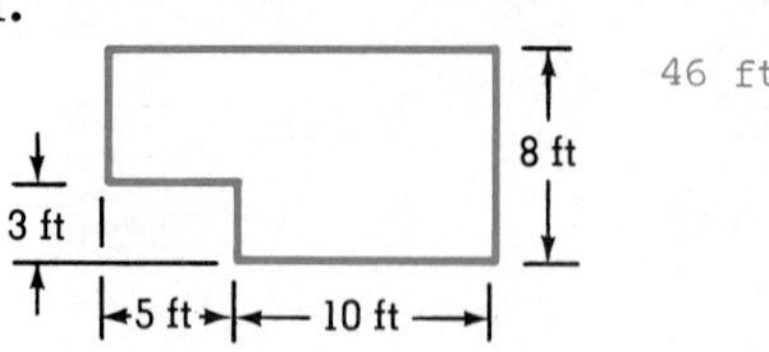

46 ft

2.

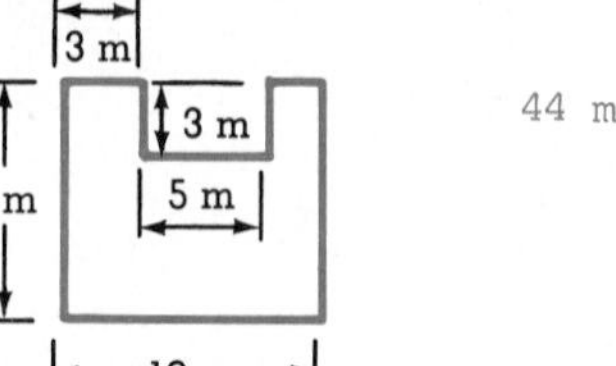

44 m

3.

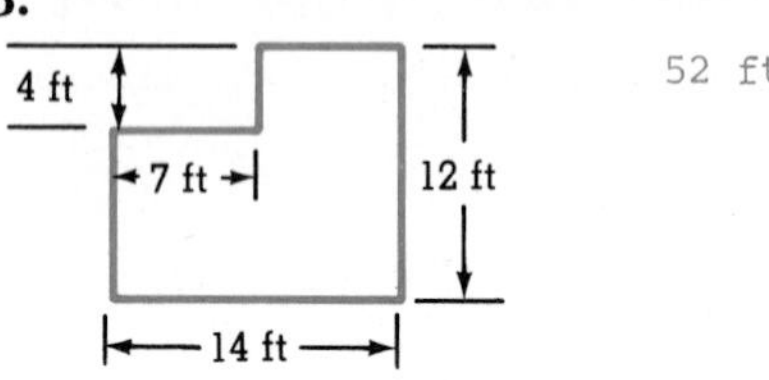

52 ft

4.

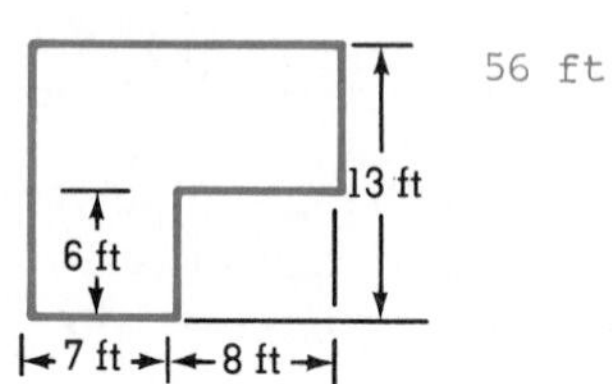

56 ft

5.

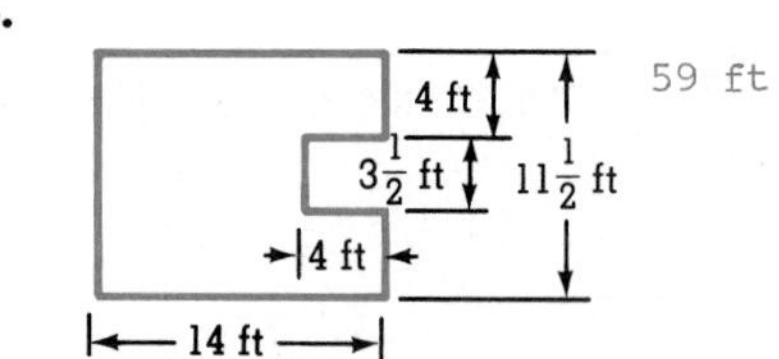

59 ft

6.

69 ft

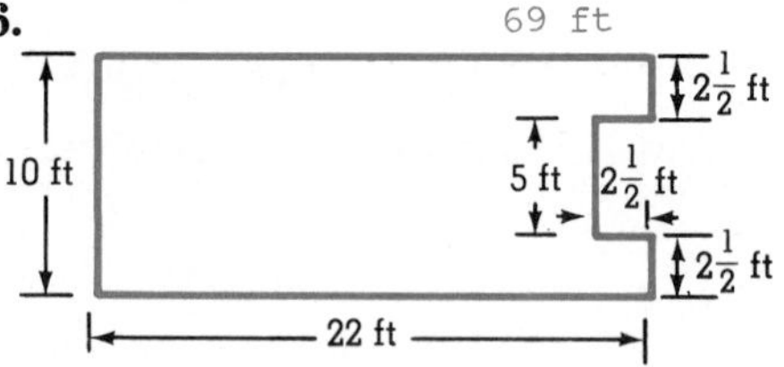

7.

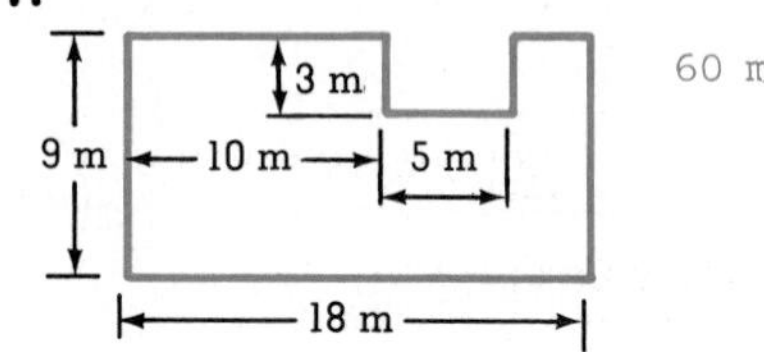

60 m

8.

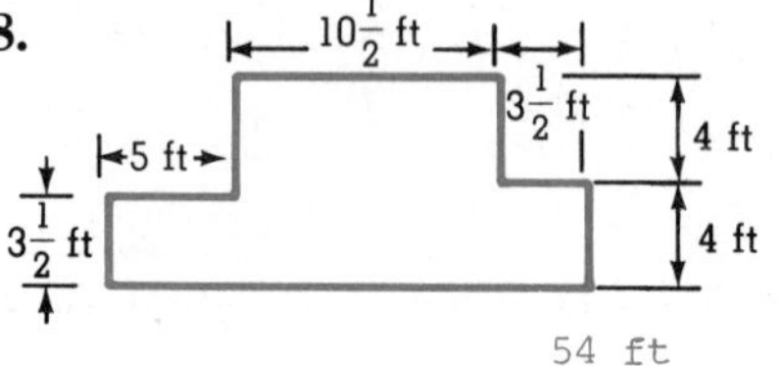

54 ft

9.

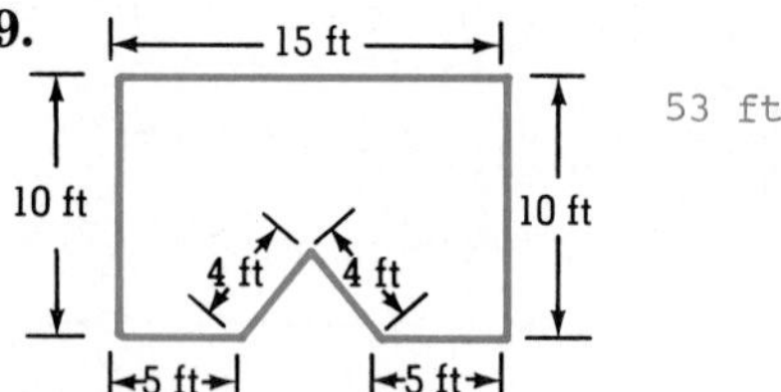

53 ft

10.

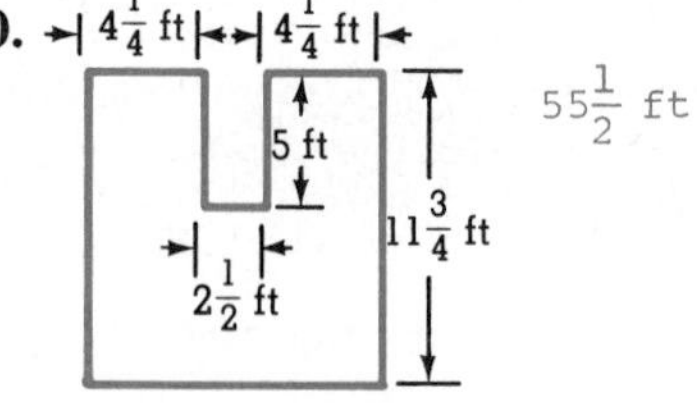

$55\frac{1}{2}$ ft

Written **Find the perimeter for each of the following. Assume all polygons shown are regular.**

1.

9.2 m

2.

$40\frac{1}{2}$ ft

$6\frac{3}{4}$ ft

3.

$16\frac{2}{3}$ in.

4.

44.8 c

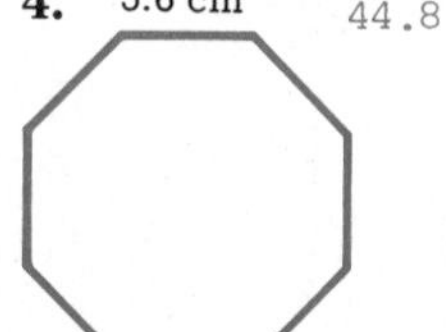

Find the measure of one side of each of the following regular polygons. The perimeter is given.

5. 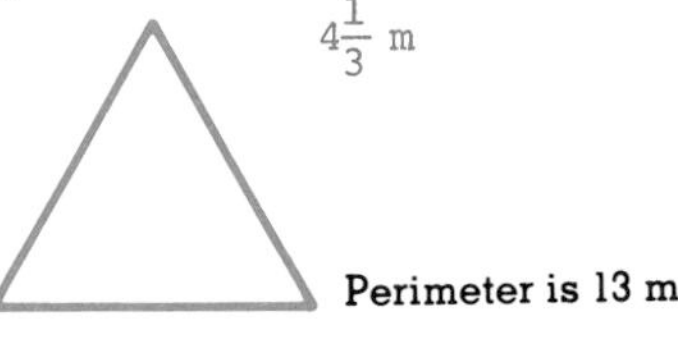
$4\frac{1}{3}$ m

Perimeter is 13 m.

6. 
6.2 cm

Perimeter is 24.8 cm.

7. 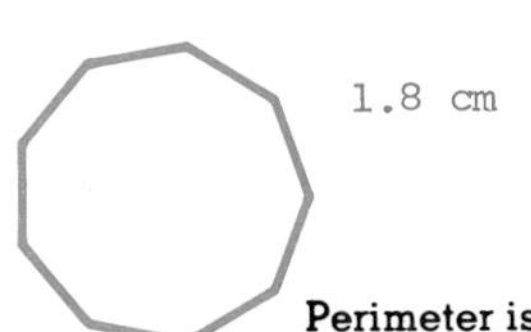
1.8 cm

Perimeter is 16.2 cm.

8. 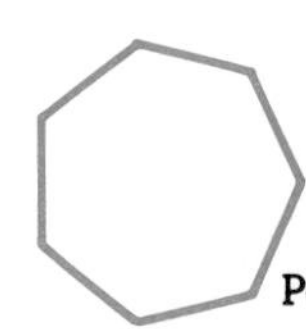
$7\frac{1}{4}$ ft

Perimeter is $50\frac{3}{4}$ ft.

The length and width of rectangles are given below. Find the perimeter for each.

9. 3.4 m, 1.6 m 10.0 m
10. 3.2 m, 1.4 m 9.2 m
11. $3\frac{1}{8}$ in., $1\frac{1}{4}$ in. $8\frac{3}{4}$ in.
12. $17\frac{1}{2}$ ft, $16\frac{2}{3}$ ft $68\frac{1}{3}$ ft
13. 43.8 mi, 38 mi 163.6 mi
14. 34.5 mm, 27.9 mm 124.8 mm
15. 25.7 cm, 2.1 cm 55.6 cm
16. $22\frac{1}{2}$ yd, 15 yd 75 yd
17. $5\frac{1}{4}$ in., $4\frac{3}{4}$ in. 20 in.

For each of the following, the perimeter and width of a rectangle are given. Find the length for each.

18. 141.4 km, 33.4 km 37.3 km
19. 21.6 mi, 6.9 mi 3.9 mi
20. 19.4 cm, 9.3 cm 0.4 cm
21. 12 in., $3\frac{1}{2}$ in. $2\frac{1}{2}$ in.
22. $18\frac{1}{4}$ ft, $7\frac{3}{4}$ ft $1\frac{3}{8}$ ft
23. $10\frac{2}{3}$ yd, $3\frac{1}{4}$ yd $2\frac{1}{12}$ yd

For each of the following regular polygons, the length of a side is given. Find the perimeter for each.

24. decagon, 15.4 cm 154 cm
25. hexagon, 12 ft 72 ft
26. pentagon, $4\frac{1}{4}$ in. $21\frac{1}{4}$ in.
27. square, 24.9 mm 99.6 mm
28. octagon, 32.3 mi 258.4 mi
29. nonagon, $3\frac{1}{3}$ yd 30 yd

For each of the following regular polygons, the perimeter is given. Find the length of a side for each.

30. square, 15.40 mm 3.85 cm
31. pentagon, 12.0 m 2.4 m
32. hexagon, 69 yd $11\frac{1}{2}$ yd
33. heptagon, 21.7 cm 3.1 cm
34. octagon, $55\frac{1}{2}$ ft $6\frac{15}{16}$ ft
35. nonagon, 6.3 km 0.7 km

Answer each question.

36. How many inches of lead molding are needed to put around 24 hexagons and 15 rhombuses of stained glass with sides measuring $1\frac{1}{2}$ inches? 306 in.

37. How many feet of chain link fencing are needed for an L-shaped yard measuring 35 feet by 20 feet by 32 feet by 20 feet by 67 feet by 40 feet? 214 ft

38. How many yards of lace trim should be purchased to make borders for two rectangular tablecloths each with width 4 feet and length 6 feet? $13\frac{1}{3}$ yd

39. How many centimeters of metal edging are needed for a rectangular table measuring 2.5 meters by 5 meters? 1500 cm

7–8 Solids

Objective: to identify faces, edges, and vertices of polyhedra

The soup can, the basketball, and the pyramid are examples of geometric solids. Solids are boundaries that enclose a part of space.

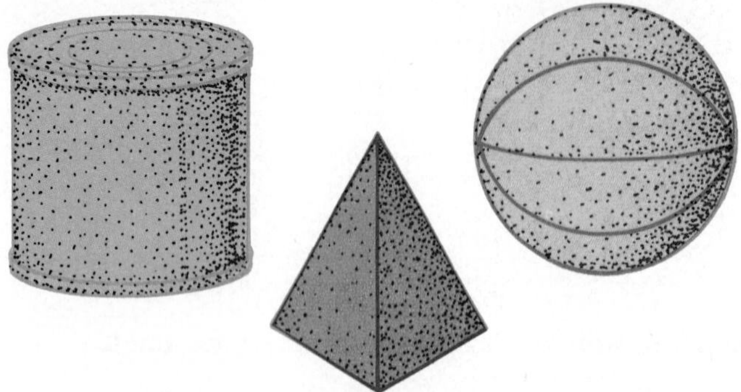

The labeled surface of the soup can and the basketball are curved. The surfaces of the pyramid are flat. These flat surfaces form polygons. Solids with flat surfaces that form polygons are called **polyhedrons.**

The flat surfaces formed by polygons and their interiors are called **faces.** Pairs of faces that intersect at line segments are called **edges.**

A polygon separates a plane into three parts, the interior, the exterior, and the polygon itself.

The faces of a convex polyhedron are convex polygons.

Three or more edges intersect at a point called a **vertex.**

The following table lists the 4 faces, 6 edges, and 4 vertices for the polyhedron at the right.

Faces	Edges		Vertices
$\triangle ABC$	$\overline{AB}$	$\overline{DC}$	A
$\triangle BCD$	$\overline{BD}$	$\overline{AC}$	B
$\triangle ACD$	$\overline{AD}$	$\overline{BC}$	C
$\triangle ABD$			D

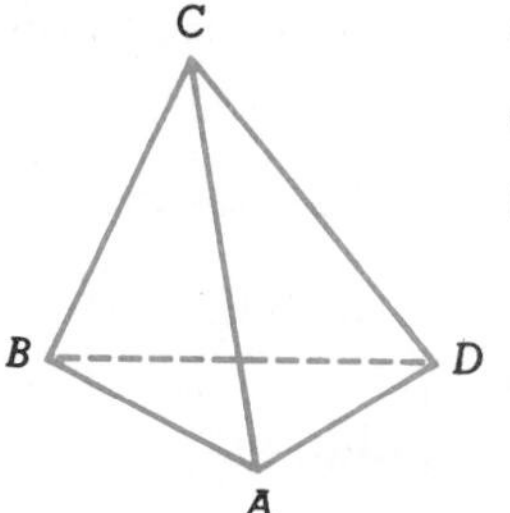

Three dimensional models are most useful for discussion purposes.

example

1 Name the faces, edges, and vertices of the polyhedron at the right.

The 7 faces are quadrilaterals $AEJF$, $DEJI$, $CDIH$, $BCHG$, $ABGF$, and pentagons $ABCDE$ and $FGHIJ$.

The 15 edges are $\overline{AB}$, $\overline{BC}$, $\overline{CD}$, $\overline{DE}$, $\overline{EA}$, $\overline{FG}$, $\overline{GH}$, $\overline{HI}$, $\overline{IJ}$, $\overline{JF}$, $\overline{FA}$, $\overline{GB}$, $\overline{HC}$, $\overline{ID}$, and $\overline{JE}$.

The 10 vertices are A, B, C, D, E, F, G, H, I, and J.

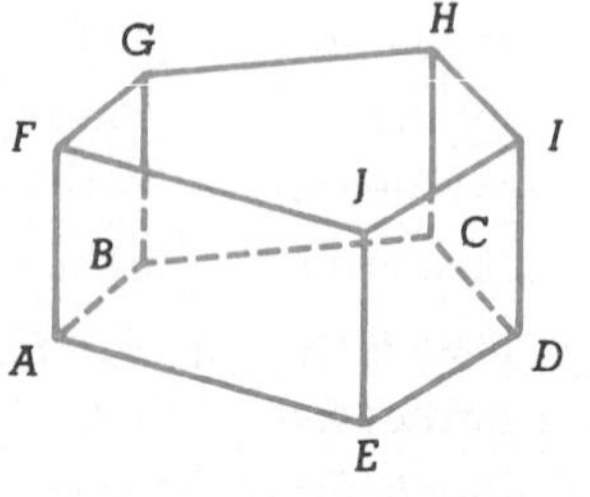

Each face of the polyhedron at the right forms a regular polygon. All the polygons formed are congruent to each other. Therefore, each edge has the same measure. Polyhedrons with such properties are called **regular polyhedrons.**

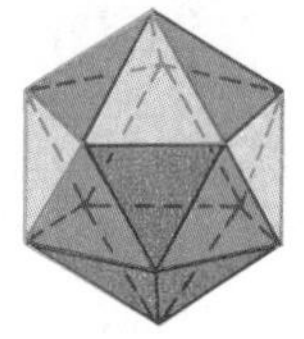

A polyhedron must have *at least* three polygons intersecting at each vertex. Also, the total degree measures of the angles formed must be *less than* 360. Thus, there are only five types of regular polyhedrons. Point out the figures below and include the table at the bottom of the page with regard to the discussion of: only five regular polyhedrons.

Two polygons do not form a polyhedron.

If the sum of the angle degree measures at a vertex is 360, the figure is flat.

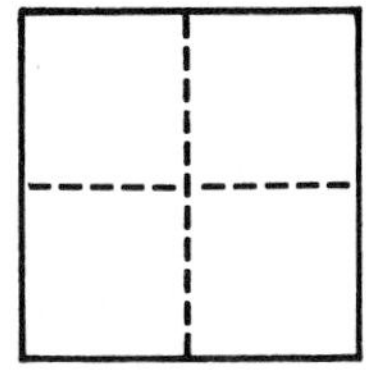

The five regular polyhedrons often are called **Platonic solids.** Each are named according to the number of faces.

Students can make models or mobiles of solids using straws and/or construction paper.

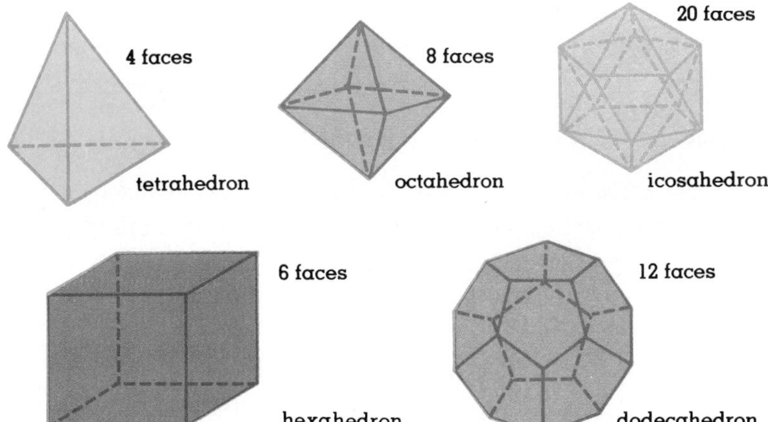

The different regular polyhedrons are determined by the regular polygons that form the faces.

regular polyhedron	regular polygon	degree measure of one angle	number of angles at vertex	total degree measure of angles at vertex
tetrahedron	triangle	60	3	180
octahedron	triangle	60	4	240
icosahedron	triangle	60	5	300
hexahedron	square	90	3	270
dodecahedron	pentagon	108	3	324

Note that totals in the last column must be less than 360, otherwise the figure is flat.

EN: Ex: 1-10, Wr: 1-19, E ; AV: Ex: 1-10, Wr: 1-19 odds, E ; pp. 238-9, Wr: 1-37 odds

exercises

FN: Ex: 1-10, Wr: 1-8, 9-19 odds; pp. 238-9, Wr: 2-36 evens

Exploratory **Name the faces, edges, and vertices for each of the following polyhedra.**
For answers to exercises 1-3, see the Teacher's Guide.

1.

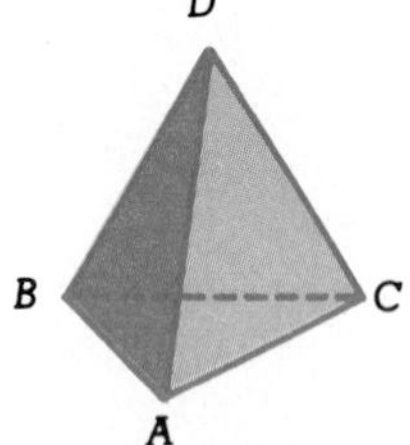

2.

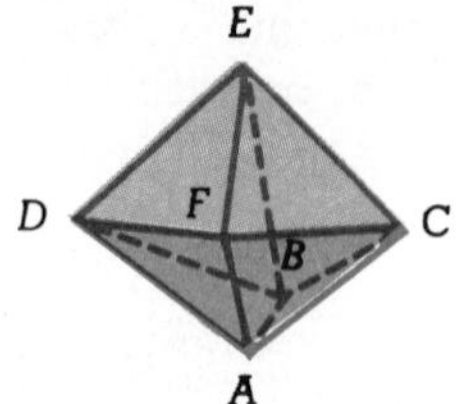

3.

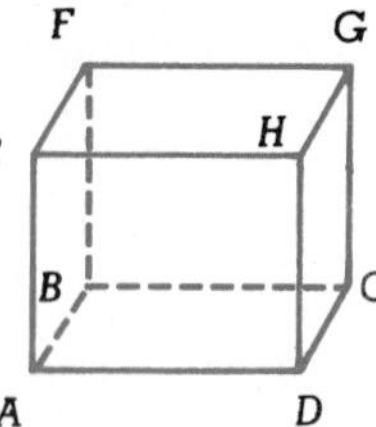

4. The sum of the degree measures of the angles formed at one vertex of a convex polyhedron must be less than what number? 360

5–7. Find the number of polygons intersecting at vertex D for each polyhedron in exercises **1–3.** 5. 3 6. 4 7. 3

8–10. Find the sum of the degree measures at vertex D for each regular polyhedron in exercises **1–3.**
8. 180 9. 240 10. 270

Written **For each of the following, name the type of polygons that form the faces.**

1. tetrahedron triangle
2. hexahedron square
3. octahedron triangle
4. dodecahedron pentagon

5–8. Find the degree measure of one angle for a face of each polyhedron in exercises **1–4.**
5. 60 6. 90 7. 60 8. 108

For each of the following, given are a possible number of polygons intersecting at one vertex of a polyhedron. Find the sum of the degree measures of the angles formed at that vertex.

9. 4 equilateral triangles 240
10. 6 equilateral triangles 360
11. 3 squares 270
12. 4 squares 360
13. 5 squares 450
14. 3 regular pentagons 324
15. 3 regular hexagons 360
16. 2 regular octagons 270

For each of the following, give the number of faces, vertices, and edges.

17. tetrahedron 4 faces, 4 vertices, 6 edges
18. hexahedron 6 faces, 8 vertices, 12 edges
19. octahedron 8 faces, 6 vertices, 12 edges

Regular Polyhedrons — excursions in geometry

The Swiss mathematician Leonhard Euler discovered that the number of faces, vertices, and edges of a regular polyhedron are related by the following formula.

$$\left(\begin{array}{c}\text{number of}\\ \text{faces}\end{array}\right)+\left(\begin{array}{c}\text{number of}\\ \text{vertices}\end{array}\right)=\left(\begin{array}{c}\text{number of}\\ \text{edges}\end{array}\right)+2$$

$$F + V = E + 2$$

Exercise **Verify Euler's formula by substituting the values from written exercises 17–19.** See the Teacher's Guide.

Vocabulary

polygon (207)
consecutive sides (207)
consecutive angles (207)
n-gon (208)
convex polygon (208)
concave polygon (208)
regular polygon (208)
diagonal (211)
exterior angles (213)
interior angles (213)
parallelogram (216)
rectangle (224)
rhombus (225)
square (226)
trapezoid (230)
bases of a trapezoid (230)
legs of a trapezoid (230)
isosceles trapezoid (230)
base angles of a trapezoid (230)
median of a trapezoid (232)
perimeter (236)
polyhedron (240)
regular polyhedron (241)
Platonic solids (241)

Chapter Summary

1. Definition of Polygon: A figure is a polygon if and only if it meets all of the following conditions.
    1. It is formed by three or more coplanar segments called sides.
    2. Sides that have a common endpoint are noncollinear.
    3. Each side intersects exactly two of the other sides, but only at their endpoints. (207)
2. Theorem 7–1: If a convex polygon has n sides and S is the sum of the degree measures of its angles, then $S = (n - 2)180$. (211)
3. Problem-Solving Procedure: **1.** Define a variable. **2.** Write an equation. **3.** Solve the equation. **4.** Check the solution. **5.** Answer the problem. (212)
4. Theorem 7–2: If a polygon is convex, then the sum of the degree measures of the exterior angles, one at each vertex, is 360. (213)
5. Definition of Parallelogram: A quadrilateral is a parallelogram if and only if each pair of opposite sides are parallel. (216)

6. Theorem 7–3: If a quadrilateral is a parallelogram, then a diagonal separates it into two congruent triangles. (216)
7. Theorem 7–4: If a quadrilateral is a parallelogram, then its opposite angles are congruent. (217)
8. Theorem 7–5: If a quadrilateral is a parallelogram, then its opposite sides are congruent. (217)
9. Theorem 7–6: If a quadrilateral is a parallelogram, then its diagonals bisect each other. (217)
10. Theorem 7–7: If both pairs of opposite sides of a quadrilateral are congruent, then the quadrilateral is a parallelogram. (220)
11. Theorem 7–8: If two sides of a quadrilateral are parallel and congruent, then the quadrilateral is a parallelogram. (221)
12. Theorem 7–9: If the diagonals of a quadrilateral bisect each other, then the quadrilateral is a parallelogram. (221)
13. Definition of Rectangle: A quadrilateral is a rectangle if and only if it is a parallelogram with four right angles. (224)
14. Theorem 7–10: If a quadrilateral is a rectangle, then its diagonals are congruent. (224)
15. Definition of Rhombus: A quadrilateral is a rhombus if and only if it is a parallelogram with all four sides congruent. (225)
16. Theorem 7–11: If a quadrilateral is a rhombus, then each diagonal bisects a pair of opposite angles. (225)
17. Theorem 7–12: If a quadrilateral is a rhombus, then its diagonals are perpendicular. (226)
18. Definition of Square: A quadrilateral is a square if and only if it is a rectangle and all four sides are congruent. (226)
19. Definition of Trapezoid: A quadrilateral is a trapezoid if and only if it has exactly one pair of parallel sides. (230)
20. Theorem 7–13: If a trapezoid is isosceles, then each pair of base angles is congruent. (230)
21. Theorem 7–14: If a trapezoid is isosceles, then its diagonals are congruent. (231)
22. Theorem 7–15: If a quadrilateral is a trapezoid, then the median is parallel to the bases, and its measure is one-half the sum of the measures of the bases. (232)
23. Definition of Perimeter: The sum of the measures of the sides of a polygon is the measure of the perimeter of the polygon. (236)
24. Perimeter of a Rectangle (Theorem 7–16): If a rectangle has a perimeter of P units, a length of ℓ units, and a width of w units, then $P = 2(\ell + w)$. (236)
25. Perimeter of a Regular Polygon (Theorem 7–17): If a regular n-gon has a perimeter of P units and a side measures s units, then $P = ns$. (237)
26. Polyhedrons are geometric solids with flat surfaces that form polygons. (240)
27. Regular polyhedrons have faces that are regular polygons. All the polygons formed are congruent to each other. Each edge has the same measure. There are only five regular polyhedrons. (241)

Chapter Review

7–1 Use the polygon to answer each of the following.

1. Name the vertices.
2. Name the sides.
3. Name the angles.
4. Classify the polygon by the number of sides.
5. Classify the polygon as *convex* or *concave*.
6. Classify the polygon as *regular* or *not regular*.

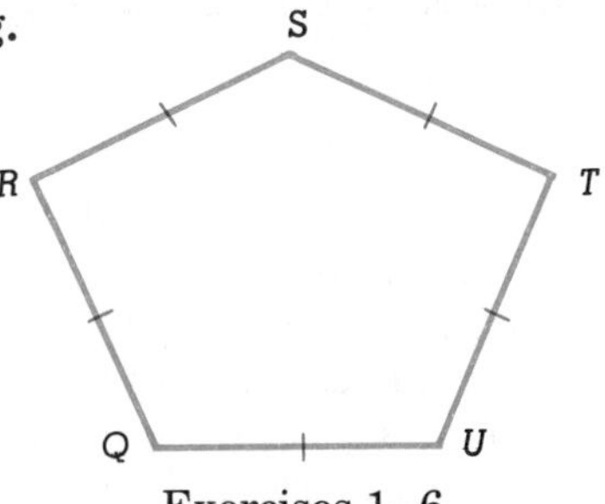

Exercises 1–6

7–2 For each of the following convex polygons, find the sum of the degree measures of the angles.

7. hexagon 720
8. pentagon 540
9. 12-gon 1800

10–12. Suppose each polygon in exercises **7–9** are regular polygons. Find the degree measure of one angle. 10. 120 11. 108 12. 150

13. Find the degree measure of one exterior angle of a regular nonagon. 40

7–3 Use the parallelogram to answer each of the following.

14. If $BE = 45$, find BD. 90
15. If $CD = 7.2$, find BA. 7.2
16. If $m\angle 1 = 2a + 5$ and $m\angle 2 = 3a - 7$, find a. 12
17. If $m\angle BCD = 6x + 3$ and $m\angle DAB = 3x + 12$, find x. 3
18. If $m\angle ABC = 4y + 9$ and $m\angle BCD = 3y + 24$, find y. 21
19. If $AC = 16.4$, find EC. 8.2

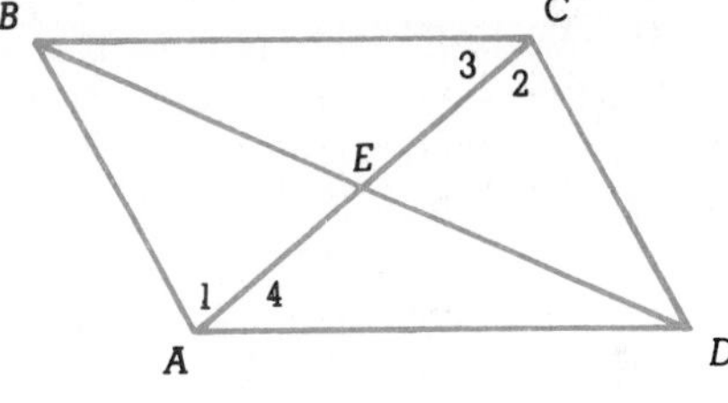

Exercises 14–19

7–4 Prove each of the following.

20. **Given:** $\angle 1$ and $\angle 2$ are supplementary.
$\angle 2 \cong \angle 3$
Prove: Quadrilateral *PQRS* is a parallelogram.

21. **Given:** $\square ABCD$
$\overline{AE} \cong \overline{CF}$
Prove: Quadrilateral *EBFD* is a parallelogram.

For answers to exercises 20-21, see the Teacher's Guide.

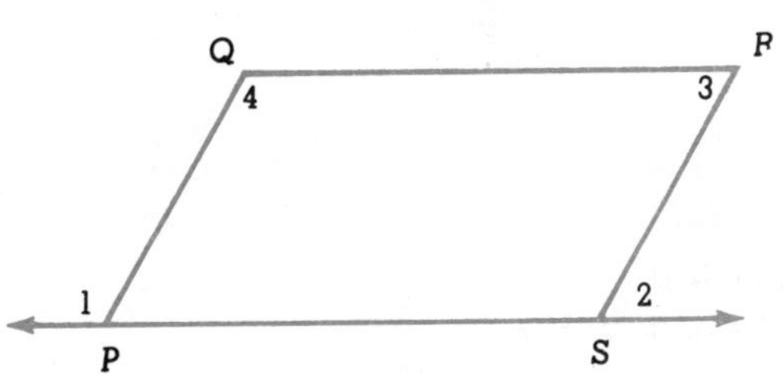

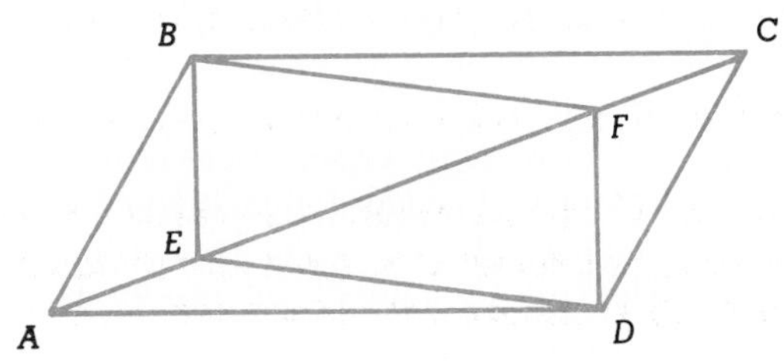

7–5 Determine whether or *not* each of the following statements must be true. Write *yes* or *no*.

22. The diagonals of a rhombus bisect each other. yes

23. The diagonals of a rectangle bisect the opposite angles. no

24. All sides of parallelograms are congruent. no

25. Every square is a rhombus. yes

Use the rhombus to answer each of the following.

26. Suppose $AE = 6$, find AC. 12

27. Suppose $m\angle ABE = 23\frac{3}{4}$, find $m\angle ABC$. $47\frac{1}{2}$

28. Find $m\angle CED$. 90

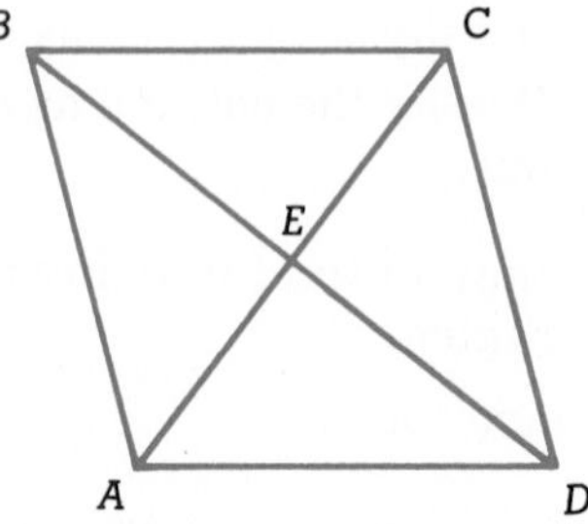

Exercises 26–28

For answers to exercises 29-30, see the Teacher's Guide.

7–6 Prove each of the following.

29. **Given:** $\overline{BC} \parallel \overline{AD}$, $\overline{AB} \nparallel \overline{CD}$
$\overline{AB} \cong \overline{DC}$
Prove: $\triangle AED$ is isosceles.

30. **Given:** $\overline{RS} \parallel \overline{PV}$
$\overline{QT}$ is a median of trapezoid $PRSV$.
Prove: W is the midpoint of $\overline{RV}$.

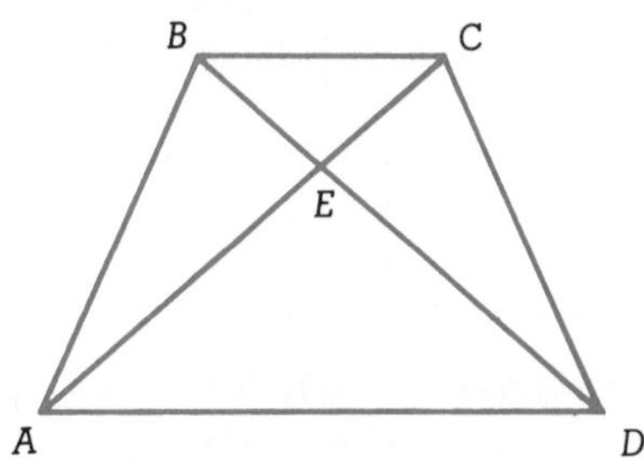

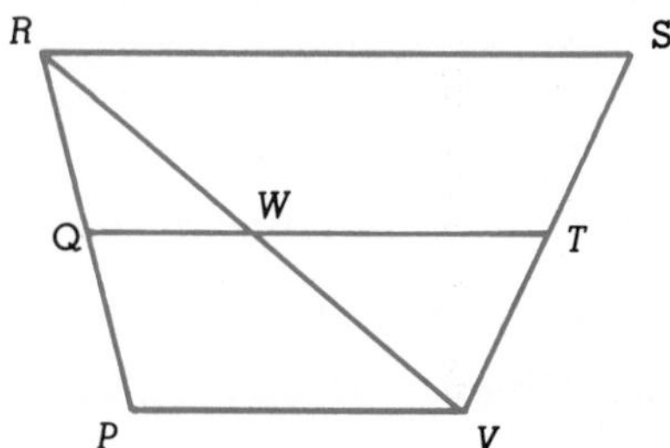

7–7 Find the perimeter for each of the following.

31. rectangle with length 4.2 m and width 3.8 m 16 m

32. regular octagon with each side measuring $4\frac{1}{4}$ ft 34 ft

33. How many centimeters of lead are needed to put around 25 hexagons of stained glass each with sides measuring 5.7 centimeters? 855 cm

7–8 34. Find the sum of the degree measures of the angles formed at each vertex of a icosahedron. 300

Chapter Test

Solve each of the following.

1. Find the number of diagonals that can be drawn for a decagon. 35
2. Find the sum of the degree measure of the angles of a 15-gon. 2340
3. Find the degree measure of one exterior angle of a regular pentagon. 72
4. Find the degree measures of one angle of a regular octagon. 135

Use $\square QRST$ for each of the following.

5. If $m\angle RST = 45$, find $m\angle QRS$. 135
6. If $m\angle QRS = 6x + 4$, find $m\angle QTS$. 6x + 4
7. If $RT = 18$, find PR. 9
8. If $QP = 12$, find SQ. 24
9. If $m\angle QTS = 4x - 2$ and $m\angle TSR = 5x - 7$, find x. 21
10. If $RP = 8x - 3$ and $PT = 6x + 5$, find x. 4

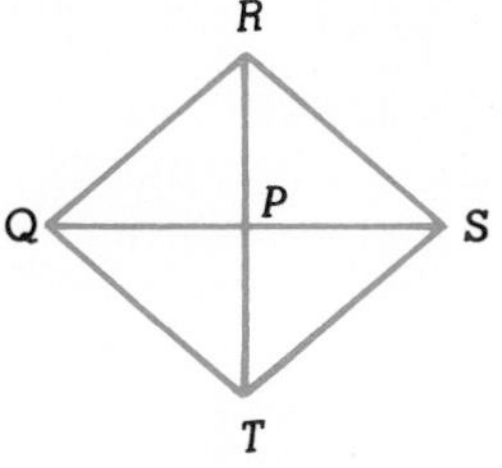

Exercises 5–10

Prove each of the following. For answers to exercises 11-14, see the Teacher's Guide.

11. **Given:** $\square ABCD$, $\overline{AC} \cong \overline{BD}$
Prove: $\square ABCD$ is a rectangle.

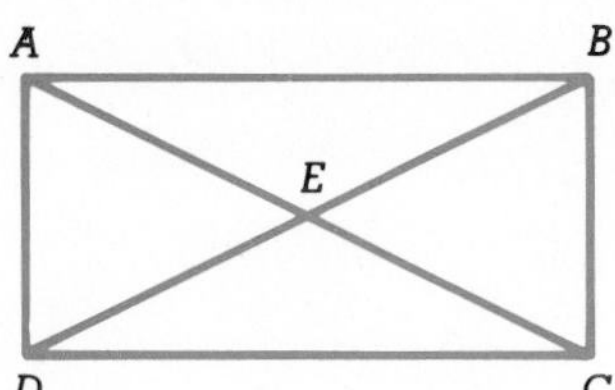

12. **Given:** $\square LMNP$, $\overline{MP} \perp \overline{LN}$
Prove: $\square LMNP$ is a rhombus.

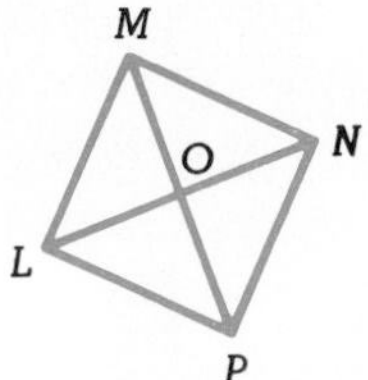

13. **Given:** $\overline{BC} \parallel \overline{AD}$, $\overline{AB} \nparallel \overline{CD}$
$\overline{AB} \cong \overline{DC}$
Prove: $\triangle ABC \cong \triangle DCB$

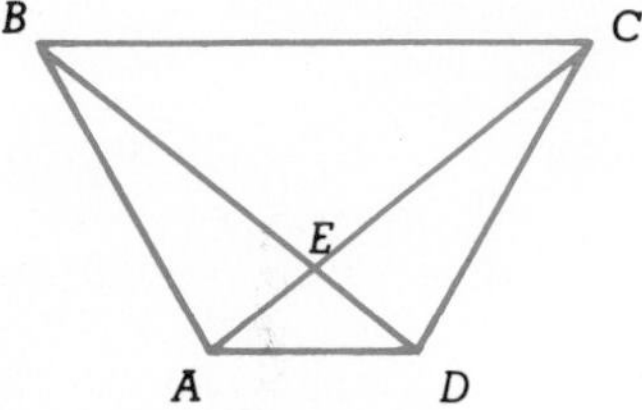

14. **Given:** $\overline{PQ} \parallel \overline{RS}$, $\overline{PQ} \cong \overline{SR}$
T is the midpoint of $\overline{QP}$.
V is the midpoint of $\overline{RS}$.
Prove: Quadrilateral $TQRV$ is a parallelogram.

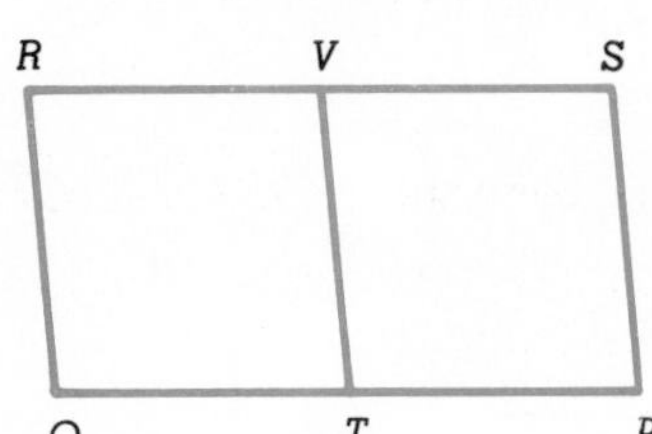

Solve each problem.

15. Suppose the bases of a trapezoid measure 6.8 mm and 15.7 mm. Find the measure of the median. 11.25 mm
16. Suppose a rectangle measures $2\frac{1}{2}$ inches by $1\frac{3}{4}$ inches. Find its perimeter. $8\frac{1}{2}$ in.

chapter 8 Similarity

The concepts of similarity are used in art and design. Plastic parts for models of the latest-style planes, cars, and ships are built to scale. Model makers plan models using the concepts of similarity.

8–1 Ratios and Proportions

Objectives: to write ratios for problems, to write and solve proportions for problems

Team records often are compared using ratios. For example, the newspaper records show that the National Basketball Association team from Kansas City won 34 of the 54 games it has played to date. The ratio of games won to games played is $\frac{34}{54}$ or about 0.630.

A **ratio** is a comparison of two numbers. The ratio of a to b can be expressed as $\frac{a}{b}$ where b is *not* zero.

WESTERN CONFERENCE Midwest Division		
Milwaukee	19	10
Kansas City	15	14
Denver	10	18
Chicago	8	20
Utah	5	21

example

1 The pitch of a roof is the ratio of the rise to the run. If a roof has a rise measuring 3.6 m and a run measuring 1.9 m, what is the pitch?

$$\text{pitch} = \frac{\text{rise}}{\text{run}}$$

$$= \frac{3.6}{1.9}$$

$$\approx 1.895$$

The pitch to 1 decimal place is 1.9.

A **proportion** shows that two ratios are equivalent. For example, Boston and New York are tied in the Atlantic Division. The two teams have the same percentage. The ratios of games won to games played are the same.

$$\frac{24}{48} = \frac{27}{54}$$

The equation that shows two ratios equivalent is a proportion.

Every proportion has two **cross products.** In the proportion $\frac{24}{48} = \frac{27}{54}$, the cross products are 24 times 54 and 48 times 27. The cross products of a proportion are equal.

$$\frac{24}{48} \times \frac{27}{54}$$
$$24 \times 54 = 48 \times 27$$
$$1296 = 1296$$

48 and 27 are called the means.
24 and 54 are called the extremes.

Point out that this theorem is biconditional.

For any numbers a and c, and any nonzero numbers b and d, $\frac{a}{b} = \frac{c}{d}$ if and only if $ad = bc$.

Theorem 8–1 Equality of Cross Products

This theorem is proven in Example 3 along with Written exercise 31.

examples

2 **A racing car uses alcohol for fuel. The alcohol weighs 4.8 pounds per gallon and is burned with a fuel to air ratio of 1 to 15. Use a proportion to find how many pounds of air are used in burning 1 gallon of alcohol.**

Let x stand for the amount of air used in pounds.

$$\frac{4.8}{x} = \frac{1}{15}$$
$$x = 4.8 \times 15$$
$$= 72$$

The car will use 72 pounds of air in burning 1 gallon of alcohol.

3 **Prove that for any numbers a and c, and any nonzero numbers b and d, if $\frac{a}{b} = \frac{c}{d}$, then $ad = bc$.**

Given: $\frac{a}{b} = \frac{c}{d}$, b and d are nonzero.

Prove: $ad = bc$

Proof:

STATEMENTS	REASONS
1. $\frac{a}{b} = \frac{c}{d}$, b and d are nonzero	1. Given
2. $bd\left(\frac{a}{b}\right) = bd\left(\frac{c}{d}\right)$	2. Postulate 2–8: Multiplication Property of Equality
3. $ad\left(\frac{b}{b}\right) = bc\left(\frac{d}{d}\right)$	3. Postulate 2–10: Commutative Property for Multiplication and Postulate 2–11: Associative Property for Multiplication
4. $ad = bc$	4. Postulate 2–9: Substitution and Postulate 2–12: Identity Property for Multiplication

EN: Wr:10-30 evens, 31; p. 252, AR:9-10; AV: Ex:1-23 odds, Wr:1-31 odds; p. 252, AR: 2-10 evens

exercises

FN: Ex: 1-20, Wr: 1-31 odds; p. 252, AR: 1-10

Exploratory **Use the standings listed at the right to find the ratio of games won to games played for each team.**

1. Kansas City
2. Denver
3. Milwaukee
4. Indiana
5. Chicago
6. Utah
7. New York
8. Atlanta
9. Boston
10. Detroit
11. Houston $\frac{14}{26}$ = 0.538
12. Washington $\frac{10}{23}$ = 0.435

1. $\frac{15}{29}$ = 0.517
2. $\frac{10}{28}$ = 0.357
3. $\frac{19}{29}$ = 0.655
4. $\frac{12}{28}$ = 0.429
5. $\frac{8}{28}$ = 0.286
6. $\frac{5}{26}$ = 0.192
7. $\frac{14}{27}$ = 0.519
8. $\frac{17}{29}$ = 0.586
9. $\frac{20}{26}$ = 0.769
10. $\frac{8}{27}$ = 0.296

EASTERN CONFERENCE		
Atlantic Division	W	L
Boston	20	6
Philadelphia	20	7
New York	14	13
Washington	10	13
New Jersey	11	16
Central Division		
Atlanta	17	12
Houston	14	12
San Antonio	14	13
Cleveland	13	17
Indiana	12	16
Detroit	8	19
WESTERN CONFERENCE		
Midwest Division		
Milwaukee	19	10
Kansas City	15	14
Denver	10	18
Chicago	8	20
Utah	5	21

Gears on bicycles are called sprockets. To find bicycle gear ratios, you must first find the ratio of the number of rear sprocket teeth to the number of front sprocket teeth. Find the ratio for each of the following to two decimal places.

13. 12 rear sprocket teeth 0.50
24 front sprocket teeth

14. 13 rear sprocket teeth 0.50
26 front sprocket teeth

15. 13 rear sprocket teeth 0.25
52 front sprocket teeth

16. 14 rear sprocket teeth 0.33
42 front sprocket teeth

17. 15 rear sprocket teeth 0.33
45 front sprocket teeth

18. 15 rear sprocket teeth 0.27
55 front sprocket teeth

19. 20 rear sprocket teeth 0.40
50 front sprocket teeth

20. 20 rear sprocket teeth 0.67
30 front sprocket teeth

21. 12 rear sprocket teeth 0.32
38 front sprocket teeth

22. 24 rear sprocket teeth 0.55
44 front sprocket teeth

23. 26 rear sprocket teeth 0.57
46 front sprocket teeth

24. 24 rear sprocket teeth 0.44
54 front sprocket teeth

Written **Solve each of the following proportions using cross products.**

1. $\frac{11}{24} = \frac{x}{24}$ 11
2. $\frac{5}{8} = \frac{20}{x}$ 32
3. $\frac{t}{18} = \frac{5}{6}$ 15
4. $\frac{14}{b} = \frac{7}{8}$ 16
5. $\frac{1.2}{1.6} = \frac{k}{4}$ 3
6. $\frac{7}{12} = \frac{9.8}{m}$ 16.8
7. $\frac{b}{3.24} = \frac{1}{8}$ 0.405
8. $\frac{7.29}{a} = \frac{27}{9}$ 2.43
9. $\frac{x}{30 - x} = \frac{2}{3}$ 12
10. $\frac{5 + x}{8 + x} = \frac{3}{4}$ 4
11. $\frac{3 - n}{n + 1} = \frac{2}{1}$ $\frac{1}{3}$
12. $\frac{n + 3}{10} = \frac{3n - 2}{8}$ 2

Proportions can be used to change a fraction to a percent. For example, to change $\frac{5}{6}$ to a percent, you solve the proportion $\frac{5}{6} = \frac{n}{100}$. For each of the following use a proportion to change the fraction to a percent.

13. $\frac{5}{8}$ 62.5% **14.** $\frac{1}{12}$ $8.\overline{3}\%$ or $8\frac{1}{3}\%$ **15.** $\frac{1}{3}$ $33.\overline{3}\%$ or $33\frac{1}{3}\%$ **16.** $\frac{3}{16}$ 18.75%

17. $\frac{3}{8}$ 37.5% **18.** $\frac{7}{8}$ 87.5% **19.** $\frac{5}{12}$ $41.\overline{6}\%$ **20.** $\frac{3}{4}$ 75%

21. $\frac{4}{5}$ 80% **22.** $\frac{3}{5}$ 60% **23.** $\frac{1}{10}$ 10% **24.** $\frac{6}{10}$ 60%

Use proportions to solve each of the following.

25. Ann Towns plays basketball for a university team. Last season she attempted 156 field goals and made 117. What percent of the field goals attempted did she make? 75% $\frac{117}{156} = \frac{n}{100}$

26. The mixture for a finish coat of concrete is 1 part cement to 2 parts sand. How much cement should be mixed with 15 pounds of sand? 7.5 pounds of cement $\frac{1}{2} = \frac{n}{15}$

27. The sales tax on $140 is $8.40. What is the rate of sales tax? (Hint: Find a percent.) 6% $\frac{8.40}{140} = \frac{x}{100}$

28. A designated hitter made 8 hits in 9 games. If he continues hitting at that rate, how many hits will he make in 108 games? 96 hits $\frac{8}{9} = \frac{x}{108}$

29. A recipe for preparing material to dye calls for 4 parts alum to 1 part washing soda. How much washing soda should be used for 150 grams of alum? 37.5 g $\frac{4}{1} = \frac{150}{x}$

30. An old cake recipe calls for 2 parts butter to 3 parts sugar. How much butter should be used with $4\frac{1}{2}$ cups of sugar? 3 cups $\frac{2}{3} = \frac{x}{4.5}$

31. Prove that for any numbers a and c, and any nonzero numbers b and d, if $ad = bc$, then $\frac{a}{b} = \frac{c}{d}$. See the Teacher's Guide.

Factoring Equations — algebra review

Quadratic equations can be solved by factoring as follows.

Example **Solve $x^2 - 2x - 15 = 0$ by factoring.**

$$x^2 - 2x - 15 = 0$$
$$(x - 5)(x + 3) = 0$$
$$x - 5 = 0 \text{ or } x + 3 = 0$$
$$x = 5 \text{ or } \quad x = {}^-3$$

The solutions are 5 and $^-3$.

Exercises **Solve each equation.**

1. $(x - 4)(x + 5) = 0$ 4, -5
2. $(y - 3)(y + 7) = 0$ 3, -7
3. $(a + 6)(a + 2) = 0$ -6, -2
4. $(m - 8)(m - 1) = 0$ 8, 1
5. $b^2 + 3b - 10 = 0$ 2, -5
6. $y^2 - 4y - 21 = 0$ 7, -3
7. $x^2 + 4x + 4 = 0$ -2
8. $c^2 - 12c + 36 = 0$ 6
9. $2x^2 + 5x + 3 = 0$ $\frac{-3}{2}$, -1
10. $2a^2 + 9a + 4 = 0$ $\frac{-1}{2}$, -4

careers

Advertising Designer

Larry Koans is an advertising designer. One of his tasks is to determine the sizes of the different parts of the copy on a page. Proportions are used to determine reductions or enlargements of photographs.

Larry reduces the photograph at the left to fit the advertising page at the right. The original photograph is $4\frac{3}{4}$ in. wide by $6\frac{5}{8}$ in. long. He wants to reduce the photograph to fit a $1\frac{1}{2}$ in. width.

The percent of original size is found as follows.

new width / old width $\quad \frac{1.50}{4.75} = \frac{n}{100}$ $\quad$ *percent means parts per hundred*

$$4.75n = 150$$

$$n = 31.57$$

The percent of original size to the nearest tenth is 31.6%.

A percent greater than 100% is called an enlargement.

Exercises **Use the following dimensions to find the percent of original size to the nearest tenth.**

	Original		Final
	Width	**Length**	**Width**
1. 80%	5 in.	9 in.	4 in.
3. 85.7%	14 in.	20 in.	12 in.

	Original		Final
	Width	**Length**	**Length**
2. 66.7%	$4\frac{1}{2}$ in.	6 in.	4 in.
4. 178.6%	$6\frac{1}{4}$ in.	7 in.	$12\frac{1}{2}$ in.

5. State the numbers of the exercises that represent enlargements. 4

8–2 Properties of Proportions

Objectives: to name properties of proportions, to prove properties of proportions, to apply properties of proportions to geometric figures

Proportions have many interesting properties. The properties can be derived using cross products and the properties of equality. The following chart summarizes these properties.

Emphasize that the denominators must be nonzero.

For any numbers a, b, c, and d, the following properties hold whenever all denominators are nonzero.	
If $\frac{a}{b} = \frac{c}{d}$, then $\frac{a}{c} = \frac{b}{d}$.	***Theorem 8–2***
If $\frac{a}{b} = \frac{c}{d}$, then $\frac{b}{a} = \frac{d}{c}$.	***Theorem 8–3***
$\frac{a}{b} = \frac{c}{d}$ if and only if $\frac{a+b}{b} = \frac{c+d}{d}$.	***Theorem 8–4 Addition Property of Proportions***
$\frac{a}{b} = \frac{c}{d}$ if and only if $\frac{a-b}{b} = \frac{c-d}{d}$.	***Theorem 8–5 Subtraction Property of Proportions***
$\frac{a}{b} = \frac{c}{d}$ if and only if $\frac{a}{b} = \frac{a+c}{b+d}$ or $\frac{c}{d} = \frac{a+c}{b+d}$.	***Theorem 8–6 Summation Property of Proportions***

Students prove Theorems 8-2, 8-3, 8-5, and 8-6 in Written exercises 7-12.

example

1 **Prove that for any numbers a, b, c, and d, if $\frac{a}{b} = \frac{c}{d}$, then $\frac{a+b}{b} = \frac{c+d}{d}$, whenever all denominators are nonzero.** This is the proof of Theorem 8-4 in one direction.

Given: $\frac{a}{b} = \frac{c}{d}$

Prove: $\frac{a+b}{b} = \frac{c+d}{d}$

Proof:

STATEMENTS	REASONS
1. $\frac{a}{b} = \frac{c}{d}$	**1.** Given
2. $ad = bc$	**2.** Theorem 8–1: Equality of Cross Products
3. $ad + bd = bc + bd$	**3.** Postulate 2–7: Addition Property of Equality
4. $(a + b)d = b(c + d)$	**4.** Postulate 2–14: Distributive Property
5. $\frac{a+b}{b} = \frac{c+d}{d}$	**5.** Theorem 8–1: Equality of Cross Products

The figures above show special rectangles, called **golden rectangles.** Golden rectangles have interesting mathematical properties. For example, the measures of their sides are always in the ratio of about 1 to 1.618. *This ratio is called the* golden ratio.

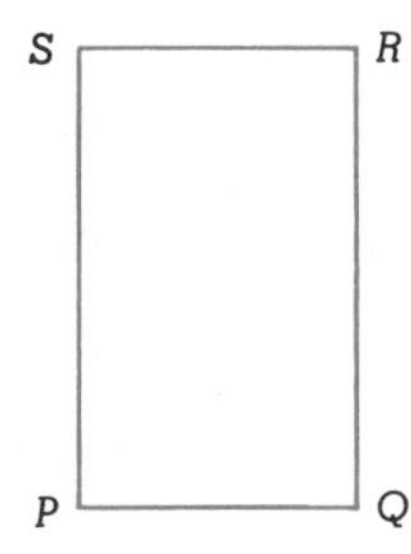

Draw other similar polygons to help reinforce proportional parts.

The two rectangles above are golden rectangles.

$$\frac{AB}{BC} = \frac{AB}{DA} = \frac{CD}{CB} = \frac{CD}{DA} \approx \frac{1}{1.618}$$

$$\frac{PQ}{QR} = \frac{PQ}{PS} = \frac{RS}{RQ} = \frac{RS}{SP} \approx \frac{1}{1.618}$$

The symbol ≈ means "approximately equal to."

Using properties of proportions, you can show that there is a correspondence between the rectangles so that the measures of their corresponding sides are **proportional.**

$$\frac{AB}{PQ} = \frac{BC}{QR} = \frac{CD}{RS} = \frac{DA}{SP}$$

example

2 Given that $\frac{AB}{BC} \approx \frac{1}{1.618}$ and $\frac{PQ}{QR} \approx \frac{2}{1.618}$, show $\frac{AB}{PQ} = \frac{BC}{QR}$.

$\frac{AB}{BC} \approx \frac{1}{1.618}$ $\quad \frac{PQ}{QR} \approx \frac{1}{1.618}$ *Given*

$\frac{AB}{BC} = \frac{PQ}{QR}$ *Substitution*

$\frac{AB}{PQ} = \frac{BC}{QR}$ *Theorem 8–2*

EN: Ex: 1-15 odds, Wr: 4-14 evens; p. 257, E ; p. 253, C: 3, 4; AV: Ex: 2-16 evens, Wr: 1-13 odds; pp. 251-2, Wr: 10-18 evens, 26, 28; p. 253, C: 1-5

exercises

Exploratory **Name the property shown in each of the following.**

1. If $\frac{3}{1} = \frac{6}{2}$, then $\frac{3-1}{1} = \frac{6-2}{2}$. Theorem 8-5
2. If $\frac{3}{1} = \frac{6}{2}$, then $\frac{2}{1} = \frac{4}{2}$. Theorem 8-5
3. If $\frac{3}{1} = \frac{6}{2}$, then $\frac{4}{1} = \frac{8}{2}$. Theorem 8-4
4. If $\frac{3+1}{1} = \frac{6+2}{2}$, then $\frac{3}{1} = \frac{6}{2}$. Theorem 8-4
5. If $\frac{6}{8} = \frac{7}{x}$, then $\frac{8}{6} = \frac{x}{7}$. Theorem 8-3
6. If $\frac{2}{10} = \frac{1}{y}$, then $\frac{y}{10} = \frac{1}{2}$. Post. 2-5, Theorem 8-2
7. If $\frac{3}{4} = \frac{3+y}{8}$, then $\frac{3}{4} = \frac{y}{4}$. Theorem 8-6
8. If $\frac{2}{3} = \frac{x}{6}$, then $\frac{2}{3} = \frac{x+2}{9}$. Theorem 8-6
9. If $\frac{12}{b} = \frac{11}{a}$, then $\frac{a}{b} = \frac{11}{12}$. Post. 2-5, Theorem 8-2
10. If $\frac{x}{27} = \frac{y}{13}$, then $\frac{x}{y} = \frac{27}{13}$. Theorem 8-2
11. If $\frac{25}{14} = \frac{7}{AB}$, then $\frac{14}{25} = \frac{AB}{7}$. Theorem 8-3
12. If $\frac{25}{14} = \frac{7}{AB}$, then $\frac{AB}{14} = \frac{7}{25}$. Post. 2-5, Theorem 8-2
13. If $\frac{PQ}{QR} = \frac{PQ}{SP}$, then $\frac{QR}{SP} = \frac{PQ}{PQ}$. Post. 2-5, Theorem 8-2
14. If $\frac{CD}{BC} = \frac{RS}{QR}$, then $\frac{CD}{RS} = \frac{BC}{QR}$. Theorem 8-2
15. If $\frac{CD}{RS} = \frac{BC}{QR}$, then $\frac{RS}{CD} = \frac{QR}{BC}$. Theorem 8-3
16. If $\frac{DF+BD}{BD} = \frac{DG+FH}{FH}$, then $\frac{DF}{BD} = \frac{DG}{FH}$. Theorem 8-4

FN: Ex: 1-16, Wr: 1-13 odds; pp. 251-2, Wr: 2-28 evens; p. 253, C: 1-5

Written **Suppose the measures of corresponding sides of the polygons at the right are proportional. For each of the following, find PS.**

1. $AB = 5, AD = 2, PQ = 3$ 1.2
2. $CB = 7, DA = 7, RQ = 3$ 3
3. $CD = 6.3, RS = 4.5, AD = 7.0$ 5
4. $QP = 2.1, BA = 2.8, DA = 3.2$ 2.4
5. $AD = 91.0, AB = 84.7, PQ = 12.1$ 13
6. $CD = 43.6, DA = 21.8, SR = 33.0$ 16.5

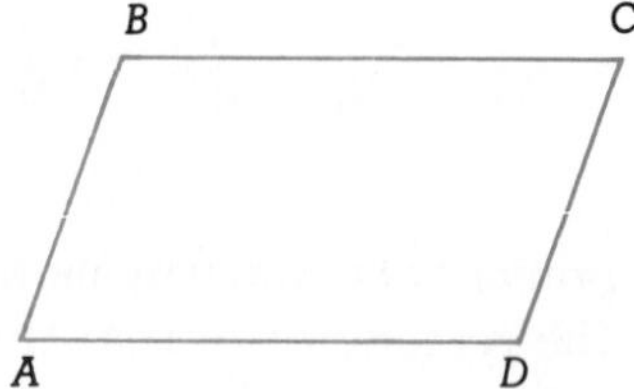

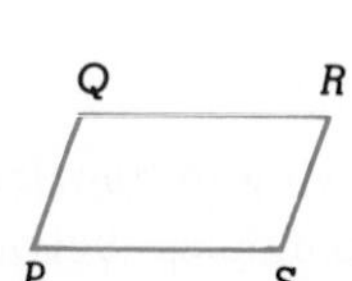

A corresponds to P
B corresponds to Q
C corresponds to R
D corresponds to S

Prove each of the following whenever all denominators are nonzero.

7. For any numbers a, b, c, and d, if $\frac{a}{b} = \frac{c}{d}$, then $\frac{a}{c} = \frac{b}{d}$.

8. For any numbers a, b, c, and d, if $\frac{a}{b} = \frac{c}{d}$, then $\frac{b}{a} = \frac{d}{c}$.

9. For any numbers a, b, c, and d, if $\frac{a}{b} = \frac{c}{d}$, then $\frac{a - b}{b} = \frac{c - d}{d}$.

10. For any numbers a, b, c, and d, if $\frac{a - b}{b} = \frac{c - d}{d}$, then $\frac{a}{b} = \frac{c}{d}$.

11. For any numbers a, b, c, and d, if $\frac{a}{b} = \frac{a + c}{b + d}$, then $\frac{a}{b} = \frac{c}{d}$.

12. For any numbers a, b, c, and d, if $\frac{a}{b} = \frac{c}{d}$, then $\frac{c}{d} = \frac{a + c}{b + d}$.

Answer each of the following.

13. John Frank is a potter making a rectangular clay plaque 25 inches by 36 inches. The plaque shrinks uniformly in the oven to a 30 inches length. What is the width after the plaque shrinks? $\frac{36}{30} = \frac{25}{w}$

    $20.8\overline{3}$ inches

14. Cindy Lawyer has a 55 cm by 60 cm oil painting. She wants to paint a copy that will fit a 40 cm width. What will be the corresponding length? $\frac{55}{40} = \frac{60}{\ell}$ $43.\overline{63}$ cm

Pentagram — excursions in geometry

The pentagram or star pentagon was a distinctive mark of the Pythagorean society. The five-pointed star can be made by drawing all the diagonals of a regular pentagon.

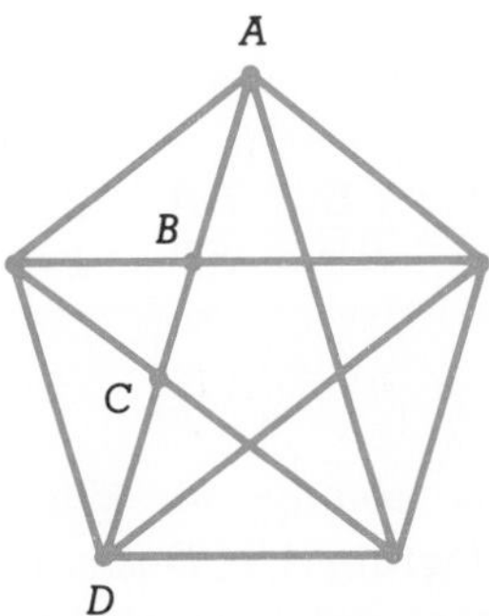

The concept of mean proportional can be illustrated with the pentagram. It can be proven that $\frac{BC}{AB} = \frac{AB}{AC}$.

Exercise **Find AB if $BC = 2.5$ and $AC = 6.5$.** $AB = \sqrt{16.25} \approx 4.03$

8–3 Similar Polygons

Objectives: to identify similar polygons, to use properties of similar polygons to solve problems

Enlargements of an original photograph are shown below. All the copies have the same shape but differ in size.

Ask students to name objects that have the same shape but different sizes.

In geometry, figures that have the same shape, but may differ in size are called **similar figures.**

The word "may" suggests that similar figures can be the same size or congruent.

Corresponding parts of polygons are used to tell if they are similar. For example, the parallelograms *ABCD* and *PQRS* are similar.

$\angle A \cong \angle P$
$\angle B \cong \angle Q$
$\angle C \cong \angle R$
$\angle D \cong \angle S$

$$\frac{AB}{PQ} = \frac{BC}{QR} = \frac{CD}{RS} = \frac{DA}{SP} = \frac{2}{1}$$

It may be necessary to help students identify proportional parts.

The symbol $\sim$ means *similar* or *is similar to.* We write, $\square ABCD \sim \square PQRS$, and we say *parallelogram ABCD is similar to parallelogram PQRS.* The order of letters indicates the vertices that correspond.

Two polygons are similar if and only if there is a correspondence such that their corresponding angles are congruent and the measures of their corresponding sides are proportional.

Definition of Similar Polygons

For two polygons to be similar, there are two conditions to be proven. If *only one* of the conditions is proven, then the polygons may *not* be similar.

The corresponding angles for these two figures are congruent. The measures of the corresponding sides are *not* proportional.

The measures of corresponding sides are proportional for these two figures. The corresponding angles are *not* congruent. Write out the proportions.

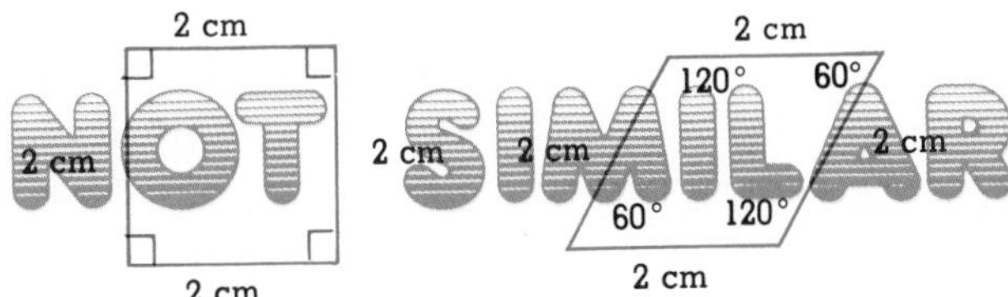

example

1 Determine whether or *not* all squares are similar.

All squares have four right angles, and all right angles are congruent. Thus, any correspondence between squares will have corresponding angles congruent.

All four sides of a square are congruent. Thus, the measures of each set of corresponding sides form equal ratios. That is, the measures of the corresponding sides are proportional.

Therefore, all squares are similar.

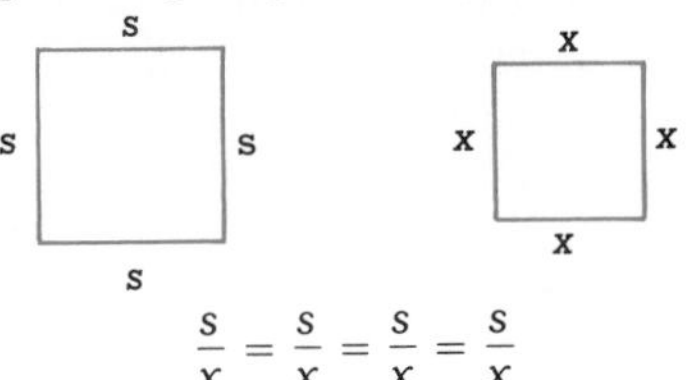

$$\frac{s}{x} = \frac{s}{x} = \frac{s}{x} = \frac{s}{x}$$

If s = x, are the squares similar? yes

Ask if all rectangles are similar. See Written exercise 3.

If the measures of some parts of two similar figures are known, then it may be possible to find the measures of other parts.

example

2 Suppose quadrilaterals *ABCD* and *PQRS* are similar. Find the value of x.

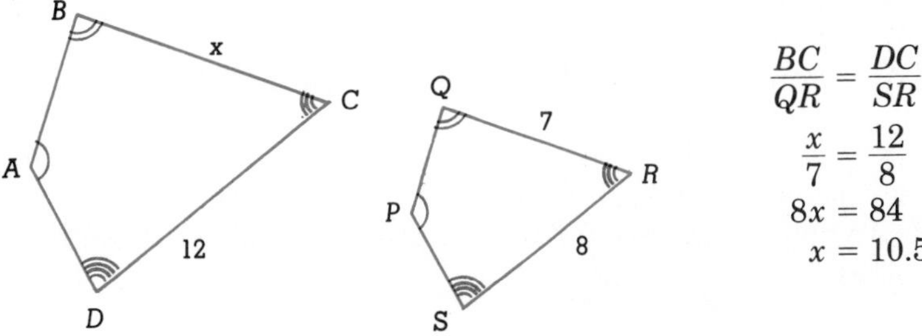

$$\frac{BC}{QR} = \frac{DC}{SR}$$

$$\frac{x}{7} = \frac{12}{8}$$

$$8x = 84$$

$$x = 10.5$$

example

3 **Imagine that a triangle is formed by connecting Atlanta, Cleveland, and New York. Such a triangle is similar to the one shown on the map. It is 405 miles by air from Cleveland to New York. How far is it from New York to Atlanta?**

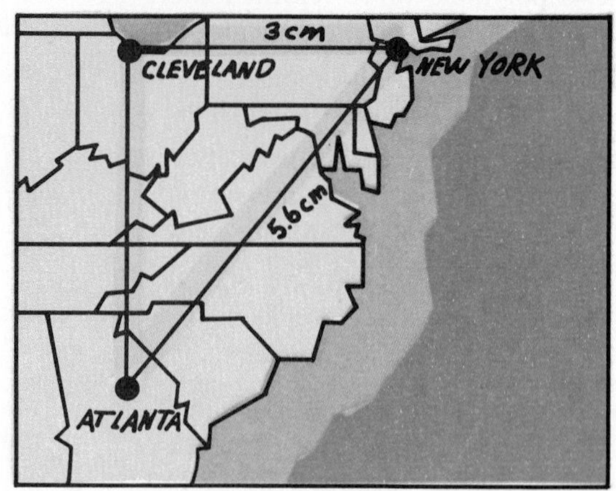

$$\frac{\textit{map distance Cle.–N.Y.}}{\textit{actual distance Cle.–N.Y.}} = \frac{\textit{map distance N.Y.–Atl.}}{\textit{actual distance N.Y.–Atl.}}$$

$$\frac{3}{405} = \frac{5.6}{x}$$

$$3x = 2268$$

$$x = 756$$

The distance from New York to Atlanta is 756 miles.

EN: Ex: 7, 8, Wr: 1-10, 14-22; AV: Ex: 1-8, Wr: 1-10, 11-21 odds; pp. 256-7, Wr: 4-14 evens p. 257,

exercises

FN: Ex: 1-8, Wr: 1-10, 11-21 odds; pp. 256-7, Wr: 2-14 evens

Exploratory **For each of the following list the information needed to show that the figures in each pair are similar.** For answers to exercises 1-4, see the Teacher's Guide.

1. $\triangle ABC \sim \triangle DEF$

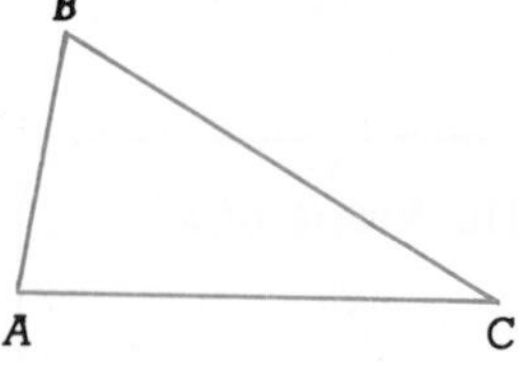

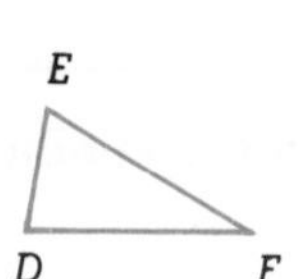

2. polygon $PQRS \sim$ polygon $ABCD$

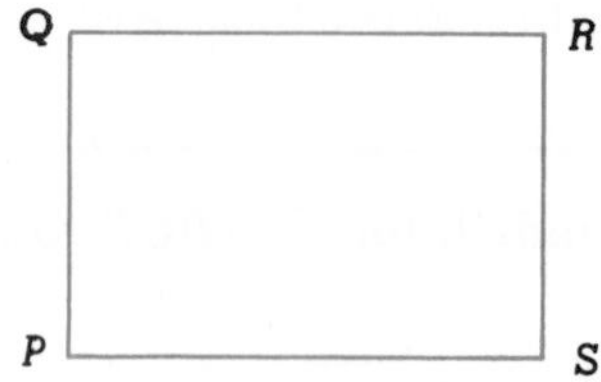

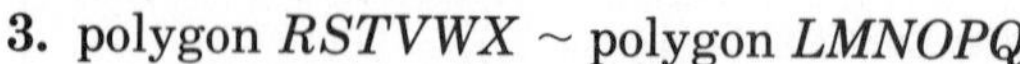

3. polygon $RSTVWX \sim$ polygon $LMNOPQ$

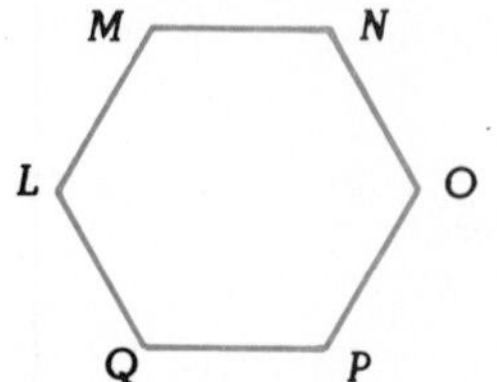

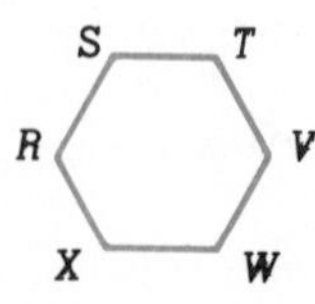

4. polygon $ABCD \sim$ polygon $NMLP$

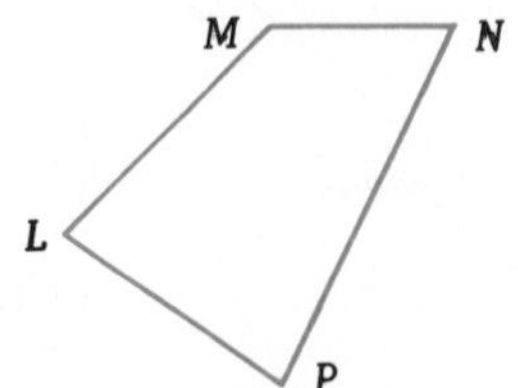

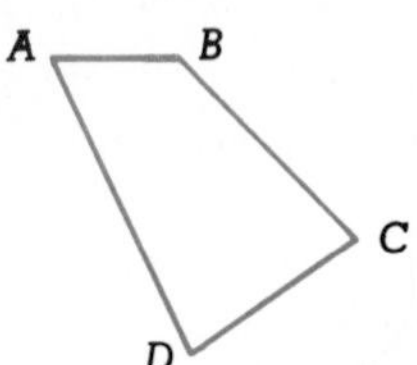

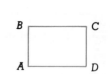

Determine whether or *not* the figures in each pair are similar.

yes **5.**

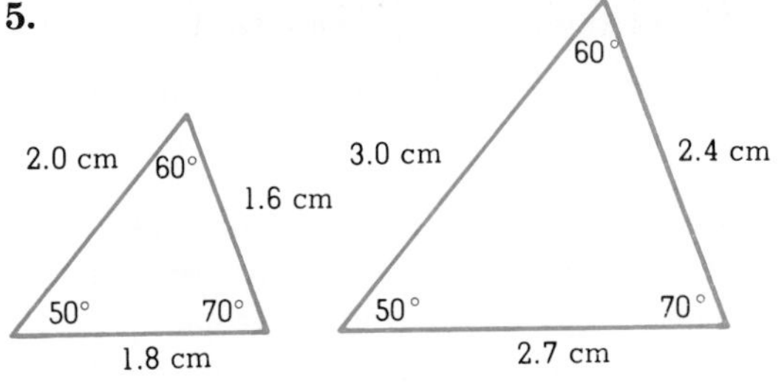

no **6.**

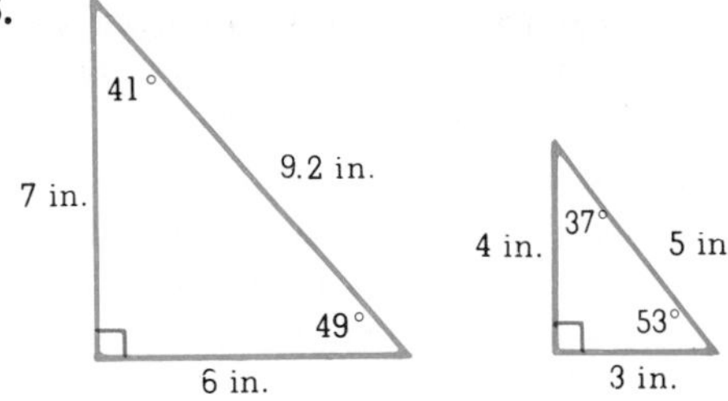

yes **7.**

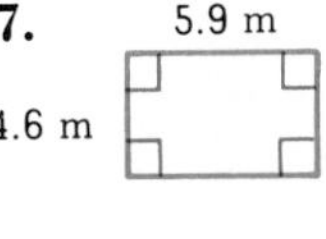

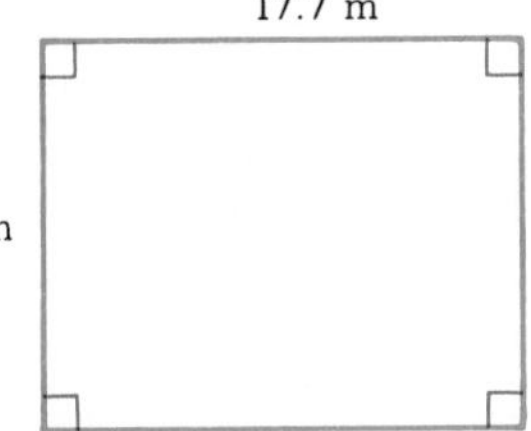

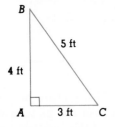

no **8.**

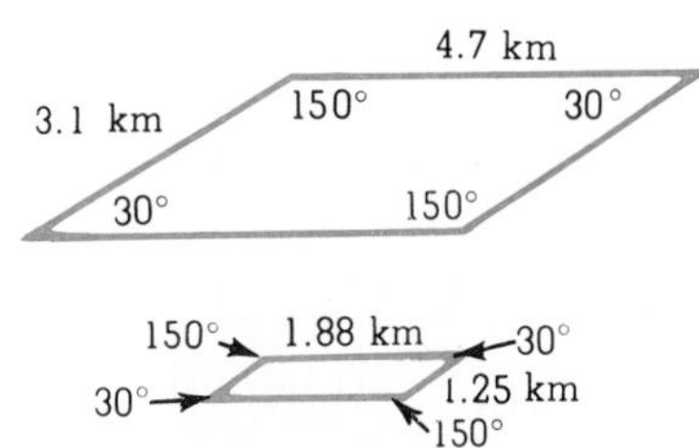

For reasons to exercises 1-10, see the Teacher's Guide.

Written **Determine whether the following are *true* or *false*. Then, explain your answer.**

1. All equilateral triangles are similar. true
2. All isosceles triangles are similar. false
3. All rectangles are similar. false
4. All regular hexagons are similar. true
5. All rhombuses are similar. false
6. Congruent triangles are similar. true
7. All trapezoids are similar. false
8. All parallelograms are similar. false
9. Similar quadrilaterals are congruent. false
10. Congruent quadrilaterals are similar. true

For each of the following, find the values of x and y.

11. $\triangle ABC \sim \triangle FED$ $x = 1\frac{2}{3}$ $y = \frac{4}{3}$

B, 5 ft, 4 ft, A, 3 ft, C

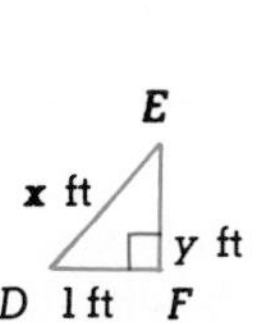

12. $\square ABCD \sim \square FGHE$ $x = 12$ $y = 12$

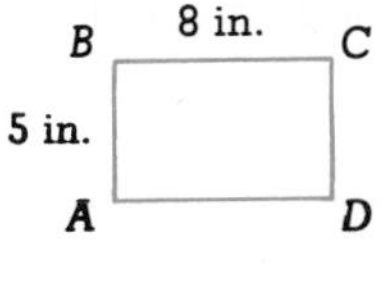

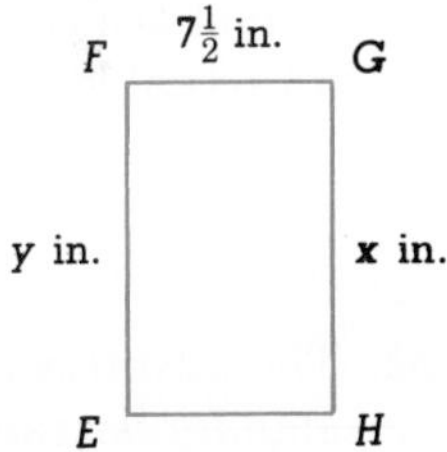

13. trapezoid *PQRS* ~ trapezoid *VWTU*
$x = 15$ $y = 35$

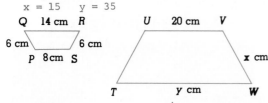

Q 14 cm R, 6 cm, 6 cm, P 8cm S

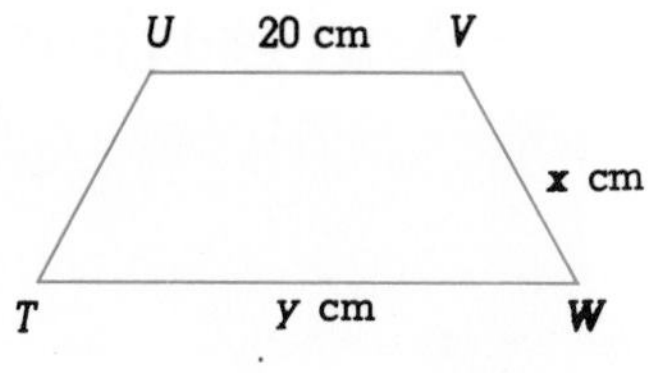

14. pentagon *ABCDE* ~ pentagon *PQRST*
$x = 1\frac{7}{8}$ $y = 3\frac{3}{4}$

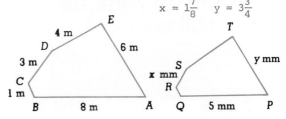

E, 4 m, D, 6 m, 3 m, C, 1 m, B, 8 m, A

T, S, y mm, x mm, R, Q, 5 mm, P

Prove each of the following. For answers to exercises 15-18, see the Teacher's Guide.

15. Similarity of triangles is reflexive.
16. Similarity of triangles is symmetric.
17. Similarity of triangles is transitive.
18. If two triangles are congruent, then the triangles are similar.

Answer each of the following.

19. The poster shown below has a width of 14 inches and a height of 21 inches. The manufacturer plans to issue an enlarged poster with an 18 inch width. Find the new height. $\frac{14}{18} = \frac{21}{x}$ 27 inches

20. Joan Shaull designs automobiles using scale drawings. Suppose one length on a model is 1.2 cm and corresponds with 3 cm on the drawing. Find the length on the model that measures 2 cm on the drawing. $\frac{1.2}{3} = \frac{x}{2}$ 0.8 cm

21. Figures seen in the picture shown are similar to the actual figure. Suppose the width of the building is actually 208 m and it is 2.6 cm wide in the picture. If one side of the building measures 3 cm, find its actual length. $\frac{208}{2.6} = \frac{x}{3}$ 240 m

22. The advertisement shown illustrates the growth in boxcar shipments. The picture of the smaller boxcar has a length of 6 cm and corresponds with the 7.2 cm length of the picture of the larger boxcar. If the height of the larger car is 2.4 cm, find the height of the smaller car. $\frac{6}{x} = \frac{7.2}{2.4}$ 2 cm

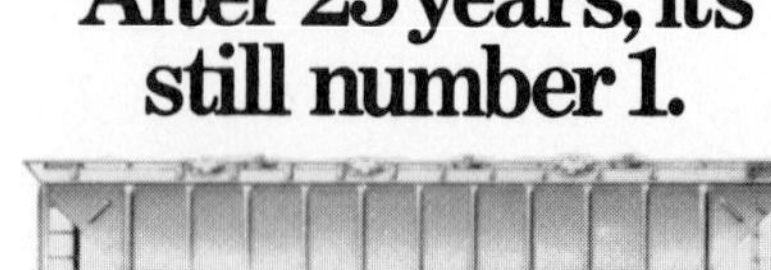

8–4 Similar Triangles

Objectives: to recognize the conditions for similar triangles, to use the tests for similar triangles in proofs and other problem-solving situations

To show that two triangles are similar, it is *not* necessary to prove all the conditions of the definition of similar polygons. The following postulate tells you that the shape of a triangle is completely determined by the measures of its angles.

If two angles of one triangle are congruent to two corresponding angles of another triangle, then the triangles are similar.

Postulate 8–1
AA Similarity

example

It may be helpful to redraw these triangles separately to help students visualize the proportional parts.

1 **Prove the following.**

Given: $\overline{ST} \parallel \overline{PR}$
$QS = 3$
$SP = 1$
$TR = 1.2$

Prove: $QT = 3.6$

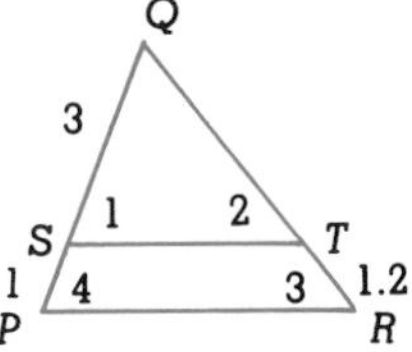

Proof:

STATEMENTS	REASONS
1. $\overline{ST} \parallel \overline{PR}$	**1.** Given
2. $\angle QST \cong \angle QPR$ $\angle QTS \cong \angle QRP$	**2.** Theorem 6–9: If two parallel lines are cut by a transversal, then each pair of corresponding angles are congruent.
3. $\triangle SQT \sim \triangle PQR$	**3.** Postulate 8–1: AA Similarity
4. $\frac{QT}{QR} = \frac{QS}{QP}$	**4.** Definition of Similar Polygons
5. $QS = 3$ $SP = 1$ $TR = 1.2$	**5.** Given
6. $QP = QS + SP$ $= 3 + 1$ $= 4$ $QR = QT + TR$ $= QT + 1.2$	**6.** Definition of Between and Postulate 2–9: Substitution
7. $\frac{QT}{QT + 1.2} = \frac{3}{4}$	**7.** Postulate 2–9: Substitution
8. $4QT = 3(QT + 1.2)$ $= 3QT + 3.6$	**8.** Theorem 8–1: Equality of Cross Products and Postulate 2–14: Distributive Property
9. $QT = 3.6$	**9.** Postulate 2–7: Subtraction Property of Equality

To check triangles for similarity, it is only necessary to test angle measures. Could similarity of triangles be checked by testing the measures of corresponding sides for proportionality? yes

Remind students that polygons other than triangles must meet both conditions of similarity in order to be similar.

Point out how this theorem differs from SSS congruence.

Theorem 8–7 SSS Similarity

If there is a correspondence between the two triangles so that the measures of their corresponding sides are proportional, then the two triangles are similar.

Emphasize that these conditions must be true for all three pairs of sides.

example

2 Prove Theorem 8–7.

Given: $\frac{PQ}{AB} = \frac{QR}{BC} = \frac{RP}{CA}$

Prove: $\triangle BAC \sim \triangle QPR$

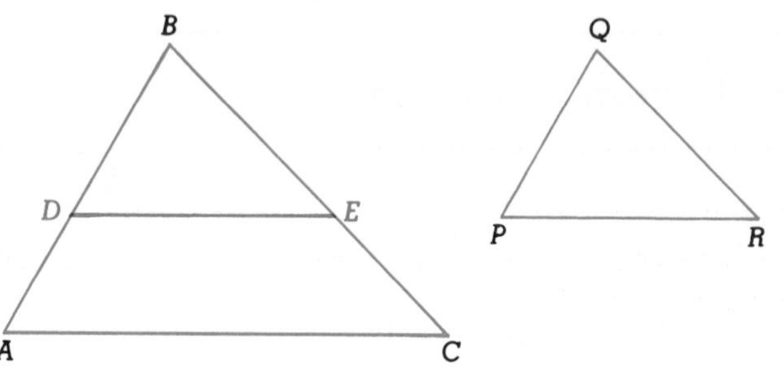

Proof:

STATEMENTS	REASONS
1. $\frac{PQ}{AB} = \frac{QR}{BC} = \frac{RP}{CA}$	1. Given
2. Locate D on $\overline{AB}$ so that $\overline{DB} \cong \overline{PQ}$.	2. Postulate 2–2: Ruler Postulate and Definition of Congruent Segments
3. Draw $\overline{DE}$ so that $\overline{DE} \parallel \overline{AC}$.	3. Postulate 6–1: Parallel Postulate
4. $\angle BDE \cong \angle A$	4. Theorem 6–9: If two parallel lines are cut by a transversal, then each pair of corresponding angles are congruent.
5. $\triangle BDE \sim \triangle BAC$	5. Postulate 8–1: AA Similarity
6. $\frac{DB}{AB} = \frac{BE}{BC} = \frac{ED}{CA}$	6. Definition of Similar Polygons
7. $DB = PQ$	7. Definition of Congruent Segments
8. $\frac{DB}{AB} = \frac{QR}{BC} = \frac{RP}{CA}$	8. Postulate 2–9: Substitution
9. $\frac{QR}{BC} = \frac{BE}{BC}$ $\frac{RP}{CA} = \frac{ED}{CA}$	9. Postulate 2–6: Transitive Property of Equality
10. $QR = BE$, $RP = ED$	10. Postulate 2–8: Multiplication Property of Equality
11. $\overline{QR} \cong \overline{BE}$, $\overline{RP} \cong \overline{ED}$	11. Definition of Congruent Segments

12. $\triangle BDE \cong \triangle QPR$	**12.** Postulate 4–1: SSS Congruence
13. $\angle B \cong \angle Q$, $\angle BDE \cong \angle P$	**13.** Definition of Congruent Triangles
14. $\triangle BAC \sim \triangle QPR$	**14.** Postulate 8–1: AA Similarity

Students prove this theorem in Written exercise 7.

If the measures of two sides of a triangle are proportional to the measures of two corresponding sides of another triangle, and the included angles are congruent, then the triangles are similar.

Theorem 8–8
SAS Similarity

Draw a diagram to illustrate this theorem.

EN: Wr: 1-8; AV: Ex: 1-6, Wr: 1-5 odds; pp. 261-2, Wr: 12-22 evens

exercises

FN: Ex: 1-6, Wr: 1-5; pp. 261-2, Wr: 12-22 evens

Exploratory **Use each figure and the information given to determine whether or *not* each pair of triangles are similar.**

1.

yes

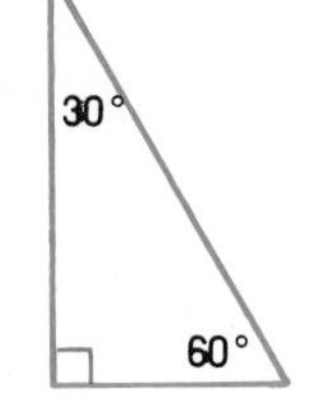

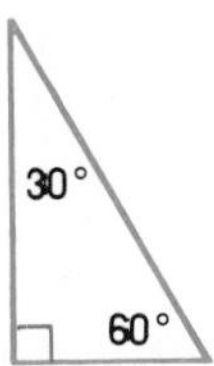

2.

yes

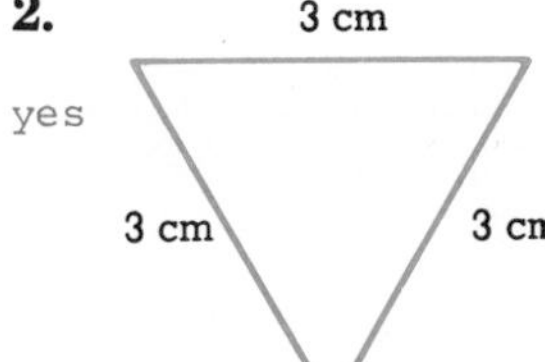

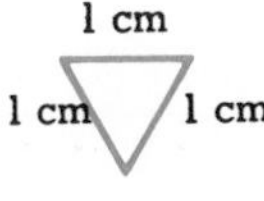

3.

no

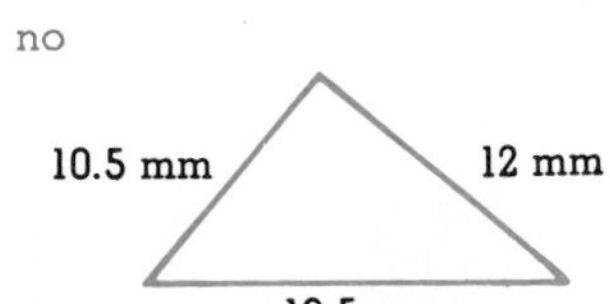

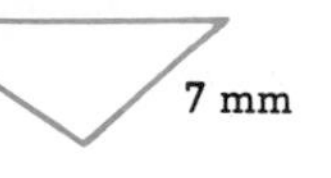

4.

yes

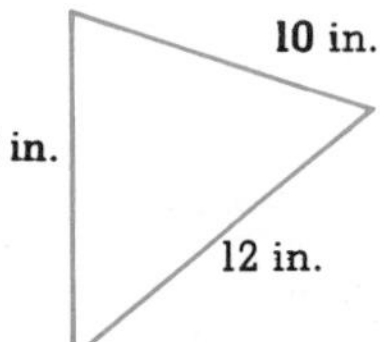

5.

yes

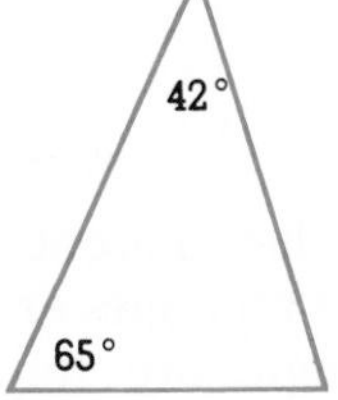

65° 42°

6.

no

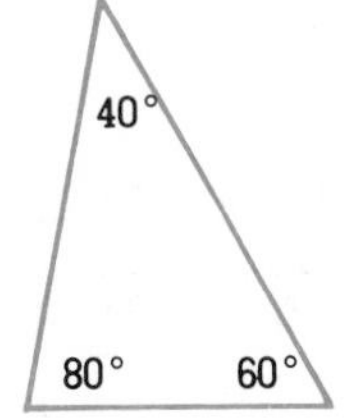

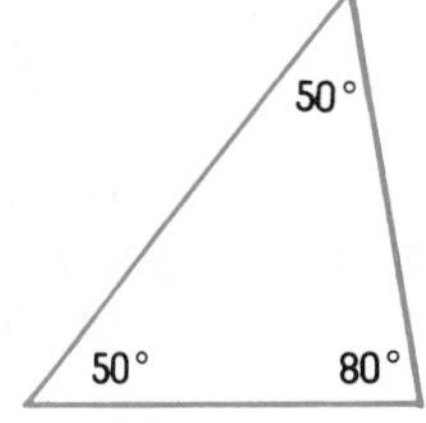

Suggest that students can draw triangles separately to help find proportional parts.

Written **For each of the following, use the figure at the right and the given information to find the value of x.**

1. $QR = x + 4$
$RS = 2x + 3$
$QP = 3$
$TS = 5$
$\frac{x + 4}{2x + 3} = \frac{3}{5}$ $11 = x$

2. $TS = 6$
$QP = 4$
$RS = \frac{1}{4}x + 1$
$QR = 3x - 5$
$\frac{3x - 5}{\frac{1}{4}x + 1} = \frac{4}{6}$ $x = 2$

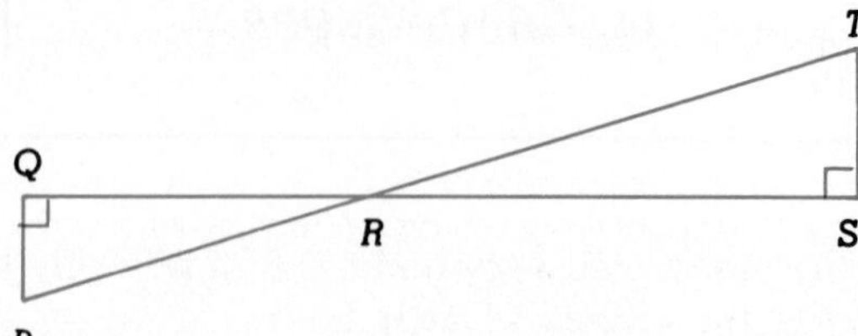

Exercises 1 and 2

For answers to exercises 3-8, see the Teacher's Guide.

Prove each of the following.

3. **Given:** $\angle D$ is a right angle.
$\overline{BE} \perp \overline{AC}$
Prove: $\triangle ADC \sim \triangle ABE$

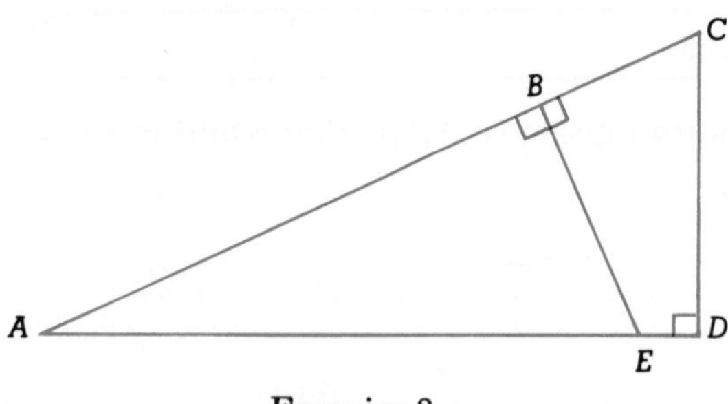

Exercise 3

4. **Given:** $\overline{QS} \parallel \overline{PT}$
Prove: $\triangle QRS \sim \triangle TRP$

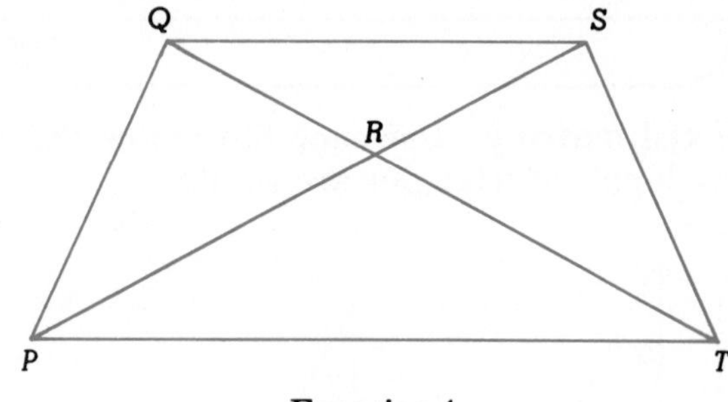

Exercise 4

5. **Given:** $\angle Q$ is a right angle.
$\square WSTV$ is a square.
Prove: $\triangle PWS \sim \triangle TVR$

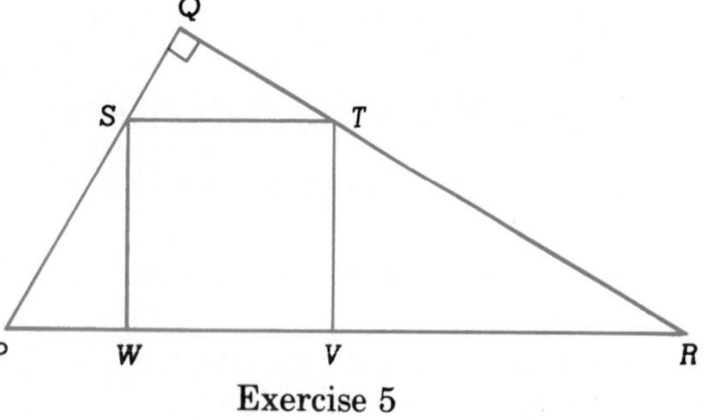

Exercise 5

6. **Given:** $\overline{PR} \cong \overline{TR}$
$\overline{VQ} \perp \overline{PR}$
$\overline{VS} \perp \overline{RT}$
Prove: $\frac{PQ}{TS} = \frac{VQ}{VS}$

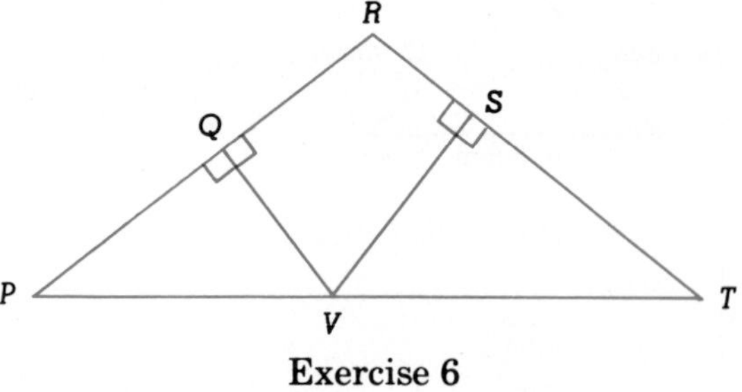

Exercise 6

7. Theorem 8–8

8. If the measures of the sides adjacent to the right angles of two right triangles are proportional, then the triangles are similar.

8–5 Proportional Parts

Objective: to recognize and use the relationships between parallels and proportional parts of triangles in problem solving

Proportional parts of a triangle can be used to prove that lines are parallel.

If a line intersects two sides of a triangle, and separates the sides into segments of proportional lengths, then the line is parallel to the third side.

Theorem 8–9

example

1 **Prove Theorem 8–9.**

Given: $\frac{BA}{CB} = \frac{DE}{CD}$

Prove: $\overleftrightarrow{BD} \parallel \overline{AE}$

These triangles can be redrawn separately to help show the proportional parts.

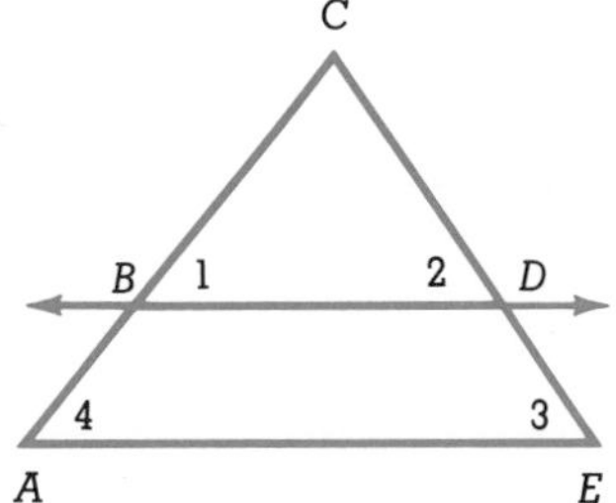

Proof:

STATEMENTS	REASONS
1. $\frac{BA}{CB} = \frac{DE}{CD}$	**1.** Given
2. B is between C and A. D is between C and E.	**2.** Given
3. $CA = CB + BA$; $CE = CD + DE$	**3.** Definition of Between
4. $BA = CA - CB$; $DE = CE - CD$	**4.** Postulate 2–7: Subtraction Property of Equality
5. $\frac{CA - CB}{CB} = \frac{CE - CD}{CD}$	**5.** Postulate 2–9: Substitution
6. $\frac{CA}{CB} = \frac{CE}{CD}$	**6.** Theorem 8–5: Subtraction Property of Proportions
7. $\angle C \cong \angle C$	**7.** Theorem 3–1: Congruence of angles is reflexive.
8. $\triangle CBD \sim \triangle CAE$	**8.** Theorem 8–8: SAS Similarity
9. $\angle 1 \cong \angle 4$	**9.** Definition of Similar Polygons
10. $\overleftrightarrow{BD} \parallel \overline{AE}$	**10.** Theorem 6–5: In a plane, if two lines are cut by a transversal so that a pair of corresponding angles are congruent, then the two lines are parallel.

Each floor of an A-frame is the base of a triangle with part of the roof as sides. Also, each floor is parallel to the ground floor. The following theorem tells you that, because the floors are parallel, the triangles formed are similar.

It is assumed that the line does not pass through the vertex.

If a line is parallel to one side of a triangle and intersects the other two sides, then it separates the sides into segments of proportional lengths.

Theorem 8–10

example

2 Prove Theorem 8–10.

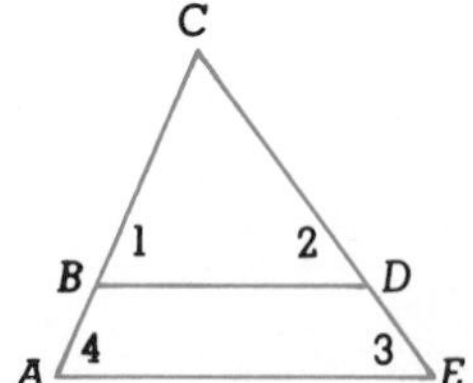

Given: $\overline{BD} \parallel \overline{AE}$

Prove: $\frac{BA}{CB} = \frac{DE}{CD}$

Proof:

STATEMENTS	REASONS
1. $\overline{BD} \parallel \overline{AE}$	**1.** Given
2. $\angle 1 \cong \angle 4$ $\angle 2 \cong \angle 3$	**2.** Theorem 6–9: If two parallel lines are cut by a transversal, then each pair of corresponding angles are congruent.
3. $\triangle ACE \sim \triangle BCD$	**3.** Postulate 8–1: AA Similarity
4. $\frac{CA}{CB} = \frac{CE}{CD}$	**4.** Definition of Similar Polygons
5. B is between A and C. D is between C and E.	**5.** Given
6. $CA = BA + CB$ $CE = DE + CD$	**6.** Definition of Between
7. $\frac{BA + CB}{CB} = \frac{DE + CD}{CD}$	**7.** Postulate 2–9: Substitution
8. $\frac{BA}{CB} = \frac{DE}{CD}$	**8.** Theorem 8–4: Addition Property of Proportions

The proof of the following theorem is based on Theorems 8–9 and 8–10.

Students complete a proof of this theorem in Written exercise 11.

If a segment has as its endpoints the midpoints of two sides of a triangle, then it is parallel to the third side and its length is one-half the length of the third side.

Theorem 8–11

In the triangle below, suppose that B is the midpoint of $\overline{AC}$ and D is the midpoint of $\overline{CE}$.

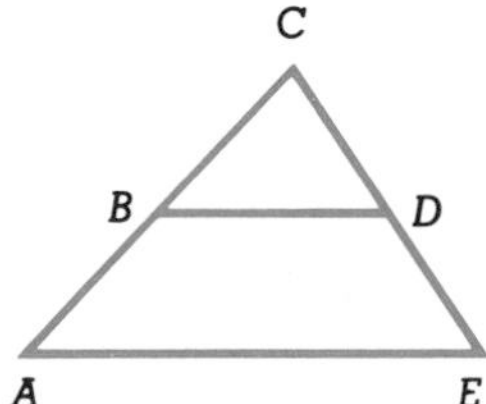

By Theorem 8–11, $\overline{BD} \parallel \overline{AE}$ and $BD = \frac{1}{2} AE$.

Three or more parallel lines separate transversals into proportional parts as stated below.

If three parallel lines intersect two transversals, then they divide the transversals proportionally.

Theorem 8–12

If three parallel lines cut off congruent segments on one transversal, then they cut off congruent segments on any transversal.

Theorem 8–13

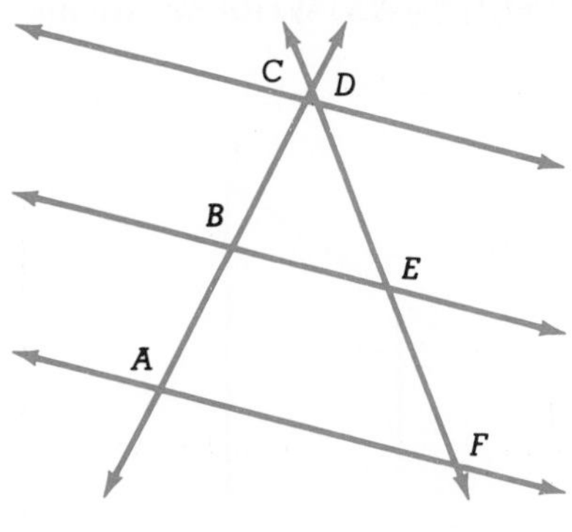

In the figure at the left, $\overleftrightarrow{CD} \parallel \overleftrightarrow{BE} \parallel \overleftrightarrow{AF}$. Transversals, $\overleftrightarrow{AC}$ and $\overleftrightarrow{FD}$, have been separated into proportional segments. Sample proportions are listed below.

$$\frac{CB}{BA} = \frac{DE}{EF}; \frac{CA}{DF} = \frac{BA}{EF}; \frac{AC}{BC} = \frac{FD}{ED}$$

You may want students to name other proportions in class discussion.

EN: Ex: 7-19 odds, Wr: 2-10 evens, 11; AV: Ex: 1-19 odds, Wr: 1-11 odds; p. 266, Wr: 2-6 evens

exercises

FN: Ex: 1-20, Wr: 1-10; p. 266, Wr: 6

Exploratory **In the figure, $BD \parallel AE$. Use this figure to determine whether or *not* each of the following must be true.**

1. $\frac{CB}{BA} = \frac{CD}{DE}$ yes
2. $\frac{CD}{CB} = \frac{DE}{BA}$ yes
3. $\frac{AC}{BC} = \frac{ED}{DC}$ no
4. $\frac{CB}{BA} = \frac{DE}{DC}$ no
5. $\frac{BC}{ED} = \frac{AB}{CD}$ no
6. $\frac{CB}{CD} = \frac{CA}{CE}$ yes
7. $\frac{CB}{CD} = \frac{BA}{DE}$ yes
8. $\frac{AB}{BC} = \frac{DE}{CD}$ yes
9. $\frac{AC}{DC} = \frac{EC}{BC}$ no
10. $\frac{AC}{EC} = \frac{DC}{BC}$ no
11. $\frac{CA}{BA} = \frac{CE}{DE}$ yes
12. $\frac{BA}{DE} = \frac{CA}{CE}$ yes

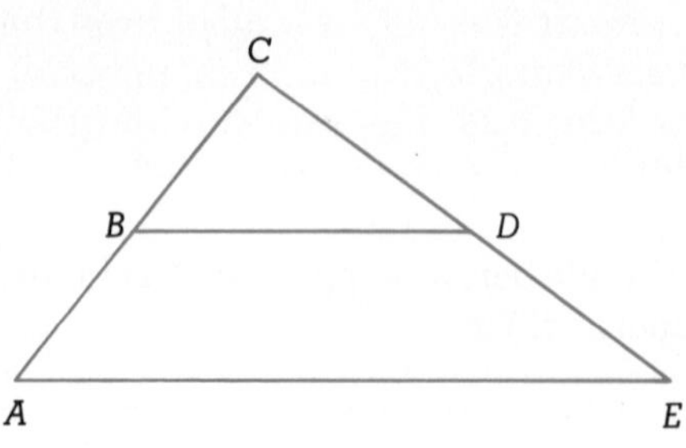

In the figure below, $\overleftrightarrow{YA} \parallel \overleftrightarrow{OE} \parallel \overleftrightarrow{BR}$. Use the figure to complete each of the following.

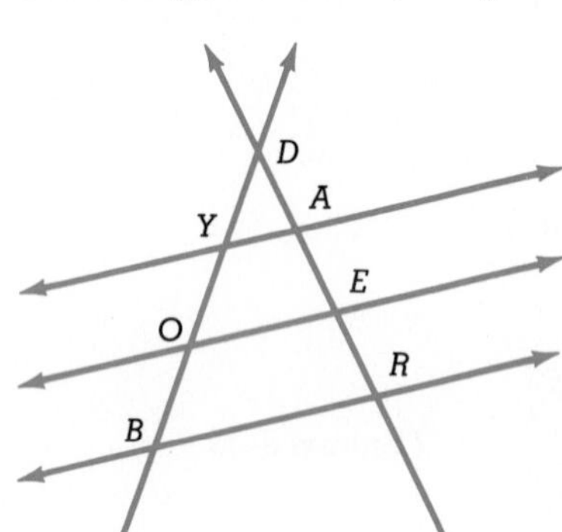

13. $\frac{YO}{OB} = \frac{AE}{\blacksquare}$ ER
14. $\frac{YB}{OB} = \frac{\blacksquare}{ER}$ AR
15. $\frac{\blacksquare}{AE} = \frac{YB}{YO}$ AR
16. $\frac{DY}{YO} = \frac{DA}{\blacksquare}$ AE
17. $\frac{DR}{\blacksquare} = \frac{DB}{YB}$ AR
18. $\frac{\blacksquare}{AE} = \frac{DO}{YO}$ DE
19. $\frac{AE}{DR} = \frac{\blacksquare}{DB}$ YO
20. $\frac{ER}{\blacksquare} = \frac{OB}{DO}$ DE

Written **For each of the following, determine whether or *not* $\overline{QT} \parallel \overline{RS}$. Write *yes* or *no*.**

1. $PR = 30$
   $PQ = 9$
   $PT = 12$
   $PS = 18$ $\quad \frac{9}{30} \overset{?}{=} \frac{12}{18}$ no
2. $QR = 22$
   $TS = 9$
   $RP = 65$
   $SP = 27$ $\quad \frac{65}{22} \overset{?}{=} \frac{27}{9}$ no
3. $RP = 13.5$
   $RQ = 7.2$
   $TP = 4.2$
   $SP = 9.0$ $\quad \frac{13.5}{7.2} \overset{?}{=} \frac{9.0}{4.8}$ yes
4. $PQ = 34.88$
   $RQ = 18.32$
   $PS = 33.25$
   $TS = 11.45$ yes

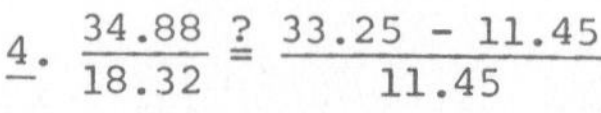
4. $\frac{34.88}{18.32} \overset{?}{=} \frac{33.25 - 11.45}{11.45}$

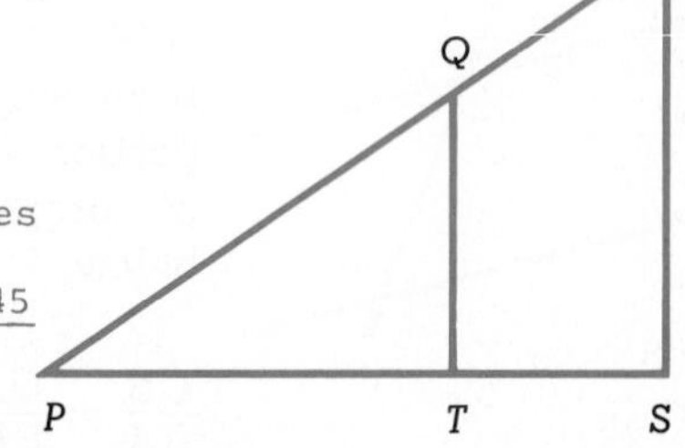

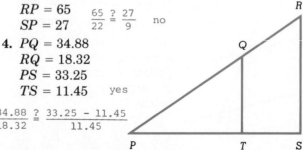

For each of the following, use the figure at the right and the given information to find the value of x.

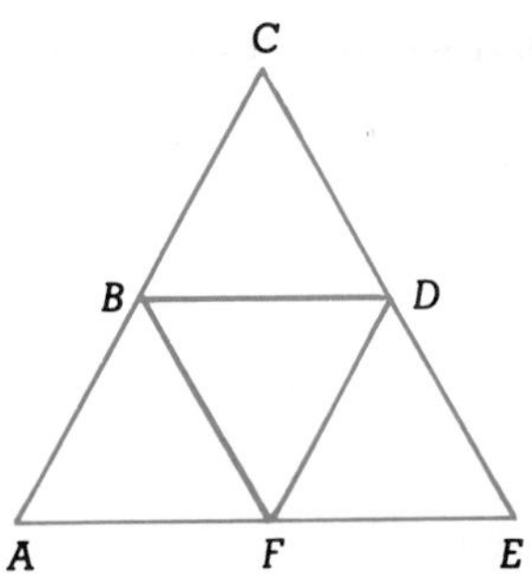

5. $\overline{BD} \parallel \overline{AE}$
   $AB = 6$
   $DE = 8$
   $DC = 4$
   $BC = x$ 3

6. $\overline{AC} \parallel \overline{DF}$
   $DC = 7$
   $DE = 5$
   $FA = 8$
   $FE = x$ $5\frac{5}{7}$

7. $\overline{DF} \parallel \overline{CA}$
   $AF = 3.42$
   $FE = 3.35$
   $DE = 6.7$
   $CD = x$ 6.84

8. $\overline{FB} \parallel \overline{CE}$
   $AB = 4.90$
   $AF = 5.62$
   $FE = 8.43$
   $BC = x$ 7.35

9. $\overline{EC} \parallel \overline{FB}$
   $AF = x + 2$
   $FE = 5$
   $AB = x$
   $BC = 3$ 3

10. $\overline{AE} \parallel \overline{DB}$
    $CB = x$
    $CD = x - 2$
    $BA = 5$
    $DE = 1$ 2.5

11. Complete the following proof.

Given: Q is the midpoint of $\overline{RP}$.
S is the midpoint of $\overline{RT}$.

Prove: $\overline{QS} \parallel \overline{PT}$
$QS = \frac{1}{2}PT$

Proof:

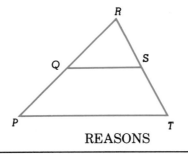

STATEMENTS	REASONS
1. Q is the midpoint of $\overline{RP}$. S is the midpoint of $\overline{RT}$.	1. Given
2. $QR = PQ$, $SR = TS$	2. Definition of Midpoint
3. $RP = PQ + QR$, $TR = TS + SR$	3. Definition of Between
4. $RP = QR + QR$, $TR = SR + SR$	4. Postulate 2–9: Substitution
5. $RP = 2\,QR$, $TR = 2\,SR$	5. Postulate 2-7
6. $\frac{RP}{QR} = 2$, $\frac{TR}{SR} = 2$	6. Postulate 2–8: Division Property of Equality
7. $\frac{RP}{QR} = \frac{TR}{SR}$	7. Postulate 2–9: Substitution
8. $\angle R \cong \angle R$	8. Theorem 3-1
9. $\triangle RPT \sim \triangle RQS$	9. SAS Similarity
10. $\angle RPT \cong \angle RQS$	10. Definition of Similar Polygons
11. $\overline{QS} \parallel \overline{PT}$	11. Theorem 6-5
12. $\frac{RP}{QR} = \frac{PT}{QS}$	12. Theorem 8-10
13. $\frac{PT}{QS} = 2$	13. Postulate 2–9: Substitution
14. $QS = \frac{1}{2}PT$	14. Postulate 2–8: Division Property of Equality

8–6 Parts of Similar Polygons

Objective: to recognize and use the proportional relationships of corresponding perimeters, altitudes, angle bisectors, and medians of similar triangles

When two triangles are similar, the measures of their corresponding sides are proportional. What about their corresponding altitudes, medians, and so on? Are the measures of these proportional to the measures of the corresponding sides of the triangles? yes

By using the Summation Property of Proportions, you can show that the measures of corresponding perimeters are proportional to the measures of corresponding sides of similar triangles.

In the figure at the left, suppose $\triangle ABC \sim \triangle PQR$.

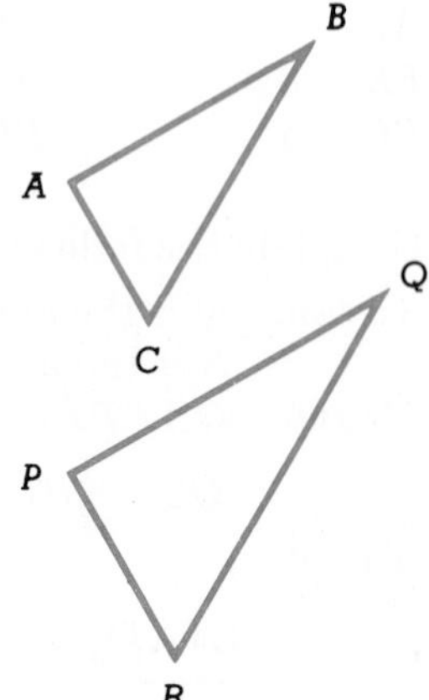

$$\frac{AB}{PQ} = \frac{BC}{QR} = \frac{CA}{RP}$$ *Definition of Similar Triangles*

$$\frac{AB}{PQ} = \frac{AB + BC}{PQ + QR}$$ *Summation Property of Proportions*

$$\frac{AB + BC}{PQ + QR} = \frac{CA}{RP}$$ *Substitution*

$$\frac{AB + BC + CA}{PQ + QR + RP} = \frac{CA}{RP}$$ *Summation Property of Proportions*

This procedure can be repeated as many times as necessary to prove that corresponding perimeters are proportional to corresponding sides for any set of similar polygons.

If two triangles are similar, then the measures of corresponding perimeters are proportional to the measures of corresponding sides. ***Theorem 8–14***

example

1 In the figure at the right, suppose $\triangle ABD \sim \triangle ADC$. If the perimeter of $\triangle ABD$ measures 37, the perimeter of $\triangle ADC$ measures 71, and $AD = 16$, find AB.

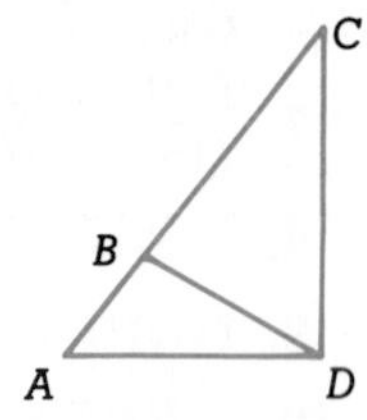

$$\frac{AB}{AD} = \frac{AB + BD + DA}{AD + DC + CA}$$

$$\frac{AB}{16} = \frac{37}{71}$$

$$71 \cdot AB = 37 \cdot 16$$

$$AB = \frac{37 \cdot 16}{71}$$

$$\approx 8.3$$

In the figure below, suppose $\triangle ABC \sim \triangle PQR$. Then $\angle A \cong \angle P$ because they are corresponding angles. Since $\overline{BD}$ is an altitude of $\triangle ABC$, it forms a right angle, $\angle BDA$. Similarly, $\angle QSP$ is a right angle. By AA Similarity, $\triangle ABD \sim \triangle PQS$. Thus, $\frac{BD}{QS} = \frac{BA}{QP}$.

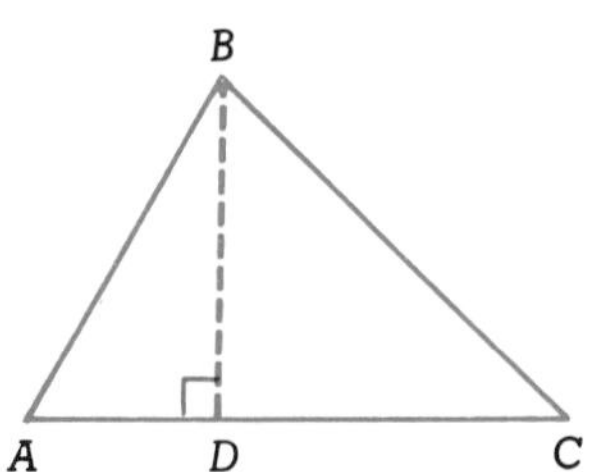

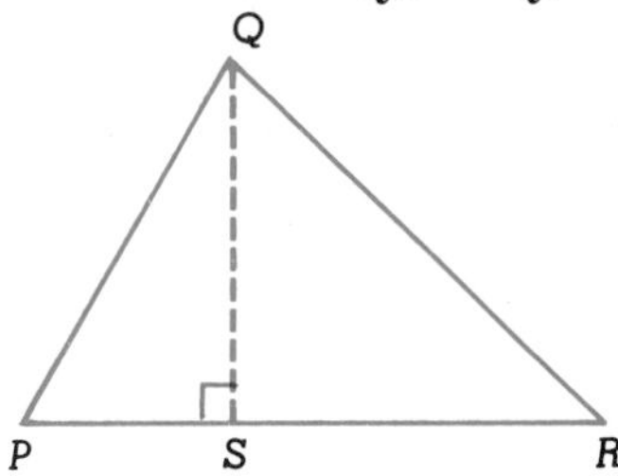

Help students find the corresponding parts.

If two triangles are similar, then the measures of corresponding altitudes are proportional to the measures of corresponding sides.

Theorem 8–15

Students prove this theorem in Written exercises 9-10.

Suppose $\triangle RST \sim \triangle EFG$ in the figure below. $\angle SRT \cong \angle FEG$ because they are corresponding angles. $\overrightarrow{RV}$ bisects $\angle SRT$ and $\overrightarrow{EH}$ bisects $\angle FEG$. Then $\angle SRV \cong \angle FEH$. Using AA Similarity, $\triangle RSV \sim \triangle EFH$. Thus, $\frac{RV}{EH} = \frac{RS}{EF}$.

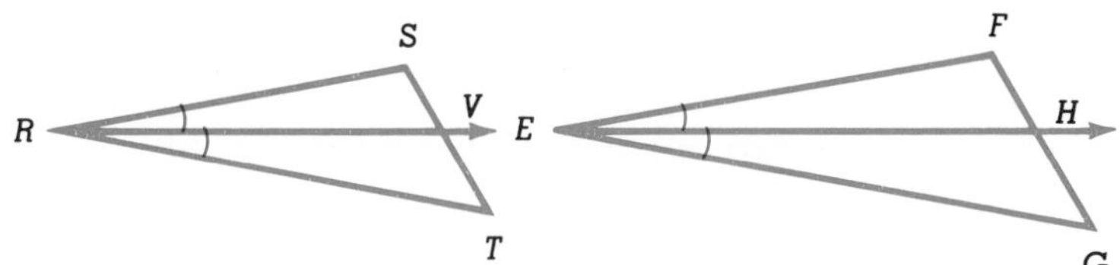

If two triangles are similar, then the measures of corresponding angle bisectors of the triangles are proportional to the measures of corresponding sides.

Theorem 8–16

Students plan a proof for this theorem in Written exercise 11.

example

2 State five different proportions for $\triangle KLM$ and $\triangle WXY$ if $\triangle KLM \sim \triangle WXY$.

The proportions include the following.

$$\frac{AM}{BY} = \frac{LM}{XY}, \frac{AM}{BY} = \frac{KM}{WY}$$

$$\frac{AM}{BY} = \frac{KL}{WX}, \frac{AL}{LM} = \frac{BX}{XY}$$

$$\frac{KA + AM + MK}{WB + BY + YW} = \frac{KA}{WB}$$

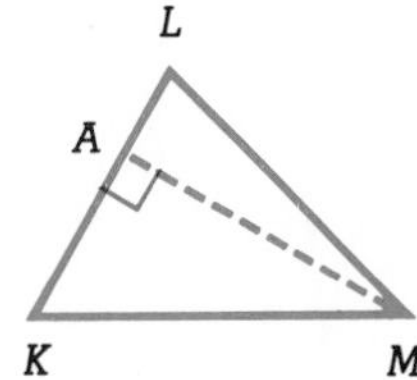

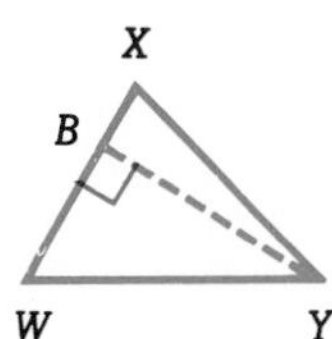

If two triangles are similar, then the measures of corresponding medians are proportional to the measures of corresponding sides.

Theorem 8–17

Students prove this theorem in Written exercise 12 in conjunction with Example 3.

example

3 Plan a proof for Theorem 8–17.

Given: $\triangle ABC \sim \triangle PQR$
$\overline{BD}$ is a median of $\triangle ABC$.
$\overline{QS}$ is a median of $\triangle PQR$.

Prove: $\dfrac{BD}{QS} = \dfrac{BA}{QP}$

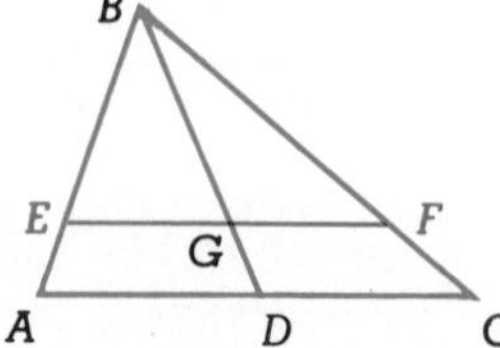

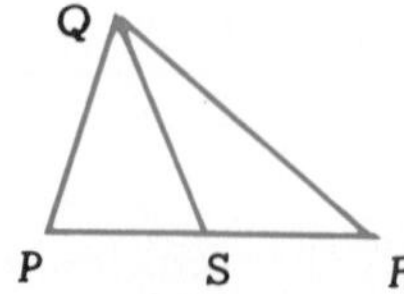

Proof:

Draw $\overline{EF}$ so that $\overline{BE} \cong \overline{QP}$ and $\angle BEF \cong \angle QPR$.

Since $\triangle ABC \sim \triangle PQR$, conclude that $\angle QPR \cong \angle BAC$. Thus, by transitivity of angle congruence, $\angle BEF \cong \angle BAC$. Since $\angle ABD$ is congruent to itself, AA Similarity implies that $\triangle BEG \sim \triangle BAD$.

Since $\overline{BD}$ is a median of $\triangle ABC$ and $\overline{QS}$ is a median of $\triangle PQR$, then D is the midpoint of $\overline{AC}$ and S is the midpoint of $\overline{PR}$.

Using proportions and substitution, show that $\triangle BEG \cong \triangle QPS$ by SAS. Then, substitute in proportions to show that $\dfrac{BD}{QS} = \dfrac{BA}{QP}$.

EN: Ex: 1-4, 7-9, Wr: 4-12; AV: Ex: 1-11 odds, Wr: 1-11 odds; pp. 270-1, Wr: 2-10 evens

exercises

FN: Ex: 1-12, Wr: 1-6; p. 271, Wr: 11

Exploratory **In the figure, $\triangle EFG \sim \triangle QRS$. $\overline{GH}$ bisects $\angle EGF$ and $\overline{ST}$ bisects $\angle QSR$. Determine whether or *not* each of the following *must be* true.**

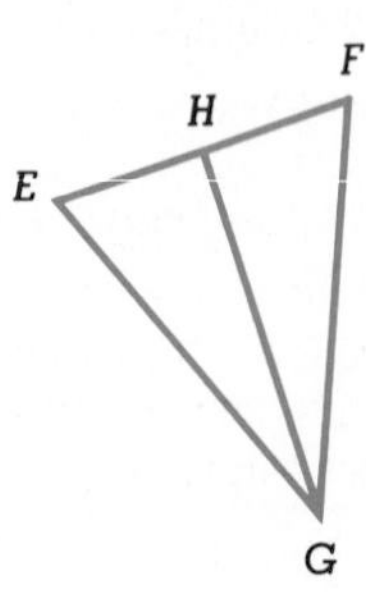

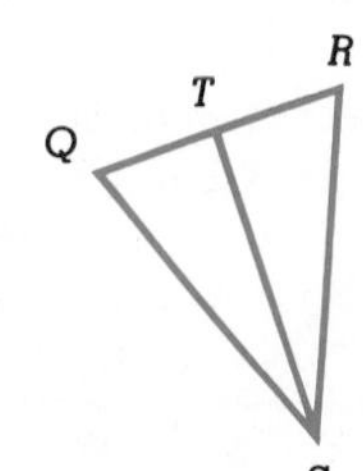

1. $\dfrac{HG}{TS} = \dfrac{EF}{QR}$ yes

2. $\dfrac{TS}{HG} = \dfrac{RQ}{FG}$ no

3. $\dfrac{TS}{HG} = \dfrac{SQ}{GE}$ yes

4. $\dfrac{FG}{RS} = \dfrac{HG}{TS}$ yes

5. $\dfrac{FE}{RQ} = \dfrac{TS}{HG}$ no

6. $\dfrac{ST}{QS} = \dfrac{GH}{EG}$ yes

In the figure at the right, $\triangle ABC \sim \triangle PQR$. Also, $\overline{BD}$ is an altitude of $\triangle ABC$, and $\overline{QS}$ is an altitude of $\triangle PQR$. Determine whether or *not* each of the following *must be* true.

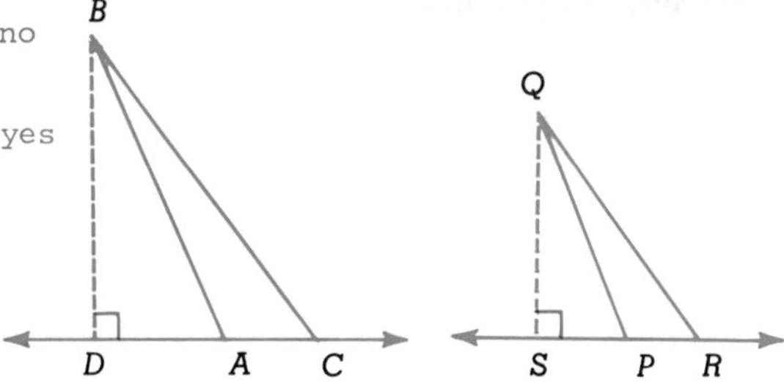

7. $\frac{BD}{QS} = \frac{AB}{PQ}$ yes
8. $\frac{AD}{PS} = \frac{QR}{BC}$ no
9. $\frac{QP}{AB} = \frac{BD}{QS}$ no
10. $\frac{QR}{BC} = \frac{QS}{BD}$ yes
11. $\frac{BD}{QS} = \frac{AC}{PR}$ yes
12. $\frac{AB}{BD} = \frac{PQ}{QS}$ yes

For answers to exercises 1-2, see the Teacher's Guide.

Written **In the figure, $\triangle TVX \sim \triangle LMO$.**

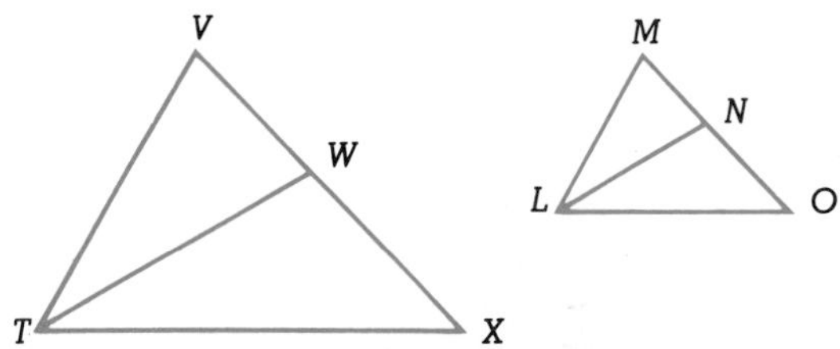

1. Suppose $\overline{WT}$ bisects $\angle VTX$, and $\overline{NL}$ bisects $\angle MLO$. State eight different proportions that follow from this information.
2. Suppose $\overline{TW}$ is a median of $\triangle TVX$, and $\overline{LN}$ is a median of $\triangle LMO$. State eight different proportions that follow from this information.

In the figure, $\triangle WXY \sim \triangle JKL$, $\overline{XZ}$ is a median for $\triangle WYZ$, and $\overline{KM}$ is a median for $\triangle JKL$. Use the given information to find each of the following.

3. $KM = 3$; $XZ = 4$
   $KL = 6$; $XY = ■$ 8
4. $XZ = ■$; $KM = 4$
   $WY = 10$; $JL = 8$ 5

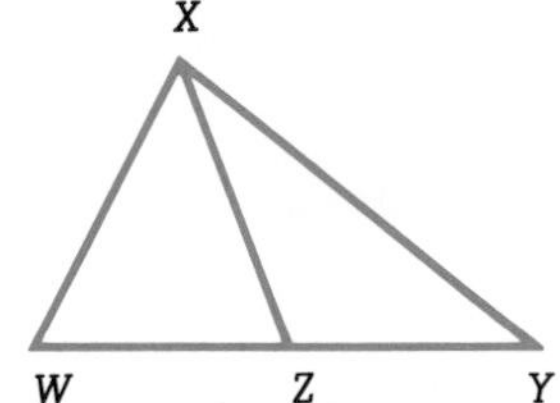

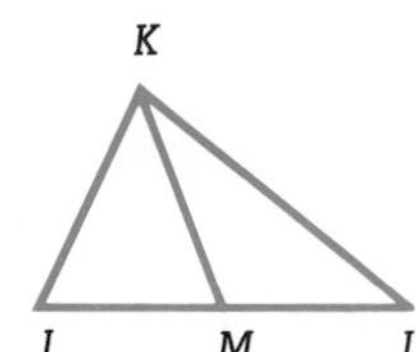

Solve each problem.

5. Suppose $\triangle PQR \sim \triangle ABC$. If $PR = 1.8$, $AC = 1.2$, and the measure of the perimeter of $\triangle ABC$ is 3.4, find the measure of the perimeter of $\triangle PQR$. 5.1
6. Suppose $\triangle LMN \sim \triangle XYZ$. If the perimeter of $\triangle LMN$ measures 7.6, $LM = 1.0$, $MN = 5.8$, and $XY = 2.7$, find XZ. 2.16
7. The perimeters of two equilateral triangles measure 18.0 and 41.4. Suppose an altitude of the first triangle measures 5.2. Find the measure of the altitude of the second triangle. 11.96
8. The perimeters of two similar triangles measure 51.3 and 27.0. Suppose an angle bisector of the first triangle measures 17.1. Find the measure of the corresponding angle bisector in the second triangle. 9
9. Plan a proof for Theorem 8–15.
10. Prove Theorem 8–15.
11. Plan a proof for Theorem 8–16.
12. Prove Theorem 8–17.

For answers to exercises 9-12, see the Teacher's Guide.

8–7 Using Similarity

Objective: to use properties of similarity in problem-solving situations

Properties of similar triangles can be used to solve practical problems such as the following.

> Jeane Johnston measured the height of an oak tree by placing a mirror a short distance from the tree, on a level surface, and facing up. She stood where she could see the top of the tree in the mirror. The mirror was 6 feet from the tree. Jeane was $\frac{1}{2}$ foot from the mirror and her eyes were 5 feet from the ground. A beam of light forms the same angle with a mirror as its reflection. Find the height of the tree.

The problem asks for the height of the tree. Let x stand for the measure of the height.

Define a variable.

Make a drawing.

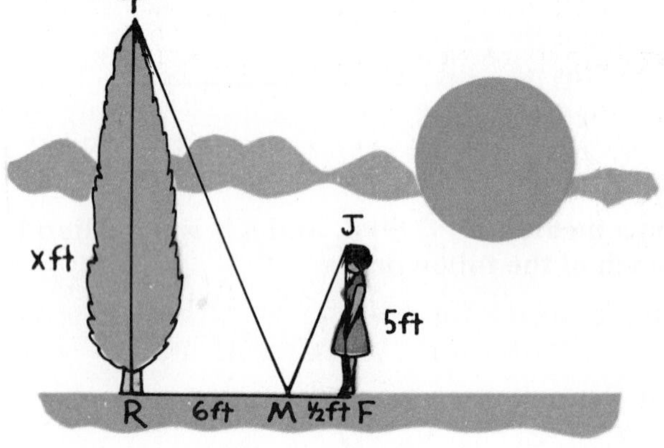

Notice the two triangles in the drawing. The angles of reflection, $\angle TMR$ and $\angle JMF$, are congruent.

Assume that Jeane and the tree are both perpendicular to the ground. Also, $\angle TMR \cong \angle JMF$ since they represent the angles formed by a beam of light and its reflection. Thus, $\triangle TMR \sim \triangle JMF$ by AA Similarity and the measures of corresponding sides are proportional.

Write a proportion.

$$\frac{TR}{JF} = \frac{RM}{FM}$$

$$\frac{x}{5} = \frac{6}{\frac{1}{2}}$$

Solve the proportion.

$$\frac{1}{2}x = 30$$

$$x = 2 \cdot 30 \text{ or } 60$$

The tree is 60 feet tall.

Answer the problem.

1. **Define a variable.**
2. **Make a drawing.**
3. **Write a proportion.**
4. **Solve the proportion.**
5. **Answer the problem.**

Problem Solving Procedure for Proportions

example

1 **A triangle is made from a 12-inch length of metal. The piece of metal tapers from 8 inches wide to a point. Find the width of the tapered metal for a length of 15 inches.**

Point out how helpful it is to draw a diagram to analyze a problem.

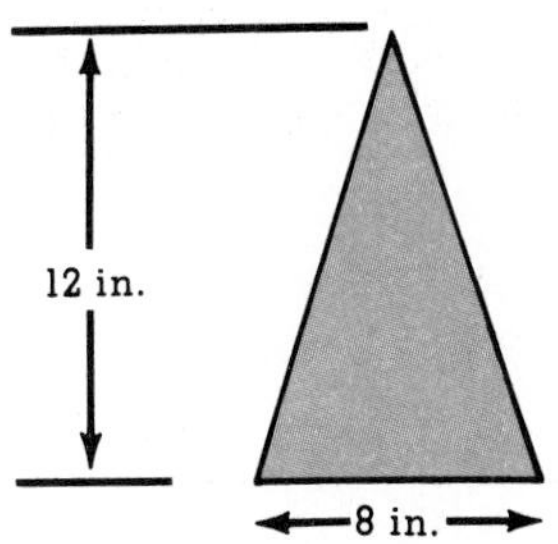

Let x stand for the width of the metal for a length of 15 inches.

Define a variable.

Make a drawing.

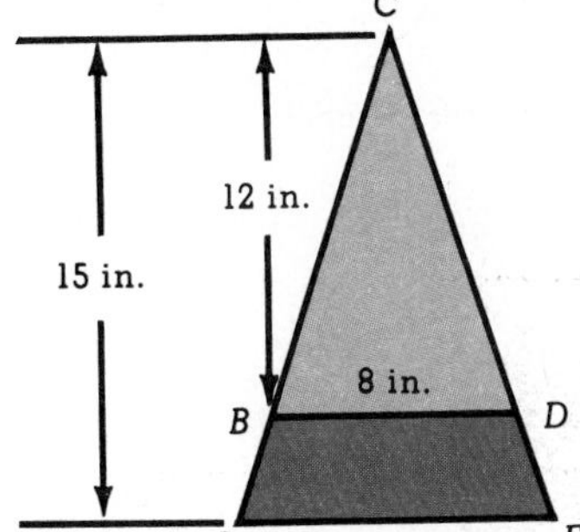

Assume $\overline{BD} \parallel \overline{AE}$. Thus, $\triangle BCD \sim \triangle ACE$. By Theorem 8–15, the measures of corresponding altitudes of similar triangles are proportional to the measures of corresponding sides.

Write a proportion.

$$\frac{AE}{BD} = \frac{\text{altitude of } \triangle ACE}{\text{altitude of } \triangle BCD}$$

$$\frac{x}{8} = \frac{15}{12}$$

Solve the proportion.

$$12x = 120$$

$$x = 10$$

The width of the tapered metal is 10 inches.

Answer the problem.

example

2 **A hypsometer shown at the right can be used to measure the height of a tree. Sight through the straw to the top of the tree. Note where the free-hanging string crosses the scale. Suppose Gene Pulski used the readings shown. His eye was 167 cm from the ground, and he was 15 m, or 1500 cm, from the tree. Find the height of the tree.**

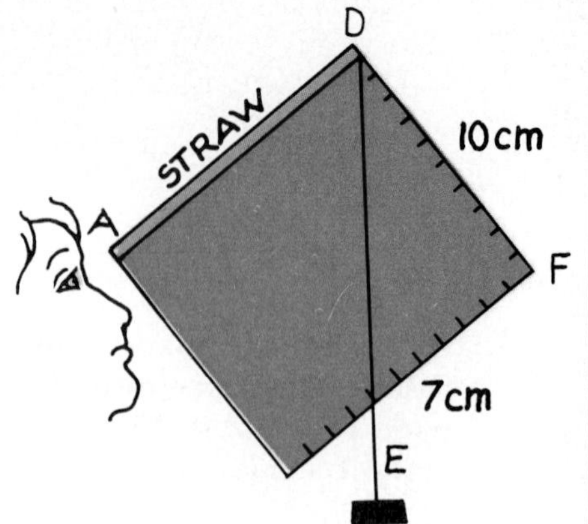

Let x stand for the measure of the distance from eye level to the tip of the tree. *Define a variable.*

Make a drawing.

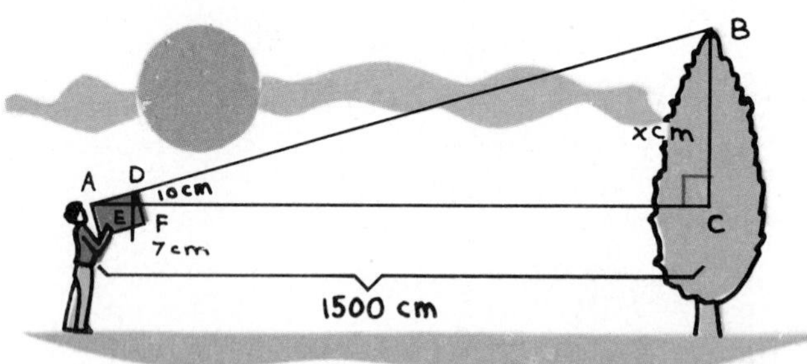

First, assume that $\angle DFE$ and $\angle BCA$ are right angles. $\overline{DE} \parallel \overline{BC}$, and $\overline{AD} \parallel \overline{EF}$.

$\angle FED \cong \angle ADE$	*They are alternate interior angles of $\overline{AD}$ and $\overline{EF}$.*
$\angle ADE \cong \angle ABC$	*They are corresponding angles of $\overline{DE}$ and $\overline{BC}$.*
$\angle FED \cong \angle ABC$	*Angle congruence is transitive.*
$\angle DFE \cong \angle BCA$	*All right angles are congruent.*
$\triangle DEF \sim \triangle ABC$	*AA Similarity*

The measures of corresponding sides of similar triangles are proportional.

$$\frac{BC}{EF} = \frac{AC}{DF}$$

$\frac{\text{vertical}}{\text{horizontal scale}} = \frac{\text{horizontal}}{\text{vertical scale}}$ *Write a proportion.*

$$\frac{x}{7} = \frac{1500}{10}$$

Solve the proportion.

$$10x = 10{,}500$$

$$x = 1050$$

Emphasize this correspondence relationship between the scales of the hypsometer and the triangle's sides.

The tree is 1050 + 167 or 1217 cm tall. *Answer the problem.*

example

3 **Ann Lawson made a camera from a box. Suppose the film is 1.8 cm from the lens and the person being photographed is 360 cm from the camera. Find the height of the image on the film if the height of the person is 260 cm.**

Let h stand for the height of the image on the film. *Define a variable.*

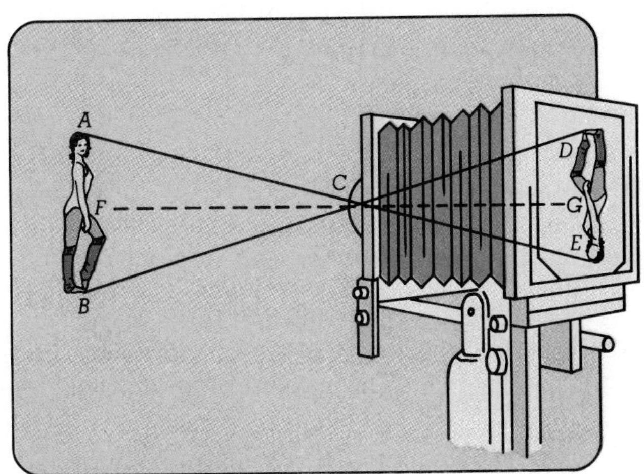

Make a drawing.

The dashed lines are the altitudes of $\triangle ABC$ and $\triangle EDC$.

Assume that $\overline{AB} \parallel \overline{DE}$.

$\angle ACB \cong \angle ECD$ — *They are vertical angles of $\overline{AE}$ and $\overline{BD}$.*
$\angle BAC \cong \angle DEC$ — *They are alternate interior*
$\angle ABC \cong \angle EDC$ — *angles of $\overline{AB}$ and $\overline{DE}$.*
$\triangle ABC \sim \triangle EDC$ — *AA Similarity*

The measures of the corresponding altitudes of similar triangles are proportional to the measures of corresponding sides.

$$\frac{AB}{FC} = \frac{ED}{GC}$$

Help students recognize these proportions. *Write a proportion.*

$$\frac{260}{360} = \frac{x}{1.8}$$

Solve the proportion.

$$360x = 468$$
$$x = 1.3$$

The height of the image on the film is 1.3 cm. *Answer the problem.*

EN: Wr: 1-6; AV: Ex: 1-4, Wr: 1-6; p. 275, Wr: 4-12 evens

exercises

FN: Ex: 1-4, Wr: 1-6; p. 275, Wr: 7-10

Exploratory Answer each of the following.

1. A triangle is made from an 8 cm length of metal. The piece of metal tapers from 4 cm wide to a point. Find the width of the tapered metal for a length of 9 cm. 4.5 cm
2. A triangle is made from a 5 cm length of metal. The piece of metal tapers from 3 cm wide to a point. Find the width of the tapered metal for a length of 6 cm. 3.6 cm
3. Elena Rogelio used a hypsometer to measure the height of a chestnut tree. She had a reading of 10 cm on the vertical scale and 5.5 cm on the horizontal scale. She was 20 m from the tree. Elena's eyes are 1.5 m from the ground. Find the height of the tree in meters. 11 + 1.5 = 12.5 m
4. Lamar Presley measured the height of a pecan tree by sighting the top of the tree in a mirror that was a short distance from the tree and facing up. The mirror was 6.0 m from the tree. Lamar was 0.9 m from the mirror and his eyes were 1.8 m from the ground. Find the height of the tree. 12 m

Some students may need help with Exploratory exercise 3 by relating it to Example 2.

Written Answer each of the following.

1. A tower casts a shadow 64 feet long. A 6-foot tall pole near the tower casts a shadow 8 feet long. How tall is the tower? 48 ft
2. A flag pole casts a shadow 3 meters long. A woman near the pole casts a shadow. 0.75 meters long. The woman is 1.5 meters tall. How tall is the flag pole? 6 m
3. Use similar triangles to find the length of the lake. 2.7 mi

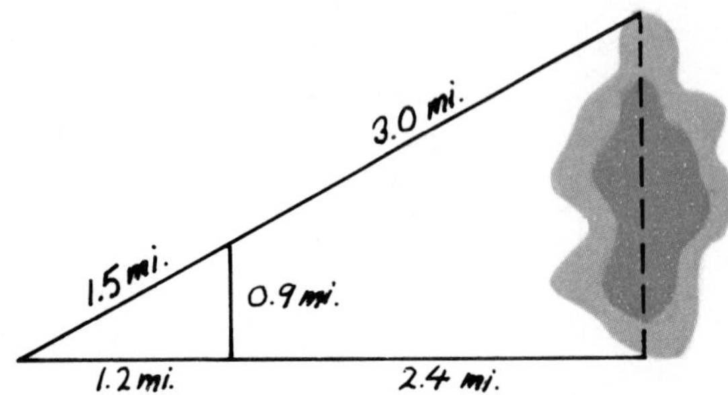

4. Most T.V. screens have similar shapes. The measure of the diagonal is used to give screen size. Suppose the dimensions of a 9-inch screen are $5\frac{1}{2}$ inches by $7\frac{1}{2}$ inches. Find the dimensions of an 18-inch screen. 11 in. by 15 in.
5. Suppose a person is 300 cm from a camera lens, and the film is 1.3 cm from the lens. If the person is 180 cm tall, how tall is his image on the film? 0.78 cm
6. Suppose film is 1.3 cm from a camera lens and can have an image no more than 4.5 cm tall. If the person in front of the lens is 180 cm tall, how far from the lens can he be for a full length picture? 52 cm

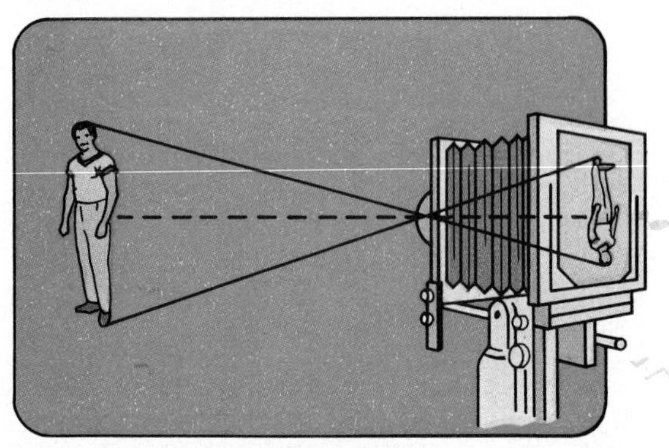

Vocabulary

ratio (249)
proportion (249)
cross products (250)
similar figures (258)

Chapter Summary

1. A ratio is a comparison of two numbers by division. The ratio of a to b is $\frac{a}{b}$ where b is not zero. (249)
2. An equation of the form $\frac{a}{b} = \frac{c}{d}$ which states that two ratios are equal is called a proportion. (249)
3. Equality of Cross Products (Theorem 8–1): For any numbers a and c, and any nonzero numbers b and d, $\frac{a}{b} = \frac{c}{d}$ if and only if $ad = bc$. (250)
4. Properties of Proportion: (254)

For any numbers a, b, c, and d, the following properties hold whenever all denominators are nonzero.	
Theorem 8–2	If $\frac{a}{b} = \frac{c}{d}$, then $\frac{a}{c} = \frac{b}{d}$.
Theorem 8–3	If $\frac{a}{b} = \frac{c}{d}$, then $\frac{b}{a} = \frac{d}{c}$.
Theorem 8–4: Addition Property of Proportions	$\frac{a}{b} = \frac{c}{d}$ if and only if $\frac{a+b}{b} = \frac{c+d}{d}$.
Theorem 8–5: Subtraction Property of Proportions	$\frac{a}{b} = \frac{c}{d}$ if and only if $\frac{a-b}{b} = \frac{c-d}{d}$.
Theorem 8–6: Summation Property of Proportions	$\frac{a}{b} = \frac{c}{d}$ if and only if $\frac{a}{b} = \frac{a+c}{b+d}$ or $\frac{c}{d} = \frac{a+c}{b+d}$.

5. Definition of Similar Polygons: Two polygons are similar if and only if there is a correspondence such that their corresponding angles are congruent and the measures of their corresponding sides are proportional. (258)
6. AA Similarity (Postulate 8–1): If two angles of one triangle are congruent to two corresponding angles of another triangle, then the triangles are similar. (263)
7. SSS Similarity (Theorem 8–7): If there is a correspondence between two triangles so that the measures of their corresponding sides are proportional, then the two triangles are similar. (264)
8. SAS Similarity (Theorem 8–8): If the measures of two sides of a triangle are proportional to the measures of two corresponding sides of another triangle, and the included angles are congruent, then the triangles are similar. (265)
9. Theorem 8–9: If a line intersects two sides of a triangle and separates the sides into segments of proportional lengths, then the line is parallel to the third side. (267)
10. Theorem 8–10: If a line is parallel to one side of a triangle and intersects the other two sides, then it separates the sides into segments of proportional lengths. (268)
11. Theorem 8–11: If a segment has as its endpoints the midpoints of two sides of a triangle, then it is parallel to the third side and its length is one-half the length of the third side. (269)
12. Theorem 8–12: If three parallel lines intersect two transversals, then they divide the transversals proportionally. (269)
13. Theorem 8–13: If three parallel lines cut off congruent segments on one transversal, then they cut off congruent segments on any transversal. (269)
14. Theorem 8–14: If two triangles are similar, then the measures of corresponding perimeters are proportional to the measures of corresponding sides. (272)
15. Theorem 8–15: If two triangles are similar, then the measures of corresponding altitudes are proportional to the measures of corresponding sides. (273)
16. Theorem 8–16: If two triangles are similar, then the measures of corresponding angle bisectors of the triangles are proportional to the measures of corresponding sides. (273)
17. Theorem 8–17: If two triangles are similar, then the measures of corresponding medians are proportional to the measures of corresponding sides. (274)
18. Problem Solving Procedure for Proportions: (277)
    1. Define a variable.
    2. Make a drawing.
    3. Write a proportion.
    4. Solve the proportion.
    5. Answer the problem.

Chapter Review

8–1 Write the cross products for each of the following and solve.

$5 \cdot 3 = x \cdot 2$ **1.** $\frac{5}{x} = \frac{2}{3}$ $7.5 = x$

2. $\frac{x}{9} = \frac{7}{15}$ $x \cdot 15 = 9 \cdot 7$ $x = 4.2$

3. $\frac{1}{x} = \frac{5}{x + 5}$ $1(x + 5) = 5x$ $1.25 = x$

4. $\frac{n + 4}{3} = \frac{5n - 3}{8}$ $(n + 4)8 = 3(5n - 3)$ $5\frac{6}{7} = n$

Solve each of the following.

5. Two gears have a ratio of 5 to 4. If the larger gear has 60 teeth, find the number of teeth in the other gear. $\frac{5}{4} = \frac{60}{x}$ 48 teeth

6. A certain metal is composed of 85% copper and 15% zinc. How many pounds of copper are there in 25 pounds of the metal? $\frac{x}{25} = \frac{85}{100}$ 21.25 pounds

8–2 Determine whether each of the following is true or false.

7. If $\frac{a}{b} = \frac{c}{d}$, then $\frac{a}{b} = \frac{d}{c}$. false

8. If $\frac{a}{b} = \frac{c}{d}$, then $\frac{a + b}{b} = \frac{c + d}{d}$. true

Prove each of the following. For answers to exercises 9-10, see the Teacher's Guide.

9. Prove that for any numbers, a, b, c, and d, if $\frac{a}{b} = \frac{c}{d}$, then $\frac{a - b}{c - d} = \frac{b}{d}$ whenever all denominators are nonzero.

10. Prove that for any numbers a, b, c, and d, if $\frac{a + c}{b + d} = \frac{a}{b}$, then $\frac{a}{b} = \frac{c}{d}$ whenever all denominators are nonzero.

8–3 For each of the following, write *yes* or *no*. Then explain your answer.

11. All congruent triangles are similar. yes

12. All similar triangles are congruent. no

For reasons to exercises 11-12, see the Teacher's Guide.

For the following, find the values of *x* and *y*.

13. $\square QRST \sim \square MNOP$ x = 9 y = 30

14. $\triangle ABC \sim \triangle GFE$ x = 8 y = 10

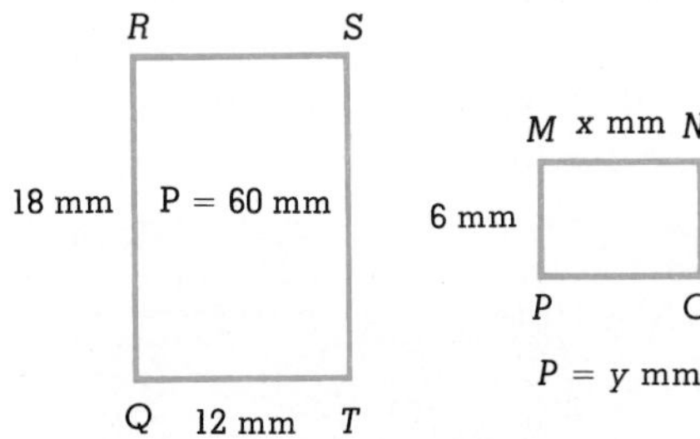

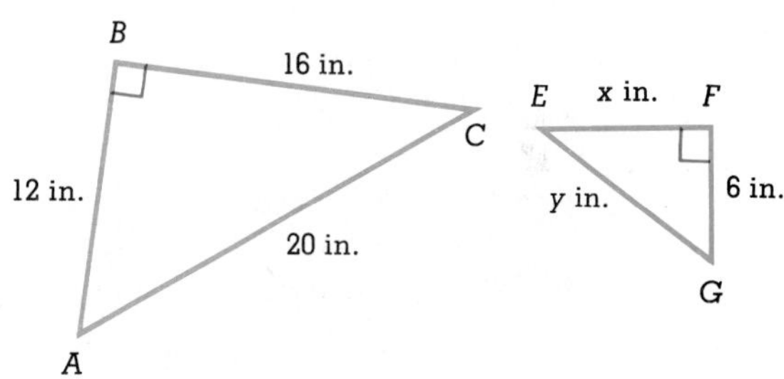

For answers to exercises 15-16, see the Teacher's Guide.

Prove each of the following.

15. Given: $\frac{PR}{QS} = \frac{RS}{QP}$, $\overline{QR} \parallel \overline{PS}$, isosceles trapezoid $PQRS$

Prove: $\triangle PQR \sim \triangle SRQ$

16. Given: $\overline{QR} \parallel \overline{PS}$

Prove: $\frac{QT}{TS} = \frac{TR}{PT}$

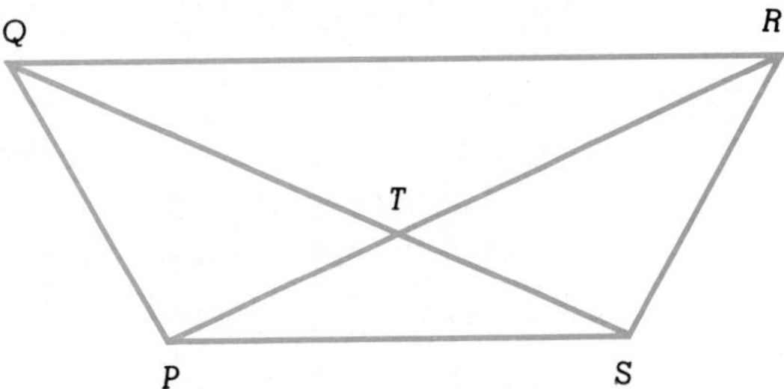

8–5 For each of the following, determine whether or *not* $\overline{BD} \parallel \overline{AE}$. Write *yes* or *no*.

17. $CB = 18$
$AC = 28$
$DE = 5$
$CE = 14$
$\frac{10}{18} \stackrel{?}{=} \frac{5}{9}$ yes

18. $EC = 48$
$BA = 4$
$CD = 34$
$CA = 16$
$\frac{4}{12} \stackrel{?}{=} \frac{14}{34}$ no

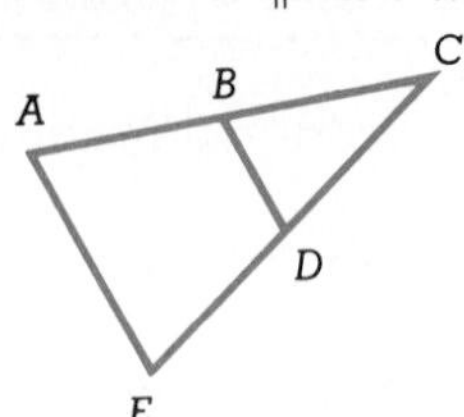

Use the figure and the given information to find the value of *x*.

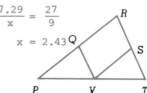

19. $\overline{SV} \parallel \overline{PR}$
$TS = 5 + x$
$TV = 8 + x$ $\frac{8 + x}{4} = \frac{5 + x}{3}$
$VP = 4$
$SR = 3$ $4 = x$

20. $\overline{RT} \parallel \overline{QV}$ $\frac{7.29}{x} = \frac{27}{9}$
$TV = 7.29$
$PV = x$ $x = 2.43$
$PQ = 9$
$QR = 27$

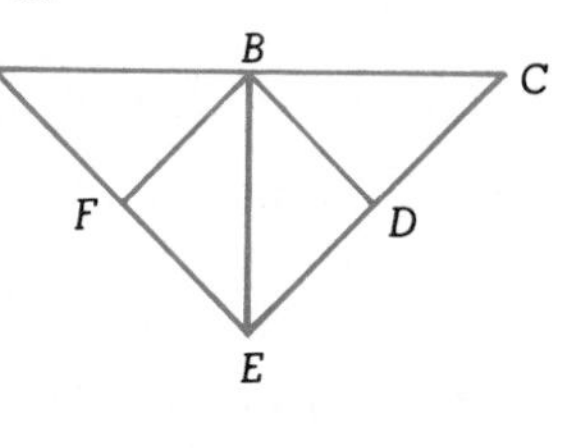

8–6 Use the figure and the given information to find the value of *x*.

21. $\triangle ABE \sim \triangle AEC$
$\overline{BE}$ bisects $\angle AEC$.
$\overline{BF}$ bisects $\angle ABE$.
$AB = 4$
$FB = 3$ $\frac{4}{x} = \frac{3}{4}$
$AE = x$
$EB = 4$ $5\frac{1}{3} = x$

22. $\triangle CEA \sim \triangle CBE$
B is the midpoint of $\overline{AC}$.
$\overline{BD}$ is a median of $\triangle EBC$.
$BE = x + 3$
$BD = 4$ $\frac{x + 3}{4} = \frac{6}{5}$
$CE = 6$
$CB = 5$ $x = 1.8$

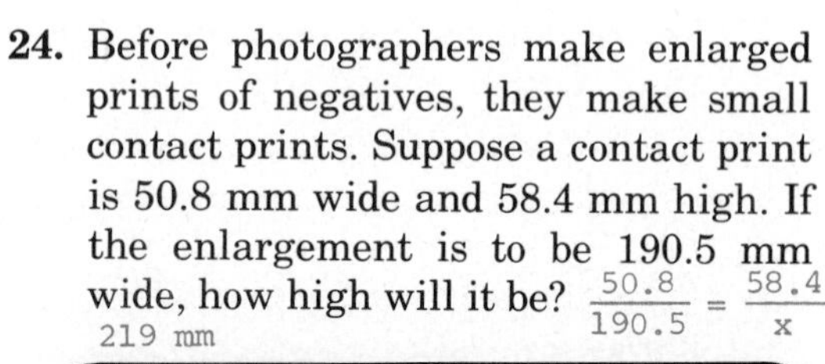

8–7 Answer each of the following.

23. A light pole casts a shadow 42 feet long. A man standing next to the pole casts a shadow 12 feet long. If the man is $5\frac{3}{4}$ feet tall, how tall is the light pole?
$\frac{x}{5.75} = \frac{42}{12}$ 20.125 ft

24. Before photographers make enlarged prints of negatives, they make small contact prints. Suppose a contact print is 50.8 mm wide and 58.4 mm high. If the enlargement is to be 190.5 mm wide, how high will it be? $\frac{50.8}{190.5} = \frac{58.4}{x}$
219 mm

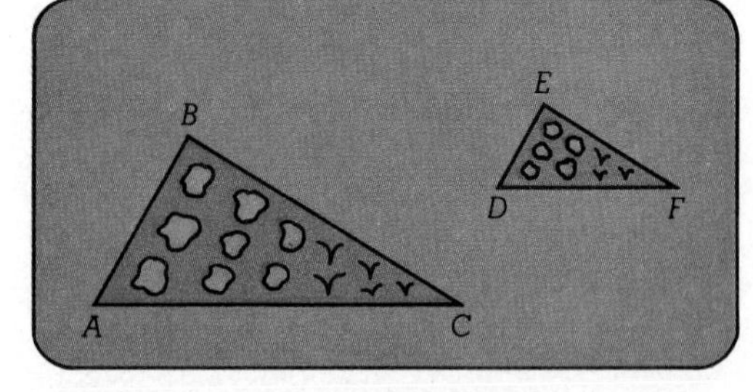

25. An attic window has a triangular shape as shown by $\triangle ACE$. A crossbar $\overline{BD}$ is parallel to the base $\overline{AE}$. Also, B and D are midpoints of their respective sides. The crossbar has a length of $3\frac{1}{2}$ feet. What is the length of the base $\overline{AE}$? 7 ft

26. Two gardens are shaped like similar triangles. The perimeter of the larger garden is 10.5 m and the perimeter of the smaller garden is 5.6 m. If one side of the larger garden is 3.6 m long, find the measure of the corresponding side of the smaller garden. 1.92 m

Chapter Test

Solve each proportion.

1. $\frac{x}{28} = \frac{60}{16}$ 105
2. $\frac{15}{33} = \frac{50}{x}$ 110
3. $\frac{1}{15} = \frac{x}{7}$ $\frac{7}{15}$
4. $\frac{5}{5x + 4} = \frac{2}{3}$ $\frac{7}{10}$
5. $\frac{21}{1 - x} = \frac{7}{x}$ $\frac{1}{4}$
6. $\frac{x - 1}{5 - x} = \frac{3}{5}$ $2\frac{1}{2}$

Use the figure at the right and the given information to find the value of x.

7. $\triangle RWP \sim \triangle VST$
   $PW = x$
   $QW = 1$
   $SU = 5$
   $ST = x + 5$
   $\frac{x}{x + 5} = \frac{1}{5}$
   $x = 1\frac{1}{4}$

8. $\triangle WRS \sim \triangle VUS$
   $SW = 3$
   $RS = 1\frac{1}{3}$
   $SU = x + \frac{2}{3}$
   $SV = 2$
   $\frac{3}{2} = \frac{1\frac{1}{3}}{x + \frac{2}{3}}$
   $x = \frac{2}{9}$

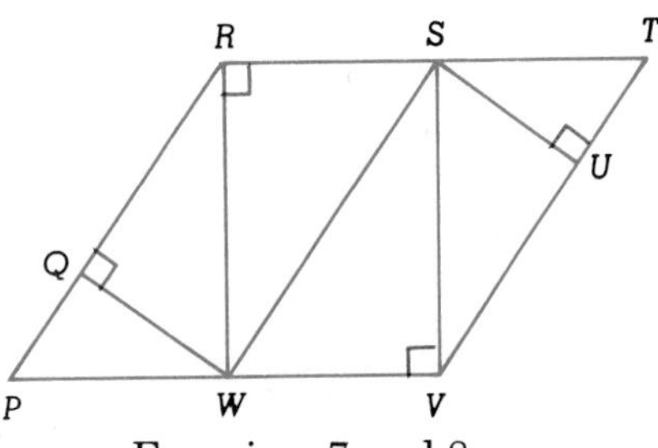

Exercises 7 and 8

Prove each of the following.

9. **Given:** $\triangle ABC \sim \triangle RSP$
   D is the midpoint of $\overline{AC}$.
   Q is the midpoint of $\overline{PR}$.
   $\overline{TP}$ bisects $\angle SPQ$.
   $\overline{EC}$ bisects $\angle BCD$.
   Prove: $\frac{QT}{DE} = \frac{SP}{BC}$

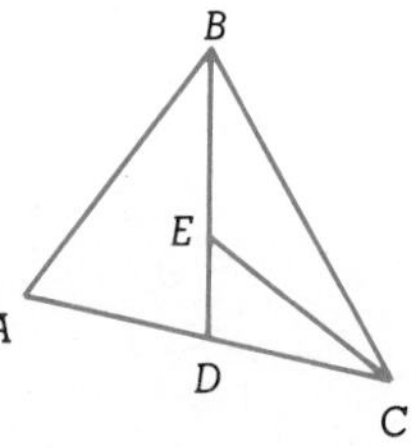

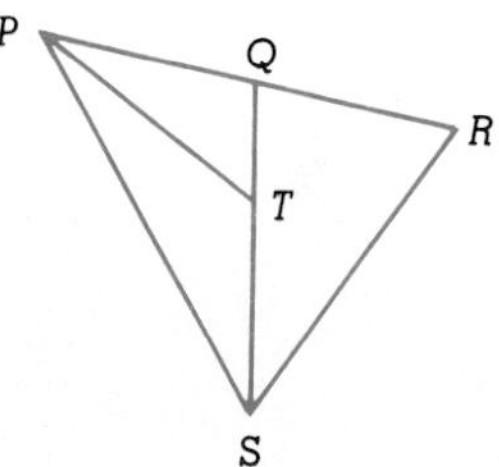

Exercise 9

For answers to exercises 9-10, see the Teacher's Guide.

10. If two triangles are similar, then the measures of corresponding altitudes are proportional to the measures of corresponding perimeters.

Solve each of the following.

11. Use similar triangles to find the distance AB across the river. $\frac{48}{0.4} = \frac{x}{0.3}$ 36 mi

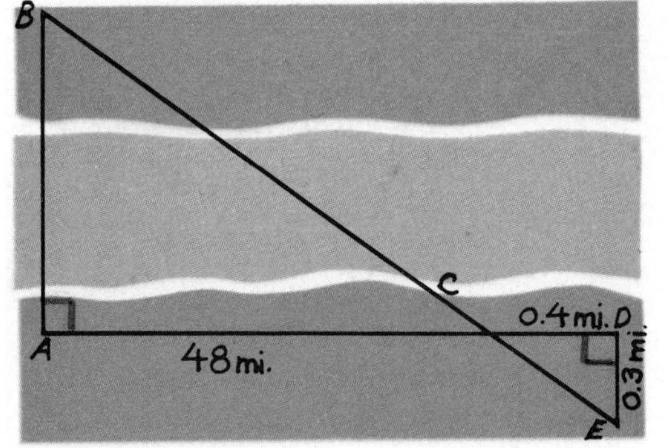

12. Fritz Gundlach measured the height of a building by sighting the top of the building in a mirror that was on the ground and facing up. The mirror was $17\frac{1}{2}$ ft from the building and Fritz was $2\frac{5}{8}$ ft from the mirror. If Fritz's eyes were 6 ft from the ground, how tall is the building? $\frac{2\frac{5}{8}}{17\frac{1}{2}} = \frac{6}{x}$
    40 ft

chapter

9 Right Triangles

The part of a sundial that casts the shadow has a triangular shape. Its construction is based on several right triangles that represent its position with respect to the sun.

Objectives: to find the square and square root of a number, to simplify square roots, to identify rational and irrational roots, to find decimal approximations of roots using a table

9–1 Square Roots

Suppose $\triangle ABD \sim \triangle BCD$ in the figure at the right. Then, the following proportion can be written.

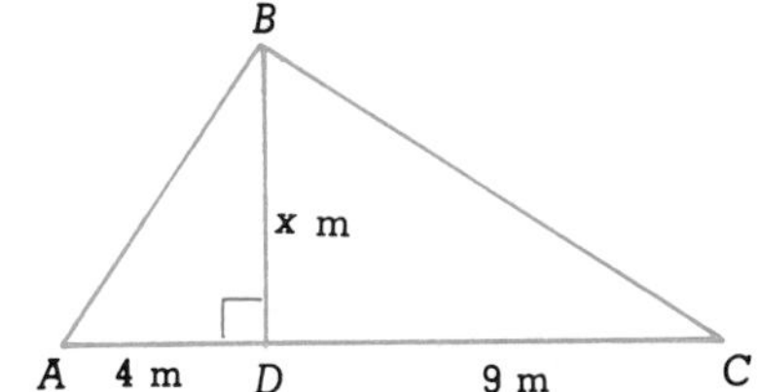

$$\frac{DC}{BD} = \frac{BD}{DA}$$

To find the value of x, make the appropriate substitutions in the proportion.

$$\frac{9}{x} = \frac{x}{4}$$

$DC = 9$, $BD = x$, $DA = 4$

Then, cross multiply.

$$x \cdot x = 9 \cdot 4$$
$$x^2 = 36$$

Squaring a number means using that number as a factor two times. The inverse of squaring is finding the **square root.** To find the square root of 36, you must find two equal factors whose product is 36.

Since 6 times 6 is 36, one square root of 36 is 6. Since $^-6$ times $^-6$ is 36, another square root of 36 is $^-6$.

What is the value of x in the problem above?

Since x represents a distance measure, only the nonnegative or principal square root or 6 has meaning.

For any numbers a and b, if $a^2 = b$, then a is a square root of b.

Definition of Square Root

The symbol $\sqrt{\ }$, called a **radical sign,** indicates a nonnegative square root. The expression under the radical sign is called the **radicand.** Emphasize that the principal square root is nonnegative.

$\sqrt{36} = 6$ — *$\sqrt{36}$ indicates the principal, or nonnegative, square root of 36.*

$^-\sqrt{36} = {^-6}$ — *$^-\sqrt{36}$ indicates the negative square root of 36.*

$\pm\sqrt{36} = \pm 6$ — *$\pm\sqrt{36}$ indicates both square roots of 36.*

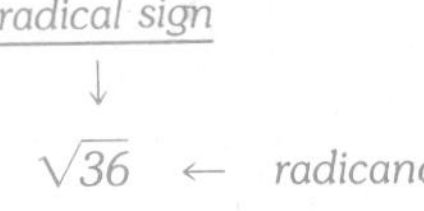

examples

1 Find $\sqrt{49}$.

Since $7^2 = 49$, it follows that $\sqrt{49} = 7$.

2 Find $^-\sqrt{100}$.

Since the square root of 100 is 10, it follows that $^-\sqrt{100} = {^-10}$.

To simplify a square root such as $\sqrt{196}$, find the square root of any perfect square factor of the radicand. Use the prime factorization of 196 to do this.

Use this opportunity to review prime factorization.

$$\begin{aligned}\sqrt{196} &= \sqrt{2 \cdot 2 \cdot 7 \cdot 7} && \textit{Find the prime factorization of 196.}\\ &= \sqrt{2^2 \cdot 7^2}\\ &= \sqrt{2^2} \cdot \sqrt{7^2}\\ &= 2 \cdot 7 \text{ or } 14 && \textbf{Check: } 14^2 = 196\end{aligned}$$

An important property of square roots was used to simplify $\sqrt{196}$.

Postulate 9–1 Product Property of Square Roots

For any nonnegative numbers a and b, $\sqrt{ab} = \sqrt{a} \cdot \sqrt{b}$.

Point out that $\sqrt{(-6)(-7)} \neq \sqrt{-6} \cdot \sqrt{-7}$.

A similar property for quotients of square roots also can be used to simplify square roots.

Postulate 9–2 Quotient Property of Square Roots

For any nonnegative numbers a and b with $b \neq 0$, $\sqrt{\frac{a}{b}} = \frac{\sqrt{a}}{\sqrt{b}}$.

examples

3 **Simplify $\sqrt{300}$.**

$$\begin{aligned}\sqrt{300} &= \sqrt{2 \cdot 2 \cdot 3 \cdot 5 \cdot 5} && \textit{Find the prime factorization of 300.}\\ &= \sqrt{2^2 \cdot 3 \cdot 5^2}\\ &= \sqrt{2^2} \cdot \sqrt{3} \cdot \sqrt{5^2} && \textit{Use the product property of square roots.}\\ &= 2 \cdot \sqrt{3} \cdot 5\\ &= 10\sqrt{3}\end{aligned}$$

Check: $(10\sqrt{3})^2 = 100 \cdot 3$ or 300

4 **Simplify $\sqrt{\frac{16}{9}}$.**

$$\begin{aligned}\sqrt{\frac{16}{9}} &= \frac{\sqrt{16}}{\sqrt{9}} && \textit{Use the quotient property of square roots.}\\ &= \frac{4}{3}\end{aligned}$$

Check: $\left(\frac{4}{3}\right)^2 = \frac{16}{9}$

The method used to simplify $\frac{\sqrt{5}}{\sqrt{2}}$ is called **rationalizing the denominator.** Notice that the denominator becomes a rational number.

$$\frac{\sqrt{5}}{\sqrt{2}} = \frac{\sqrt{5}}{\sqrt{2}} \cdot \frac{\sqrt{2}}{\sqrt{2}}$$

Notice that $\frac{\sqrt{2}}{\sqrt{2}}$ is equal to 1.

$$= \frac{\sqrt{10}}{\sqrt{4}}$$

$$= \frac{\sqrt{10}}{2}$$

A square root is said to be simplified when the following conditions are met.

1. The radicand has no perfect square factor other than 1.
2. The radicand does *not* contain a fraction.
3. No radical appears in the denominator of a fraction.

Some numbers such as 5 and 13 have square roots that are *not* integers or rational numbers. These square roots are **irrational numbers.**

To compute with irrational numbers, you often use decimal approximations. Tables of square roots give approximations.

Such a table is given on page 548.

Emphasize that these are approximations.

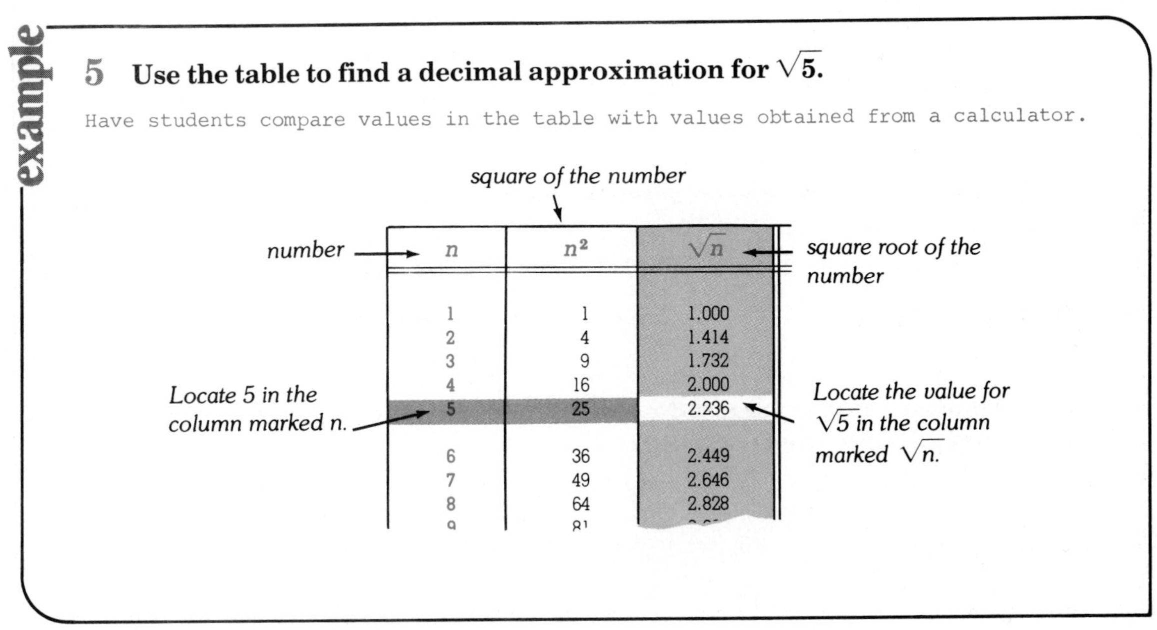
example
5 Use the table to find a decimal approximation for √5.
Have students compare values in the table with values obtained from a calculator.
square of the number
number
square root of the number
Locate 5 in the column marked n.
Locate the value for √5 in the column marked √n.

n	n^2	$\sqrt{n}$
1	1	1.000
2	4	1.414
3	9	1.732
4	16	2.000
5	25	2.236
6	36	2.449
7	49	2.646
8	64	2.828

exercises

Exploratory **Find the square of each number.**

1. 8 64 **2.** 12 144 **3.** $^-7$ 49 **4.** $^-11$ 121 **5.** 0.2 0.04

6. 0.1 0.01 **7.** $\frac{2}{5}$ $\frac{4}{25}$ **8.** $\frac{4}{9}$ $\frac{16}{81}$ **9.** 1.3 1.69 **10.** $^-2.5$ 6.25

Simplify.

11. $\sqrt{64}$ 8 **12.** $^-\sqrt{144}$ -12 **13.** $^-\sqrt{49}$ -7 **14.** $\sqrt{49}$ 7 **15.** $\sqrt{0.04}$ 0.2

16. $\sqrt{0.01}$ 0.1 **17.** $\pm\sqrt{1.69}$ ±1.3 **18.** $\sqrt{6.25}$ 2.5 **19.** $\sqrt{\frac{4}{25}}$ $\frac{2}{5}$ **20.** $\pm\sqrt{\frac{16}{81}}$ $\pm\frac{4}{9}$

Written **Write the principal square root of each of the following.**

1. 1 1 **2.** 100 10 **3.** 0.25 0.5 **4.** 1.21 1.1 **5.** 0.09 0.3

6. $\frac{16}{121}$ $\frac{4}{11}$ **7.** $\frac{49}{4}$ $\frac{7}{2}$ **8.** 0.0025 0.05 **9.** 169 13 **10.** 16,900 130

Simplify each of the following and determine whether the answer is a rational number or an irrational number.

11. $\sqrt{256}$ 16, r **12.** $\sqrt{361}$ 19, r **13.** $\sqrt{900}$ 30, r **14.** $\sqrt{484}$ 22, r **15.** $\sqrt{80}$ $4\sqrt{5}$, irr

16. $\sqrt{72}$ $6\sqrt{2}$, irr **17.** $\sqrt{75}$ $5\sqrt{3}$, irr **18.** $\sqrt{54}$ $3\sqrt{6}$, irr **19.** $\sqrt{5}\sqrt{15}$ $5\sqrt{3}$, irr **20.** $\sqrt{8}\sqrt{2}$ 4, r

21. $\sqrt{\frac{5}{4}}$ $\frac{\sqrt{5}}{2}$, irr **22.** $\sqrt{\frac{2}{9}}$ $\frac{\sqrt{2}}{3}$, irr **23.** $\sqrt{\frac{1}{8}}$ $\frac{\sqrt{2}}{4}$, irr **24.** $\frac{1}{\sqrt{2}}$ $\frac{\sqrt{2}}{2}$, irr **25.** $\frac{5}{\sqrt{3}}$ $\frac{5\sqrt{3}}{3}$, irr

26. $\sqrt{\frac{1}{3}}$ $\frac{\sqrt{3}}{3}$, irr **27.** $\sqrt{\frac{5}{3}}$ $\frac{\sqrt{15}}{3}$, irr **28.** $\sqrt{\frac{7}{2}}$ $\frac{\sqrt{14}}{2}$, irr **29.** $\frac{\sqrt{21}}{\sqrt{14}}$ $\frac{\sqrt{6}}{2}$, irr **30.** $\sqrt{\frac{2}{3}}\sqrt{\frac{5}{2}}$ $\frac{\sqrt{15}}{3}$, irr

Find the approximate value of each of the following. Use the table of Squares and Approximate Square Roots on page 548.

31. $\sqrt{76}$ 8.718 **32.** $\sqrt{21}$ 4.583 **33.** $\sqrt{17}$ 4.123 **34.** $\sqrt{61}$ 7.810 **35.** $\sqrt{6} - \sqrt{12}$ -1.015

36. $\sqrt{15} + \sqrt{19}$ 8.232 **37.** $\sqrt{\frac{7}{2}}$ 1.871 **38.** $\sqrt{\frac{5}{3}}$ 1.291 **39.** $\sqrt{200}$ 14.14 **40.** $\sqrt{175}$ 13.230

Solve for x. Approximate the values of x to three decimal places. Use the table of Squares and Approximate Square Roots on page 548.

41. $x^2 - 40 = 0$ ±6.325 **42.** $x^2 = \frac{3}{2}$ ±1.225 **43.** $x^2 + 16 = 64$ ±6.928

44. $100 + x^2 = 121$ ±4.583 **45.** $x^2 + (\sqrt{5})^2 = (\sqrt{30})^2$ ±5 **46.** $(\sqrt{11})^2 + (4)^2 = x^2$ ±5.196

47. $\frac{3}{x} = \frac{x}{12}$ ±6 **48.** $\frac{3}{x} = \frac{x}{7}$ ±4.583 **49.** $\frac{5}{x} = \frac{x}{9}$ ±6.708

Objectives: to find the geometric mean for a pair of numbers, to solve problems using relationships between parts of a right triangle and the altitude

9–2 The Geometric Mean

When the altitude to the hypotenuse of a right triangle is drawn, two smaller triangles are formed. These two triangles are similar to each other, and both are similar to the original triangle.

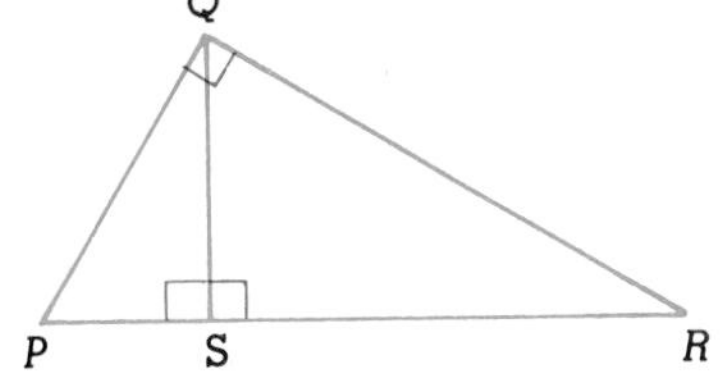

$\triangle PQR \sim \triangle PSQ \sim \triangle QSR$

If an altitude is drawn from the vertex of the right angle to the hypotenuse of a right triangle, then the two triangles formed are similar to the given triangle and to each other.

Theorem 9–1

example

Help students find the corresponding parts in these triangles.

1 Prove Theorem 9–1.

Given: $\angle PQR$ is a right angle.
$\overline{QS}$ is an altitude of right $\triangle PQR$.

Prove: $\triangle PQR \sim \triangle PSQ$
$\triangle PQR \sim \triangle QSR$
$\triangle PSQ \sim \triangle QSR$

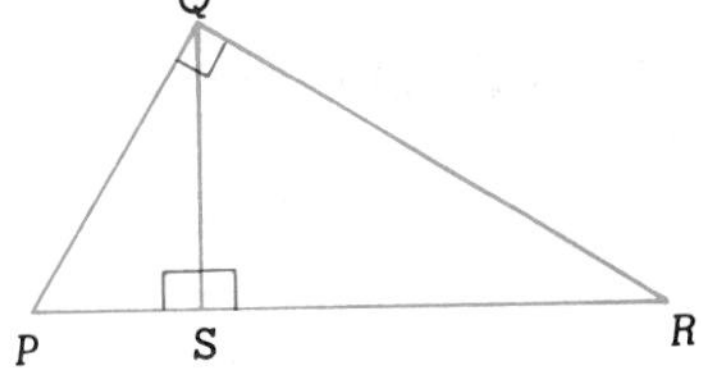

Proof:

STATEMENTS	REASONS
1. $\angle PQR$ is a right angle.	1. Given
2. $\overline{QS}$ is an altitude of right $\triangle PQR$.	2. Given
3. $\overline{QS} \perp \overline{PR}$	3. Definition of Altitude
4. $\angle PSQ$ is a right angle. $\angle QSR$ is a right angle.	4. Definition of Perpendicular
5. $\angle PQR \cong \angle PSQ$ $\angle PQR \cong \angle QSR$ $\angle PSQ \cong \angle QSR$	5. Theorem 3–6: If two angles are right angles, then the angles are congruent.
6. $\angle P \cong \angle P$ $\angle R \cong \angle R$	6. Theorem 3–1: Congruence of angles is reflexive, symmetric, and transitive.
7. $\triangle PQR \sim \triangle PSQ$ $\triangle PQR \sim \triangle QSR$	7. Postulate 8–1: AA Similarity
8. $\angle SQP \cong \angle QRP$	8. Definition of Similar Triangles
9. $\triangle PSQ \sim \triangle QSR$	9. Postulate 8–1: AA Similarity

By Theorem 9–1, the two smaller triangles in the figure at the right are similar. Thus, corresponding sides are proportional, and the following proportion can be written.

$$\frac{4}{6} = \frac{6}{9}$$

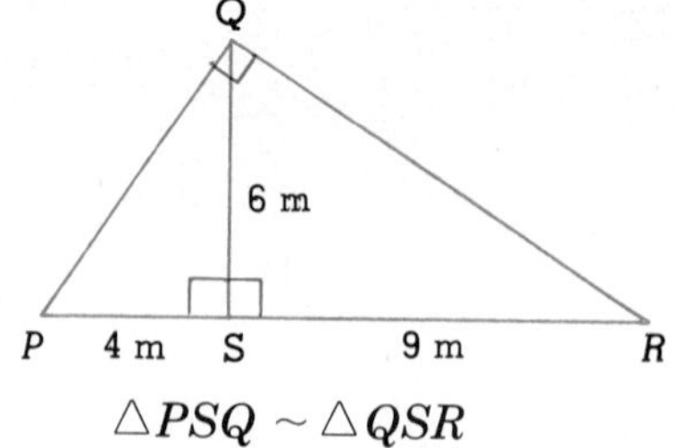

$\triangle PSQ \sim \triangle QSR$

Notice that the denominator of the first fraction is 6 and the numerator of the second fraction also is 6. This number, 6, is the **geometric mean** between 4 and 9. The geometric mean is sometimes called mean proportional.

For any positive numbers a and b, x is the geometric mean between a and b if and only if $\frac{a}{x} = \frac{x}{b}$ and x is positive.

Definition of Geometric Mean

The proportions also can be written $\frac{x}{b} = \frac{a}{x}$.

examples

2 **Find the geometric mean between 4 and 10.**

Let x represent the geometric mean.

$\frac{4}{x} = \frac{x}{10}$ *Definition of geometric mean*

$x^2 = 40$ *Equality of cross products*

$x = \sqrt{40}$ *Definition of square root and the geometric*

$x = 2\sqrt{10}$ *mean is positive*

The geometric mean is $2\sqrt{10}$. In general the solution to $x^2 = 40$ is $\pm 2\sqrt{10}$.

Show that the value of the geometric mean between a and b is $\sqrt{ab}$.

Let x represent the geometric mean.

$\frac{a}{x} = \frac{x}{b}$ *Definition of geometric mean*

$x^2 = ab$ *Equality of cross products*

$x = \sqrt{ab}$ *Definition of square root and the geometric mean is positive*

The proofs of the following theorems are based on the fact that the triangles formed are similar.

The measure of the altitude drawn from the right angle to the hypotenuse of a right triangle is the geometric mean between the measures of the two segments of the hypotenuse.

Theorem 9–2

Students prove this theorem in Written exercise 29.

example

4 **Find the measure of altitude, $\overline{AE}$, in the figure.**

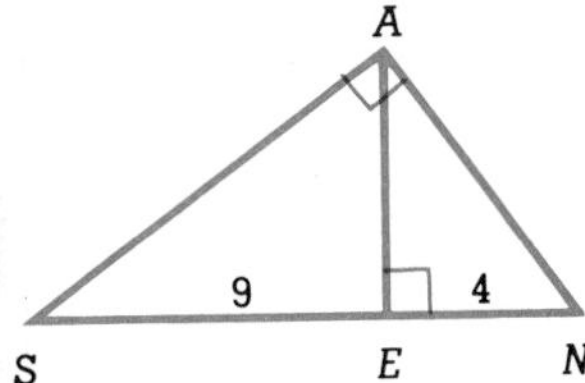

$\frac{SE}{AE} = \frac{AE}{NE}$	*Theorem 9–2*
$\frac{9}{AE} = \frac{AE}{4}$	*Substitution*
$(AE)^2 = 36$	*Equality of cross products.*
$AE = 6$	*Definition of square root and the geometric mean is positive.*

If the altitude is drawn to the hypotenuse of a right triangle, then the measure of a leg of the triangle is the geometric mean between the measure of the hypotenuse and the measure of the segment of the hypotenuse adjacent to that leg.

Theorem 9–3

Students prove this theorem in Written exercise 30.

example

5 **Find the measure of sides *TS* and *SP* in the figure.**

$TP = TO + OP$

Therefore, $TP = 25$.

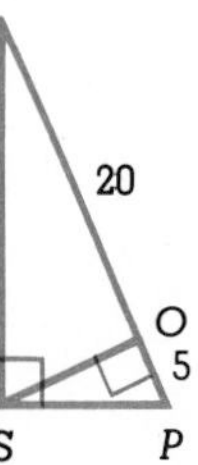

$\frac{OP}{SP} = \frac{SP}{TP}$ and $\frac{TO}{TS} = \frac{TS}{TP}$	*Theorem 9–3*
$\frac{5}{SP} = \frac{SP}{25}$ and $\frac{20}{TS} = \frac{TS}{25}$	*Substitution*
$(SP)^2 = 125$ and $(TS)^2 = 500$	*Equality of cross products*
$SP = 5\sqrt{5}$ and $TS = 10\sqrt{5}$	

EN: Ex: 13-16, Wr: 1-25 odds, 27-30; AV: Ex: 1-15 odds, Wr: 1-25 odds, 28-30; p. 290, Wr: 26-48 evens

exercises

FN: Ex: 1-16, Wr: 1-26; p. 290, Wr: 16-48 evens

Exploratory **Find the geometric mean for each pair of numbers.**

1. 2 and 8 4 **2.** 3 and 12 6 **3.** 2 and 18 6 **4.** 5 and 20 10
5. 9 and 16 12 **6.** 2 and 50 10 **7.** 1 and 36 6 **8.** 16 and 1 4
9. 4 and 4 4 **10.** 2 and 32 8 **11.** 72 and 2 12 **12.** 8 and 8 8
13. 27 and 3 9 **14.** 5 and 45 15 **15.** 16 and 4 8 **16.** 18 and 8 12

Written **Find the geometric mean for each pair of numbers.**

1. 3 and 5 $\sqrt{15}$ **2.** 4 and 6 $2\sqrt{6}$ **3.** 5 and 8 $2\sqrt{10}$ **4.** 2 and 10 $2\sqrt{5}$
5. 24 and 6 12 **6.** 5 and 4 $2\sqrt{5}$ **7.** 12 and 4 $4\sqrt{3}$ **8.** 25 and 4 10
9. 15 and 5 $5\sqrt{3}$ **10.** 8 and 10 $4\sqrt{5}$ **11.** 18 and 3 $3\sqrt{6}$ **12.** 4 and 18 $6\sqrt{2}$
13. $\frac{1}{4}$ and 9 $\frac{3}{2}$ **14.** 4 and $\frac{1}{9}$ $\frac{2}{3}$ **15.** $\frac{2}{5}$ and $\frac{5}{2}$ 1 **16.** $\frac{2}{3}$ and $\frac{1}{3}$ $\frac{\sqrt{2}}{3}$
17. $\frac{1}{4}$ and $\frac{3}{4}$ $\frac{\sqrt{3}}{4}$ **18.** $\frac{2}{3}$ and $\frac{1}{2}$ $\frac{\sqrt{3}}{3}$ **19.** $\frac{1}{2}$ and $\frac{1}{4}$ $\frac{\sqrt{2}}{4}$ **20.** $\frac{1}{3}$ and $\frac{1}{4}$ $\frac{\sqrt{3}}{6}$

Use the figure at the right to answer each of the following. Approximate each answer to three decimal places.

21. Find BD if $AD = 3$ and $DC = 10$. $\sqrt{30} \approx 5.477$
22. Find BD if $AD = 5$ and $DC = 9$. $\sqrt{45} \approx 6.708$
23. Find AB if $AC = 8$ and $AD = 3$. $\sqrt{24} \approx 4.899$
24. Find BD if $DC = 12$ and $AD = 3$. 6
25. Find BC if $AD = 3$ and $DC = 4$. $\sqrt{28} \approx 5.292$
26. Find BA if $DA = 4$ and $DC = 4$. $\sqrt{32} \approx 5.657$

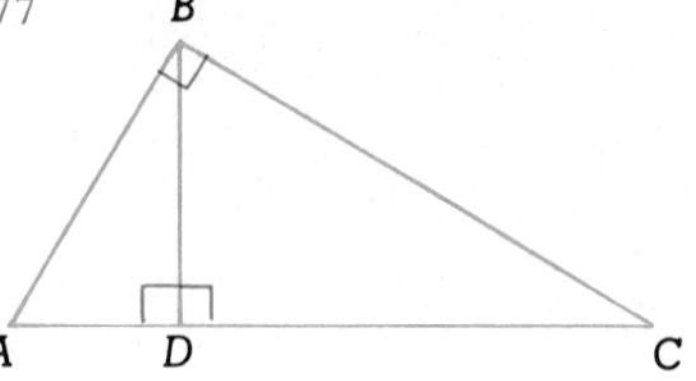

Answer each of the following.

27. **Given:** $VQ = 6$, $QR = 4$
$\overline{RV} \perp \overline{PV}$, $\overline{VQ} \perp \overline{PR}$
Find: PQ, PR, PV, and VR

PQ = 9, PR = 13, VR = $2\sqrt{13}$, PV = $3\sqrt{13}$

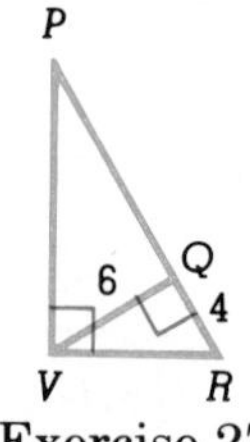

Exercise 27

28. AG = 9.6, GF = 5.4, DG = 7.2, EF = 3.24, CD = 4.32, CG = 5.76, BC = 2.7648

28. **Given:** $\overline{AD} \perp \overline{DF}$, $\overline{DG} \perp \overline{AF}$, $\overline{GE} \perp \overline{DF}$, $\overline{GC} \perp \overline{AD}$, $\overline{CH} \perp \overline{AF}$, $\overline{BH} \perp \overline{AD}$, $\overline{HJ} \perp \overline{CG}$
$AF = 15$, $AD = 12$, $DF = 9$
Find: AG, GF, DG, EF, CD, CG and BC

A calculator is recommended for exercise 28, otherwise large fraction answers will result.

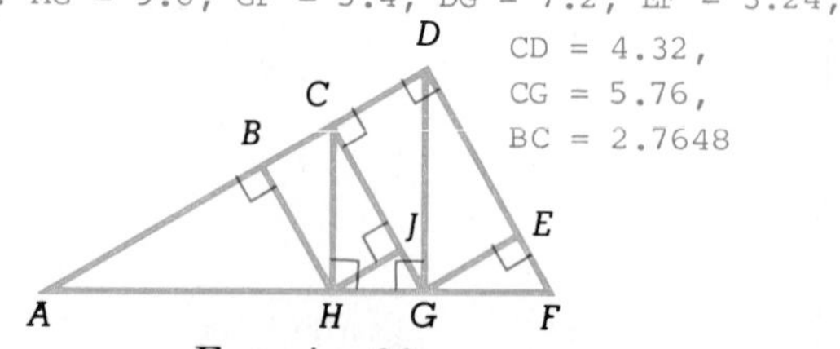

Exercise 28

29. Prove Theorem 9–2. **30.** Prove Theorem 9–3.

For answers to exercises 29-30, see the Teacher's Guide.

Objectives: to recognize Pythagorean Triples, to use the Pythagorean Theorem or its converse as a test for right triangles, to solve problems using the Pythagorean Theorem or its converse

9–3 The Pythagorean Theorem

The following theorem has been studied and used for thousands of years. A Chinese manuscript from about 1000 B.C. illustrates this theorem. It is named after Pythagoras, a Greek mathematician from the sixth century. There are many proofs of the Pythagorean theorem. President Garfield presented his own special proof of the theorem in 1876.

Theorem 9–4
Pythagorean Theorem

If a triangle is a right triangle, then the sum of the squares of the measures of the legs equals the square of the measure of the hypotenuse.

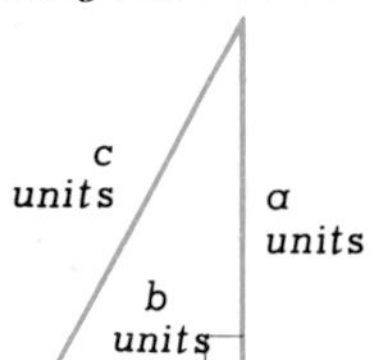

By the Pythagorean Theorem, $a^2 + b^2 = c^2$. A proof of the Pythagorean Theorem follows.

Note, there are many different proofs of the Pythagorean Theorem.

example

1 Prove the Pythagorean Theorem.

Given: $\triangle ABC$ is a right triangle.
Prove: $(BC)^2 + (CA)^2 = (AB)^2$

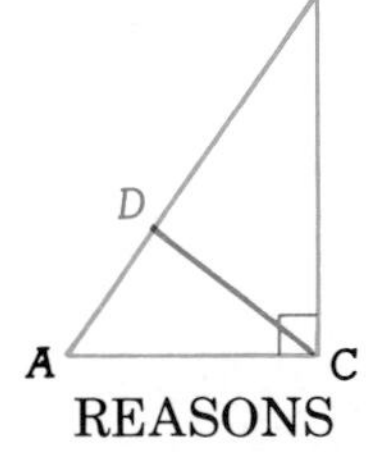

Proof:

STATEMENTS	REASONS
1. Draw altitude $\overline{CD}$.	1. Theorem 6–14: Given a line and a point *not* on the line, there is exactly one line through the point that is perpendicular to the given line.
2. $\triangle ABC$ is a right triangle.	2. Given
3. $\frac{AB}{BC} = \frac{BC}{BD}$, $\frac{AB}{CA} = \frac{CA}{DA}$	3. Theorem 9–3: If the altitude is drawn to the hypotenuse of a right triangle, then the measure of a leg of the triangle is the geometric mean between the measure of the hypotenuse and the measure of the segments of the hypotenuse adjacent to that leg.
4. $(BC)^2 = AB \cdot BD$, $(CA)^2 = AB \cdot DA$	4. Theorem 8–1: Equality of Cross Products
5. $(BC)^2 + (CA)^2 = AB \cdot BD + AB \cdot DA$	5. Postulate 2–7: Addition of Equality
6. $(BC)^2 + (CA)^2 = AB(BD + DA)$	6. Postulate 2–14: Distributive Property
7. $AB = BD + DA$	7. Definition of Between
8. $(BC)^2 + (CA)^2 = (AB)^2$	8. Postulate 2–9: Substitution

If the square of the measure of the longest side of a triangle does *not* equal the sum of the squares of the measures of the other two sides, then the triangle is *not* a right triangle. Suppose $a^2 + b^2 = c^2$ is true for a given triangle. Can you conclude that the triangle is a right triangle? The answer is yes.

The first sentence is the contrapositive of the Pythagorean Theorem. Recall that the contrapositive of a true statement also is a true statement.

Theorem 9–5 Converse of the Pythagorean Theorem

If the sum of the squares of the measures of two sides of a triangle equals the square of the measure of the longest side, then the triangle is a right triangle.

Students prove this theorem in Written exercise 24.

Together, the Pythagorean Theorem and its converse provide a useful test for right triangles.

examples

2 Determine whether or *not* a triangle with sides measuring 11.5 centimeters, 16.1 centimeters, and 20.7 centimeters is a right triangle.

Recall that if the measures of two angles of a triangle are unequal, then the measures of the sides opposite those angles are unequal in the same order. As a result, the hypotenuse of a right triangle is its longest side. Thus, it is only necessary to check one equation.

$$(20.7)^2 \stackrel{?}{=} (16.1)^2 + (11.5)^2$$
$$428.49 \stackrel{?}{=} 259.21 + 132.25$$
$$428.49 \neq 391.46$$

Since the equation is *not* true, the triangle is *not* a right triangle.

3 Determine whether or *not* a triangle with sides measuring 4 inches, $5\frac{1}{3}$ inches, and $6\frac{2}{3}$ inches is a right triangle.

The hypotenuse of a right triangle is its longest side. Thus, it is only necessary to check one equation.

$$\left(6\frac{2}{3}\right)^2 \stackrel{?}{=} (4)^2 + \left(5\frac{1}{3}\right)^2$$
$$\left(\frac{20}{3}\right)^2 \stackrel{?}{=} (4)^2 + \left(\frac{16}{3}\right)^2$$
$$\frac{400}{9} \stackrel{?}{=} 16 + \frac{256}{9}$$
$$\frac{400}{9} = \frac{400}{9}$$

Since the equation is true, the triangle is a right triangle.

Many practical problems can be solved by using the Pythagorean Theorem or its converse.

example

4 **The diagram shows a truss for a roof. The rise of the roof is 9 feet. The run is 18 feet on one part and 12 feet on the other. Find the lengths of both the long rafters and the short rafters, *not* counting the overhang. Round the answer to the nearest foot.**

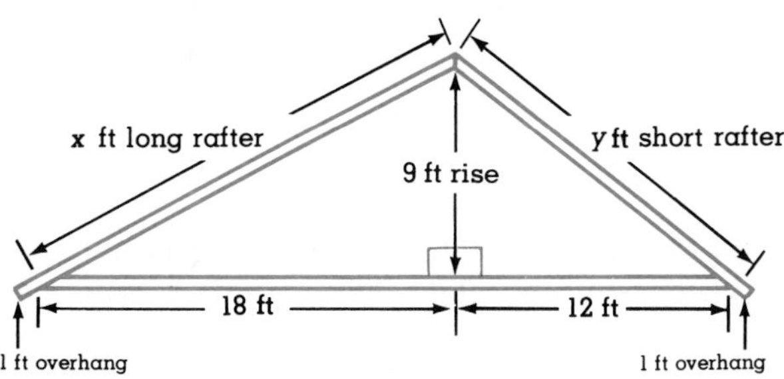

Let x be the measure of the long rafter. Let y be the measure of the short rafter. *Define variables.*

Two right triangles are formed. One measures 18 feet by 9 feet by x feet. The other measures 12 feet by 9 feet by y feet.

$x^2 = 18^2 + 9^2 \qquad y^2 = 12^2 + 9^2$ *Write equations.*

Solve the equations.

$$\begin{aligned} x^2 &= 18^2 + 9^2 \\ x^2 &= 324 + 81 \\ x^2 &= 405 \\ x &= 9\sqrt{5} \\ x &\approx 9 \cdot 2.236 \\ &\approx 20.124 \\ &\approx 20 \end{aligned} \qquad \begin{aligned} y^2 &= 12^2 + 9^2 \\ y^2 &= 144 + 81 \\ y^2 &= 225 \\ y &= 15 \end{aligned}$$

The length of the long rafter is about 20 feet and the short rafter is 15 feet. *Answer the problem.*

EN: Wr: 1-17 odds, 19-23; AV: Ex: 7-12, Wr: 1-17 odds, 19-23; p. 294, Wr: 10-26 evens

exercises

FN: Ex: 1-12, Wr: 1-18; p. 294, Wr: 27-28

Exploratory **Three integers that can be measures for the three sides of a right triangle are called a Pythagorean triple. Determine whether or *not* each of the following is a Pythagorean triple.**

1. 5, 10, 12 no
2. 12, 16, 20 yes
3. 15, 20, 25 yes
4. 24, 32, 40 yes
5. 9, 12, 15 yes
6. 8, 15, 17 yes
7. 3, 4, 5 yes
8. 9, 12, 14 no
9. 30, 40, 50 yes
10. 3, 6, 8 no
11. 20, 21, 29 yes
12. 9, 40, 41 yes

Written **For each of the following, determine whether or *not* it is possible to draw a right triangle with sides of the given measures. Write *yes* or *no*.**

1. 1.6, 3.0, 3.4 yes
2. 2.2, 2.4, 3.3 no
3. 3.87, 4.47, 5.91 no
4. 0.27, 0.36, 0.45 yes
5. $1, \sqrt{2}, \sqrt{3}$ yes
6. $\sqrt{3}, \sqrt{4}, \sqrt{5}$ no
7. $\sqrt{5}, \sqrt{6}, \sqrt{7}$ no
8. $2, 2\frac{1}{3}, 3\frac{2}{3}$ no
9. $2, 2\frac{2}{3}, 3\frac{1}{3}$ yes

For each of the following, find the measure of the hypotenuse of a right triangle with legs of the given measures. Round each nonintegral answer to one decimal place.

10. 5, 12 13 = c
11. 12, 16 20 = c
12. 3, 6 $\sqrt{45} \approx 6.7 \approx c$
13. 5, 8 $\sqrt{89} \approx 9.4 \approx c$
14. 11.2, 10 $15.0 \approx c$
15. 6, 10.3 $11.9 \approx c$

For each of the following, find the value of x. Round each answer to one decimal place.

16. $x \approx 4.9$

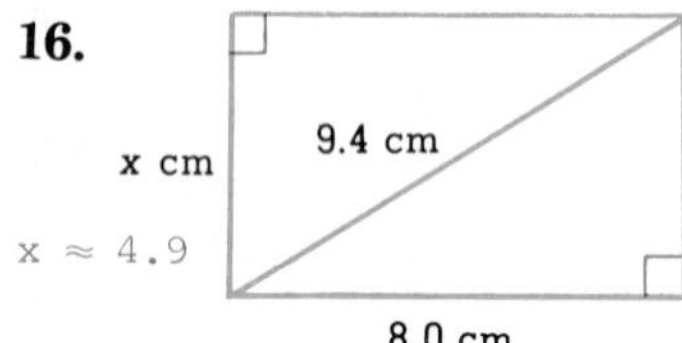

17. $x \approx 13.6$

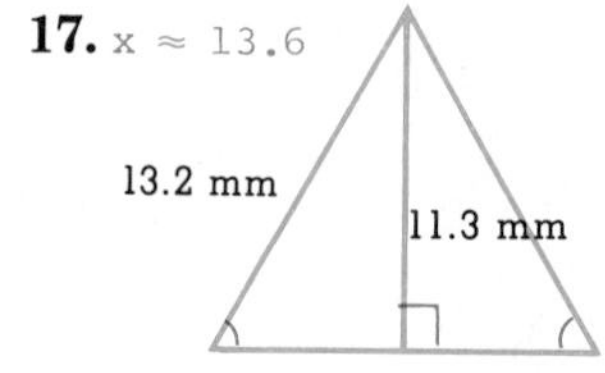

18. $9.8 \approx x$

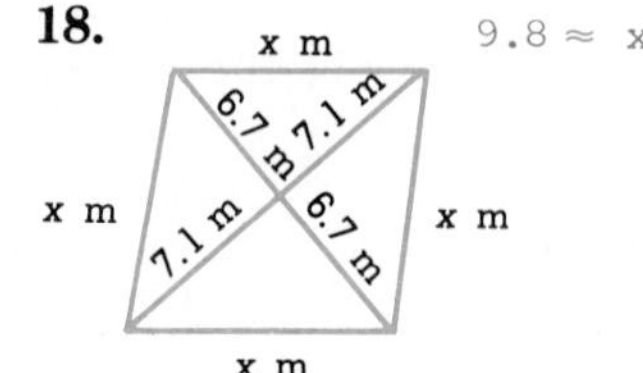

19. A stair stringer is a board that supports stairs. Suppose a set of stairs is to rise 8 feet over a length of 15 feet. Find the length of the stair stringer to the nearest tenth of a foot. 17 ft

20. A picket fence is to have a gate 42 inches wide. The gate is 54 inches high. Find the length of a diagonal brace for the gate to the nearest inch. 68 in.

21. In a rectangular container all pairs of intersecting edges are perpendicular. What is the length of the longest rod that would fit inside the container at the right? 13 units

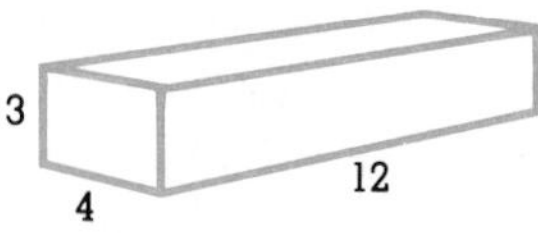

22. A plane flies 300 km due north, 400 km due east, and then 500 km due south. How far is the plane from its starting point? State the answer to the nearest kilometer. 447 km

23. The rafters of a roof truss are perpendicular to each other. The lengths are 24 ft and 32 ft. Find the rise of the roof. 19.2 ft

24. Prove Theorem 9–5. See the Teacher's Guide.

Objective: to find measures of parts of squares and equilateral triangles by using properties of 30°- 60° and isosceles right triangles

9–4 Special Right Triangles

The diagonal of a square and the sides of the square form two isosceles right triangles. By using the Pythagorean Theorem, it is possible to develop a formula relating the length of the diagonals to the length of a side.

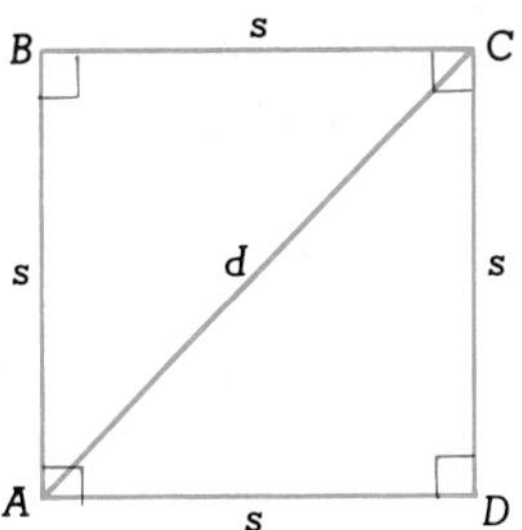

Let s be the measure of each side of a square.
Let d be the measure of a diagonal of the square.

$$d^2 = s^2 + s^2$$
$$d^2 = 2s^2$$
$$d = s\sqrt{2}$$

Encourage students to learn how to derive these facts.

If each acute angle of a right triangle has a degree measure of 45, then the hypotenuse measures $\sqrt{2}$ times the measure of a leg.

Theorem 9–6

The altitude of an equilateral triangle and the sides of the triangle form two congruent right triangles. Using the Pythagorean Theorem, it is possible to develop a formula relating the length of the altitude to the length of a side.

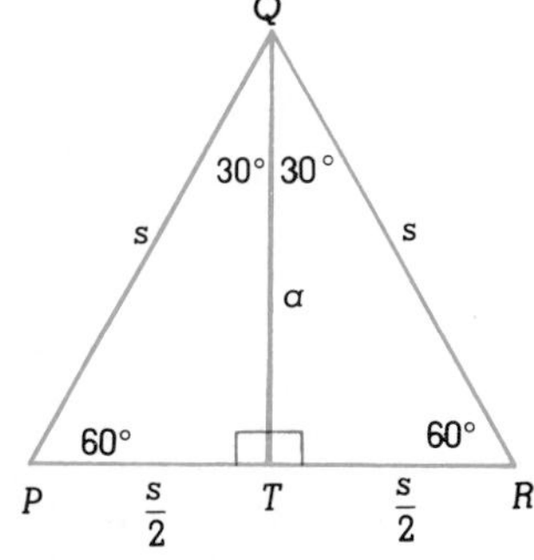

Let s be the measure of each side of an equilateral triangle.
Let a be the measure of an altitude of the triangle.

$$s^2 = a^2 + \left(\frac{s}{2}\right)^2$$
$$a^2 = s^2 - \left(\frac{s}{2}\right)^2$$
$$a^2 = \frac{3s^2}{4}$$
$$a = \frac{s\sqrt{3}}{2}$$

If the acute angles of a right triangle have degree measures of 30 and 60, then the measure of the hypotenuse is 2 times the measure of the shorter leg and the measure of the longer leg is $\sqrt{3}$ times the measure of the shorter leg.

Theorem 9–7

Note that the shorter leg is opposite the smallest angle.

The properties of the special right triangles can be used to solve a variety of problems.

example

1 **Consecutive bases of a square-shaped baseball diamond are 90 feet apart. Find the distance from home plate to second base. Round your answer to the nearest foot.**

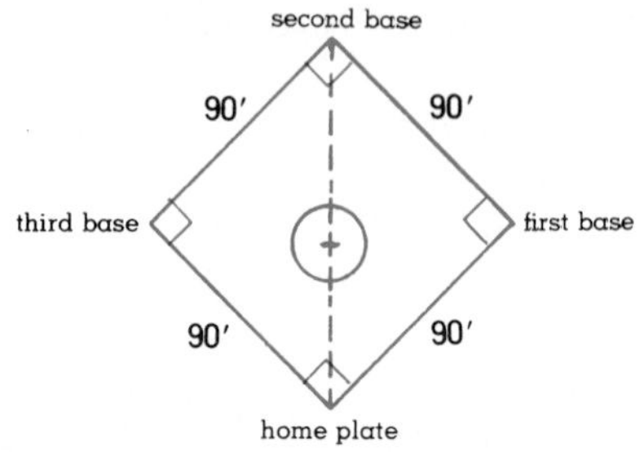

A line segment from home plate to second base is the diagonal of a square with side measuring 90 feet.

$$\begin{aligned} d &= s\sqrt{2} \\ &= 90\sqrt{2} \\ &\approx 90 \cdot 1.414 \text{ or } 127.26 \end{aligned}$$

The distance from home plate to second base is about 127 feet.

EN: Ex: 4, 8, 12, 16, 20, 24, Wr: 1-19 odds, 20-25, Ch: 1-2; AV: Ex: 1-23 odds, Wr: 1-19 odds; p. 298, Wr: 2-18 evens

exercises

FN: Ex: 1-24, Wr: 1-19; p. 298, Wr: 19-23

Exploratory **For each of the following, the length of each of the sides of a square is given. Find the length of the diagonals of each square.**

1. 1 ft $\sqrt{2}$ ft
2. 3 cm $3\sqrt{2}$ cm
3. 2 in. $2\sqrt{2}$ in.
4. 12 in. $12\sqrt{2}$ in.
5. 45 mm $45\sqrt{2}$ mm
6. 10 yd $10\sqrt{2}$ yd
7. 1.8 m $1.8\sqrt{2}$ m
8. 2.5 cm $2.5\sqrt{2}$ cm
9. 31.2 m $31.2\sqrt{2}$ m
10. $\frac{3}{4}$ ft $\frac{3}{4}\sqrt{2}$ ft
11. $4\frac{2}{3}$ yd $4\frac{2}{3}\sqrt{2}$ yd
12. $1\frac{1}{2}$ ft $1\frac{1}{2}\sqrt{2}$ ft

For each of the following, the length of each of the sides of an equilateral triangle is given. Find the length of the altitudes of each triangle.

13. 1 in. $\frac{\sqrt{3}}{2}$ in.
14. 1 m $\frac{\sqrt{3}}{2}$ in.
15. 4 cm $2\sqrt{3}$ cm
16. 6 yd $3\sqrt{3}$ yd
17. 25 cm $\frac{25\sqrt{3}}{2}$ cm
18. 14 m $7\sqrt{3}$ m
19. 2.5 cm $1.25\sqrt{3}$ cm
20. 1.4 m $0.7\sqrt{3}$ m
21. $\frac{2}{3}$ yd $\frac{\sqrt{3}}{3}$ yd
22. $\frac{1}{4}$ ft $\frac{\sqrt{3}}{8}$ ft
23. $2\frac{3}{4}$ ft $\frac{11\sqrt{3}}{8}$ ft
24. $2\frac{1}{3}$ yd $\frac{7\sqrt{3}}{6}$ yd

Written **Find the value of x to the nearest tenth.**

1. 7.1

x cm

5.0 cm

5.0 cm

2. 5.2

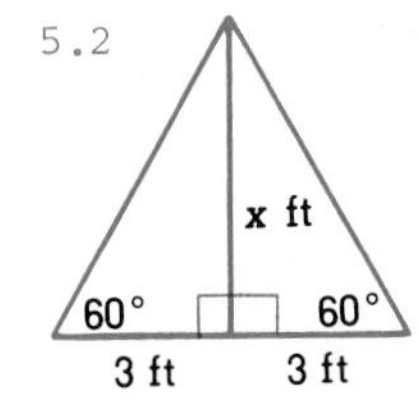

3. 13.0

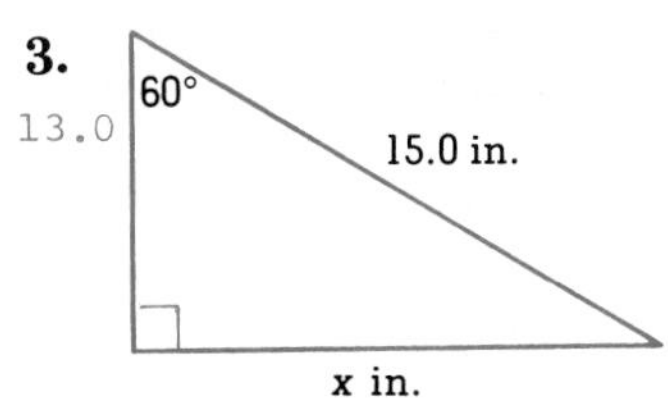

4. 10.1

x mm

45°

45°

14.3 mm

5. 4.9

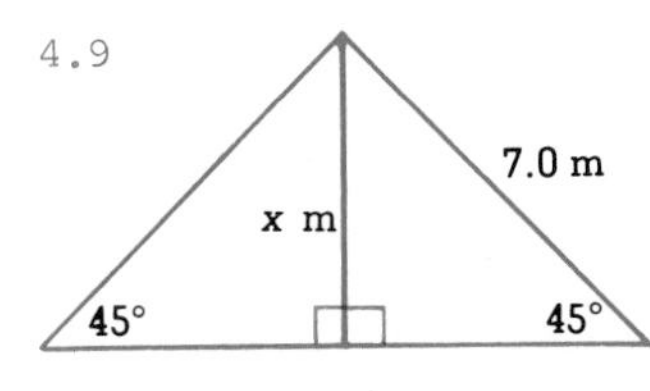

6. 1.4

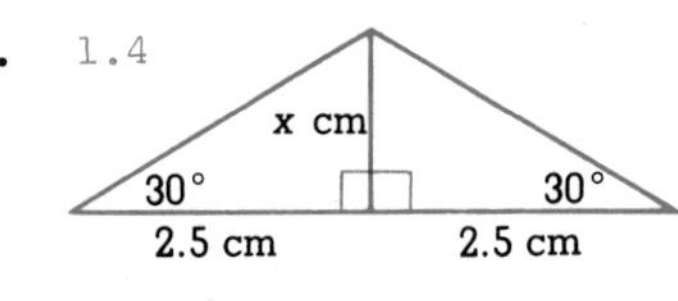

7. 1.0

x m

60°

30°

1.2 m

8. 4.2

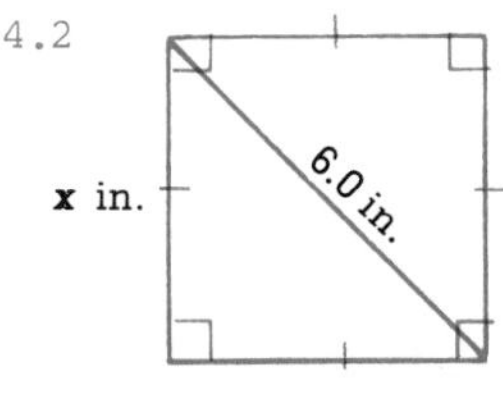

9. 18.0

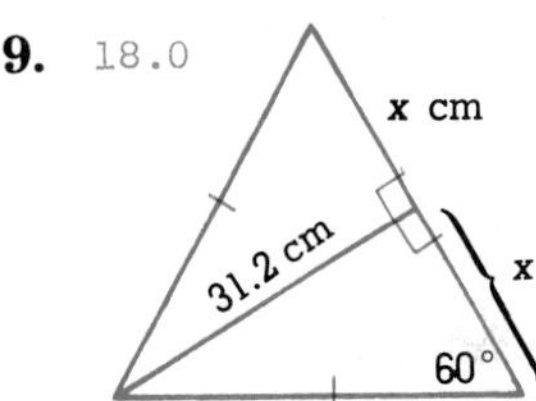

10. 11.0

5.5 m

30°

x m

30°

11. 6.0

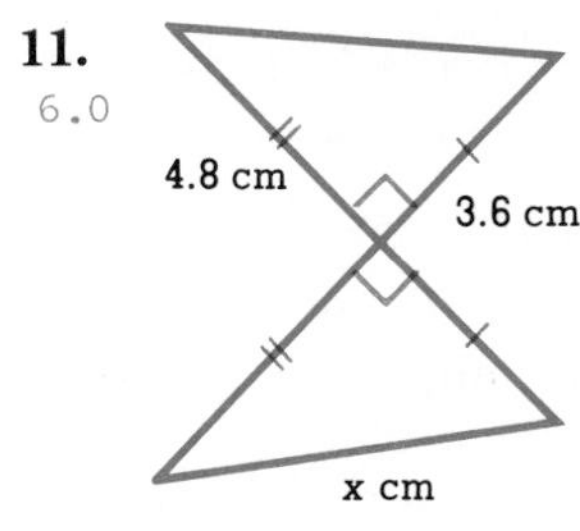

12. 5.0

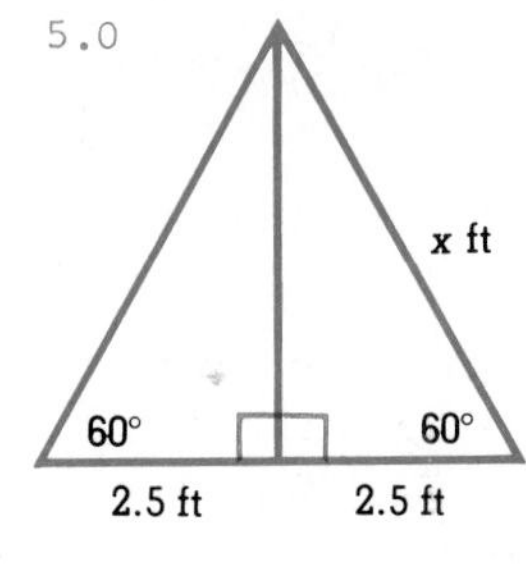

13. 5.3

7.5 m

45°

x m

14. 5.5

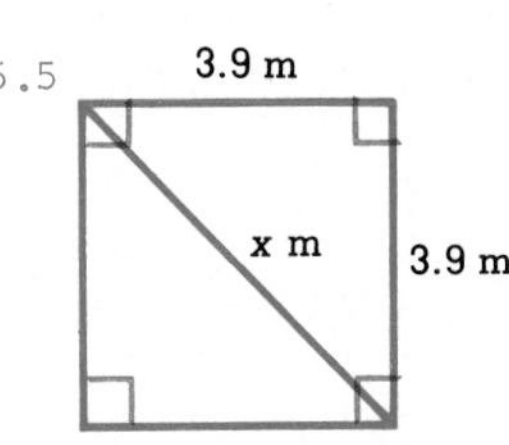

15. 14.8

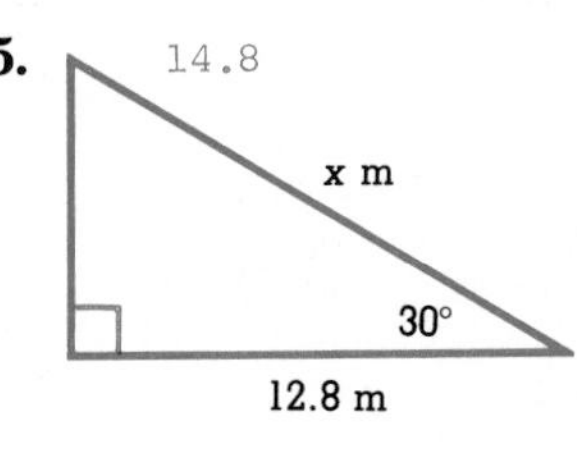

Solve each problem. Round each answer to the nearest tenth.

16. Consecutive bases of a square-shaped baseball diamond are 90 feet apart. Find the distance from first base to third base. 127.3 ft

17. Find the measure of the diagonal of a square nut if each side measures 3 centimeters. 4.2 cm

18. The perimeter of an equilateral triangle is 2.4 units. Find the measure of an altitude of the triangle. 0.7 units

19. The measure of an altitude of an equilateral triangle is 5.2. Find the perimeter of the triangle. 18.0 units

Use the figure at the right to find the value for each of the following.

20. u $\sqrt{2}$

21. v $\sqrt{3}$

22. w 2

23. x $\sqrt{5}$

24. y $\sqrt{6}$

25. z $\sqrt{7}$

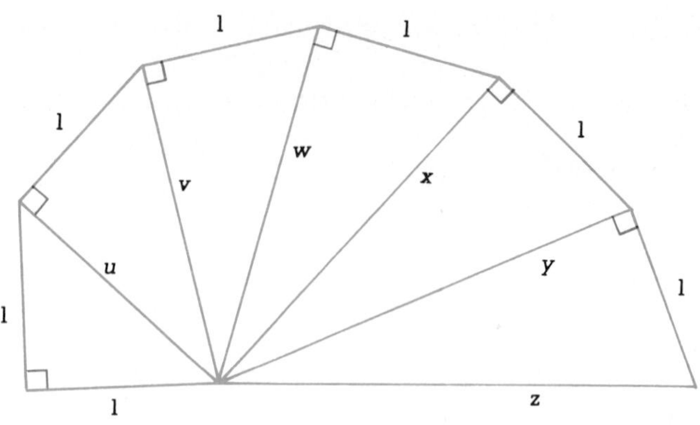

Challenge **Suppose each edge of the cube at the right measures s units.**

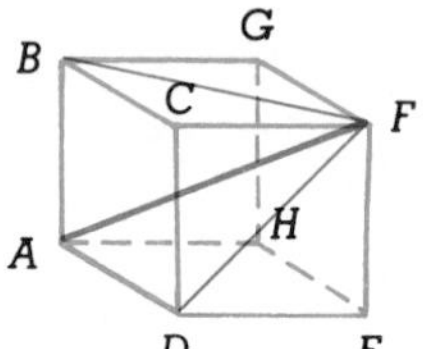

1. Develop a formula for the measure of the distance from A to F in terms of s. AF = $s\sqrt{3}$
2. Find the degree measure of $\angle BFD$. m $\angle BFD$ = 60

Heron's Formula — excursions in geometry

One formula for the area of a triangle is $A = \frac{1}{2}bh$ where b represents the measure of the base of the triangle and h represents the measure of the height of the triangle. Do you suppose there is a formula to find the area of a triangle when you only know the lengths of its sides?

In the first century A.D., a Greek mathematician of Alexandria named Heron (or Hero) developed such a formula. The formula is: Area = $\sqrt{s(s-a)(s-b)(s-c)}$, where a, b, and c are the measures of the lengths of the sides of the triangle and $s = \frac{1}{2}(a + b + c)$.

Exercise **Use Heron's formula to find the area of $\triangle HIJ$ in the cube below.**

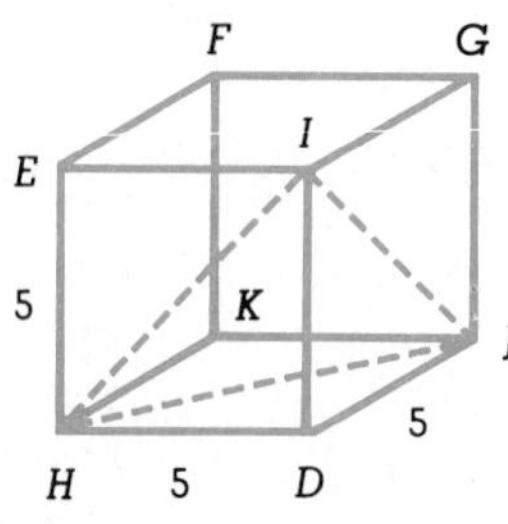

Area = $\frac{25}{2}\sqrt{3}$ square units

9–5 Trigonometry

Objectives: to express trigonometric ratios as a fraction in simplest form and as a decimal, to recognize trigonometric relationships from right triangles

Notice that for the 30°–60° right triangles below, the ratios of the measure of the side opposite the 30° angle to the measure of the hypotenuse are equal.

Calculators may be helpful with this lesson.

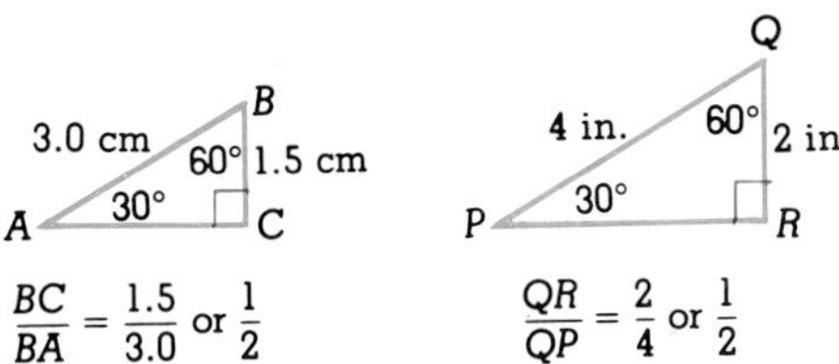

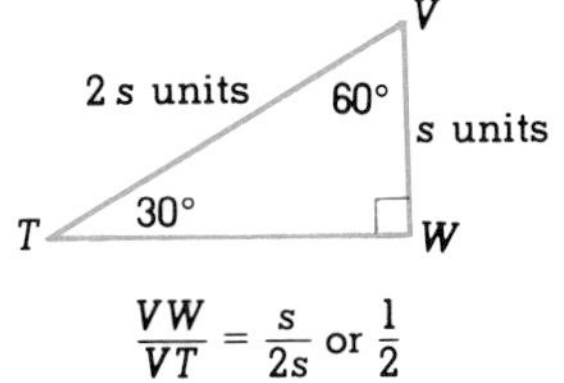

$\frac{BC}{BA} = \frac{1.5}{3.0}$ or $\frac{1}{2}$ $\frac{QR}{QP} = \frac{2}{4}$ or $\frac{1}{2}$ $\frac{VW}{VT} = \frac{s}{2s}$ or $\frac{1}{2}$

Consider the two triangles at the right. They are right triangles and $\angle A \cong \angle P$. Thus, the triangles are similar. How do the ratios $\frac{BC}{AB}$ and $\frac{QR}{PQ}$ compare?

Because the triangles are similar, the ratios are equal.

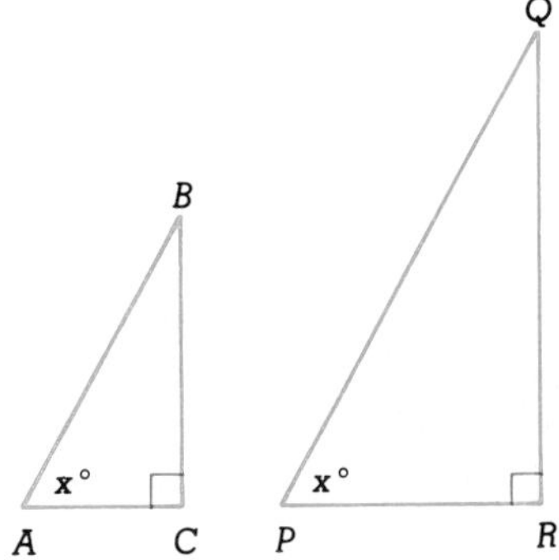

A ratio of the measures of two sides of a right triangle is called a **trigonometric ratio.** The value of a trigonometric ratio depends only on the measure of an acute angle. It does *not* depend on the size of the triangle.

Emphasize that these ratios are based on right triangles.

The three most common trigonometric ratios are defined in the following way.

A ratio is the sine of an acute angle of a right triangle if and only if it is the ratio of the measure of the leg opposite the acute angle to the measure of the hypotenuse.

Definition of Sine

A ratio is the cosine of an acute angle of a right triangle if and only if it is the ratio of the measure of the leg adjacent to the acute angle to the measure of the hypotenuse.

Definition of Cosine

A ratio is the tangent of an acute angle of a right triangle if and only if it is the ratio of the measure of the leg opposite the acute angle to the measure of the leg adjacent to the acute angle.

Definition of Tangent

The sine of angle A is abbreviated $\sin A$. The abbreviation $\cos A$ is used for cosine A and $\tan A$ for tangent A.

The trigonometric ratios for $\angle A$ of $\triangle ABC$ are as follows.

$$\sin A = \frac{BC}{AB}$$

$$\cos A = \frac{CA}{AB}$$

$$\tan A = \frac{BC}{CA}$$

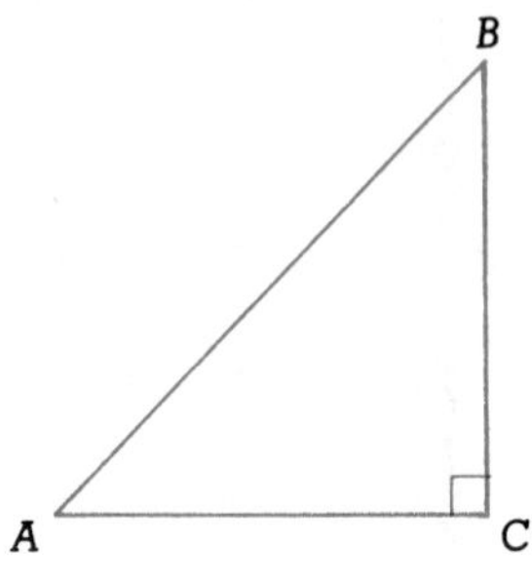

If the degree measure of $\angle A$ is 45, then we can write $\sin 45°$, $\cos 45°$, and $\tan 45°$.

Given the measures of the sides of a triangle, the values of sine, cosine, and tangent can be calculated.

example

1 **Find sin 45°, cos 45°, and tan 45°.**

An isosceles right triangle has a 45° angle. According to Theorem 9–6, the hypotenuse measures $\sqrt{2}$ times the measure of a side.

$$\sin 45° = \sin A = \frac{BC}{AB} = \frac{s}{s\sqrt{2}} = \frac{s}{s\sqrt{2}} \cdot \frac{\sqrt{2}}{\sqrt{2}} = \frac{\sqrt{2}}{2}$$

$$\cos 45° = \cos A = \frac{CA}{BA} = \frac{s}{s\sqrt{2}} = \frac{\sqrt{2}}{2}$$

$$\tan 45° = \tan A = \frac{BC}{CA} = \frac{s}{s} = 1$$

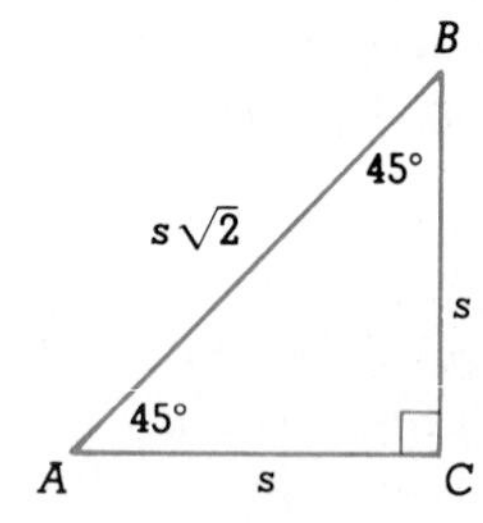

Thus, $\sin 45° = \frac{\sqrt{2}}{2}$, $\cos 45° = \frac{\sqrt{2}}{2}$, and $\tan 45° = 1$.

EN: Ex: 2-18 evens, Wr: 2-20 evens; p. 302, E ; AV: Ex: 1-18, Wr: 1-21 odds; pp. 301-2, Wr: 12-20 evens, 21-25; Ch: 1-2

exercises

Exploratory **For the three triangles at the right, express each of the following as a fraction in simplest form.**

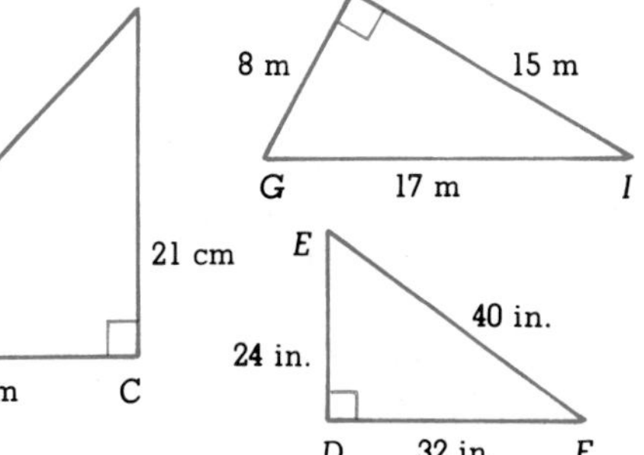

1. sin A 21/29	**2.** cos A 20/29	**3.** tan A 21/20
4. sin B 20/29	**5.** cos B 21/29	**6.** tan B 20/21
7. sin E 4/5	**8.** cos E 3/5	**9.** tan E 4/3
10. sin F 3/5	**11.** cos F 4/5	**12.** tan F 3/4
13. sin G 15/17	**14.** cos G 8/17	**15.** tan G 15/8
16. sin I 8/17	**17.** cos I 15/17	**18.** tan I 8/15

FN: Ex: 1-18, Wr: 1-21 odds; p. 302, Wr: 20-25

Written **For each of the following triangles, express the sine, cosine, and tangent of each acute angle to three decimal places.** For answers to exercises 1-6, see the Teacher's Guide.

1.

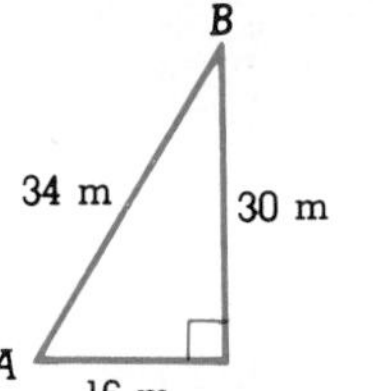

2.

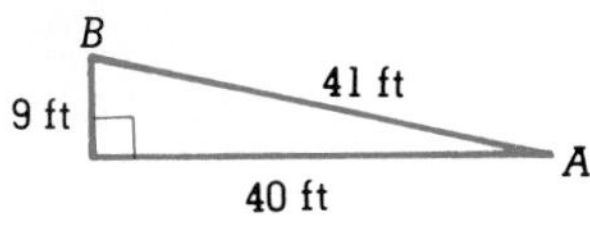

3.

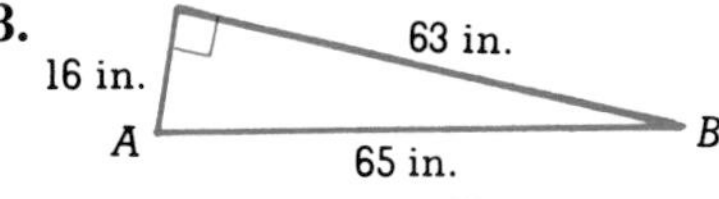

4.

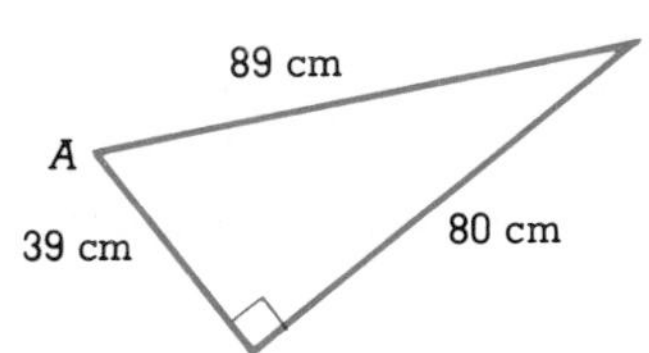

5.

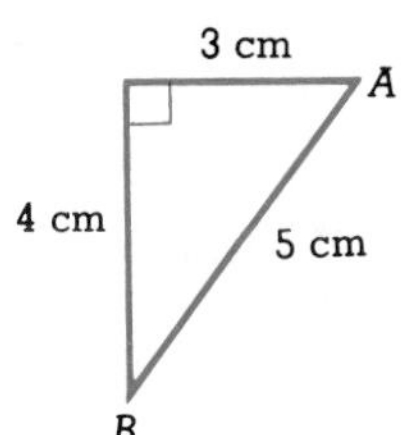

6.

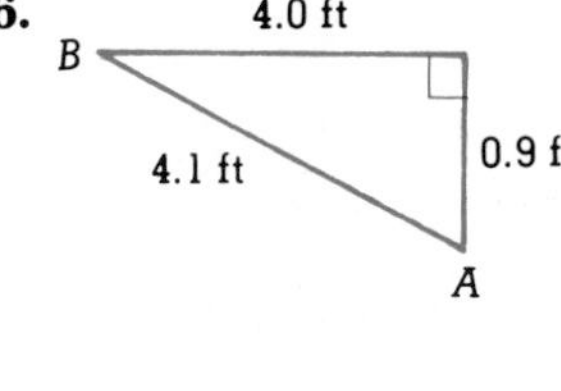

Find each of the following.

7. Find sin 30°. 1/2 **8.** Find cos 30°. $\sqrt{3}/2$ **9.** Find tan 30°. $\sqrt{3}/3$

10. Find sin 60°. $\sqrt{3}/2$ **11.** Find cos 60°. 1/2 **12.** Find tan 60°. $\sqrt{3}$

13. If $\angle A$ and $\angle B$ are complementary angles of a triangle, how are sin A and cos B related? They are equal.

In exercises 14-21, the reciprocals of trigonometric functions are used to find the solutions.

Use the figures to state the trigonometric ratio for each of the angles and the value given.

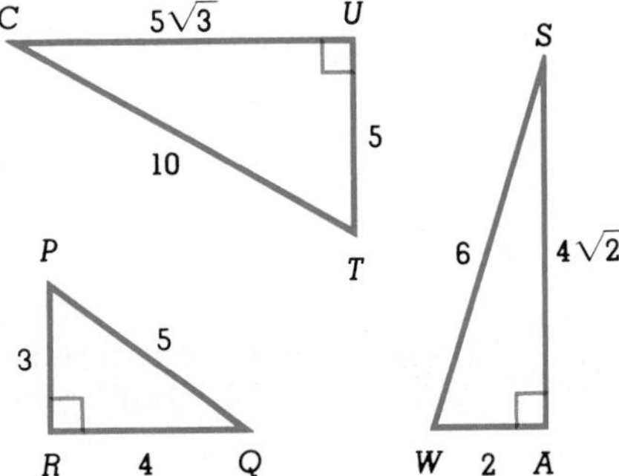

14. $\frac{3}{5}$; $\angle Q$ sin Q **15.** $\frac{6}{4\sqrt{2}}$; $\angle W$ $\frac{1}{\sin W}$

16. $\frac{1}{\sqrt{3}}$; $\angle C$ tan C **17.** $\frac{5\sqrt{3}}{10}$; $\angle T$ sin T

18. $\frac{3}{4}$; $\angle Q$ tan Q **19.** 3; $\angle W$ $\frac{1}{\cos W}$

20. 1.25; $\angle P$ $\frac{1}{\sin P}$ **21.** 2; $\angle C$ $\frac{1}{\sin C}$

careers

Recreation Supervisor

David Wagoner is a recreation supervisor for a city Parks and Recreation Department. He is checking the blueprints for the construction of swings for the park. Each swing will be 2.0 meters tall. What will be the length of one leg of a swing set?

The equilateral triangle at the left represents the swings. Since $\overline{BD}$ is an altitude of the triangle, the following equation can be written.

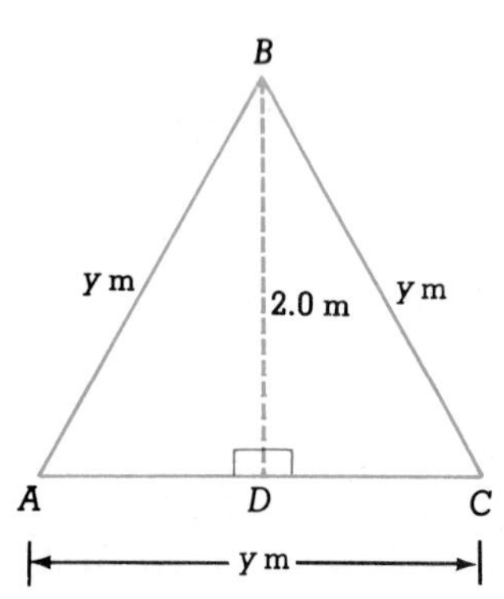

$$BD = \frac{y\sqrt{3}}{2}$$

To find y, the measure of a leg, substitute 2.0 for BD and solve the equation for y.

$$2.0 = \frac{y\sqrt{3}}{2}$$
$$4.0 = y\sqrt{3}$$
$$y = \frac{4.0}{\sqrt{3}}$$
$$\approx \frac{4.0}{1.7}$$
$$\approx 2.4$$

Each leg is approximately 2.4 meters long.

Exercises **Given each of the following heights for swings, find the lengths of the legs. Round each answer to one decimal place.**

1. 3.0 meters 3.5 m **2.** 4.0 meters 4.6 m **3.** 8.0 feet 9.2 ft **4.** 6.0 feet 6.9 ft

9–6 Trigonometric Tables

Objective: to use trigonometric tables to approximate values of trigonometric ratios or to find the measurement of angles to the nearest degree

A table of values can be used to find decimal approximations for trigonometric ratios. Such a table is given on page 549.

example

1 **Find cos 48°.**

Angle	sin	cos	tan
45°	0.7071	0.7071	1.0000
46°	0.7193	0.6947	1.0355
47°	0.7314	0.6820	1.0724
48°	0.7431	0.6691	1.1106
49°	0.7547	0.6561	1.1504
50°	0.7660	0.6428	1.1918
51°	0.7771	0.6293	1.2349
52°	0.7880	0.6157	1.2799
53°	0.7986	0.6018	1.3270

Locate 48° in the column marked Angle.

Locate the value for cos 48° in the column marked cos.

An approximate value for cos 48° is 0.6691.

A table also can be used to find the measure of an angle, given a trigonometric ratio.

example

2 **Given cos A = 0.5446, find $m\angle A$.**

Locate 0.5446 in the column marked *cos*.

Angle	sin	cos	tan
54°	0.8090	0.5878	1.3764
55°	0.8192	0.5736	1.4281
56°	0.8290	0.5592	1.4826
57°	0.8387	0.5446	1.5399
58°	0.8480	0.5299	1.6003
59°	0.8572	0.5150	1.6643
60°	0.8660	0.5000	1.7321
61°	0.8746	0.4848	1.8040
62°	0.8829	0.4695	1.8807
63°	0.8910	0.4540	1.9626
64°	0.8988	0.4384	2.0503
65°	0.9063	0.4226	2.1445

Locate the measure of the angle in the column marked Angle.

The degree measure of $\angle A$ is about 57.

If a given value does *not* match any entry in a table, choose the closest value from the table.

example

3 Given tan $B = 0.1234$, find $m\angle B$.

Look in the column marked *tan*.

Angle	sin	cos	tan
0°	0.0000	1.0000	0.0000
1°	0.0175	0.9998	0.0175
2°	0.0349	0.9994	0.0349
3°	0.0523	0.9986	0.0524
4°	0.0698	0.9976	0.0699
5°	0.0872	0.9962	0.0875
6°	0.1045	0.9945	0.1051
7°	0.1219	0.9925	0.1228
8°	0.1392	0.9903	0.1405
9°	0.1564	0.9877	0.1584
10°	0.1736	0.9848	0.1763
11°	0.1908	0.9816	0.1944
12°	0.2079	0.9781	0.2126

Locate the measure of the angle in the column marked Angle.

The value of 0.1234 is between 0.1228 and 0.1405. It is closer to 0.1228.

The degree measure of $\angle B$ is about 7.

EN: Ex: 1-12, Wr: 14-28 evens, 46-58 evens, 70-84 evens; p. 306, C: 1-2; AV: Ex: 1-12, Wr: 1-83 odds; p. 305, Wr: 2-20 evens; p. 306, C: 1-4

exercises

Exploratory **Use the table at the back of this book on page 549 to answer each of the following.**

1. Name the least possible value for sine. 0.0000
2. Name the measurement of an angle for which the sine is at its minimum. 0°
3. Name the greatest possible value for sine. 1.0000
4. Name the measurement of an angle for which the sine is at its maximum. 90°
5. Name the least possible value for cosine. 0.0000
6. Name the measurement of an angle for which the cosine is at its minimum. 90°
7. Name the greatest possible value for cosine. 1.0000
8. Name the measurement of an angle for which the cosine is at its maximum. 0°
9. Name the least possible value for tangent. 0.0000
10. Name the greatest possible value for tangent. values go to infinity
11. Name the measurement of the angle for which sine and cosine are equal. 45°
12. Name the value of the tangent of the angle for which sine and cosine are equal. 1.0000

FN: Ex: 1-12, Wr: 1-83 odds; p. 305, Wr: 2-20 evens; p. 306, C: 1-4

Written **Use the table at the back of this book on page 549 to find the value of the following ratios.**

1. sin 0° 0.0000	**2.** sin 32° 0.5299	**3.** cos 0° 1.0000	**4.** tan 0° 0.0000
5. cos 69° 0.3584	**6.** tan 29° 0.5543	**7.** sin 58° 0.8480	**8.** cos 10° 0.9848
9. tan 38° 0.7813	**10.** sin 44° 0.6947	**11.** tan 45° 1.0000	**12.** tan 89° 57.2900
13. cos 22° 0.9272	**14.** tan 79° 5.1446	**15.** cos 36° 0.8090	**16.** cos 45° 0.7071
17. sin 13° 0.2250	**18.** cos 90° 0.0000	**19.** tan 50° 1.1918	**20.** sin 63° 0.8910
21. tan 84° 9.5144	**22.** sin 18° 0.3090	**23.** cos 16° 0.9613	**24.** tan 90° infinity
25. tan 51° 1.2349	**26.** cos 58° 0.5299	**27.** sin 89° 0.9998	**28.** sin 90° 1.0000

Use the table to find the measurement of each angle to the nearest degree.

29. $\sin A = 0.1045$ 6°	**30.** $\sin B = 0.5000$ 30°
31. $\cos C = 0.8988$ 26°	**32.** $\tan D = 0.3839$ 21°
33. $\tan E = 2.0503$ 64°	**34.** $\sin F = 0.7431$ 48°
35. $\cos P = 0.2588$ 75°	**36.** $\tan Q = 3.0777$ 72°
37. $\sin R = 0.9994$ 88°	**38.** $\tan S = 0.7002$ 35°
39. $\sin T = 0.8988$ 64°	**40.** $\sin V = 0.9205$ 67°
41. $\cos M = 0.3000$ 73°	**42.** $\tan N = 0.1500$ 9°
43. $\cos A = 0.7777$ 39°	**44.** $\cos P = 0.6$ 53°
45. $\tan L = 4.00$ 76°	**46.** $\tan T = 25$ 88°
47. $\sin X = 0.3$ 17°	**48.** $\tan Z = 0.15$ 9°
49. $\cos W = 0.65$ 49°	**50.** $\tan F = 1.75$ 60°
51. $\sin Q = 0.25$ 14°	**52.** $\cos E = 0.25$ 76°
53. $\tan R = 1.500$ 56°	**54.** $\cos G = 0.999$ 3°
55. $\sin H = 0.999$ 88°	**56.** $\sin A = \frac{1}{2}$ 30°
57. $\cos T = \frac{4}{5}$ 37°	**58.** $\tan Z = \frac{3}{4}$ 37°

Find the value of each of the following to four decimal places.

59. cos 30° − sin 30° 0.3660	**60.** cos 60° − sin 30° 0.0000
61. sin 90° + cos 30° 1.8660	**62.** cos 30° + cos 60° 1.3660
63. tan 45° + tan 0° 1.0000	**64.** tan 0° + cos 90° 0.0000
65. 3 sin 30° − sin 90° 0.5000	**66.** cos 60° − 2 cos 30° -1.2320
67. 2 tan 30° − tan 60° -0.5773	**68.** tan 60° − 2 tan 30° 0.5773
69. 2 sin 45° − sin 90° 0.4142	**70.** 2 cos 45° − cos 90° 1.4142
71. $\frac{1}{2}$ sin 60° − sin 30° -0.0670	**72.** $\frac{1}{2}$ cos 60° + sin 30° 0.7500
73. tan 45° + tan 60° 2.7321	**74.** tan 45° − $\frac{1}{2}$ tan 60° 0.1340
75. $\frac{1}{2}$(sin 60° + sin 30°) 0.6830	**76.** $\frac{1}{2}$(tan 45° − tan 30°) 0.2113

77. $\sin 30° - \cos 60°$ 0.0000

78. $\tan 45° + \sin 0°$ 1.0000

79. $\sin 90° + \cos 0°$ 2.0000

80. $\sin 90° - \tan 0°$ 1.0000

81. $\sin 45° - \cos 45°$ 0.0000

82. $\sin 45° - \tan 45°$ -0.2929

83. $\cos 60° + 2 \sin 90°$ 2.5000

84. $\cos 90° - 3 \cos 30°$ -2.5980

The Exponential Shift Key

Any number less than $\pm 1 \times 10^{-8}$ or greater than ± 99999999 must be entered in the calculator in scientific notation. Many calculators have an exponential shift key [EE↓] for this purpose.

Example **Enter 6237×10^{23}.**

ENTER:	6237	[EE↓]		23		[=]
DISPLAY:	6237.	6237.00	6237.	23	6.237	26

The number 6237×10^{23} expressed in scientific notation is 6.237 26 or 6.237×10^{26}. For some calculators, while 6.237 26 is in the display, pressing the [EE↓] key several times decreases the exponent by 1 and the decimal point moves one place to the right.

Exercises **Use the exponential shift key to enter each of the following in scientific notation.** For answers to exercises 1-16, see the Teacher's Guide.

1. 75.03×10^{15}
2. 0.159×10^{13}
3. 0.067×10^{18}
4. 7102×10^{21}
5. 56.75×10^{30}
6. $^{-}159.2 \times 10^{10}$
7. 5308×10^{32}
8. $^{-}0.00078 \times 10^{-16}$
9. $^{-}12.48 \times 10^{8}$
10. 0.58001×10^{-20}
11. $^{-}16.03 \times 10^{-31}$
12. 0.0072×10^{35}

Compute each of the following.

13. $(0.56 \times 10^{5}) + (3.45 \times 10^{8})$
14. $(66.23 \times 10^{9}) - (21.05 \times 10^{5})$
15. $(31.6 \times 10^{-2})(101.6 \times 10^{-1})$
16. $(0.004 \times 10^{-3}) \div (35.7 \times 10^{-12})$

9–7 Using Trigonometry

Objectives: to use trigonometric ratios to find missing measures of right triangles, to recognize angles of depression or elevation, to use trigonometry to solve problems

Trigonometric ratios can be used to find missing measures of right triangles.

examples

1 For the triangle, find $m\angle A$ to the nearest degree.

$$\tan A = \frac{BC}{AC}$$

$$\tan A = \frac{45}{55}$$

$$\tan A \approx 0.8182$$

$$m\angle A \approx 39°$$

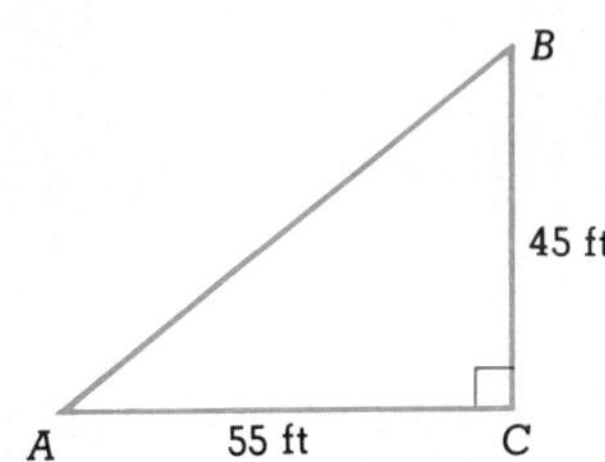

Show students that neither sin nor cos is helpful in this situation.

2 For the triangle, find QR to the nearest tenth of a millimeter.

$$\cos R = \frac{PR}{QR}$$

$$\cos 25° = \frac{42.0}{QR}$$

$$QR = \frac{42.0}{\cos 25°}$$

$$QR \approx \frac{42.0}{0.9063}$$

$$QR \approx 46.3$$

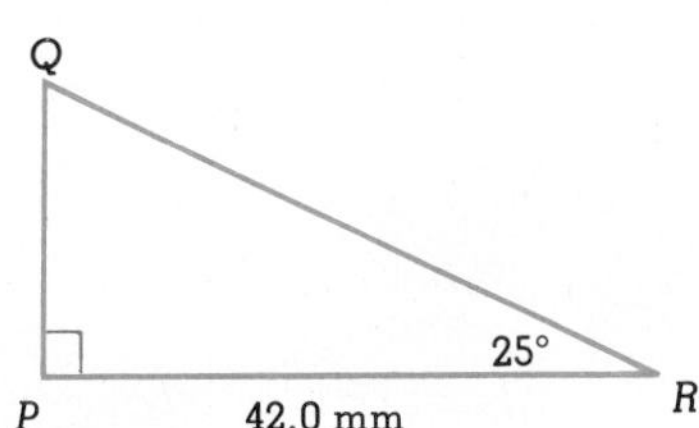

3 For the triangle, find TV and VW to the nearest tenth of a centimeter.

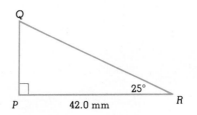

$$\sin W = \frac{TV}{TW}$$

$$\sin 40° = \frac{TV}{26.0}$$

$$TV = 26.0 \sin 40°$$

$$TV \approx 26.0\,(0.6428)$$

$$TV \approx 16.7$$

$$\cos W = \frac{VW}{TW}$$

$$\cos 40° = \frac{VW}{26.0}$$

$$VW = 26.0 \cos 40°$$

$$VW \approx 26.0\,(0.7660)$$

$$VW \approx 19.9$$

To see the top of a peak or an object in the sky, a person must look up rather than looking straight ahead. An **angle of elevation** is formed by the line of sight and a horizontal line.

A person in a tower or on a cliff must look down to see an object below. This person's line of sight forms an **angle of depression** with a horizontal line.

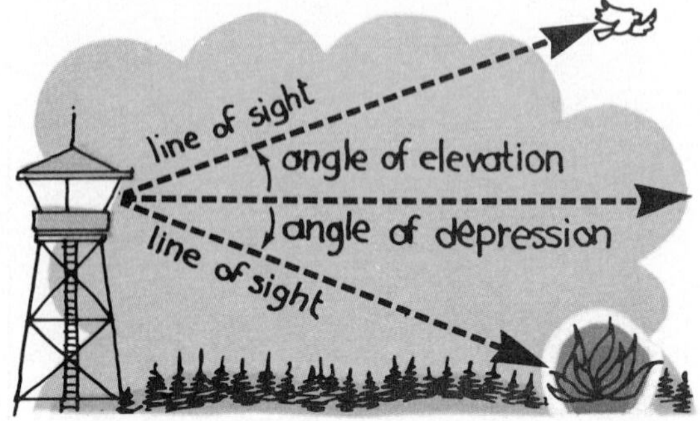

example

4 A surveyor is 100.0 meters from a dam. The angle of elevation to the top of the dam is 26°. The surveyor's instrument is 1.73 meters above the ground. Find the height of the dam to the nearest hundredth.

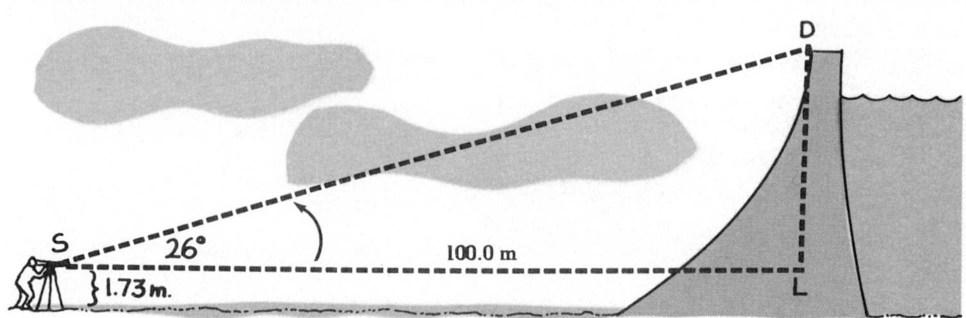

$$\tan 26° = \frac{DL}{100.0}$$

$$0.4877 \approx \frac{DL}{100.0}$$

$$48.77 \approx DL$$

The height of the dam is about $48.77 + 1.73$ or 50.50 meters.

EN: Ex: 1-3, 8-10, Wr: 6-20 evens; p. 310, Cal: 1-11 odds, 13-16; p. 315, TG: 1-2;
AV: Ex: 1-11 odds, Wr: 1-21 odds; pp. 309-10, Wr: 60-84 evens; p. 310, Cal: 1-16

exercises

FN: Ex: 1-12, Wr: 1-21; pp. 309-10, Wr: 46-84 evens; p. 310, Cal: 1-6

Exploratory **Name the angles of elevation and depression in each of the following.**

1. E: ∠ BCA, D: ∠ DBC

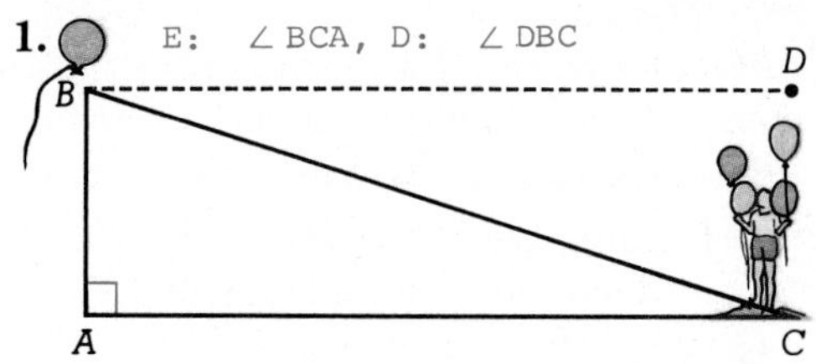

2. E: ∠ FEG, D: ∠ HFE

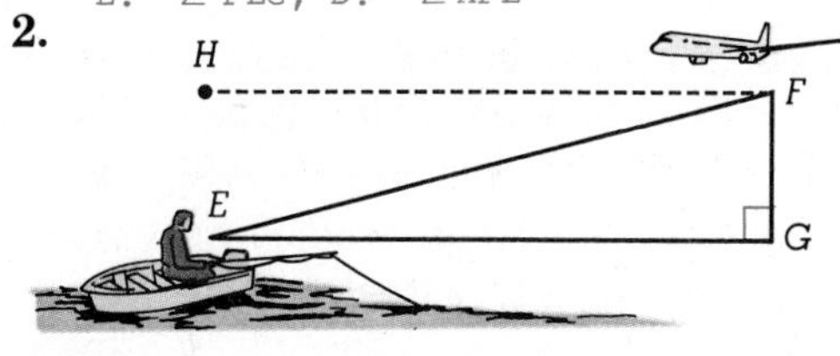

3. E: ∠ YXZ, D: ∠ WYX

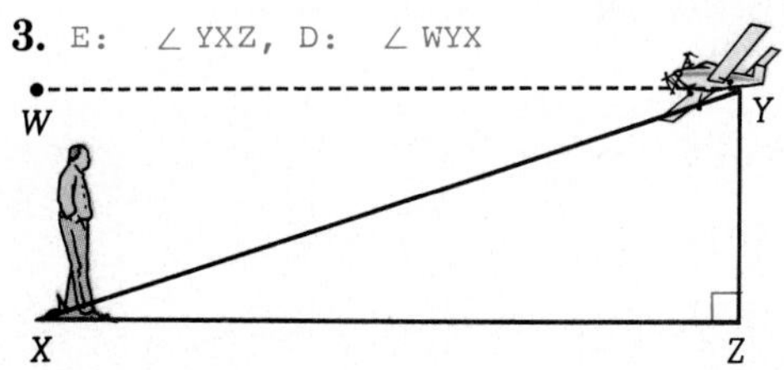

4. E: ∠ SUR, D: ∠ TSU

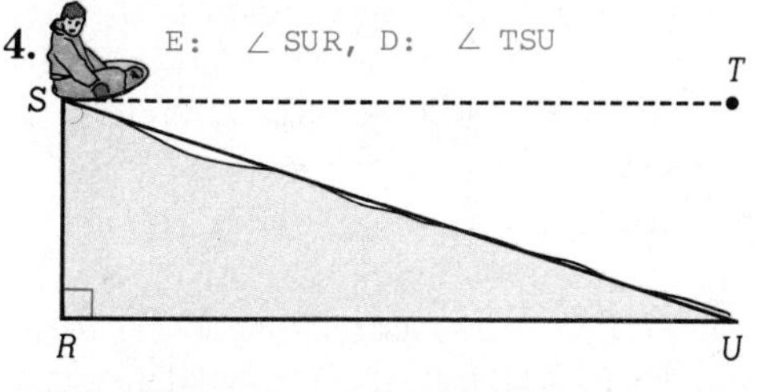

5. E: ∠ JHK, D: ∠ IJH

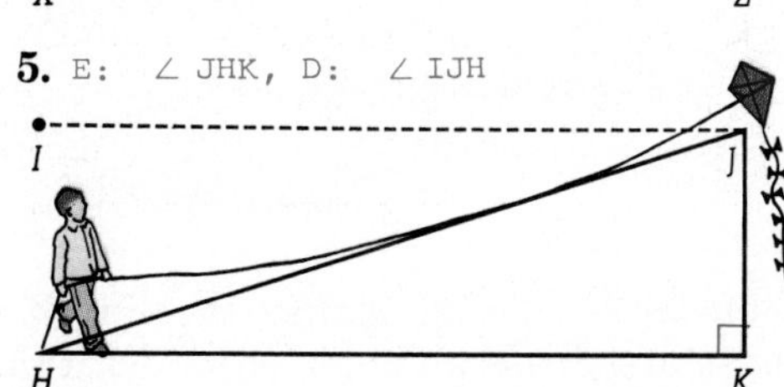

6. E: ∠ LNO, D: ∠ MLN

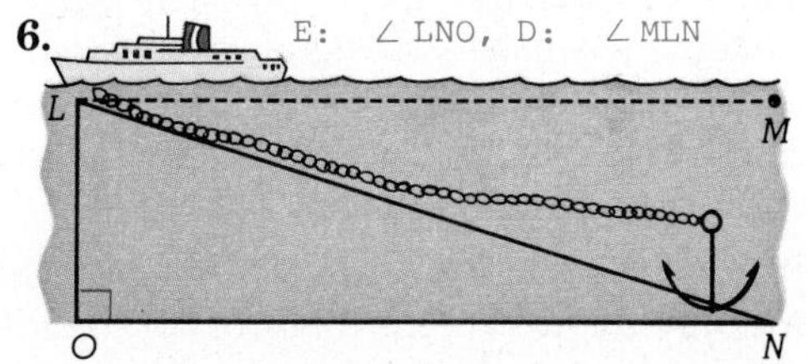

For each of the following, state an equation that would enable you to answer each problem. Use a triangle similar to $\triangle PRQ$.

7. Given $m\angle P = 15$ and $PQ = 37$, find QR. sin 15° = QR/37
8. Given $m\angle Q = 72$ and $PR = 13$, find QR. tan 72° = 13/QR
9. Given $m\angle P = 47$ and $QR = 10$, find PQ. sin 47° = 10/PQ
10. Given $QR = 21.5$ and $m\angle Q = 87$, find PR. tan 87° = PR/21.5
11. Given $PR = 13.4$ and $m\angle P = 16$, find PQ.
12. Given $PR = 31.8$ and $m\angle P = 19$, find PQ.

11. cos 16° = 13.4/PQ 12. cos 19° = 31.8/PQ

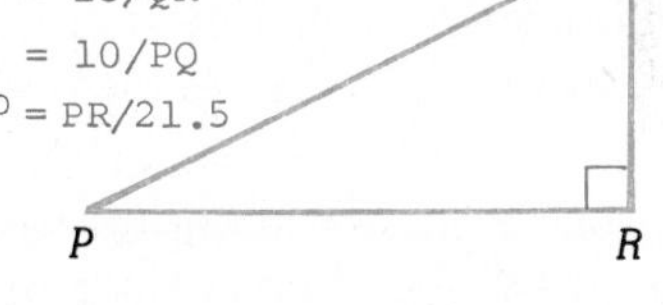

Written **Use a triangle similar to $\triangle ABC$ to help answer each problem.**

1. Given $m\angle B = 32$ and $AB = 74$, find AC. 39.21
2. Given $m\angle B = 43$ and $AB = 90$, find BC. 65.83
3. Given $AB = 14$ and $AC = 6$, find $m\angle A$. 65
4. Given $AB = 60$ and $AC = 20$, find $m\angle A$. 71
5. Given $AC = 5$ and $BC = 12$, find $m\angle B$. 23
6. Given $BC = 4$ and $AC = 3$, find $m\angle B$. 37
7. Given $m\angle B = 34$ and $BC = 15$, find AC. 10.12
8. Given $m\angle A = 62$ and $AC = 20$, find BC. 37.61
9. Given $m\angle A = 68$ and $BC = 98$, find AB. 105.7
10. Given $m\angle B = 32$ and $AC = 10$, find AB. 18.87

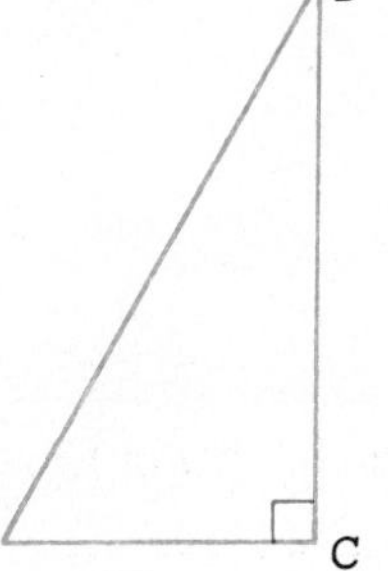

Answer each of the following. Round all answers to the nearest hundredth unless otherwise indicated.

11. A surveyor is 100.00 meters from a bridge. The angle of elevation to the top of the bridge is 35°. The surveyor's instrument is 1.45 meters above the ground. Find the height of the bridge. 71.47 m

12. A surveyor is 100.00 meters from a building. The angle of elevation to the top of the building is 23°. The surveyor's instrument is 1.55 meters above the ground. Find the height of the building. 44.00 m

13. To secure a 500-meter radio tower against high winds, guy wires are attached to a ring on the tower. The ring is 5 meters from the top. The wires form a 15° angle with the tower. Find the distance from the tower to the guy wire anchor in the ground. 132.61 m

14. In a parking garage, each level is 20 feet apart. Each ramp to a level is 130 feet long. Find the measure of the angle of elevation for each ramp. 9°

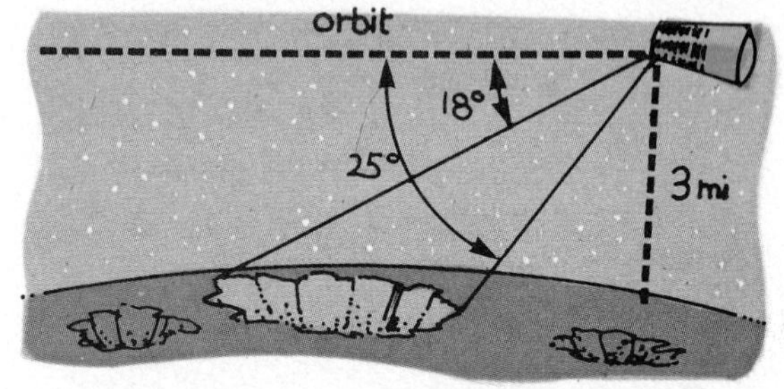

15. Before Apollo 11 descended to the surface of the moon, it made one orbit at a distance of 3 miles from the surface. At one point in its orbit, the onboard guidance system measured the angles of depression to the near and far edges of a huge crater. The angles measured 25° and 18°. Find the distance across the crater. 2.8 mi

16. A lighthouse built at sea level is 150 feet high. From its top, the angle of depression of a buoy is 25°. Find, to the nearest foot, the distance from the buoy to the foot of the lighthouse. 322 ft

17. A ladder is leaning against the side of a house and forms an angle of 65° with the ground. The foot of the ladder is 8 feet from the building. Find the length of the ladder to the nearest foot. 19 ft

18. At a certain time of day, the angle of elevation of the sun is 44°. Find, to the nearest meter, the shadow cast by a building 30 meters high. 31 m

19. A road rises vertically 40 feet over a horizontal distance of 630 feet. What is the angle of elevation of the road? 4°

20. A train in the mountains rises 10 feet for every 250 feet it moves along the track. Find the angle of elevation of the track. 2°

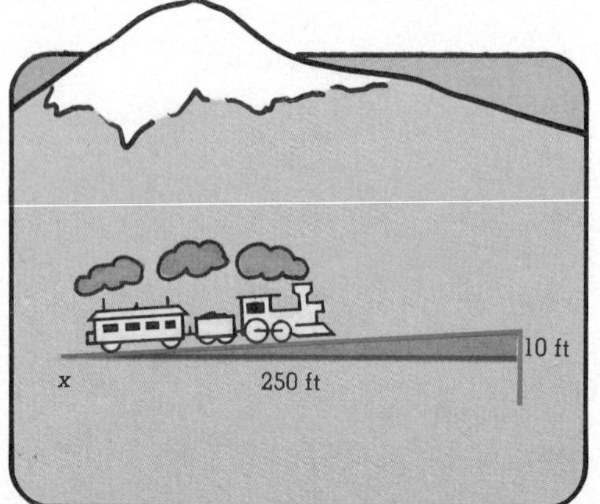

21. A plane rose from take-off and flew at an angle of 11° with the ground. When it reached an altitude of 500 feet, what was the horizontal distance the plane had flown? 2572 ft

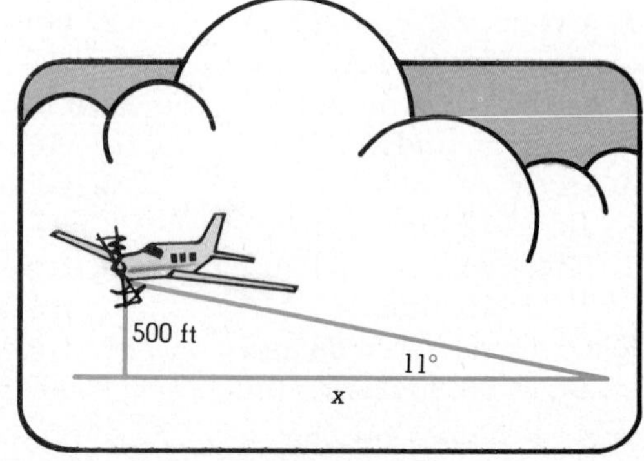

topics in geometry — Elliptic Geometry

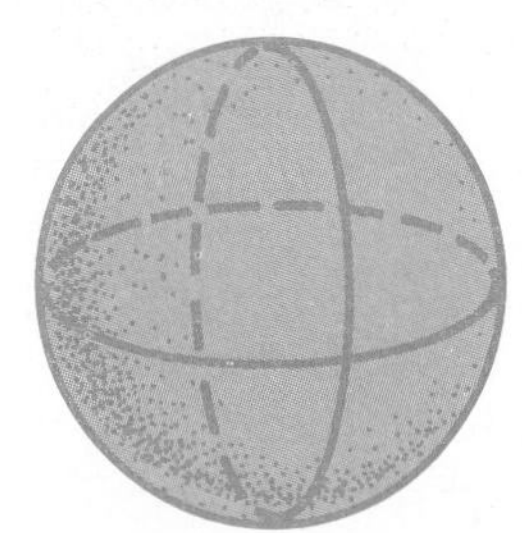

On the surface of a sphere such as the earth, the shortest distance between two points is an arc of a great circle. Therefore, navigators consider great circles as "lines" of a special kind of two-dimensional geometry called **spherical geometry.**

The giant step of extending this geometry from two dimensions to three or more was taken by the German mathematician Bernhard Riemann in the latter half of the 19th century. The new type of non-Euclidean geometry that Riemann developed was called **Riemannian** or **elliptic geometry.**

Two postulates of elliptic geometry contradict two important Euclidean postulates. One of Euclid's postulates states that a straight line extends indefinitely. Elliptic geometry replaces this postulate with the idea that if a line is extended it will meet itself.

Euclidean Postulate

A straight line extends indefinitely.

Elliptic Postulate

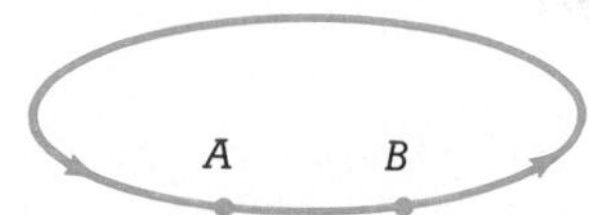

If a line is extended, it will meet itself.

In elliptic geometry lines are finite, yet unbounded. Suppose you were to walk the "line" of the earth's equator. You would be walking in a straight line and yet if you were to map your journey it would appear as a circle. The distance you walked would be a finite length and yet you could travel around the earth forever in that line and never reach an end. Thus, the terms are finite, yet unbounded.

The other Euclidean postulate that elliptic geometry does *not* satisfy is the parallel postulate. In elliptic geometry the Euclidean parallel postulate is replaced by: In a plane, given a line ℓ and a point P *not* contained in ℓ, there exists *no* line through P and parallel to ℓ.

Elliptic geometry includes most of Euclid's postulates. One of these is the idea that when two lines intersect they intersect in just one point. To satisfy this postulate in elliptic geometry the concept of "point" had to be changed. If two lines intersect in elliptic geometry they intersect in what appears to be two points. By the new definition what appears to be two points is really only one.

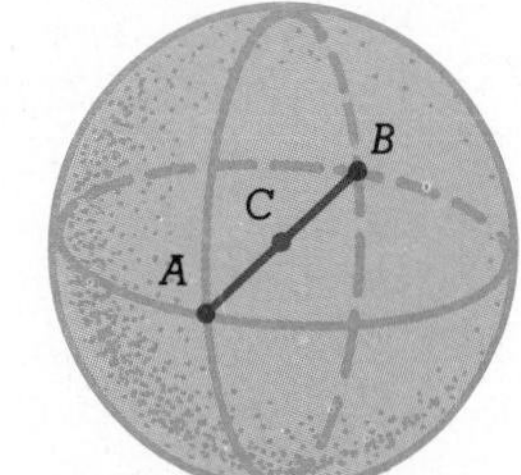

A and B are considered one point.

Exercises Answer each of the following using a reference.

1. Write a brief biographical sketch of Bernhard Riemann.
2. Draw a diagram depicting why parallel lines do *not* exist in elliptic geometry.

For answers to exercises 1-2, see the Teacher's Guide.

Vocabulary

square root (287)
radical sign (287)
principal square root (287)
rationalizing the denominator (289)
irrational numbers (289)
geometric mean (292)
trigonometric ratio (303)
sine (303)
cosine (303)
tangent (304)

Chapter Summary

1. Definition of Square Root: For any numbers a and b, if $a^2 = b$, then a is a square root of b. (287)
2. The radical sign indicates a nonnegative square root. (287)
3. Product Property of Square Roots (Postulate 9–1): For any nonnegative numbers a and b, $\sqrt{ab} = \sqrt{a} \cdot \sqrt{b}$. (288)
4. Quotient Property of Square Roots (Postulate 9–2): For any nonnegative numbers a and b with $b \neq 0$, $\sqrt{\frac{a}{b}} = \frac{\sqrt{a}}{\sqrt{b}}$. (288)
5. A square root is said to be simplified when the following conditions are met. (289)
   1. The radicand has no perfect square factor other than 1.
   2. The radicand does *not* contain a fraction.
   3. No radical appears in the denominator of a fraction.
6. Theorem 9–1: If an altitude is drawn from the vertex of the right angle to the hypotenuse of a right triangle, then the two triangles formed are similar to the given triangle and to each other. (291)
7. Definition of Geometric Mean: For any positive numbers a and b, x is the geometric mean between a and b if and only if $\frac{a}{x} = \frac{x}{b}$ and x is positive. (292)
8. Theorem 9–2: The measure of the altitude drawn from the right angle to the hypotenuse of a right triangle is the geometric mean between the measures of the two segments of the hypotenuse. (292)
9. Theorem 9–3: If the altitude is drawn to the hypotenuse of a right triangle, then the measure of a leg of the triangle is the geometric mean between the measure of the hypotenuse and the measure of the segment of the hypotenuse adjacent to that leg. (293)
10. The Pythagorean Theorem (Theorem 9–4): If a triangle is a right triangle, then the sum of the squares of the measures of the legs equals the square of the measure of the hypotenuse. (295)
11. Converse of the Pythagorean Theorem (Theorem 9–5): If the sum of the squares of the measures of two sides of a triangle equals the square of the measure of the longest side, then the triangle is a right triangle. (296)

12. Theorem 9–6: If each acute angle of a right triangle has a degree measure of 45, then the hypotenuse measures $\sqrt{2}$ times the measure of a leg. (299)
13. Theorem 9–7: If the acute angles of a right triangle have degree measures of 30 and 60, then the measure of the hypotenuse is 2 times the measure of the shorter leg and the measure of the longer leg is $\sqrt{3}$ times the measure of the shorter leg. (300)
14. Definition of Sine: A ratio is the sine of an acute angle of a right triangle if and only if it is the ratio of the measure of the leg opposite the acute angle to the measure of the hypotenuse. (303)
15. Definition of Cosine: A ratio is the cosine of an acute angle of a right triangle if and only if it is the ratio of the measure of the leg adjacent to the acute angle to the measure of the hypotenuse. (303)
16. Definition of Tangent: A ratio is the tangent of an acute angle of a right triangle if and only if it is the ratio of the measure of the leg opposite the acute angle to the measure of the leg adjacent to the acute angle. (304)
17. A table can be used to find decimal approximations for values of trigonometric ratios. (307)

Chapter Review

9–1 State the principal square root of each expression.

1. 25 5 2. 0.04 0.2 3. $\frac{81}{16}$ $\frac{9}{4}$ 4. 75 $5\sqrt{3}$ 5. $\frac{5}{3}$ $\frac{\sqrt{15}}{3}$ 6. $\frac{1}{2}$ $\frac{\sqrt{2}}{2}$

Find the approximate value of each expression. Use the table of Squares and Approximate Square Roots.

7. $\sqrt{175}$ 13.23 8. $\sqrt{6} - \sqrt{15}$ -1.424 9. $\sqrt{\frac{7}{3}}$ 1.528

9–2 Use the figure at the right to answer each of the following. Approximate each answer to the nearest tenth.

10. Find BD if $AD = 4.0$ and $DC = 6.0$. 4.9 ≈ BD
11. Find AB if $AC = 18.0$ and $AD = 4.0$. AB ≈ 8.5
12. Find BC if $AD = 4\frac{8}{9}$ and $DC = \frac{1}{9}$. 0.7 ≈ BC
13. Find BA if $AD = \frac{1}{3}$ and $DC = \frac{1}{4}$. AB ≈ 0.4

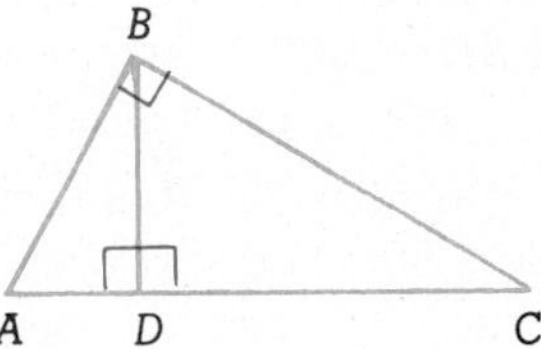

9–3 **For each of the following, determine whether or *not* it is possible to draw a right triangle with sides of the given measures. Write *yes* or *no*.**

14. 0.9, 2.1, 2.3 no
15. 0.9, 4.0, 4.1 yes
16. 4, 4, $4\sqrt{2}$ yes
17. 4, $7\frac{1}{2}$, $8\frac{1}{2}$ yes
18. $\sqrt{5}$, $\sqrt{7}$, $\sqrt{12}$ yes
19. $\sqrt{5}$, $\sqrt{6}$, $\sqrt{11}$ yes

For each of the following, find the measure of the hypotenuse of a right triangle with legs of the given measure. Round each answer to the nearest tenth.

20. 9.4, 8.0 12.3
21. 7.1, 6.7 9.8
22. 8.0, 15.0 17.0

9–4 **For each of the following, find the value of x. Round each answer to the nearest tenth.**

23. 4.2

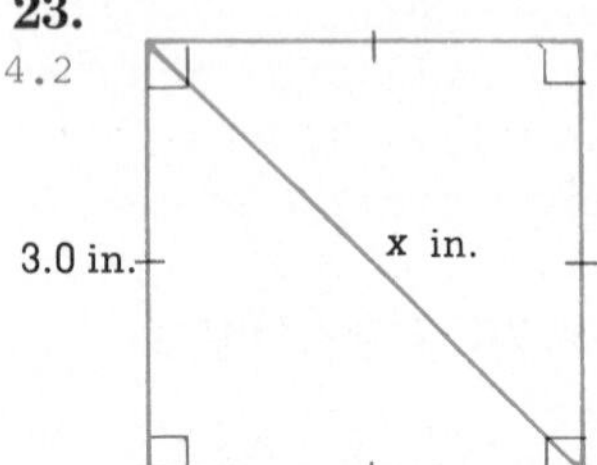

24. 2.7

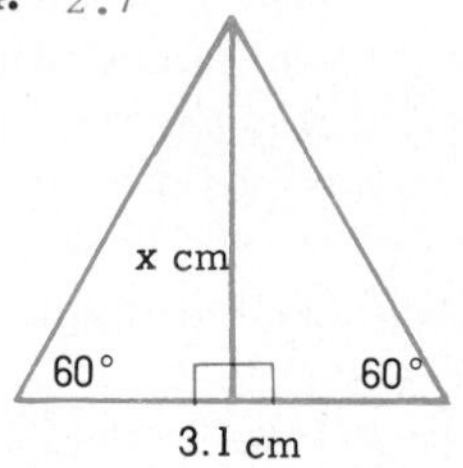

25. 10.0

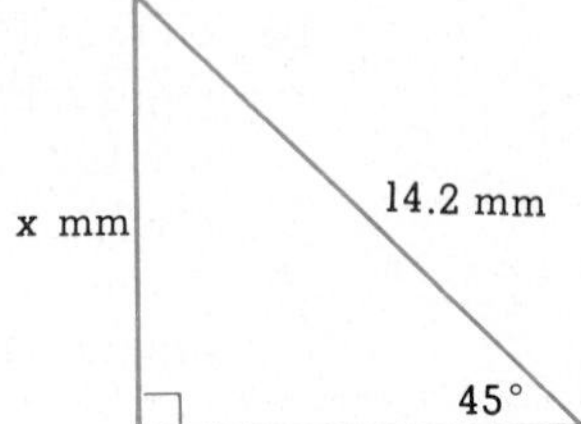

9–5 **For each of the following triangles, express the sine, cosine, and tangent of each acute angle to the nearest tenth.** For answers to exercises 26-27, see the Teacher's Guide.

26.

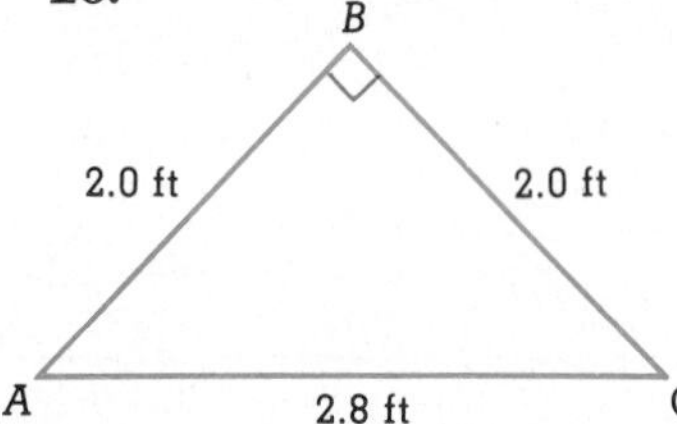

27.

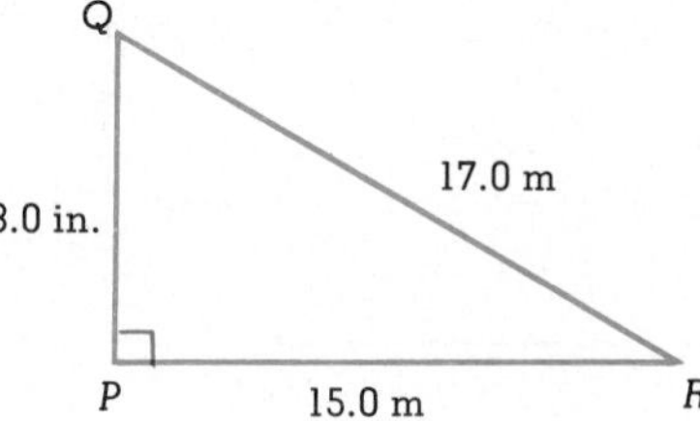

9–6 **Find the approximate value of each expression. Use the table of Trigonometric Ratios.**

28. sin 14° 0.2419
29. cos 33° 0.8387
30. tan 51° 1.2349

Find the measurement of each angle to the nearest degree.

31. sin A = 0.5000 30
32. cos B = 0.3200 71
33. tan C = 0.95 44

9–7 **Use a triangle similar to $\triangle ABC$ to help answer each problem.**

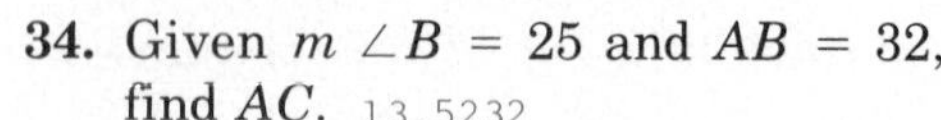

34. Given $m\angle B = 25$ and $AB = 32$, find AC. 13.5232

35. Given $m\angle A = 52$ and $AB = 7.5$, find BC. 5.91

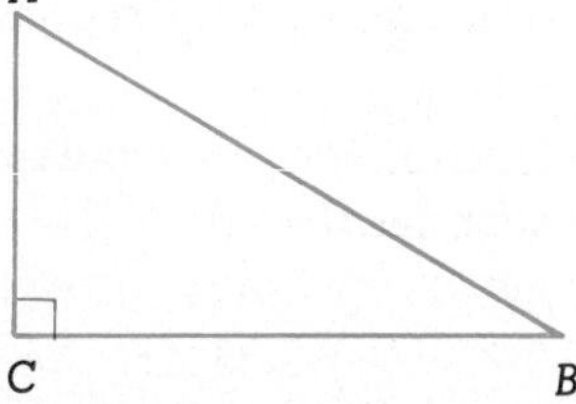

36. A surveyor is 350.0 m from a mountain peak. The angle of elevation to the top of the peak is 85°. The surveyor's instrument is 1.7 m above the ground. Find the height of the mountain peak to the nearest tenth of a meter. 4002.2 m

Chapter Test

For each of the following pairs of numbers, find the geometric mean. Approximate each answer to the nearest tenth.

1. 3.0 and 12.0 6.0
2. 11.0 and 11.0 11.0
3. 5.0 and 4.0 4.5
4. $\frac{1}{3}$ and $\frac{1}{2}$ 0.4
5. $\sqrt{2}$ and $2\sqrt{2}$ 2.0
6. $\frac{3}{4}$ and $\frac{4}{3}$ 1.0

For each of the following, determine whether or *not* it is possible to draw a right triangle with sides of the given measures. Write *yes* or *no*.

7. 16, 30, 34 yes
8. 0.3, 0.4, 0.5 yes
9. $\sqrt{7}, 2\sqrt{6}, 5$ no
10. $\frac{1}{3}, \frac{1}{4}, \frac{1}{5}$ no

For each of the following, find the value of x. Round each answer to the nearest tenth.

11. 6.6

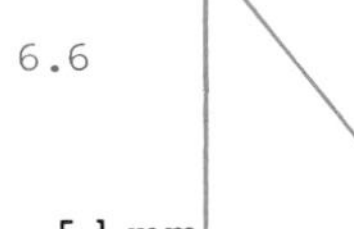

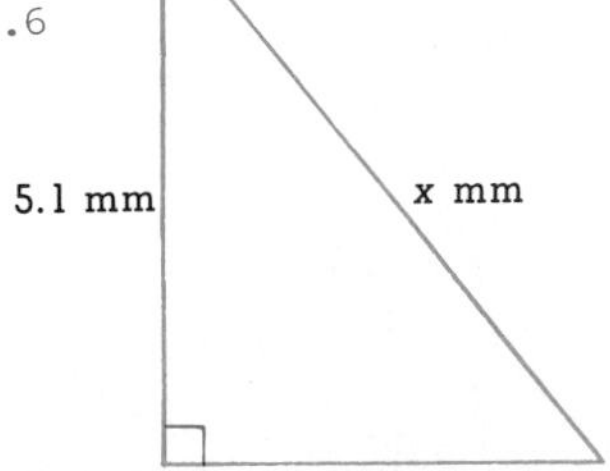

12. 5.9

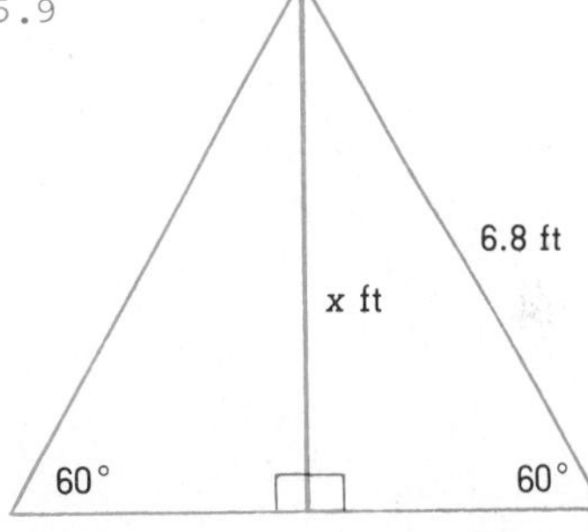

13. 5.2

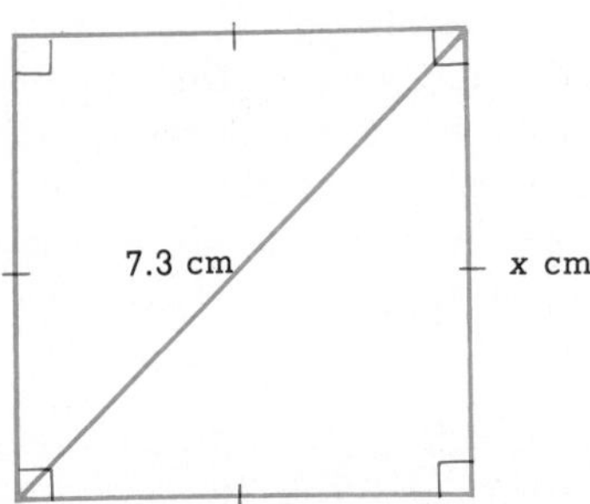

14. 4.2

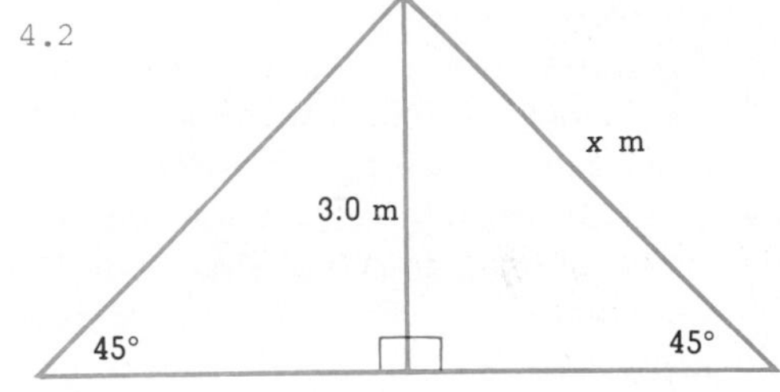

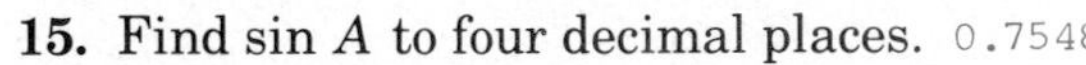

Use the figure to answer each problem.

15. Find sin A to four decimal places. 0.7548
16. Find sin C to four decimal places. 0.6560
17. Find tan A to four decimal places. 1.1506
18. Find cos C to four decimal places. 0.7548
19. Find $m\angle A$ to the nearest degree. 49
20. Find $m\angle C$ to the nearest degree. 41

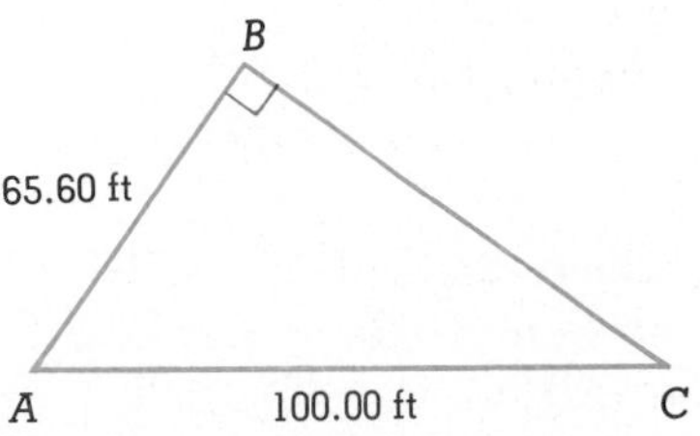

21. A flag pole casts a shadow 20 feet long when the angle of elevation of the sun measures 43°. Find the height of the pole to the nearest foot. 19 ft

cumulative review

State whether the following are *true* or *false*.

1. A point has only one dimension. false
2. A line contains at least two points. true
3. If two distinct planes intersect, then their intersection is exactly one point. false
4. The contrapositive of a statement is the same as the inverse of the converse of the statement. true
5. If P is between M and N, then P, M, and N are collinear. true
6. If $PM = MQ$, then M always is the midpoint of $\overline{PQ}$. false
7. An angle is defined as the union of two rays with a common endpoint. false
8. Vertical angles are equal in measure. true
9. Perpendicular lines form acute angles. false
10. The acute angles of a right triangle are supplementary. false
11. In an equilateral triangle all the medians and altitudes are congruent. true
12. The longest side of a right triangle is the hypotenuse. true
13. A triangle can have sides whose measures are 23, 7, and 16. false
14. Two parallel lines are everywhere equidistant. true
15. Regular polygons are always convex. true

Answer each of the following.

16. The degree measure of one angle of a regular polygon is 140. Name the polygon. nonagon (9 sides)
17. How many diagonals can be drawn in a regular heptagon? 14
18. An exterior angle of a regular polygon has a degree measure of 1. How many sides does the polygon have? 360
19. Find the measure of the other base of a trapezoid if the measures of a base and median are 12 and 29 respectively. 46
20. Find the perimeter of a regular polygon if one of its angles has a degree measure of 140 and one of its sides has a measure of 10. 9(10) or 90
21. How many faces does an icosahedron have? 20
22. In the figure at the right, $\overline{BC} \parallel \overline{DE}$, $AB = 4$, $AC = 3$, $BC = 2$, and $CE = 4$. Find BD and DE. $BD = \frac{16}{3}$, $DE = \frac{14}{3}$

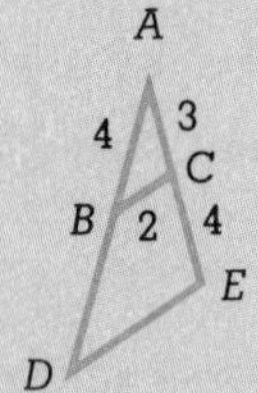

Exercise 22

23. In the figure at the right, $\triangle ABD \sim \triangle DBC$, $DB = 5$, $AB = 4$, and $AD = 3$. Find the perimeter of $\triangle DBC$. 15

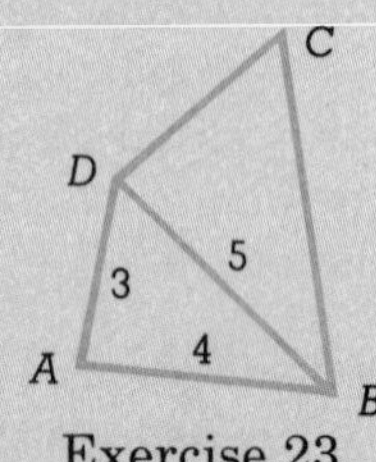

Exercise 23

Simplify each of the following.

24. $\sqrt{80}$ $4\sqrt{5}$

25. $\sqrt{12a^2b^3c^4}$ $2abc^2\sqrt{3b}$

26. Find the geometric mean between 5 and 20. 10

27. Given $NT = 4$, $MT = 3$, $\angle MNR$ is a right angle, and $\angle NTR$ is a right angle, find MN, TR, and NR.

$MN = 5$, $TR = \frac{16}{3}$, $NR = \frac{20}{3}$

N
4
M 3 T R

Exercise 27

28. Given $ST = 5\sqrt{2}$, $\overline{TO} \perp \overline{SP}$, $\overline{ST} \perp \overline{TP}$, and $m\angle TPO = 30$, find TO, OP, and TP.

$TP = 5\sqrt{6}$, $TO = \frac{5}{2}\sqrt{6}$, $OP = \frac{5}{2}\sqrt{18}$ or $\frac{15}{2}\sqrt{2}$

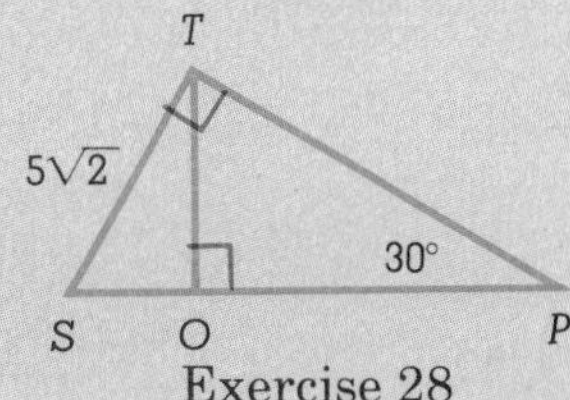

Exercise 28

29. Find the measure of the height, BC, in the diagram of the tree at the right.

49.99 ft or about 50 ft

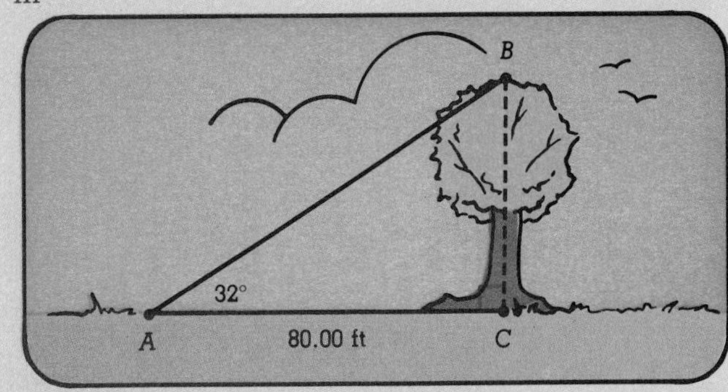

Complete each of the following.

30. opposite angles of a parallelogram are congruent.

31. The diagonals of a parallelogram bisect each other.

32. The diagonals of a rhombus bisect the angles of the rhombus.

33. The median of a trapezoid is parallel to the bases.

34. The mean proportional is also called geometric mean.

35. "For any right triangle, the square of the measure of the hypotenuse equals the sum of the squares of the measures of the legs," is called the ______ Theorem. Pythagorean

chapter 10 Circles and Spheres

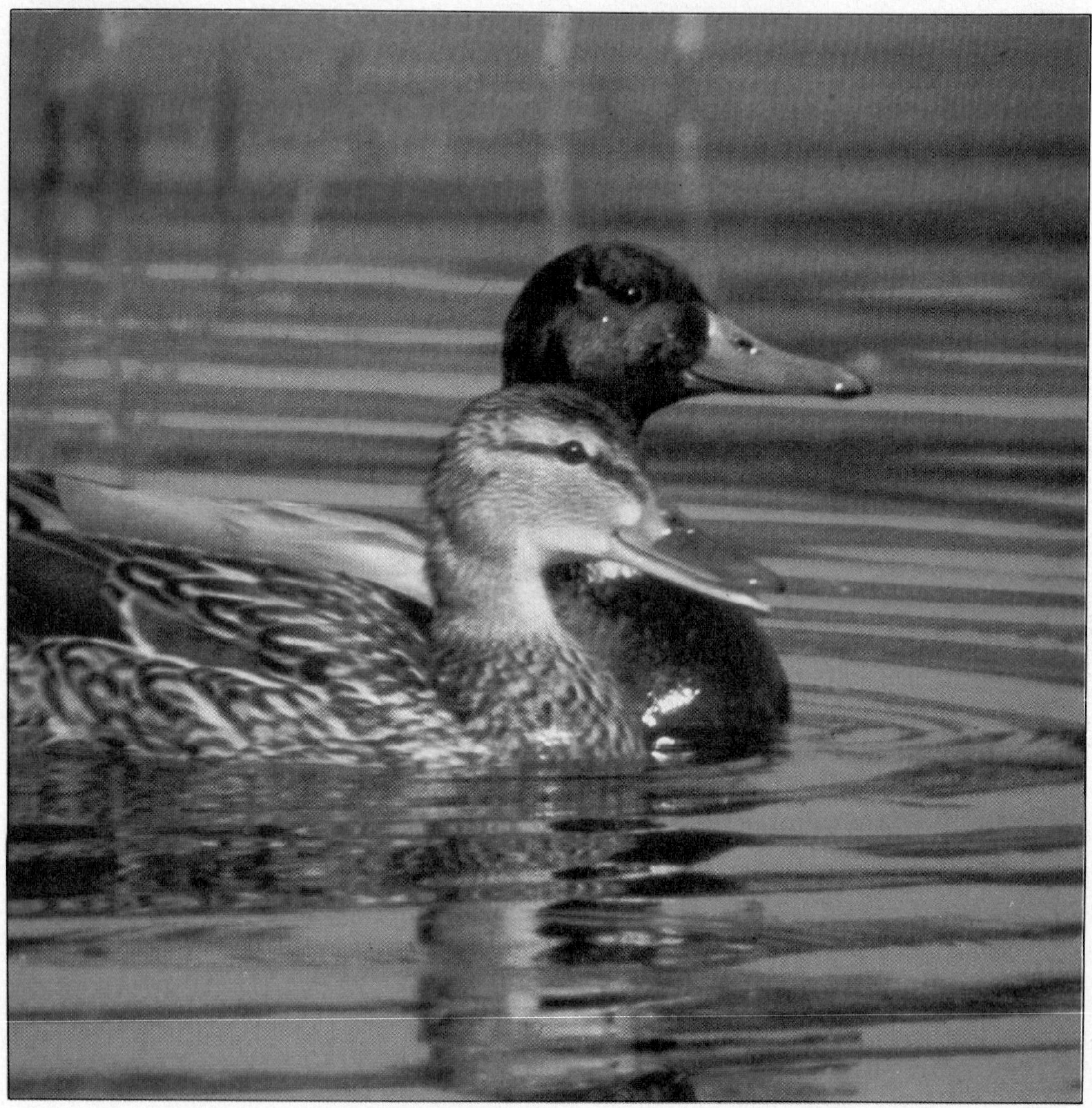

The photograph above provides a graphic illustration of circles. A circle is the set of points in a plane that are a given distance from a given point in the plane.

Emphasis should be made on "in one plane" for lessons 10-1 through 10-7.

Objectives: to name parts of circles, to determine relationships between lines and circles

10–1 Parts of Circles

To irrigate the cornfields shown in the photograph, water is sprayed from pipes that rotate about central points. Circular patterns result. Notice that all the points along the edge of a field are the same distance from the center. Each edge forms a **circle.**

A figure is a circle if and only if it is the set of all points in a plane that are a given distance from a given point in the plane, called the center.

Definition of Circle

Usually, circles are named by their centers. For example, the circle at the right is called circle P. This is symbolized $\odot P$.

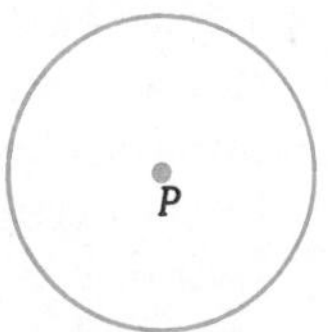

The following figures show segments that are related to circles.

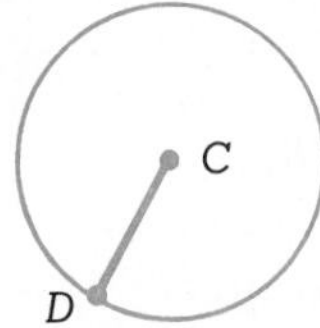

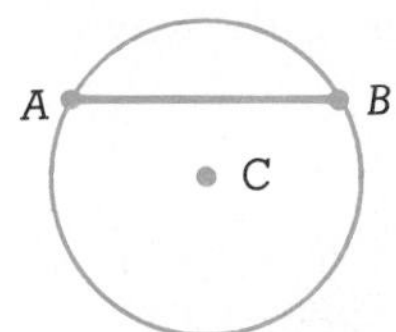

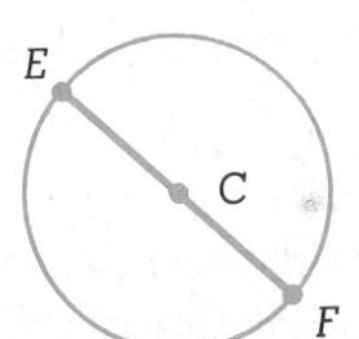

A **radius** of a circle is a segment whose endpoints are the center of the circle and a point on the circle. $\overline{CD}$ is a radius of $\odot C$.

A **chord** of a circle is a segment whose endpoints are points on the circle. $\overline{AB}$ is a chord of $\odot C$.

Note that a diameter is also a chord.

A **diameter** of a circle is a chord which contains the center of the circle. $\overline{EF}$ is a diameter of $\odot C$.

It follows from the definition of a circle that all the radii of a circle are congruent. Also, all the diameters of a circle are congruent.

How are the measure of a radius and the measure of a diameter of a circle related? $d = 2r$

A circle separates a plane into three parts. The parts are the **interior,** the **exterior,** and the **circle** itself.

Suppose a point is in the *interior* of a circle. The measure of the segment joining the point to the center is *less than* the measure of the radius.

Suppose a point is in the *exterior* of a circle. The measure of the segment joining the point to the center is *greater than* the measure of the radius.

$PI < PR$

$PE > PR$

In a plane, a line can intersect a circle in one of two ways.

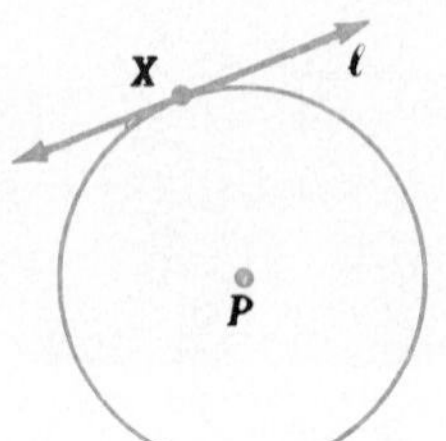

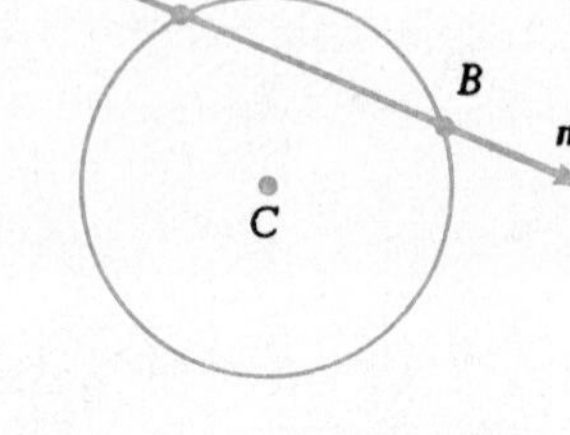

A line can intersect a circle in exactly one point. Such a line is a **tangent** to the circle. The point of intersection is the **point of tangency.** In the figure above, line ℓ is tangent to $\odot P$ at X.

A line can intersect a circle in exactly two points. Such a line is a **secant** of the circle. A secant of a circle contains a chord of the circle. In the figure above, line m contains the chord $\overline{AB}$ and is a secant of $\odot C$.

The following theorem guarantees that these are the only ways lines can intersect a circle.

In a plane, if a line contains a point in the interior of a circle, then the line intersects the circle in exactly two points.

Theorem 10–1

1 **All points of $\odot P$ are 4 units from P. Suppose $PA = 5$ and $PB = 2$. Determine whether $\overleftrightarrow{AB}$ intersects $\odot P$ in *zero points, one point,* or *two points.***

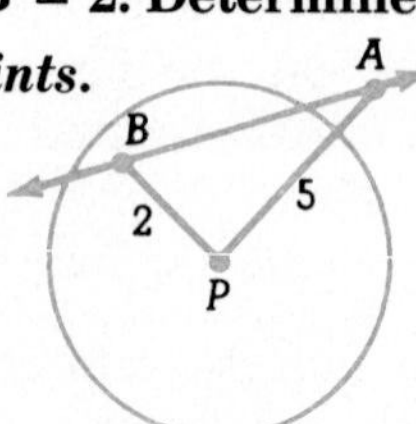

B must be in the interior of $\odot P$ because the measure of the distance from P to B is less than the measure of the radius of the circle. Thus, by Theorem 10–1, $\overleftrightarrow{AB}$ intersects the circle in exactly two points.

A line that is tangent to two circles in the same plane is called a **common tangent** of the two circles. There are two types of common tangents.

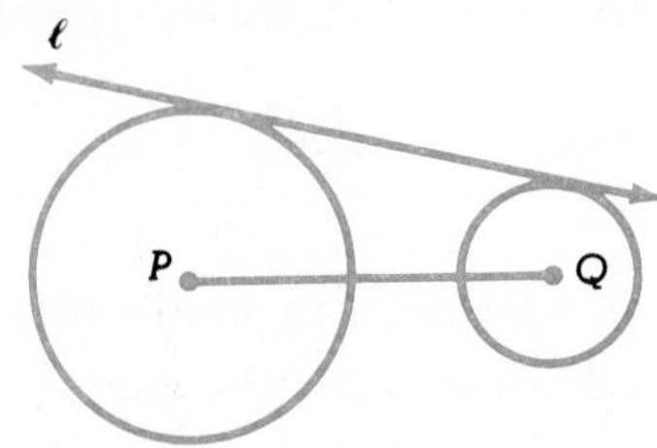

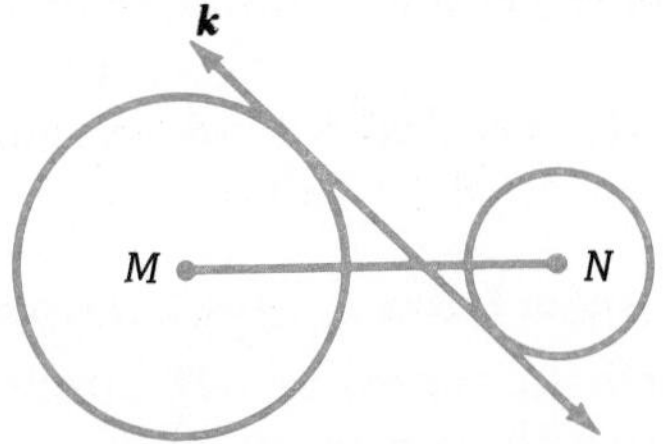

A common tangent that does not intersect the segment whose endpoints are the centers of the circles is a **common external tangent.** In the figure above, line ℓ is a common external tangent to $\odot P$ and $\odot Q$.

A common tangent that intersects the segment whose endpoints are the centers of the circles is a **common internal tangent.** In the figure above, line k is a common internal tangent to $\odot M$ and $\odot N$.

example

2 How many common tangents can be drawn to $\odot Q$ and $\odot P$?

There are 4 common tangents to $\odot Q$ and $\odot P$.

Lines ℓ and m are common external tangents and lines j and k are common internal tangents.

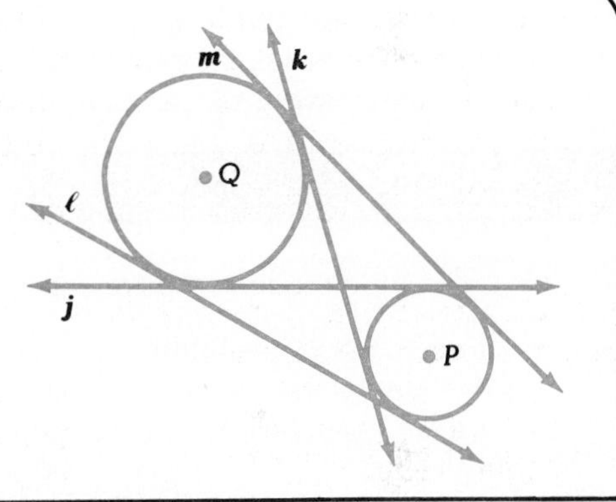

EN: Ex: 5-7 Wr: 1-15; p. 326, E: 1; AV: Ex: 1-10, Wr: 1-15; p. 326, E: 1-4

exercises

FN: Ex: 1-10, Wr: 1-15; p. 326, E: 1-4

Exploratory **Use the figure to answer each of the following.**

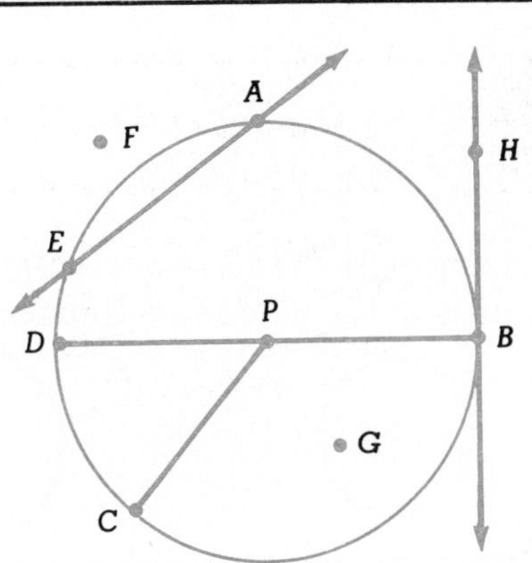

1. Name the center of the circle. P
2. Name the circle. $\odot$ P
3. Name three radii of the circle. $\overline{PD}$, $\overline{PB}$, $\overline{PC}$
4. Name a diameter of the circle. $\overline{DB}$
5. Name a chord of the circle. $\overline{EA}$ or $\overline{DB}$
6. Name a tangent of the circle. $\overleftrightarrow{HB}$
7. Name a secant of the circle. $\overleftrightarrow{EA}$
8. Name two points in the interior of the circle. G, P
9. Name two points in the exterior of the circle. F, H
10. Name five points that lie on the circle. A, B, C, D, E

Written **For each of the following, write *yes* or *no*.**

1. A diameter of a circle is the longest chord of the circle. yes
2. A radius of a circle is a chord of the circle. no
3. A chord of a circle is a secant of the circle. no
4. A secant of a circle is always a diameter of the circle. no
5. Two radii of a circle always form a diameter of the circle. no
6. A radius of a circle is tangent to the circle. no

Suppose all points of $\odot R$ are 6 units from R and $\overleftrightarrow{AB}$ and $\odot R$ are in the same plane. For each of the following, determine whether $\overleftrightarrow{AB}$ intersects $\odot R$ in *zero points*, *one point*, or *two points*. There may be more than one answer.

7. $RA = 5.2$, $RB = 7.9$ 2 points
8. $RA = 6.0$, $RB = 3.3$ 2 points
9. $RA = 6.0$, $RB = 6.0$ 2 points
10. $RA = 7.9$, $RB = 9.7$ 0, 1, or 2 points

Prove each of the following. For answers to exercises 11-15, see the Teacher's Guide.

11. If the diameter of a circle measures d units and the radius of the circle measures r units, then $d = 2r$.
12. If X is a point in the interior of $\odot P$, then there are points A and B on $\odot P$ so that X is between A and B.

Draw two different circles that have the common tangents described in the following.

13. one common internal tangent and two common external tangents
14. no common internal tangents and two common external tangents
15. no common internal tangents and one common external tangent

Centers of Circles — excursions in geometry

The following procedure can be used to find the center of a circle.

Place a sheet of paper over the circle so one corner touches the circle.

The paper intersects the circle at two other points, A and B. Draw chord $\overline{AB}$.

Place the paper so the corner touches the circle at a different point. Draw $\overline{EF}$.

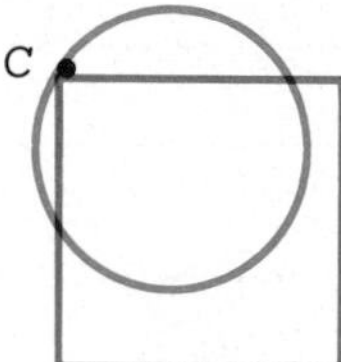

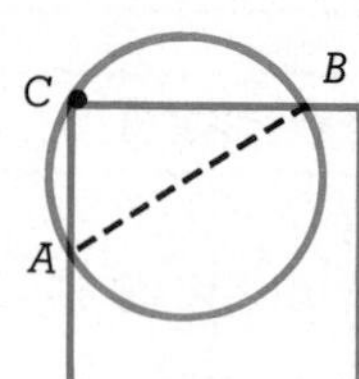

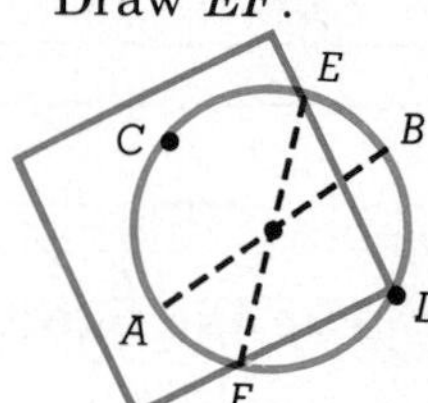

The intersection of $\overline{AB}$ and $\overline{EF}$ is the center of the circle.

Exercises **Trace each of the following circles. Find the center and the length of the radius to the nearest millimeter.**

1. 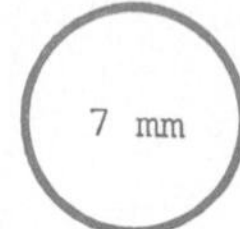

2. 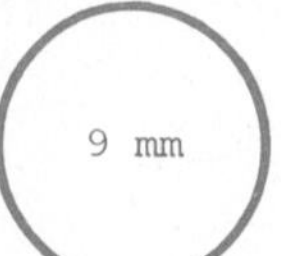

3. 

4. 

10–2 Angles and Arcs

Objectives: to recognize major or minor arcs, or semicircles, to find the degree measures of arcs and central angles

Two rays can be drawn from the center of a circle to form an angle. If the rays and the circle are in the same plane, such an angle is called a **central angle.**

words arc ACB
symbols $\widehat{ACB}$

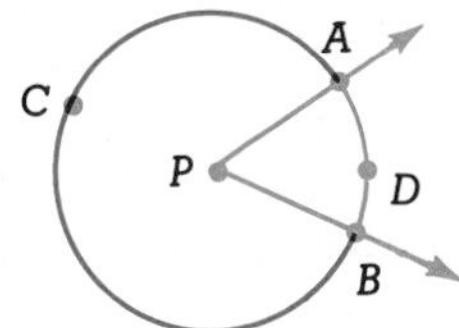

arc AB *words*
$\widehat{AB}$ *symbols*

A central angle separates a circle into **arcs.** For example, in the figure above, $\angle APB$ is a central angle of $\odot P$. Points A and B, and all points of the circle interior to $\angle APB$ form a **minor arc** called $\widehat{AB}$ or $\widehat{ADB}$. Points A and B, and all points of the circle exterior to $\angle APB$ form a **major arc** called $\widehat{ACB}$. *Three letters are needed to name a major arc. Why?* Emphasize the need to use three letters in order to differentiate the major from the minor arc.

$\widehat{ADB}$ and $\widehat{BDA}$ name the same minor arc.

A line containing the diameter of a circle separates the circle into two **semicircles.** In the figure, $\widehat{XRY}$ and $\widehat{XSY}$ are semicircles.

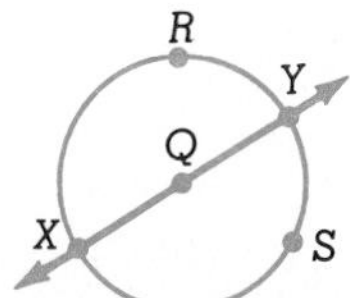

Arcs are measured by their corresponding central angles.

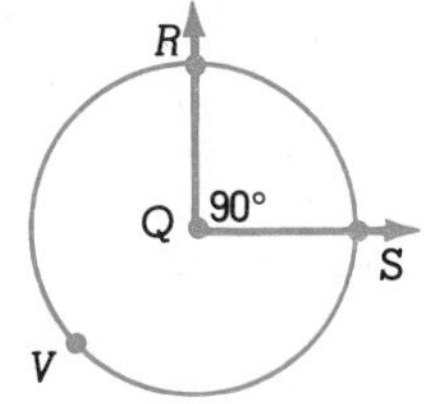

The degree measure of $\widehat{RS}$ is 90. *words*
$m\widehat{RS} = 90$ *symbols*

The degree measure of a minor arc is the degree measure of its central angle. The degree measure of a major arc is 360 minus the degree measure of its central angle. The degree measure of a semicircle is 180.

Definition of Arc Measure

As with angles, measures of arcs can be added to find measures of other arcs. For example, $m\widehat{PQ} = 110$ and $m\widehat{QR} = 120$. Thus, $m\widehat{PQR} = 230$.

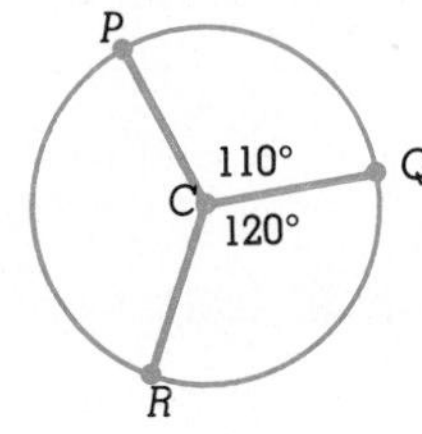

If Q is a point on $\overset{\frown}{PQR}$, then $m\overset{\frown}{PQ} + m\overset{\frown}{QR} = m\overset{\frown}{PQR}$.

Postulate 10–1 Arc Addition Postulate

The sum of the degree measures of all of the arcs of a circle is 360. Why?

The sum of the degree measures of the central angles is 360.

example

1 In $\odot P$, $m\angle APB = 30$ and $\overline{AC}$ is a diameter. Find $m\overset{\frown}{AB}$, $m\overset{\frown}{ACB}$, $m\overset{\frown}{BC}$, and $m\overset{\frown}{BAC}$.

The central angle of $\overset{\frown}{AB}$ and $\overset{\frown}{ACB}$ is $\angle APB$. Thus, $m\overset{\frown}{AB} = 30$. $\overset{\frown}{ACB}$ is a major arc for $\angle APB$. Thus, $m\overset{\frown}{ACB} = 360 - 30$ or 330.

By the Arc Addition Postulate, $m\overset{\frown}{AB} + m\overset{\frown}{BC} = m\overset{\frown}{ABC}$. Since $m\overset{\frown}{AB} = 30$ and $\overset{\frown}{ABC}$ is a semicircle, the following holds.

$$30 + m\overset{\frown}{BC} = 180$$
$$m\overset{\frown}{BC} = 180 - 30 \text{ or } 150$$

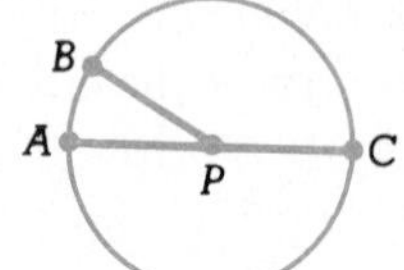

Finally, $\overset{\frown}{BAC}$ is a major arc for $\angle BPC$ which measures 150. Thus, $m\overset{\frown}{BAC} = 360 - 150$ or 210.

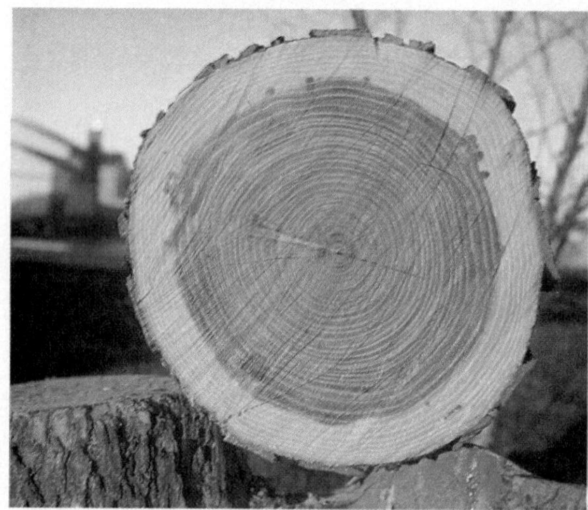

All circles have the same shape, but *not all* circles have the same size. Notice that the tree rings share a common center but have radii of different lengths. Circles that lie in the same plane and have the same center are called **concentric circles.**

All circles are similar.

As the tree rings show, circles with radii having different lengths are *not* congruent. For two circles to be congruent, their radii *must have* the same length.

Two circles are congruent if and only if their radii are congruent.

Definition of Congruent Circles

Two arcs of a circle are congruent if and only if they have the same measure.

In a circle or in congruent circles, two central angles are congruent if and only if their minor arcs are congruent. ***Theorem 10–2***

EN: Wr: 9-16, 10-15, 22-27, 28-46 evens; p. 330, AR: 5-9; Av: Ex: 1-15 odds, Wr: 1-35 odds; p. 330, AR: 1-9

exercises

FN: Ex: 1-16, Wr: 1-35; p. 330, AR: 1-9

Exploratory **For each of the following, determine whether it is a *minor arc*, a *major arc*, or a *semicircle* of $\odot M$.**

1. $\widehat{AB}$ minor **2.** $\widehat{ECA}$ major **3.** $\widehat{BAE}$ 3. semicircle **4.** $\widehat{BDE}$ 4. semicircle
5. $\widehat{DCE}$ major **6.** $\widehat{CBD}$ major **7.** $\widehat{DAB}$ major **8.** $\widehat{AE}$ minor
9. $\widehat{BC}$ minor **10.** $\widehat{BCD}$ minor **11.** $\widehat{BDC}$ major **12.** $\widehat{AD}$ minor
13. $\widehat{CBA}$ 13. semicircle **14.** $\widehat{DC}$ minor **15.** $\widehat{ACD}$ major **16.** $\widehat{CAE}$ major

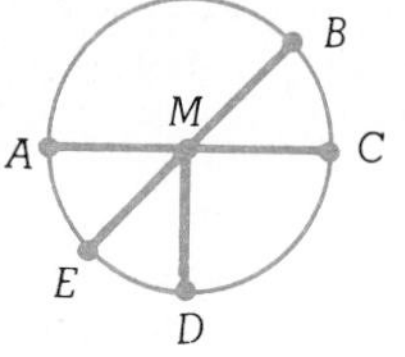

Written **Answer the following if in $\odot P$, $m\angle WPX = 28$, $m\angle ZPY = 38$, and $\overline{WZ}$ and $\overline{XV}$ are diameters.**

1. Find $m\widehat{YZ}$. 38 **2.** Find $m\widehat{WX}$. 28 **3.** Find $m\angle VPZ$. 28
4. Find $m\widehat{VZ}$. 28 **5.** Find $m\widehat{VWX}$. 180 **6.** Find $m\widehat{ZVW}$. 180
7. Find $m\widehat{WYZ}$. 180 **8.** Find $m\widehat{ZXW}$. 180 **9.** Find $m\angle XPY$. 114
10. Find $m\widehat{XY}$. 114 **11.** Find $m\widehat{XWY}$. 246 **12.** Find $m\widehat{WZX}$. 332
13. Find $m\widehat{VW}$. 152 **14.** Find $m\angle VPW$. 152 **15.** Find $m\widehat{WVY}$. 218

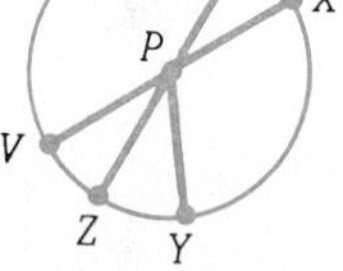

Exercises 1–15

Answer the following if in $\odot C$, $m\angle BCY = 2x$, $m\angle BCQ = 4x + 15$, $m\angle QCX = 2x + 5$, and $\overline{XY}$ and $\overline{AB}$ are diameters.

16. Find the value of x. 20 **17.** Find $m\widehat{BY}$. 40 **18.** Find $m\widehat{BQ}$. 95
19. Find $m\widehat{QX}$. 45 **20.** Find $m\widehat{YQ}$. 135 **21.** Find $m\angle YCQ$. 135
22. Find $m\widehat{BX}$. 140 **23.** Find $m\angle BCX$. 140 **24.** Find $m\widehat{XA}$. 40
25. Find $m\widehat{QA}$. 85 **26.** Find $m\angle QCA$. 85 **27.** Find $m\widehat{XYA}$. 320

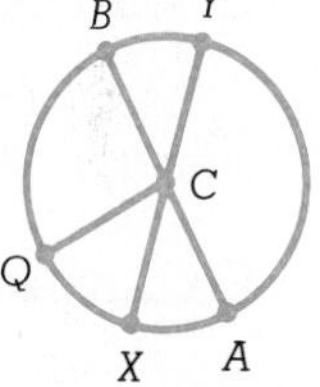

Exercises 16–27

For each of the following, write *yes* or *no*.

28. If $m\widehat{AB} = 32$ and $m\widehat{XY} = 32$, then $\widehat{AB} \cong \widehat{XY}$. no

29. If $\widehat{AB} \cong \widehat{XY}$, and $m\widehat{AB} = 32$, then $m\widehat{XY} = 64$. no

30. Two congruent circles have congruent radii. yes

31. All radii of a circle are congruent. yes

32. Two concentric circles never have congruent radii. no

33. If two circles have the same center, they are congruent. no

34. If two central angles are congruent, then their corresponding minor arcs are congruent. no

35. If two minor arcs are congruent, then their corresponding central angles are congruent. yes

Answer each of the following. For answers to exercises 36-38, see the Teacher's Guide.

36. Prove that in two congruent circles, if two minor arcs are congruent then their corresponding central angles are congruent.

37. Prove that in two congruent circles, if two central angles are congruent, then their corresponding minor arcs are congruent.

38. Suppose a wheel has 30 spokes evenly spaced and numbered consecutively from 1 through 30. Find the degree measure of the central angle formed by spokes 1 and 14.

In the figure, A is the center of two concentric circles with radii $\overline{AQ}$ and $\overline{AR}$. Also, $m\angle SAR = 32$, and $m\angle RAW = 112$.

39. Find $m\widehat{SR}$. 32 **40.** Find $m\widehat{TX}$. 144 **41.** Find $m\widehat{XQ}$. 112

42. Find $m\widehat{WR}$. 112 **43.** Find $m\widehat{SW}$. 144 **44.** Find $m\widehat{TQ}$. 32

45. Find $m\widehat{TYX}$. 216 **46.** Find $m\widehat{SZW}$. 216

47. Use your answers to exercises 39–46 to help answer the following question. Can two arcs have the same measure but not be congruent? yes

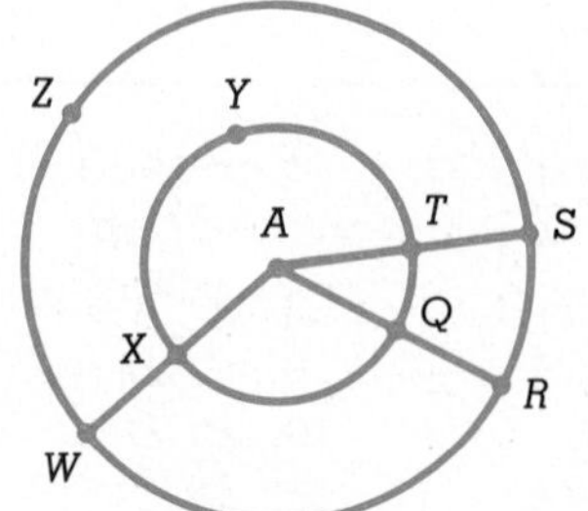

Exercises 39–47

Radical Equations algebra review

To solve a radical equation, first isolate the radical expression on one side of the equals sign. Then square both sides of the equation to eliminate the radical.

Example **Solve $\sqrt{3x} + 1 = 4$.**

$$\sqrt{3x} + 1 = 4$$

$$\sqrt{3x} = 3 \quad \textit{Isolate the radical.}$$

$$3x = 9 \quad \textit{Square both sides.}$$

$$x = 3$$

Exercises **Solve each equation.**

1. $\sqrt{x} = 6$ 36

2. $4 + \sqrt{2y} = 6$ 2

3. $\sqrt{5a + 6} = 11$ 23

4. $2\sqrt{10} = \sqrt{x}$ 40

5. $\sqrt{\frac{3m}{5}} - 1 = 2$ 15

6. $\frac{8}{\sqrt{6x - 8}} = 4$ 2

7. $\sqrt{3b + 4} - 2 = 13$ $73\frac{2}{3}$

8. $\sqrt{x + 8} = x + 1$ $\frac{-1 + \sqrt{29}}{2}$

9. $6\sqrt{n^2 - 4} = 12$ $\pm 2\sqrt{2}$

10–3 Arcs and Chords

Objective: to recognize and to use the relationships between arcs, chords, and other parts of circles

When a minor arc and a chord have the same endpoints, we call the arc the **arc of the chord.** For example, in the figure at the right $\overset{\frown}{PQ}$, is the arc of $\overline{PQ}$.

Chords and their arcs are related in the following way.

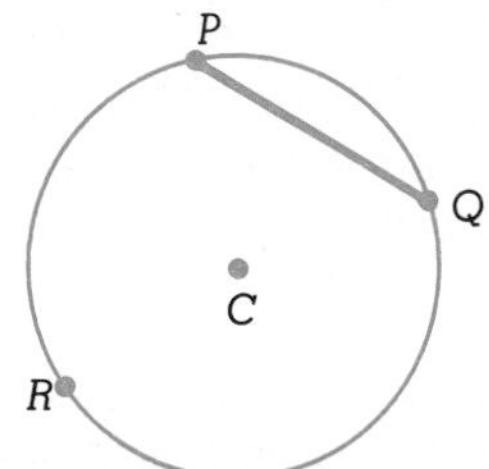

In a circle or in congruent circles, two minor arcs are congruent if and only if their corresponding chords are congruent.

Theorem 10–3

The proof of this theorem is based on congruent triangles. The following example shows how they are used to prove one part of the theorem. The second part of the proof of Theorem 10-3 is done by students in Written exercise 15.

example 1 **Prove that if two arcs of a circle are congruent, then their corresponding chords are congruent.**

Given: $\overset{\frown}{AB} \cong \overset{\frown}{PQ}$

C is the center of the circle.

Prove: $\overline{AB} \cong \overline{PQ}$

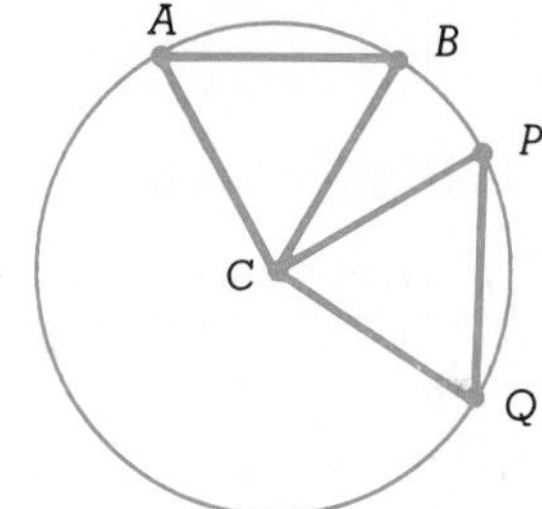

Proof:

STATEMENTS	REASONS
1. Draw radii $\overline{AC}$, $\overline{BC}$, $\overline{PC}$, and $\overline{QC}$ and chords $\overline{AB}$ and $\overline{PQ}$.	1. Postulate 1–1: Through any two points there is exactly one line.
2. $\overline{AC} \cong \overline{PC}$ $\overline{BC} \cong \overline{QC}$	2. Definition of Circle
3. $\overset{\frown}{AB} \cong \overset{\frown}{PQ}$, $\odot C$	3. Given
4. $\angle ACB \cong \angle PCQ$	4. Theorem 10–2: In a circle or in congruent circles, if two minor arcs are congruent, then their central angles are congruent.
5. $\triangle ACB \cong \triangle PCQ$	5. Postulate 4–3: SAS
6. $\overline{AB} \cong \overline{PQ}$	6. Definition of Congruent Triangles

The midpoint of an arc separates the arc into two congruent arcs. In $\odot C$, point M is the midpoint of $\overparen{AB}$ because $\overparen{AM} \cong \overparen{MB}$, and we say that $\overline{CM}$ bisects $\overparen{AB}$. By using congruent triangles, it can be shown that $\overline{CM}$ also bisects $\overline{AB}$. In addition, $\overline{CM} \perp \overline{AB}$.

Suppose a diameter or radius of a circle is perpendicular to a chord. Does it bisect the chord or its arc? yes

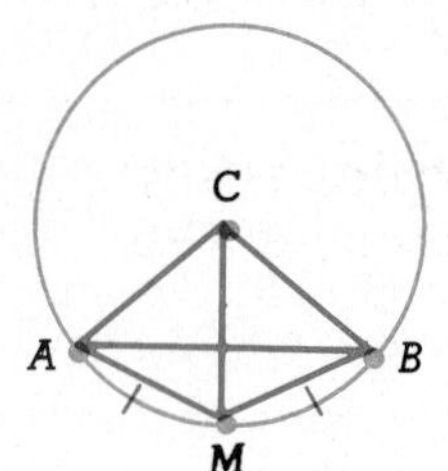

In a circle, if a diameter is perpendicular to a chord, then it bisects the chord and its arcs.

Theorem 10–4

Students prove this theorem in Written exercise 18.

2 **Suppose a chord of a circle is 24 centimeters long and is 9 centimeters from the center of the circle. Find the length of the radius.**

Let $\overline{AD}$ represent the chord, and draw $\overline{BC}$ perpendicular to $\overline{AD}$. Then, $BC = 9$.

By Theorem 10–4, $\overline{BC}$ bisects $\overline{AD}$. Thus, AC and $CD = \frac{24}{2}$ or 12.

$\overline{AB}$ is a radius of the circle and the hypotenuse of a right triangle with sides measuring 12 and 9 centimeters, respectively.

$$(AB)^2 = 12^2 + 9^2$$
$$= 225$$
$$AB = 15$$

Thus, the radius is 15 centimeters long.

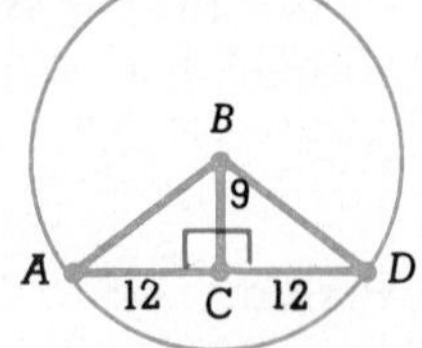

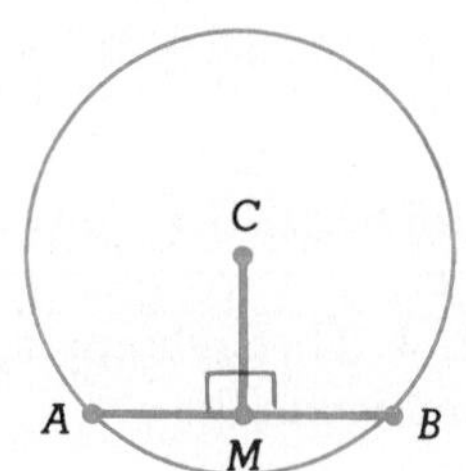

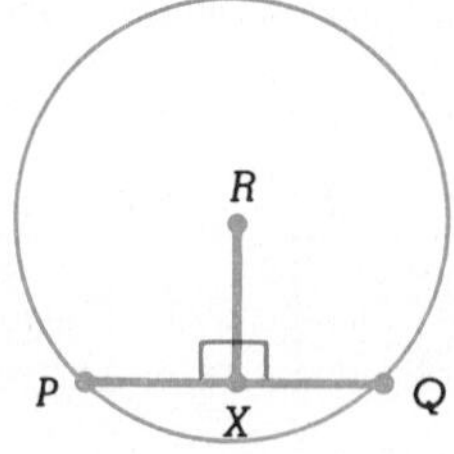

Suppose $\odot C$ and $\odot R$ are congruent, and $\overline{AB} \cong \overline{PQ}$. Are the chords the same distance from the centers of the circles? yes

Suppose, instead, that you know the chords to be equidistant from the centers of the circles. Could you conclude that the chords are congruent? yes

In a circle or in congruent circles, two chords are congruent if and only if they are equidistant from the center.

Theorem 10–5

Students prove this theorem in Written exercises 19 and 20.

EN: Ex: 1-7 odds, Wr: 11-25 odds, 26-29; AV: Ex: 1-7, Wr: 1-25 odds; p. 329-30, Wr: 32-46 evens

exercises

FN: Ex: 1-7, Wr: 1-16; p. 330, Wr: 36-46

Exploratory **For each of the following, name the theorem or theorems that justify the statement. Use $\odot P$.**

1. Theorem 10-3 2. Theorem 10-3 3. Theorem 10-5 4. Theorem 10-4 5. Theorem 10-4 6. Theorem 10-5 7. Theorem 10-4

1. If $\overline{BC} \cong \overline{AD}$, then $\widehat{BC} \cong \widehat{AD}$.
2. If $\widehat{BC} \cong \widehat{AD}$, then $\overline{BC} \cong \overline{AD}$.
3. If $\overline{BC} \cong \overline{AD}$, then $PQ = PR$.
4. If $\overline{PF} \perp \overline{AD}$, then $\widehat{AF} \cong \widehat{FD}$.
5. If $\overline{PQ} \perp \overline{BC}$, then $\overline{BQ} \cong \overline{QC}$.
6. If $PQ = PR$, then $\overline{CB} \cong \overline{DA}$.
7. If $\overline{FX} \perp \overline{AD}$, then $\widehat{AX} \cong \widehat{XD}$.

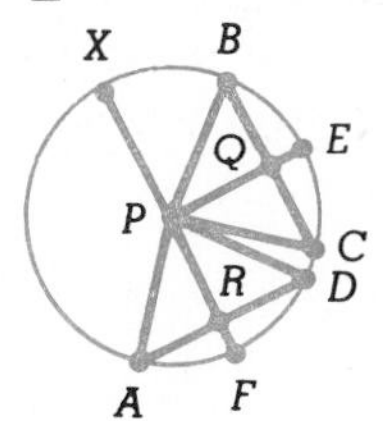

Exercises 1–7

Written **For $\odot A$ answer the following if $\overline{SY} \perp \overline{QT}$, and $\overline{YS}$ and $\overline{ZR}$ are diameters.**

1. Name a segment congruent to $\overline{VT}$. $\overline{QV}$
2. Name the midpoint of $\widehat{QT}$. S
3. Name the midpoint of $\overline{TQ}$. V
4. Name an arc congruent to $\widehat{QY}$. $\widehat{YT}$
5. Name an arc congruent to $\widehat{ST}$. $\widehat{QS}$
6. Name a segment congruent to $\overline{RZ}$. $\overline{SY}$
7. Which segment is longer, $\overline{WA}$ or $\overline{VA}$? $\overline{WA}$
8. Which segment is longer, $\overline{QT}$ or $\overline{YS}$? $\overline{YS}$
9. If W is the midpoint of $\overline{QV}$, then R is the midpoint of $\widehat{QS}$. Write *yes* or *no*. no
10. If X is the midpoint of $\widehat{ZXR}$, how is $\overline{XA}$ related to $\overline{ZR}$? They are perpendicular.

Exercises 1–10

Answer each of the following.

11. Suppose a chord of a circle is 10 inches long and is 12 inches from the center of the circle. Find the length of the radius. 13 in.
12. Suppose a chord of a circle is 18 centimeters long and is 12 centimeters from the center of the circle. Find the length of the radius. 15 cm
13. Suppose the diameter of a circle is 20 centimeters long and a chord is 16 centimeters long. Find the distance between the chord and the center of the circle. 6 cm
14. Suppose the diameter of a circle is 10 inches long and a chord is 6 inches long. Find the distance between the chord and the center of the circle. 4 in.

Prove each of the following. For answers to exercises 15-29, see the Teacher's Guide.

15. If two chords of a circle are congruent, then their corresponding arcs are congruent.
16. If two congruent circles each contain a chord that is congruent to the other chord, then the corresponding arcs are congruent.

17. If a radius of a circle bisects an arc of a circle, then it bisects the corresponding chord.

18. Theorem 10–4

19. If two chords of a circle are congruent, then they are equidistant from the center of the circle.

20. If two chords of a circle are equidistant from the center of the circle, then the two chords are congruent.

21. In a circle, if a chord is a perpendicular bisector of another chord, then the first chord is a diameter of the circle.

22. In a circle, if one chord is longer than another chord, then the longer chord is closer to the center of the circle.

23. **Given:** $\overline{AC}$ is a diameter.
$\overline{AC} \perp \overline{BD}$
Prove: $\widehat{BC} \cong \widehat{DC}$

24. **Given:** $\overline{AC}$ is a diameter.
$\overline{AC} \perp \overline{BD}$
Prove: $\triangle EBC \cong \triangle EDC$

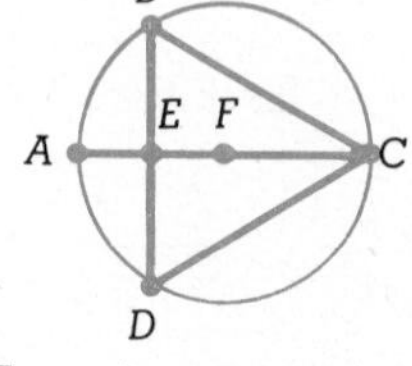

Exercises 23 and 24

25. **Given:** $\widehat{PTS} \cong \widehat{QST}$
$\overline{RS} \cong \overline{RT}$
Prove: $\triangle PQR$ is isosceles.

26. **Given:** $\overline{RQ} \cong \overline{RP}$
$\widehat{QS} \cong \widehat{PT}$
Prove: $\triangle SRT$ is isosceles.

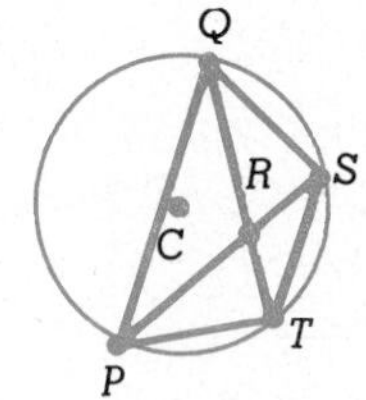

Exercises 25 and 26

Use the following information in exercises 27–29.

Given: $\overline{FE}$ is a diameter of $\odot A$.
$\overline{UT}$ is a diameter of $\odot P$.
$\overline{FE} \perp \overline{BD}$
$\overline{UT} \perp \overline{QS}$

27. **Given:** $\odot A$ and $\odot P$ are congruent.
$\overline{BC} \cong \overline{QR}$
Prove: $\widehat{BD} \cong \widehat{QS}$

28. **Given:** $\overline{AE} \cong \overline{PT}$
$\overline{AC} \cong \overline{PR}$
Prove: $\overline{BC} \cong \overline{QR}$

29. **Given:** $\overline{AC} \cong \overline{PR}$
$\overline{CD} \cong \overline{RS}$
Prove: $\widehat{BE} \cong \widehat{QT}$

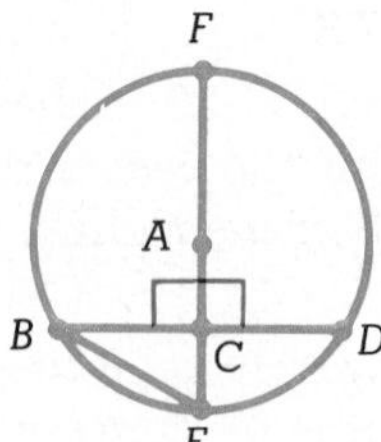

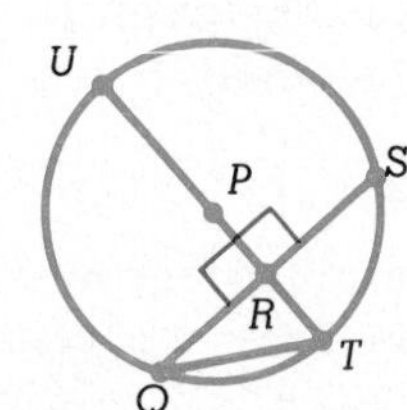

Exercises 27–29

10–4 Inscribed Angles

Objectives: to recognize intercepted arcs and inscribed angles, to find the measures of inscribed angles, to use properties of inscribed figures to solve problems

In each of the figures below, the angles intercept arcs of the circles. The **intercepted arcs** are shown in red.

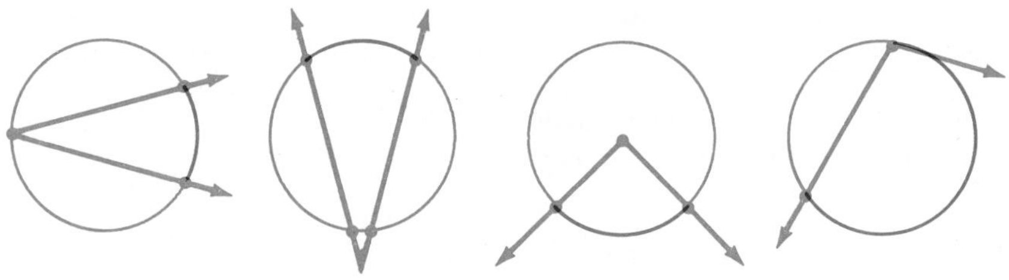

Note that one angle intercepts two arcs.

Definition of Intercepted Arc

An angle intercepts an arc if and only if each of the following conditions hold.

1. **The endpoints of the arc lie on the angle.**
2. **All points of the arc, except the endpoints, are in the interior of the angle.**
3. **Each side of the angle contains an endpoint of the arc.**

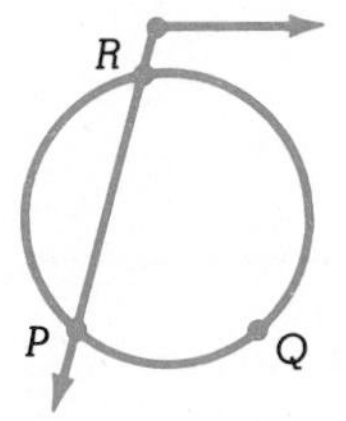

$\overset{\frown}{PQR}$ is not an intercepted arc.

In the figure at the right, $\angle ABC$ intercepts an arc of a circle, and the vertex of the angle lies on the circle. Such an angle is called an **inscribed angle.** We say that $\angle ABC$ intercepts $\overset{\frown}{AC}$ and is inscribed in $\overset{\frown}{ABC}$.

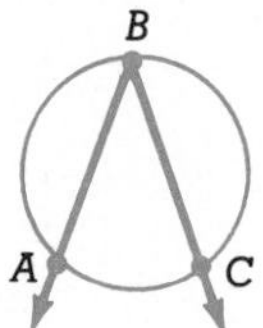

Definition of Inscribed Angle

An angle is an inscribed angle if and only if its vertex lies on a circle and its sides contain chords of the circle.

The measures of inscribed angles are related to the measures of their intercepted arcs.

In the figure at the right, $\angle QPR$ is an inscribed angle which intercepts $\widehat{QR}$. By using the Isosceles Triangle Theorem and the Exterior Angle Theorem, you can show that $m\angle QPR = \frac{1}{2}(m\angle QCR)$.

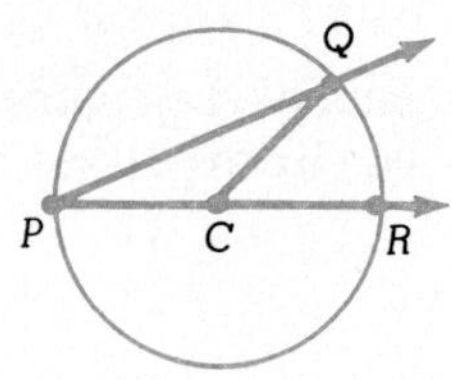

Since $\angle QCR$ is a central angle of $\odot C$, $m\angle QCR = m\widehat{QR}$. Thus, $m\angle QPR = \frac{1}{2}(m\widehat{QR})$.

Point out that ∠ QPR could intercept a major arc just as well as a minor arc.

The following deductions show how to find the measures of inscribed angles whose sides do *not* contain diameters of a circle.

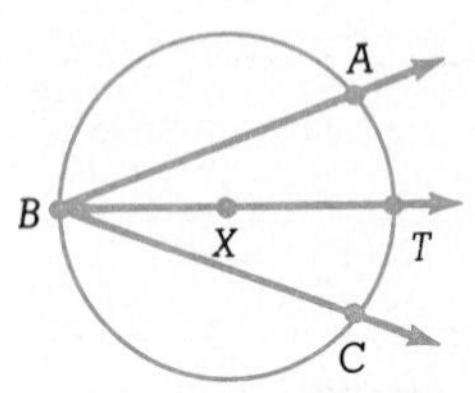

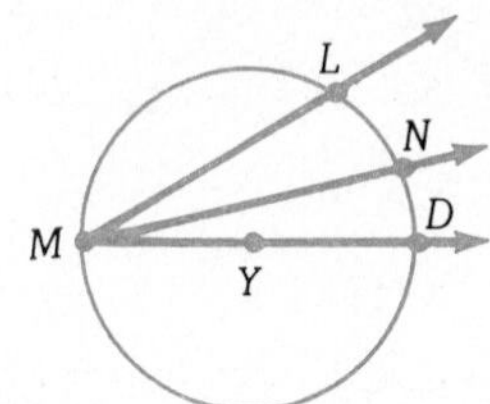

$$\begin{aligned} m\angle ABC &= m\angle ABT + m\angle TBC \\ &= \frac{1}{2}(m\widehat{AT}) + \frac{1}{2}(m\widehat{TC}) \\ &= \frac{1}{2}(m\widehat{AT} + m\widehat{TC}) \\ &= \frac{1}{2}m\widehat{AC} \end{aligned}$$

$$\begin{aligned} m\angle LMN &= m\angle LMD - m\angle NMD \\ &= \frac{1}{2}(m\widehat{LD}) - \frac{1}{2}(m\widehat{ND}) \\ &= \frac{1}{2}(m\widehat{LD} - m\widehat{ND}) \\ &= \frac{1}{2}m\widehat{LN} \end{aligned}$$

If an angle is inscribed in a circle, then the measure of the angle equals one-half the measure of its intercepted arc.

Theorem 10–6

1 In the figure, $m\widehat{PQ} = 112$, $m\widehat{QS} = 54$, and $m\widehat{ST} = 88$. Find $m\angle 1$, $m\angle 2$, and $m\angle 3$.

$$\begin{aligned} m\widehat{PQ} + m\widehat{QS} + m\widehat{ST} + m\widehat{TP} &= 360 \\ 112 + 54 + 88 + m\widehat{TP} &= 360 \\ m\widehat{TP} &= 106 \end{aligned}$$

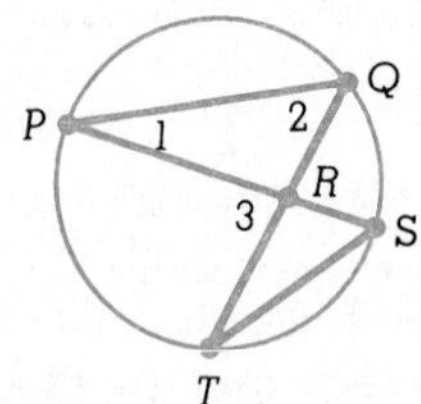

$$\begin{aligned} m\angle 1 &= \frac{1}{2}(m\widehat{QS}) \\ &= \frac{1}{2}(54) \\ &= 27 \end{aligned} \qquad \begin{aligned} m\angle 2 &= \frac{1}{2}(m\widehat{TP}) \\ &= \frac{1}{2}(106) \\ &= 53 \end{aligned}$$

$$\begin{aligned} m\angle 3 &= m\angle 1 + m\angle 2 \\ &= 27 + 53 \\ &= 80 \end{aligned}$$

The proofs of the following theorems are based on Theorem 10–6.

Students prove the following theorem in Written exercise 25.

If two inscribed angles of a circle or congruent circles intercept congruent arcs, then the angles are congruent. *Theorem 10–7*

If an angle is inscribed in a semicircle, then the angle is a right angle. *Theorem 10–8*

example

2 Prove Theorem 10–8.

Given: $\widehat{PQR}$ is a semicircle of $\odot C$.

Prove: $\angle PQR$ is a right angle.

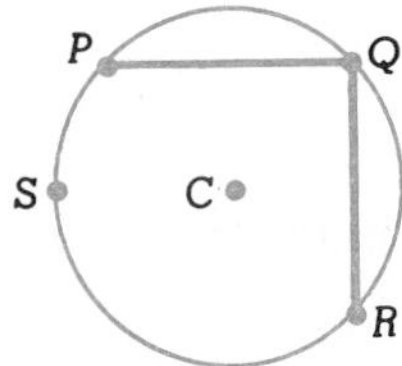

Proof:

STATEMENTS	REASONS
1. $\widehat{PQR}$ is a semicircle of $\odot C$.	1. Given
2. $\widehat{PSR}$ is a semicircle of $\odot C$.	2. Definition of Semicircle
3. $m\widehat{PSR} = 180$	3. Definition of Arc Measure
4. $m\angle PQR = \frac{1}{2}(m\widehat{PSR})$	4. Theorem 10–6: The measure of an inscribed angle of a circle equals one-half the measure of its intercepted arc.
5. $m\angle PQR = \frac{1}{2}(180)$ or 90	5. Postulate 2–9: Substitution
6. $\angle PQR$ is a right angle.	6. Definition of Right Angle

A *polygon* is *inscribed* in a circle if and only if each of its vertices lies on the circle. For example, in the figure, quadrilateral $PQRS$ is inscribed in $\odot C$.

Since the measures of the arcs of a circle total 360, the opposite angles of an inscribed quadrilateral are related in a special way.

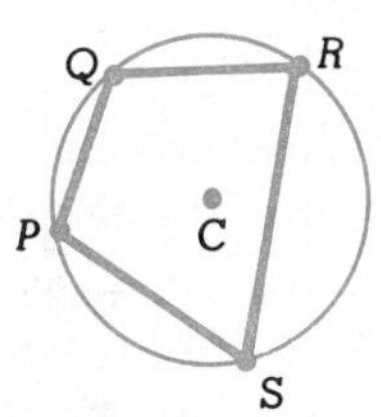

If the angles of a quadrilateral are inscribed in a circle, then each pair of opposite angles are supplementary. *Theorem 10–9*

Students prove this theorem in Written exercise 26.

EN: Wr: 1-21 odds, 23-29; AV: Ex: 1-5, Wr: 1-25 odds; p. 334, Wr: 18-24 evens, 26-29

exercises

FN: Ex: 1-6, Wr: 1-29 odds; p. 334, Wr: 18-26 evens, 27, 29

Exploratory **For each of the following, name the arc or arcs intercepted by the given angle. Then, determine whether or *not* each angle is an inscribed angle. Write *yes* or *no*.**

1. $\widehat{BC}$, yes

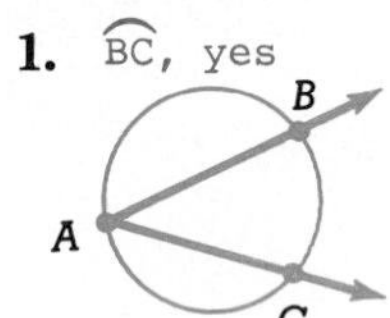

2. $\widehat{DF}$, no

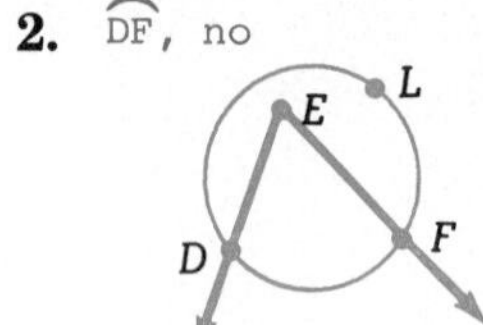

3. $\widehat{KH}$, $\widehat{IJ}$, no

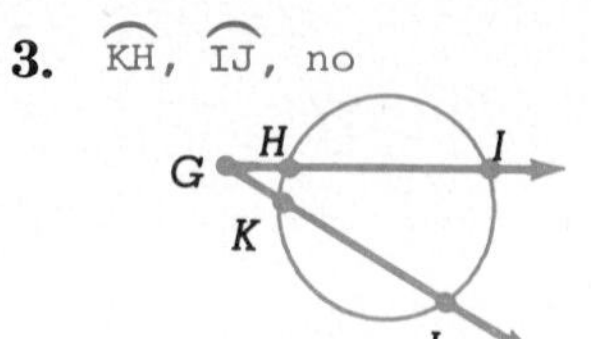

4. $\widehat{LN}$, $\widehat{LTO}$, no

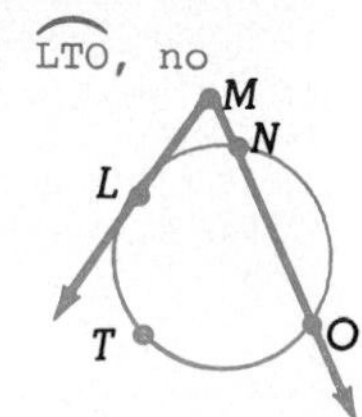

5. $\widehat{QT}$, $\widehat{RS}$, no

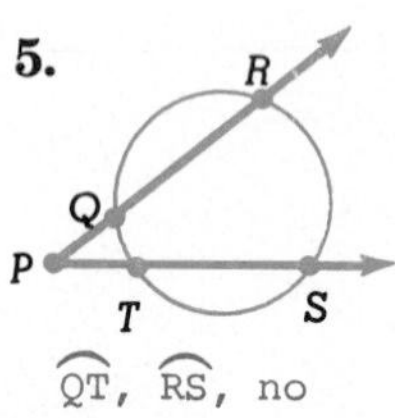

6. $\widehat{WU}$, $\widehat{WXU}$, no

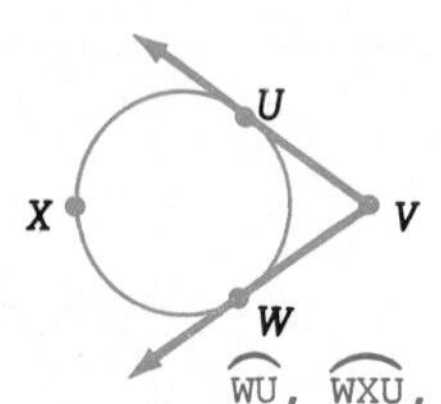

7. $\widehat{YZ}$, yes

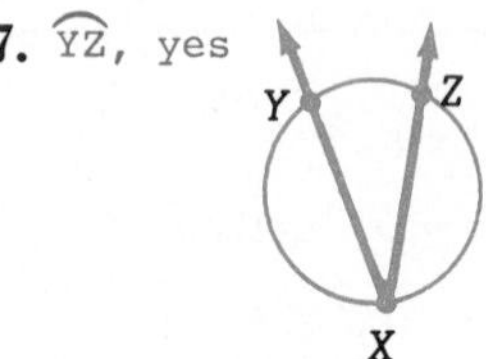

8. $\widehat{ACB}$, no

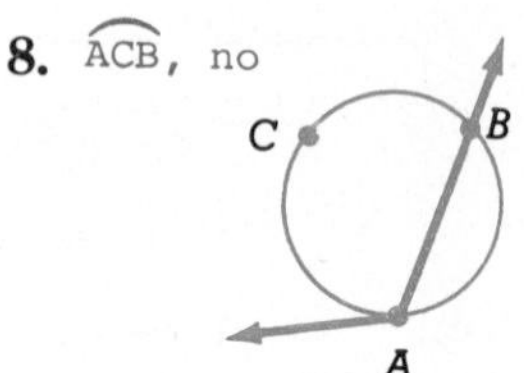

Written **Find the measure for each of the following if in $\odot X$, $\overline{AB} \parallel \overline{DC}$, $m\widehat{BC} = 94$, and $m\angle AXB = 104$.**

1. $\widehat{AB}$ 104	**2.** $\angle BAC$ 47	**3.** $\angle BDC$ 47
4. $\angle BCA$ 52	**5.** $\angle ADB$ 52	**6.** $\angle ADC$ 99
7. $\angle XAB$ 38	**8.** $\angle ABX$ 38	**9.** $\angle ACD$ 47
10. $\angle BCD$ 99	**11.** $\angle DEC$ 86	**12.** $\angle AED$ 94
13. $\angle EAD$ 34	**14.** $\widehat{DC}$ 68	**15.** $\angle BAD$ 81
16. $\angle DBC$ 34	**17.** $\widehat{AD}$ 94	**18.** $\angle ABD$ 47

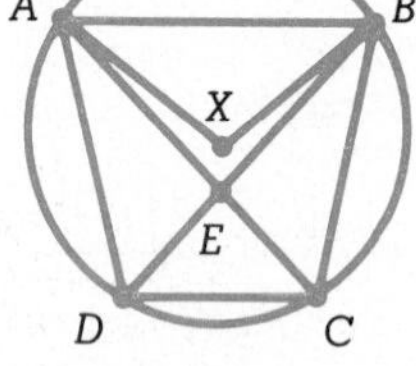

Exercises 1–18

The figure shows a regular hexagon inscribed in $\odot P$ with radius measuring 12 units. Answer each of the following.

19. Find the length of each side. 12 units

20. Find the distance of each side from the center of the circle. $6\sqrt{3}$ units

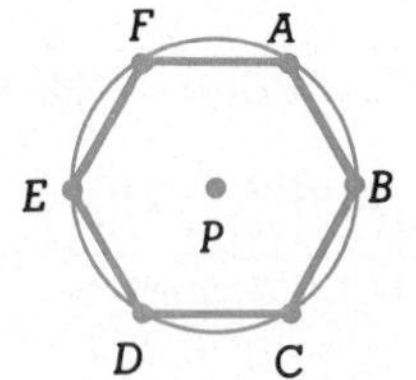

Exercises 19 and 20

The figure shows an equilateral triangle inscribed in $\odot Q$ with radius measuring 12 units. Answer each of the following.

21. Find the length of each side. $12\sqrt{3}$ units

22. Find the distance from each side of the triangle to the center of the circle. 6 units

Exercises 21 and 22

Prove each of the following. For answers to exercises 23-29, see the Teacher's Guide.

23. The measure of an inscribed angle that has a side that contains a diameter is one-half the measure of its intercepted arc.

24. The bisector of an inscribed angle separates the intercepted arc into two congruent arcs.

25. Theorem 10–7

26. Theorem 10–9

27. **Given:** $\overline{ZY}$ is a diameter of $\odot A$.
$\widehat{XY} \cong \widehat{ZW}$

Prove: $\angle XYZ \cong \angle WZY$

28. **Given:** $\overline{XY} \parallel \overline{ZW}$
$\overline{ZY}$ is a diameter of $\odot A$.

Prove: $\widehat{XY} \cong \widehat{ZW}$

29. **Given:** $\overline{ZY}$ is a diameter of $\odot A$.
$\widehat{XZ} \cong \widehat{YW}$

Prove: $\triangle ZXY \cong \triangle YWZ$

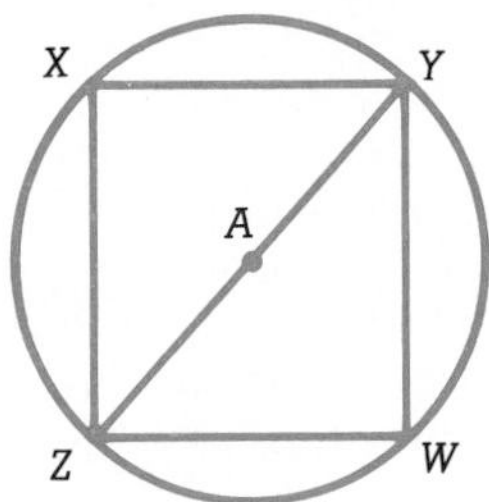

Exercises 27–29

Uses in Transportation — computers

Computers are becoming very important in many forms of transportation. For example, computers have helped airlines solve problems in such areas as flight reservations, traffic control, and scheduling.

Using computers to control flight reservations has helped airlines provide a better service to their customers. Computers are used by airline clerks and travel agents to gain access to up-to-the-minute information on seat availability for all flights.

Air traffic control is another area in which computers have proven beneficial. Once a plane is airborne, air traffic controllers monitor its speed, altitude, and location with the help of computers. The location of each plane is plotted by the computer on the controller's display scope.

Computers can help airlines plan schedules so connecting flights are available on the most traveled routes. Also, computers can schedule crews so each crew does not work beyond safety limits.

There are similar uses for computers in other forms of transportation. Railroads, for instance, have the same needs for control as airlines. To avoid major collisions, the speed, direction, and location of trains must be known. Computers are used to provide this information. Truckers also use computers to acquire information concerning loads on new jobs as well as updates on old jobs.

10–5 Tangents

Objective: to use properties of tangents of circles to solve problems

In a plane, a line that intersects a circle in exactly one point is called a **tangent.** Also, segments and rays that are contained in the tangent and intersect the circle are said to be tangent to the circle.

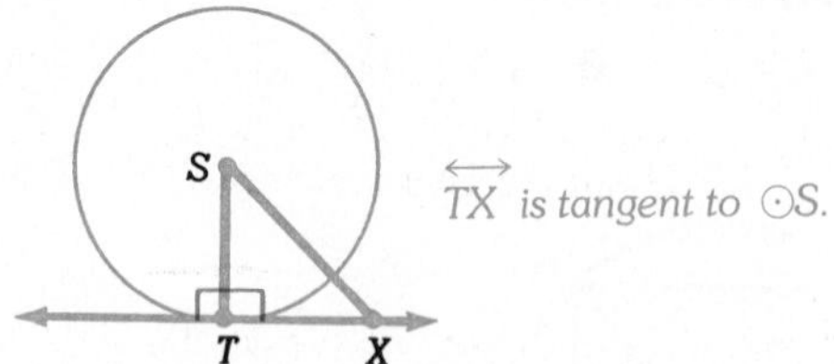

$\overleftrightarrow{TX}$ *is tangent to* $\odot S$.

In the figure, S is the center of the circle, and T is the **point of tangency.** X is in the exterior of the circle and $\overline{ST}$ is a radius. Thus, $SX > ST$. A similar inequality holds for any point in the exterior of the circle.

The shortest segment from a point to a line is the perpendicular segment. Thus, $\overline{ST} \perp \overleftrightarrow{TX}$.

Students prove this theorem in Written exercise 22.

If a line is tangent to a circle, then it is perpendicular to the radius drawn to the point of tangency.

Theorem 10–10

1 In $\odot C$, $\overline{QR}$ and $\overline{QP}$ are tangents and $m\angle RPC = 15$. Find $m\angle Q$.

Since $\overline{CR}$ and $\overline{CP}$ are radii, they are congruent. Thus, by the Isosceles Triangle Theorem, $\angle RPC \cong \angle PRC$, and $m\angle PRC = 15$.

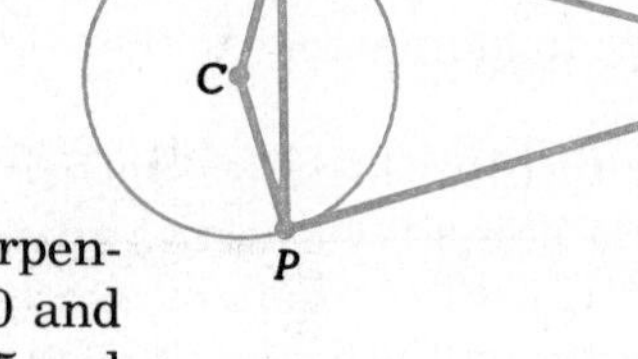

Since $\overline{QR}$ and $\overline{QP}$ are tangents, they are perpendicular to the radii. Therefore, $m\angle CPQ = 90$ and $m\angle CRQ = 90$. Thus, $m\angle PRQ = 90 - 15$ or 75 and $m\angle QPR = 90 - 15$ or 75.

The sum of the degree measures of the angles of a triangle is 180.

$$\begin{aligned} m\angle Q + m\angle PRQ + m\angle QPR &= 180 \\ m\angle Q + \quad 75 \quad + \quad 75 \quad &= 180 \\ m\angle Q &= 30 \end{aligned}$$

The converse of Theorem 10–10 also holds, and provides one method for identifying tangents to a circle.

In a plane, if a line is perpendicular to a radius of a circle at its endpoint on the circle, then the line is a tangent.

Theorem 10–11

Students prove this theorem in Written exercise 23.

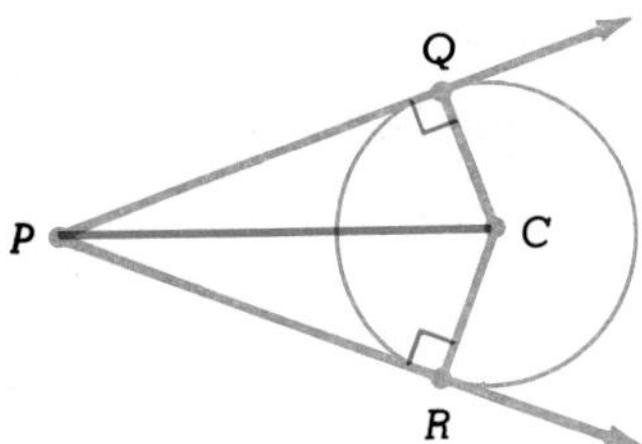

From a point exterior to a circle it is possible to draw two tangents. For example $\overrightarrow{PQ}$ and $\overrightarrow{PR}$ are both tangent to $\odot C$. Also, $\overline{PQ}$ and $\overline{PR}$ are **tangent segments.**

By drawing $\overline{PC}$, two right triangles are formed. These triangles are congruent by HL, and thus the following conclusion can be made.

If two segments from the same exterior point are tangent to a circle, then they are congruent.

Theorem 10–12

Students prove this theorem in Written exercise 24.

example

2 In the figure, both $\overline{AB}$ and $\overline{AC}$ are tangent to $\odot P$. Suppose $PB = 10$ and $AP = 26$. Find AC.

By Theorem 10–10, if a line is tangent to a circle, then it is perpendicular to the radius drawn to the point of tangency. Thus, $\overline{PB} \perp \overline{AB}$ and $\overline{PC} \perp \overline{AC}$, and $\triangle ABP$ and $\triangle ACP$ are right triangles.

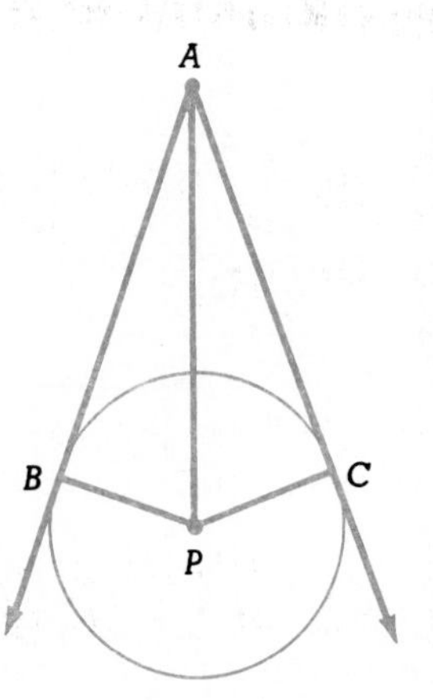

$(AB)^2 + (PB)^2 = (AP)^2$	*Pythagorean Theorem*
$(AB)^2 + 10^2 = 26^2$	*Substitution*
$(AB)^2 = 26^2 - 10^2$	*Subtraction Property of Equality*
$AB = \sqrt{576}$ or 24	

By Theorem 10–12, the two tangent segments, $\overline{AB}$ and $\overline{AC}$, are congruent. Thus, $AC = AB = 24$.

A *polygon* is *circumscribed* about a circle if and only if each side of the polygon is tangent to the circle.

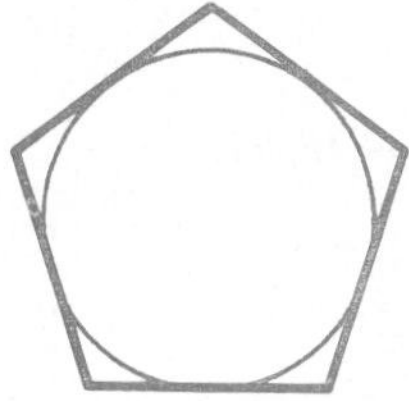

The circle is inscribed in the polygon.

Must a circumscribed polygon be regular? The answer is *no*. But, it is possible to show that a polygon is regular if and only if it can be inscribed in and circumscribed about two concentric circles.

EN: Ex: 1-6, Wr: 2-30 evens, 31; AV: Ex: 1-6, Wr: 1-29 odds; pp. 338-9, 20-28 evens

exercises

FN: Ex: 1-6, Wr: 1-21; pp. 338-9, Wr: 12-26 evens

Exploratory **Answer each of the following.**

1. How many tangents can be drawn to a circle through a point outside the circle? 2
2. How many tangents can be drawn to a circle through a point inside the circle? 0
3. How many tangents can be drawn to a circle through a point on the circle? 1
4. Can a radius of a circle be a tangent of the circle? State *yes* or *no*. no
5. Are the sides of a circumscribed polygon chords or tangents of the circle? tangents
6. Are the sides of an inscribed polygon chords or tangents of the circle? chords

Written **For each of the following, find the value of x. Assume C is the center of the circle.**

1. 12

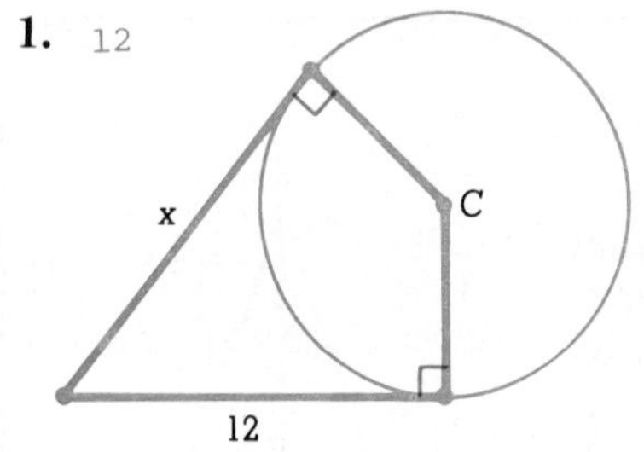

2. $\sqrt{193}$

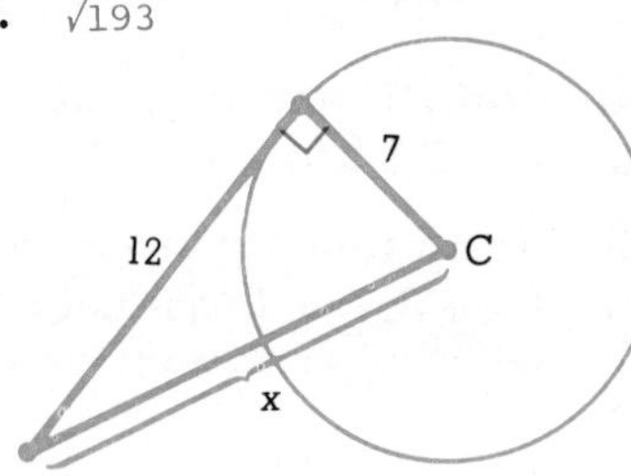

3. 14

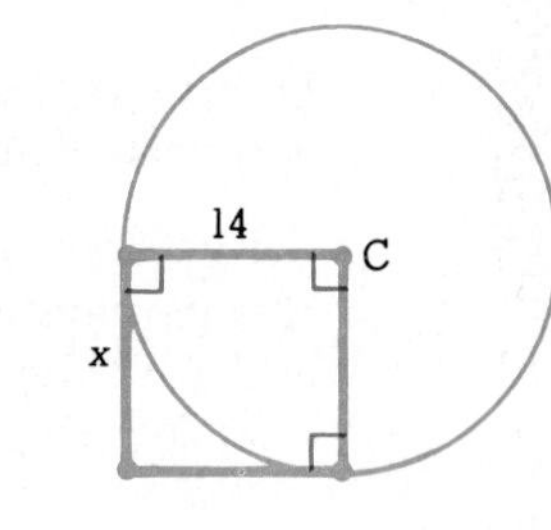

4. 12

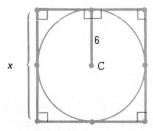

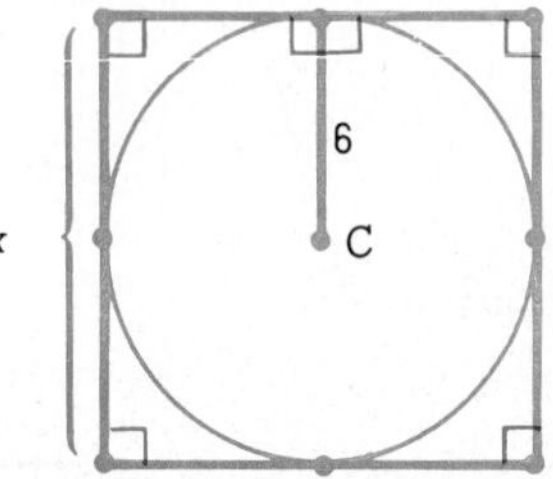

5. 8

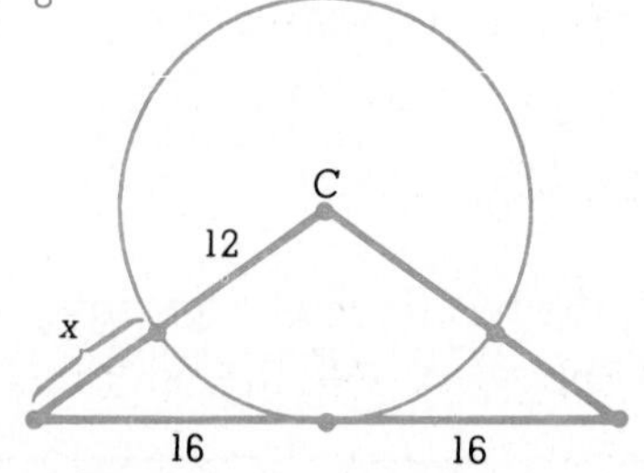

6. 16

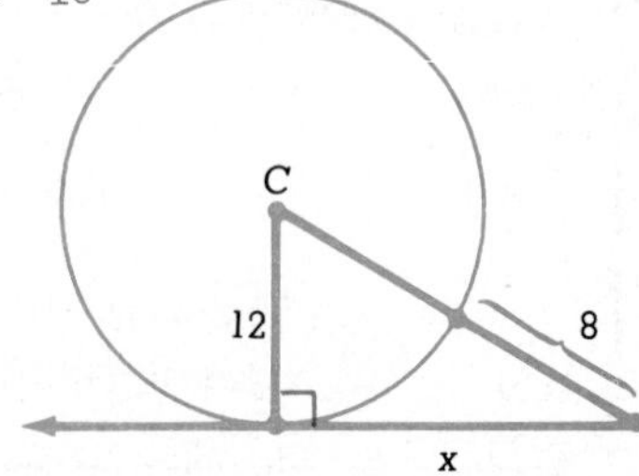

In the figure, $\overline{AB}$ and $\overline{CD}$ both are tangent to $\odot P$ and $\odot Q$. Also, $AP = 8$, $BQ = 5$, and $m\angle CPE = 45$. Find the measures for each of the following.

7. $\widehat{CE}$ 45
8. $\angle PCG$ 90
9. $\angle CGP$ 45
10. $\overline{CG}$ 8
11. $\angle QDC$ 90
12. $\angle FGD$ 45
13. $\angle FQD$ 45
14. $\widehat{DF}$ 45
15. $\overline{DQ}$ 5
16. $\overline{DG}$ 5
17. $\overline{DC}$ 13
18. $\overline{PG}$ $8\sqrt{2}$
19. $\overline{GQ}$ $5\sqrt{2}$
20. $\overline{PQ}$ $13\sqrt{2}$
21. $\overline{AB}$ $\sqrt{329}$

Point out that $\overline{AB}$ is externally tangent and that $\overline{CD}$ is internally tangent.

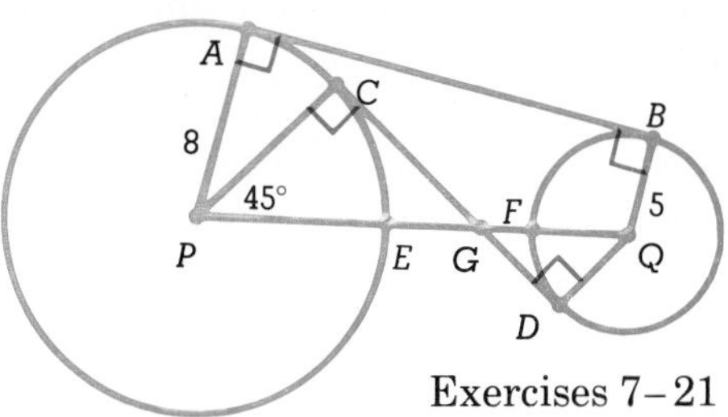

Exercises 7–21

Prove each of the following. For answers to exercises 22-31, see the Teacher's Guide.

22. Theorem 10–10
23. Theorem 10–11
24. Theorem 10–12

25. **Given:** $\overleftrightarrow{AC}$ is tangent to $\odot P$.
$\widehat{DB} \cong \widehat{BE}$
Prove: $\overline{AB} \cong \overline{BC}$

26. **Given:** $\overleftrightarrow{AC}$ is tangent to $\odot P$.
$\angle PAB \cong \angle PCB$
Prove: $\widehat{DB} \cong \widehat{BE}$

27. **Given:** $\triangle APC$ is isosceles.
$\widehat{DB} \cong \widehat{BE}$
Prove: $\overleftrightarrow{AC}$ is tangent to $\odot P$.

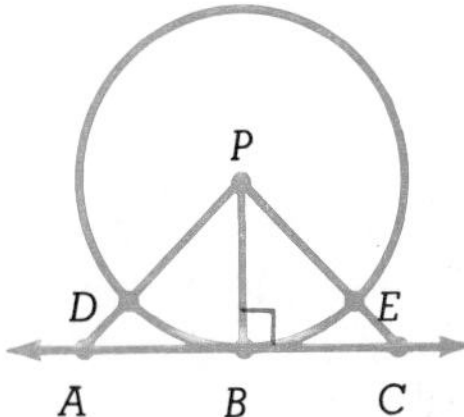

Exercises 25–27

28. **Given:** $\overleftrightarrow{AF}$ and $\overleftrightarrow{CF}$ are tangent to $\odot B$.
Prove: $\triangle ADF \cong \triangle CDF$

29. **Given:** $\overleftrightarrow{AF}$ and $\overleftrightarrow{CF}$ are tangent to $\odot B$.
Prove: $\overline{BF} \perp \overline{AC}$

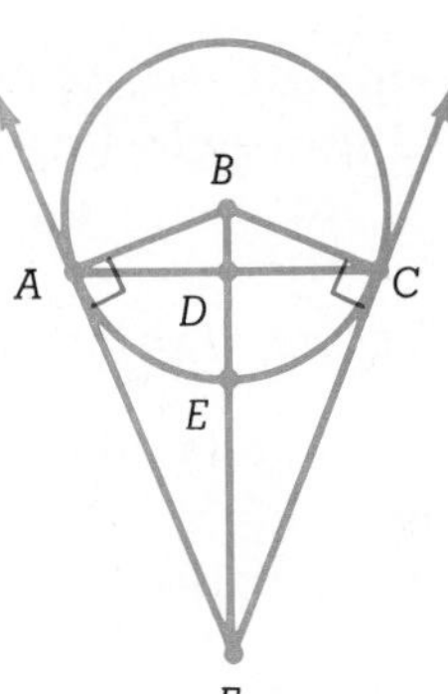

Exercises 28 and 29

30. **Given:** $\overleftrightarrow{WX}$, $\overleftrightarrow{XY}$, $\overleftrightarrow{YZ}$, and $\overleftrightarrow{ZW}$ are tangent to $\odot P$.
$\overline{WX} \parallel \overline{ZY}$, $\overline{WZ} \parallel \overline{XY}$
$\overline{WT} \cong \overline{TP}$
Prove: Quadrilateral $WXYZ$ is a rectangle.

This proof can be extended to prove quadrilateral WXYZ is a square. This can be very challenging for students.

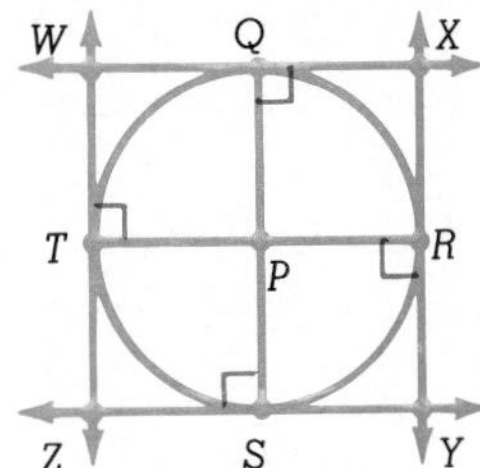

Exercise 30

31. If a hexagon can be inscribed in and circumscribed about two concentric circles, then the polygon is regular.

10–6 Measuring Angles

Objective: to find the measure of angles formed by the intersection of secants and tangents in relation to intercepted arcs

Two secants intersect to form angles that intercept arcs in three different ways.

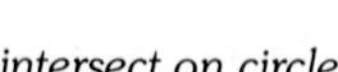

intersect on circle

intersect inside circle

intersect outside circle

In each case, the measure of the angle formed is related to the measures of the intercepted arcs. If the secants intersect on the circle, an inscribed angle is formed. Its measure is one-half the measure of the intercepted arc. The following theorems describe the other two cases.

If two secants intersect in the interior of a circle, then the measure of an angle formed is one-half the sum of the measures of the arcs intercepted by the angle and its vertical angle. ***Theorem 10–13***

If two secants intersect in the exterior of a circle, then the measure of an angle formed is one-half the positive difference of the measures of the intercepted arcs. ***Theorem 10–14***

Students prove the following theorem in Written exercise 34.

1 In $\odot P$, $m\angle CBD = 52$, $m\widehat{CD} = 39$ and $\overline{AD}$ is a diameter. Find $m\widehat{DE}$.

$$m\angle CBD = \frac{1}{2}(m\widehat{AE} + m\widehat{CD})$$

$$52 = \frac{1}{2}(m\widehat{AE} + 39)$$

$$104 = m\widehat{AE} + 39$$

$$65 = m\widehat{AE}$$

$$m\widehat{AED} = 180$$

$$m\widehat{DE} + m\widehat{AE} = 180$$

$$m\widehat{DE} + 65 = 180$$

$$m\widehat{DE} = 115$$

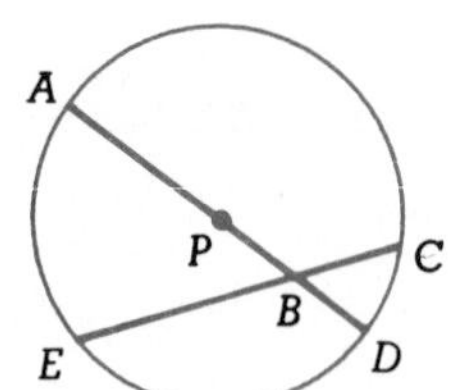

example

2 Prove Theorem 10–14.

Given: $\overline{AC}$ and $\overline{AD}$ intersect at A.
A is exterior to a circle.

Prove: $m\angle BAD = \frac{1}{2}(m\widehat{CD} - m\widehat{BE})$

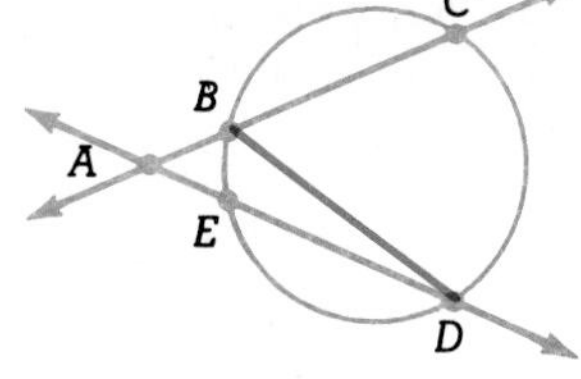

Proof:

STATEMENTS	REASONS
1. Draw chord $\overline{BD}$.	1. Postulate 1–1: Through any two points there is exactly one line.
2. $m\angle BAD + m\angle ADB = m\angle CBD$	2. Theorem 5–1: Exterior Angle Theorem
3. $m\angle BAD = m\angle CBD - m\angle ADB$	3. Postulate 2–7: Subtraction Property of Equality
4. $\angle CBD$ and $\angle BDA$ are inscribed angles.	4. Definition of Inscribed Angles
5. $m\angle CBD = \frac{1}{2}m\widehat{CD}$ $m\angle ADB = \frac{1}{2}m\widehat{BE}$	5. Theorem 10–6: If an angle is inscribed in a circle, then the measure of the angle equals one-half the measure of its intercepted arc.
6. $m\angle BAD = \frac{1}{2}m\widehat{CD} - \frac{1}{2}m\widehat{BE}$	6. Postulate 2–9: Substitution
7. $m\angle BAD = \frac{1}{2}(m\widehat{CD} - m\widehat{BE})$	7. Postulate 2–14: Distributive Property

A tangent and a secant, or two tangents, intercept arcs in several ways. In each case, the measure of the angle formed is related to the intercepted arcs.

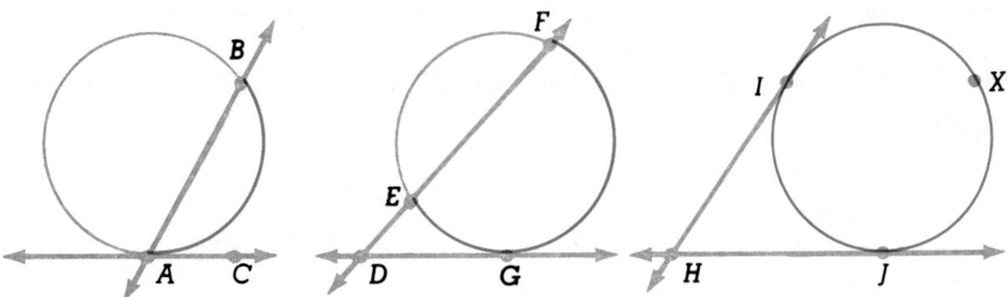

$m\angle BAC = \frac{1}{2}m(\widehat{BA})$ $m\angle FDG = \frac{1}{2}(m\widehat{FG} - m\widehat{GE})$ $m\angle IHJ = \frac{1}{2}(m\widehat{IXJ} - m\widehat{IJ})$

If a secant and a tangent intersect at the point of tangency, then the measure of each angle formed is one-half the measure of its intercepted arc.

Theorem 10–15

Students prove this theorem in Written exercise 35.

If a secant and a tangent, or two tangents, intersect in the exterior of a circle, then the measure of the angle formed is one-half the positive difference of the measures of the intercepted arcs.

Theorem 10–16

Students prove this theorem in Written exercises 36 and 37.

EN: Ex: 1-4, Wr: 2-36 evens, 40-42; AV: Ex: 1-4, Wr: 1-37 odds; p. 343, Wr: 10-28 evens

exercises

FN: Ex: 1-6, Wr: 1-34; p. 343, Wr: 8-22 evens, 23-27 odds

Exploratory **For each of the following, measurements of certain arcs are given. Find the degree measure of each numbered angle. Assume lines that appear tangent are tangent.**

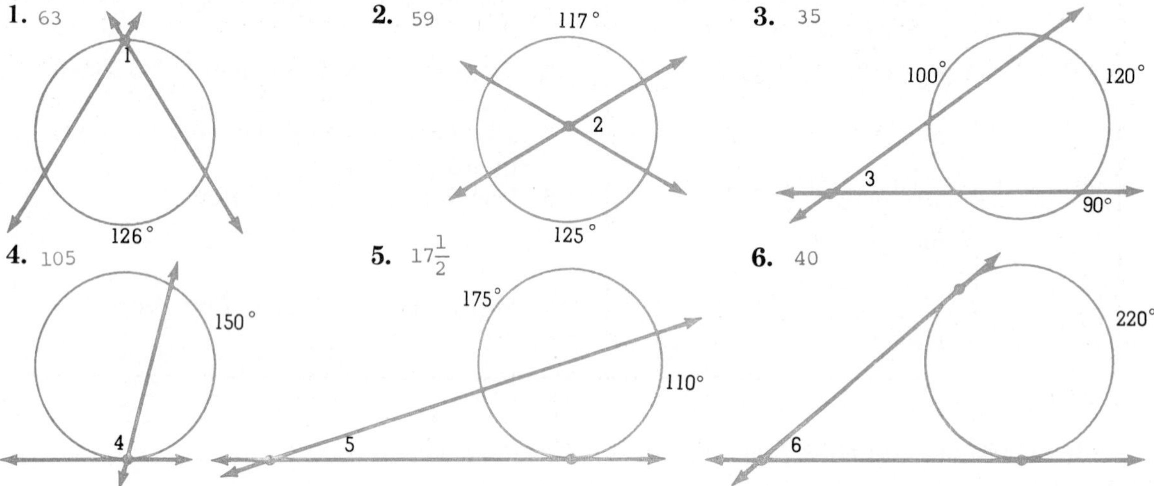

Written **In the figure, $m\widehat{BC} = 84$, $m\widehat{CD} = 38$, $m\widehat{DE} = 64$, $m\widehat{EF} = 60$, and $\overleftrightarrow{AB}$ and $\overleftrightarrow{AF}$ are tangents. Find each of the following.**

1. $m\widehat{BF}$ 114
2. $m\widehat{BDF}$ 246
3. $m\angle 1$ 66
4. $m\widehat{BFC}$ 276
5. $m\angle 2$ 138
6. $m\angle 9$ 42
7. $m\widehat{BFE}$ 174
8. $m\angle 3$ 87
9. $m\angle 4$ 49
10. $m\angle 5$ 131
11. $m\widehat{FBC}$ 198
12. $m\angle 6$ 69
13. $m\widehat{FBD}$ 236
14. $m\angle 7$ 118
15. $m\angle 8$ 38

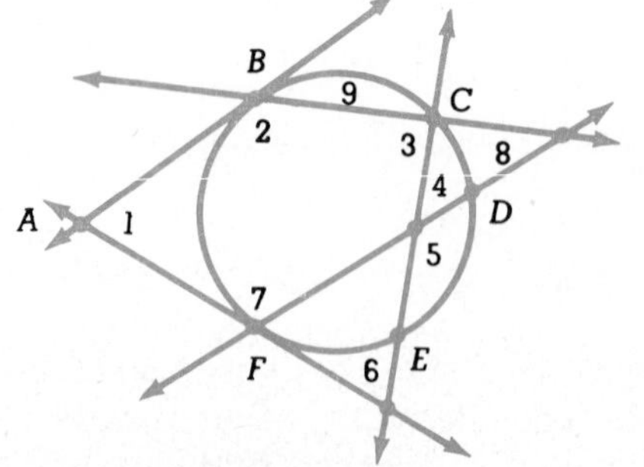

Exercises 1–15

In the figure, $m\angle 1 = 2x$, $m\angle 1 = m\angle 2$, $m\widehat{RYT} = 4x + 4$, $m\widehat{YT} = 3x - 20$, $m\angle 4 = 3x + 14$, and $\overleftrightarrow{ST}$ and $\overleftrightarrow{SR}$ are tangents. Find each of the following.

16. the value of x 22
17. $m\angle 1$ 44
18. $m\angle 2$ 44
19. $m\widehat{RYT}$ 92
20. $m\widehat{YT}$ 46
21. $m\widehat{YR}$ 46
22. $m\widehat{TW}$ 134
23. $m\widehat{RW}$ 134
24. $m\angle 4$ 80
25. $m\widehat{TWV}$ 160
26. $m\widehat{VW}$ 26
27. $m\angle 3$ 100
28. $m\widehat{TRV}$ 200
29. $m\widehat{RV}$ 108
30. $m\angle 5$ 36
31. $m\widehat{YV}$ 154
32. $m\angle 6$ 144
33. $m\angle 7$ 144

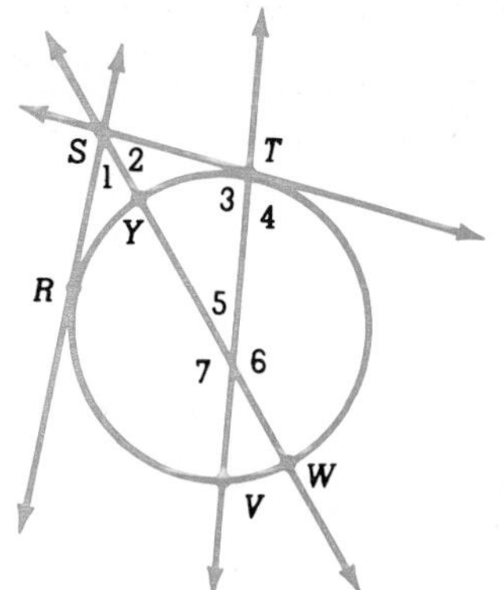

Exercises 16–33

Prove each of the following. For answers to exercises 34-43, see the Teacher's Guide.

34. Theorem 10–13
35. Theorem 10–15
36. If a secant and a tangent intersect in the exterior of a circle, then the measure of the angle formed is one-half the positive difference of the measures of the intercepted arcs.
37. If two tangents intersect in the exterior of a circle, then the measure of the angle formed is one-half the positive difference of the measures of the intercepted arcs.

Discuss in class the case of two circles being tangent to one another.

38. **Given:** $\overleftrightarrow{FA}$ is tangent to $\odot P$ and $\odot E$ at A. $\overline{AE} \perp \overline{EB}$
Prove: $m\widehat{AD} = 90$
39. **Given:** $\overleftrightarrow{FA}$ is tangent to $\odot P$ and $\odot E$ at A.
Prove: $m\angle CAF = \frac{1}{2} m\angle CEA$

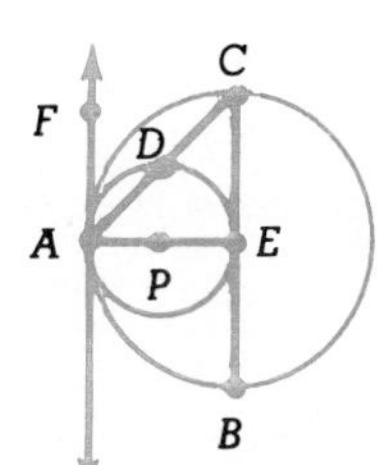

Exercises 38 and 39

40. **Given:** $\overline{RP} \perp \overline{QT}$
$\overline{RT} \perp \overline{QS}$
Prove: $m\widehat{PT} = m\widehat{ST}$
41. **Given:** $m\widehat{PT} = m\widehat{ST}$
Prove: $m\angle PXT = m\angle SVT$

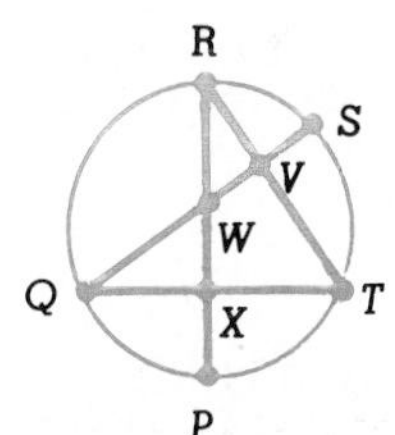

Exercises 40 and 41

42. **Given:** $\widehat{NS} \cong \widehat{RT}$
$\widehat{SNM} \cong \widehat{TRM}$
Prove: $\triangle PMQ$ is isosceles.
43. **Given:** $\widehat{NS} \cong \widehat{RT}$
$\angle NPS \cong \angle RQT$
Prove: $\angle NPM \cong \angle RQM$

Exercises 42 and 43

10–7 Segments

Objectives: to use properties of segments of chords, secants, and tangents to solve problems

Angles formed by intersecting chords are related to arcs of the circle. In addition, the segments formed by the intersecting chords are related.

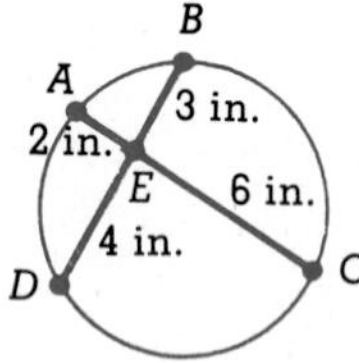

In the figure, the segments of $\overline{AC}$ are $\overline{AE}$ and $\overline{EC}$. The segments of $\overline{BD}$ are $\overline{BE}$ and $\overline{ED}$.

$$AE \cdot EC = 2 \cdot 6 = 12 \qquad BE \cdot ED = 3 \cdot 4 = 12$$

If two chords intersect in a circle, then the product of the measures of the segments of one chord equals the product of the measures of the segments of the other chord. *Theorem 10–17*

The proof of the theorem is based on properties of similar triangles.

example

1 Prove Theorem 10–17.

Given: $\overline{AC}$ and $\overline{BD}$ intersect at E.
Prove: $AE \cdot EC = BE \cdot ED$

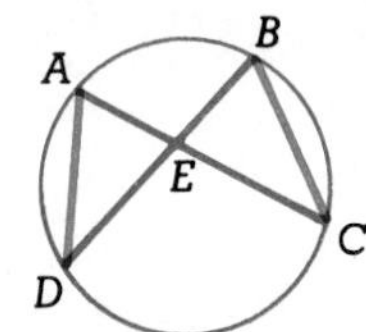

Proof:

STATEMENTS	REASONS
1. Draw $\overline{AD}$ and $\overline{BC}$.	1. Postulate 1–1: Through any two points there is exactly one line.
2. $\angle A \cong \angle B$ $\angle D \cong \angle C$	2. Theorem 10–7: If two inscribed angles intercept congruent arcs, then the angles are congruent.
3. $\triangle DAE \sim \triangle CBE$	3. Postulate 8–1: AA Similarity
4. $\frac{AE}{BE} = \frac{ED}{EC}$	4. Definition of Similar Polygons
5. $AE \cdot EC = BE \cdot ED$	5. Theorem 8–1: Equality of Cross Products

In the figure, both $\overline{RP}$ and $\overline{RT}$ are called **secant segments.** They contain chords of the circle. The parts of these segments that are exterior to the circle are called **external secant segments.** In the figure, $\overline{RQ}$ and $\overline{RS}$ are external secant segments.

The measures of the segments of the figure are related in an interesting way.

$RQ \cdot RP$	$RS \cdot RT$
$4 \cdot 10$	$5 \cdot 8$
40	40

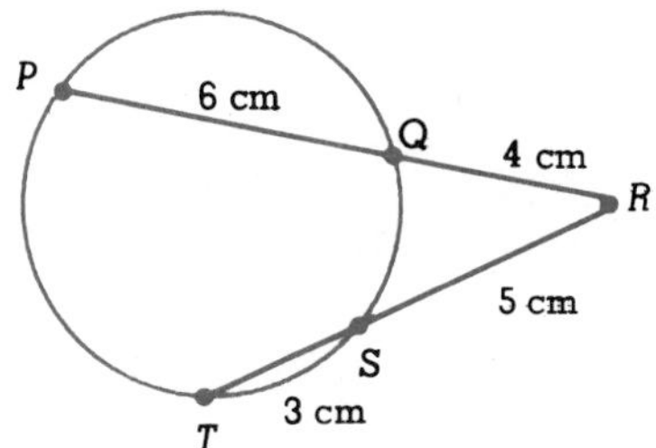

To prove the following theorem, draw a figure like the one shown above. Connect P and S, and T and Q. Show that $\triangle PSR \sim \triangle TQR$. Then, write a proportion and find its cross product.

If two secant segments are drawn to a circle from an exterior point, then the product of the measures of one secant segment and its external secant segment equals the product of the measures of the other secant segment and its external secant segment.

Theorem 10–18

Students prove this theorem in Written exercise 19.

The figure shows a tangent segment and a secant segment drawn to a circle from an exterior points. By drawing $\overline{XW}$ and $\overline{XZ}$ several triangles are formed.

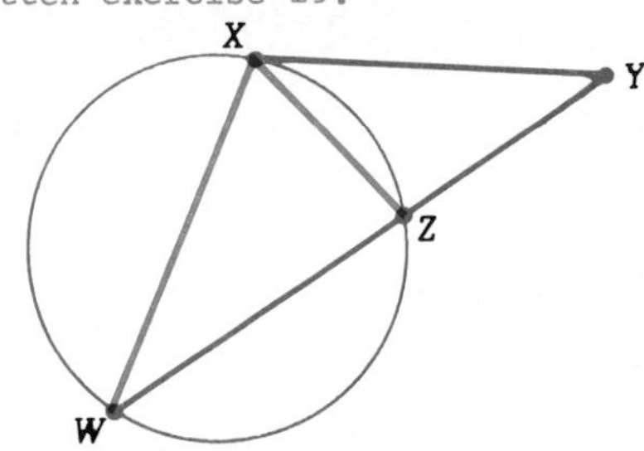

$\overline{XY}$ is a tangent segment.

$\triangle YXZ \sim \triangle YWX$	*AA Similarity*
$\dfrac{XY}{YW} = \dfrac{YZ}{XY}$	*Definition of Similarity*
$XY^2 = YW \cdot YZ$	*Equality of Cross Products*

If a tangent segment and a secant segment are drawn to a circle from an exterior point, then the square of the measure of the tangent segment equals the product of the measures of the secant segment and its external secant segment.

Theorem 10–19

Students prove this theorem in Written exercise 20.

examples

2 **In the figure, $\overline{BC}$ is a tangent segment. Find the value of x.**

$$AC \cdot DC = (BC)^2$$
$$(x + 6.6)(x) = (8)^2$$
$$x^2 + 6.6x = 64$$
$$x^2 + 6.6x - 64 = 0$$

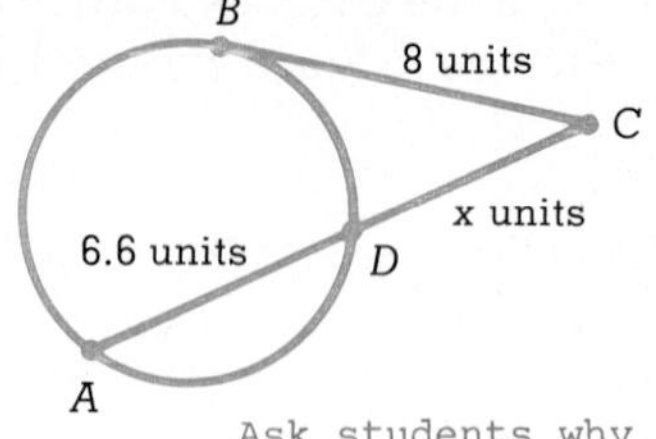

Ask students why the -11.95 is not used as an answer.

$$x = \frac{^-(6.6) \pm \sqrt{(6.6)^2 - 4(1)(^-64)}}{2(1)}$$
$$= \frac{^-(6.6) \pm \sqrt{43.56 + 256}}{2}$$
$$\approx \frac{^-6.6 \pm 17.3}{2}$$
$$\approx 5.35 \text{ or } ^-11.95$$

Use the quadratic formula. a is 1, b is 6.6, and c is $^-64$.

Why is $^-11.95$ not used?

x is approximately equal to 5.35.

EN: Ex: 1-3, Wr: 1-17 odds, 18-22; p. 352, C: 1-2; AV: Ex: 1-9, Wr: 1-21 odds; p. 347, Wr: 26-38 evens; p. 352, C: 1-2

exercises

FN: Ex: 1-9, Wr: 1-12, 13-19 odds; p. 347, Wr: 35-39; p. 352, C: 1-2

Exploratory **For each of the following, state the equation you would use to find the value of x. Assume segments that appear tangent are tangent.**

1. 3x = 4(9)

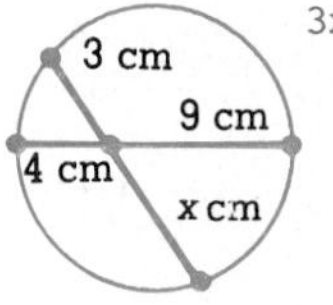

2. 3x = 7(2)

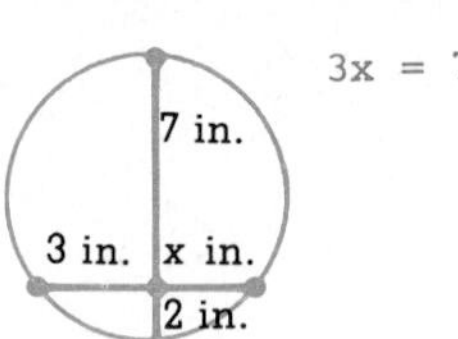

3. 5(5 + x) = 4(12)

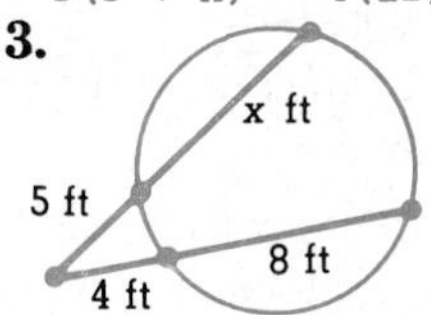

4. 3(8) = 4(x + 4)

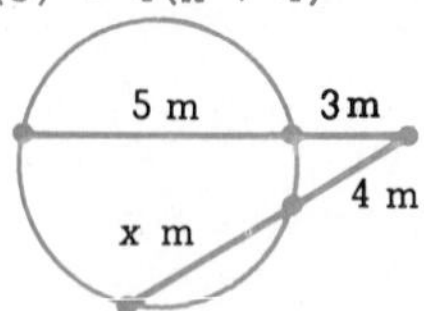

5. 20^2 = (x + 10)10

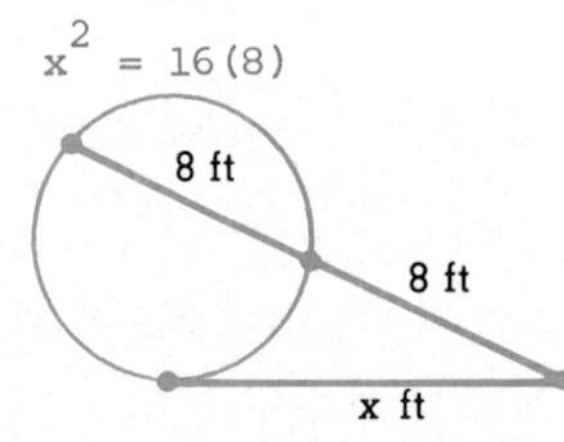

6. 3x = 7(3)

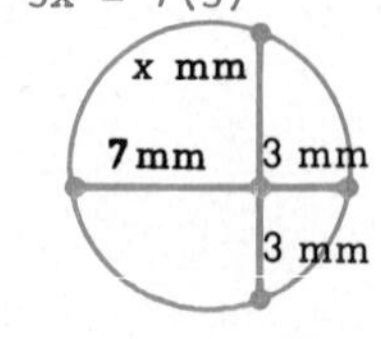

7. 3(12) = x(5 + x)

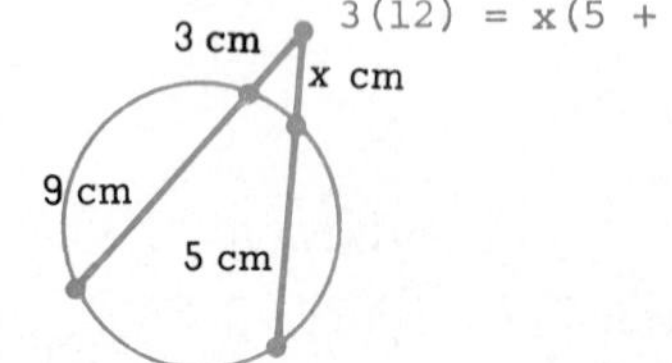

8. x^2 = 16(8)

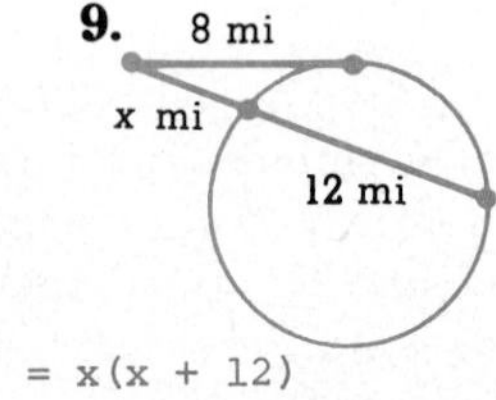

9. 8^2 = x(x + 12)

8 mi
x mi
12 mi

Written **For each of the following, find the value of x. Assume segments that appear tangent are tangent.**

1. 12

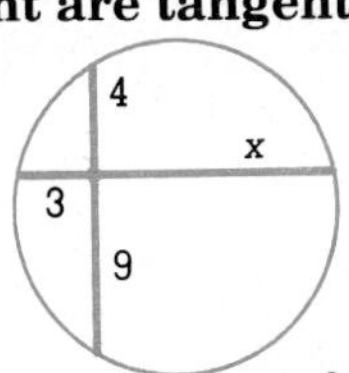

2. $\frac{14}{3}$

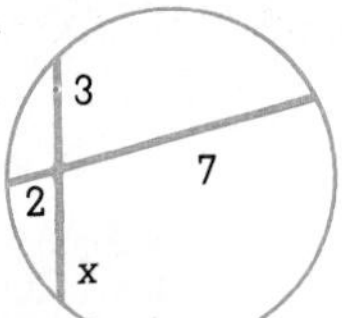

3 7 2 x

3. 0.3

0.9 3.6 x 1.2

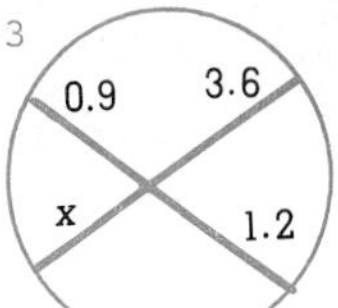

4. $\frac{17}{8}$

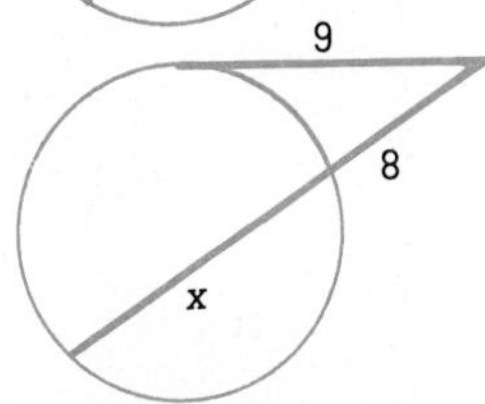

5. 5

10 3x 5

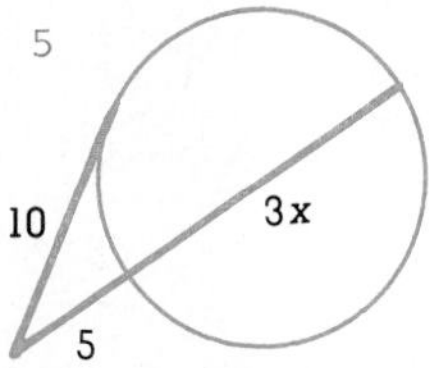

6. 0.46

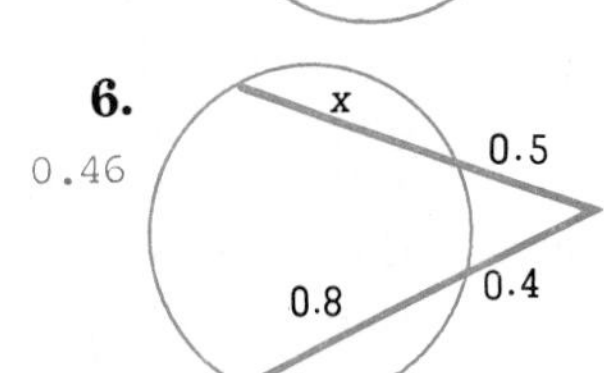

7. 5

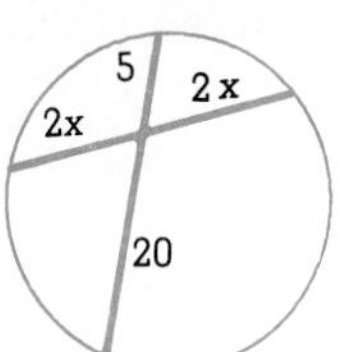

8. 1.2

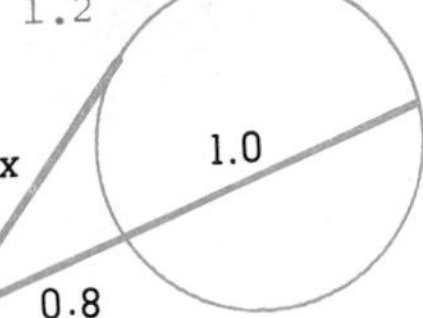

9. 5

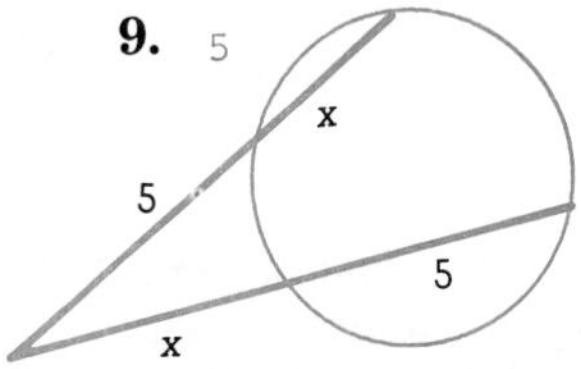

x 5 5 x

10. $\frac{-5 + \sqrt{73}}{2}$

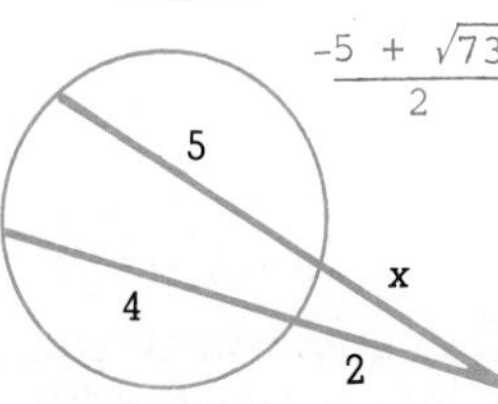

11. 2

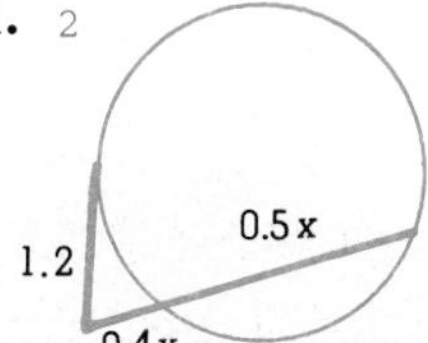

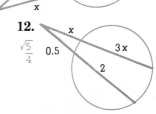

12. $\frac{\sqrt{5}}{4}$

x 0.5 3x 2

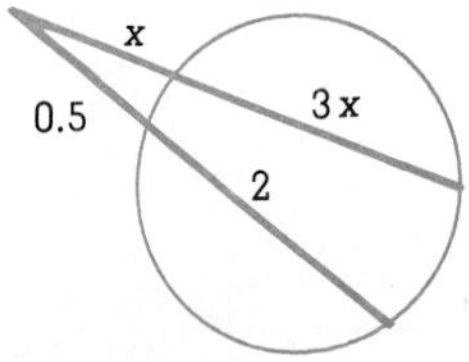

In the figure, $\overline{AB}$ is a tangent segment. Use the figure to solve each problem. Round each answer to the nearest tenth.

13. Suppose $FH = 6$, $HD = 2$, and $HE = 3$. Find CH. 4

14. Suppose $AD = 16$, $FD = 8$, and $AG = 6$. Find GC. 15.3

15. Suppose $AC = 21$, $AF = 8$, and $FD = 8$. Find AG. 6.1

16. Suppose $CH = 20$, $EH = 10.5$, and $DH = 8$. Find FH. 26.3

17. Suppose $AF = 16$, $FH = 6$, and $DH = 2$. Find BA. 19.6

18. Suppose $GC = 15.3$ and $GA = 6.0$. Find AB. 11.3

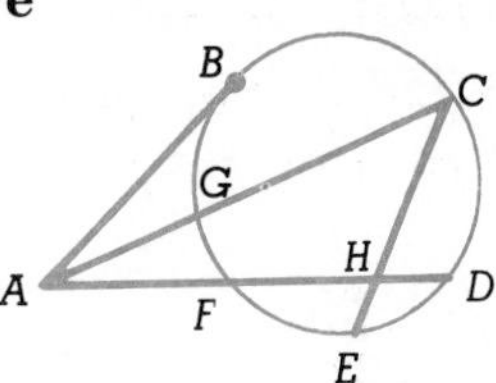

Exercises 13–18

Prove each of the following. For answers to exercises 19-22, see the Teacher's Guide.

19. Theorem 10–18

20. Theorem 10–19

21. Given: $\overleftrightarrow{CF}$ is tangent to $\odot P$ and $\odot Q$ at F.

Prove: $CA \cdot CB = CE \cdot CD$

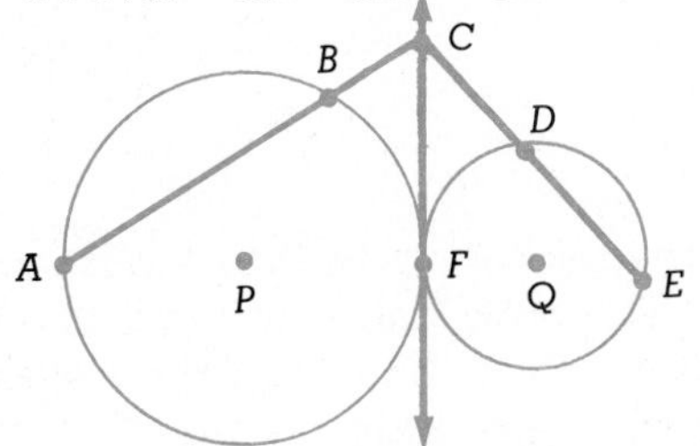

22. Given: $\overleftrightarrow{GM}$ is tangent to $\odot R$ and $\odot S$ at M.

Prove: $GH \cdot GL = GJ \cdot GK$

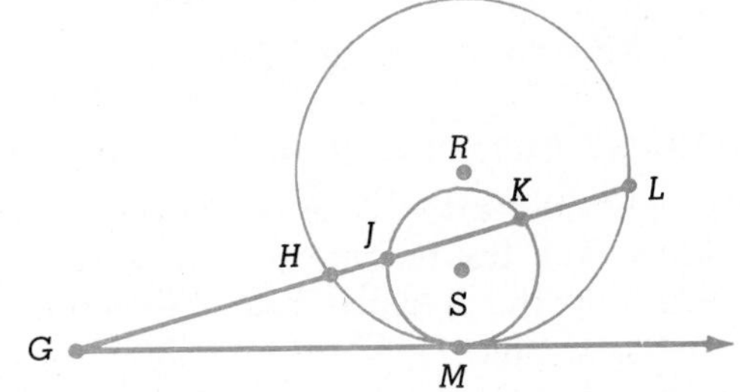

careers

Seismologist

Russ Lindsey is a seismologist. One of his tasks is to determine the size and the location of earthquakes. He uses an instrument called a seismograph that records the time of travel and the intensity of shockwaves.

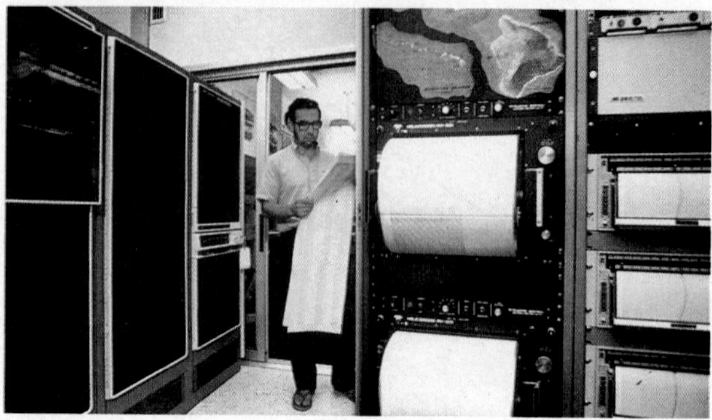

Shockwaves move in a circular manner from the center of the earthquake as shown below.

The **focus** is the origin of the earthquake beneath the earth's surface.

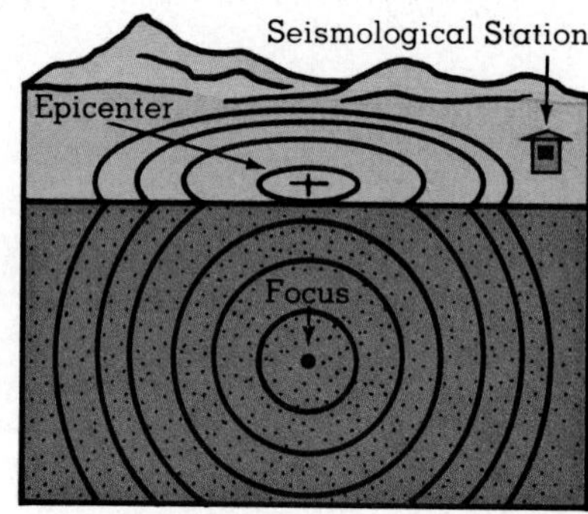

The **epicenter** is the point on the earth's surface above the focus of the earthquake.

Example **Assume the shockwaves travel at a constant rate of 8 km per second. It takes 13 minutes for the first waves to reach the station. Find the approximate distance from the epicenter to the seismological station.**

$rt = d$ *Use rate × time = distance.*

$8 \cdot 780 = d$ *r is 8, t is 13·60 or 780.*

$6240 = d$

The distance is about 6240 km.

Exercises **Answer each of the following.**

1. The constant rate of a shockwave is 9.1 km/s. The travel time of the wave is 11 min. Find the distance from the epicenter to the station. 6006 km
2. An earthquake occurred 9700 km from the station. The wave took 23 minutes to reach the station. Find the rate of the waves in km/s to the nearest km. 7 km/s

10–8 Spheres

Objective: to recognize and define basic properties of spheres

In space, many congruent circles can be drawn using the same center. Considered together, all these circles form a **sphere.**

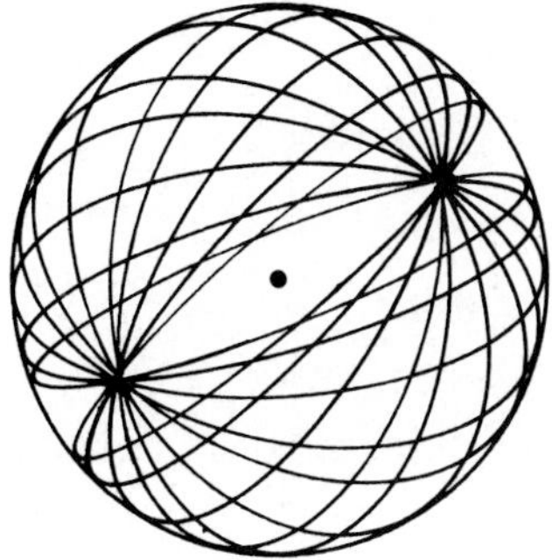

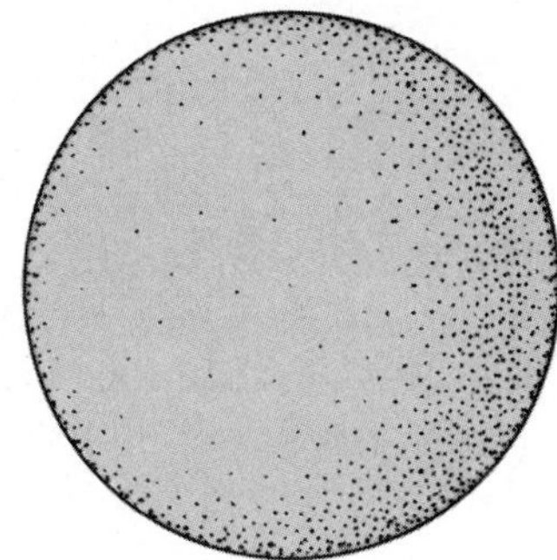

Emphasize that a sphere is a hollow shell and not solid.

In space, a figure is a sphere if and only if it is the set of all points that are a given distance from a given point, called the center.

Definition of Sphere

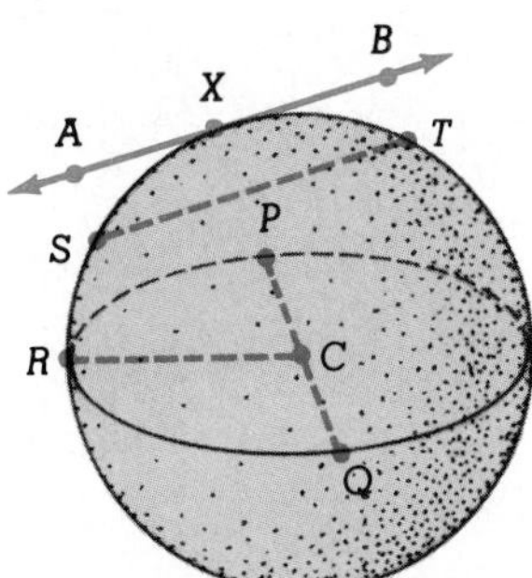

A **radius** of a sphere is a segment whose endpoints are the *center* and *a point on the sphere*. In the figure above, $\overline{CR}$ is a radius.

A **chord** of a sphere is a segment whose endpoints are *points on the sphere*. In the figure above, $\overline{TS}$ is a chord.

A **diameter** of a sphere is a segment that *contains the center,* and whose *endpoints are points on the sphere*. In the figure above, $\overline{PQ}$ is a diameter. A diameter could be defined as a chord containing the center.

A **tangent** to a sphere is a line that *intersects the sphere in exactly one point*. In the figure above, $\overleftrightarrow{AB}$ is tangent to the sphere at X.

A plane can intersect a sphere in one of three ways.

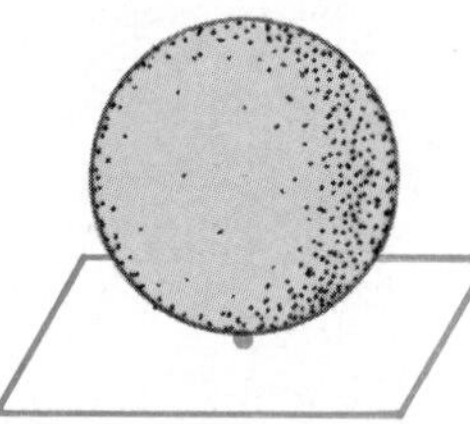

A plane may be tangent to the sphere.

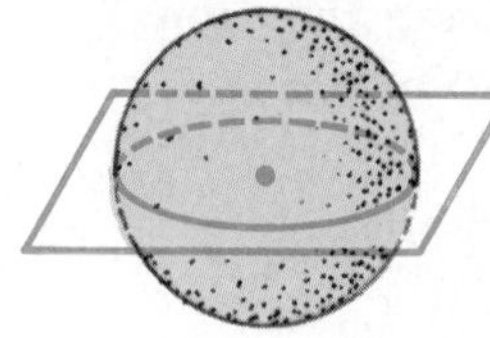

A plane may intersect the sphere and contain the center of the sphere.

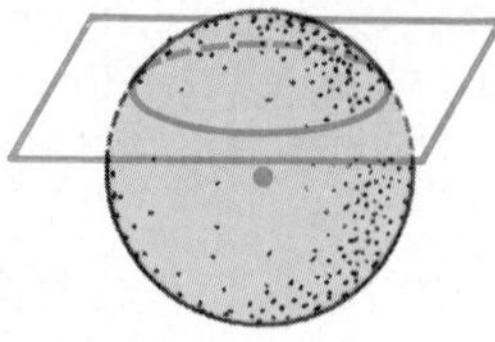

A plane may intersect the sphere but *not* contain the center of the sphere.

example

1 **Prove that the intersection of a sphere and a plane is a circle if the intersection contains more than one point.**

Suppose X and Y are two points in the intersection of sphere P and plane $\mathscr{A}$. Draw $\overline{PQ}$ so that $\overline{PQ} \perp \mathscr{A}$ and Q lies in $\mathscr{A}$. Next, draw $\overline{QX}$, $\overline{QY}$, $\overline{PX}$, and $\overline{PY}$. $\overline{PQ} \perp \overline{QX}$ and $\overline{PQ} \perp \overline{QY}$, since $\overline{PQ} \perp \mathscr{A}$. Thus, $\triangle PQX \cong \angle PQY$ because they are right angles.

Since $\overline{PX}$ and $\overline{PY}$ are both radii of the sphere, $\overline{PX} \cong \overline{PY}$. Also, $\overline{PQ} \cong \overline{PQ}$. So, $\triangle PQX \cong \triangle PQY$ by HL.

As a result, $\overline{QX} \cong \overline{QY}$, and X and Y are equidistant from Q. They lie on the circle with Q as a center and radius measuring QY. In addition, any point on the circle is in $\mathscr{A}$.

Suppose Z is a point on $\odot Q$. Then, $\overline{QZ} \cong \overline{QY}$. Also, $\overline{PQ} \perp \overline{QZ}$ because $\overline{PQ} \perp \mathscr{A}$. Because, $\overline{PQ} \cong \overline{PQ}$, the two right triangles, $\triangle PQY$ and $\triangle PQZ$ are congruent. Thus, $PY = PZ$ and Z must be on the sphere.

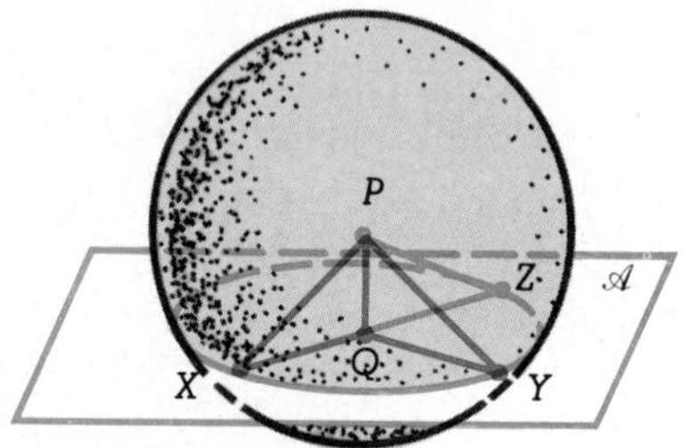

If a plane intersects a sphere in more than one point, then the intersection is a circle.

Theorem 10–20

Suppose a plane intersects a sphere in more than one point and contains the center of the sphere. The intersection is called a **great circle.** A great circle has the same center as the sphere and its radii are also radii of the sphere.

Each great circle separates a sphere into two hemispheres.

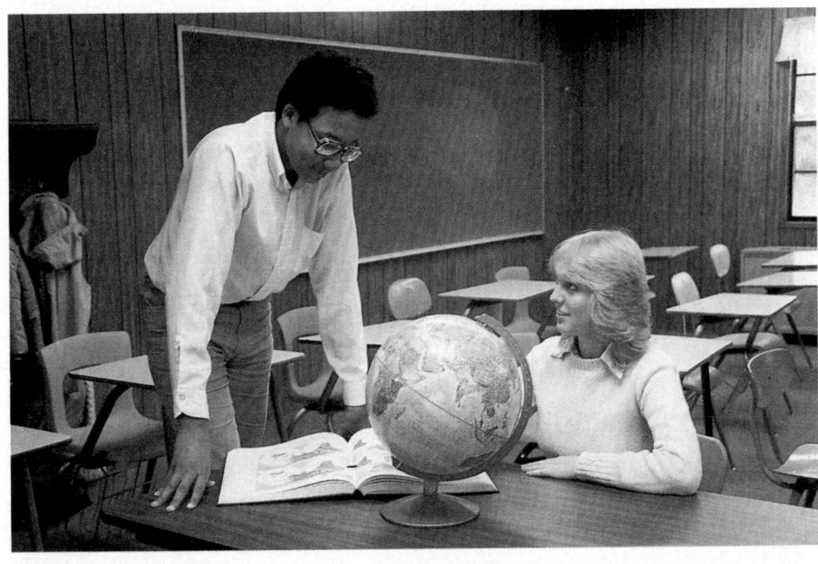

The surface of a globe is a model of a sphere. Each north-south meridian represents a great circle. Of the parallels of latitude, only the equator represents a great circle.

EN: Wr: 1-14, 15-35 odds; p. 356, Ch: 1-4, AV: Ex: 1-11 odds, Wr: 1-14, 15-35 odds; p. 356, Ch: 1-2; p. 351, Wr: 6-18 evens, 21

exercises

FN: Ex: 1-12, Wr: 1-20, 21-35 odds; p. 351, Wr: 14-20 evens

Exploratory **Describe each of the following as a model of a *circle,* a *sphere,* or *neither.***

1. ball bearing sphere
2. basketball hoop circle
3. Jupiter sphere
4. basketball sphere
5. car tire circle
6. corona of eclipse circle
7. orbit of electron circle
8. cross section of pipe circle
9. telephone dial circle
10. ping pong ball sphere
11. helicopter pad neither
12. record circle

Written **For each of the following, write *yes* or *no.***

1. A diameter of a sphere is a chord of the sphere. yes
2. A radius of a sphere is a chord of the sphere. no
3. All radii of a sphere are congruent. yes
4. All diameters of a sphere are congruent. yes
5. All great circles of a sphere are congruent. yes
6. A plane and a sphere may intersect in exactly two points. no

7. A diameter of a great circle is a diameter of the sphere. yes

8. A diameter of a sphere is a diameter of a great circle of the sphere. yes

9. A secant of a sphere intersects the sphere in exactly one point. no

10. A radius of a sphere intersects the sphere in exactly one point. yes

11. Two spheres may intersect in exactly one point. yes

12. Two great circles of a sphere may intersect in exactly one point. no

13. Two great circles of a sphere intersect in exactly two points. yes

14. Two spheres may intersect in exactly two points. no

Write *if and only if* definitions for each of the following.

For answers to exercises 15-26, see the Teacher's Guide.

15. radius of a sphere
16. chord of a sphere
17. great circle of a sphere
18. diameter of a sphere
19. interior of a sphere
20. exterior of a sphere
21. line tangent to a sphere
22. plane tangent to a sphere
23. secant of a sphere
24. hemisphere
25. congruent spheres
26. arc of a sphere

Have students draw a figure to illustrate each situation.

Suppose C is the center of a sphere, I is in the interior of the sphere, and E is in the exterior of the sphere answer each of the following questions about the sphere.

27. In how many points does $\overline{IE}$ intersect the sphere? one

28. In how many points does $\overleftrightarrow{IE}$ intersect the sphere? two

29. In how many points does $\overrightarrow{IE}$ intersect the sphere? one

30. In how many points does $\overrightarrow{EI}$ intersect the sphere? two

31. In how many points does $\overline{CE}$ intersect the sphere? one

32. In how many points does $\overline{CI}$ intersect the sphere? none

33. How many chords contain I? infinitely many

34. How many radii contain I? one

35. Prove that if $\overline{PR}$ and $\overline{QS}$ are diameters of a sphere, then $PQRS$ is a rectangle.

See the Teacher's Guide.

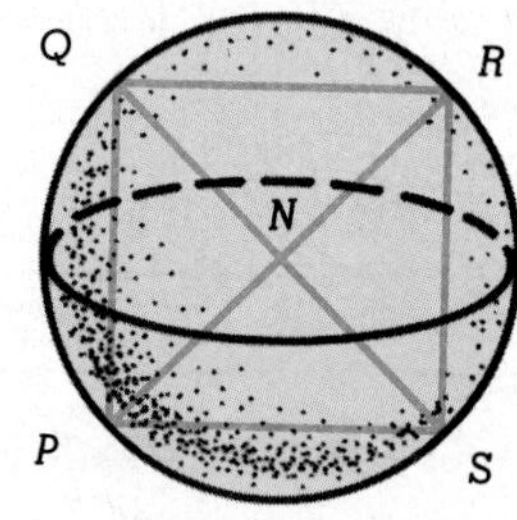

Exercise 35

Challenge

In the figure, P is the center of the sphere and the plane, $\mathscr{B}$, intersects the sphere in $\odot R$.

1. Suppose $PS = 25$ and $PR = 7$. Find RS. 24
2. Suppose $PS = 15$ and $PR = 9$. Find RS. 12
3. Suppose $PS = 13$ and $RS = 12$. Find PR. 5
4. Suppose $PS = 26$ and $RS = 24$. Find PR. 10

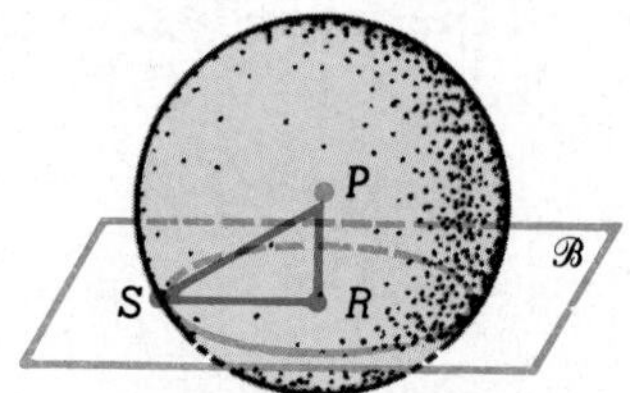

Vocabulary

circle (323)
radius (323)
chord (323)
diameter (323)
interior of a circle (324)
exterior of a circle (324)
tangent (324)
secant (324)
common external tangent (325)
common internal tangent (325)
central angle (327)
minor arc (327)
major arc (327)
semicircle (327)
concentric circles (328)
intercepted arc (335)
inscribed angle (335)
inscribed polygon (337)
tangent segment (341)
circumscribed polygon (342)
secant segment (349)
external secant segment (349)
sphere (353)
great circle (355)

Chapter Summary

1. Definition of Circle: A figure is a circle if and only if it is the set of all points in a plane that are a given distance from a given point in the plane, called the center. (323)
2. Theorem 10–1: In a plane, if a line contains a point in the interior of a circle, then the line intersects the circle in exactly two points. (324)
3. Definition of Arc Measure: The degree measure of a minor arc is the degree measure of its central angle. The degree measure of a major arc is 360 minus the degree measure of its central angle. The degree measure of a semicircle is 180. (327)
4. Arc Addition Postulate (Postulate 10–1): If Q is a point on $\widehat{PQR}$, then $m\widehat{PQ} + m\widehat{QR} = m\widehat{PQR}$. (328)
5. Definition of Congruent Circles: Two circles are congruent if and only if their radii are congruent. (328)
6. Theorem 10–2: In a circle or in congruent circles, two central angles are congruent if and only if their minor arcs are congruent. (329)
7. Theorem 10–3: In a circle or in congruent circles, two minor arcs are congruent if and only if their corresponding chords are congruent. (331)

8. Theorem 10–4: In a circle, if a diameter is perpendicular to a chord, then it bisects the chord and its arcs. (332)
9. Theorem 10–5: In a circle or in congruent circles, two chords are congruent if and only if they are equidistant from the center. (332)
10. Theorem 10–6: If an angle is inscribed in a circle, then the measure of the angle equals one-half the measure of its intercepted arc. (336)
11. Theorem 10–7: If two inscribed angles intercept congruent arcs, then the angles are congruent. (337)
12. Theorem 10–8: If an angle is inscribed in a semicircle, then the angle is a right angle. (337)
13. Theorem 10–9: If the angles of a quadrilateral are inscribed in a circle, then each pair of opposite angles are supplementary. (337)
14. Theorem 10–10: If a line is tangent to a circle, then it is perpendicular to the radius at the point of tangency. (340)
15. Theorem 10–11: In a plane, if a line is perpendicular to a radius of a circle at its endpoint on the circle, then the line is a tangent. (341)
16. Theorem 10–12: If two segments from the same exterior point are tangent to a circle, then they are congruent. (341)
17. Theorem 10–13: If two secants intersect in the interior of a circle, then the measure of an angle formed is one-half the sum of the measures of the arcs intercepted by the angle and its vertical angle. (344)
18. Theorem 10–14: If two secants intersect in the exterior of a circle, then the measure of an angle formed is one-half the positive difference of the measures of the intercepted arcs. (344)
19. Theorem 10–15: If a secant and a tangent intersect at the point of tangency, then the measure of each angle formed is one-half the measure of its intercepted arc. (345)
20. Theorem 10–16: If a secant and a tangent, or two tangents, intersect in the exterior of a circle, then the measure of the angle formed is one-half the positive difference of the measures of the intercepted arcs. (346)
21. Theorem 10–17: If two chords intersect in a circle, then the product of the measures of the segments of one chord equals the product of the measures of the segments of the other chord. (348)
22. Theorem 10–18: If two secant segments are drawn to a circle from an exterior point, then the product of the measures of one secant segment and its external secant segment equals the product of the measures of the other secant segment and its external secant segment. (349)
23. Theorem 10–19: If a tangent segment and a secant segment are drawn to a circle from an exterior point, then the square of the measure of the tangent segment equals the product of the measures of the secant segment and its external secant segment. (349)
24. Definition of Sphere: In space, a figure is a sphere if and only if it is the set of all points that are a given distance from a given point, called the center. (353)

25. Theorem 10–20: If a plane intersects a sphere in more than one point, then the intersection is a circle. (354)

Chapter Review

10–1 Solve each of the following.

1. A radius of a circle is a chord of the circle. Write *yes* or *no*. no

2. A diameter of a circle is a chord of the circle. Write *yes* or *no*. yes

3. Write an if and only if definition for the diameter of a circle. A segment is a diameter of a circle if and only if its endpoints are on the circle and it contains the center of the circle.

10–2 In $\odot P$, $\overline{XY}$ and $\overline{AB}$ are diameters.

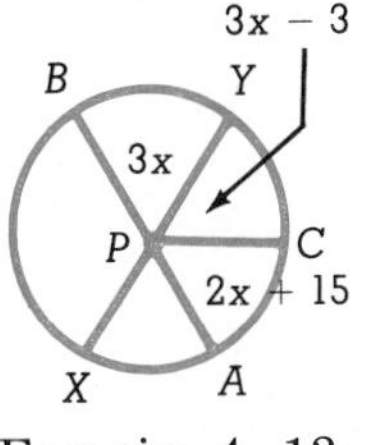

Exercise 4–13

4. Find the value of x. 21

5. Find $m\angle BPY$. 63

6. Find $m\widehat{YAX}$. 180

7. Find $m\angle YPC$. 60

8. Find $m\angle BPC$. 123

9. Find $m\widehat{BX}$. 117

10. Find $m\angle CPA$. 57

11. Find $m\angle XPA$. 63

12. Find $m\widehat{CA}$. 57

13. Find $m\widehat{BC}$. 123

10–3 Answer each of the following.

14. **Given:** $\overline{AB}$ is a diameter of $\odot E$.
$\overline{AB} \perp \overline{CD}$
Prove: $\widehat{CB} \cong \widehat{DB}$ See the Teacher's Guide.

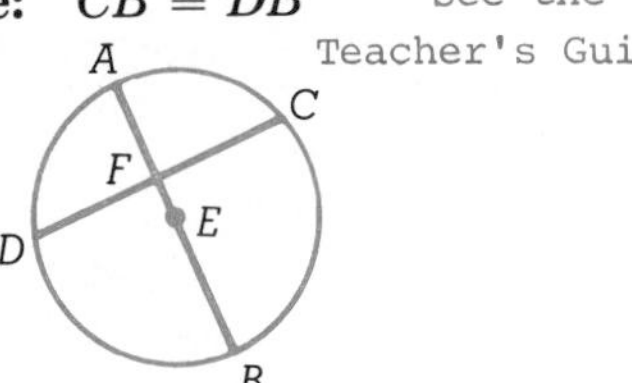

Exercise 14

15. Suppose a chord of a circle is 16 centimeters long and is 6 centimeters from the center of the circle. Find the length of the radius. 10 cm

10–4 In $\odot P$, $\overline{AB} \parallel \overline{CD}$, $m\widehat{BD} = 72$, and $m\angle CPD = 144$. Find the degree measure for each of the following.

Exercises 16–23

16. $\angle DPB$ 72

17. $\angle DAB$ 36

18. $\widehat{CD}$ 144

19. $\angle CPA$ 72

20. $\widehat{CA}$ 72

21. $\angle CDA$ 36

22. $\widehat{AB}$ 72

23. $\angle APB$ 72

10–5 For each of the following, find the value of x. Assume C is the center of each circle and that segments that appear tangent are tangent.

24. 12

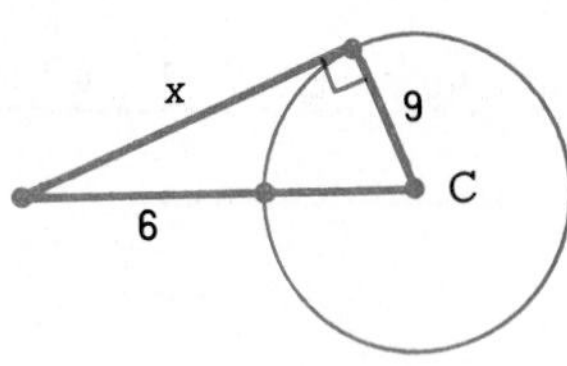

25. $3\sqrt{2}$

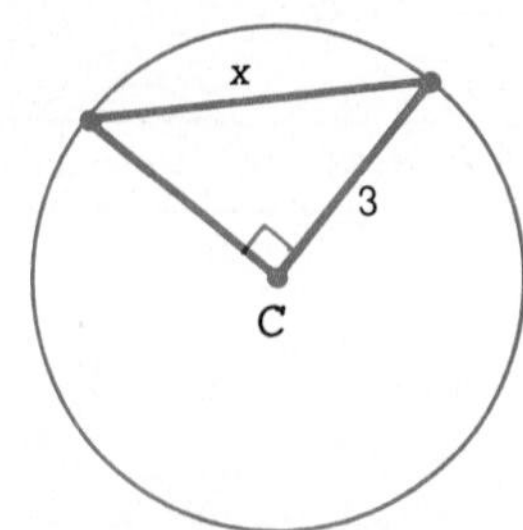

26. 6

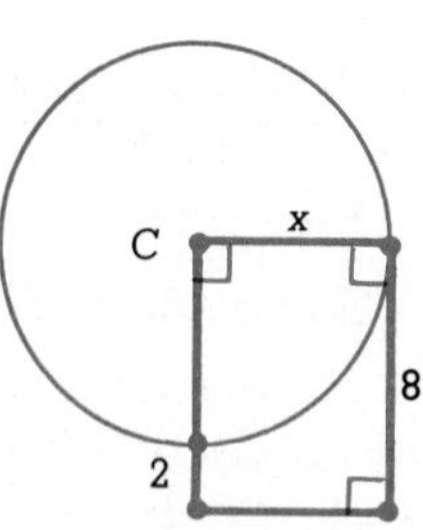

27. Determine whether the sides of a circumscribed polygon are chords or tangents of the circle. tangents

10–6 In $\odot P$, $m\widehat{AB} = 29$, $m\angle AEB = 42$, $m\widehat{BG} = 18$, and $\overline{AC}$ is a diameter. Find each of the following.

28. $m\angle DEC$ 42

29. $m\widehat{CD}$ 55

30. $m\angle GFD$ $18\frac{1}{2}$

31. $m\widehat{AD}$ 125

32. $m\angle AED$ 138

33. $m\widehat{GC}$ 133

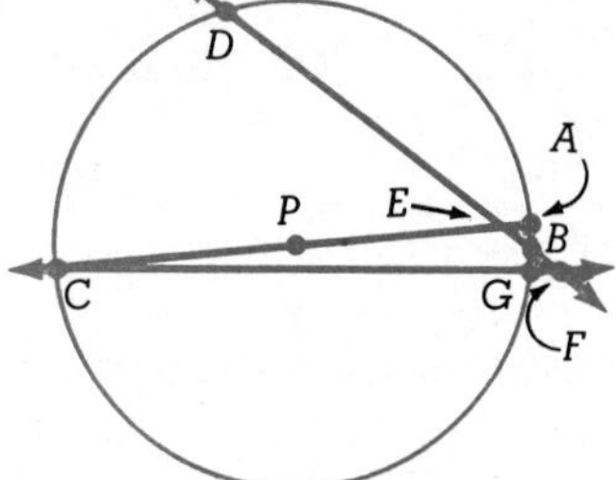

10–7 For each of the following, find the value of x. Assume the segment in exercise 35 is tangent.

34. 6 cm

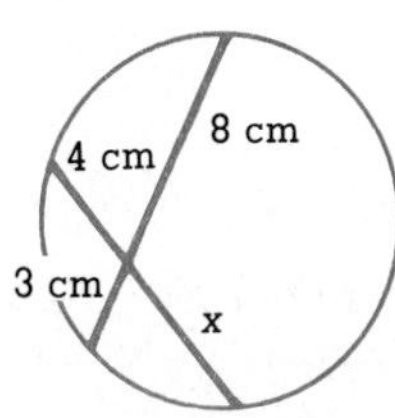

35. 0.806 ft

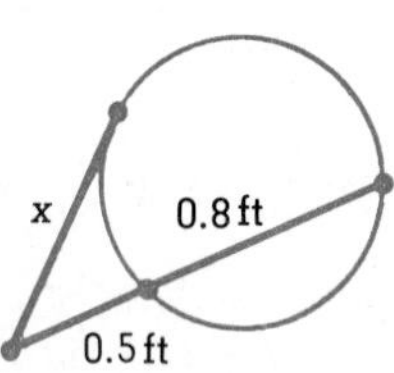

36. $15\frac{1}{3}$ cm

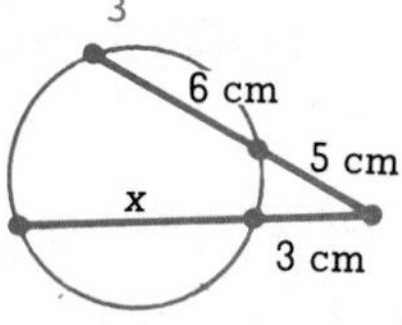

10–8 Answer each of the following.

37. A radius of a sphere is a chord of the sphere. Write *yes* or *no*. no

38. All great circles of a sphere are congruent. Write *yes* or *no*. yes

Suppose C is the center of a sphere, I is in the interior of the sphere, and E is in the exterior of the sphere. Solve each problem about the sphere.

39. In how many points does $\overrightarrow{EI}$ intersect the sphere? two

40. How many chords contain E? none

41. In how many points does $\overline{IC}$ intersect the sphere? none

42. In how many points does $\overline{EC}$ intersect the sphere? one

Chapter Test

1. Write an if and only if definition for the radius of a circle. A segment is a radius of a circle if and only if its endpoints are the center of the circle and a point on the circle.

For each of the following, find the value of x. Assume C is the center of each circle and that segments that appear tangent are tangent.

2. 10

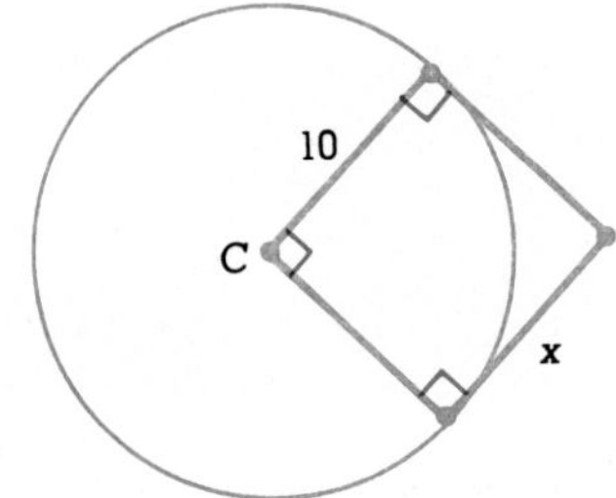

3. 4

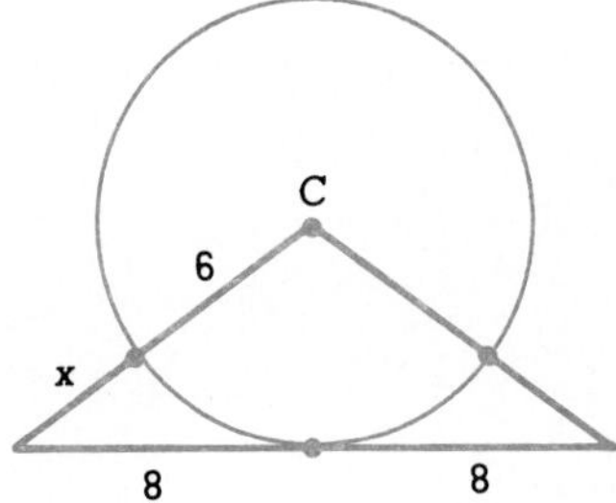

4. 15

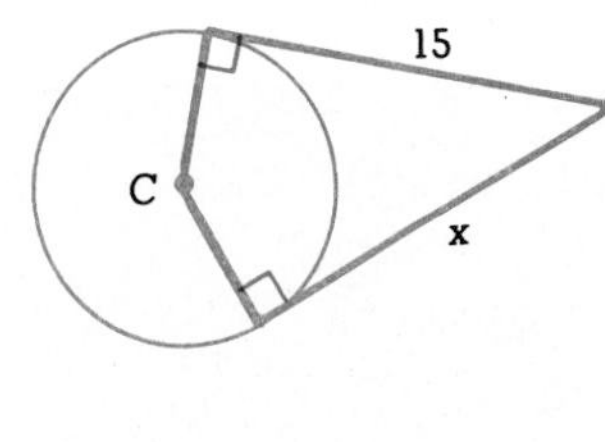

5. 7

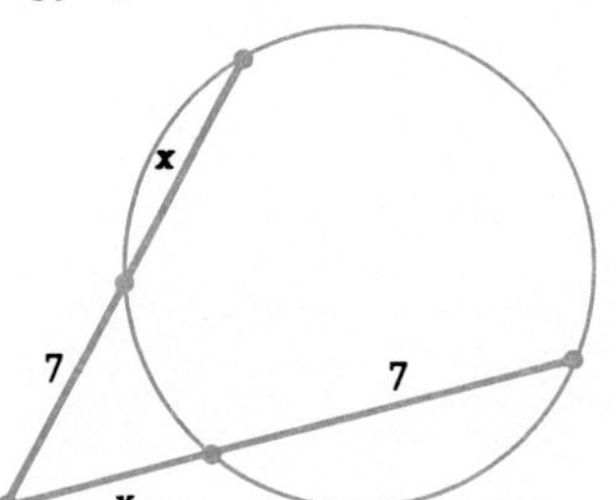

6. 6

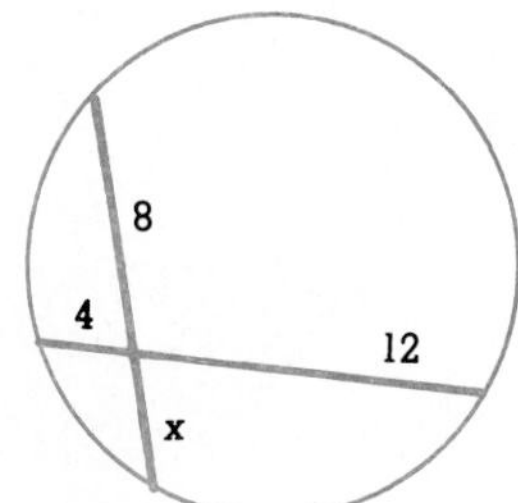

7. 5.35

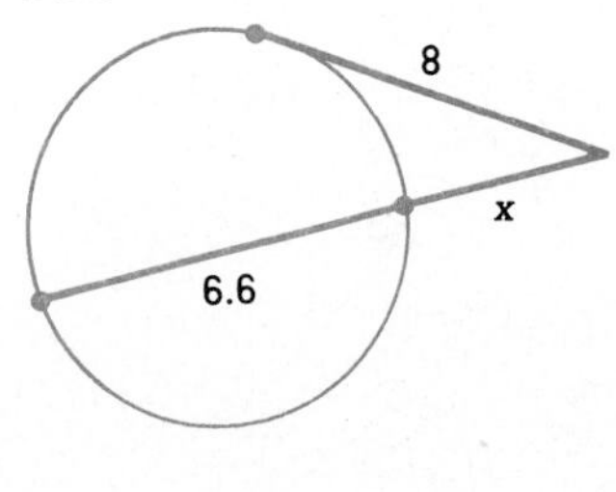

Answer each of the following.

8. Suppose the diameter of a circle is 10 inches long and a chord is 6 inches long. Find the distance between the chord and the center of the circle. 4 in.

9. Determine whether the sides of an inscribed polygon are chords or tangents of the circle. chords

10. Two spheres may intersect in exactly two points. Write *yes* or *no*. no

In $\odot P$, $\overline{AB} \parallel \overline{CD}$, $m\widehat{BD} = 42$, $m\widehat{BE} = 12$, and $\overline{CF}$ and $\overline{AB}$ are diameters. Find each of the following.

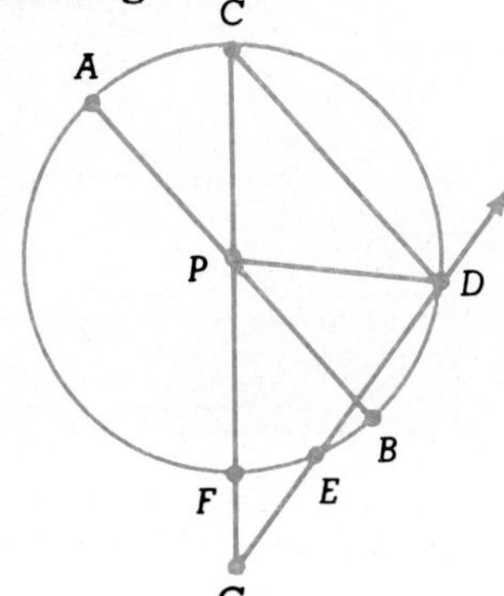

11. $m\angle BPD$ 42
12. $m\widehat{AC}$ 42
13. $m\angle APC$ 42
14. $m\widehat{CD}$ 96
15. $m\angle BPF$ 42
16. $m\widehat{FB}$ 42
17. $m\widehat{AF}$ 138
18. $m\widehat{FE}$ 30
19. $m\angle FCD$ 42
20. $m\angle EDC$ 105

chapter 11 Area and Volume

Farmers use the concepts of area and volume to determine their yield and profit.

Objectives: to find the area and perimeter of a rectangle, to find the width of a rectangle given its length and area

11–1 Defining Area

The amount of surface a carpet covers is called the **area** of the surface. For example, a 9-foot by 12-foot carpet covers 108 square feet (ft^2) of surface.

A polygon separates the planes into three parts, the polygon, the interior, and the exterior. Together, a polygon and its interior are called a **polygonal region.**

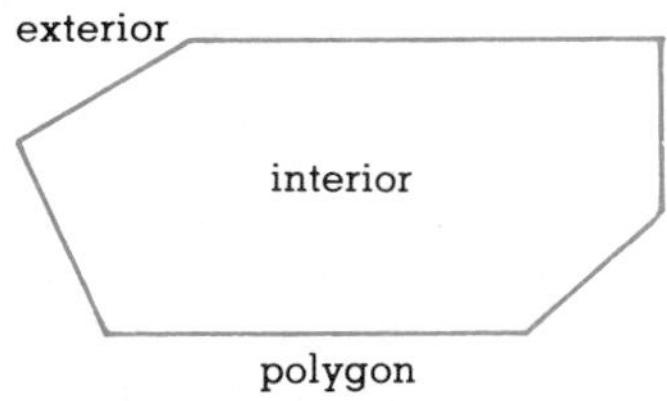

polygon

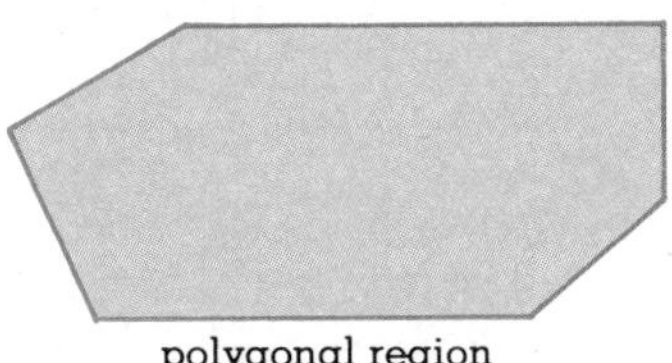

polygonal region

Area measurements are used to compare polygonal regions.

For any polygonal region and a given unit of measure, there is a unique positive number called the measure of the area of the region.

Postulate 11–1 Area Postulate

Area will mean the amount of surface covered by a polygonal region. Thus, for example, the area of a square is the amount of surface covered by the square and its interior.

If each side measures 1 unit, we say that the area is 1 square unit. Thus, a square one centimeter (cm) wide and one centimeter long has an area of 1 square centimeter (cm^2).

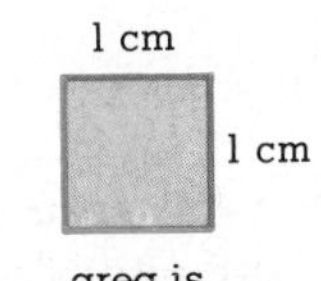

area is
1 square centimeter

Emphasize that area is measured in square units.

The area of a region may differ depending on the unit of measure. For example, the area of the square region at the right is 1 square inch. The area of the region also is about 6.45 square centimeters.

In a given situation, we do *not* always state the unit of measure. If no units are stated, assume the same unit is used for all measurements.

Two figures are congruent if all the sides and angles of one figure are congruent to the corresponding sides and angles of the other figure.

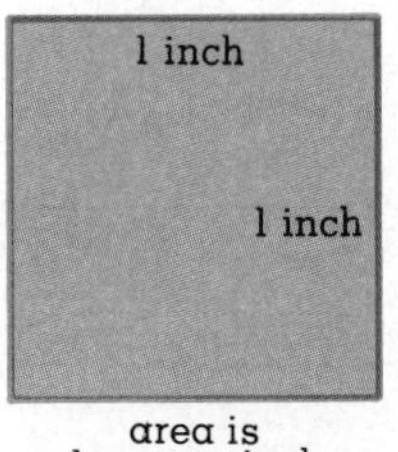

area is
1 square inch

Using the following postulates, it is possible to find the areas of various regions.

If two figures are congruent, then they have exactly the same area.

Postulate 11–2

If a polygonal region is separated into nonoverlapping regions, then the sum of the areas of these regions equals the area of the entire region.

Postulate 11–3
Area Addition Postulate

Nonoverlapping regions are regions that have no interior points in common.

The rectangular region at the right is separated into 12 congruent squares whose sides are 1 centimeter long. Thus, the area of each square is 1 square centimeter. By the Area Addition Postulate, the area of the rectangle is 12 square centimeters.

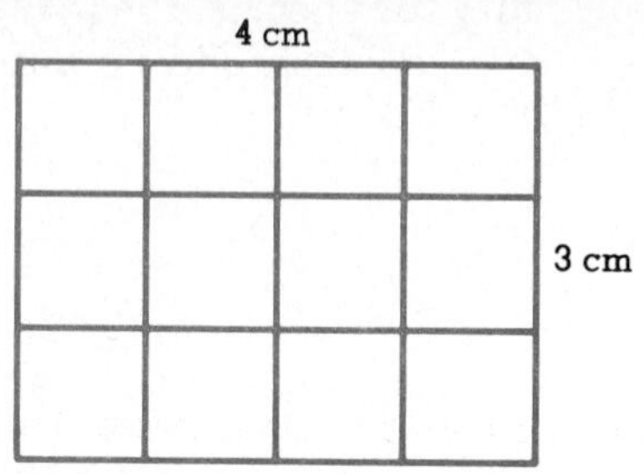

This and many similar examples suggest the following postulate.

If a rectangle has an area of A square units, a length of ℓ units, and a width of w units, then $A = \ell w$.

Postulate 11–4
Area of a Rectangle

examples

1 **Find the area of a rectangle that has a length of 6.1 m and a width of 3.7 m.**

$A = \ell w$ — *Postulate 11–4*

$= 6.1 \times 3.7$

$= 22.57$

The area of the rectangle is 22.57 square meters (m^2).

2 **Develop a formula for the area of a square, if each side is s units long. Let A stand for the area of the square.**

$A = \ell w$ — *A square is a rectangle.*

$= s \cdot s$ — *Replace ℓ by s and w by s.*

$= s^2$

The formula is $A = s^2$.

If a square has an area of A square units, and each side is s units long, then $A = s^2$.

Theorem 11–1
Area of a Square

EN: Ex: 9-12, Wr: 1-31 odds; p. 366, E: 1-4, AV: Ex: 5-12, Wr: 1-31 odds; p. 366, E: 1-4

exercises

FN: Ex: 1-12, Wr: 1-16, 17-31 odds; p. 366, E: 1-4

Exploratory Answer each of the following.

1. Draw as many rectangles as you can that are separated into 24 one-centimeter squares. Name the dimensions for each rectangle.
2. Draw as many rectangles as you can that are separated into 36 one-centimeter squares. Name the dimensions for each rectangle.

For answers to exercises 1-2, see the Teacher's Guide.

Find the measure of the area and perimeter of each rectangle described below.

3. 6 units by 6 units $A = 36, P = 24$
4. 9 units by 4 units $A = 36, P = 26$
5. 12 units by 3 units $A = 36, P = 30$
6. 18 units by 2 units $A = 36, P = 40$
7. 5 units by 5 units $A = 25, P = 20$
8. 6 units by 4 units $A = 24, P = 20$

Determine whether each of the following is *true* or *false*.

9. If two rectangles have the same area, then they have the same perimeter. false
10. If two rectangles have the same perimeter, then they have the same area. false
11. If two squares have the same area, then they have the same perimeter. true
12. If two squares have the same perimeter, then they have the same area. true

Written Find the area of each rectangle described below.

1. 5 centimeters by 4 centimeters 20 cm^2
2. 7 inches by 4 inches 28 in.^2
3. 10 feet by 12 feet 120 ft^2
4. 3.5 inches by 10 inches 35 in.^2
5. 42.5 centimeters by 53.4 centimeters 2269.5 cm^2
6. 16.3 meters by 21.2 meters 345.56 m^2
7. 29 miles by 23 miles 667 mi^2
8. 48 yards by 38 yards 1824 yd^2
9. $5\frac{1}{2}$ miles by $3\frac{1}{3}$ miles $18\frac{1}{3}\text{ mi}^2$
10. $4\frac{1}{3}$ yards by $2\frac{2}{3}$ yards $11\frac{5}{9}\text{ yd}^2$
11. $5\frac{1}{2}$ inches by $4\frac{1}{4}$ inches $23\frac{3}{8}\text{ in.}^2$
12. $\frac{3}{4}$ foot by $\frac{1}{4}$ foot $\frac{3}{16}\text{ ft}^2$
13. x feet by $(x + 3)$ feet $(x^2 + 3x)\text{ft}^2$
14. $2k$ centimeters by $(k + 1)$ centimeters
15. $(3a + 1)$ inches by $(4a + 2)$ inches
16. $(9w - 3)$ miles by $(4w - 1)$ miles

14. $(2k^2 + 2k)\text{cm}^2$ 15. $(12a^2 + 10a + 2)\text{in.}^2$ 16. $(36w^2 - 21w + 3)\text{mi}^2$

Find the width of each rectangle given the length and area.

17. 10 inches, 35 square inches 3.5 in.
18. 48 yards, 1824 square yards 38 yd
19. 21.2 meters, 345.56 square meters 16.3 m
20. 21 kilometers, 239.4 square kilometers 11.4 km
21. $4\frac{1}{3}$ yards, $11\frac{5}{9}$ square yards $2\frac{2}{3}$ yd
22. $30\frac{1}{2}$ feet, 610 square feet 20 ft
23. $3\frac{1}{2}$ feet, $7\frac{7}{8}$ square feet $2\frac{1}{4}$ ft
24. $2\frac{1}{2}$ feet, $5\frac{5}{6}$ square feet $2\frac{1}{3}$ ft

Find the area of each shaded region. Note that all angles are right angles.

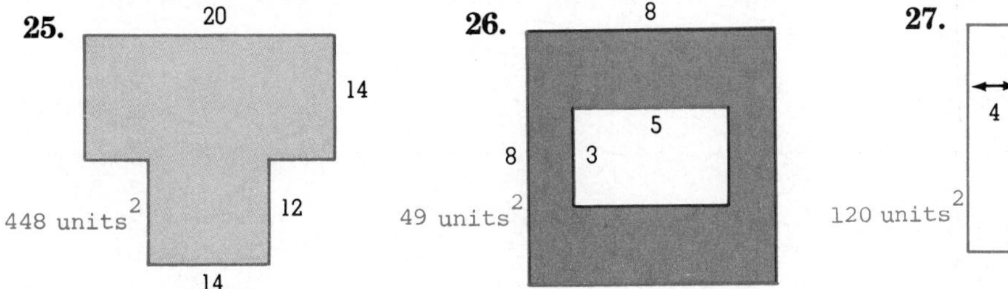

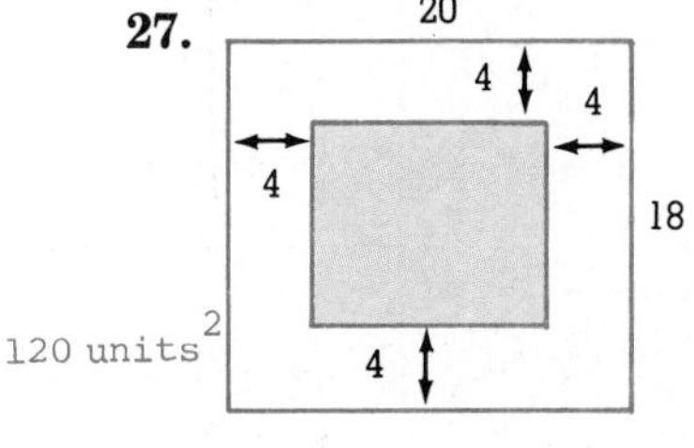

28. 36

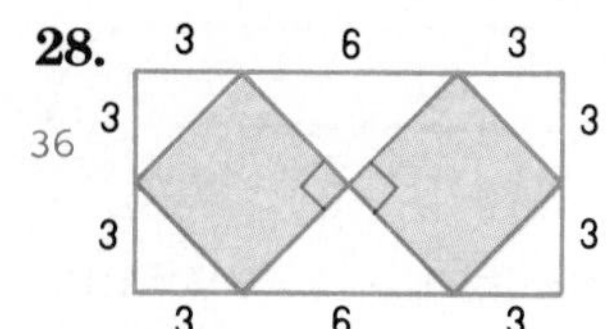

29. 12.5

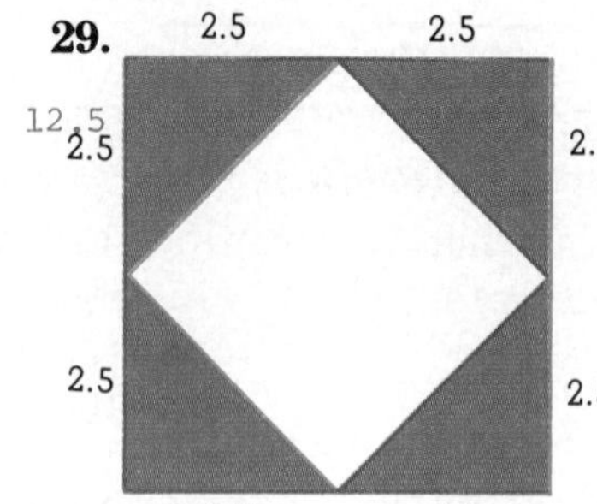

30. 650

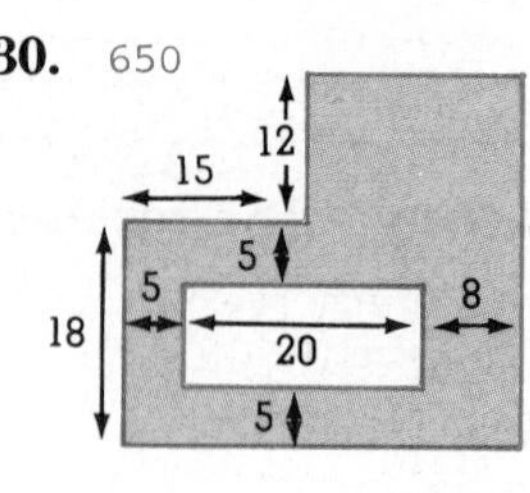

Answer each of the following.

31. A rectangular field to be planted with grain is 150 meters wide and 160 meters long. One bushel of grain plants 100 square meters of land. How many bushels are needed to plant the field? 240 bags

32. A rectangular window is $5\frac{1}{2}$ feet by 4 feet. The window is to be filled with stained glass. Most stained glass costs about $12 per square foot. Estimate the cost of stained glass for the window. $264

Pick's Theorem — excursions in geometry

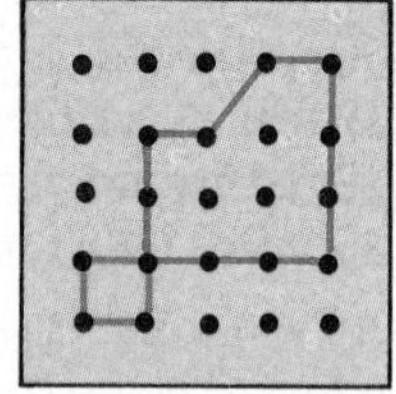

A geoboard usually is a square piece of wood with an arrangement of nails on its surface. The nails are in rows and columns of 5 each for a total of 25 nails.

A variety of geometric figures can be formed by looping rubber bands around the nails on a geoboard. The figure at the right shows two such figures. The area of the region outlined in green is 1 square unit.

Pick's Theorem gives a formula for the area of a region outlined on a geoboard.

> If the area of a region on a geoboard is A square units, the borders of the region touch x nails, and there are y nails in the interior, then $A = \frac{x}{2} + y - 1$.

Example **Find the area of the region outlined in red in the figure shown above.**

$$A = \frac{x}{2} + y - 1$$ *x is 11 and y is 3.*

$$= \frac{11}{2} + 3 - 1$$

$$= 7\frac{1}{2}$$

Exercises **Find the area for each of the following regions. Use Pick's Theorem.**

1. 5

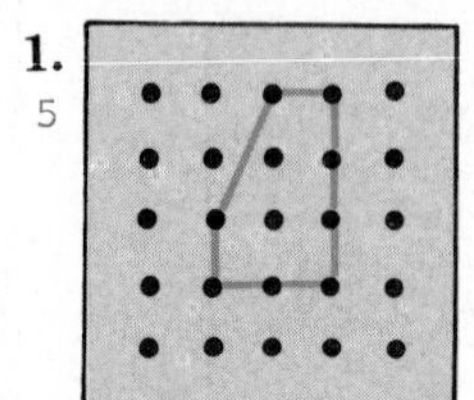

2. 8

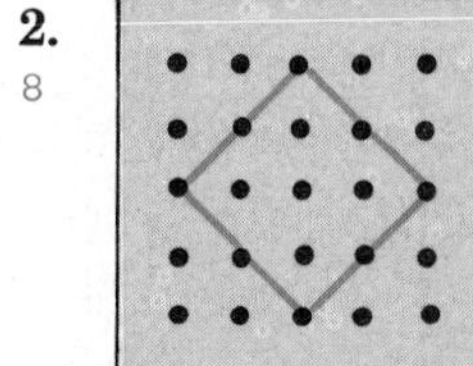

3. 8

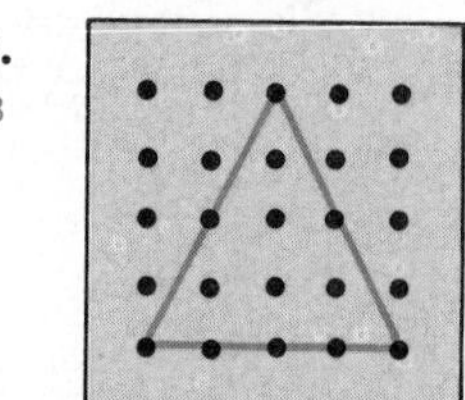

4. 10

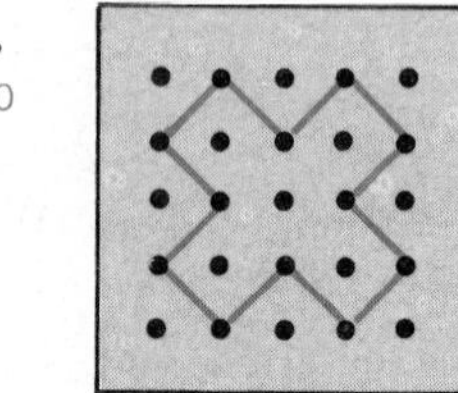

11–2 Area Formulas

Objectives: to recognize the base(s) and altitude(s) of parallelograms, triangles, and trapezoids, to find the areas of parallelograms, triangles, and trapezoids

Any side of a parallelogram may be called the **base** of the parallelogram. For each base there is a corresponding **altitude.** An altitude of a parallelogram is a segment that is perpendicular to the line containing the base and which has its endpoints on the lines containing the base and the opposite side.

For each parallelogram shown below, one base is 10 units long, and its corresponding altitude is 7 units long.

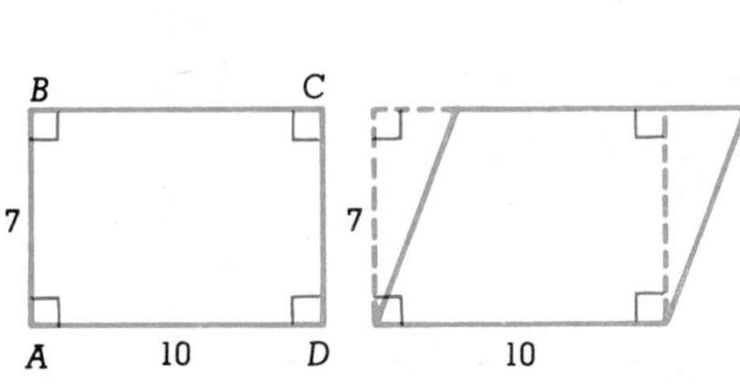

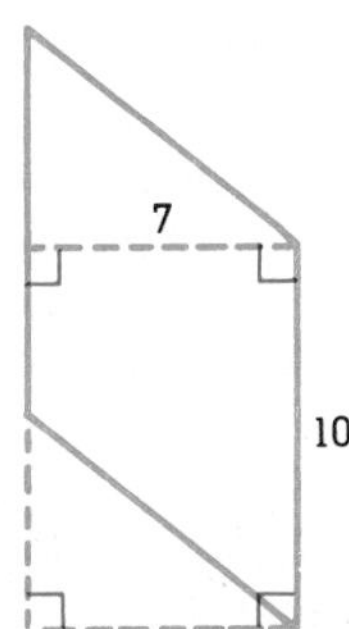

By using the Area Addition Postulate and congruence, it is possible to show that each region has the same area, 7×10 or 70 square units.

If a parallelogram has an area of A square units, a base of b units, and a corresponding altitude of h units, then $A = bh$.

Theorem 11–2
Area of a Parallelogram

example

1 **Prove Theorem 11–2.**

Given: $\square PQRS$
$PS = b$ Locate T between R and Q
$TS = h$ and draw altitude $\overline{ST}$.
The area of $\square PQRS$ is A square units.

Prove: $A = bh$

Proof:

Extend $\overline{RQ}$ and draw $\overline{PV}$ so that $\overline{PV} \perp \overleftrightarrow{RQ}$. Then $PV = h$ and quadrilateral $PVTS$ is a rectangle with a length of h units and a width of b units.

Since $\overline{PQ} \cong \overline{SR}$, show $\triangle PVQ \cong \triangle STR$ by HL. Thus, by the Area Addition Postulate, show that the area of the parallelogram is the same as the area of the rectangle. Thus, $A = bh$.

The area of a triangle is related to the area of a parallelogram. For example, consider ▱$PQRS$.

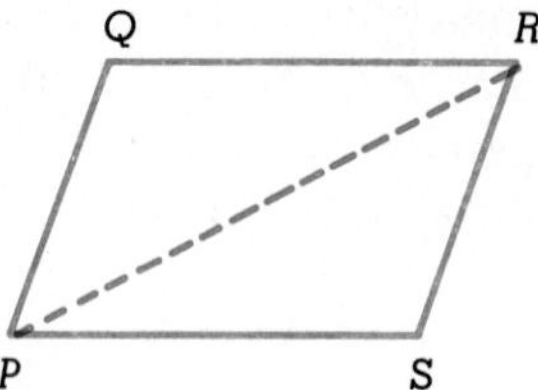

Draw the diagonal $\overline{PR}$ to form $\triangle PQR$ and $\triangle RSP$. We know $\triangle PQR$ and $\triangle RSP$ are congruent by SAS. If the area of ▱$PQRS$ is A square units, then the sum of the areas of $\triangle PQR$ and $\triangle RSP$ is A square units. Therefore it follows that each triangle has half the area of the parallelogram. This conclusion suggests the following theorem.

Have students identify the base and altitude for a variety of triangles including obtuse, acute, and right triangles.

Theorem 11–3
Area of a Triangle

If a triangle has an area of A square units, a base of b units, and a corresponding altitude of h units, then $A = \frac{1}{2}bh$.

Students prove this theorem in Written exercise 27.

A diagonal of a trapezoid separates the trapezoid into two triangles. The formula for the area of a trapezoid can be found by finding the areas of triangles.

An altitude of the trapezoid is a segment perpendicular to the lines containing the bases of the trapezoid, and with its endpoints on the bases. Notice that the measure h of $\overline{QT}$ is the measure of the altitudes of both triangles.

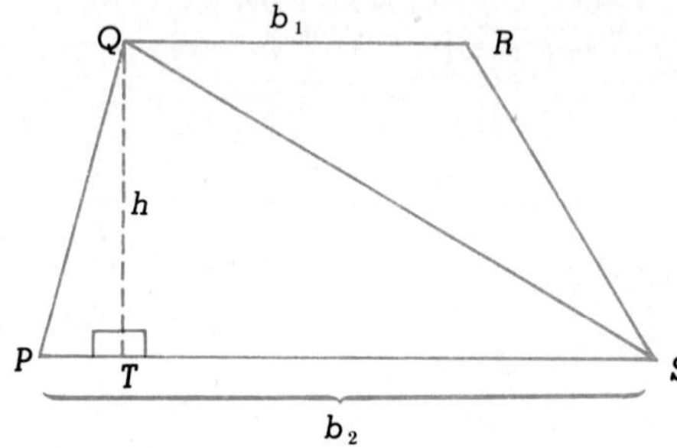

Provide examples of trapezoids in a variety of positions and have students identify bases and altitude.

$$\begin{aligned} \text{area of trapezoid } PQRS &= \text{area } \triangle PQS + \text{area } \triangle QRS \\ &= \frac{1}{2}b_2h + \frac{1}{2}b_1h \\ &= \frac{1}{2}h(b_2 + b_1) \end{aligned}$$

Emphasize in the trapezoid above that $\overline{QT}$ is an altitude of both triangles.

Theorem 11–4
Area of a Trapezoid

If a trapezoid has an area of A square units, bases of b_1 units and b_2 units, and an altitude of h units, then $A = \frac{1}{2}h(b_1 + b_2)$.

Students prove this theorem in Written exercise 28.

example

2 Find the area of the isosceles trapezoid whose bases are 20 units and 32 units, and whose legs measure 10 units each.

Draw the altitudes shown at the right. Two right triangles are formed with a leg of 6 units and hypotenuse of 10 units. Use the Pythagorean Theorem to find the length of the altitude.

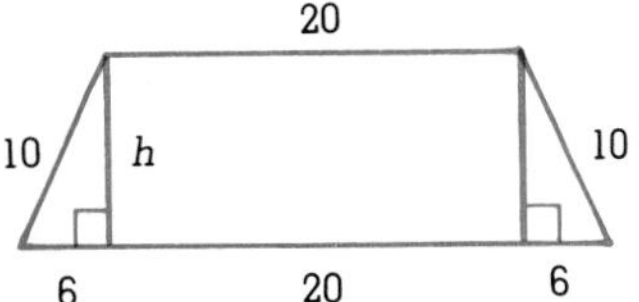

$$h^2 + 6^2 = 10^2$$
$$h^2 = 10^2 - 6^2$$
$$= 100 - 36$$
$$= 64$$
$$h = 8$$

Then, use the formula to find the area of the trapezoid.

$$A = \frac{1}{2}h(b_1 + b_2)$$
$$= \frac{1}{2}(8)(20 + 32)$$
$$= \frac{1}{2}(8)(52)$$
$$= 208 \qquad \text{The area is 208 square units.}$$

EN: Ex: 3, 7, 13, Wr: 1-10, 21-30; AV: Ex: 1-17 odds, Wr: 1-10, 11-29 odds; pp. 365-6, Wr: 2-32 evens

exercises

FN: Ex: 1-18, Wr: 1-10, 11-29 odds; pp. 365-6, Wr: 18-32 evens

Exploratory **Find the area of each parallelogram given the following measurements for the base and altitude respectively.**

1. 12 inches and 8 inches 96 in.^{2}
2. 6 feet and 2 feet 12 ft^2
3. 2 centimeters and 9 centimeters 18 cm^2
4. 4 yards and 5 yards 20 yd^2
5. 21 millimeters and 12 millimeters 252 mm^2
6. 9 meters and 4 meters 36 m^2

Find the area of each triangle given the following measurements for the base and altitude respectively.

7. 7 centimeters and 12 centimeters 42 cm^2
8. 11 miles and 10 miles 55 mi^2
9. $4\frac{1}{2}$ inches and 2 inches $4\frac{1}{2}$ in.^{2}
10. 9 meters and 2.6 meters 11.7 m^2
11. 4.95 feet and 1.02 feet 2.5245 ft^2
12. 120 millimeters and 63.5 millimeters 3810 mm^2

Find the area of each trapezoid described below.

13. bases 9 centimeters and 2 centimeters
altitude 7 centimeters 38.5 cm^2
14. bases 16 meters and 11 meters
altitude 11 meters 148.5 m^2
15. bases 30 miles and 20 miles
altitude 34 miles 850 mi^2
16. bases 55 centimeters and 40 centimeters
altitude 21 centimeters 997.5 cm^2
17. bases 12 inches and 4 inches
altitude 8 inches 64 in.^{2}
18. bases 7 feet and 5 feet
altitude 5 feet 30 ft^2

Written **Copy and complete the chart below.**

	base	altitude	area of parallelogram	
1.	10 feet	4 ft	40 square feet	11. 8 ft = h
2.	$2\frac{1}{2}$ in.	8 inches	20 square inches	12. 5 in. = b
3.	4.7 meters	2.8 meters	13.16 m^2	13. A = 6.58 m^2
4.	13.6 centimeters	5.05 cm	68.68 square centimeters	14. h = 10.1 cm
5.	1.3 m	16 meters	20.8 square meters	15. b = 2.6 m
6.	1.3 ft	12 feet	15.6 square feet	16. 2.6 ft = b
7.	$4\frac{1}{2}$ inches	$4\frac{1}{2}$ inches	$20\frac{1}{4}$ $in.^2$	17. A = $10\frac{1}{8}$ $in.^2$
8.	$1\frac{3}{4}$ feet	$1\frac{19}{21}$ ft^2	$3\frac{1}{3}$ square feet	18. h = $3\frac{17}{21}$ ft
9.	$(2x + 8)$ meters	x meters	$(2x^2 + 8x)m^2$	19. A = $(x^2 + 4x)m^2$
10.	$3k$ inches	k inches	$3k^2 in.^2$	20. A = $\frac{3}{2}k^2 in.^2$

11–20. Complete the chart in exercises 1–10 for triangles.

Find the area of each of the following regions.

21.

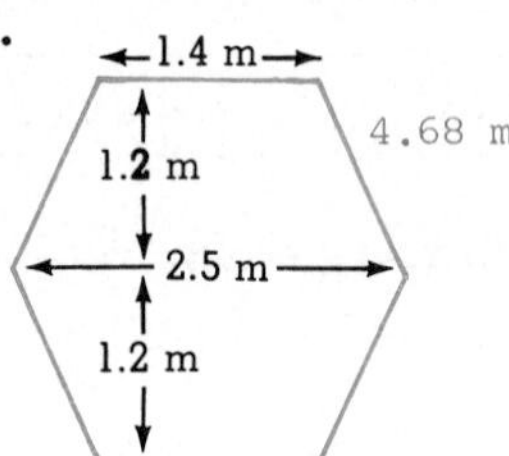

22.

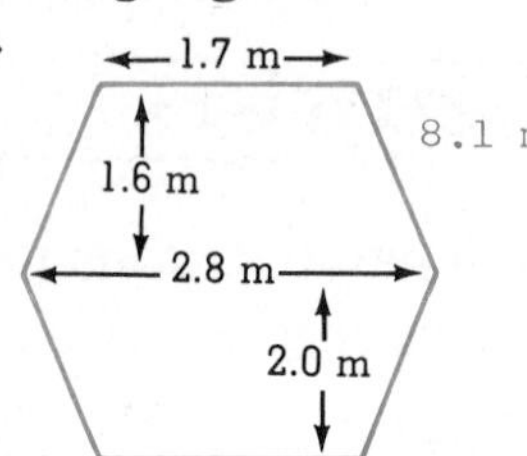

23.

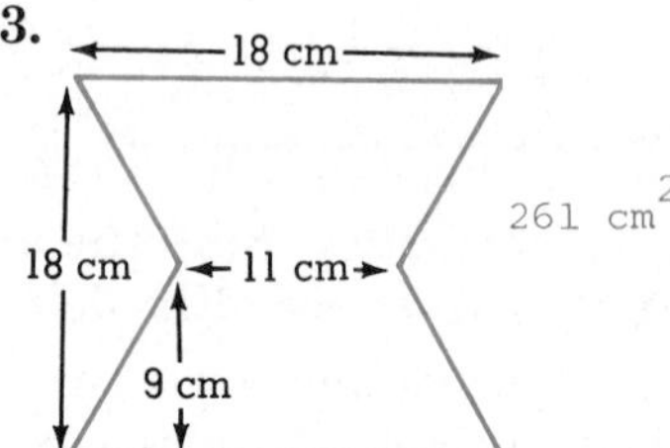

24.

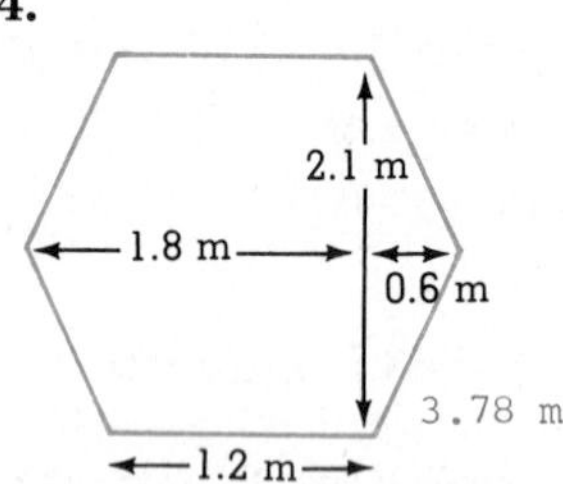

25.

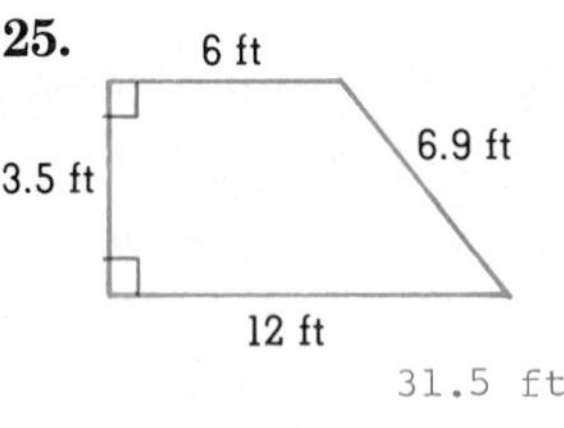

26.

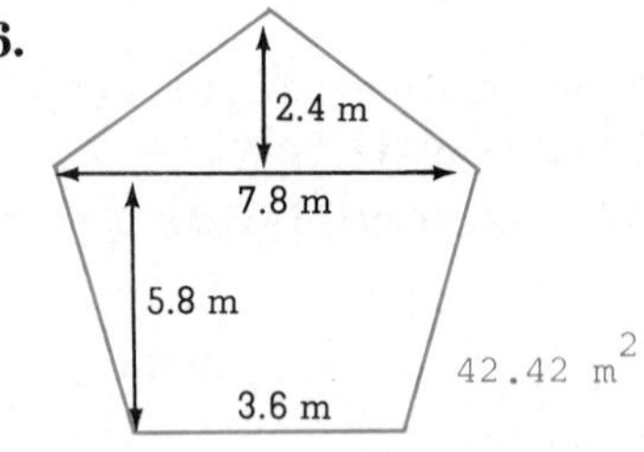

Answer each problem. For answers to exercises 27-28, see the Teacher's Guide.

27. Prove Theorem 11–3.

28. Prove Theorem 11–4.

29. Find the area of an isosceles trapezoid whose bases are 8 units and 13 units and whose legs are 6.5 units. 63 $units^2$

30. Find the area of an isosceles trapezoid whose bases are 37 kilometers and 12 kilometers, and whose legs are 32.5 kilometers. 735 km^2

Objectives: to find the degree measure of a central angle of a regular polygon, to determine the radius, apothem, center, and area of a regular polygon

11–3 Regular Polygons

In the figure at the right, $\odot X$ is circumscribed about the regular hexagon. Notice that $\overline{XP}$, $\overline{XQ}$, $\overline{XR}$, $\overline{XS}$, $\overline{XT}$, and $\overline{XV}$ are radii of the circle. They also are called **radii of the regular hexagon.**

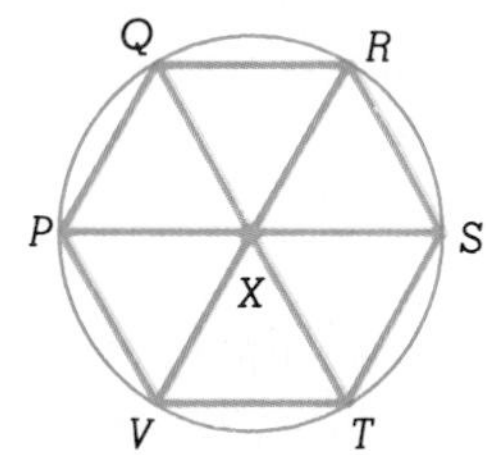

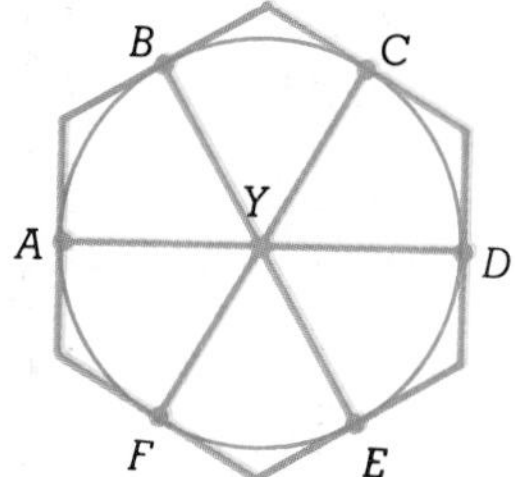

In the figure at the left, $\odot Y$ is inscribed in the regular hexagon. Notice that $\overline{YA}$, $\overline{YB}$, $\overline{YC}$, $\overline{YD}$, $\overline{YE}$, and $\overline{YF}$ are radii of the circle with endpoints at points where the hexagon is tangent to the circle. They are called **apothems of the regular hexagon.**

A segment is a radius of a regular polygon if and only if it is a radius of a circle circumscribed about the polygon. — *Definition of Radius*

A segment is an apothem of a regular polygon if and only if it is a radius of a circle inscribed in the polygon. — *Definition of Apothem*

For a regular polygon, a circle inscribed in the polygon and a circle circumscribed about the polygon have the same center. This point is also called the **center of the regular polygon.**

Point out that this theorem is a biconditional statement.

A polygon is regular if and only if a circle inscribed in the polygon and a circle circumscribed about the polygon have the same center. — *Theorem 11–5*

The circles are concentric.

A point is a center of a regular polygon if and only if it is the common center of its inscribed and circumscribed circles. — *Definition of Center of a Regular Polygon*

If a polygon is *not* regular, then the inscribed circle and the circumscribed circle may *not* exist. If the circles do exist, they may *not* have the same center.

Each side of a regular polygon is tangent to a circle inscribed in the polygon. A radius of a circle drawn to a point of tangency is perpendicular to the tangent. Thus, each apothem of a regular polygon is perpendicular to one side of the polygon.

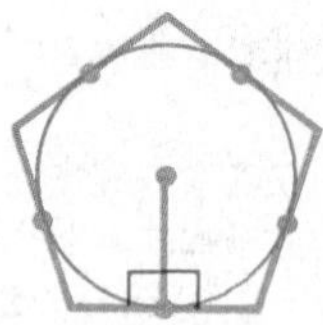

If a segment is an apothem of a regular polygon, then it is perpendicular to a side of the polygon at the point of tangency with the inscribed circle.

Theorem 11–6

Students prove this theorem in Written exercise 20.

Given the length of the apothem and one side of a regular polygon, the area can be found.

example

1 Find the area of a regular hexagon if the apothem is a units long and one side is s units long.

By drawing all the radii of the hexagon, 6 triangles such as $\triangle XYZ$ are formed. Each apothem of a regular polygon is perpendicular to a side of the polygon. Thus, the altitude of each triangle is an apothem of a units. The base of each triangle is a side of the hexagon, and is s units long.

By the Area Addition Postulate, the area of the hexagon equals the sum of the areas of the triangles.

$$A = \frac{1}{2}sa + \frac{1}{2}sa + \frac{1}{2}sa + \frac{1}{2}sa + \frac{1}{2}sa + \frac{1}{2}sa$$

$$= 6\left(\frac{1}{2}sa\right)$$

$= 3sa$ The area is $3sa$ square units.

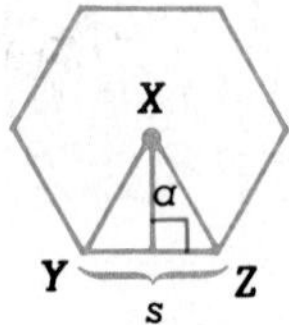

Suppose a regular polygon has an apothem of a units and a side of s units. Then, the following chart gives values for the area, based on the number of sides.

number of sides	3	4	5	6	7	8	9	10
area	$\frac{1}{2}a(3s)$	$\frac{1}{2}a(4s)$	$\frac{1}{2}a(5s)$	$\frac{1}{2}a(6s)$	$\frac{1}{2}a(7s)$	$\frac{1}{2}a(8s)$	$\frac{1}{2}a(9s)$	$\frac{1}{2}a(10s)$

Since the perimeter, p, of each polygon can be written as sn, the following theorem is suggested.

If a regular polygon has an area of A square units, a perimeter of p units, and an apothem of a units, then $A = \frac{1}{2}ap$.

Theorem 11–7
Area of a Regular Polygon

Students prove this theorem in Written exercise 21.

A central angle of a regular polygon is formed by two radii drawn to consecutive vertices.

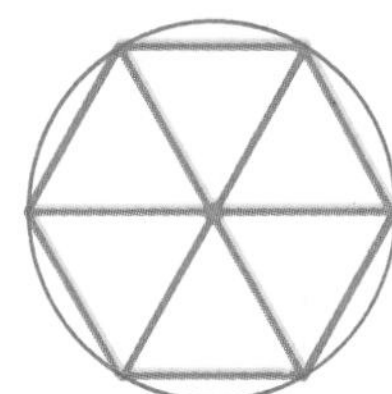

The central angles of the polygon also are central angles of a circle. The sum of their degree measures must be 360.

Why?

A regular hexagon has 6 central angles. Thus, the degree measure of each is $\frac{360}{6}$ or 60.

If a regular polygon has n sides, then the degree measure of each central angle is $\frac{360}{n}$.

Theorem 11–8

Students prove specific cases of this theorem in Written exercises 22-23.

example

2 Find the area of a regular hexagon having 6-inch sides.

Since $\angle ACB$ is a central angle its degree measure is $\frac{360}{6}$ or 60. Also, $\overline{AC} \cong \overline{BC}$, so the triangle must be equilateral. Thus, AC and BC are 6 inches.

Since the apothem $\overline{CD}$ also is an altitude, it bisects $\overline{AB}$. Thus AD and DB are 3 inches.

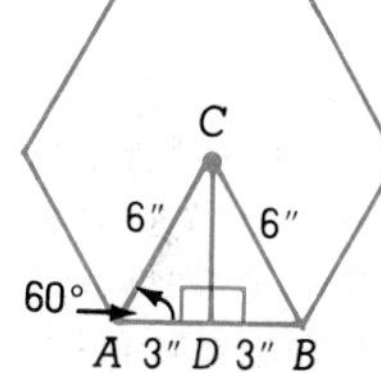

The length of the apothem can be found using either trigonometry or the Pythagorean Theorem. For a 30°–60°–90° right triangle, the length is known to be $(AD)\sqrt{3}$ or $3\sqrt{3}$ inches. Thus, the area of the hexagon is found as follows.

$$A = \frac{1}{2}ap$$

$$= \frac{1}{2}(3\sqrt{3})(6)(6) \qquad p = s \cdot n$$

$$= 54\sqrt{3}$$

$$\approx 93.5$$

The area is about 93.5 square inches.

EN: Wr: 2-28 evens; p. 375, Cal: 1-9; AV: Ex: 1-9 odds, Wr: 1-29 odds; p. 370, Wr: 12-30 evens; p. 375, Cal. 1-9

exercises

FN: Ex: 1-9, Wr: 1-5, 7-25 odds; p. 370, Wr: 12-30 evens

Exploratory **Find the degree measure of a central angle of each regular polygon with the given number of sides.**

1. 3 120	**2.** 4 90	**3.** 5 72
4. 6 36	**5.** 8 45	**6.** 9 40
7. 10 36	**8.** 12 30	**9.** 14 $25\frac{5}{7}$

Written **Complete the chart for each regular polygon described.**

	n	s	p	a	A
1.	3	4	12	$2\sqrt{3}/3$	$4\sqrt{3}$
2.	4	3	12	3/2	9
3.	6	8	48	$4\sqrt{3}$	$96\sqrt{3}$
4.	6	$4\sqrt{3}/3$	$8\sqrt{3}$	$\sqrt{3}$	12
5.	6	3.4	20.4	$1.7\sqrt{3}$	$17.34\sqrt{3}$

Find the area of each regular polygon with the following measurements. Round each answer to the nearest tenth.

6. equilateral triangle
apothem 5.8 centimeters
side 20 centimeters 174 cm^2

7. square
apothem 8 inches
side 16 inches 256 $in.^2$

8. pentagon
apothem 8.9 miles
side 13.0 miles 289.3 mi^2

9. hexagon
apothem 22 millimeters
side 19.0 millimeters 1254 mm^2

10. hexagon
apothem 8.7 meters
side 10 meters 261 m^2

11. octagon
apothem 7.5 feet
side 6.2 feet 186 ft^2

Answer each of the following.

12. Find the area of an equilateral triangle with a radius of $4\sqrt{3}$ units. $36\sqrt{3}$ $units^2$

13. Find the area of an equilateral triangle with a radius of 6 units. $27\sqrt{3}$ $units^2$

14. Find the area of a regular hexagon with an apothem of 12 centimeters. $288\sqrt{3}$ cm^2

15. Find the area of a regular hexagon with a side of 12 centimeters. $216\sqrt{3}$ cm^2

16. Find the area of a square inscribed in a circle with a radius of 10 feet. 200 ft^2

17. Find the area of a square circumscribed about a circle with a radius of 10 feet. 400 ft^2

18. Find the area of a regular pentagon with a perimeter of 16.5 inches and an apothem of 4 inches. 33 $in.^2$

19. Find the area of a regular pentagon with a perimeter of 68.3 meters and an apothem of 5 meters. 170.75 m^2

Prove each of the following. For answers to exercises 20-23, see the Teacher's Guide.

20. Theorem 11–6

21. Theorem 11–7 for a regular pentagon

22. Theorem 11–8 for a regular hexagon

23. Theorem 11–8 for an equilateral triangle

Answer each of the following.

24. Miss Smith wants to add a triangular deck in the yard behind her house. Each side is to be 18 feet long. Find the length of the railing that will fit completely around the deck. Then, find the area of the deck. P = 54 ft, A = $81\sqrt{3}$ ft^2

25. Sam is building a pen for his dogs near the barn. The pen will be a hexagon with sides of 3 meters. Find the perimeter and area of the pen. P = 18 m, A = $27\sqrt{3}/2$ m^2

Find the area of each shaded region. Assume the polygons are regular polygons.

26.

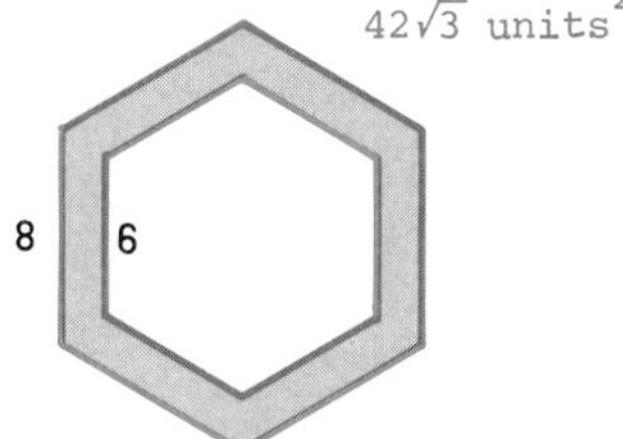

27.

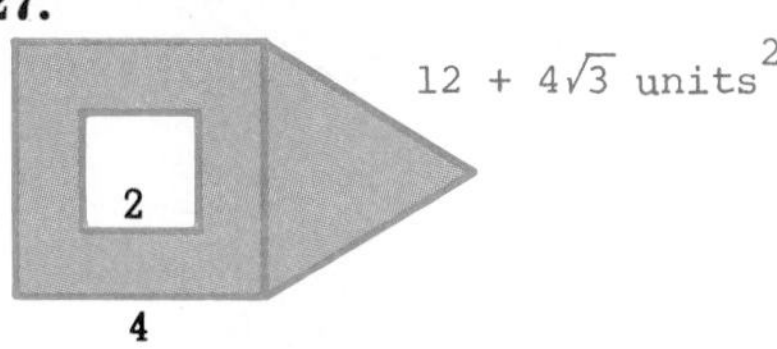

28.

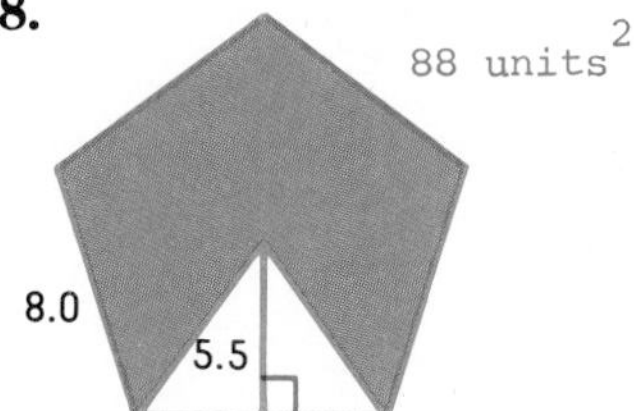

29.

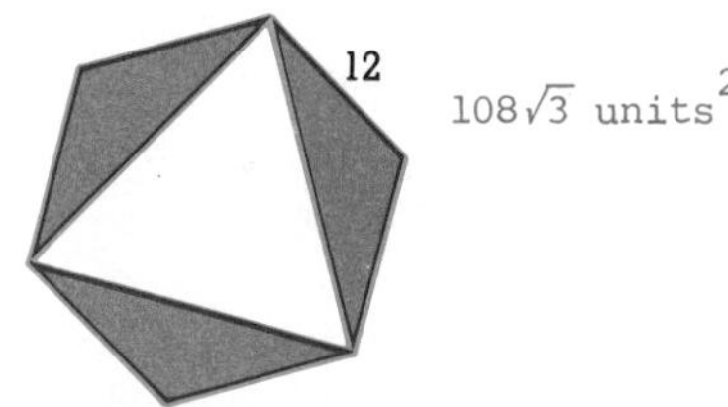

Trigonometric Functions

Some calculators have the [sin], [cos], and [TAN] keys. When one of the keys is used the appropriate function is determined.

Example: Find sin 90°.

Enter: 90 [sin] [=]

Display: 90 1 1

If your calculator has a degree/radian key, be sure the calculator is in the degree mode.

If the value of the function is given, the [INV] key can be used to find the angle. This key will provide the smallest angle whose function value has been given.

Example: Find the degree of the smallest angle whose tangent is 1.

Enter: 1 [INV] [TAN]

Display: 1 45

A 45° angle is the smallest angle that has a tangent equal to 1.

Exercise Find the value of each of the following.

1. cos 35° 0.819152 **2.** tan 120° -1.7320508 **3.** sin 45° 0.7071068

4. tan 225° 1 **5.** cos 315° 0.701068 **6.** sin 27° 0.4539905

Find the degree measure of the smallest angle for the function given.

7. tan $x = 0$ 0 **8.** cos $x = 1$ 0 **9.** sin $x = 0.5$ 30

Objectives: to find the area and circumference of a circle using either 3.14 or $\frac{22}{7}$ for π, to find the area of a sector of a circle

11–4 Circles

Suppose a wheel, such as a bicycle wheel, makes one complete revolution. The distance it travels is the same as the **circumference** of the wheel.

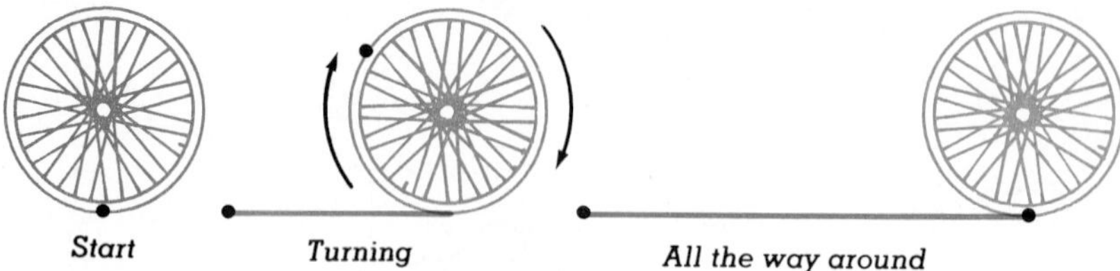

The circumference of a circle is related to the perimeter of regular polygons. The sequence of figures below suggests the relationship.

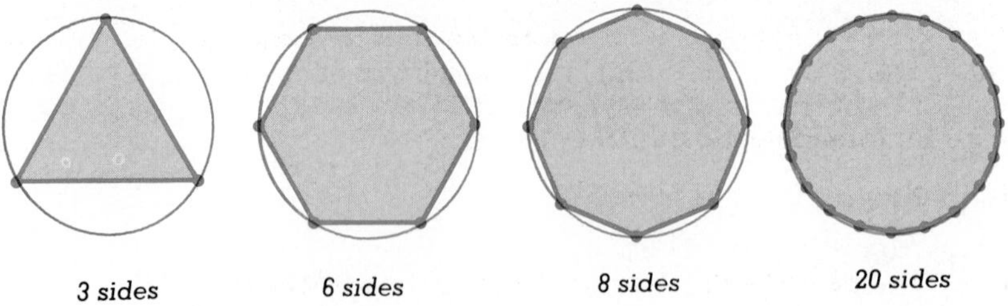

Notice that as the number of sides of the inscribed polygons increases, the polygons begin to look more and more like a circle. Thus, as the number of sides increases, the perimeter becomes closer and closer to the circumference of the circle.

Emphasize that as the number of sides increase, the polygon approaches the shape of a circle.

The circumference of a circle is the limit of the perimeter of the inscribed regular polygons as the number of sides increases.

Definition of Circumference

As the number of sides of the polygons increases, the area of the polygons becomes closer and closer to the area of the circle.

The area of a circle is the limit of the area of the inscribed polygons as the number of sides increases.

Definition of Area of Circle

The Greek letter π (pronounced pi) stands for a number that cannot be named exactly by a decimal or fraction. One decimal approximation for π is 3.14159265 and one fractional approximation for π is $\frac{22}{7}$.

Another fractional approximation for π is $\frac{355}{113}$.

Both the circumference and area of a circle are related to π.

Suppose the radius of a circle is r units. The following chart gives the approximate perimeter and area of each regular polygon inscribed in the circle.

Number of sides	3	4	5	6	8	10	20	50	100
Perimeter	$5.20r$	$5.66r$	$5.88r$	$6.00r$	$6.12r$	$6.18r$	$6.27r$	$6.28r$	$6.28r$
Area	$1.30r^2$	$2.00r^2$	$2.38r^2$	$2.60r^2$	$2.83r^2$	$2.94r^2$	$3.09r^2$	$3.13r^2$	$3.14r^2$

Compare the perimeter values in the chart with $2\pi r$. The values suggest the following formula.

If a circle has a circumference of C units and a radius of r units, then $C = 2\pi r$.

Theorem 11–9 Circumference of a Circle

Compare the area values in the chart with πr^2. The values suggest the following formula.

If a circle has an area of A square units and a radius of r units, then $A = \pi r^2$.

Theorem 11–10 Area of a Circle

example

1 Find the circumference and area of a circle with a radius of $5\frac{6}{10}$ centimeters. Use $\frac{22}{7}$ for π.

$$C = 2\pi r \approx 2\left(\frac{22}{7}\right)\left(\frac{56}{10}\right) \approx \left(\frac{44}{7}\right)\left(\frac{56}{10}\right) \approx 35\frac{1}{5}$$

$$A = \pi r^2 \approx \left(\frac{22}{7}\right)\left(\frac{56}{10}\right)^2 \approx \left(\frac{22}{7}\right)\left(\frac{3136}{100}\right) \approx 98\frac{14}{25}$$

The circumference is about $35\frac{1}{5}$ centimeters.

The area is about $98\frac{14}{25}$ square centimeters.

example

1 Find the area of a circle inscribed in an equilateral triangle whose sides are 5 centimeters. Use 3.14 for π and round your answer to the nearest hundredth.

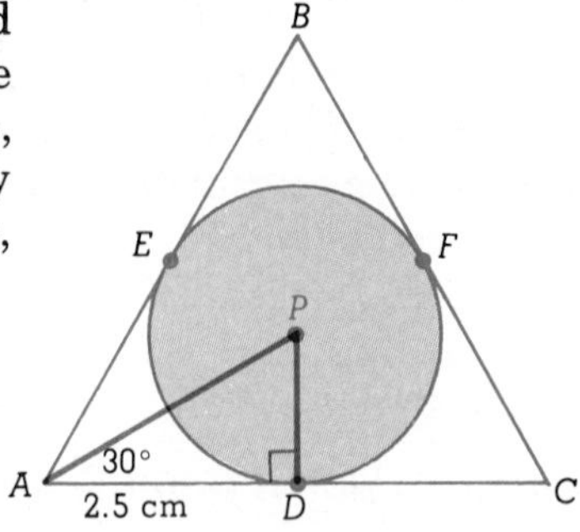

By using a theorem about tangent segments and properties of congruence, it is possible to conclude that $\overline{AD} \cong \overline{DC}$. Thus, AD is 2.5 centimeters. Also, $\overline{PA}$ bisects $\angle EAD$. Thus, $m\angle PAD = 30$. Finally $\overline{PD} \perp \overline{AD}$. Since $\triangle APD$ is a 30°–60°–90° triangle, $(PD)\sqrt{3} = AD$.

$$PD = \frac{AD}{\sqrt{3}}$$

$$PD = \frac{2.5\sqrt{3}}{3} \quad \textit{Note } AD = 2.5.$$

Then, find the area of the circle.

$$\begin{aligned} A &= \pi r^2 \\ &\approx (3.14)\left(\frac{2.5\sqrt{3}}{3}\right)^2 \quad \textit{Note } \frac{2.5\sqrt{3}}{3} \approx 1.4. \\ &\approx (3.14)(1.4)^2 \\ &\approx 6.15 \end{aligned}$$

The area of the circle is about 6.15 square centimeters.

A **sector** of a circle is a region bounded by a central angle and its intercepted arc.

The sum of the degree measures of the central angles of a circle is 360. The region bounded by a circle can be separated into exactly three sectors whose central angles measure 120°. Since the boundaries of the sectors are congruent, the sectors have the same area. As a result, the area of each sector is $\frac{1}{3}$ the area of the circle or, if the radius is r units, $\frac{1}{3}\pi r^2$.

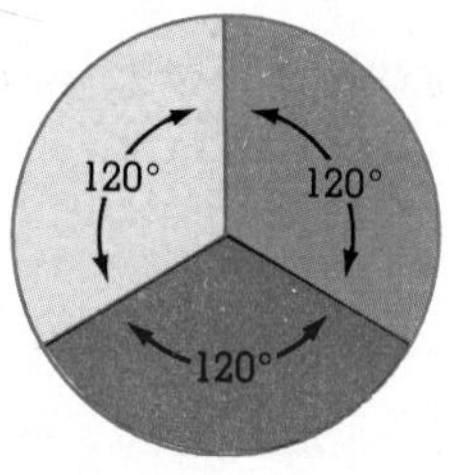

In general, the area of a sector of a circle is the fraction of the area of the circle times the area of the circle.

If a sector of a circle has an area of A square units, a central angle measurement of N degrees, and a radius of r units, then $A = \frac{N}{360}\pi r^2$.

Definition of Area of a Sector of a Circle

EN: Wr: 1-33 odds, 34-39; p. 380, E: 1-3; AV: Ex: 10-15, Wr: 1-23, 24-38 evens; pp. 374-5 Wr: 16-28 evens

exercises

FN: Ex: 1-15, Wr: 1-39, odds; pp. 374-5, Wr: 16-28 evens

Exploratory **Find the circumference and area of each circle with the given radius. Give answers in terms of π.**

1. 7 centimeters 14π, 49π
2. 10 meters 20π, 100π
3. 4 inches 8π in., 16π in.^{2}
4. 8 feet 16π ft, 64π ft^2
5. 7.4 centimeters 14.8π cm, 54.76π cm^2
6. 9.6 meters 19.2π m, 92.16π m^2
7. 2.4 kilometers 4.8π km, 5.76π km^2
8. 1.5 miles 3.0π mi, 2.25π mi^2
9. $\frac{1}{2}$ foot π ft, $\frac{\pi}{4}$ ft^2
10. $3\frac{1}{3}$ yards $6\frac{2}{3}\pi$ yd, $\frac{100}{9}\pi$ yd^2
11. $4\frac{2}{3}$ yards $9\frac{1}{3}\pi$ yd, $\frac{196}{9}\pi$ yd^2
12. $5\frac{3}{4}$ feet $11\frac{1}{2}\pi$ ft, $33\frac{1}{16}\pi$ ft^2
13. $5\sqrt{2}$ centimeters $10\sqrt{2}\pi$ cm, 50π cm^2
14. $4\sqrt{3}$ inches $8\sqrt{3}\pi$ in., 48π in.^{2}
15. $3\sqrt{2}$ inches $6\sqrt{2}\pi$ in., 18π in.^{2}

Written **Find the circumference of each circle with the given radius. Use 3.14 for π and round each answer to the nearest tenth.**

1. 7 centimeters 44.0 cm
2. 10 meters 62.8 m
3. 4 inches 25.1 in.
4. 8 feet 50.2 ft
5. 7.4 centimeters 46.5 cm
6. 9.6 meters 60.3 m
7. 2.4 kilometers 15.1 km
8. 1.5 miles 9.4 mi
9. $\frac{1}{2}$ foot 3.1 ft

Find the area of each circle with the given radius. Use $\frac{22}{7}$ for π.

10. $3\frac{1}{3}$ yards $34\frac{58}{63}$ yd^2
11. $4\frac{2}{3}$ yards $68\frac{4}{9}$ yd^2
12. $5\frac{3}{4}$ feet $103\frac{51}{56}$ ft^2
13. $5\sqrt{2}$ centimeters $157\frac{1}{7}$ cm^2
14. $4\sqrt{3}$ inches $150\frac{6}{7}$ in.^{2}
15. $3\sqrt{2}$ inches $56\frac{4}{7}$ in.^{2}

Each of the following is a measurement for a central angle of a circle. The area of the corresponding sector is what fraction of the area of its circle?

16. 40° 1/9
17. 60° 1/6
18. 30° 1/12
19. 2° 1/180
20. 45° 1/8
21. 15° 1/24
22. 18° 1/20
23. 72° 1/5

24–31. Suppose a circle has a radius of 4.6 centimeters. Find the areas of sectors formed by central angles whose measurements are given in exercises 16–23. Use 3.14 for π and round each answer to the nearest tenth.

24. 7.4 cm^2 25. 11.1 cm^2 26. 5.5 cm^2 27. 0.4 cm^2 28. 8.3 cm^2 29. 2.8 cm^2 30. 3.3 cm^2 31. 13.3 cm^2

Find each area. Use 3.14 for π and round each answer to the nearest tenth.

32. the area of a circle inscribed in a square whose sides are 7.2 meters 40.7 m^2

33. the area of a circle inscribed in a square whose diagonal is 6.5 feet 16.6 ft^2

Find the area of shaded regions.

34.

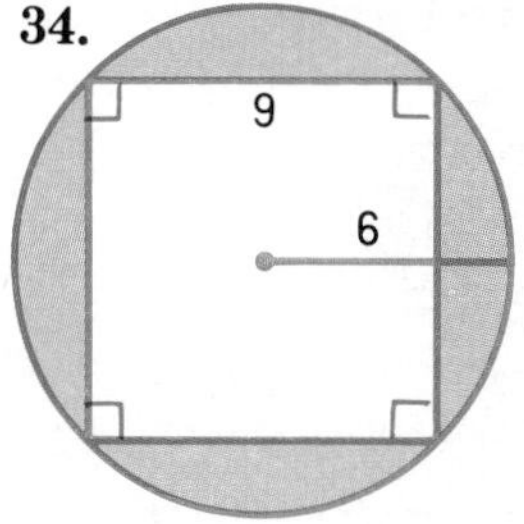

$36\pi - 81$ (or about 32.04) units^2

35.

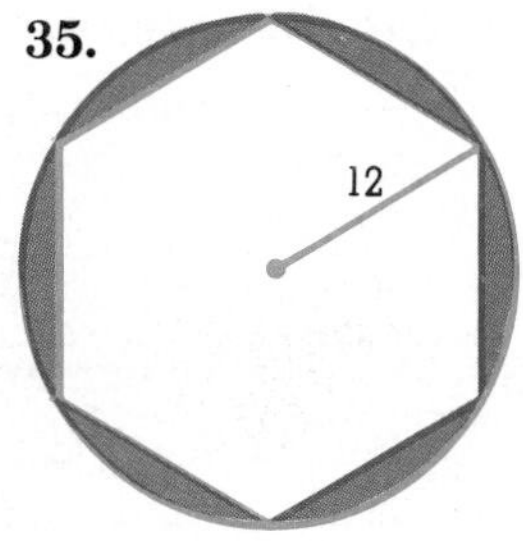

$144\pi - 216\sqrt{3}$ (or about 78.48) units^2

36.

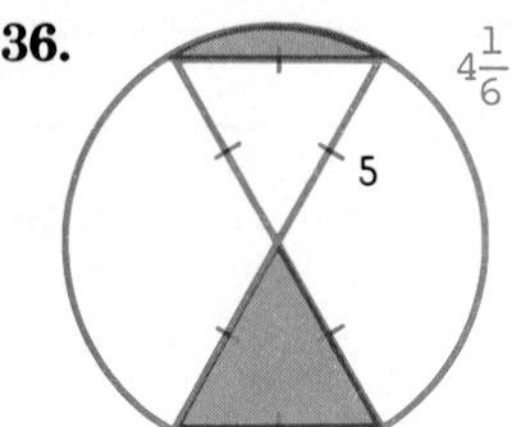

$4\frac{1}{6}\pi$ (or about 13.1) units^2

37.

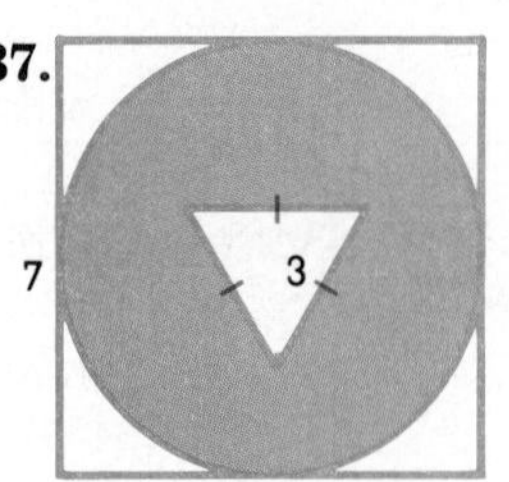

$\frac{49}{4}\pi - \frac{9}{4}\sqrt{3}$ (or about 34.58) units^2

38.

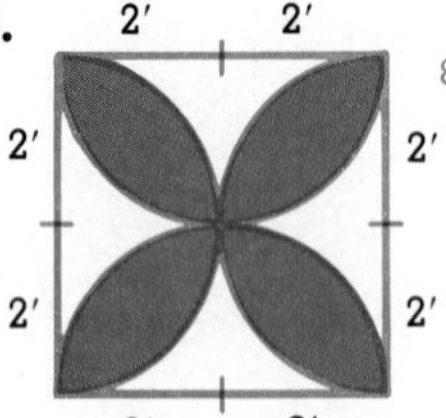

$8\pi - 16$ (or about 9.1) ft^2

39.

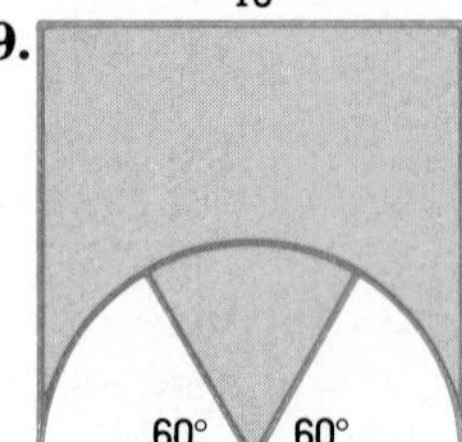

$100 - \frac{25}{3}\pi$ (or about 73.8) units^2

Drawing Figures — excursions in geometry

When three-dimensional figures are shown on paper, they are drawn in perspective. The figure on the right shows the edges of a cube drawn in perspective. Although no edges of the cube cross each other, in the drawing they appear to cross in two places. Any parts of a figure that are directly in front or behind each other from a given point of view will appear to cross in a drawing. Artists use this property to create illusions.

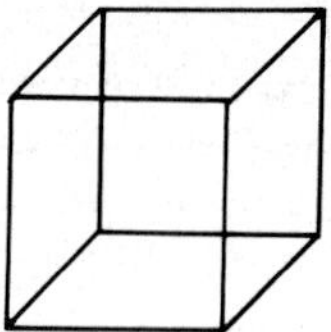

Broken lines are used to show parts that are behind others. The drawings below show two different ways of viewing a cube.

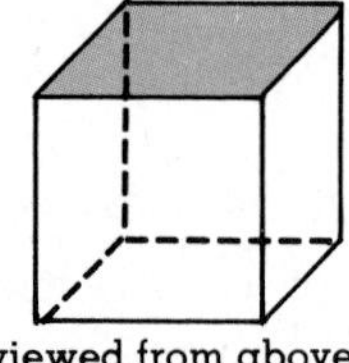

viewed from above

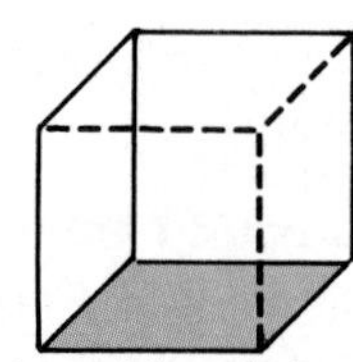

viewed from below

Exercises **Use broken lines to show two views for each of the following.**

For answers to exercises 1-3, see the Teacher's Guide.

1.

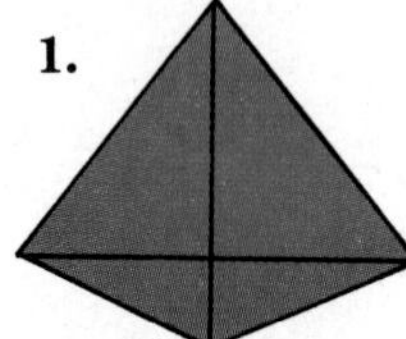

2.

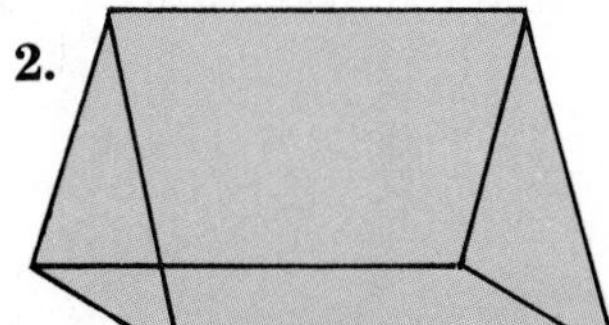

3.

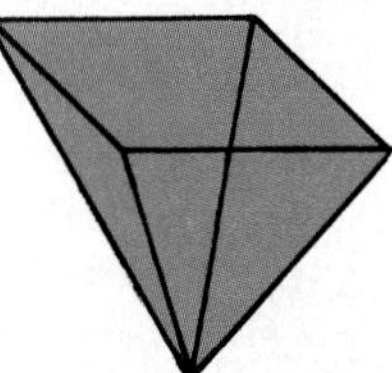

Objective: to find the lateral areas and the total surface areas of right prisms and right cylinders

11–5 Surface Area

If the figure below is traced on a piece of paper, cut out, and folded along the broken lines, it will look like a cube. The area of the figure is called the *total* **surface area,** or total area, of the cube it forms.

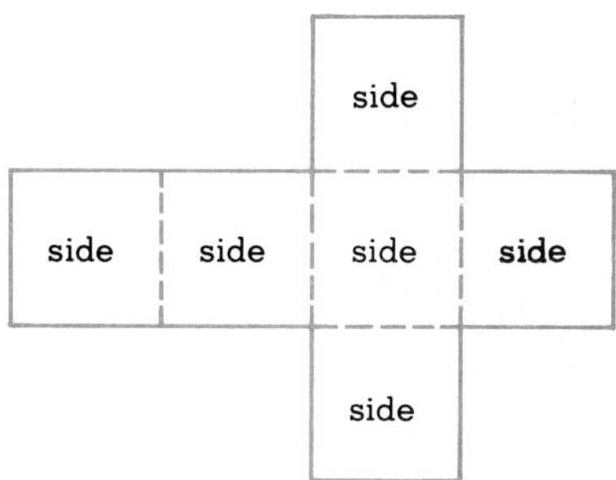

One way to find the surface area of a solid is to add the area of each face. For certain types of solids, another way is to use formulas.

One type of solid is called a **prism.** A cube and a rectangular box are both prisms. Some other prisms are shown below.

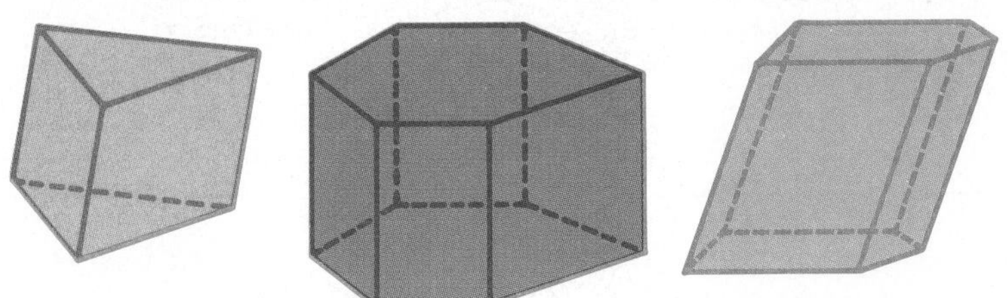

The figure at the left is an oblique prism. See annotation at bottom of page.

Prisms have the following characteristics.

1. Two faces, called **bases,** are formed by congruent polygons that lie in parallel planes.
2. The faces that are *not* bases, called **lateral faces,** are formed by parallelograms.
3. The intersections of two adjacent lateral faces are called **lateral edges** and are parallel segments.

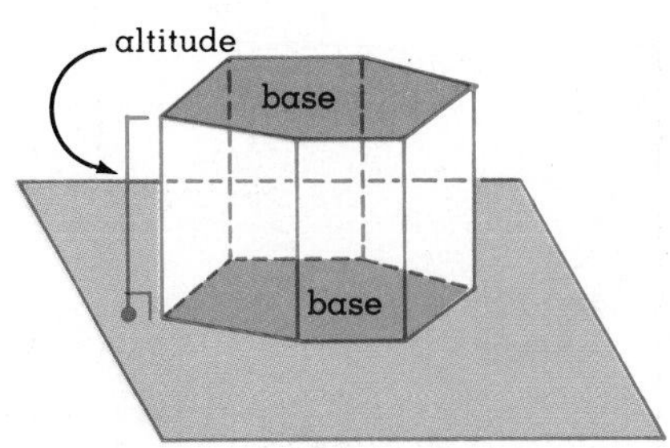

An **altitude** of a prism is a segment perpendicular to the base planes with an endpoint in each plane. The length of an altitude is called the height of the prism.

If the lateral edges of a prism also are altitudes, then the prism is a **right prism.** The lateral faces of right prisms are rectangles.

A prism that is not a right prism is called an oblique prism.

The **lateral area** of a prism is the area of all the lateral faces. As a result of the Distributive Property, the lateral area of a right prism can be found by multiplying the height by the perimeter of a base.

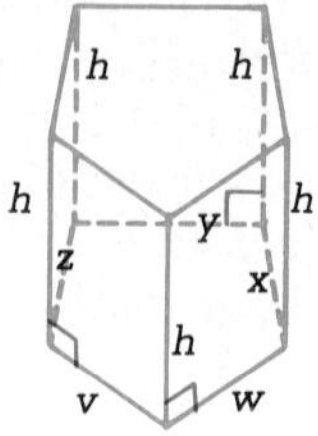

Does this hold for oblique prisms?

See Cavalieri's Principle on page 396.

$$A = vh + wh + xh + yh + zh$$
$$= (v + w + x + y + z)h$$

If a right prism has a lateral area of L square units, a height of h units, and each base has a perimeter of p units, then $L = ph$.

Theorem 11–11 Lateral Area of a Right Prism

The total surface area of a prism is found by adding the lateral area to the areas of both bases. Since the bases of a prism are congruent, they have the same area.

If the total surface area of a right prism is T square units, each base has an area of B square units, a perimeter of p units, and the height is h units, then $T = ph + 2B$.

Theorem 11–12 Total Surface Area of a Right Prism

example

1 **Find the total surface area of a right prism whose base is a right triangle with legs of 5 inches and 12 inches, and whose height is 20 inches.**

First, use the Pythagorean Theorem to find the measure of the hypotenuse.

$$\begin{aligned} a^2 &= 5^2 + 12^2 \\ &= 169 \\ a &= 13 \end{aligned}$$

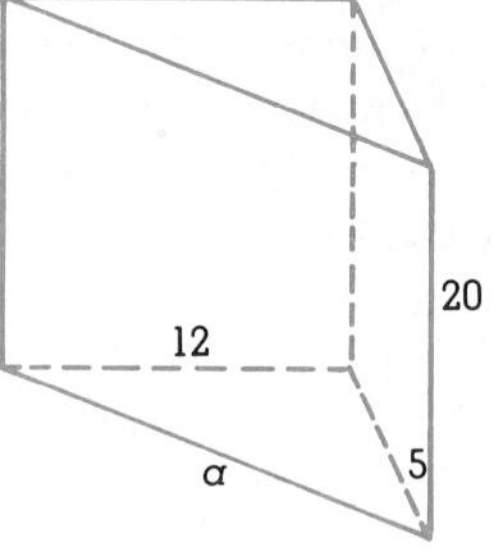

Then, find the total surface area.

$$\begin{aligned} T &= ph + 2B \\ &= (5 + 12 + 13)20 + 2\left(\frac{1}{2} \cdot 5 \cdot 12\right) \\ &= (30)20 + 2(30) \\ &= 660 \end{aligned}$$

The total surface area is 660 square inches.

The bases of a cylinder are formed by two congruent circles that lie in parallel planes. The segment whose endpoints are centers of these circles is called the **axis** of the cylinder.

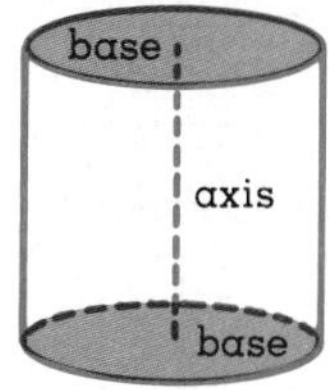

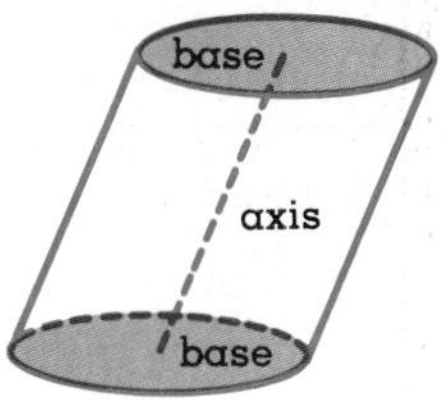

The **altitude** of a cylinder is a segment perpendicular to the base planes with an endpoint in each plane. If the axis of a cylinder also is an altitude of the cylinder, then the cylinder is called a **right cylinder.**

The cylinder at the right is an oblique cylinder. Have students compare this with an oblique prism.

The lateral area of a cylinder is the area of the curved surface. Think of the label from a cylindrical can. What is the height of the label on the can? What is the base?

The height of the label is the same as the height of the can.

The base is the same as the circumference of the circle.

If a right cylinder has a lateral area of L square units, a height of h units, and the bases have radii of r units, then $L = 2\pi rh$.

Theorem 11–13 Lateral Area of a Right Cylinder

If a right cylinder has a total surface area of T square units, a height of h units, and the bases have radii of r units, then $T = 2\pi rh + 2\pi r^2$.

Theorem 11–14 Total Surface Area of a Right Cylinder

example

2 **Find the number of square feet of cardboard needed to make the sides of 30,000 orange juice cans if they each are 6 inches tall and are 3 inches in diameter. Use 3.14 for π.**

number square inches = number cans × lateral area of one can

$$= 30{,}000 \times 2\pi rh$$

$$\approx 30{,}000 \times 2(3.14)\left(\frac{3}{2}\right)(6)$$

$$\approx 1{,}695{,}600$$

There are 12 × 12 or 144 square inches in 1 square foot.
Thus, about 1,695,600 ÷ 144 or 11,775 square feet of cardboard is needed.

EN: Wr: 1-21 odds, p. 385, Ch: 1-2; p. 386, E: 1-4; AV: Ex: 1-5, Wr: 1-14; p. 386, E: 1-4; p. 379-80, Wr: 25-39 odds

exercises

FN: Ex: 1-5, Wr: 1-15; p. 386, E: 1-4; pp. 379-80, Wr: 2-38 evens

Exploratory **Use the prism at the right to answer each of the following.**

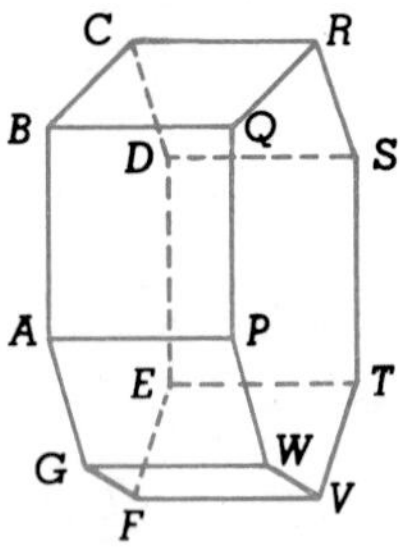

1. Name each base. heptagon RSTVWPQ, heptagon CDEFGAB
2. Tell how many sides to each base. 7
3. Tell how many lateral faces to the figure. 7
4. Name the lateral faces. CRQB, CRSD, STED, TVFE, PWGA, QPAB, WVFG
5. Suppose each polygon forming a base is regular with side of s units. Suppose the height is h units and the lateral area is L square units. Write a formula for the lateral area of the prism. $L = 7sh$

Answers to the following exercises have been computed by rounding each step to the nearest tenth. Values of square roots have been rounded to the nearest tenth.

Written **Find the lateral area and total surface area of each right prism described below.**

1. rectangular base 2 centimeters by 3 centimeters; height 6 centimeters 60 cm^2, 72 cm^2
2. rectangular base 9 meters by 6 meters; height 25 meters 750 m^2, 858 m^2
3. right triangular base with legs 6 inches and 8 inches; height 11 inches 264 $in.^2$, 312 $in.^2$
4. right triangular base with legs 18 millimeters and 12 millimeters; height 15 millimeters 450 + $90\sqrt{13}$ (or about 774) mm^2, 666 + $90\sqrt{13}$ (or about 990) mm^2
5. equilateral triangular base with sides 2.7 meters; height 5 meters 40.5 m^2, 40.5 + $3.6\sqrt{3}$ (or about 46.6) m^2
6. equilateral triangular base with sides 8.1 centimeters; height 13 centimeters 315.9 cm^2, 315.9 + $32.8\sqrt{3}$ (or about 372.7) cm^2
7. regular hexagonal base with sides 7.3 units; height 4 units 175.2 $units^2$, 175.2 + $159.8\sqrt{3}$ (or about 446.9) $units^2$
8. regular hexagonal base with sides 11.1 units; height 6 units 399.6 $units^2$, 399.6 + $369.6\sqrt{3}$ (or about 1027.9) $units^2$

Find the lateral area of each right cylinder described below. Use 3.14 for π and round each answer to the nearest tenth.

9. radius: 7 centimeters
   height: 10 centimeters 439.6 cm^2
10. radius: 4 inches
    height: 11 inches 276.3 $in.^2$
11. radius: 6 feet
    height: 10.2 feet 384.3 ft^2
12. radius: 4.5 feet
    height: 7 feet 197.8 ft^2
13. radius: 11.8 meters
    height: 23 meters 1704.4 m^2
14. radius: 26.3 centimeters
    height: 26.3 centimeters 4343.8 cm^2

Find the total surface area of each right cylinder described below. Use $\frac{22}{7}$ for π.

15. 55 m^2

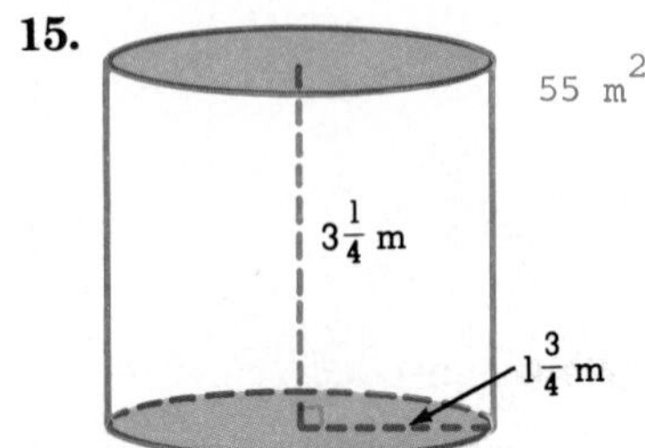

16. 22 $in.^2$

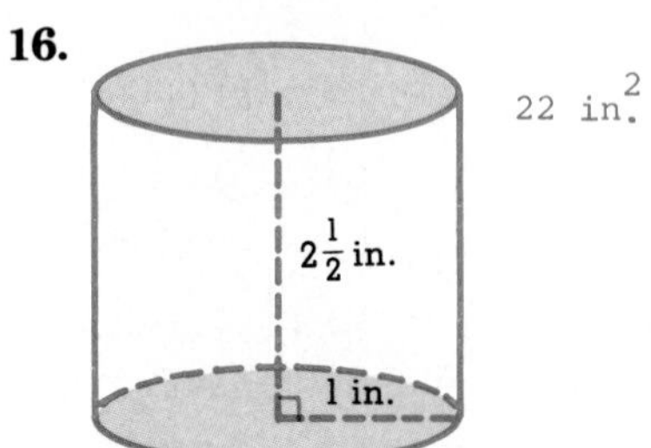

17. $35\frac{4}{9}$ ft^2

$3\frac{2}{3}$ ft

$\frac{7}{6}$ ft

18. 1672 mm^2

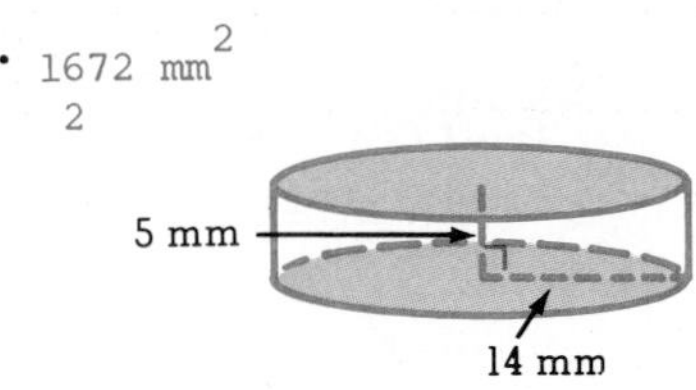

Solve each problem. Use 3.14 for π and round each answer to the nearest tenth.

19. Find the surface area of a cylindrical gas tank that is 25 feet tall and has a radius of 30 feet. 10,362 ft^2

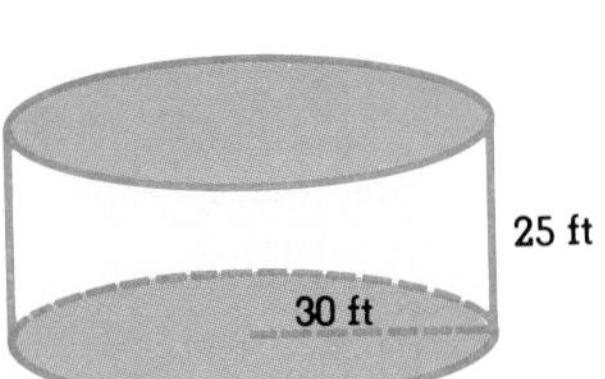

20. Find the surface area of a cylindrical water tank that is 8 meters tall and has a diameter of 8 meters. 301.4 m^2

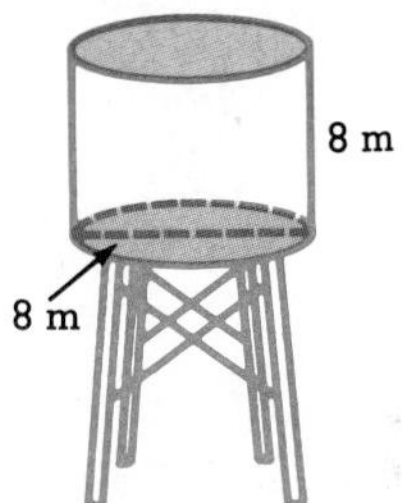

21. Suppose two different crystals occur in the shape of right prisms. One crystal has rectangular base of 2 units by 3 units with a height of 2.5 units. The other crystal has regular hexagonal bases with sides of 2.1 units and height 2.3 units. Which crystal has the greater surface area?

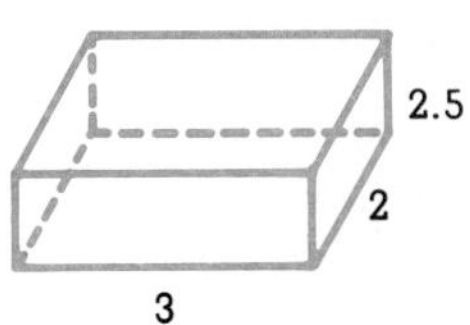

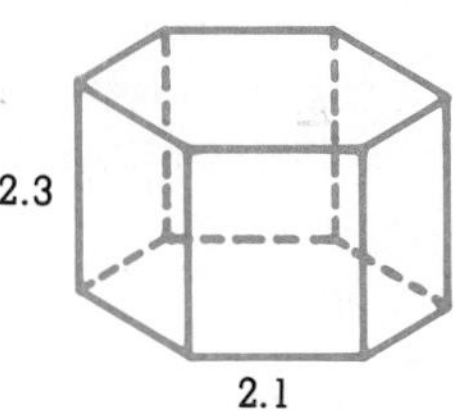

rectangular prism surface area = 37 units^2, hexagonal prism surface area = 51.9 units^2

The hexagonal prism has the greater surface area.

Challenge **Find the total surface area of each of the following oblique rectangular prisms.**

1. $150 + 50\sqrt{2}$ units^2

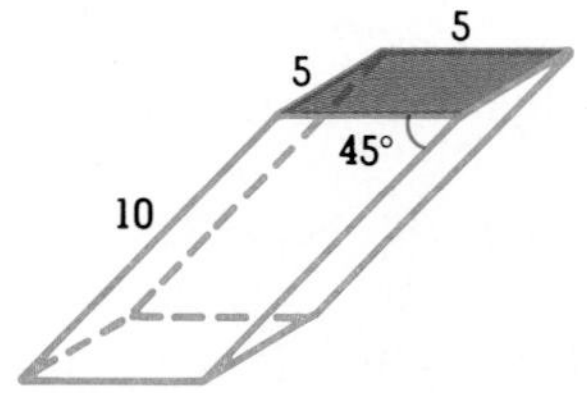

2. $352 + 120\sqrt{3}$ units^2

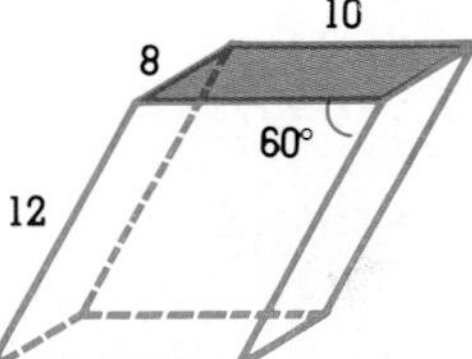

topics in geometry

Topology

Topology is a branch of geometry that deals with the distortion of geometric figures and shapes. Topics of topology include networks, mazes, map coloring, and one-sided surfaces such as the Möbius strip and the Klein bottle.

The concept of inside and outside is used frequently to explore topology. The Möbius strip is a famous illustration of this concept. Study the following steps for making a Möbius strip.

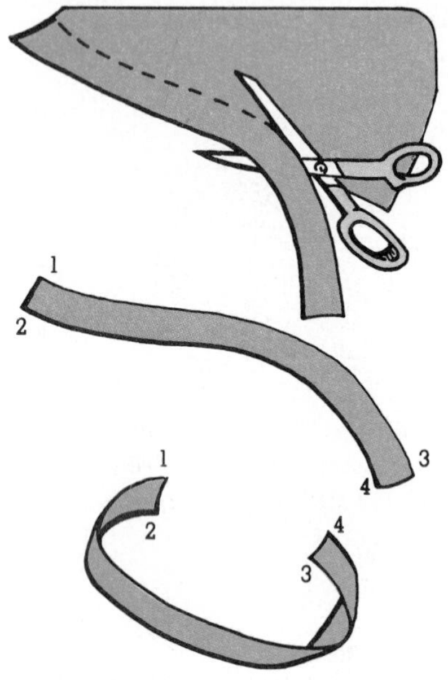

Cut a strip from a sheet of paper.

Number the ends as shown at the left.

Make a half twist on the band and join the ends, 1 to 4 and 2 to 3.

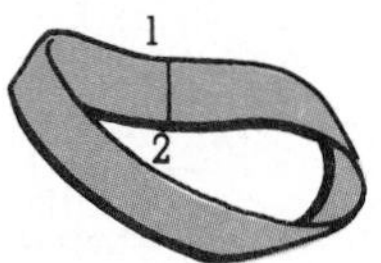

The completed band is an example of a Möbius strip (introduced by Augustus Möbius in the 19th century).

Exercises Complete each of the following.

1. Construct 2 Möbius strips using the steps shown on this page. See student's work.
2. Mark a point in the center of one strip. Then draw a line from that point which returns to that point without removing the pencil from the paper. How many sides are there to the strip? How many edges? one, one
3. Cut the Möbius strip from exercise 2 in half by cutting along the line that was drawn. How many sides are there? How many edges? two, two
4. Find a point on the second strip about one-third of the way from the edge. Cut the strip parallel to the edge and return to this point. Describe the result. There will be two intertwining strips, one is a two-sided band. The second is a new Möbius strip. See student's work.

Objectives: to find the lateral area for a regular pyramid, to find the lateral area and total surface area of a right circular cone, to find the surface area of a sphere

11–6 More about Surface Area

The figure at the right is called a **pyramid.** It has the following characteristics.

1. All the faces, except one face, intersect at a point called the **vertex.**
2. The face that does *not* intersect at the vertex is called the **base** and forms a polygon.
3. The faces meeting at the vertex are called **lateral faces** and form triangles.

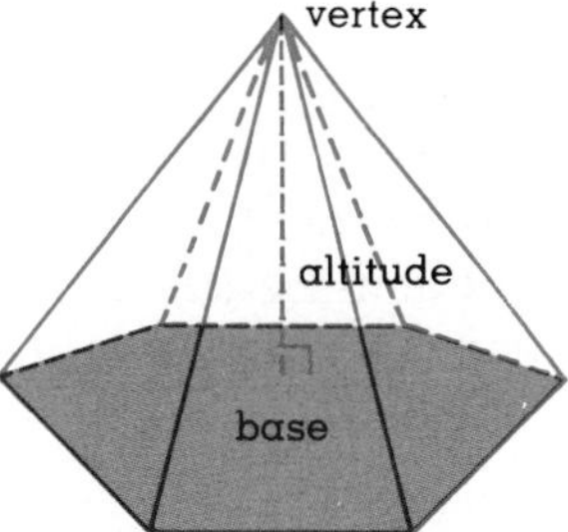

A pyramid is a **regular pyramid** if and only if its base is regular and the segment whose endpoints are the center of the base and the vertex is perpendicular to the base. This segment is called the **altitude.**

All the lateral faces of a regular pyramid form congruent isosceles triangles. The height of each lateral face is called the **slant height,** ℓ, of the pyramid.

The figure at the right is a regular hexagonal pyramid. Its lateral area can be found in the following way.

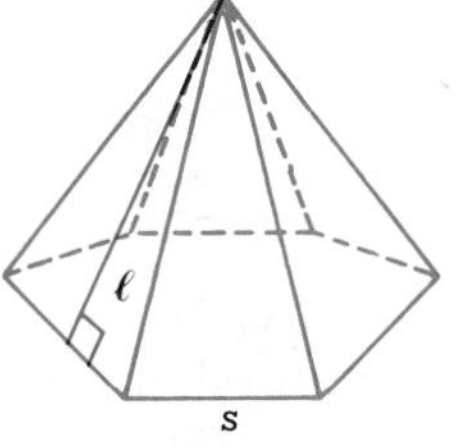

$$L = \frac{1}{2}s\ell + \frac{1}{2}s\ell + \frac{1}{2}s\ell + \frac{1}{2}s\ell + \frac{1}{2}s\ell + \frac{1}{2}s\ell$$
$$= \frac{1}{2}(s + s + s + s + s + s)\ell$$

If a regular pyramid has a lateral area of L square units, a slant height of ℓ units, and its base has a perimeter of p units, then $L = \frac{1}{2}p\ell$.

Theorem 11–15 Lateral Area for a Regular Pyramid

example

1 **Find the total surface area of a regular square pyramid in which the slant height is 10 inches and the sides of the base are 7 inches.**

total surface area = *lateral area* + *base area*

$$= \frac{1}{2}p\ell + s^2$$
$$= \frac{1}{2}(4 \cdot 7)(10) + (7)^2$$
$$= 189$$

The total surface area is 189 square inches.

The figure shown below is a **right circular cone.** It has a circular **base,** and a **vertex** at T. Its **axis,** $\overline{TC}$, is the segment whose endpoints are the vertex and the center of the base.

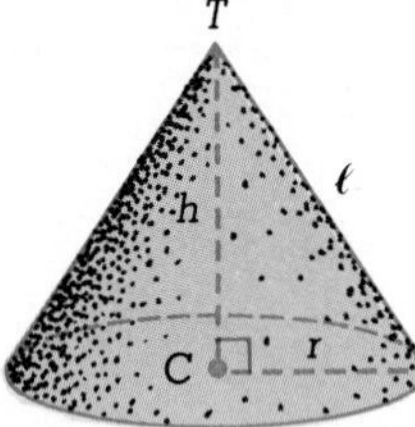

In a right circular cone, the axis is perpendicular to the base. Thus, it is the altitude of the cone. The length of any segment joining the vertex to the circle is called the **slant height.** In the cone at the left, the slant height is ℓ units.

Finding the lateral area and total surface area of a right circular cone is similar to finding those measurements for a regular pyramid.

Theorem 11–16 Lateral and Total Surface Area of a Right Circular Cone

If a right circular cone has a lateral area of L square units, a total surface area of T square units, a slant height of ℓ units, and the radius of the base is r units, then $L = \pi r\ell$ and $T = \pi r\ell + \pi r^2$.

example

2 **A right circular cone has a radius of 7.6 centimeters. Its altitude is 11.9 centimeters. Find the total surface area of the cone. Use 3.14 for π and round to the nearest tenth.**

First, use the Pythagorean Theorem to find the slant height.

$$\begin{aligned}\ell^2 &= 11.9^2 + 7.6^2\\ &= 141.61 + 57.76\\ &= 199.37\\ \ell &= \sqrt{199.37}\\ &\approx 14.1\end{aligned}$$

Then, find the total surface area.

$$\begin{aligned}T &= \pi r\ell + \pi r^2\\ &\approx (3.14)(7.6)(14.1) + (3.14)(7.6)^2\\ &\approx 336.5 + 181.4\\ &\approx 517.9\end{aligned}$$

The total surface area is about 517.9 square centimeters.

A formula for the surface area of a sphere is given in the following theorem.

If a sphere has a surface area of A square units and a radius of r units, then $A = 4\pi r^2$.

Theorem 11–17
Surface Area of a Sphere

example

3 Find the surface area of a sphere with a radius of 3 cm. Use 3.14 for π and round your answer to the nearest tenth.

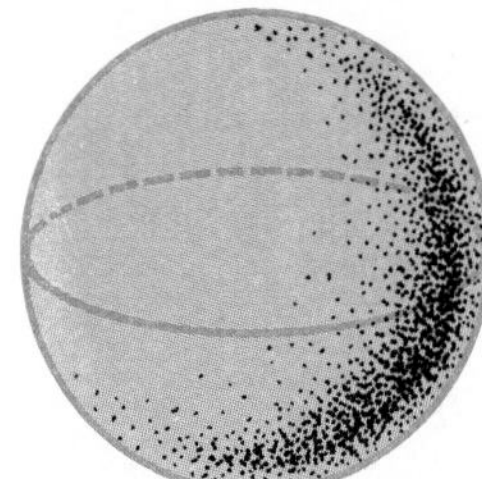

$$\begin{aligned} A &= 4\pi r^2 \\ &\approx 4(3.14)(3)^2 \\ &\approx 4(3.14)(9) \\ &\approx 113.04 \\ &\approx 113.0 \end{aligned}$$

The surface area is about 113.0 square centimeters.

EN: Ex: 1-9 odds, Wr: 1-21 odds, 22; AV: Ex: 1-9 odds, Wr: 1-21 odds; pp. 384-5, Wr: 15-21; p. 385, Ch: 1

exercises

FN: Ex: 1-10, Wr: 1-15; pp. 384-5, Wr: 16-21

Exploratory **Find the lateral area of each regular pyramid described below.**

1. triangular base with sides of 3 centimeters; slant height of 6 centimeters 27 cm^2
2. triangular base with sides of 5 centimeters; slant height of 6 centimeters 45 cm^2
3. square base with sides of 3 centimeters; slant height of 6 centimeters 36 cm^2
4. square base with sides of 5 centimeters; slant height of 6 centimeters 60 cm^2
5. pentagonal base with sides of 3 centimeters; slant height of 6 centimeters 45 cm^2
6. pentagonal base with sides of 5 centimeters; slant height of 6 centimeters 75 cm^2
7. hexagonal base with sides of 3 centimeters; slant height of 6 centimeters 54 cm^2
8. hexagonal base with sides of 5 centimeters; slant height of 6 centimeters 90 cm^2
9. octagonal base with sides of 3 centimeters; slant height of 6 centimeters 72 cm^2
10. octagonal base with sides of 5 centimeters; slant height of 6 centimeters 120 cm^2

Written **Find the lateral area of each right circular cone described below. Use 3.14 for π and round to the nearest tenth.**

1. base radius: 6 centimeters
   slant height: 10 centimeters 188.4 cm^2
2. base radius: 4 feet
   slant height: 11 feet 138.2 cm^2
3. base radius: 4.1 meters
   slant height: 10.3 meters 132.6 m^2
4. base radius: 3.2 millimeters
   slant height: 5.2 millimeters 52.2 mm^2
5. base radius: 6.9 centimeters
   slant height: 6.9 centimeters 149.5 cm^2
6. base radius: 4.4 meters
   slant height: 6.3 meters 87.0 m^2

7. base radius: $4\frac{1}{2}$ inches
slant height: $5\frac{1}{2}$ inches 77.7 in.^{2}

8. base radius: $3\frac{3}{4}$ yards
slant height: $7\frac{1}{2}$ yards 88.3 yd^2

9. base radius: 100 feet
slant height: 1200 feet 376,800 ft^2

10. base radius: 35.0 meters
slant height: 67.2 meters 7385.3 m^2

Find the total surface area for each cone described below. Use $\frac{22}{7}$ for π.

11.

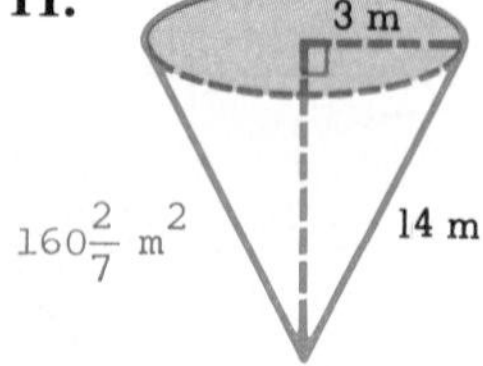

$160\frac{2}{7}$ m^2

12.

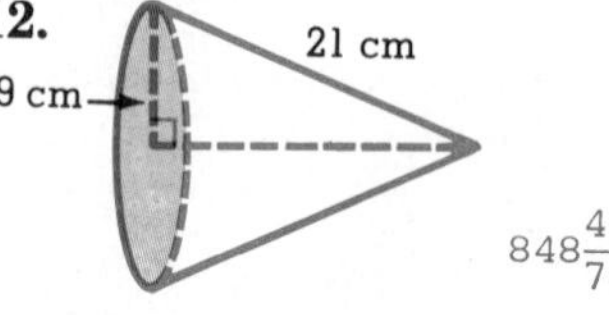

$848\frac{4}{7}$ cm^2

13.

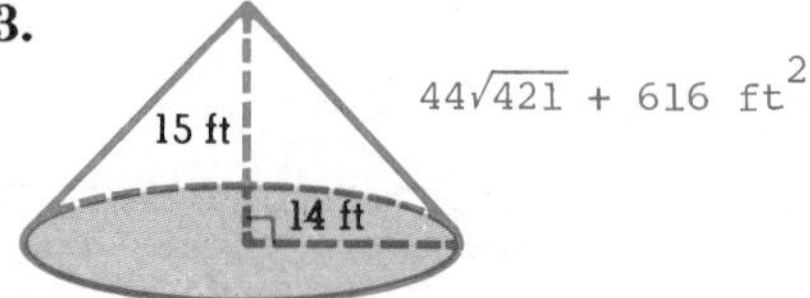

$44\sqrt{421} + 616$ ft^2

14.

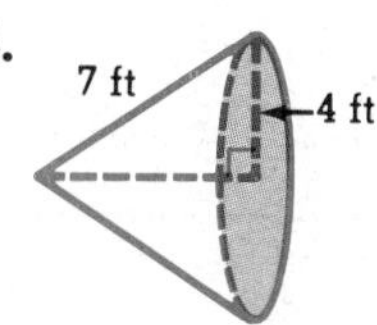

$138\frac{2}{7}$ ft^2

Find the surface area of each sphere given the following radii. Use 3.14 for π and round to the nearest tenth.

15. 10 centimeters 1256 cm^2
16. 2 inches 50.2 in.^{2}
17. 2000 feet 50,240,000 ft^2
18. 3.8 meters 181.4 m^2
19. 372 miles 1,738,103 mi^2
20. 75.3 centimeters 71,216.3 cm^2

Solve each problem.

21. The Great Pyramid is a regular pyramid with a square base. It covers about 570,000 square feet and is 480 feet tall. Find its lateral area. 922,610 ft^2

22. The radius of the earth is about 4000 mi. Find its surface area to the nearest square mile (mi^2). Use 3.14 for π. 200,960,000 mi^2

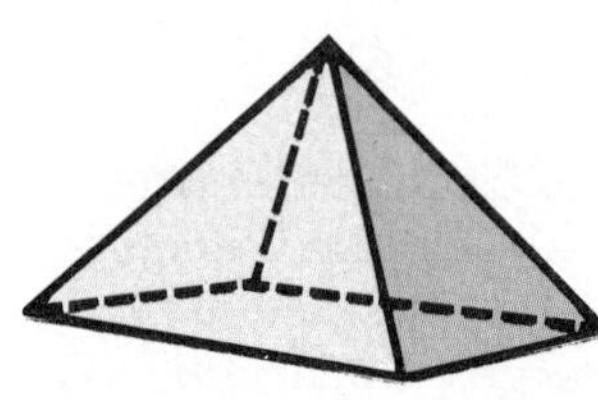

Objectives: to find the volume of a right prism, to find the volume of a right cylinder, to use the properties of volume in problem solving

11–7 Defining Volume

The photograph below shows polluted air in a major city.

About 1,640,000,000 grams of sulfur dioxide are emitted each day into the air over the city. This means that each cubic meter of air carries about 0.000082 grams of sulfur dioxide each day.

Volume is used to measure space. When each edge of a cube is 1 unit long, we say that the volume of the cube is 1 cubic unit. Thus, a cube one centimeter by one centimeter by one centimeter has a volume of one cubic centimeter (cm^3).

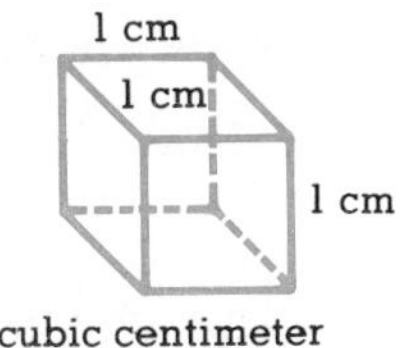

1 cubic centimeter

For any solid region and a given unit of measure, there is a unique positive number called the measure of the volume of the region.

Postulate 11–5 Volume Postulate

Volume will mean the amount of space enclosed by the figure. The volume of a figure may differ depending on the unit of measure. Before calculating the volume, each dimension must have the same unit of measure.

In a given situation, we do *not* always state the unit of measure. If no units are stated, assume the same unit is used for all measures.

Using the following postulates, it is possible to find the volumes of various regions.

If two solids are congruent, then they have exactly the same volume.

Postulate 11–6

If a solid region is separated into nonoverlapping regions, then the sum of the volumes of these regions equals the volume of the given region.

Postulate 11–7 Volume Addition Postulate

The rectangular box below is separated into 24 congruent cubes whose sides are 1 unit each. Thus, the volume of each cube is 1 cubic unit. Notice that the box has three layers, each with 2×4 or 8 cubes. By the Volume Addition Postulate, the volume of the box is 24 cubic units.

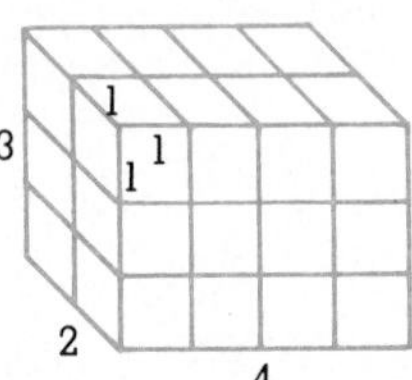

$V = (2 \times 4) \times 3$

$\quad = \text{Base area} \times \text{height}$

In a similar manner, any right prism can be separated into layers to find its volume. The example shown and many others suggest the following.

If a right prism has a volume of V cubic units, a base with an area of B square units, and a height of h units, then $V = Bh$.

Postulate 11–8

example

1 **Find the volume of a right hexagonal prism that has a base with sides of 8 centimeters and a height of 20 centimeters. Round your answer to the nearest unit.**

$$\begin{aligned} V &= Bh \\ &= \left(\frac{1}{2}ap\right)h \\ &= \frac{1}{2}(4\sqrt{3})(48)(20) \\ &\approx 3325.54 \end{aligned}$$

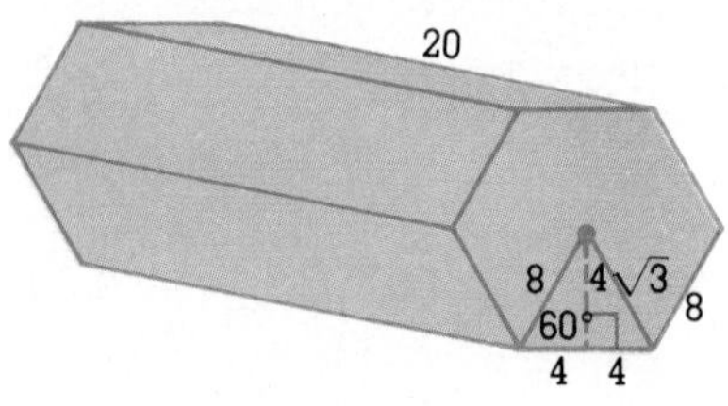

The volume is about 3326 cubic centimeters.

A right cylinder can be thought of as separated into circular layers similar to a stack of coins. The volume of the cylinder is the area of each layer times the height of the stack.

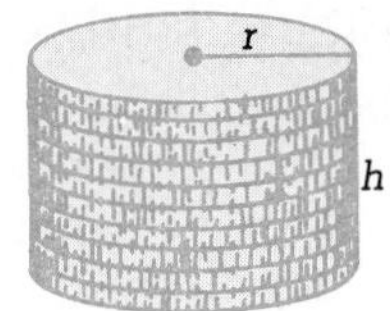

$$\text{Volume} = \text{Base area} \times \text{height}$$
$$= \pi r^2 \times h$$

If a right cylinder has a volume of V cubic units, a height of h units, and a radius of r units, then $V = \pi r^2 h$.

Theorem 11–18 Volume of a Right Cylinder

example

2 Hexagonal metal bars are made by cutting the sides from cylindrical bars. The radii of the hexagonal and cylindrical bars are 2.5 centimeters. Find the volume of waste metal from making a bar 60 centimeters long. Use 3.14 for π and round to the nearest hundredth.

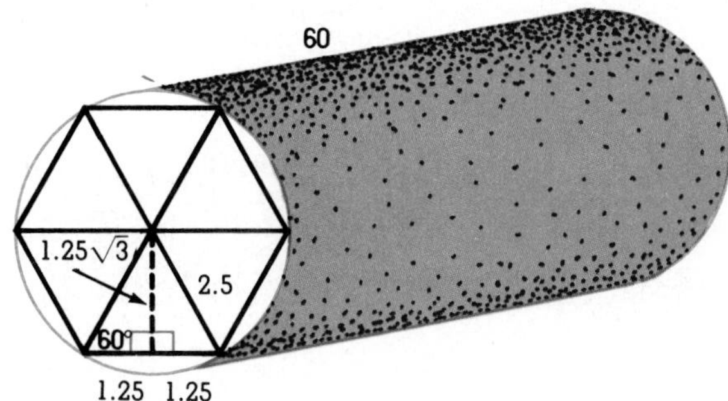

$$\begin{aligned} \text{volume waste metal} &= \text{volume cylindrical bar} - \text{volume hexagonal bar} \\ &= \pi r^2 h - Bh \\ &= \pi r^2 h - \tfrac{1}{2}aph \\ &\approx (3.14)(2.5)^2(60) - \tfrac{1}{2}(1.25\sqrt{3})(15)(60) \\ &\approx 203.22 \end{aligned}$$

About 203.22 cubic centimeters of metal are wasted.

EN: Wr: 1-19 odds; p. 390, Wr: 8-18 evens; AV: Ex: 1-3, Wr: 1-15 odds; p. 390, Wr: 8-22 evens

exercises

FN: Ex: 1-6, Wr: 1-19 odds; p. 390, Wr: 16-22

Exploratory **Find the volume of each right prism described below.**

1. area of base: 12 m^2
height: 3.5 m 42 m^3

2. area of base: 17.5 cm^2
height: 14 cm 245 cm^3

3. area of base: 16 ft^2
height: 4.2 ft 67.2 ft^3

4. area of base: 48 m^2
height: 3 m 144 m^3

5. area of base: 720 cm^2
height: 20 cm 14,400 cm^3

6. area of base: 25 m^2
height: 7 m 175 m^3

Written **Find the volume of each right prism given below.**

1. height of 3 meters; square bases with sides of 4 meters $48\ m^3$
2. height of 8 centimeters; rectangular bases 9 centimeters by 10 centimeters $720\ cm^3$
3. height of 40 inches; hexagonal bases with sides 5 inches $1500\sqrt{3}\ in.^3$
4. height of 36 inches; hexagonal bases with radius of 0.5 inches $13.5\sqrt{3}\ in.^3$
5. height of 20 centimeters; equilateral triangular bases with radius of 1.5 centimeters $33.75\sqrt{3}\ cm^3$
6. height of 27 centimeters; equilateral triangular bases with sides of 2 centimeters $27\sqrt{3}\ cm^3$

Find the volume of each right cylinder below. Use 3.14 for π and round to the nearest tenth.

7. 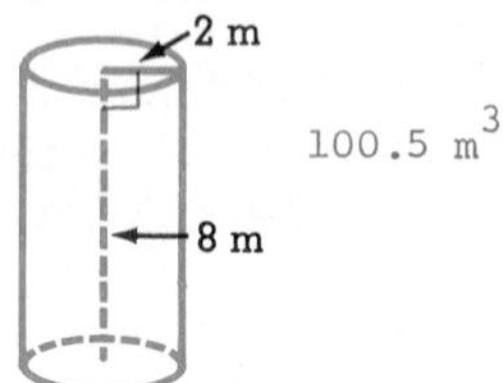

$100.5\ m^3$

8. 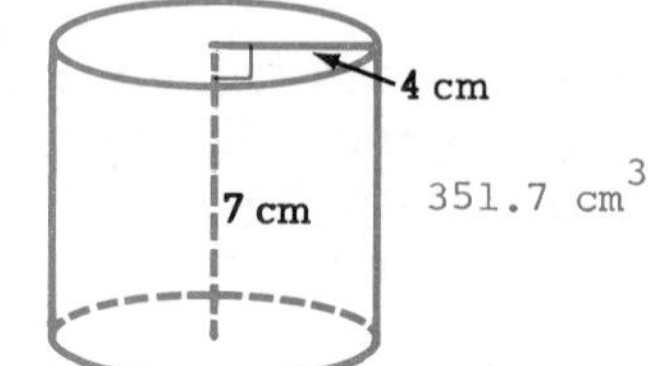

$351.7\ cm^3$

9. 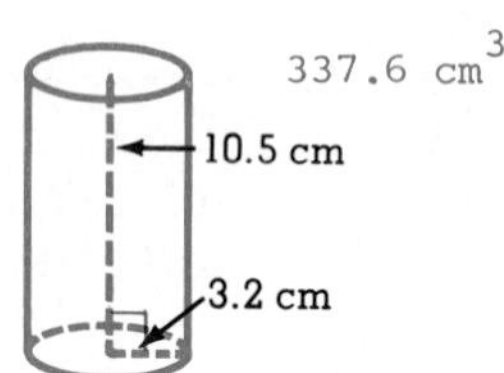

$337.6\ cm^3$

10. 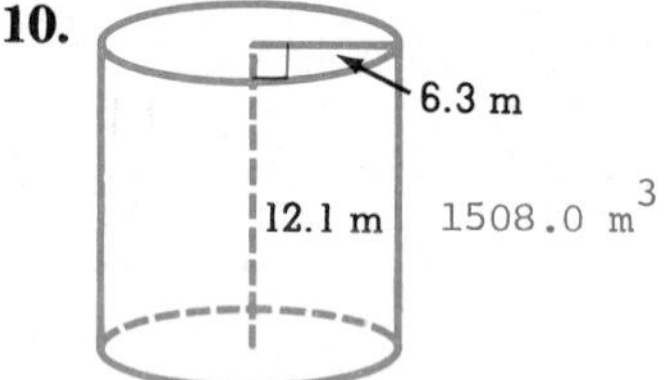

$1508.0\ m^3$

11. 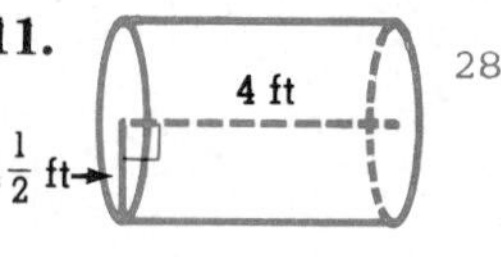

$28.3\ ft^3$

12. 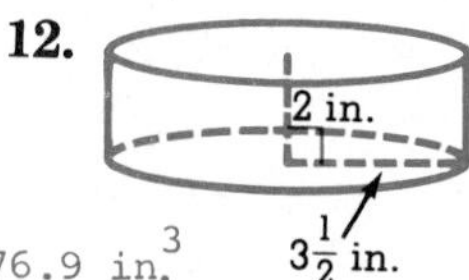

$76.9\ in.^3$

Answer each of the following.

13. A cube is 1 centimeter along each edge. Suppose the length of each edge is doubled. How does the volume of the new cube compare to the original cube? 8 times as large
14. A cube is 1 centimeter along each edge. Suppose the length of each edge is tripled. How does the volume of the new cube compare to the original cube? 27 times as large
15. A right cylinder has a height of 1 centimeter and a radius of 1 centimeter. Suppose each is doubled. How does the volume of the new cylinder compare to the original cylinder? 8 times as large
16. A right cylinder has a height of 1 centimeter and a radius of 1 centimeter. Suppose each is tripled. How does the volume of the new cylinder compare to the original cylinder? 27 times as large
17. Suppose a classroom is 30 feet long, 24 feet wide, and 10 feet high. Each person in the room must have 200 cubic feet of air. Find the maximum number of people that should be allowed in the room. 36 people
18. A driveway is 80 feet long and 12 feet wide. Blacktop will be spread over the driveway at an average depth of 2 inches. Approximate the volume of blacktop needed. (Hint: Assume the driveway is a rectangular prism.) $160\ ft^3$
19. A pipe is 100 feet long and has an inside diameter of $\frac{1}{2}$ foot. Find the number of cubic feet of oil that it can hold. $19.63\ ft^3$
20. A cube of aluminum with each edge 15 inches long is melted. Then, it is rolled into a wire with a diameter of 0.2 inches. Find the length of the wire. $\frac{337{,}500}{\pi}$ in. $\approx$ 107,484.1 in.

Objectives: to find the volume of a right pyramid, to find the volume of a right circular cone, to find the volume of a sphere, to recognize Cavalieri's Principle

11–8 More About Volume

The volume of a pyramid is less than the volume of a prism with the same base and height. Similarly, the volume of a cone is less than the volume of a cylinder with the same base and height.

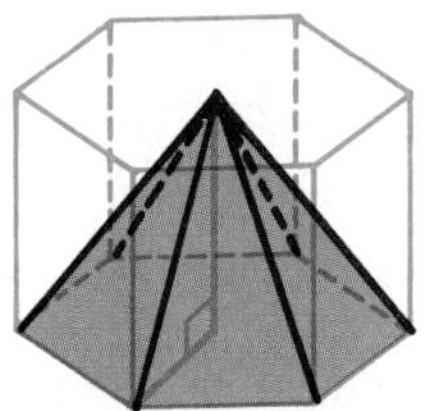

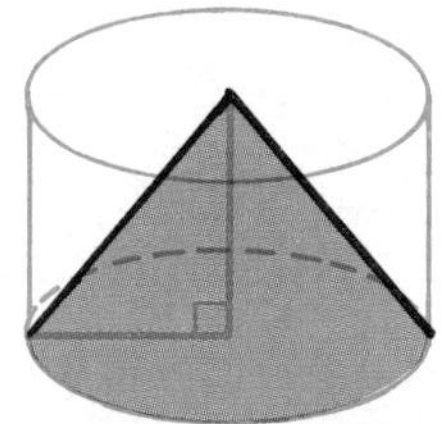

Three cones of water would fill the cylinder at the left. The volume of the cone is $\frac{1}{3}$ the volume of the cylinder. Similar reasoning applies to the pyramid and the prism.

If a right pyramid has a volume of V cubic units, a height of h units, and the area of the base is B square units, then $V = \frac{1}{3}Bh$.

Theorem 11–19 Volume of a Right Pyramid

If a right circular cone has a volume of V cubic units, a height of h units, and the area of the base is B square units, then $V = \frac{1}{3}Bh$.

Theorem 11–20 Volume of a Right Circular Cone

examples

1 Find the total volume of the two cones inside the right circular cylinder shown.

$$\text{Total Volume} = \text{Volume Top Cone} + \text{Volume Bottom Cone}$$
$$= \frac{1}{3}Bh + \frac{1}{3}Bh$$
$$= \frac{1}{3}(\pi r^2)\left(\frac{1}{2}a\right) + \frac{1}{3}(\pi r^2)\left(\frac{1}{2}a\right)$$
$$= \frac{1}{3}\pi r^2 a$$

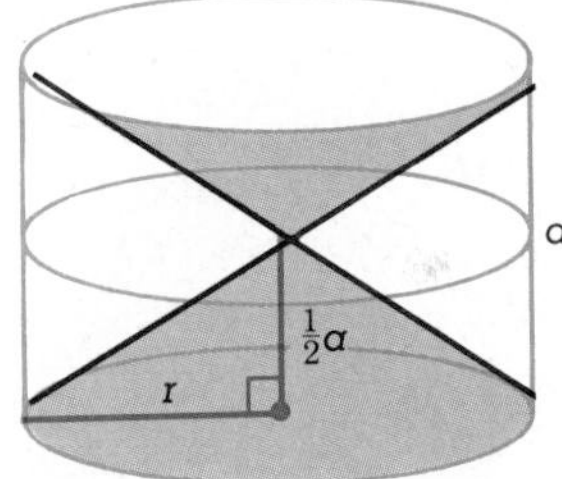

2 Find the volume of the right circular cone with a radius of 3 cm and a slant height of 5 cm. Use 3.14 for π and round to the nearest tenth.

First use the Pythagorean Theorem to find the height.

$$h^2 + r^2 = \ell^2$$
$$h^2 + 9 = 25$$
$$h = 4$$

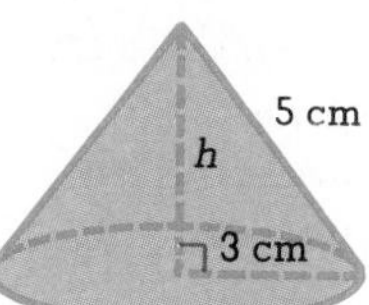

Then, find the volume.

$$V = \frac{1}{3}Bh$$
$$\approx \frac{1}{3}(3.14)(3^2)(4)$$
$$\approx 37.7$$

The volume is about 37.7 cubic centimeters.

The volume of a sphere is less than the volume of a right circular cylinder with the same radius and a height which is the same length as the diameter of the sphere.

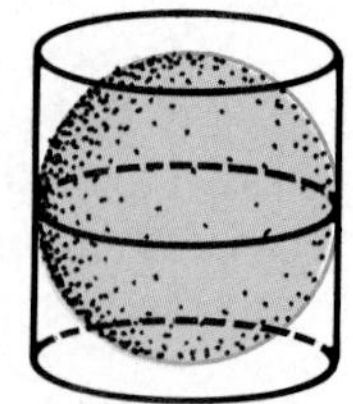

If a sphere has a volume of V cubic units and a radius of r units, then $V = \frac{4}{3}\pi r^3$.

Theorem 11–21
Volume of a Sphere

example

3 Find the volume of the given sphere. Use 3.14 for π and round the answer to the nearest cubic foot.

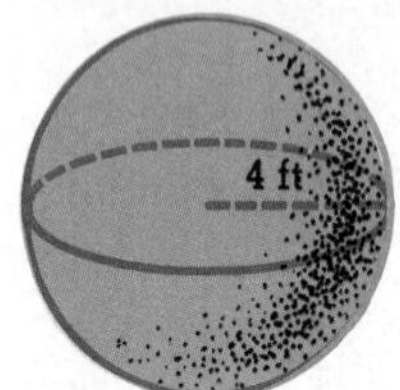

$$V = \frac{4}{3}\pi r^3$$
$$\approx \frac{4}{3}(3.14)(4^3)$$
$$\approx \frac{4}{3}(3.14)(64)$$
$$\approx 268$$

The volume is about 268 cubic feet.

The photograph shows two matching decks of cards. One deck resembles a right rectangular prism. The other deck resembles an oblique rectangular prism. The photograph suggests that the two prisms have the same volume.

A **cross section** of a solid is the intersection of the solid with a plane that is parallel to the base of the solid. In the photograph, each card represents a plane parallel to the base of the deck. Thus, the area of each card represents the area of a cross section of the prism. Notice at each level, the decks of cards have the same cross-sectional area.

The number of cards in a stack represents the measure of the height of that stack. Thus, the two decks have the same height.

If two solids have the same cross-sectional area at every level, and the same height, then they have the same volume.

Postulate 11–9
Cavalieri's Principle

As a result of Cavalieri's Principle, if a prism has a base with an area of B square units and a height of h units, then its volume is Bh cubic units, whether it is right or oblique. Similarly, the volume formulas for cylinders, cones, and pyramids hold whether they are right or oblique.

example

4 Find the volume of the cone. Use 3.14 for π and round to the nearest cubic meter.

$$V = \frac{1}{3}Bh$$
$$= \frac{1}{3}[\pi \cdot (6)^2](13)$$
$$= 156\pi$$
$$\approx 489.84 \text{ or } 490$$

The volume is about 490 cubic meters.

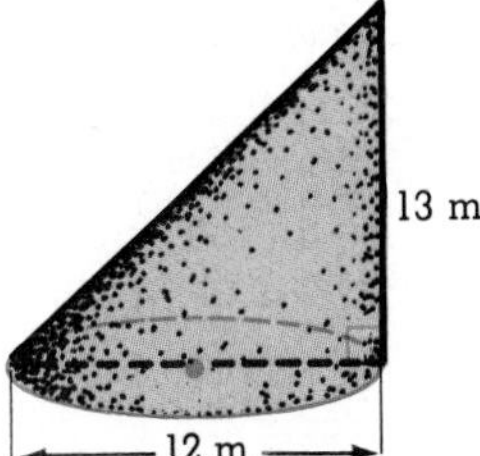

EN: Ex: 3-9 odds, Wr: 2-20 evens; p. 399, C: 1-3; AV: Ex: 1-9 odds, Wr: 2-20 evens; p. 399, C: 1-3; p. 394, Wr: 2-20 evens

exercises

FN: Ex: 1-10, Wr: 1-20; p. 394, Wr: 2-20 evens

Exploratory **Find the volume of each pyramid given below. Round your answer to the nearest tenth.**

1. area of base: 15 ft^2
   height: 7 ft 35 ft^3
2. area of base: 24 cm^2
   height: 5 cm 40 cm^3
3. area of base: 10 ft^2
   height: 3 ft 10 ft^3
4. area of base: 17 m^2
   height: 9 m 51 m^3
5. area of base: 31.2 cm^2
   height: 11.6 cm 120.6 cm^3
6. area of base: 27.9 mm^2
   height: 18.5 mm 172.1 mm^3
7. area of base: 63.5 cm^2
   height: 21.1 cm 446.6 cm^3
8. area of base: 3.49 m^2
   height: 1.3 m 1.5 m^3
9. area of base: $9\frac{1}{2}$ in^2
   height: 2 in. 6.3 $in.^3$
10. area of base: 7 ft^2
    height: $1\frac{3}{4}$ ft 4.1 ft^3

Written **Find the volume of each right circular cone given below. Use 3.14 for π and round to the nearest tenth.**

1. base radius: 5 ft
   height: 16 ft 418.7 ft^3
2. base radius: 4 m
   height: 11 m 184.2 m^3
3. base radius: 5 m
   height: 13 m 340.2 m^3
4. base radius: 9 yd
   height: 16 yd 1356.5 yd^3
5. base radius: 8.6 cm
   height: 12.0 cm 928.9 cm^3
6. base radius: 4.2 m
   height: 10.3 m 190.2 m^3
7. base radius: 100 ft
   height: 130 ft 1,360,666.7 ft^3
8. base radius: 350 mm
   height: 670 mm 85,905,166.7 mm^3

Find the volume of each of the following right circular cones. Use 3.14 for π and round to the nearest tenth.

9. 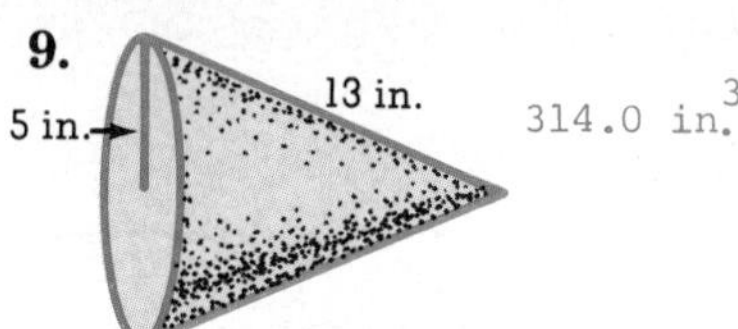

314.0 in.^3

10. 10 cm, 6 cm 301.4 cm^3

11. 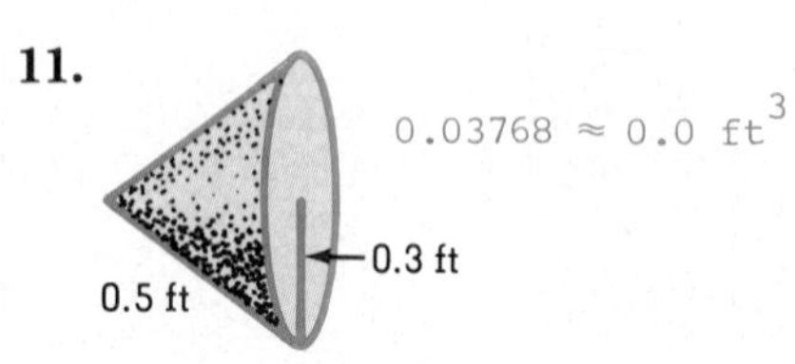

$0.03768 \approx 0.0 \text{ ft}^3$

12. 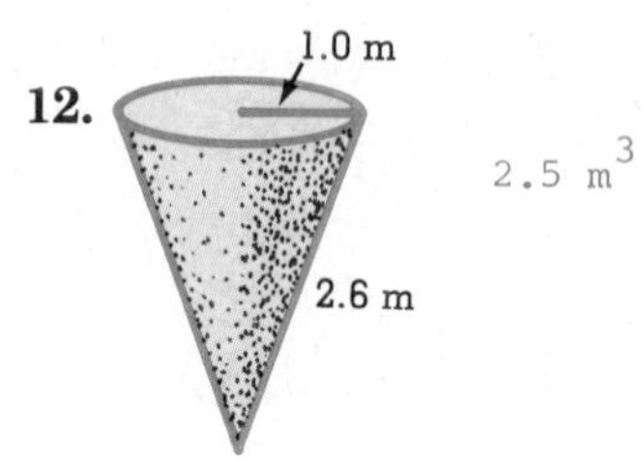

2.5 m^3

Find the volume of each sphere given below. Use 3.14 for π and round to the nearest tenth.

13. radius: 6400 kilometers $1{,}097{,}509{,}500{,}000.0 \text{ km}^3$

14. diameter: 8000 miles $267{,}946{,}666{,}666.7 \text{ mi}^3$

15. area of great circle: 50.24 square centimeters 267.9 cm^3

16. area of great circle: 28.26 square meters 113.0 m^3

Find the volume of each shaded figure.

17. 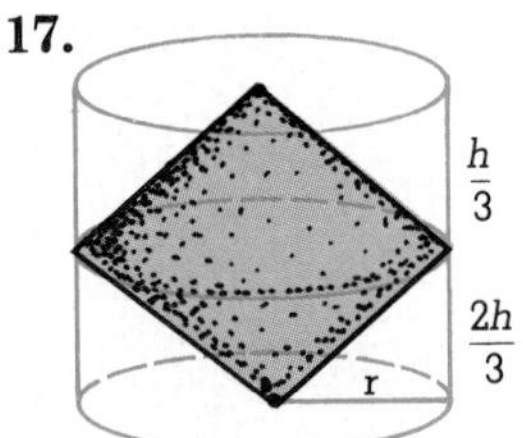

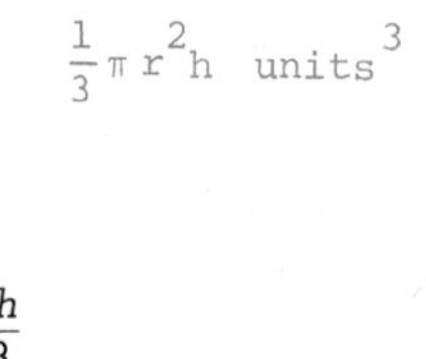

$\frac{1}{3}\pi r^2 h \text{ units}^3$

18. 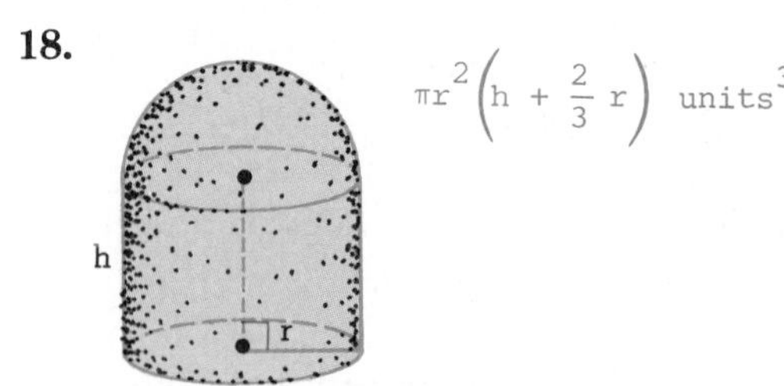

$\pi r^2\left(h + \frac{2}{3}r\right) \text{ units}^3$

19. 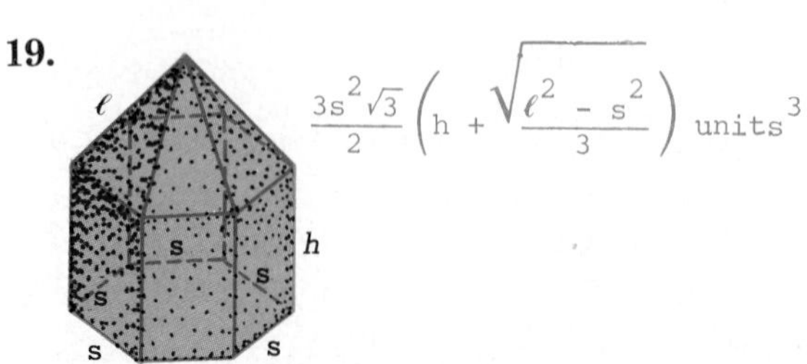

$\frac{3s^2\sqrt{3}}{2}\left(h + \sqrt{\frac{\ell^2 - s^2}{3}}\right) \text{ units}^3$

20. 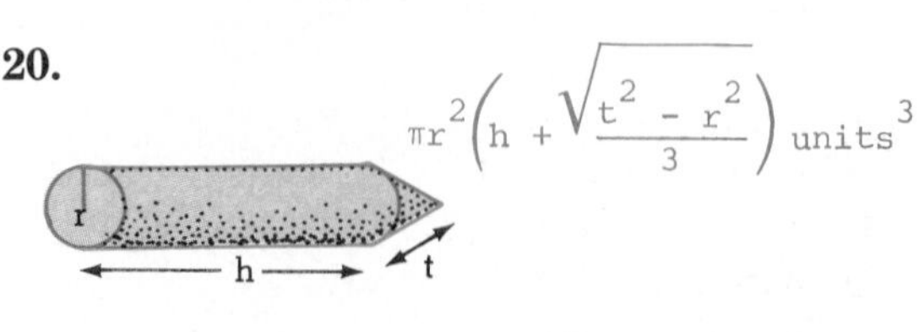

$\pi r^2\left(h + \sqrt{\frac{t^2 - r^2}{3}}\right) \text{ units}^3$

careers

Scuba Diving

Yvonne Munsie is a scuba diver doing underwater research of biological and geological forms.

The varying conditions of pressure and volume of the air supply affect the diver. Changes in pressure on the air in the lungs of the diver and the diving equipment can cause difficulty in breathing.

Several laws of physics affect divers. Boyle's Law represents the inverse relationship between pressure and volume of a gas at a constant temperature. The following formula is frequently used to state Boyle's Law.

$$P_1V_1 = P_2V_2$$

initial pressure × initial volume = new pressure × new volume

Example **A gas with a volume of 2.6 m³ is under a pressure of 2×10^5 N/m². The pressure is increased to 5×10^5 N/m². If the temperature remains unchanged, find the new volume of the gas.**

Note that a pressure of 500 N/m² means 500 newtons of force per square meter of area.

Pressure is defined as force per unit of area. The kilopascal or kPa is a frequently used unit of measure of pressure: 1 kPa = 1000 N/m^2.

$$P_1V_1 = P_2V_2$$

$$(2.6)(2 \times 10^5) = (5 \times 10^5)\ V_2$$

$$5.2 \times 10^5 = (5 \times 10^5)\ V_2$$

$$1.04 = V_2$$

The new volume is 1.04 m³.

Exercises **Complete each of the following. Assume the temperature is unchanged.**

1. $V_1 = 60$, $P_1 = 2.36 \times 10^5$
$P_2 = 3.54 \times 10^5$
Find V_2. 40

2. $V_1 = 50$, $P_1 = 2 \times 10^5$
$V_2 = 12.5$
Find P_2. 8×10^5

3. The volume of a gas is 2.0 m³ under a pressure of 1.02×10^6 N/m². The volume changes under pressure to 6.0 m³. Find the new pressure acting on the gas. 3.4×10^5 N/m^2

Vocabulary

area (363)
polygonal region (363)
radius (371)
center (371)
apothem (371)
circumference (376)
sector (378)
total surface area (381)
prism (381)
bases (381)
lateral faces (381)
lateral edges (381)
right prism (381)
oblique prism (381)
lateral area (382)
cylinder (383)
axis (383)
right cylinder (383)
pyramid (387)
regular pyramid (387)
slant height (387)
right circular cone (388)
volume (391)

Chapter Summary

1. Area Postulate (Postulate 11–1): For any polygonal region and a given unit of measure, there is a unique positive number called the measure of the area of the region. (363)
2. Postulate 11–2: If two regions are congruent, then they have exactly the same area. (364)
3. Area Addition Postulate (Postulate 11–3): If a region is separated into nonoverlapping regions, then the sum of the areas of these regions equals the area of the given region. (364)
4. Formulas for areas of polygons and circles:

   Rectangle $A = \ell w$ (364)
   Square $A = s^2$ (364)
   Parallelogram $A = bh$ (367)
   Triangle $A = \frac{1}{2}bh$ (368)
   Trapezoid $A = \frac{1}{2}h(b_1 + b_2)$ (368)
   Regular Polygon $A = \frac{1}{2}ap$ (372)
   Circle $A = \pi r^2$ (377)

5. Theorem 11–5: A polygon is regular if and only if a circle inscribed in the polygon and a circle circumscribed about the polygon have the same center. (371)
6. Theorem 11–6: If a segment is an apothem of a regular polygon, then it is perpendicular to a side of the polygon at the point of tangency with the inscribed circle. (372)
7. Circumference of a Circle (Theorem 11–9): If a circle has a circumference of C units and a radius of r units, then $C = 2\pi r$. (377)

8. Definition of Area of a Sector of a Circle: If a sector of a circle has an area of A square units, a central angle measurement of N degrees, and a radius of r units, then $A = \frac{N}{360}\pi r^2$. (378)
9. Volume Postulate (Postulate 11–5): For any solid region and a given unit of measure, there is a unique positive number called the measure of the volume of the region. (391)
10. Postulate 11–6: If two solids are congruent, then they have exactly the same volume. (392)
11. Volume Addition Postulate (Postulate 11–7): If a solid region is separated into nonoverlapping regions, then the sum of the volumes of these regions equals the volume of the given region. (392)
12. Cavalieri's Principle (Postulate 11–9): If two solids have the same cross-sectional area at every level, and the same height, then they have the same volume. (396)
13. Formulas for areas and volumes of solids:

Prism	Cylinder	Circular Cone
$L = ph$ (382)	$L = 2\pi rh$ (383)	$L = \pi r\ell$ (388)
$T = ph + 2B$ (382)	$T = 2\pi rh + 2\pi r^2$ (383)	$T = \pi r\ell + \pi r^2$ (388)
$V = Bh$ (392)	$V = \pi r^2 h$ (393)	$V = \frac{1}{3}Bh$ (395)

Regular Pyramid	Sphere
$L = \frac{1}{2}p\ell$ (387)	$A = 4\pi r^2$ (389)
$V = \frac{1}{3}Bh$ (395)	$V = \frac{4}{3}\pi r^3$ (396)

Answers to the following exercises have been rounded at the final step.

Chapter Review

11–1 Find the area for each of the following.

1. a rectangle with length of 6 feet and width of 4 feet 24 ft^2
2. a parallelogram with height of 4 feet and base of 10 feet 40 ft^2

11–2 Find the area for each of the following. Round each answer to the nearest tenth.

3. a right triangle with a base of 6 meters and a hypotenuse of 10 meters 24 m^2
4. an equilateral triangle with each side 16 centimeters long 110.9 cm^2
5. a trapezoid with bases of 14 feet and 12 feet, and a height of 10 feet 130 ft^2
6. a rhombus with diagonals of 12 inches and 20 inches 120 in.^{2}

11–3 Find the area for each of the following. Round each answer to the nearest tenth.

7. a square inscribed in a circle with radius of 25 centimeters 1250 cm^2
8. a regular hexagon with an apothem of 20 centimeters 1385.6 cm^2
9. a regular hexagon with a side of 32 centimeters 2660.4 cm^2

11–4 For each of the following, use 3.14 for π and round to the nearest tenth.

10. Find the circumference of a circle with a radius of 9.6 meters. 60.3 m
11. Find the area of a circle with a radius of 9.6 meters. 289.4 m^2
12. Find the area of a sector of a circle, if the measurement of the central angle is 72° and the radius of the circle is 5 inches. 15.7 $in.^2$

11–5 For each of the following, use 3.14 for π and round to the nearest tenth.

13. Find the lateral area of a regular octagonal prism if its base has sides of 2 centimeters and its height is 3 centimeters. 48 cm^2
14. Find the surface area of a right cylindrical gas tank if it is 7 meters tall and has a diameter of 11 meters. 431.8 m^2

11–6 For each of the following, use 3.14 for π and round to the nearest tenth.

15. Find the total surface area of a square pyramid, if each side is 3 centimeters long and its slant height is 6 centimeters. 45 cm^2
16. Find the total surface area of a right circular cone with a radius of 5 feet and a slant height of 13 feet. 282.6 ft^2

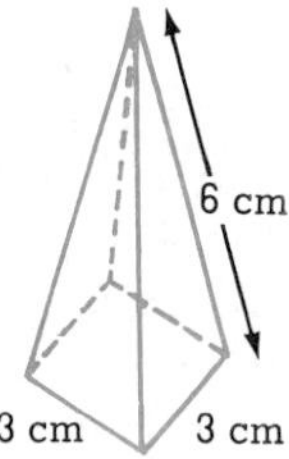

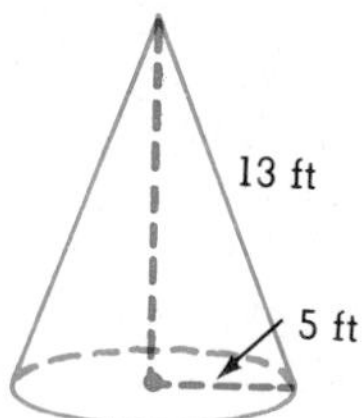

17. Find the surface area of the moon if its diameter is approximately 2160 miles. 14,649,984 mi^2

11–7 For each of the following, use 3.14 for π and round to the nearest tenth.

18. Find the volume of a hexagonal prism if its radius is 10 centimeters and its height is 20 centimeters. 5196.2 cm^3
19. Find the volume of a right circular cone if its radius is 10 centimeters and its height is 20 centimeters. 2093.3 cm^3

11–8 For each of the following, use 3.14 for π and round to the nearest tenth.

20. Find the volume of a triangular prism if its base is an equilateral triangle with sides 9 centimeters long and its height is 15 centimeters. 526.1 cm^3
21. Find the volume of a right circular cone if its height is 22 centimeters and its radius is 11 centimeters. 2786.2 cm^3
22. Find the volume of the sphere shown below. 33,493.3 ft^3

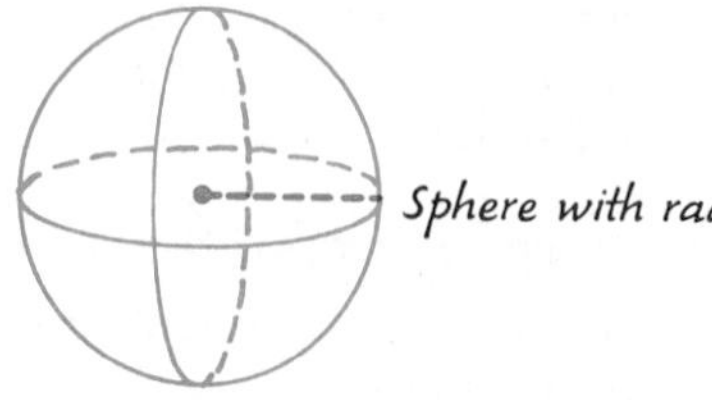

Chapter Test

Answers to the following exercises have been rounded at the final step.

Find the area for each of the following. Round each answer to the nearest tenth. Use 3.14 for π, if necessary.

1. a rectangle with length of 7.1 millimeters and width of 9.2 millimeters 65.3 mm^2
2. a parallelogram with a height of 11 inches and a base of 12 inches 132 $in.^2$
3. an equilateral triangle with each side 25 centimeters long 270.6 cm^2
4. a right triangle with a hypotenuse 13 centimeters long and one leg 5 centimeters long 30 cm^2
5. a regular hexagon with sides of 15 feet 584.6 ft^2
6. a regular hexagon with an apothem of 2.5 inches 21.7 $in.^2$
7. a circle with a diameter of 4 inches 12.6 $in.^2$
8. a circle inscribed in a square with a diagonal of 21.5 centimeters 181.4 cm^2
9. a sector of a circle, if the measurement of the central angle is 30° and the radius of the circle is 3 feet 2.4 ft^2

Find the total surface area for each of the following. Round each answer to the nearest tenth. Use 3.14 for π, if necessary.

10. a regular hexagonal prism with base sides of 5 feet and a height of 10 feet 429.9 ft^2
11. a right cylinder with base radius of 5 feet and a height of 10 feet 471 ft^2
12. a regular triangular pyramid with base sides of 23 centimeters and a slant height of 40 centimeters 1609.1 cm^2
13. a right circular cone with a radius of 27 millimeters and a height of 30 millimeters 5710.9 mm^2
14. a sphere with radius of 300 feet 1,130,400 ft^2
15. a regular square pyramid with base sides of 4 inches and a height of 6 inches 66.6 $in.^2$

Find the volume for each of the following. Round each answer to the nearest tenth. Use 3.14 for π, if necessary.

16. a regular triangular prism with base sides of 8 yards and a height of 10 yards 277.1 yd^3
17. a regular square pyramid with base sides of 4 inches and a height of 6 inches 32 $in.^3$
18. a right cylinder with a diameter of 39 centimeters and a height of 50 centimeters 59,699.3 cm^3
19. a right circular cone with a diameter of 39 centimeters and a height of 50 centimeters 19,899.8 cm^3
20. a sphere with radius of 300 feet 113,040,000 ft^3

chapter 12 Coordinates

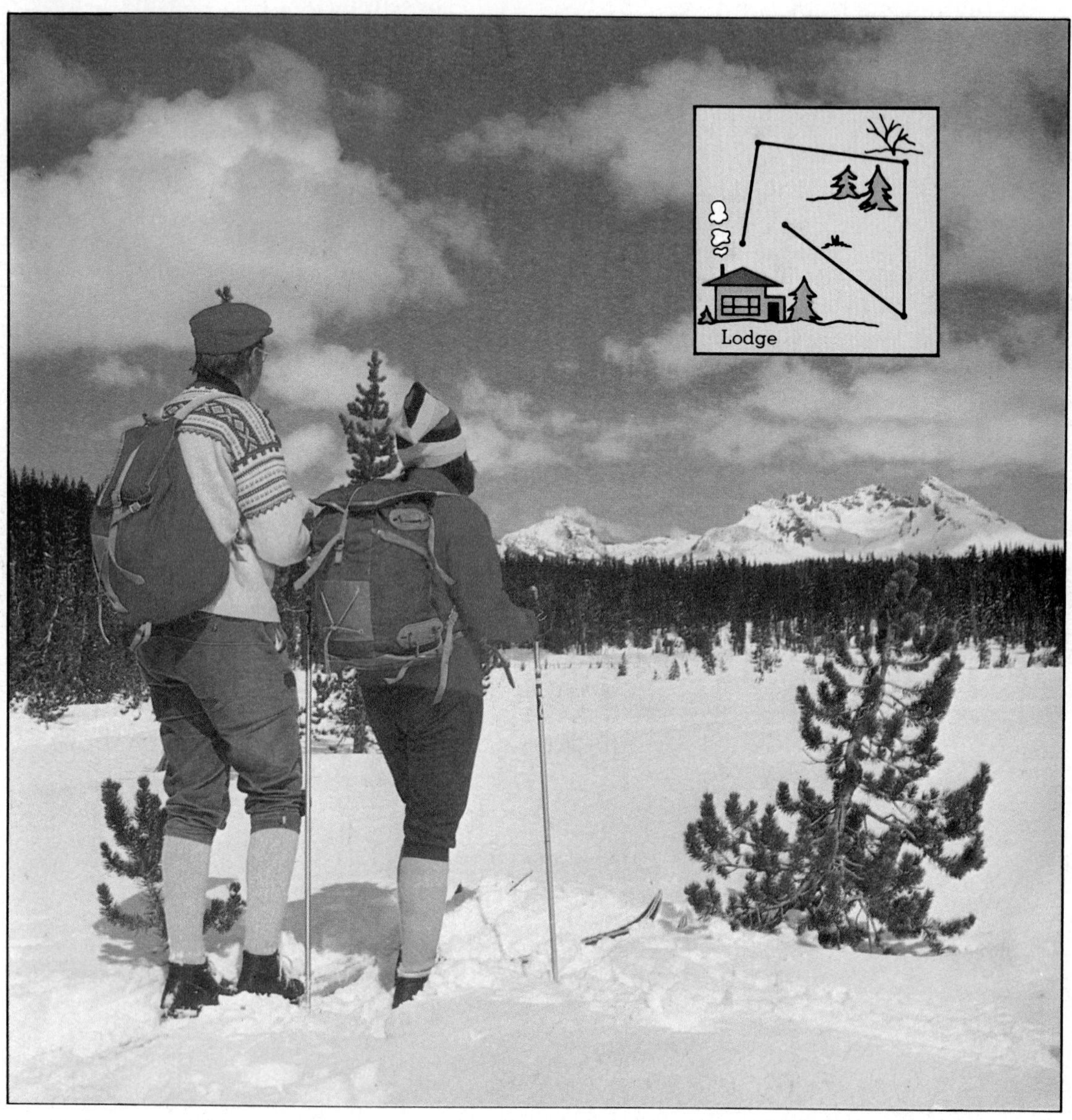

Maps are used by cross country skiers to determine the route they will take. Coordinates describe the skiers' route.

Objectives: to name the ordered pair for a point on a graph, to identify a linear equation, to graph points and linear equations

12–1 Graphing

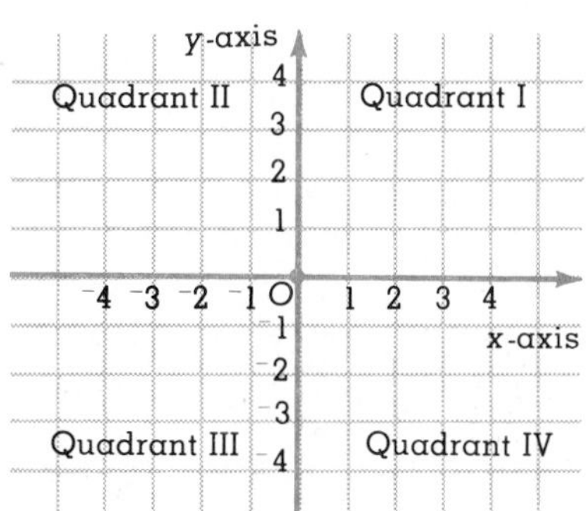

Ordered pairs of numbers can be used to locate points in a plane. Two perpendicular number lines separate the plane into four regions called **quadrants.** The horizontal number line is called the ***x*-axis.** The vertical number line is called the ***y*-axis.** Their point of intersection is called the **origin** and named *O*.

The two axes do not lie in any quadrant.
Emphasize this point.

The figure at the right shows the graph of the ordered pair (4, 2). The first component, 4, is called the ***x*-coordinate.** It tells the number of units the point lies to the left or right of the origin. The second component, 2, is called the ***y*-coordinate.** It tells the number of units the point lies above or below the origin.

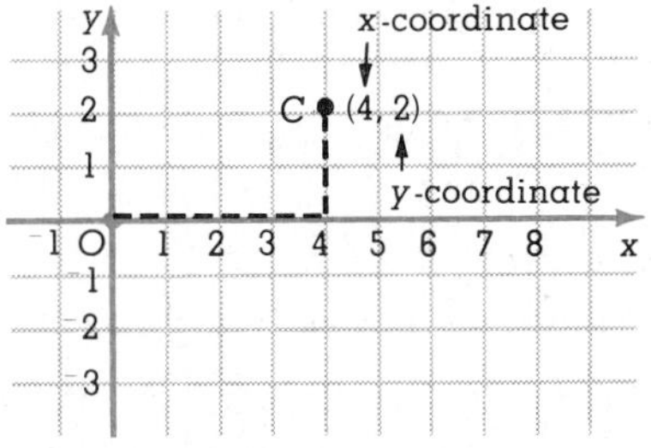

Notice that on the x-axis, the positive numbers are to the right of the origin and the negative numbers are to the left of the origin. On the y-axis, the positive numbers are above the origin and the negative numbers are below the origin.

Emphasize the order of x and y in the ordered pair.

example

1 Graph point *A* at (2, ⁻3).

Start at *O*. Move 2 units to the right. Then, move 3 units down.

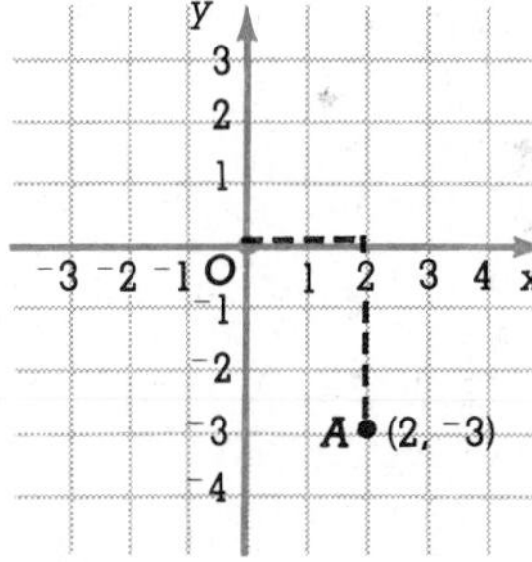

When plotting points, the following is true.

Each point in a coordinate plane corresponds to exactly one ordered pair of numbers. Each ordered pair of numbers corresponds to exactly one point in a coordinate plane.

Postulate 12–1

The solutions of $y = 2x - 1$ are ordered pairs. By substituting different values for x in the equation you can find the corresponding values for y. Some of the solutions are shown in the table below.

x	$2x - 1$	y	(x, y)
$^-2$	$2(^-2) - 1$	$^-5$	$(^-2, 5)$
$^-1$	$2(^-1) - 1$	$^-3$	$(^-1, ^-3)$
0	$2(0) - 1$	$^-1$	$(0, ^-1)$
1	$2(1) - 1$	1	$(1, 1)$
2	$2(2) - 1$	3	$(2, 3)$

For each value of x you choose, there is a corresponding value of y that satisfies the equation.

The solutions of $y = 2x - 1$ can also be shown by a graph. The figure at the left shows points for some of the solutions to $y = 2x - 1$. The figure at the right shows the line containing all the points whose ordered pairs are solutions to $y = 2x - 1$.

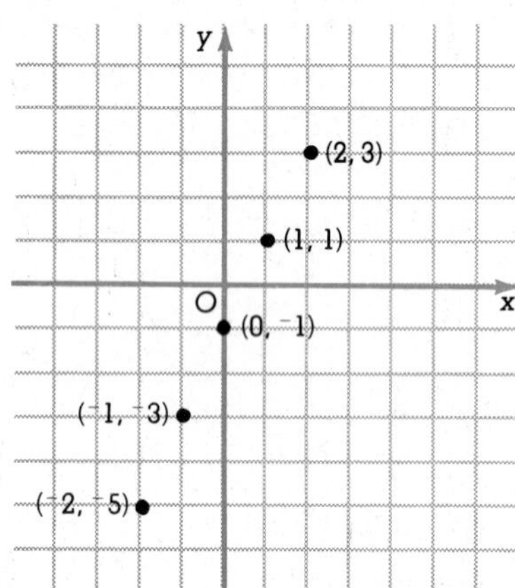

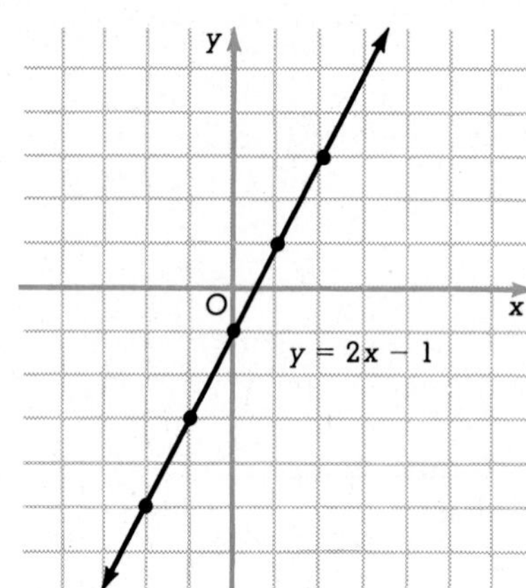

Point out the difference between the B in Ax + By = C and the b in y = mx + b.

An equation whose graph is a straight line is called a **linear equation.**

Tell students that Ax + By = C is called the standard form of a linear equation.

An equation is linear if and only if it can be written in the form $Ax + By = C$, where A, B, and C are any real numbers, and A and B are not both 0.

Definition of Linear Equation

Students should understand that the equation need not appear in the form Ax + By = C.

The equations $5x + 6y = 8$, $3x = 4y + 9$, $5x - y = \frac{1}{2}$, and $x = 4$ are linear equations. Each can be written in the form $Ax + By = C$. The equations $4x + 5y^2 = 7$ and $\frac{1}{y} + x = 3$ are *not* linear equations. Why?

$Ax + By = C$ is called standard form.

The first is a second degree equation. The second equation has the $\frac{1}{y}$ or y^{-1} term.

example

2 Graph $y = 3x - 3$.

Make a table of values for x and y. Graph the ordered pairs and connect them with a line.

x	y
$^-2$	$^-9$
$^-1$	$^-6$
0	$^-3$
1	0
2	3

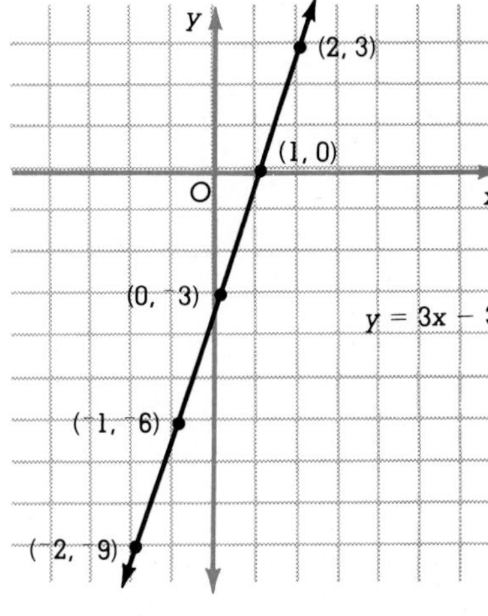

The equation $y = 3x - 3$ can be written in the form $3x - y = 3$. Therefore, it is a linear equation and the graph is a line.

According to Postulate 1–1, two points determine a line. Therefore, to graph any equation, simply find two ordered pairs that satisfy the linear equation. Then, graph the ordered pairs and connect the points with a line.

Students should be encouraged to find a third ordered pair as a check.

example

3 Graph $3x + 2y = 4$.

Transform the equation so that y is on one side by itself. Then, find at least two values for x and y that satisfy the equation.

$$3x + 2y = 4$$
$$2y = 4 - 3x$$
$$y = \frac{4 - 3x}{2}$$

x	y
0	2
2	$^-1$
4	$^-4$

The equation $3x + 2y = 4$ is a linear equation. The graph is a line.

Graph the ordered pairs and connect them with a line.

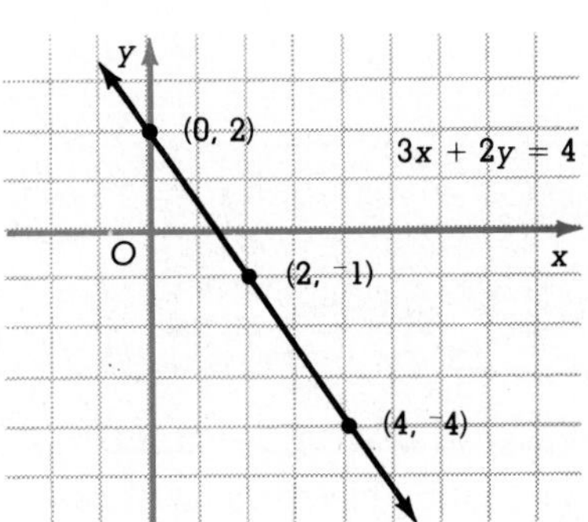

EN: Ex: 15-18, Wr: 2-18 evens, E ; AV: Ex: 1-18, Wr: 1-17 odds;

exercises

FN: Ex: 1-18, Wr: 1-17 odds

Exploratory **Name the ordered pair for each point on the graph below.**

1. A (-6,4)
2. I (-1,-4)
3. F (-6,-5)
4. W (8,4)
5. P (1,5)
6. X (8,-5)
7. Q (3,3)
8. S (0,-5)
9. B (-4,-3)
10. C (-5,0)
11. M (4,0)
12. N (3,-3)

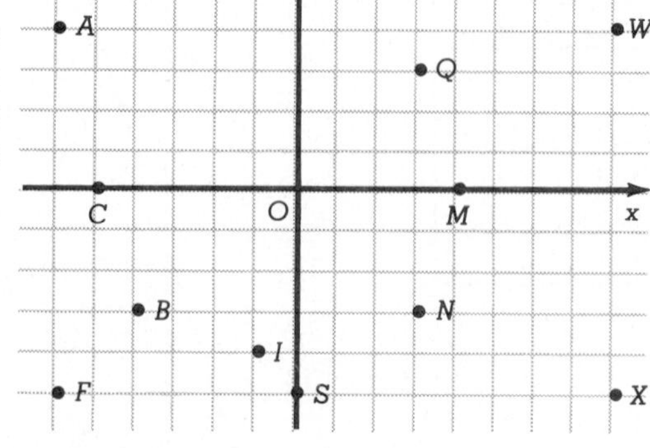

Determine whether each of the following are linear equations. Write *yes* or *no*.

13. $3x + 2y = 6$ yes
14. $y = 2x - 1$ yes
15. $y = 8$ yes
16. $3x + 4y^2 = 1$ no
17. $9x + 4y = {}^-2$ yes
18. $\frac{1}{x} + \frac{3}{4}y = 7$ no

It may be helpful to use graph paper with 4 or 5 divisions to the inch.

Written **Graph each of the following linear equations.**

For graphs to exercises 1-18, see the Teacher's Guide.

1. $y = 2x$
2. $x + y = 5$
3. $x + 2y = 6$
4. $4x - 3y = 0$
5. $y = 4x$
6. $x + y = {}^-4$
7. $x - 4y = {}^-8$
8. $5x + 2y = 0$
9. $y = {}^-x + 2$
10. $2x + y = 6$
11. $4x + 2y = 6$
12. $2x - 3y = 4$

Each of the following are the coordinates of three vertices of a rectangle. Graph them. Then, find each fourth vertex.

13. (3, 1), (3, ⁻3), (⁻5, ⁻3) (-5,1)
14. (1, 0), (3, 0), (3, 3) (1,3)
15. (⁻3, 4), (5, 4), (5, ⁻3) (-3,-3)
16. (2, ⁻2), (⁻2, ⁻2), (⁻2, ⁻5) (2,-5)
17. (2, 0), (0, 2), (⁻4, ⁻2) (-2,-4)
18. (⁻1, 0), (1, 1), (0, 3) (-2,2)

Creative Blocks — excursions in geometry

The figure below shows a block of wood with three holes.

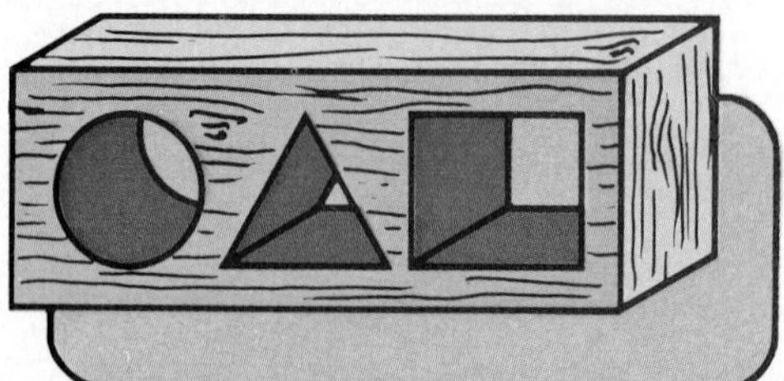

The following object is circular in one cross section, triangular in another cross section, and square in the third cross section. It represents one solution to the problem.

Describe a single, solid object that will pass through each hole and will entirely block any light during its passage.

12–2 Distances and Midpoints

Objectives: to find the distance between points, to find the midpoint of a segment

In a coordinate plane consider two points A and C with coordinates $(^-3, ^-1)$, and $(1, ^-1)$. These points lie on a horizontal line. You can use *absolute value* to find the distance between points A and C.

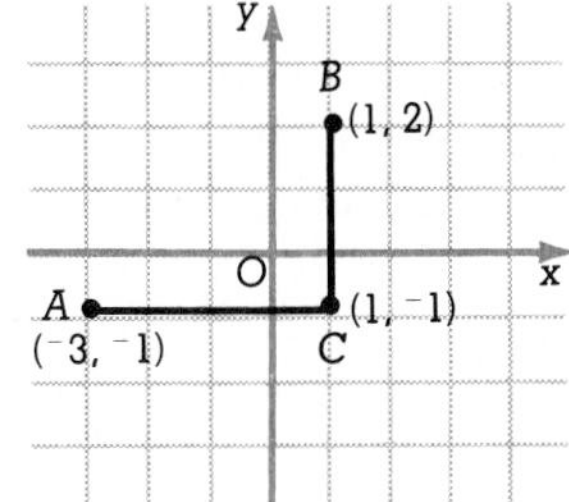

$AC = |^-3 - 1| = |^-4|$ or 4 *The difference of the x-coordinates*

The points B and C with coordinates $(1, 2)$ and $(1, ^-1)$ lie on a vertical line. The distance between points B and C is 3 units.

$BC = |2 - ^-1| = |3|$ or 3 *The difference of the y-coordinates*

Notice that the segment connecting A and B is neither horizontal nor vertical. The distance between A and B can be found by using the Pythagorean Theorem.

A review of absolute value may be helpful.

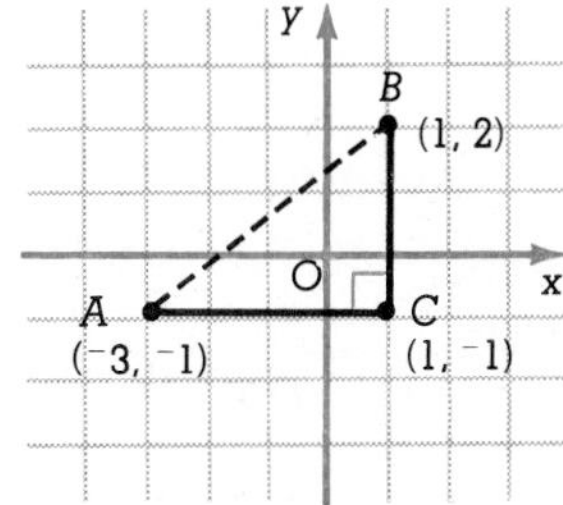

$$\begin{aligned}(AB)^2 &= (AC)^2 + (BC)^2\\ &= |^-3 - 1|^2 + |2 - ^-1|^2\\ &= 4^2 + 3^2\\ &= 16 + 9\\ &= 25\\ AB &= \sqrt{25} \text{ or } 5\end{aligned}$$

Distance is positive.

Emphasize that distance is always positive.

example

1 Find the distance between the points with coordinates $(^-2, 3)$ and $(5, ^-3)$.

A vertical line through $(^-2, 3)$ and a horizontal line through $(5, ^-3)$ intersect at $(^-2, ^-3)$. These three points are the vertices of a right triangle, $\triangle ABC$. The length of the hypotenuse is the distance between $(^-2, 3)$ and $(5, ^-3)$.
Now, use the Pythagorean Theorem.

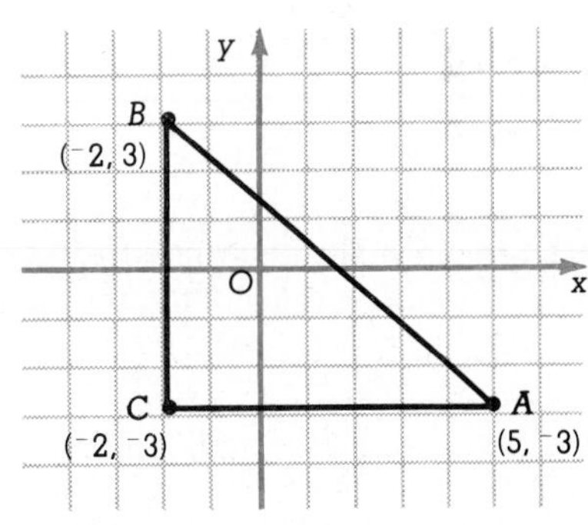

$$\begin{aligned}(AB)^2 &= (AC)^2 + (BC)^2\\ (AB)^2 &= |5 - ^-2|^2 + |3 - ^-3|^2\\ &= 7^2 + 6^2\\ &= 49 + 36\\ &= 85\\ AB &= \sqrt{85}\end{aligned}$$

This is approximately 9.22.

The Pythagorean Theorem can be used to develop a general formula for finding the distance between two points in a plane.

Suppose (x_1, y_1) and (x_2, y_2) are coordinates of the endpoints of $\overline{BA}$. Form a right triangle, $\triangle ABC$, by drawing a vertical line through (x_1, y_1) and a horizontal line through (x_2, y_2). These lines intersect at (x_1, y_2).

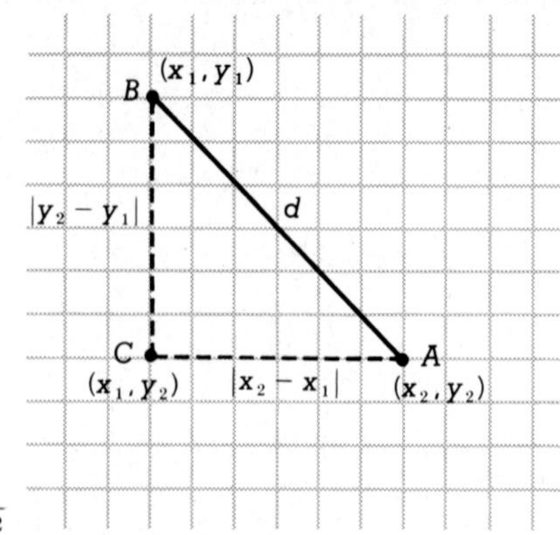

Point out that the right triangle could also be formed by locating point A at (x_2, y_1).

$$(BA)^2 = (AC)^2 + (AB)^2$$
$$d^2 = |x_2 - x_1|^2 + |y_2 - y_1|^2$$
$$d^2 = (x_2 - x_1)^2 + (y_2 - y_1)^2$$
$$d = \sqrt{(x_2 - x_1)^2 + (y_2 - y_1)^2}$$

x_1 is read "x sub one."
y_1 is read "y sub one."

The distance between two points with coordinates (x_1, y_1) and (x_2, y_2) is given by the following formula.

$$d = \sqrt{(x_2 - x_1)^2 + (y_2 - y_1)^2}$$

Theorem 12–1 Distance Formula

example

2 Use the Distance Formula to find the distance between the points with coordinates ($^-1$, 6) and (5, $^-4$).

$$d = \sqrt{(x_2 - x_1)^2 + (y_2 - y_1)^2}$$
$$= \sqrt{(5 - {}^-1)^2 + ({}^-4 - 6)^2}$$
$$= \sqrt{(6)^2 + ({}^-10)^2}$$
$$= \sqrt{36 + 100}$$
$$= \sqrt{136}$$
$$= 2\sqrt{34}$$

The distance is $2\sqrt{34}$ units.

The Distance Formula can be used to show that a given point on a segment is the midpoint of that segment.

Example 3 assumes that (3,1) is on the line segment.

example

3 Show that the point represented by (3, 1) is the midpoint of a segment having endpoints whose coordinates are (6, $^-1$) and (0, 3).

distance between (3, 1) and (6, $^-1$)

$$d = \sqrt{(6 - 3)^2 + ({}^-1 - 1)^2}$$
$$= \sqrt{(3)^2 + ({}^-2)^2}$$
$$= \sqrt{9 + 4}$$
$$= \sqrt{13}$$

distance between (3, 1) and (0, 3)

$$d = \sqrt{(0 - 3)^2 + (3 - 1)^2}$$
$$= \sqrt{({}^-3)^2 + (2)^2}$$
$$= \sqrt{9 + 4}$$
$$= \sqrt{13}$$

The Distance Formula also can be used to find the coordinates of the midpoint of a segment.

example

4 Find the coordinates of M, the midpoint of a segment having endpoints whose coordinates are (2, 3) and (6, 7).

Form trapezoid $ABQP$ by drawing vertical segments through A, through B, and through M to the x-axis. Since $\overline{MR}$ is the median of the trapezoid, R is the midpoint of $\overline{PQ}$. Thus, the x-coordinate of R is also the x-coordinate of M. Use the Definition of Midpoint to find the x-coordinate of M.

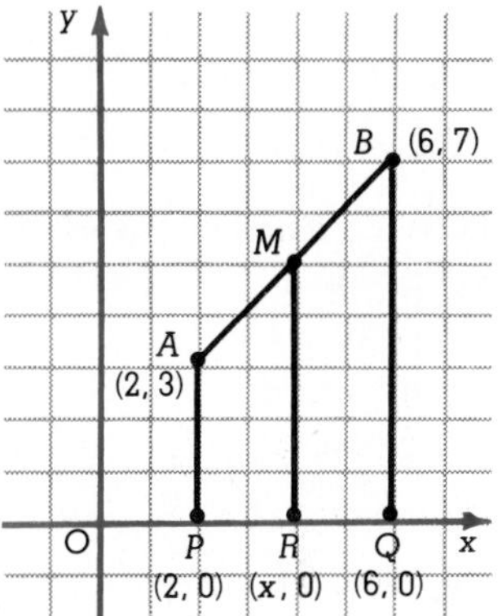

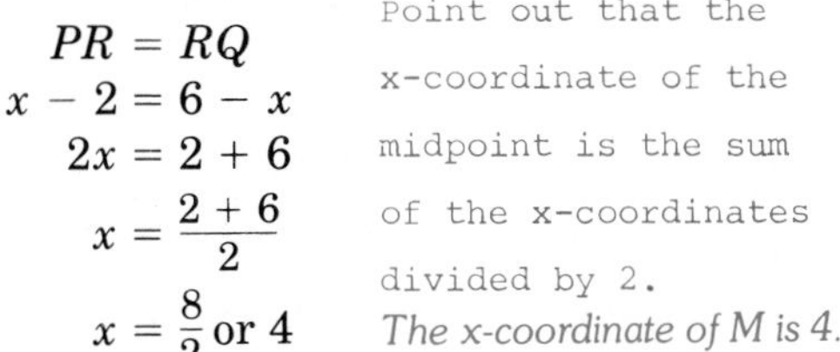

$$PR = RQ$$
$$x - 2 = 6 - x$$
$$2x = 2 + 6$$
$$x = \frac{2 + 6}{2}$$
$$x = \frac{8}{2} \text{ or } 4$$

Point out that the x-coordinate of the midpoint is the sum of the x-coordinates divided by 2.

The x-coordinate of M is 4.

To find the y-coordinate of M, form trapezoid $ABCD$ by drawing horizontal segments through A, through B, and through M to the y-axis. Since $\overline{MG}$ is the median of the trapezoid, G is the midpoint of $\overline{CD}$. Thus, the y-coordinate of G is also the y-coordinate of M. Use the Definition of Midpoint to find the y-coordinate of G.

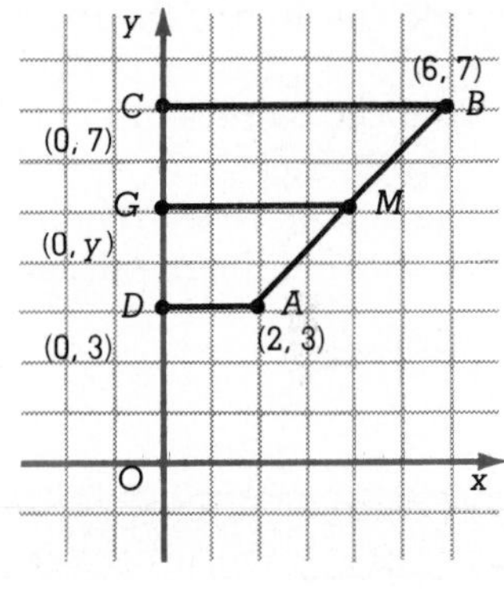

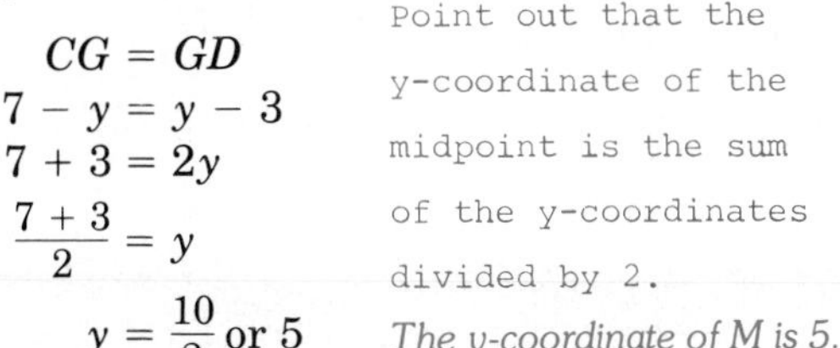

$$CG = GD$$
$$7 - y = y - 3$$
$$7 + 3 = 2y$$
$$\frac{7 + 3}{2} = y$$
$$y = \frac{10}{2} \text{ or } 5$$

Point out that the y-coordinate of the midpoint is the sum of the y-coordinates divided by 2.

The y-coordinate of M is 5.

The coordinates of M are (4, 5).

Example 4 suggests the following theorem.

If the coordinates of A and B are (x_1, y_1) and (x_2, y_2) respectively, then the midpoint M of $\overline{AB}$ has coordinates $\left(\frac{x_1 + x_2}{2}, \frac{y_1 + y_2}{2}\right)$.

Theorem 12–2
Midpoint Formula

EN: Ex: 1, 4, 7, 10; Wr: 1-29 odds, 31-35; AV: Ex: 1-11 odds, Wr: 1-15; p. 408, Wr: 2-18 evens

exercises

FN: Ex: 1-12, Wr: 1-15; p. 408, Wr: 2-18 evens

Exploratory **Find the distance between each of the following pairs of points.**

1. (5, 0), (12, 0) 7
2. (0, 3), (0, 6) 3
3. ($^-6$, 0), ($^-2$, 0) 4
4. (1, 2), (3, 4) $2\sqrt{2}$
5. (2, 3), (5, 7) 5
6. ($^-1$, $^-2$), ($^-3$, $^-4$) $2\sqrt{2}$

Find the coordinates of the midpoint of each segment that has endpoints with the following coordinates.

7. (0, 4), (0, 0) (0,2)
8. (6, 0), (13, 0) $\left(\frac{19}{2}, 0\right)$
9. ($^-3$, 2), ($^-5$, 6) (-4,4)
10. ($^-1$, $^-2$), ($^-3$, $^-6$) (-2,-4)
11. (4, 6), ($^-2$, $^-3$) $\left(1, \frac{3}{2}\right)$
12. ($^-1$, $^-7$), (6, 1) $\left(\frac{5}{2}, -3\right)$

Written **Find the distance between each of the following pairs of points.**

1. (2, 3), (8, 9) $6\sqrt{2}$
2. (15, 0), (0, 15) $15\sqrt{2}$
3. (1, 1), (8, 8) $7\sqrt{2}$
4. ($^-7$, $^-5$), ($^-10$, $^-9$) 5
5. (0, 3), (5, 7) $\sqrt{41}$
6. ($^-2$, $^-6$), ($^-6$, $^-2$) $4\sqrt{2}$
7. (4, 6), (0, $^-4$) $2\sqrt{29}$
8. (6, 0), ($^-4$, $^-8$) $2\sqrt{41}$
9. (0, 0), (3, 4) 5
10. (0, 0), (p, q) $\sqrt{p^2 + q^2}$
11. (a, c), (c, a) $|a - c|\sqrt{2}$
12. $(0, r)$, $(0, {}^-r)$ $2|r|$
13. $(4, a)$, $({}^-8, b)$ $\sqrt{144 + (a - b)^2}$
14. $\left(\frac{2}{3}, \frac{4}{5}\right)$, $\left(\frac{1}{3}, \frac{2}{5}\right)$ $\frac{1}{15}\sqrt{61}$
15. (0.2, 0.7), (0.4, 0.9) $\frac{1}{5}\sqrt{2}$

16–30. Find the coordinates of the midpoint of each segment that has endpoints with the coordinates given in written exercises **1–15.** 16. (5,6) 17. (7.5,7.5) 18. (4.5,4.5) 19. (-8.5,-7) 20. (2.5,5) 21. (-4,-4) 22. (2,1) 23. (1,-4) 24. (1.5,2)

31. The vertices of a rectangle have the coordinates (4, 1), ($^-5$, 1), ($^-5$, $^-3$), and (4, $^-3$). Find the perimeter of the rectangle. 26

32. Find the area of the rectangle in exercise **31.** 36

33. Find the measure of each diagonal of the rectangle in exercise **31.** $\sqrt{97}$ for each diagonal

34. Find the coordinates of the center of a circle whose diameter has endpoints with coordinates ($^-6$, $^-8$), and (5, 7). (-0.5,-0.5)

35. The center of a circle has coordinates ($^-8$, 3). One endpoint of a diameter has coordinates (5, 4). Find the coordinates of the other endpoint of the diameter. (-21,2)

25. $\left(\frac{p}{2}, \frac{q}{2}\right)$ 26. $\left(\frac{a + c}{2}, \frac{c + a}{2}\right)$ 27. (0,0) 28. $\left(-2, \frac{a + b}{2}\right)$ 29. $\left(\frac{1}{2}, \frac{3}{5}\right)$ 30. (0.3,0.8)

Uses in Banking — computers

Banks use computers to store data as well as to keep account of daily transactions. For example, when a checking account is opened, the computer assigns a number to the account. As deposits are made and withdrawals are completed, the computer keeps a running total by adding or subtracting as necessary. The computer processes this information at such a rate of speed that the time of processing is reduced from weeks to minutes.

Savings accounts, loans, and savings clubs are all kept up-to-date using a computer. Computers also make 24-hour self-service windows possible. In some areas, customers are able to make purchases using a special plastic credit card that deducts the amount from the customer's checking account.

Objectives: to describe the slope of a line, to determine the slope of a line from (1) a table and (2) pairs of points, to find the coordinate of a point if given the slope and a point

12–3 Slope

A staircase has two parts, the stringers and the steps. The stringers slope from one floor to the next and support the steps. The vertical and horizontal measurements of the stairs affect the steepness of the stringers.

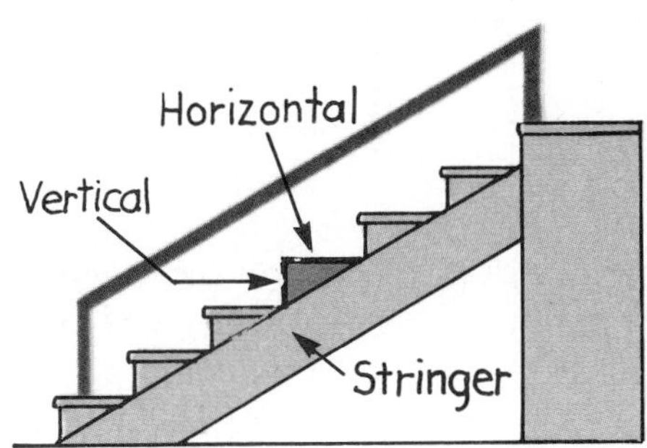

The measure of the slope or steepness, of a line is found by comparing the change in vertical units to the change in horizontal units. For example, in the graph of $y = 2x$, a vertical change of 2 units is accompanied by a horizontal change of 1 unit.

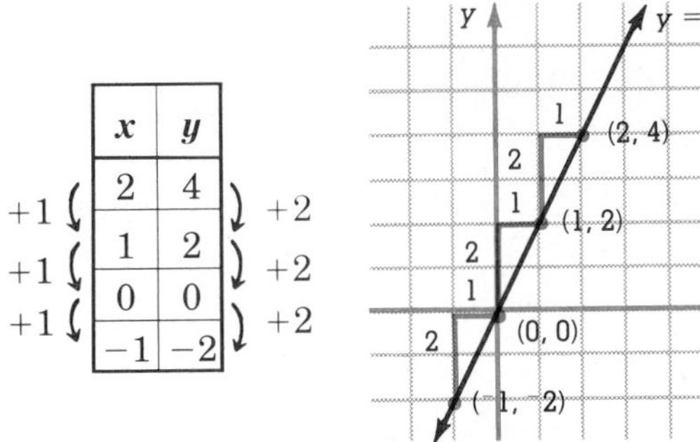

x	y
2	4
1	2
0	0
−1	−2

Notice that the vertical change is the difference of the y-coordinates and the horizontal change is the difference of the corresponding x-coordinates. You can use a ratio to compare the two differences.

Students may refer to the vertical and horizontal changes as the rise and the run respectively.

$$\text{slope} = \frac{\text{difference of the } y\text{-coordinates}}{\text{difference of the corresponding } x\text{-coordinates}}$$

$$= \frac{2}{1} \text{ or } 2$$

Emphasize that the difference of corresponding coordinates must be followed.

Definition of Slope

The slope of a line containing two points with coordinates (x_1, y_1) and (x_2, y_2) is given by the following formula.

$$m = \frac{y_2 - y_1}{x_2 - x_1} \quad \text{where } x_2 \neq x_1$$

Point out that $m = \frac{y_1 - y_2}{x_1 - x_2}$ is true also.

example

1 Determine the slope of each of the following lines.

A.

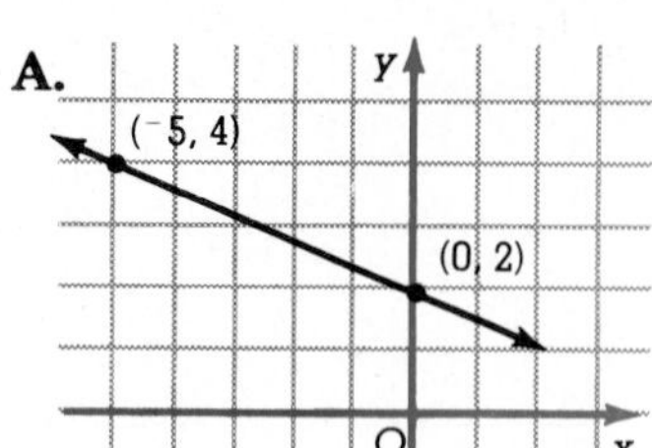

B.

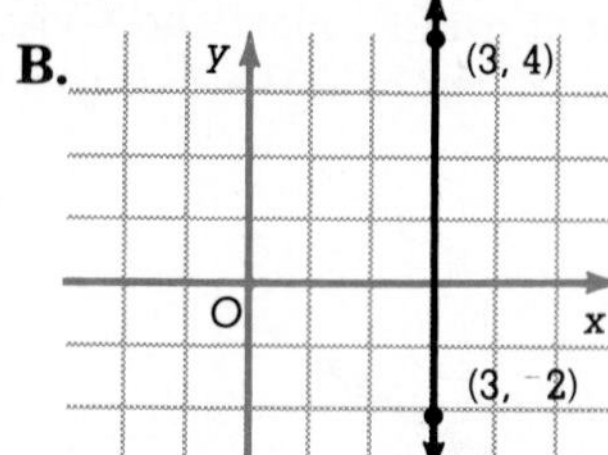

C.

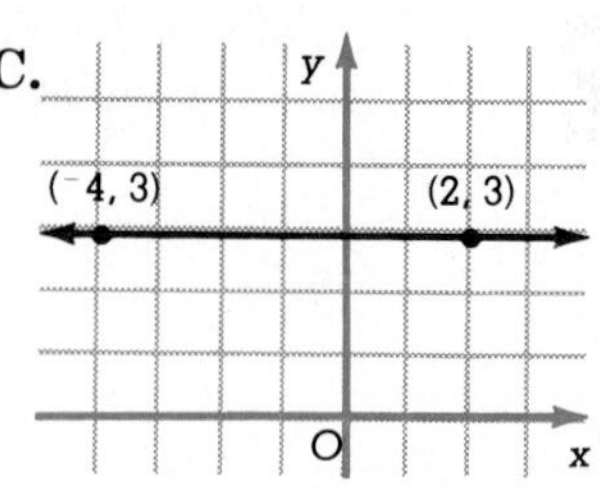

Be careful that students do <u>not</u> write $m = \frac{y_2 - y_1}{x_1 - x_2}$.

A. $m = \frac{y_2 - y_1}{x_2 - x_1}$

$= \frac{2 - 4}{0 - {}^-5}$

$= \frac{{}^-2}{5}$

$= -\frac{2}{5}$

The slope is $-\frac{2}{5}$.

B. $m = \frac{y_2 - y_1}{x_2 - x_1}$

$= \frac{{}^-2 - 4}{3 - 3}$

$= \frac{{}^-6}{0}$

The slope is undefined.

C. $m = \frac{y_2 - y_1}{x_2 - x_1}$

$= \frac{3 - 3}{2 - {}^-4}$

$= \frac{0}{6}$

$= 0$

The slope is non-zero.

The following conclusions about slope can be made.

If the line *rises* to the right, then the slope is *positive.*

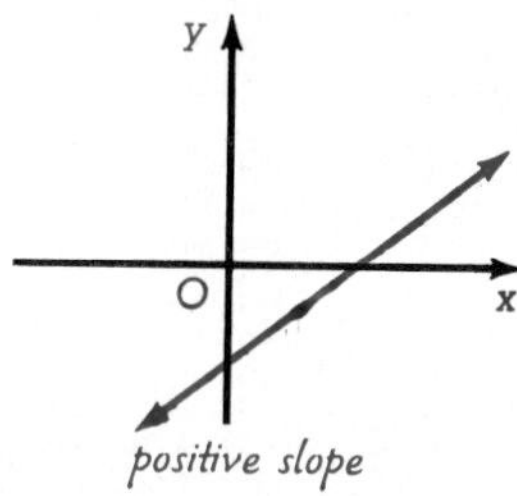

positive slope

If the line *falls* to the right, then the slope is *negative.*

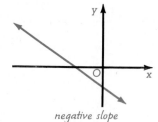

negative slope

Several chalkboard examples can be used to reinforce these concepts and aid in the recognition of these cases by students.

If the line is *vertical,* then the slope is *undefined.*

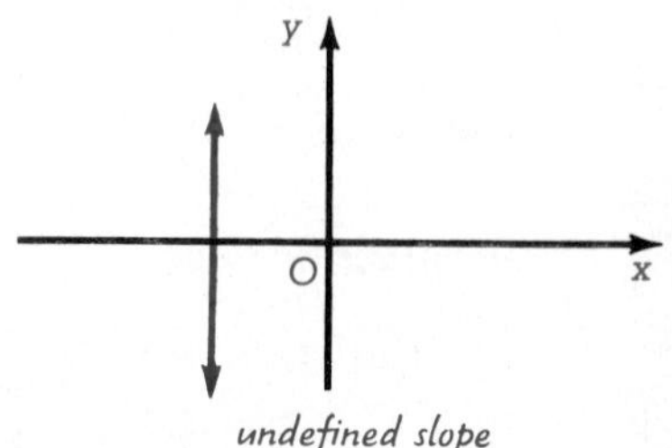

undefined slope

If the line is *horizontal,* then the slope is *0.*

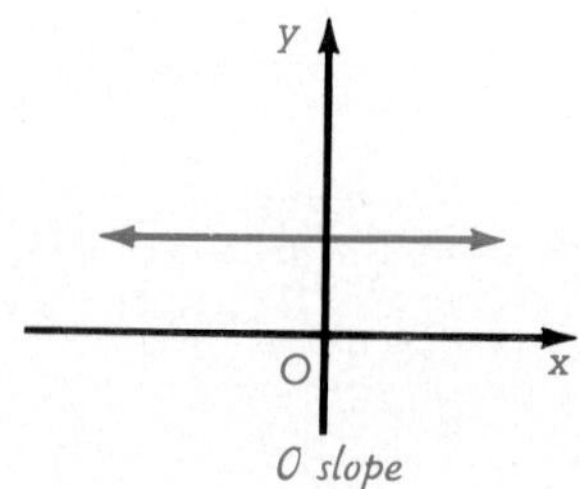

0 slope

examples

2 The following lines are parallel. Determine the slope of each line.

$$\text{slope of } \ell = \frac{0 - {}^-4}{{}^-2 - {}^-3} = \frac{4}{1} \text{ or } 4$$

$$\text{slope of } m = \frac{4 - 0}{4 - 3} = \frac{4}{1} \text{ or } 4$$

Notice that the slopes are the same.

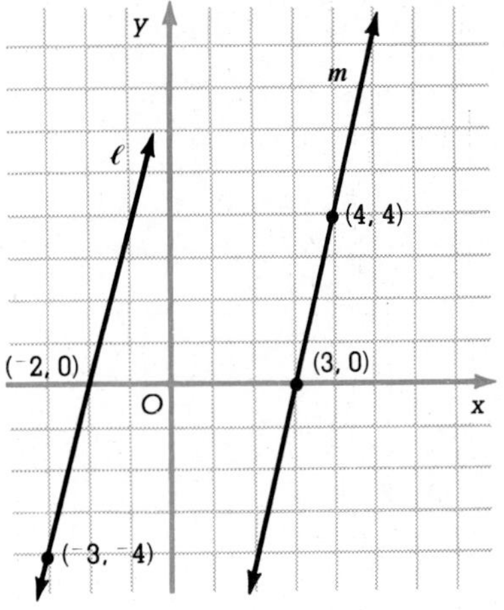

3 The following lines are perpendicular. Determine the slope of each line.

$$\text{slope of } a = \frac{4 - {}^-3}{1 - {}^-1} = \frac{7}{2}$$

$$\text{slope of } b = \frac{3 - 1}{{}^-4 - 3} = \frac{2}{{}^-7} \text{ or } -\frac{2}{7}$$

$$\frac{7}{2} \cdot \left(-\frac{2}{7}\right) = {}^-1$$

Notice that the product of their slopes is ⁻1.

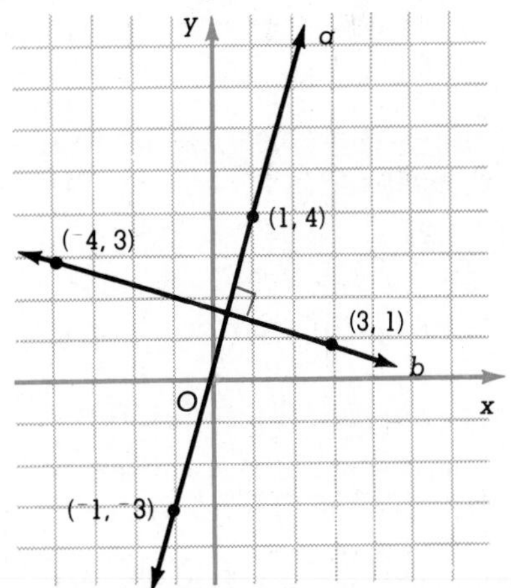

Discuss why nonvertical is part of Theorem 12-4.

In general, the following theorems can be stated.

Remind students that the slope for vertical lines is undefined.

Two lines have the same slope if and only if they are parallel and nonvertical. *Theorem 12–3*

Two nonvertical lines are perpendicular if and only if the product of their slopes is ⁻1. *Theorem 12–4*

Illustrate these theorems with other examples similar to Examples 2 and 3.

EN: Ex: 1-8, Wr: 1-13 odds, 14-19; Ch: 1-4; AV: Ex: 1-8, Wr: 1-15 odds, Ch: 1-2; p. 412, Wr: 16-35

exercises

FN: Ex: 1-10, Wr: 1-13; p. 412, Wr: 16-35

Exploratory **Describe the slope of each of the following.**

1. vertical lines undefined slope
2. horizontal lines zero slope
3. nonvertical perpendicular lines
4. nonvertical parallel lines
5. lines that rise to the right positive slope
6. lines that fall to the right negative slope

3. The product of their slopes is -1.
4. The slopes are equal.

For each table, state the change in y and the change in x. Then, determine the slope of the line passing through the points whose coordinates are listed in each table.

7.

x	y
0	0
1	2
2	4
3	6

change in y: 2, change in x: 1, slope: 2

8.

x	y
$^-2$	2
$^-1$	1
0	0
1	$^-1$

change in y: -1, change in x: 1, slope: -1

9.

x	y
6	$^-8$
3	$^-4$
0	0
$^-3$	4

change in y: 4, change in x: -3, slope: $-\frac{4}{3}$

10.

x	y
4	4
3	3
2	2
1	1

change in y: -1, change in x: -1, slope: 1

Written **Find the slope of the lines passing through the pairs of points whose coordinates are listed below.**

1. (4, 6), (3, 4) 2
2. ($^-7$, 4), (2, 9) 5/9
3. (6, 3), ($^-7$, 3) 0
4. ($^-4$, 11), ($^-6$, 3) 4
5. (6, 9), (4, 6) 3/2
6. (4, 8), (4, 6) undefined slope
7. ($^-8$, 1), ($^-5$, $^-8$) -3
8. (3, $^-2$), (5, $^-9$) -7/2
9. (4, 7), (10, $^-5$) -2

Determine the value of r so that a line through the points with the given coordinates has the slope listed.

10. (r, $^-5$), (5, 3); slope $= \frac{2}{3}$ -7
11. (9, r), (6, 3); slope $= -\frac{1}{3}$ 2
12. (8, r), (12, 6); slope $= \frac{1}{2}$ 4
13. (r, 3), (5, 9); slope $= 2$ 2

Answer each of the following.

14. Find the value of y if the points $A(1, 4)$, $B(3, 2)$, and $C(8, y)$ are collinear. (Hint: Use slope.) -3
15. Find the slope of any line parallel to a line passing through points with coordinates of (4, $^-3$) and ($^-8$, 10). 13/-12
16. Find the slope of any line perpendicular to the line passing through points with coordinates (3, 8) and ($^-7$, $^-12$). $-\frac{1}{2}$
17. Find the slope of each side of quadrilateral $ABCD$ to determine if it is a rectangle. The vertices are $A(2, 4)$, $B(5, 8)$, $C(13, 2)$, and $D(10, ^-2)$.

17. $\overline{AB}$: 4/3, $\overline{CD}$: 4/3, $\overline{BC}$: -3/4, $\overline{AD}$: -3/4

18. Are the graphs of $3x + 4y = 7$ and $6x + 8y = 10$ parallel? Yes, the slopes are both -3/4.
19. Are the graphs of $2x + 5y = 15$ and $5x + 2y = 2$ perpendicular? No, since $-\frac{2}{5} \cdot -\frac{5}{2} \neq -1$.

Challenge **Answer each of the following for $\triangle ABC$ whose vertices are $A(3, 2)$, $B(6, ^-3)$, and $C(1, ^-2)$.**

1. Find the slope of the median to $\overline{AC}$. -3/4
2. Find the slope of the median to $\overline{BC}$. -9
3. Find the slope of the median to $\overline{AB}$. 3/7
4. Change the coordinates for B so that $\triangle ABC$ is a right triangle. Any point satisfying $(x - 2)^2 + (y - 0)^2 = 5$ except (3,2) and (1,-2).

Objectives: to determine the slope and y-intercept from the equation of a line, to rewrite an equation in slope-intercept form, to write the equation of a line satisfying certain given conditions

12–4 Equations for a Line

The graph of $y = 3x + 2$ is shown below.

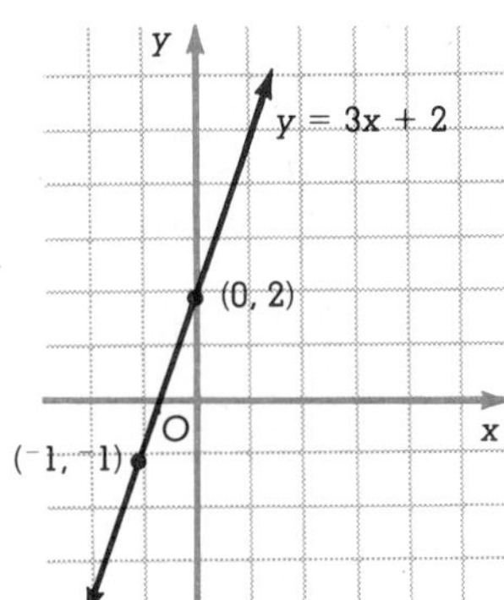

Notice that (0, 2) and (⁻1, ⁻1) represent points on the line. The coordinates can be used to find the slope of the line.

$$m = \frac{^-1 - 2}{^-1 - 0}$$
$$= \frac{^-3}{^-1} \text{ or } 3$$

Compare the slope of the line to the coefficient of x in $y = 3x + 2$. The graph of $y = 3x + 2$ crosses the y-axis when y is 2. This value, 2, is called the ***y*-intercept** of the line.

In general, any linear equation can be written in the form $y = mx + b$. The slope of the line is m and its y-intercept is b. This form is called the **slope-intercept form.**

Emphasize that "m" represents the slope and "b" represents the y-intercept.

The equation of the line having a slope *m* and *y*-intercept *b* is *y* = *mx* + *b*.

Theorem 12–5 Slope-Intercept Form

Point out the difference between the b in y = mx + b and the B in Ax + By = C.

examples

1 Write the equation of the line having a slope of 4 and *y*-intercept ⁻3.

Substitute the values for slope and y-intercept into the slope-intercept form.

$$y = mx + b$$
$$= 4x + {}^-3 \quad \text{Substitute 4 for m and } {}^-3 \text{ for b.}$$
$$= 4x - 3$$

The equation is $y = 4x - 3$.

2 Name the slope and *y*-intercept of 5*x* + 3*y* = 6. Rewrite the equation in slope-intercept form.

$$5x + 3y = 6$$
$$3y = {}^-5x + 6 \quad \text{Subtraction Property of Equality}$$
$$y = -\frac{5}{3}x + 2 \quad \text{Division Property of Equality}$$

The slope is $-\frac{5}{3}$. The y-intercept is 2.

Suppose the slope and the coordinates of one point on a line are known. Can the equation of the line be determined? yes The coordinates of a point on a line whose slope is 4 are (2, 3). Let (x, y) be the coordinates of another point on the line.

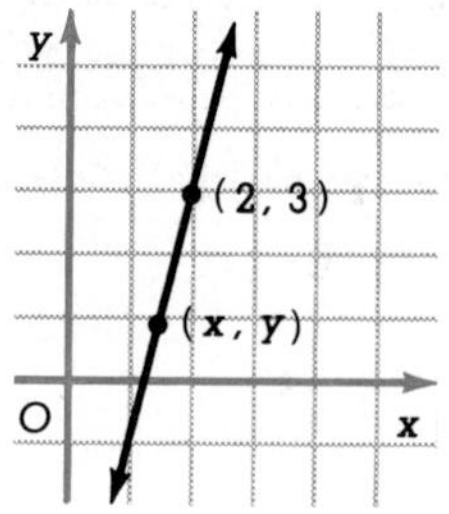

Some teachers may want to use the two point form. $y - y_1 = \frac{y_2 - y_1}{x_2 - x_1}(x - x_1)$

$$m = \frac{y_2 - y_1}{x_2 - x_1}$$

$$4 = \frac{y - 3}{x - 2} \quad \textit{Substitution}$$

$$y - 3 = 4(x - 2) \quad \textit{Multiplication Property of Equality}$$

This equation is said to be in **point-slope form.** *Could this equation be changed to either standard form or slope-intercept form?* yes Remind students that the standard form is Ax + By = C.

The equation of the line passing through the point whose coordinates are (x_1, y_1) and which has a slope m is $y - y_1 = m(x - x_1)$.

Theorem 12–6 Point-Slope Form

examples

3 Find the equation of the line passing through the point whose coordinates are $(^-3, 2)$ and having a slope of 5. Write the equation in the point-slope form.

Substitute $^-3$, 2, and 5 into the point-slope form.

$$y - y_1 = m(x - x_1) \quad \textit{Point-Slope Form}$$

$$y - 2 = 5(x - {}^-3) \quad \textit{Substitution}$$

4 Find the equation of the line passing through points whose coordinates are $(3, ^-6)$ and $(^-2, 1)$.

Find the slope of the line.

$$m = \frac{y_2 - y_1}{x_2 - x_1} \quad \textit{Definition of Slope}$$

$$m = \frac{1 - (^-6)}{^-2 - 3} \quad \textit{Substitution}$$

$$= \frac{7}{^-5}$$

Substitute either $(3, ^-6)$ or $(^-2, 1)$ and $-\frac{7}{5}$ into the point-slope form.

$$y - y_1 = m(x - x_1) \quad \textit{Point-Slope Form}$$

$$y - (^-6) = -\frac{7}{5}(x - 3) \quad \textit{Substitution}$$

Using the other point, $y - 1 = -\frac{7}{5}(x - (^-2))$.

This equation can also be written as $y = -\frac{7}{5}x - \frac{9}{5}$ or $7x + 5y = {}^-9$.

slope-intercept form or standard form

EN: Ex: 5-11 odds, Wr: 1-15 odds, 17-26; AV: Ex: 1-12, Wr: 1-19 odds; p. 416, Wr: 6-14 evens, 16-19

exercises

FN: Ex: 1-12, Wr: 1-25 odds; p. 416, Wr: 14-19

Exploratory **Determine the slope and y-intercept of the graph of each of the following.**

1. $y = -\frac{3}{4}x + 2$ m = $-\frac{3}{4}$, b = 2

2. $y = {}^-3x + 5$ m = -3, b = 5

3. $y = 4x - 3$ m = 4, b = -3

4. $y = \frac{1}{2}x + 6$ m = $\frac{1}{2}$, b = 6

5. $y = 3x - 5$ m = 3, b = -5

6. $y = mx + b$ slope = m, y-intercept = b

7. $y = 6$ m = 0, b = 6

8. $x = {}^-3$ undefined slope, no y-intercept

Write an equation of the line satisfying the given conditions.

9. $m = 6$, y-intercept is $^-5$ y = 6x - 5

10. $m = {}^-2$, y-intercept is 3 y = -2x + 3

11. $m = 4$, through a point at (1, 3)
y - 3 = 4(x - 1) or y = 4x - 1

12. $m = {}^-7$, through a point at (2, 4)
y - 4 = -7(x - 2) or y = -7x + 18

Written **Write an equation of the line satisfying the given conditions.**

1. $m = 2$, y-intercept is $^-3$ y = 2x - 3

2. $m = -\frac{1}{3}$, y-intercept is 0.4 y = $-\frac{1}{3}$x + 0.4

3. $m = {}^-4$, y-intercept is 7 y = -4x + 7

4. $m = 0$. y-intercept is $^-5$ y = -5

5. $m = 0$, through a point at ($^-4$, 8) y = 8

6. $m = 7$, through a point at (10, $^-3$) y = 7x - 73

7. $m = -\frac{2}{3}$, through a point at ($^-2$, $^-2$)

8. $m = \frac{1}{5}$, through a point at $\left(\frac{1}{2}, -\frac{1}{3}\right)$

9. parallel to the graph of $y = 3x + 4$, through a point at (3, 7) y = 3x - 2

10. parallel to the y-axis, through a point at (3, 9) x = 3

11. parallel to the x-axis, through a point at ($^-3$, $^-6$) y = -6

12. parallel to the y-axis, through a point at (2, 6) x = 2

13. perpendicular to the graph of $y = {}^-2x+1$, through a point (3, $^-7$) y = $\frac{1}{2}$x - $\frac{17}{2}$

14. perpendicular to the graph of $3x-5y = 6$, through a point ($^-4$, $^-5$) y = $-\frac{5}{3}$x - $\frac{35}{3}$

15. passing through points at ($^-7$, 4) and ($^-7$, $^-5$) x = -7

16. passing through points at ($^-3$, $^-7$) and (6, $^-1$) y = $\frac{2}{3}$x - $\frac{15}{3}$

7. y = $-\frac{2}{3}$x - $\frac{10}{3}$ 8. y = $\frac{1}{5}$x - $\frac{13}{30}$

Determine the slope and y-intercept of the graph of each of the following.

17. $y = 5x - 3$ m = 5, b = -3

18. $y = \frac{1}{2}x + 6$ m = $\frac{1}{2}$, b = 6

19. $2x - y = 4$ m = 2, b = -4

20. $^-9x + 3y = 6$ m = 3, b = 2

21. $4x - 3y = 5$ m = $\frac{4}{3}$, b = $-\frac{5}{3}$

22. $^-6x + 5y = 7$ m = $\frac{6}{5}$, b = $\frac{7}{5}$

Answer each of the following.

23. Write the equation of a line that has a slope of $^-5$ and bisects a segment whose endpoints have coordinates ($^-4$, 10) and (5, $^-7$). y = -5x + 4

24. Write the equation of a line that is the perpendicular bisector of a segment whose endpoints have coordinates ($^-3$, $^-7$) and (12, 14). y = $-\frac{5}{7}$x + $\frac{47}{7}$

25. Write the equation of a line that bisects two segments, one whose endpoints have coordinates ($^-2$, $^-3$) and ($^-6$, 5), and the other whose endpoints have coordinates (1, 4) and ($^-8$, 7). y = 9x + 37

26. If a line passes through points at (3, 6) and ($^-4$, 9), an equation of the line can be written as $y - 6 = -\frac{3}{7}(x - 3)$ or $y - 9 = -\frac{3}{7}(x + 4)$. Show that the two equations are equivalent. See the Teacher's Guide.

Objective: to find the solution of a system of equations by graphing, substitution, or by the elimination method

12–5 Systems of Equations

The graphs of $y = 2x + 1$ and $y = {}^{-}2x + 5$ are shown below.

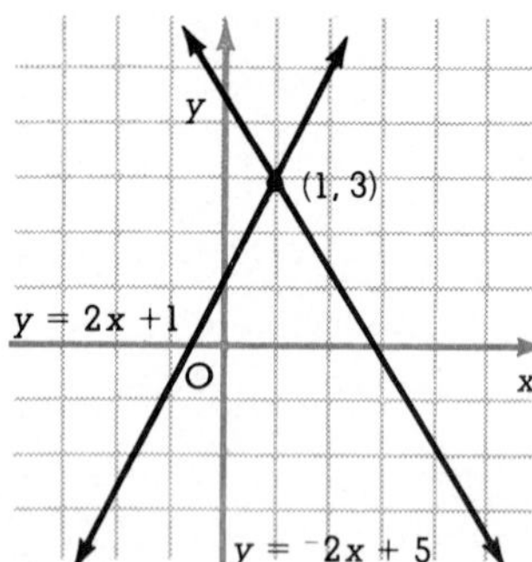

Notice that the graphs intersect at the point with coordinates (1, 3). Since this point lies on the graph of each equation, its coordinates satisfy both $y = 2x + 1$ and $y = {}^{-}2x + 5$. You can check this as follows.

$y = 2x + 1$	$y = {}^{-}2x + 5$
$3 \stackrel{?}{=} 2(1) + 1$	$3 \stackrel{?}{=} {}^{-}2(1) + 5$
$3 = 3$	$3 = 3$

A review of this from algebra may be helpful.

The equations $y = 2x + 1$ and $y = {}^{-}2x + 5$ together are called a **system of equations.** The solution of this system of equations is (1, 3).

example

1 Graph the equations $x + y = 6$ and $y = 2x$. Then, find the solution of the system of equations.

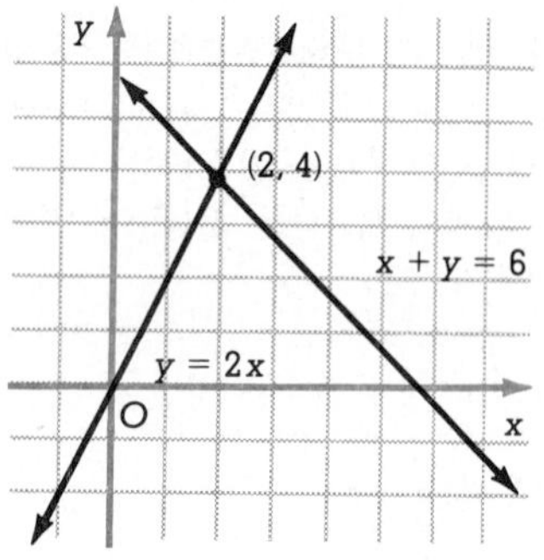

The graphs intersect at (2, 4). Therefore, (2, 4) is the solution of the system of equations $x + y = 6$ and $y = 2x$.

A system of equations can be solved by algebraic methods as well as by graphing. Two such methods are the **substitution method** and the **elimination method.**

examples

2 Use the substitution method to solve the following system of equations.

$y = x - 3$
$3x + 5y = 9$

By the first equation, y is equal to $x - 3$. Therefore, $x - 3$ can be substituted for y in the second equation.

$3x + 5y = 9$
$3x + 5(x - 3) = 9$ *Substitute $x - 3$ for y.*

The resulting equation has only one variable, x. Solve the equation.

$$3x + 5x - 15 = 9$$
$$8x - 15 = 9$$
$$8x = 24$$
$$x = 3$$ *The x-coordinate is 3.*

Now, find y by substituting 3 for x in the first equation.

$y = x - 3$

$y = 3 - 3$ *Substitute 3 for x.*

$y = 0$ *The y-coordinate is 0.*

The solution is (3, 0). *Check in the original equation.*

Emphasize checking in the original equation.

3 **Use the elimination method to solve the following system of equations.**

$3x + 4y = 6$

$2x + 3y = 5$

This method is usually used when both equations are written in the same form.

Sometimes adding or subtracting two equations will eliminate a variable. In this case, adding or subtracting the two equations will not eliminate a variable. However, suppose both sides of the first equation are multiplied by 2, and both sides of the second equation are multiplied by $^-3$. Then, the system can be solved by adding the equations.

$3x + 4y = 6$ → *Multiply by 2.* → $6x + 8y = 12$

$2x + 3y = 5$ → *Multiply by $^-3$.* → $^-6x - 9y = ^-15$

Now, add to eliminate x. Then, solve for y.

Point out that there is more than one way to solve a system of equations. This system could be solved by multiplying the first equation by 3 and the second equation by 4, then subtract.

$$6x + 8y = 12$$ *Add.*
$$^-6x - 9y = ^-15$$
$$^-y = ^-3$$ *The variable x is eliminated.*
$$y = 3$$

Finally, substitute 3 for y in the first equation. Then, solve for x.

$$3x + 4y = 6$$
$$3x + 4(3) = 6$$
$$3x + 12 = 6$$
$$3x = ^-6$$
$$x = ^-2$$

3 could also be substituted in the second equation.

The solution is ($^-2$, 3). *Check in the original equation.*

EN: Wr: 1-16, AR: 1-6; AV: Ex: 1-10, Wr: 1-12, AR: 1-4; p. 419, Wr: 6-20 evens, 21-26

exercises

FN: Ex: 1-10, Wr: 1-12, AR: 1-2; p. 419, Wr: 2-26 evens

Exploratory **State the coordinates of the point of intersection of each pair of lines.**

1. a and b (-10,6)
2. a and c (-2,2)
3. a and d (2,0)
4. b and d (6,2)
5. b and c (-2,4)
6. d and y-axis (0,-1)
7. c and the x-axis (-2,0)

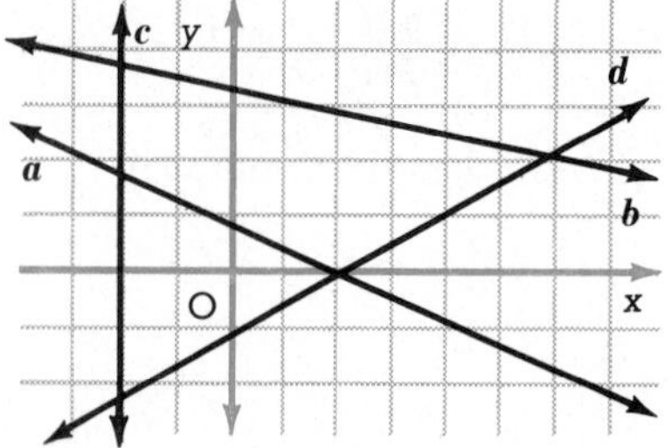

State the letter of the ordered pair(s) that satisfies each equation.

8. $x + 3y = 6$ a. (0, 2) b. ($^-1$, 4) c. (6, 0) d. ($^-3$, 3)
9. $2x - 5y = {}^-1$ a. (0, 5) b. (2, 1) c. ($^-0.5$, 0) d. ($^-2$, $^-1$)
10. $3x = 15$ a. (5, 1) b. (5, 0) c. (0, 5) d. (5, 8)

Written **Graph each pair of equations. Then, state the solution of each system of equations.** For graphs to exercises 1-6, see the Teacher's Guide.

1. $x + y = 6$, $x - y = 2$ (4,2)
2. $y = x - 1$, $x + y = 11$ (6,5)
3. $3x - 2y = 10$, $x + y = 0$ (2,-2)
4. $x + 2y = 7$, $y = 2x + 1$ (1,3)
5. $y = x + 3$, $3y + x = 5$ (-1,2)
6. $y = 4x$, $x + y = 5$ (1,4)

Solve each system of equations by an algebraic method.

7. $x - y = {}^-5$, $x + y = 25$ (10,15)
8. $x - y = 6$, $x + y = 5$ $(5\frac{1}{2}, -\frac{1}{2})$
9. $x + 2y = 5$, $2x + y = 7$ (3,1)
10. $y = 3x$, $x + 2y = {}^-21$ (-3,-9)
11. $3x + 4y = {}^-7$, $2x + y = {}^-3$ (-1,-1)
12. $y = x - 1$, $4x - y = 19$ (6,5)
13. $x = y + 10$, $2y = x - 6$ (14,4)
14. $12 - 3y = {}^-4x$, $40 + 4x = 10y$ (0,4)
15. $9x + y = 20$, $3x + 3y = 12$ (2,2)
16. The graphs of $y = 2$, $x - y = 0$, and $3y = {}^-2x + 30$ intersect to form a triangle. Find the coordinates of the vertices of the triangle. Then, find the area of the triangle. Area = 20; 16. A = (2,2); B = (6,6); C = (12,2)

Quadratic Formula — algebra review

Example **Solve $2x^2 - 3x - 4 = 0$ using the quadratic formula.**

$$x = \frac{{}^-b \pm \sqrt{b^2 - 4ac}}{2a}$$ *The Quadratic Formula*

$$= \frac{{}^-({}^-3) \pm \sqrt{({}^-3)^2 - 4(2)({}^-4)}}{2(2)}$$ *Substitute $^-3$ for b, 2 for a, and $^-4$ for c.*

$$= \frac{3 \pm \sqrt{41}}{4}$$

For answers to exercises 1-6, see the Teacher's Guide.

Exercises **Use the quadratic formula to solve each equation.**

1. $x^2 + 4x - 1 = 0$
2. $x^2 - 5x - 2 = 0$
3. $3x^2 + 6x + 1 = 0$
4. ${}^-2x^2 - 7x + 5 = 0$
5. $10 = x^2 - 4x$
6. $x^2 + x = 3$

Objectives: to determine the center and the measure of the radius from the equation of a circle, to write the equation for a circle using the center and the measure of the radius

12–6 Circles

Circles are used to locate points on a radar scope.

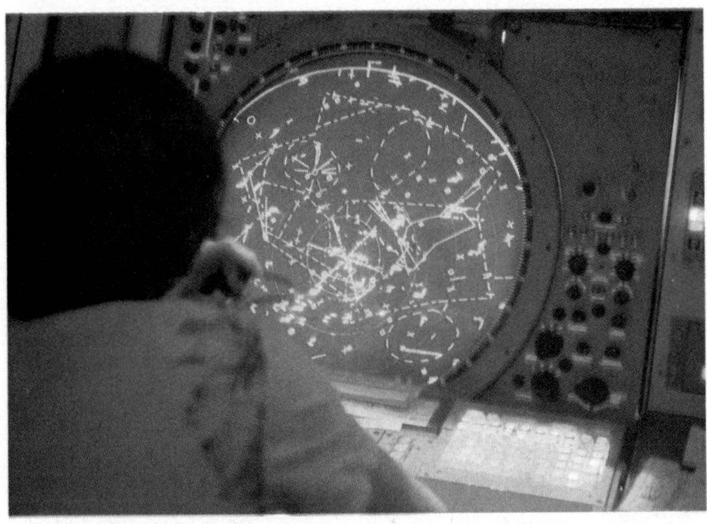

The distance formula can be used to develop an equation for the graph of the circle.

This concept may be new to students and may require more in depth explanation.

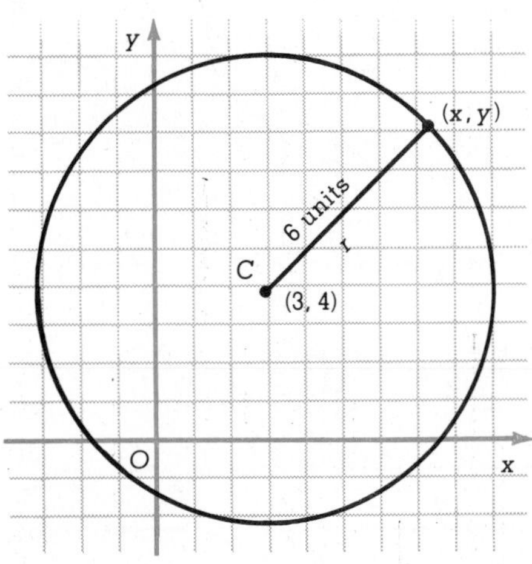

The circle at the left has its center at (3, 4). The length of the radius is 6 units. Suppose (x, y) represents any point on the circle. This point must be 6 units from the center.

The distance between (x, y) and (3, 4) is 6 units.

$$\sqrt{(x-3)^2 + (y-4)^2} = 6$$
$$(x-3)^2 + (y-4)^2 = 6^2 \quad \textit{Square both sides.}$$
$$(x-3)^2 + (y-4)^2 = 36$$

The equation of a circle with center at (3, 4) and radius measuring 6 units is $(x-3)^2 + (y-4)^2 = 36$.

The equation of a circle can be written in the form given below.

The equation of a circle with center at (h, k) and radius measuring r units is $(x-h)^2 + (y-k)^2 = r^2$.

Theorem 12–7 General Equation of a Circle

examples

1 **Find the equation of a circle whose center is at (0, 0) and whose radius is 4 inches long.**

The distance between (0, 0) and a point on the circle (x, y) is 4 units.

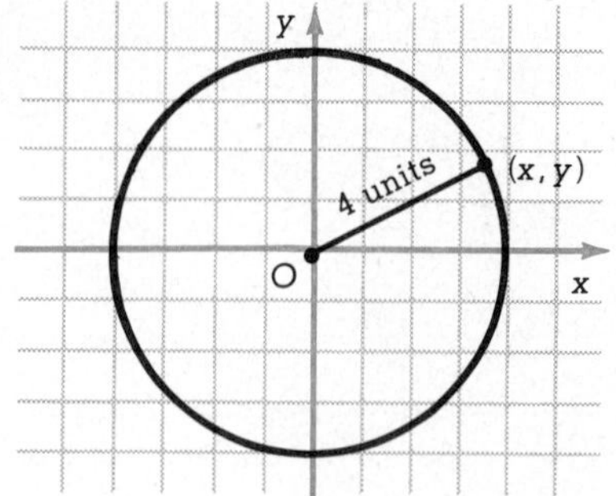

$$\sqrt{(x-0)^2+(y-0)^2}=4$$
$$x^2+y^2=4^2$$
$$x^2+y^2=16$$

The equation of the circle is $x^2 + y^2 = 16$.

It may be desirable with Enriched classes to use the completing the square method for finding $(x - h)^2 + (y - k)^2 = r^2$.

2 **Graph the circle whose equation is $(x + 1)^2 + (y - 4)^2 = 25$.**

First, rewrite the equation in the form $(x - h)^2 + (y - k)^2 = r^2$.

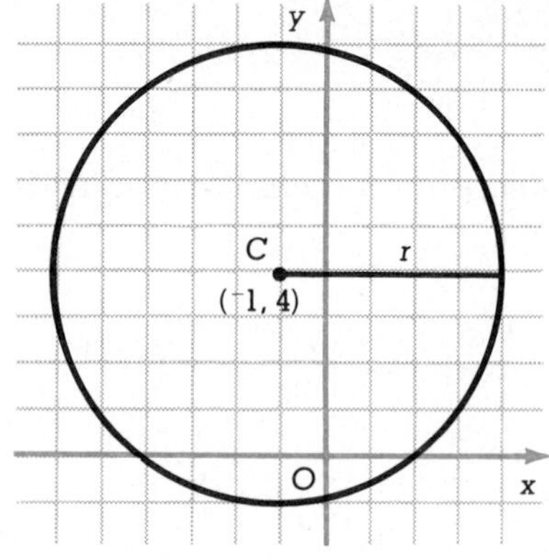

$$(x+1)^2+(y-4)^2=25$$
$$(x-{}^-1)^2+(y-4)^2=5^2$$

Therefore, $h = {}^-1$, $k = 4$, and $r = 5$.
The center is $({}^-1, 4)$.
The radius is 5 units long.

EN: Ex: 2-10 evens, Wr: 2-30 evens, 31-34, AV: Ex: 1-10, Wr: 1-8, 15-26; p. 422, Wr: 13-16

exercises

FN: Ex: 1-10, Wr: 1-10, 15-26; p. 422, Wr: 13-16

Exploratory Determine the center and measure of the radius for each circle whose equation is given below.

1. $x^2 + y^2 = 16$ (0,0), r = 4
2. $(x + 2)^2 + (y + 7)^2 = 81$ (-2,-7), r = 9
3. $x^2 + y^2 - 25 = 0$ (0,0), r = 5
4. $\left(x + \frac{1}{2}\right)^2 + \left(y + \frac{1}{3}\right)^2 = \frac{16}{25}$ $\left(-\frac{1}{2}, -\frac{1}{3}\right)$, $r = \frac{4}{5}$
5. $(x - 4)^2 + (y - 6)^2 = 9$ (4,6), r = 3
6. $(x - 2)^2 + (y - 5)^2 = 49$ (2,5), r = 7
7. $(x - 3)^2 + (y - 12)^2 - 36 = 0$ (3,12), r = 6
8. $(x + 5)^2 + (y - 7)^2 = 100$ (-5,7), r = 10
9. $(x + 8)^2 + (y - 9)^2 = 81$ (-8,9), r = 9
10. $(x + 4)^2 + y^2 - 121 = 0$ (-4,0), r = 11

Written **For each of the following, write the equation of the circle. The coordinates of the center and measure of the radius are given.**

1. $(0, 0), 5$ $\quad x^2 + y^2 = 25$

2. $(0, 0), 7$ $\quad x^2 + y^2 = 49$

3. $(3, 4), 6$ $\quad (x - 3)^2 + (y - 4)^2 = 36$

4. $(1, 2), 3$ $\quad (x - 1)^2 + (y - 2)^2 = 9$

5. $(^{-}1, ^{-}1), \frac{1}{4}$ $\quad (x + 1)^2 + (y + 1)^2 = \frac{1}{16}$

6. $(^{-}4, 3), \frac{4}{3}$ $\quad (x + 4)^2 + (y - 3)^2 = \frac{16}{9}$

7. $(^{-}2, 8), \sqrt{2}$ $\quad (x + 2)^2 + (y - 8)^2 = 2$

8. $(^{-}5, 9), \sqrt{20}$ $\quad (x + 5)^2 + (y - 9)^2 = 20$

9. $(0, 0), \sqrt{14}$ $\quad x^2 + y^2 = 14$

10. $(0, 0), \frac{1}{2}$ $\quad x^2 + y^2 = \frac{1}{4}$

11. $(6, 0), 12$ $\quad (x - 6)^2 + y^2 = 144$

12. $(0, ^{-}5), 9$ $\quad x^2 + (y + 5)^2 = 81$

13. $\left(3, \frac{1}{2}\right), \frac{4}{5}$ $\quad (x - 3)^2 + (y - \frac{1}{2})^2 = \frac{16}{25}$

14. $\left(-\frac{3}{4}, 6\right), \sqrt{18}$ $\quad (x + \frac{3}{4})^2 + (x - 6)^2 = 18$

Determine the center and measure of the radius for each circle whose equation is given below.

15. $x^2 + y^2 = 121$ $\quad (0,0), r = 11$

16. $(x - 9)^2 + (y - 10)^2 = 1$ $\quad (9,10), r = 1$

17. $x^2 + (y - 3)^2 - 4 = 0$ $\quad (0,3), r = 2$

18. $0 = {^{-}y^2} - x^2 + 10$ $\quad (0,0), r = \sqrt{10}$

19. $(x + 3)^2 + (y - 4)^2 = 20$ $\quad (-3,4), r = 2\sqrt{5}$

20. $(x + 7)^2 + (y + 3)^2 = 50$ $\quad (-7,-3), r = 5\sqrt{2}$

21. $(x - 7)^2 + (y + 5)^2 = 4$ $\quad (7,-5), r = 2$

22. $x^2 + y^2 = 64$ $\quad (0,0), r = 8$

23. $y^2 = 16 - x^2$ $\quad (0,0), r = 4$

24. $(x + 1)^2 = 11 - y^2$ $\quad (-1,0), r = \sqrt{11}$

25. $(x + 7)^2 + (y + 3)^2 = 3$ $\quad (-7,-3), r = \sqrt{3}$

26. $x^2 + (y - 3)^2 = 25$ $\quad (0,3), r = 5$

27. $(x + 4)^2 + \left(y - \frac{1}{2}\right)^2 = 6$ $\quad (-4,\frac{1}{2}), r = \sqrt{6}$

28. $(x - 4)^2 + y^2 = \frac{16}{25}$ $\quad (4,0), r = \frac{4}{5}$

29. $(x + 5)^2 + (y - 2)^2 = \frac{3}{4}$ $\quad (-5,2), r = \frac{\sqrt{3}}{2}$

30. $x^2 + (y + 5)^2 = \frac{81}{64}$ $\quad (0,-5), r = \frac{9}{8}$

Answer each of the following.

31. Write the equation of the circle that has a diameter whose endpoints are at (2, 7) and $(^{-}6, 15)$. $\quad (x + 2)^2 + (y - 11)^2 = 32$

32. Write the equation of the circle that has a diameter of 12 units and a center at $(^{-}4, ^{-}7)$. $\quad (x + 4)^2 + (y + 7)^2 = 36$

33. The x-axis and the y-axis are both tangent to a circle that has its center in the second quadrant and a radius of 5. Write the equation of the circle.

$(x + 5)^2 + (y - 5)^2 = 25$

34. The graphs of $x = 4$ and $y = {^{-}1}$ are both tangent to a circle that has its center in the fourth quadrant and a diameter of 14. Write the equation of the circle.

$(x - 11)^2 + (y + 8)^2 = 49$

Challenge **Determine the center and the measure of the radius for each circle whose equation is given below.**

1. $c = (2,3), r = 5$

2. $c = (-3,-6), r = 7$

1. $x^2 - 4x + 4 + y^2 - 6y + 9 = 25$

2. $x^2 + 6x + 9 + y^2 + 12y + 36 = 49$

3. $x^2 - 2x + y^2 + 6y = 111$ $\quad c = (1,-3), r = 11$

4. $x^2 + 4x + y^2 + 18y + 81 = 0$ $\quad c = (-2,-9), r = 2$

12–7 Coordinate Proofs

Objectives: to position and label figures in a coordinate plane, to plan and write a coordinate proof

Theorems can be proven using coordinate geometry.

example

1 Prove that the diagonals of a square are perpendicular.

Given: Square $PQRS$

Prove: $\overleftrightarrow{PR} \perp \overleftrightarrow{QS}$

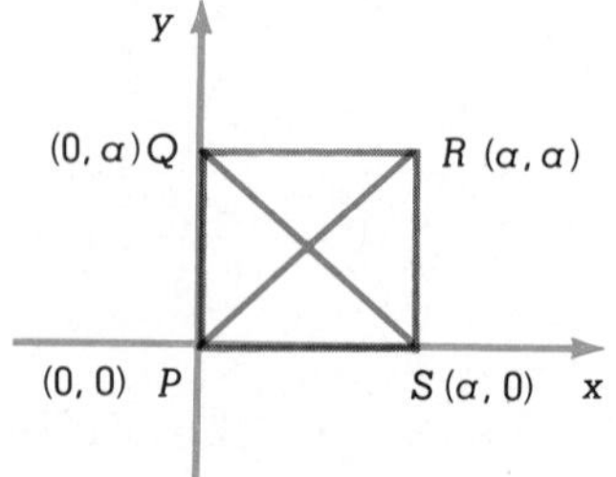

Proof:

By Theorem 12–4, the product of the slopes of perpendicular lines is $^-1$.

First, find the slope of $\overleftrightarrow{PR}$ and of $\overleftrightarrow{QS}$.

$$\text{slope of } \overleftrightarrow{PR} = \frac{a - 0}{a - 0} = \frac{a}{a} \text{ or } 1$$

$$\text{slope of } \overleftrightarrow{QS} = \frac{0 - a}{a - 0} = \frac{^-a}{a} \text{ or } {^-1}$$

Then, find the product of the slopes.

$$\text{slope of } \overleftrightarrow{PR} \cdot \text{slope of } \overleftrightarrow{QS} = 1 \cdot {^-1} \text{ or } {^-1}$$

Therefore, the diagonals are perpendicular.

Point out that students should minimize the number of variables introduced.

Placing the geometric figure in a coordinate plane is an important part of planning a coordinate proof. In most cases, the following suggestions will help you place figures for your proofs.

Placing Figures on a Coordinate Plane

1. **Use the origin as a vertex or center.**
2. **Place at least one side of a polygon on a coordinate axis.**
3. **Keep the figure within the first quadrant.**

Step 3 may not always be possible but should be attempted when possible.

example

2 Position and label a right triangle on the coordinate plane.

Use the origin as the vertex of the right angle.
Place the legs of the triangle on the positive axes.

Label the vertices P, Q, and R. Since Q is on the y-axis, its x-coordinate is 0. Since R is on the x-axis, its y-coordinate is 0. Since P is at the origin, both coordinates are 0.

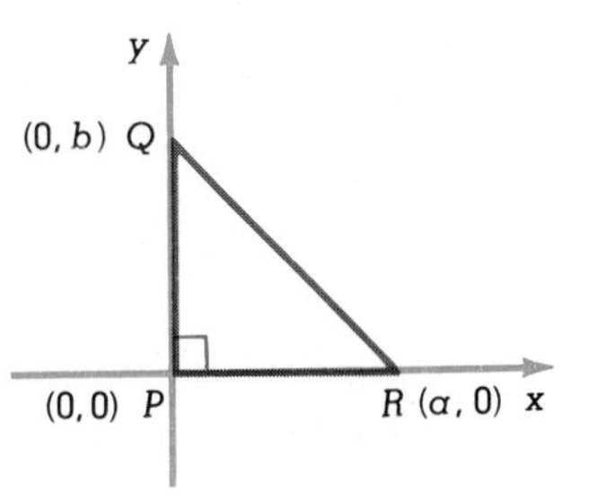

The Exploratory exercises can be used in conjunction with a discussion of positioning and labeling figures in the coordinate plane.

The most common ways of positioning and labeling several figures on the coordinate plane are shown below.

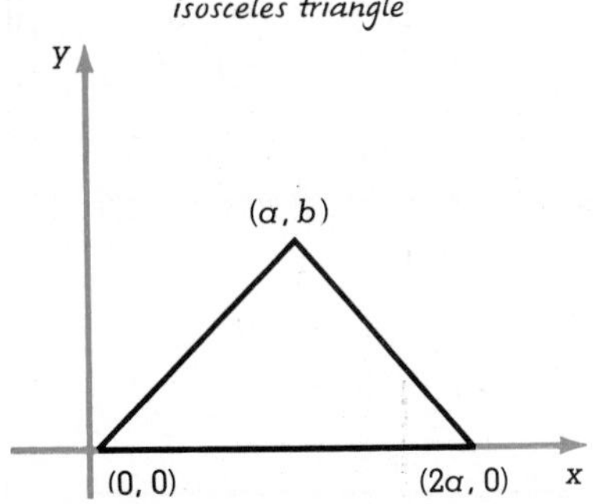

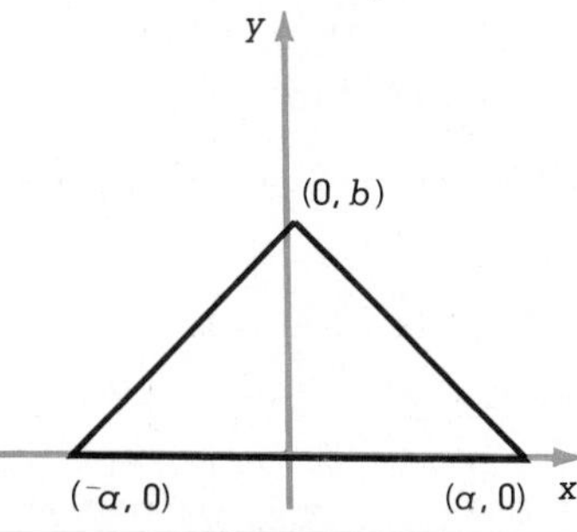

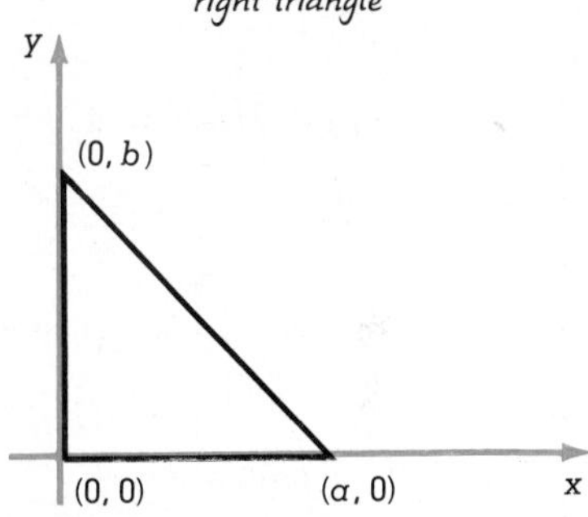

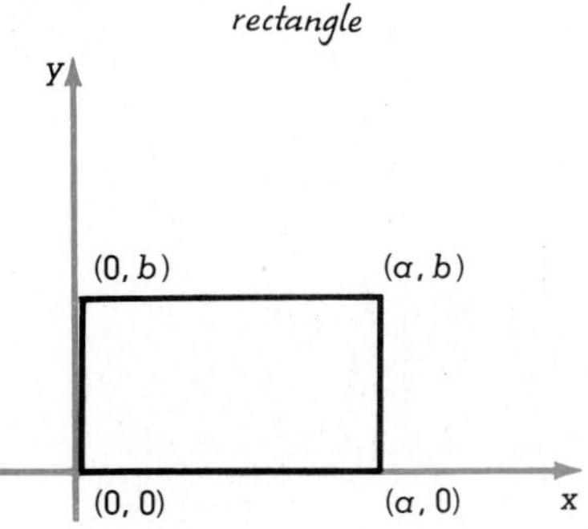

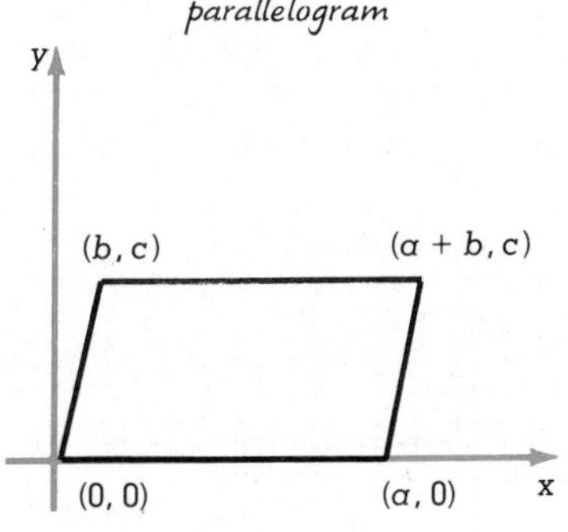

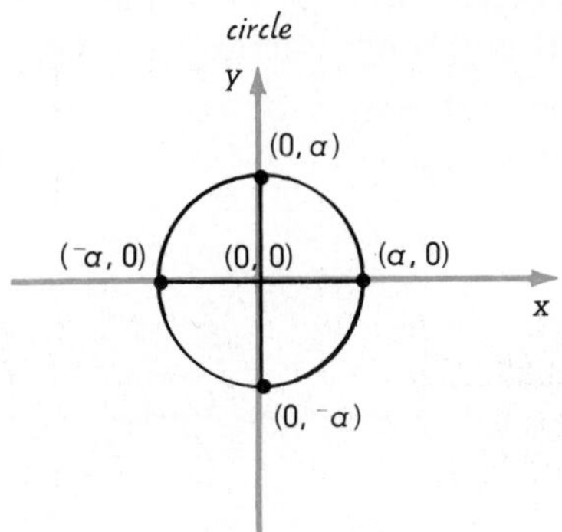

example

3 **Prove that the midpoint of the hypotenuse of a right triangle is equidistant from the vertices.**

Given: $\angle QPR$ is a right angle.
M is the midpoint of $\overline{QR}$.

Prove: M is equidistant from Q, P, and R.

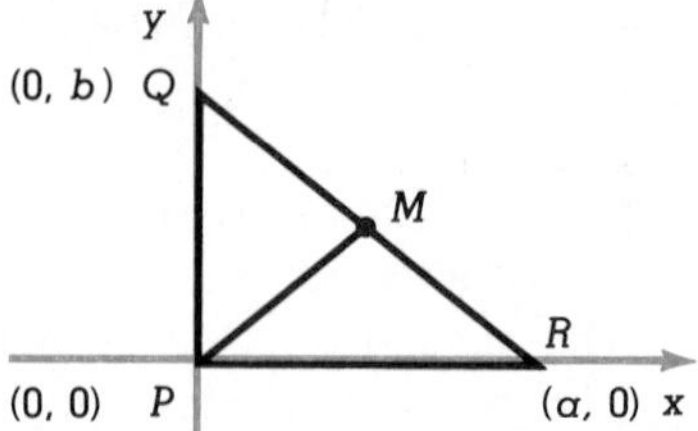

Proof:

By the Midpoint Formula, the coordinates of M are $\left(\frac{a}{2}, \frac{b}{2}\right)$.

Use the Distance Formula to find MR and PM.

$$MR = \sqrt{\left(\frac{a}{2} - a\right)^2 + \left(\frac{b}{2} - 0\right)^2} = \sqrt{\left(\frac{^-a}{2}\right)^2 + \left(\frac{b}{2}\right)^2} = \sqrt{\frac{a^2 + b^2}{4}}$$

$$PM = \sqrt{\left(\frac{a}{2} - 0\right)^2 + \left(\frac{b}{2} - 0\right)^2} = \sqrt{\left(\frac{a}{2}\right)^2 + \left(\frac{b}{2}\right)^2} = \sqrt{\frac{a^2 + b^2}{4}}$$

Therefore, $MR = PM$. Also, by the definition of midpoint, $QM = MR$. Thus, $QM = MR = PM$ and M is equidistant from Q, P, and R.

EN: Ex: 1-5 odds, Wr: 1-14; p. 425, Ch: 1-4; AV: Ex: 1-6, Wr: 1-6, 7-13 odds; p. 425, Wr: 9-14, 27-34, Ch: 1-2

exercises

FN: Ex: 1-6, Wr: 1-6, 7-13 odds; p. 425, Wr: 11-14, 27-34

Exploratory **For each of the following, name the missing coordinates without introducing new variables.**

1.

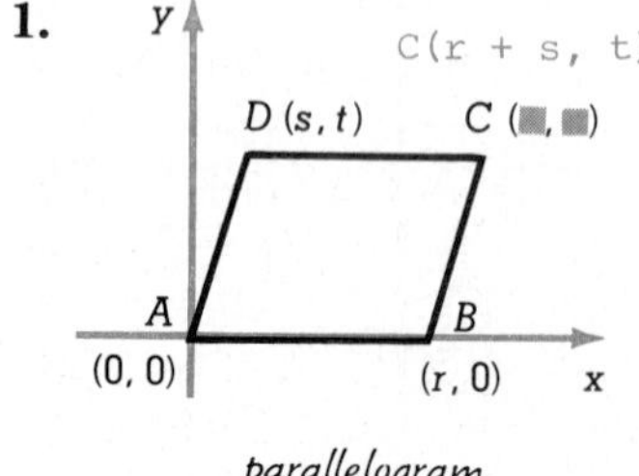

parallelogram

2.

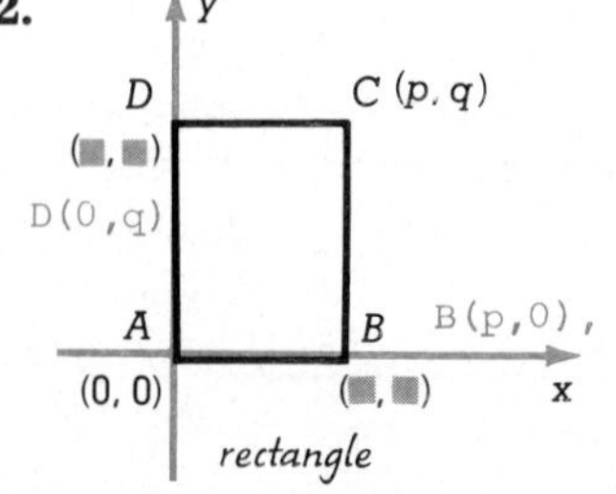

rectangle

3. R(-b,2b)

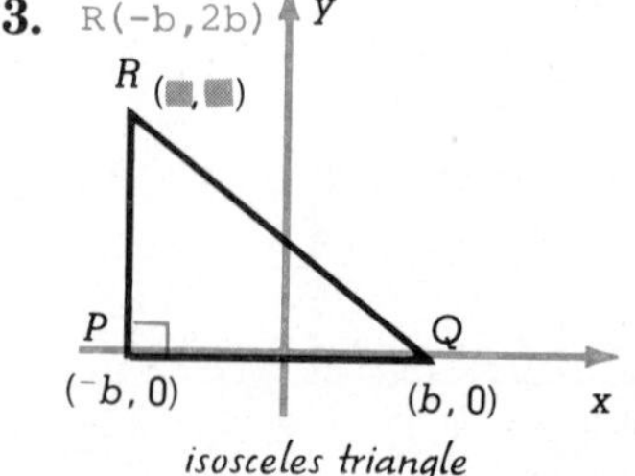

isosceles triangle

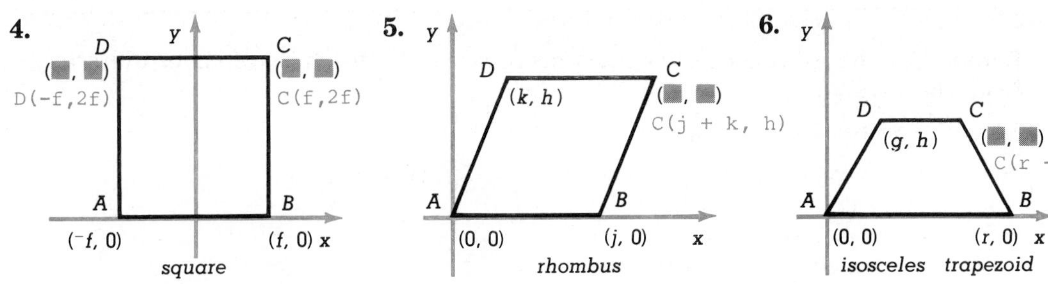

Written **For each of the following, name the missing coordinates without introducing new variables.**

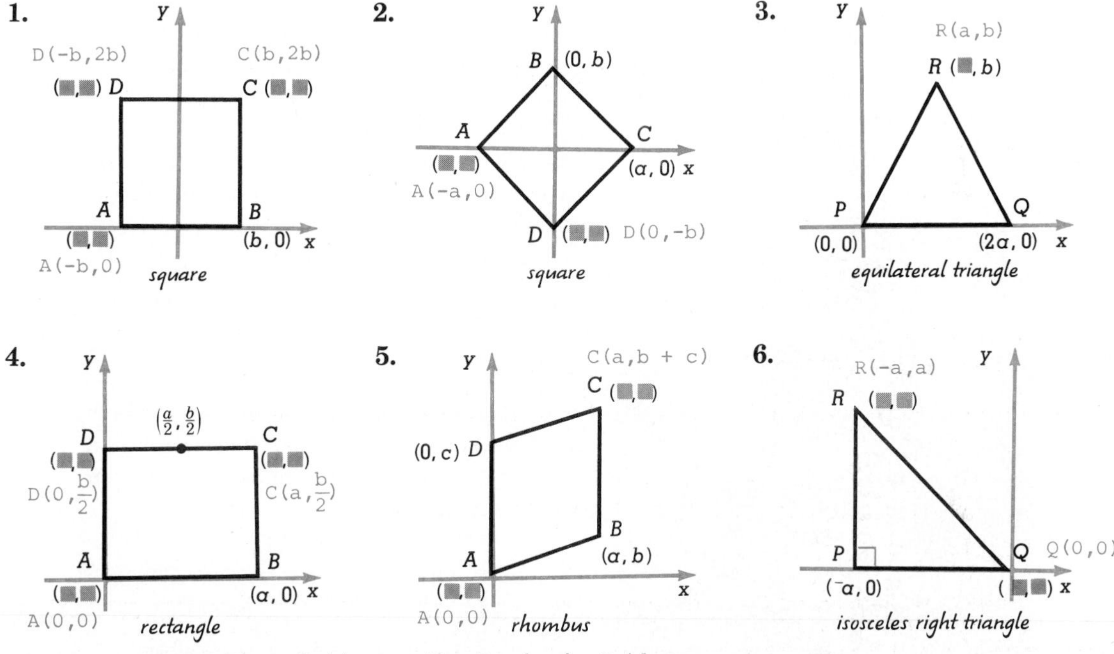

For answers to exercises 7-14, see the Teacher's Guide.

For each of the following theorems name the given, the prove statement, and draw a diagram you would use in a formal proof. Then, prove the theorem.

7. The diagonals of a rectangle are congruent.
8. The diagonals of a rhombus are perpendicular.
9. The diagonals of an isosceles trapezoid are congruent.
10. The diagonals of a parallelogram bisect each other.
11. Opposite sides of a parallelogram are congruent.
12. The segments that join the midpoints of consecutive sides of a rectangle form a rhombus.
13. The length of the median of a trapezoid is one-half the sum of the lengths of the bases.
14. The segments that join the midpoints of consecutive sides of an isosceles trapezoid form a rhombus.

careers

Drafter

Ben Shriver is employed as a drafter. He is preparing a three-dimensional drawing of an architect's concept for a building. The drawings provide the builder with a detailed view of the building from various sides.

One type of drawing that Ben prepares is called a perspective.

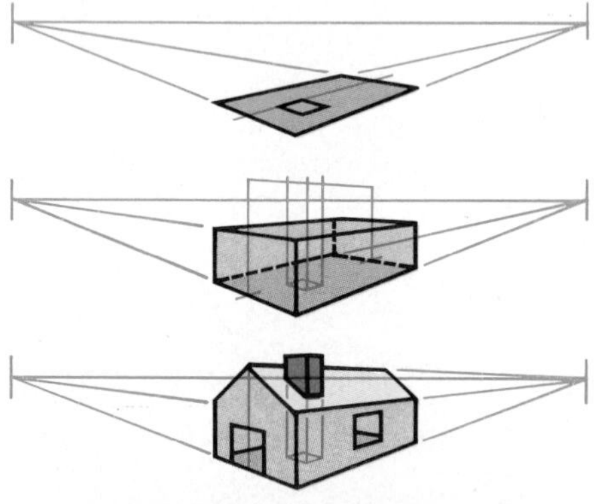

The perspective drawings at the left show parallel sides extended to meet at a point called the vanishing point.

Perspectives are named as 1-, 2-, or 3-point perspective drawings. The drawing at the left is a 2-point perspective drawing. Why? There are 2 vanishing points.

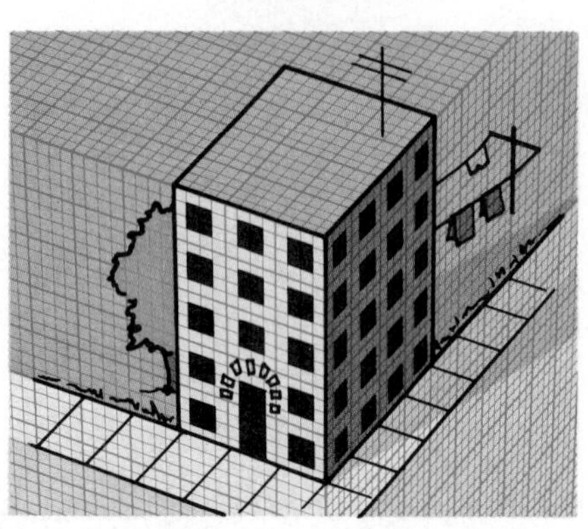

The drawing at the left has been done on a perspective grid. Compare this grid with coordinate graph paper as used in your geometry class.

Notice that the axes of the perspective grid intersect at angles other than 90°.

Exercises **Determine whether each drawing below represents a *1-, 2-,* or *3-point perspective.***

3-point

2-point

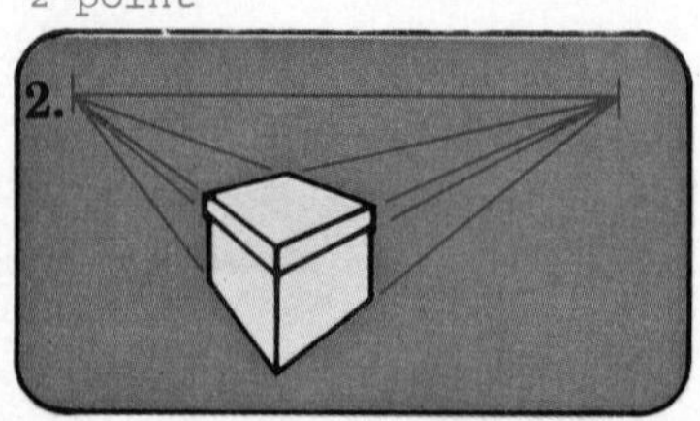

1-point

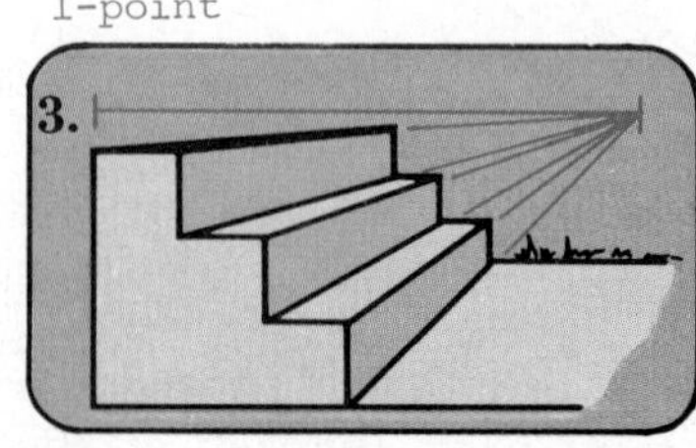

4. Choose an object and sketch 1-, 2-, and 3- point perspective drawings.
See student's work. Answers may vary.

Objectives: to determine the distance between a pair of points in space, to determine the midpoint of a segment in space, to determine the center and the measure of the radius of a sphere, to write the equation of a sphere given the center and the radius

12–8 Coordinates in Space

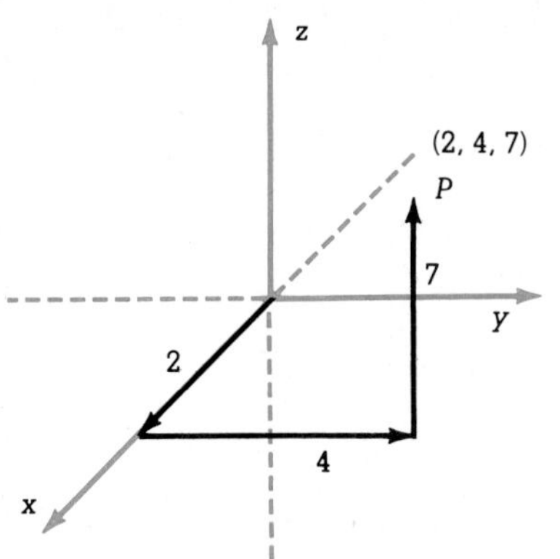

The two-dimensional coordinate system can be extended to a three-dimensional coordinate system in space. The x-axis, the y-axis, and the z-axis are perpendicular to each other. A point in space is represented by an ordered triple of real numbers (x, y, z). In the figure at the left, the ordered triple (2, 4, 7) represents point P.

2 is the x-coordinate.
4 is the y-coordinate.
7 is the z-coordinate.

The Pythagorean Theorem can be used to find the distance between two points in space.

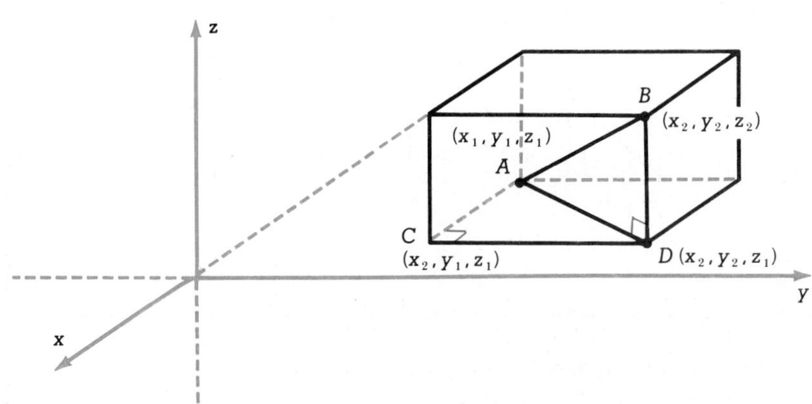

The distance between points A and B on $\triangle ABD$ is found as follows.

$(AB)^2 = (AD)^2 + (BD)^2$ *Pythagorean Theorem*

$= (AC)^2 + (CD)^2 + (BD)^2$ *Substitute $(AC)^2 + (CD)^2$ for $(AD)^2$.*

$AB = \sqrt{(AC)^2 + (CD)^2 + (BD)^2}$ *Find the square root of both sides.*

Ask students why $|x_2 - x_1|^2 = (x_2 - x_1)^2$

But, $AC = |x_2 - x_1|$, $CD = |y_2 - y_1|$, and $BD = |z_2 - z_1|$.

$AB = \sqrt{(x_2 - x_1)^2 + (y_2 - y_1)^2 + (z_2 - z_1)^2}$ *Substitution*

Given two points $A\ (x_1, y_1, z_1)$ and $B\ (x_2, y_2, z_2)$ in space, the distance between A and B is given by the following equation.

$$AB = \sqrt{(x_2 - x_1)^2 + (y_2 - y_1)^2 + (z_2 - z_1)^2}$$

Theorem 12–8
This formula is an extension of the Distance Formula in the two-dimensional coordinate system.

example

1 Find the distance between $P(6, {}^-1, 3)$ and $Q(2, 3, 5)$.

Let $(2, 3, 5)$ be (x_1, y_1, z_1) and $(6, {}^-1, 3)$ be (x_2, y_2, z_2).

$$\begin{aligned} PQ &= \sqrt{(x_2 - x_1)^2 + (y_2 - y_1)^2 + (z_2 - z_1)^2} \\ &= \sqrt{(6 - 2)^2 + ({}^-1 - 3)^2 + (3 - 5)^2} \\ &= \sqrt{4^2 + ({}^-4)^2 + ({}^-2)^2} \\ &= \sqrt{16 + 16 + 4} \\ &= \sqrt{36} \\ &= 6 \end{aligned}$$

The distance between P and Q is 6 units.

Suppose M is the midpoint of $\overline{PQ}$, a segment in space. The midpoint is represented by the following.

$$\left(\frac{x_1 + x_2}{2}, \frac{y_1 + y_2}{2}, \frac{z_1 + z_2}{2}\right)$$

This formula is an extension of the Midpoint Formula in the two-dimensional coordinate system.

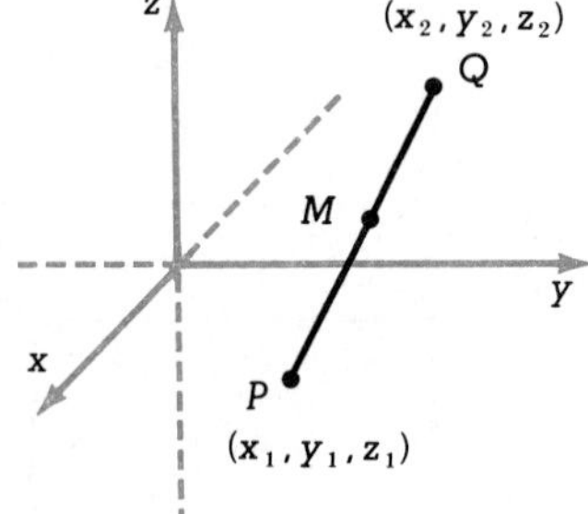

Point out the similarity between naming points in a two-dimensional space.

example

2 Find the coordinates of the midpoint of a segment in space whose endpoints P and Q have coordinates $(3, {}^-7, 0)$ and $(5, 1, 7)$.

Let $(3, {}^-7, 0)$ be (x_1, y_1, z_1) and $(5, 1, 7)$ be (x_2, y_2, z_2).

$$\left(\frac{x_1 + x_2}{2}, \frac{y_1 + y_2}{2}, \frac{z_1 + z_2}{2}\right)$$

$$\left(\frac{3 + 5}{2}, \frac{{}^-7 + 1}{2}, \frac{0 + 7}{2}\right)$$

$$\left(\frac{8}{2}, \frac{{}^-6}{2}, \frac{7}{2}\right)$$

$$\left(4, {}^-3, \frac{7}{2}\right)$$

The midpoint of $\overline{PQ}$ is represented by $\left(4, {}^-3, \frac{7}{2}\right)$.

The formula for the equation of a sphere is an extension of the formula for the equation of a circle.

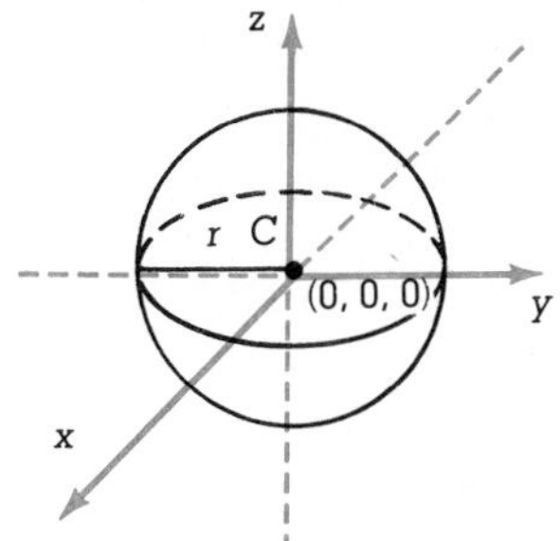

The equation of a sphere whose center is at (0, 0, 0) and whose radius is r units in length is as follows.

$$x^2 + y^2 + z^2 = r^2$$

The equation of a sphere whose center is at (i, j, k) and that has a radius measuring r units is as follows.

$$(x - i)^2 + (y - j)^2 + (z - k)^2 = r^2$$

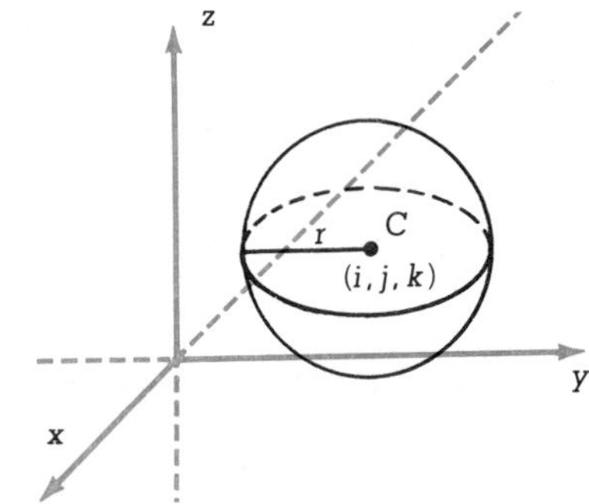

example

3 Write the equation of a sphere whose center is at (3, ⁻2, 4) and that has a radius measuring 6 units.

Let $i = 3, j = {}^-2, k = 4$, and $r = 6$.

$$(x - i)^2 + (y - j)^2 + (z - k)^2 = r^2$$
$$(x - 3)^2 + (y - {}^-2)^2 + (z - 4)^2 = 6^2$$
$$(x - 3)^2 + (y + 2)^2 + (z - 4)^2 = 36$$

The equation of the sphere is $(x - 3)^2 + (y + 2)^2 + (z - 4)^2 = 36$.

EN: Ex: 3, 4, 7, 8, 11, 12, Wr: 1-33 odds; p. 430, C: 1-4; AV: Ex: 1-12, Wr: 1-33 odds; p. 429, Wr: 8-14 evens; p. 430, C: 1-4

exercises

FN: Ex: 1-12, Wr: 1-20, 21-27 odds; p. 429, Wr: 8-14 evens

Exploratory **Find the distance between each of the following pairs of points.**

1. $A(0, 0, 0)$, $B(0, 4, 0)$ 4

2. $P(0, 0, 0)$, $Q(3, 4, 0)$ 5

3. $R(0, 0, 0)$, $S(2, 1, 1)$ $\sqrt{6}$

4. $C(2, 4, 5)$, $D(2, 4, 7)$ 2

Determine the midpoint of the segment whose endpoints are given.

5. $A(1, 3, {}^-2), B(7, {}^-3, 2)$ (4,0,0)
6. $C({}^-5, 4, {}^-2), D(5, {}^-4, 2)$ (0,0,0)
7. $P(0, 0, 6), Q({}^-1, 8, 10)$ $(-\frac{1}{2},4,8)$
8. $R(14, {}^-10, {}^-8), S({}^-4, 2, 6)$ (5,-4,-1)

Determine the center and the measure of the radius for each sphere whose equation is given below.

9. $(x - 3)^2 + (y - 8)^2 + (z - 2)^2 = 49$ c = (3,8,2), r = 7
10. $x^2 + y^2 + z^2 = 7$ c = (0,0,0), r = $\sqrt{7}$
11. $(x + 4)^2 + (y - 2)^2 + (z + 1)^2 = 25$ c = (-4,2,-1), r = 5
12. $x^2 + y^2 + (z - 2)^2 = 2$ c = (0,0,2), r = $\sqrt{2}$

Written **Find the distance between each of the following pairs of points.**

1. $A(0, 0, 0), B(3, 0, 2)$ $\sqrt{13}$
2. $S(0, 4, 0), T(2, 0, 0)$ $2\sqrt{5}$
3. $C(0, 0, 0), D(0, {}^-4, 2)$ $2\sqrt{5}$
4. $L(1, 2, 3), M(0, 0, 0)$ $\sqrt{14}$
5. $P(3, 4, \sqrt{11}), Q(0, 0, 0)$ 6
6. $E(3, 7, {}^-1), F(4, 8, 9)$ $\sqrt{102}$
7. $R({}^-1, {}^-4, 3), S(2, {}^-5, 1)$ $\sqrt{14}$
8. $H({}^-2, {}^-4, {}^-3), J({}^-3, {}^-4, {}^-2)$ $\sqrt{2}$
9. $M(2, 2, 2), N({}^-5, 1, 7)$ $5\sqrt{3}$
10. $P(6, 1, 3), Q(10, 8, 6)$ $\sqrt{74}$

Determine the midpoint of the segment whose endpoints are given.

11. $A(0, {}^-4, 2), B(3, 0, 2)$ $(\frac{3}{2},-2,2)$
12. $S({}^-6, 3, {}^-1), T(6, 3, 1)$ (0,3,0)
13. $C(2, {}^-5, 1), D(3, 2, 4)$ (5/2,-3/2,5/2)
14. $R(2, 7, 4), S(0, 8, {}^-4)$ (1,15/2,0)
15. $P({}^-1, 8, 10), Q(0, 0, 0)$ (-1/2,4,5)
16. $H(4, {}^-4, 2), J(8, {}^-4, 6)$ (6,-4,4)

Determine the center and the measure of the radius for each sphere whose equation is given below.

17. c = (6,5,-1),r = 9
18. c = (-2,-3,2),r = 10

17. $(x - 6)^2 + (y - 5)^2 + (z + 1)^2 = 81$
18. $(x + 2)^2 + (y + 3)^2 + (z - 2)^2 = 100$
19. $x^2 + (y - 3)^2 + z^2 = 4$ c = (0,3,0),r = 2
20. $(x + 1)^2 + (y - 8)^2 + z^2 = 11$

20. c = (-1,8,0), r = $\sqrt{11}$

Write the equation of the sphere having the coordinates of the center and the measure of the radius given below.

21. (0, 0, 0), 3 $x^2 + y^2 + z^2 = 9$
22. (0, 3, 1), 1 $x^2 + (y - 3)^2 + (z - 1)^2 = 1$
23. $({}^-1, 2, 4)$, 4 $(x + 1)^2 + (y - 2)^2 + (z - 4)^2 = 16$
24. $(6, {}^-2, 3)$, 12 $(x - 6)^2 + (y + 2)^2 + (z - 3)^2 = 144$
25. $(2, \frac{1}{2}, 1), \frac{1}{3}$ $(x - 2)^2 + (y - \frac{1}{2})^2 + (z - 1)^2 = \frac{1}{9}$
26. $\left({}^-5, 0, \frac{2}{3}\right), \frac{3}{5}$ $(x + 5)^2 + y^2 + (z - \frac{2}{3})^2 = \frac{9}{25}$

Answer each of the following.

27. Find the perimeter of a triangle whose vertices are $A(6, 4, 1)$, $B(4, 6, 0)$, and $C(3, {}^-2, 3)$. P = 10 + $\sqrt{74}$ or about 18.6
28. Find the perimeter of a triangle whose vertices are $P(0, 0, 0)$, $Q(3, 4, \sqrt{11})$ and $R(0, 5, 0)$. P = 11 + $\sqrt{21}$ or about 15.6

The diameter of a sphere has endpoints $A({}^-3, 5, 7)$ and $B(5, {}^-1, 5)$. Use this information to answer each of the following.

29. Determine the center. (1,2,6)
30. Determine the measure of the radius. 30. $\sqrt{26}$ or about 5.1
31. Write the equation of the sphere. $(x - 1)^2 + (y - 2)^2 + (z - 6)^2 = 26$
32. Sketch the graph of the sphere. See student's work.

Answer the following.

33. Find the distance between $A(7, 5, 6)$ and $B(3, 1, 4)$ using the Pythagorean Theorem. AB = 6

Vocabulary

ordered pair (405)
quadrant (405)
axis (405)
origin (405)
coordinate (405)
linear equation (406)
distance formula (410)
midpoint formula (411)
slope (413)
slope-intercept form (417)
point-slope form (418)
system of equations (420)
equation of a circle (423)
equation of a sphere (433)

Chapter Summary

1. Postulate 12–1: Each point in a coordinate plane corresponds to exactly one ordered pair of numbers. Each ordered pair of numbers corresponds to exactly one point in a coordinate plane. (405)
2. Definition of Linear Equation: An equation is linear if and only if it can be written in the form $Ax + By = C$, where A, B, and C are any real numbers and A and B are not both 0. (406)
3. Distance Formula (Theorem 12–1): The distance between two points with coordinates (x_1, y_1) and (x_2, y_2) is given by the following formula. (410)
$$d = \sqrt{(x_2 - x_1)^2 + (y_2 - y_1)^2}$$
4. Midpoint Formula (Theorem 12–2): If the coordinates of A and B are (x_1, y_1) and (x_2, y_2) respectively, then the midpoint M of $\overline{AB}$ has coordinates $\left(\frac{x_1 + x_2}{2}, \frac{y_1 + y_2}{2}\right)$. (411)
5. Definition of Slope: The slope of a line containing two points with coordinates (x_1, y_1) and (x_2, y_2) is given by the following formula. (413)
$$m = \frac{y_2 - y_1}{x_2 - x_1}$$
6. If the line is vertical, then the slope is undefined; if the line is horizontal, then the slope is zero. (414)
7. Theorem 12–3: Two lines have the same slope if and only if they are parallel and nonvertical. (415)
8. Theorem 12–4: Two nonvertical lines are perpendicular if and only if the product of their slopes is $^-1$. (415)
9. Slope-Intercept Form (Theorem 12–5): The equation of the line having a slope m, and y-intercept b is $y = mx + b$. (417)
10. Point-Slope Form (Theorem 12–6): The equation of the line passing through the point whose coordinates are (x_1, y_1) and which has a slope m is $y - y_1 = m(x - x_1)$. (418)
11. A system of equations can be solved by three methods: graphing, the substitution method, and the elimination method. (420)

12. General Equation of a Circle (Theorem 12–7): The equation of a circle with center at (h, k) and radius measuring r units is $(x - h)^2 + (y - k)^2 = r^2$. (423)

13. Placing figures in a coordinate plane: (426)
    1. Use the origin as a vertex or center.
    2. Place at least one side of a polygon on a coordinate axis.
    3. Keep the figure within the first quadrant.

14. In a three dimensional coordinate system in space, the x-axis, the y-axis, and the z-axis are perpendicular to each other. A point in space is represented by an ordered triple of real numbers (x, y, z). (431)

15. Theorem 12–8: Given two points $A(x_1, y_1, z_1)$ and $B(x_2, y_2, z_2)$ in space, the distance between A and B is given by the following equation. (431)

$$AB = \sqrt{(x_2 - x_1)^2 + (y_2 - y_1)^2 + (z_2 - z_1)^2}$$

16. Given two points $P(x_1, y_1, z_1)$ and $Q(x_2, y_2, z_2)$ in space, the midpoint of $\overline{PQ}$ is represented by the following. (432)

$$\left(\frac{x_1 + x_2}{2}, \frac{y_1 + y_2}{2}, \frac{z_1 + z_2}{2}\right)$$

17. The equation of a sphere whose center is at (i, j, k) and that has a radius measuring r units is as follows. (433)

$$(x - i)^2 + (y - j)^2 + (z - k)^2 = r^2$$

Chapter Review

For graphs to exercises 1-10, see the Teacher's Guide.

12–1 Graph each of the following linear equations.

1. $x = 4$
2. $3x + y = 5$
3. $^-5x + 2y = 0$
4. $3x - 6y = 9$
5. $y = {}^-x + 1$
6. $2x = y - 1$

Each of the following are the coordinates of three vertices of a rectangle. Graph them. Then, determine each fourth vertex.

7. $(^-2, 2), (1, 2), (1, ^-4)$ (-2,-4)
8. $(0, 0), (1, ^-1), (^-3, ^-5)$ (-4,-4)
9. $(^-6, 4), (^-4, 6), (^-2, 4)$ (-4,2)
10. $(1, 0), (5, 0), (5, 6)$ (1,6)

12–2 Find the distance between each of the following pairs of points.

11. $(0, 3), (4, 0)$ 5
12. $(^-3, ^-5), (3, 5)$ $2\sqrt{34}$
13. $(6, r), (4, r)$ 2
14. $\left(\frac{2}{5}, \frac{3}{5}\right), \left(\frac{1}{10}, \frac{3}{10}\right)$ $\frac{3}{10}\sqrt{2}$
15. $(a, b), (b, a)$ $|a - b|\sqrt{2}$
16. $(0.1, 0.3), (0.2, 0.4)$ $\frac{\sqrt{2}}{10}$

Determine the coordinates of the midpoints of each segment that has endpoints with the following coordinates.

17. $(^-4, 2), (^-4, 5)$ (-4,7/2) **18.** $(5, 0), (12, 0)$ (17/2,0) **19.** $(^-2, ^-3), (^-4, ^-7)$ (-3,-5)

20. $(0, 0), (0, 5)$ $\left(0, \frac{5}{2}\right)$ **21.** $\left(\frac{1}{2}, \frac{1}{3}\right), \left(1, \frac{2}{3}\right)$ $\left(\frac{3}{4}, \frac{1}{2}\right)$ **22.** $(4, 6), (5, 7)$ $\left(\frac{9}{2}, \frac{13}{2}\right)$

23. The center of a circle has coordinates $(^-6, ^-8)$. One endpoint of a diameter has coordinates $(0, 0)$. Determine the coordinates of the other endpoint of the diameter. (-12,-16)

12–3 Determine the slope of the lines passing through the following pairs of points whose coordinates are listed below.

24. $(5, 2), (^-6, 2)$ 0 **25.** $(^-2, 1), (^-5, 3)$ -2/3 **26.** $(3, 6), (9, ^-6)$ -2

27. $(3, 8), (3, 6)$ undefined **28.** $(2, 6), (5, 2)$ -4/3 **29.** $(^-3, 10), (^-7, 2)$ 2

Determine the value of r so that a line through the points with the given coordinates has the slope listed.

30. $(r, 6), (1, 5)$; slope $= \frac{1}{5}$ 6 **31.** $(4, r), (^-2, 4)$; slope $= \frac{1}{2}$ 7

32. $(5, 3), (8, r)$; slope $= 0$ 3 **33.** $(r, ^-2), (5, r)$; slope $= 1$ 3/2

34. Find the value of x if the points $A(x, 4)$, $B(0, 2)$, and $C(2, 0)$ are collinear. -2

12–4 Determine the slope and y-intercept of the graphs of each of the following.

35. $y = 4x + 6$ m = 4, b = 6 **36.** $y = ^-8$ m = 0, b = -8

37. $x = 7$ m undefined, no y-intercept **38.** $4x - 6y = 8$ m = 2/3, b = -4/3

Write an equation of the line satisfying the given conditions.

39. $m = 3$, y-intercept is $^-1$ $y = 3x - 1$ **40.** $m = 0$, through a point at $\left(\frac{1}{2}, \frac{1}{3}\right)$ $y = \frac{1}{3}$

41. m is undefined; through a point at $(4, 6)$ $x = 4$ **42.** $m = \frac{2}{3}$, y-intercept is $^-5$ $y = \frac{2}{3}x - 5$

43. Write the equation of a line passing through points whose coordinates are $(^-2, ^-6)$ and $(5, 0)$. $y = \frac{6}{7}x - \frac{30}{7}$

For graphs to exercises 44-45, see the Teacher's Guide.

12–5 Graph each pair of equations. Then, state the solution of each system of equations.

44. $x + y = 4$
$x - y = 2$ (3,1)

45. $y = x - 2$
$2x + y = 13$ (5,3)

Solve each system of equations by an algebraic method.

46. $y = 2x - 1$
$x + y = 7$ $\left(\frac{8}{3}, \frac{13}{3}\right)$

47. $3x - 4y = ^-1$
$^-2x + y = ^-1$ (1,1)

48. $3x + y = 5$
$2x + 3y = 8$ (1,2)

49. $4x + 5y = 29$
$3x - 2y = 16$ (6,1)

12–6 Determine the center and the measure of the radius for each circle whose equation is given below.

50. $x^2 + y^2 = 36$ c = (0,0), r = 6 **51.** $(x + 2)^2 + y^2 = 12$ c = (-2,0), r = $2\sqrt{3}$

52. $(x + 3)^2 + (y - 6)^2 = 16$ c = (-3,6), r = 4 **53.** $x^2 + (y - 5)^2 = \frac{64}{121}$ c = (0,5), r = $\frac{8}{11}$

For each of the following, write the equation of the circle. The center and measure of the radius are given.

54. (2, 3), 8 $(x - 2)^2 + (y - 3)^2 = 64$

55. (0, 0), 0.3 $x^2 + y^2 = 0.09$

56. ($^-$7, 8), 5 $(x + 7)^2 + (y - 8)^2 = 25$

57. $\left(-\frac{2}{3}, 5\right), \frac{6}{7}$ $\left(x + \frac{2}{3}\right)^2 + (y - 5)^2 = \frac{36}{49}$

58. Find the equation of the circle that has a diameter of 12 units and a center at ($^-$5, $^-$6).
$(x + 5)^2 + (y + 6)^2 = 36$

12–7 For each of the following, name the missing coordinates without introducing new letters.

59.

(-a,2a) (■,■) (a,2a) (■,■)

(■,■) (-a,0) (a, 0)

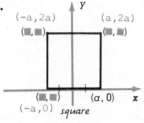

square

60.

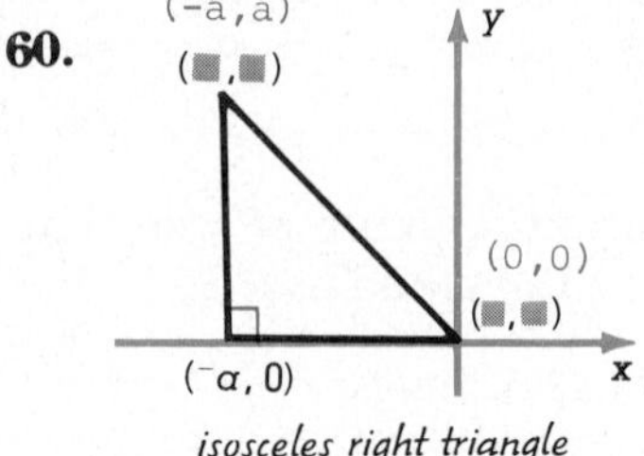

isosceles right triangle

61. Name the given and the prove statement and then draw a diagram you would use to prove that the diagonals of a rhombus are perpendicular. See the Teacher's Guide.

12–8 Find the distance between each of the following pairs of points.

62. (0, 0, 0), (0, $^-$3, 7) $\sqrt{58}$

63. (3, 3, 3), ($^-$6, 0, 6) $3\sqrt{11}$

64. (0, 8, 0), (4, 0, 0) $4\sqrt{5}$

65. (5, 0, 2), (9, 7, 5) $\sqrt{74}$

Determine the midpoint of the segment whose endpoints are given.

66. ($^-$5, 2, 0), (5, 2, 0) (0,2,0)

67. (1, 6, 4), (0, 7, $^-$3) $\left(\frac{1}{2}, \frac{13}{2}, \frac{1}{2}\right)$

68. (3, $^-$3, 1), (7, $^-$3, 5) (5,-3,3)

69. (2, 4, 6), (0, 2, 4) (1,3,5)

Determine the center and the measure of the radius for each sphere whose equation is given below.

70. $(x - 4)^2 + (y - 1)^2 + (z + 2)^2 = 100$ c = (4,1,-2), r = 10

71. $x^2 + y^2 + z^2 = 144$ c = (0,0,0), r = 12

72. $(x + 1)^2 + y^2 + (z - 5)^2 = 4$ c = (-1,0,5), r = 2

73. $(x + 3)^2 + (y + 4)^2 + (z - 1)^2 = 13$ c = (-3,-4,1), r = $\sqrt{13}$

Write the equation of the sphere having the center and the measure of the radius given below.

74. (0, 0, 0), 5 $x^2 + y^2 + z^2 = 25$

75. (9, $^-$6, 4), 8 $(x - 9)^2 + (y + 6)^2 + (z - 4)^2 = 64$

76. ($^-$1, 2, $^-$3), 4 $(x + 1)^2 + (y - 2)^2 + (z + 3)^2 = 16$

77. $\left(^-2, 1, \frac{2}{5}\right), \frac{2}{7}$ $(x + 2)^2 + (y - 1)^2 + \left(z - \frac{2}{5}\right)^2 = \frac{4}{49}$

Chapter Test

For graphs to exercises 1-2, see the Teacher's Guide.

Graph each of the following linear equations.

1. $x + 2y = 6$
2. $x = {}^-3$

Find the distance between each of the following pairs of points.

3. (2, 3), (6, 7) $4\sqrt{2}$
4. $\left(\frac{2}{3}, \frac{4}{5}\right), \left(\frac{1}{3}, \frac{2}{5}\right)$ $\frac{\sqrt{61}}{15}$

Determine the coordinates of the midpoint of each segment that has endpoints with the coordinates given below.

5. (0, 4), (6, 8) (3,6)
6. ($^-$5, 7), ($^-$5, 9) (-5,8)

Determine the slope of the lines passing through the following pairs of points whose coordinates are given below.

7. ($^-$4, 11), ($^-$6, 3) 4
8. (5, 2), (8, 2) 0
9. (3, 7), (3, $^-$6) undefined
10. Determine the value of r so that a line through (r, 3) and (5, 9) has a slope of 2. 2
11. Write the equation of a line passing through points whose coordinates are ($^-$2, $^-$6) and (8, $^-$2). $y = \frac{2}{5}x - \frac{26}{5}$

Solve each system of equations.

12. $y = 4x$
$x + y = 5$ (1,4)
13. $3x - 2y = 10$
$x + y = 0$ (2,-2)
14. $3x + 4y = {}^-7$
$2x + y = {}^-3$ (-1,-1)

Determine the center and the measure of the radius for each circle whose equation is given below.

15. $x^2 + y^2 = 49$ c = (0,0), r = 7
16. $(x + 7)^2 + (y - 3)^2 = 3$ c = (-7,3), r = $\sqrt{3}$

For each of the following, write the equation of the circle. The center and the measure of the radius are given.

17. (0, 0), 2 $x^2 + y^2 = 4$
18. ($^-$5, $^-$6), $\sqrt{8}$ $(x + 5)^2 + (y + 6)^2 = 8$
19. (2, $^-$3), 12 $(x - 2)^2 + (y + 3)^2 = 144$

Answer each of the following.

20. Name the given, the prove statement, and draw a diagram you would use to prove that the diagonals of a rectangle are congruent. See the Teacher's Guide.
21. Determine the distance between (2, 4, 5) and (2, 4, 7). 2
22. Determine the midpoint of the segment whose endpoints are (0, $^-$4, 2) and (3, 0, 2). $\left(\frac{3}{2}, -2, 2\right)$

Determine the center and the measure of the radius for each sphere whose equation is given below.

23. $(x - 4)^2 + (y - 5)^2 + (z + 2)^2 = 81$ c = (4,5,-2), r = 9
24. $x^2 + y^2 + z^2 = 7$ c = (0,0,0), r = $\sqrt{7}$
25. Write the equation of the sphere whose diameter has endpoints at ($^-$3, 5, 7) and (5, $^-$1, 5). $(x - 1)^2 + (y - 2)^2 + (z - 6)^2 = 26$

cumulative review

For answers to exercises 1-4, see the Teacher's Guide.

Draw and label a diagram to show each of the following.

1. Points R, S, and T are coplanar.
2. Points L, M, and N are collinear.

Write the inverse and the contrapositive of each of the following statements.

3. If three points are coplanar, then they lie in the same plane.
4. If it snows, then you may ski.

Change each fraction to decimal form.

5. $-\frac{7}{8}$ -0.875
6. $4\frac{2}{3}$ $4.\overline{6}$

Change each decimal to fractional form.

7. $2.\overline{54}$ $2\frac{6}{11}$
8. $0.\overline{324}$ $\frac{12}{37}$

Determine whether each of the following is *true* or *false*.

9. $\overrightarrow{BA}$ and $\overrightarrow{BC}$ are opposite rays. true
10. $\angle ABE$ and $\angle EBC$ form a linear pair. true
11. F is in the interior of $\angle DBC$. false
12. $\angle ABE$ and $\angle DBC$ are adjacent angles. false

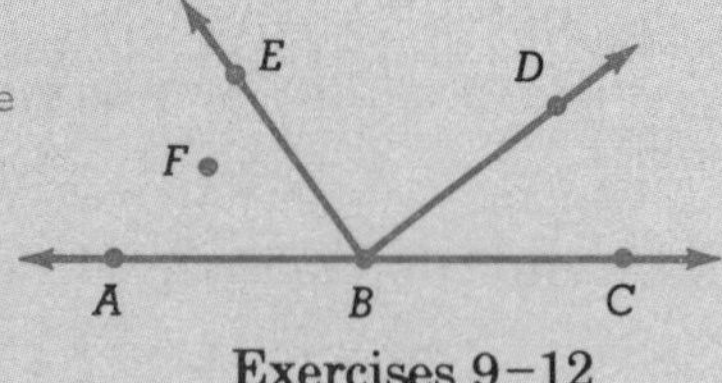

Exercises 9–12

Answer each of the following.

13. The measure of the supplement of an angle is three times the measure of the complement of the angle. What is the measure of the angle? 45
14. If $\triangle BCD$ is isosceles with $\overline{BD} \cong \overline{DC}$ and $BD = 2x - 5$ and $DC = x + 3$, then find the value of x. 8

In the figure, $\overline{AB} \cong \overline{CB}$ and $m\angle 2 = 40$. Find each of the following.

15. $m\angle 4$ 40
16. $m\angle 5$ 140
17. $m\angle 3$ 100
18. $m\angle 1$ 140

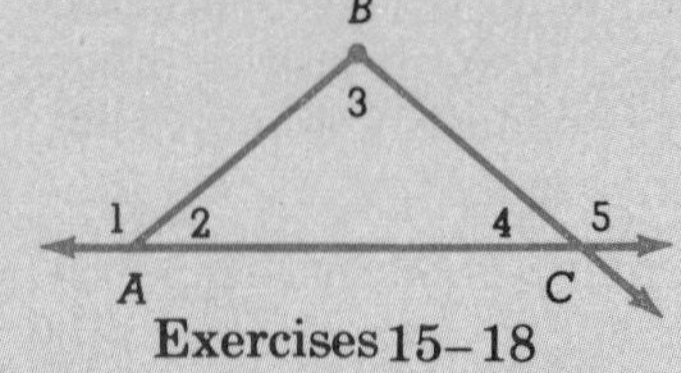

Exercises 15–18

Prove each of the following.

19. **Given:** $\triangle ABC \cong \triangle CDA$
    Prove: $\overline{BC} \parallel \overline{DA}$

20. **Given:** $\angle 2 \cong \angle 3$
    $\angle 4 \cong \angle 1$
    Prove: $\overline{AB} \cong \overline{CD}$

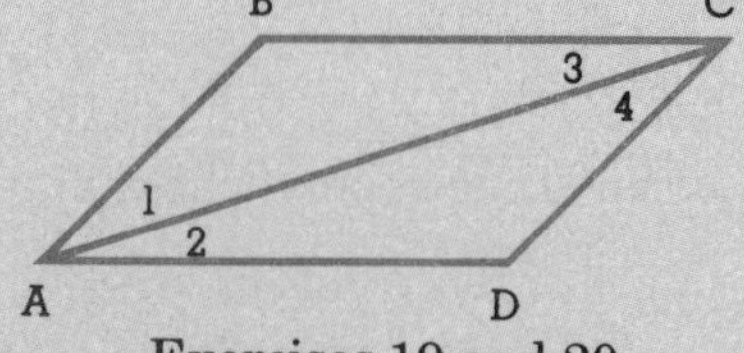

Exercises 19 and 20

For answers to exercises 19-21, see the Teacher's Guide.

Answer each of the following.

21. Draw a diagram showing a ray and a segment that are *not* parallel. see Teacher's Guide
22. Find the number of diagonals that can be drawn in a pentagon. 5
23. Find the sum of the degree measures of the angles of a 12-gon. 1800
24. If the length of a rectangle is 21 ft and the width is 16 ft, find the perimeter. 74 ft

Solve each proportion.

25. $\frac{x}{8} = \frac{13}{40}$ $\frac{13}{5}$
26. $\frac{4}{3x + 2} = \frac{2}{3}$ $\frac{4}{3}$
27. $\frac{x - 1}{5 - x} = \frac{3}{5}$ $\frac{5}{2}$

28. Find the geometric mean between $\frac{3}{4}$ and $\frac{4}{3}$. 1

In $\odot O$, $\overline{AB} \parallel \overline{CD}$, $m\angle ABO = 50$, $m\widehat{EC} = 70$, and $\overline{CB}$ is a diameter. Find each of the following.

29. $m\widehat{AEC}$ 100°
30. $m\angle 3$ 80°
31. $m\angle D$ 35°
32. $m\angle 1$ 50°

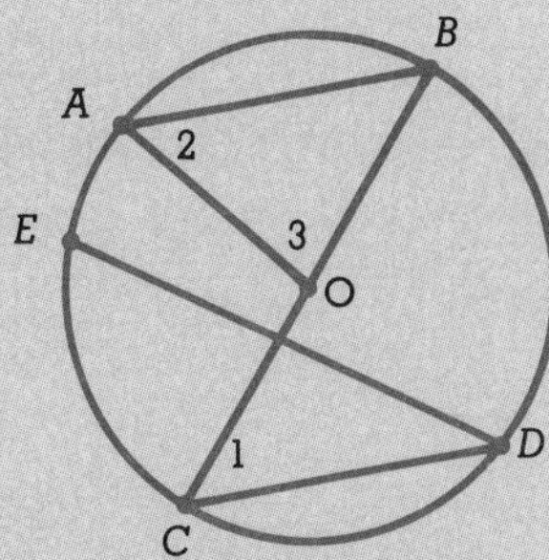

Exercises 29–32

Answer each of the following.

33. Find the area of an equilateral triangle with sides measuring 20 cm. $100\sqrt{3}$ cm^2
34. Find the area of a regular hexagon with an apothem measuring 3 inches. $18\sqrt{3}$ in.^{2}
35. Find the total surface area of a right cylinder with height of 10 ft and a radius of the base of 6 ft. Use 3.14 for π. 602.88 ft^2
36. Find the volume of a regular square pyramid with a height of 12 inches and a base with sides of 6 inches. 144 in.^{3}
37. Find the distance between the points with coordinates (4, 7) and ($^-8$, 6). $\sqrt{145}$
38. Find the coordinates of the midpoint of a segment whose endpoints are (3, 7) and (7, $^-11$). (5,2)
39. Write the equation of a circle with center at ($^-3$, 9) and radius of 13 units. $(x + 3)^2 + (y - 9)^2 = 169$
40. Determine r so that the line through (r, 3) and (5, 9) has a slope of 2. $r = 2$

chapter

13 Loci and Constructions

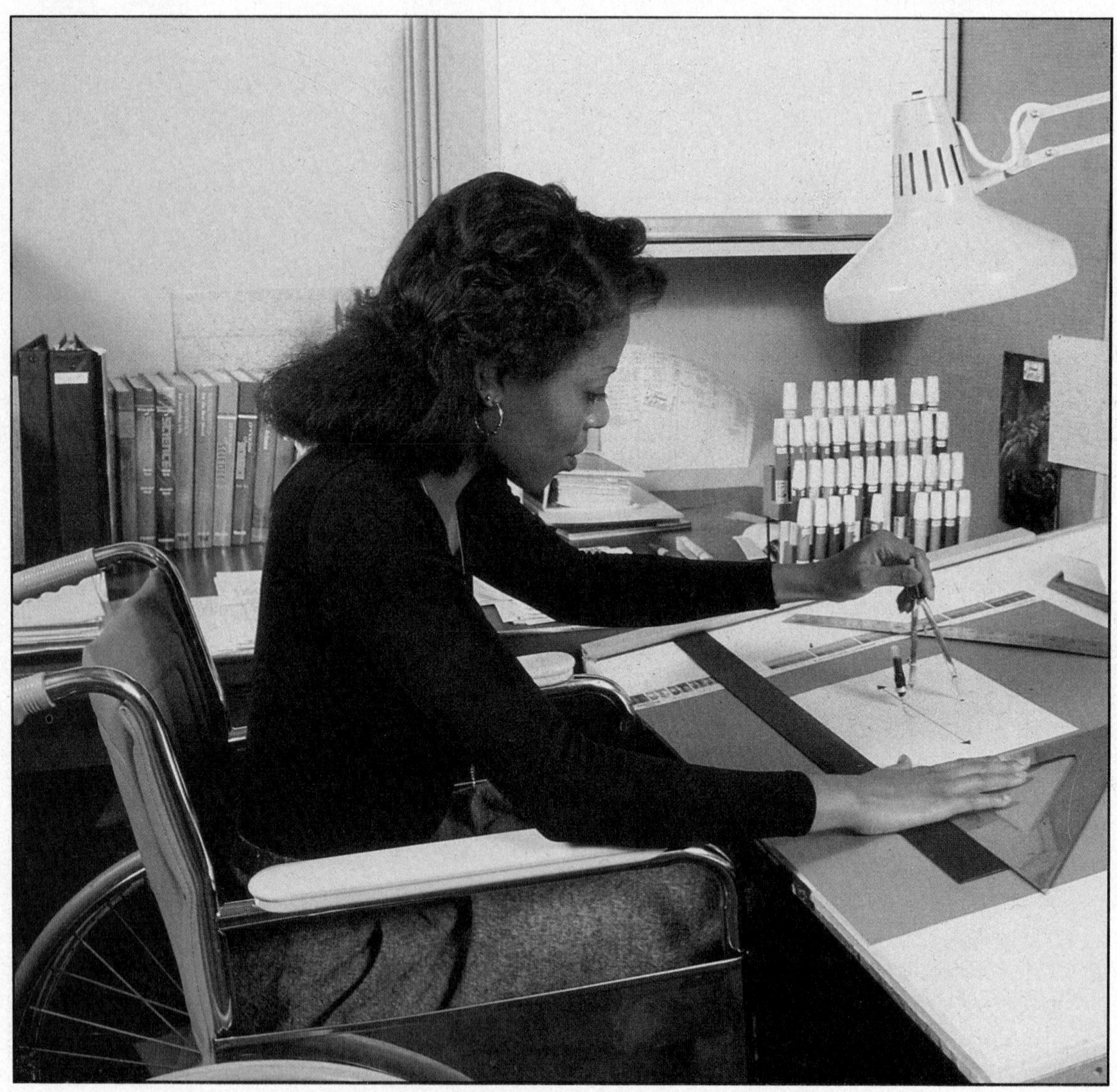

Among other instruments, artists use compasses and protractors to construct design layouts. Their work involves the basic construction ideas included in this chapter.

Objectives: to construct congruent line segments, to construct congruent angles, to construct the bisector of an angle, to translate a problem into: the given, construct statement, and diagram

13–1 Basic Constructions

It is possible to construct many geometric figures without making measurements. Two instruments are used, a **straightedge** and a **compass.**

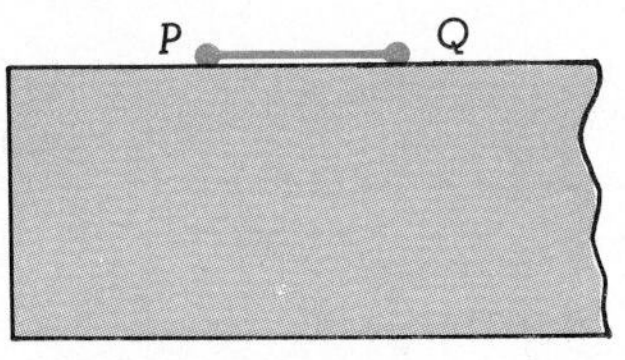

A straightedge is like an unmarked ruler. It is used to draw lines and segments. Two points, such as P and Q, lie on exactly one line. A straightedge is used to draw such a line.

A ruler may be used as a straightedge for constructions, as long as the measurement marks are not *used.*

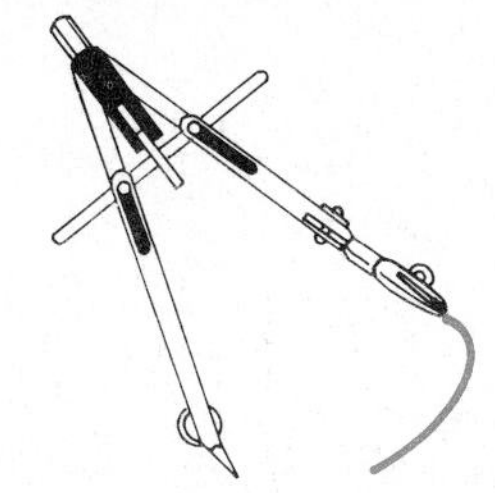

A compass is used to draw circles and arcs of circles. In a plane there is exactly one circle with a given center and radius. A compass is used to draw such a circle.

Emphasize that geometric constructions are done without making measurements.

The following construction shows how to construct a segment congruent to a given segment. *Notice the parts of the presentation,* given, construct statement, diagram, method, *and* justification.

construction

Construction 1: Construct a segment congruent to a given segment.

Given: $\overline{AB}$

Construct: $\overline{CD}$ so that $\overline{CD} \cong \overline{AB}$

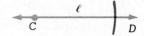

Method:

1. Use a straightedge to draw a line. Call it ℓ.
2. Choose any point on ℓ. Label it C.
3. Place the compass point on A and the pencil on B. The compass radius now has measure AB.
4. With the same compass setting, place the compass point on C. Mark an arc intersecting ℓ. Label the point D. Then, $\overline{CD} \cong \overline{AB}$.

Justification: The radius for a circle with center C has the same measure as a circle with center A and radius AB. Thus, $\overline{CD} \cong \overline{AB}$ since the radii are congruent.

construction

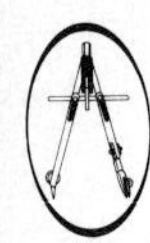

Construction 2: Construct an angle congruent to a given angle.

Given: $\angle ABC$

Construct: $\angle DEF$ so that $\angle DEF \cong \angle ABC$

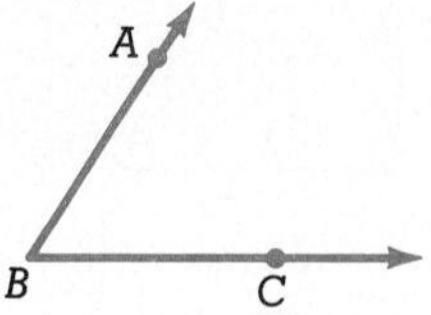

Emphasize to students that neat, accurate work is important for all constructions.

Method:

1. Draw $\overrightarrow{EF}$.

2. Using B as center, draw an arc that intersects both sides of $\angle ABC$. Call the intersection points X and Y.

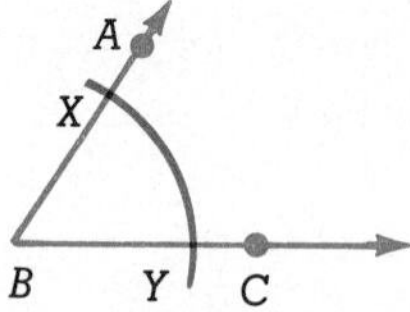

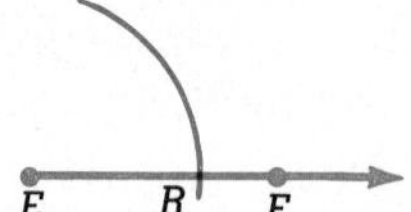

3. Keep the compass at the same setting. Using E as a center, draw an arc intersecting $\overrightarrow{EF}$. The arc may intersect either side of F. Call the intersection R.
4. Using R as a center and radius setting XY, draw an arc that intersects the arc drawn in Step 3. Call the intersection D.

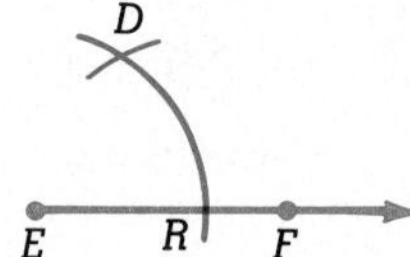

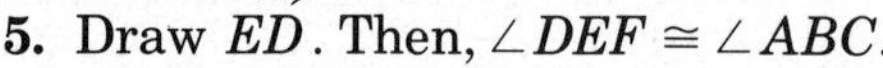

5. Draw $\overrightarrow{ED}$. Then, $\angle DEF \cong \angle ABC$.

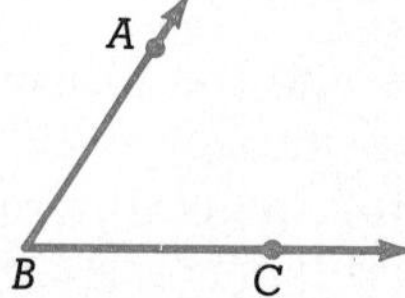

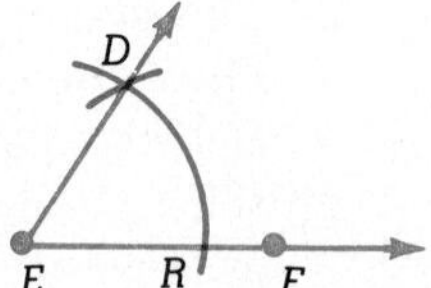

Emphasize the justification.

Justification: If $\overline{DR}$ and $\overline{XY}$ are drawn, then $\overline{DR} \cong \overline{XY}$. Also, by construction, $\overline{ED} \cong \overline{BX}$ and $\overline{ER} \cong \overline{BY}$. Thus, $\triangle DER \cong \triangle XBY$ by SSS. Then, $\angle DEF \cong \angle ABC$ by the definition of congruent triangles. *CPCTC*

Construction 3: Construct the bisector of a given angle.

Given: $\angle ABC$

Construct: $\overrightarrow{BD}$ so that $\overrightarrow{BD}$ bisects $\angle ABC$

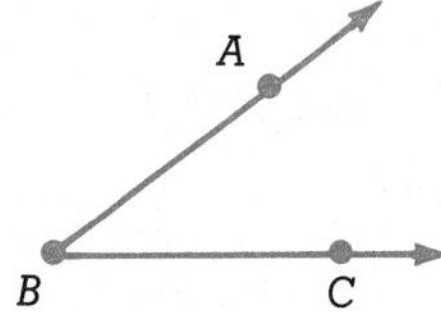

Method:

1. Using B as a center, draw an arc that intersects both sides of $\angle ABC$. Call the intersection points X and Y.

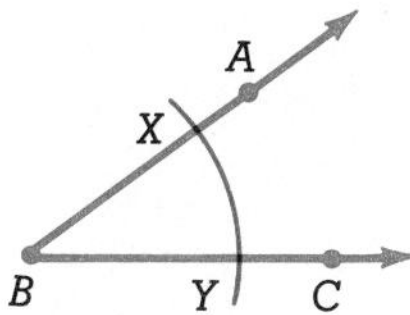

2. Keep the same compass setting. Using X as a center, draw an arc in the interior of $\angle ABC$.

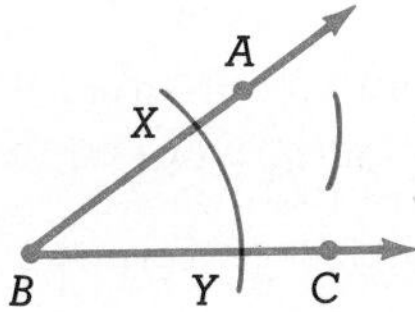

3. Keep the same compass setting. Using Y as a center, draw an arc that intersects the arc drawn in Step 2. Call the intersection D.

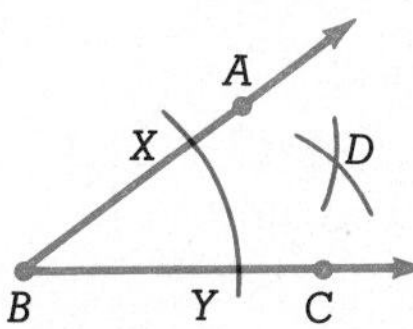

4. Draw $\overrightarrow{BD}$. Then, $\overrightarrow{BD}$ bisects $\angle ABC$.

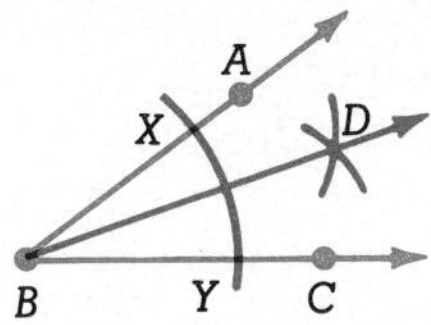

Justification: Draw $\overline{XD}$ and $\overline{YD}$. By construction, $\overline{XD} \cong \overline{YD}$ and $\overline{BX} \cong \overline{BY}$. Also, $\overline{BD} \cong \overline{BD}$. Thus, $\triangle BXD \cong \triangle BYD$ by SSS. By the definition of congruent triangles, $\angle XBD \cong \angle YBD$. Thus $\overrightarrow{BD}$ bisects $\angle ABC$.

EN: Ex: 1-2, Wr: 1-18, Ch ; AV: Ex: 1-6, Wr: 1-18; FN: Ex: 1-8, Wr: 1-16

exercises

Exploratory **For each of the following, state the given, construct statement, and draw a diagram.** For answers to exercises 1-8, see the Teacher's Guide.

1. Construct an equilateral triangle given one side.
2. Construct a triangle congruent to a given triangle.
3. Construct a segment whose measure is twice the measure of a given segment.
4. Construct a segment whose measure is three times the measure of a given segment.
5. Construct a segment whose measure is the sum of the measures of two given segments.
6. Construct an angle whose measure is twice the measure of a given angle.
7. Construct an angle whose measure is one-half the measure of a given angle.
8. Construct an angle whose measure is the sum of the measures of two given angles.

Written **On a piece of paper, draw and label two segments like the segments shown below. Then, construct segments for each of the following measures.**

1. $AB + CD$
2. $CD - AB$
3. $2AB$
4. $3CD$
5. $4AB - CD$
6. $2AB - CD$
7. $3(CD - AB)$
8. $2(AB + CD)$

For answers to exercises 1-24, see the Teacher's Guide.

On a piece of paper, draw and label two angles like the angles shown below. Then, construct angles with each of the following degree measures.

9. $2y$
10. $x - 2y$
11. $\frac{1}{2}x$
12. $\frac{1}{2}y$
13. $\frac{1}{2}(x + y)$
14. $\frac{1}{2}x + y$
15. $\frac{3}{4}x$
16. $x + \frac{1}{2}y$

Perform the following constructions.

17. Draw a segment. Then, construct an equilateral triangle with the segment as one of its sides.
18. Draw an obtuse triangle. Then, construct a triangle congruent to the triangle drawn.
19. Construct a 30° angle.
20. Construct a 15° angle.
21. Construct a 75° angle.
22. Construct a 45° angle.
23. Draw an angle and two segments. Then, construct a triangle whose sides and an included angle are congruent to the figures drawn.
24. Draw two angles and a segment. Then, construct a triangle whose angles and included side are congruent to the figures drawn.

Challenge **Inscribe in a circle, a triangle with angles constructed that are congruent to ∠1, ∠2, and ∠3 as shown at the right.** See the Teacher's Guide.

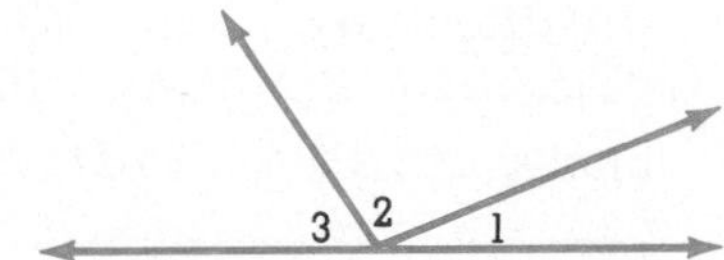

Objectives: to make constructions using parallels and perpendiculars, to construct a line ⊥ to a given line through a given point not on the line, to construct the ⊥ bisector of a segment, to construct a line ⊥ to a given line through a given point on the line, to construct a line ∥ to a given line through a point not on the line

13–2 Perpendiculars and Parallels

Notice how the following constructions are alike.

construction

Construction 4: Construct a line perpendicular to a given line and through a given point *not* on the line.

Given: P is *not* on ℓ.

Construct: $\overleftrightarrow{PQ}$ so that $\overleftrightarrow{PQ} \perp \ell$

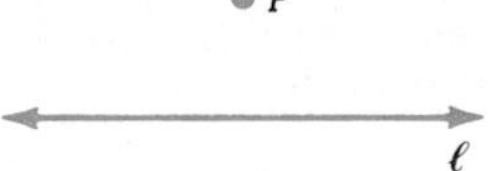

Method:

1. Using P as the center, draw two arcs that intersect ℓ. Call the intersection points V and W.

P
V W ℓ

2. Keep the same compass setting. Using V as the center, and then W as the center, draw arcs that intersect at a point other than P. Call the intersection Q.

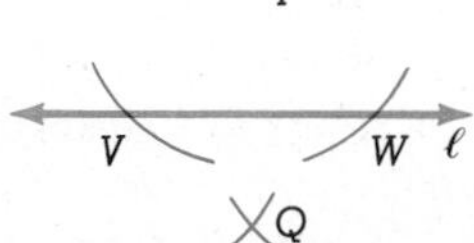

3. Draw $\overleftrightarrow{PQ}$. Then, $\overleftrightarrow{PQ} \perp \ell$.

This construction is vital to later constructions such as finding the incenter of a triangle.

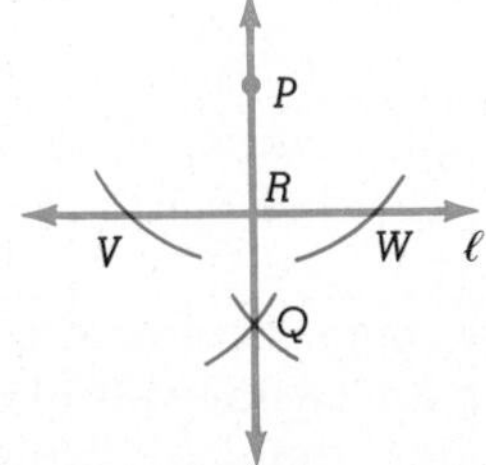

Justification: Draw $\overline{PV}$, $\overline{PW}$, $\overline{VQ}$, and $\overline{WQ}$. By construction, $\overline{PV} \cong \overline{PW}$ and $\overline{VQ} \cong \overline{WQ}$. Also, $\overline{PQ} \cong \overline{PQ}$. Thus, $\triangle PVQ \cong \triangle PWQ$. By the definition of congruent triangles, $\angle VPR \cong \angle WPR$. Also, $\overline{PR} \cong \overline{PR}$, so $\triangle VPR \cong \triangle WPR$ by SAS. The linear pair, $\angle PRV$ and $\angle PRW$ are right angles because they are congruent, supplementary angles. Thus, $\overleftrightarrow{PQ} \perp \ell$.

Construction 5: Construct the perpendicular bisector of a given segment.

Given: $\overline{AB}$

Construct: $\overleftrightarrow{PQ}$ so that $\overleftrightarrow{PQ} \perp \overline{AB}$ and $\overleftrightarrow{PQ}$ bisects $\overline{AB}$

Method:

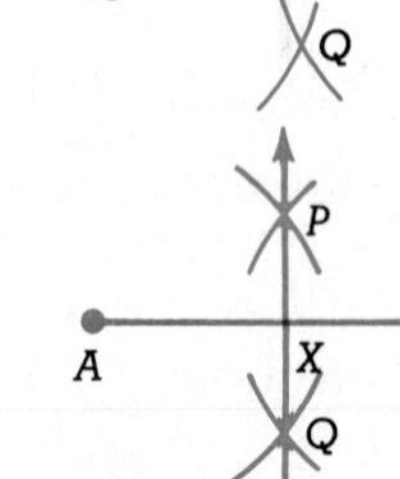

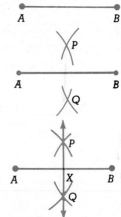

1. Set the compass with measure greater than $\frac{1}{2}AB$. Using A as a center, draw arcs on both sides of $\overline{AB}$.

2. Keep the same compass setting. Using B as a center, draw arcs intersecting the arcs in Step 1. Label the points P and Q.

3. Draw $\overleftrightarrow{PQ}$. Then $\overleftrightarrow{PQ} \perp \overline{AB}$, and $\overleftrightarrow{PQ}$ bisects $\overline{AB}$ at X.

Justification: Draw $\overline{PA}$, $\overline{PB}$, $\overline{QA}$, and $\overline{QB}$. By construction, $\overline{PA} \cong \overline{PB}$ and $\overline{QA} \cong \overline{QB}$. Also, $\overline{PQ} \cong \overline{PQ}$. Thus, $\triangle PAQ \cong \triangle PBQ$. By the definition of congruent triangles, $\angle APX \cong \angle BPX$. Also, $\overline{PX} \cong \overline{PX}$, so $\triangle APX \cong \triangle BPX$ by SAS. It follows that $\overline{AX} \cong \overline{XB}$ and $\angle PXA \cong \angle PXB$. Thus, it is possible to conclude that $\overleftrightarrow{PQ} \perp \overline{AB}$ and $\overleftrightarrow{PQ}$ bisects $\overline{AB}$.

Construction 6: Construct a line perpendicular to a given line through a given point on the line.

Given: A is on ℓ.

Construct: $\overleftrightarrow{AB}$ so that $\overleftrightarrow{AB} \perp \ell$

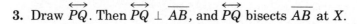

Method:

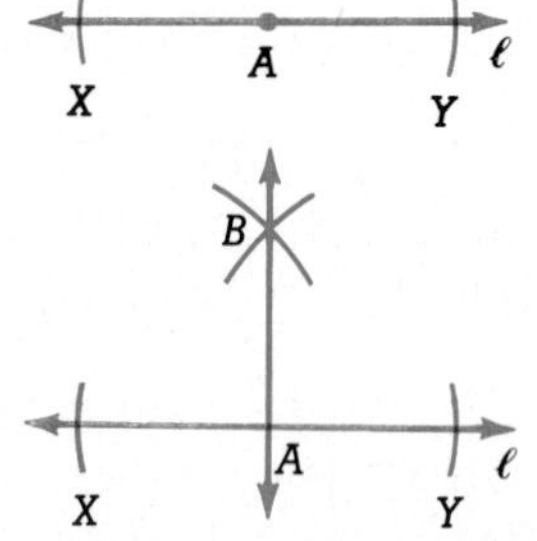

1. Using A as the center, draw two arcs with the same radius that intersect ℓ. Call the intersection points X and Y.
2. Increase the compass radius. Using X as the center, draw an arc on one side of the line.
3. Keep the same compass radius. Using Y as the center, draw an arc that intersects the arc in Step 2. Call the intersection B.
4. Draw $\overleftrightarrow{AB}$. Then $\overleftrightarrow{AB} \perp \ell$.

Justification: Draw $\overline{XB}$ and $\overline{YB}$. By construction, $\overline{XB} \cong \overline{YB}$ and $\overline{AX} \cong \overline{AY}$. Also, $\overline{AB} \cong \overline{AB}$. Thus, $\triangle AXB \cong \triangle AYB$ by SSS. By the definition of congruent triangles, $\angle BAX \cong \angle BAY$. Since $\angle BAX$ and $\angle BAY$ form a linear pair, by the Supplement Postulate they are supplementary. Congruent, supplementary angles are right angles. Thus, $\overline{AB} \perp \ell$.

According to Theorem 6–7, if two lines are perpendicular to the same line, then the two lines are parallel.

construction

Construction 7: Construct a line parallel to a given line and through a point *not* on the line.

Given: P is *not* on ℓ.

Construct: n so that $n \parallel \ell$ and n contains P.

Method:

1. Draw a line through ℓ and through P. Call it $\overleftrightarrow{PX}$.

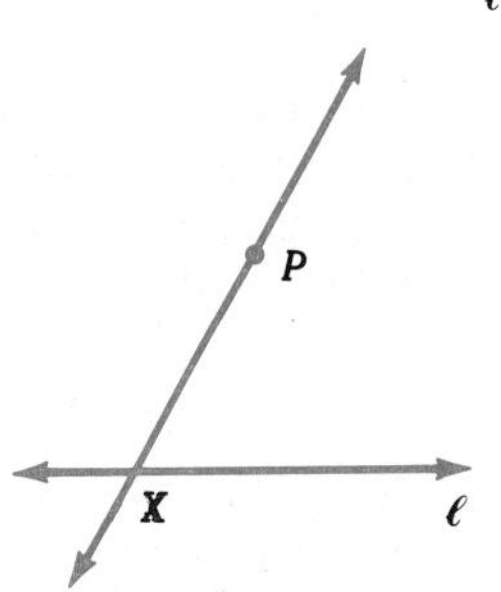

2. Copy one of the angles formed at X using P as a vertex and one side on $\overleftrightarrow{PX}$. Draw a line through P to form an angle congruent to the angle at X. Call it n. Then, $n \parallel \ell$ and n contains P.

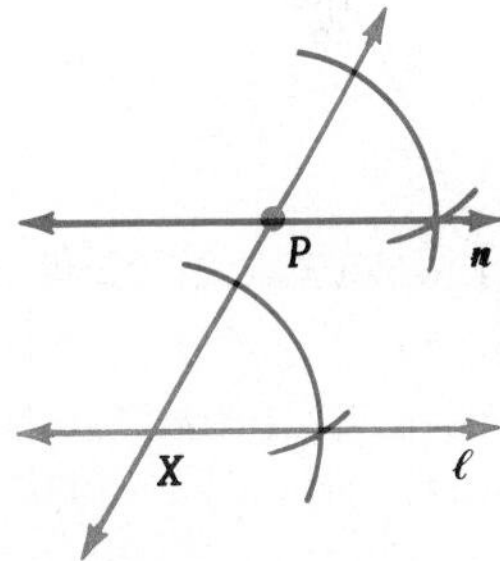

Justification: By construction, n contains P. Also, by construction, corresponding angles are congruent. Thus, $n \parallel \ell$.

EN: Ex: 1-10, Wr: 1-19 odds; p. 446, Wr: 19-24; AV: Ex: 1-10, Wr: 1-15; p. 446, Wr: 19-24

exercises

FN: Ex: 1-10, Wr: 1-15; p. 446, Wr: 17-24

Exploratory **The figure at the right shows the construction of the perpendicular bisector of $\overline{AB}$. Supply reasons for each of the following statements in the justification for the construction.**

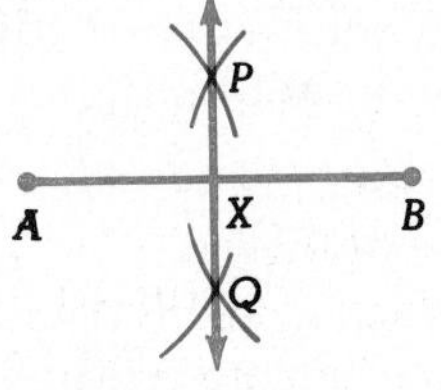

1. Draw $\overline{PA}$, $\overline{PB}$, $\overline{QA}$, and $\overline{QB}$. Postulate 1-1
2. $\overline{PA} \cong \overline{PB}$ and $\overline{QA} \cong \overline{QB}$ by construction
3. $\overline{PQ} \cong \overline{PQ}$ Theorem 2-2
4. $\triangle PAQ \cong \triangle PBQ$ SSS
5. $\angle APX \cong \angle BPX$ CPCTC
6. $\overline{PX} \cong \overline{PX}$ Theorem 2-2
7. $\triangle APX \cong \triangle BPX$ SAS
8. $\overline{AX} \cong \overline{BX}$ and $\angle PXA \cong \angle PXB$ CPCTC
9. $\overleftrightarrow{PQ}$ bisects $\overline{AB}$.
10. $\overleftrightarrow{PQ} \perp \overline{AB}$ Theorem 3-14

9. Definition of Congruent Segments, Definition of Midpoint, Definition of Bisector of a Segment

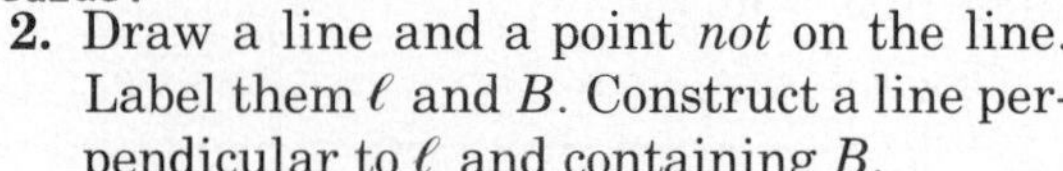

Written **Complete each of the following.**

For answers to exercises 1-19, see the Teacher's Guide.

1. Draw a line and a point on the line. Label them ℓ and A. Construct a line perpendicular to ℓ and containing A.
2. Draw a line and a point *not* on the line. Label them ℓ and B. Construct a line perpendicular to ℓ and containing B.
3. Draw a segment. Label it $\overline{PQ}$. Construct a line perpendicular to $\overline{PQ}$.
4. Draw a segment. Label it $\overline{RS}$. Construct a bisector of $\overline{RS}$.
5. Draw a line and a point *not* on the line. Label them m and P. Construct a line parallel to m and containing P.
6. Describe a method based on perpendicular lines for constructing a line parallel to a given line and through a point *not* on the line.
7. Draw a segment. Construct a square with sides congruent to the given segment.
8. Draw an acute triangle. Construct the medians of the triangle. The medians of a triangle intersect at a point which is called the centroid of the triangle.
9. Copy $\triangle ABC$. Then construct the altitudes of the triangle. The altitudes of a triangle intersect at a point which is called the orthocenter of the triangle.
10. Copy RST. Then construct the altitudes of the obtuse triangle.

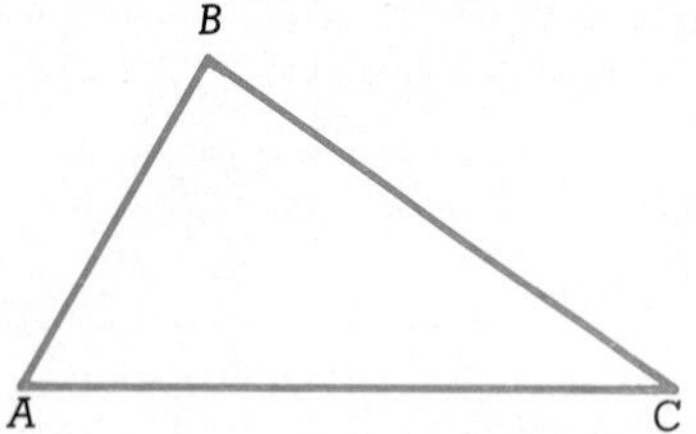

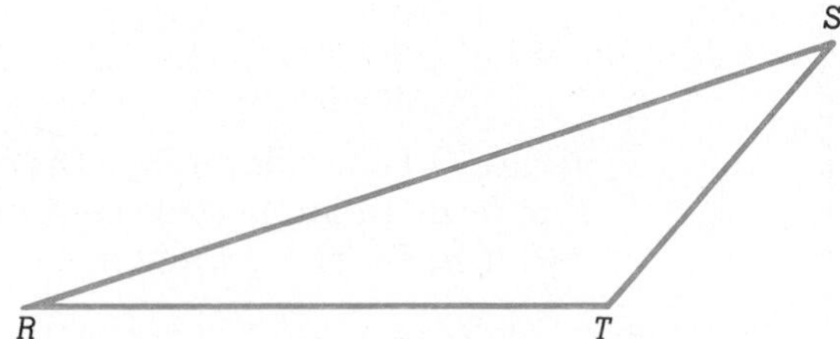

11. Draw a segment. Construct an isosceles triangle whose congruent sides are congruent to the given segment.
12. Draw an acute angle and a segment. Construct an isosceles triangle with base angles congruent to the given angle, and congruent sides congruent to the given segment.
13. Construct an isosceles right triangle.
14. Construct a $30°–60°–90°$ triangle.
15. Draw two segments and an angle. Construct a parallelogram with adjacent sides congruent to the given segments, and included angle congruent to the given angle.

Draw two segments of different lengths. Label the shorter segment $\overline{AB}$, and the other $\overline{CD}$. Draw an acute angle. Label it $x°$. Use the figures to complete each of the following.

16. Construct a rectangle with sides measuring AB and CD.
17. Construct a rhombus with diagonals measuring AB and CD.
18. Construct a right triangle with hypotenuse measuring AB and an $x°$ angle.
19. Construct an isosceles triangle with congruent sides measuring CD and vertex angle $x°$.

Objectives: to perform constructions involving circles, to construct a line tangent to a circle at a given point, to construct a line tangent to a circle through a point not on the circle, to locate the center of a circle, to circumscribe a circle about a polygon

13–3 Circles

The following show how to construct a line tangent to a circle.

constructions

Construction 8: Construct a line tangent to a given circle at a given point on the circle.

Given: $\odot P$ with A on the circle

Construct: ℓ so that ℓ is tangent to $\odot P$ at A

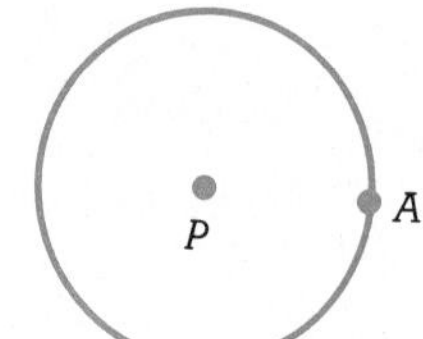

Method:

1. Draw $\overrightarrow{PA}$.
2. Construct ℓ through A and perpendicular to $\overrightarrow{PA}$. Line ℓ is tangent to $\odot P$ at A.

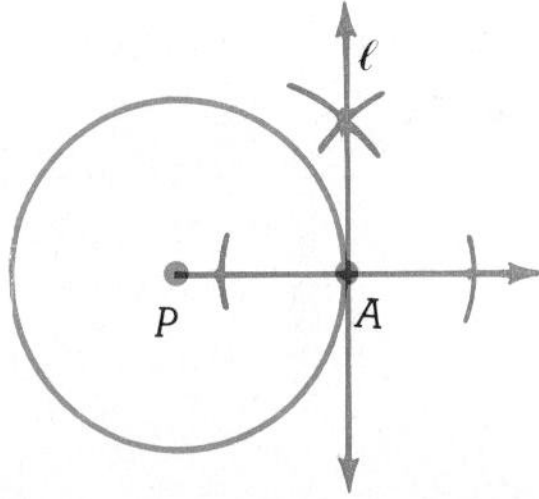

Justification: In a plane, if a line is perpendicular to a radius at a point on the circle, then the line is tangent to the circle. Thus, ℓ is tangent to $\odot P$ at A.

Construction 9: Construct a line tangent to a given circle and through a given point *not* on the circle.

Given: A *not* on $\odot C$

Construct: $\overleftrightarrow{AD}$ so that $\overleftrightarrow{AD}$ is tangent to $\odot C$

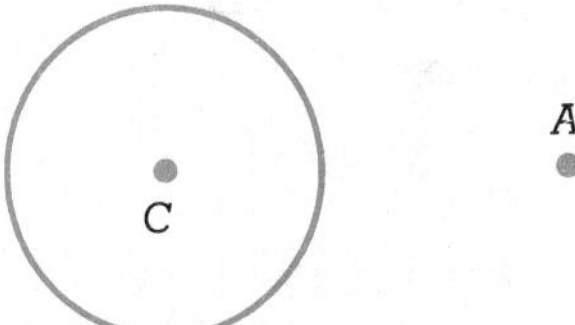

Method:

1. Draw $\overline{AC}$.
2. Construct the perpendicular bisector of $\overline{AC}$. Call it ℓ. Call X the intersection of ℓ and $\overline{AC}$.
3. Using X as the center, draw a circle with radius measuring XC. Call D and E the intersection points of the two circles.
4. Draw $\overleftrightarrow{AD}$. Then, $\overleftrightarrow{AD}$ is tangent to $\odot C$.

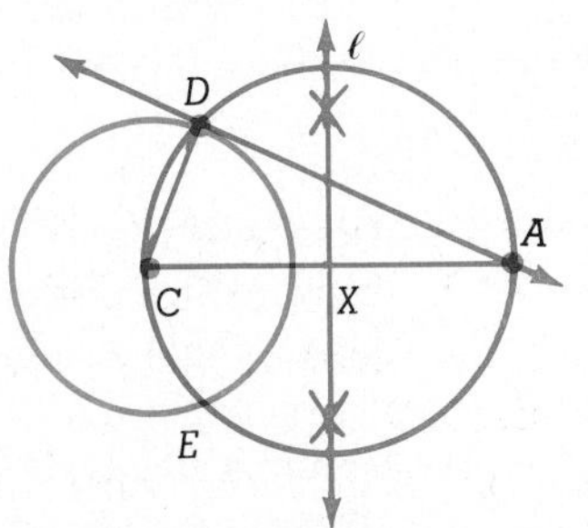

Justification: $\overline{AC}$ is a diameter of $\odot X$. Thus, $\widehat{CDA}$ is a semicircle and $\angle CDA$ is a right angle. $\overline{CD} \perp \overleftrightarrow{AD}$ implies that $\overleftrightarrow{AD}$ is tangent to $\odot C$ at D.

Point out that $\overleftrightarrow{AE}$ is also tangent to $\odot$ C.

The justifications for each of the following are based on the same theorem.

constructions

Construction 10: Locate the center of a given circle.

Given: a circle

Construct: C so that C is the center of the circle

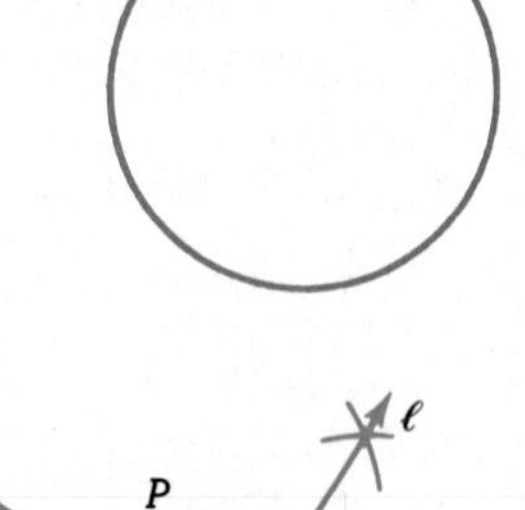

Method:

1. Draw two nonparallel chords. Call them $\overline{PQ}$ and $\overline{RS}$.
2. Construct the perpendicular bisectors for each chord. Call them ℓ and m. Call C the intersection of ℓ and m. Then, C is the center of the circle.

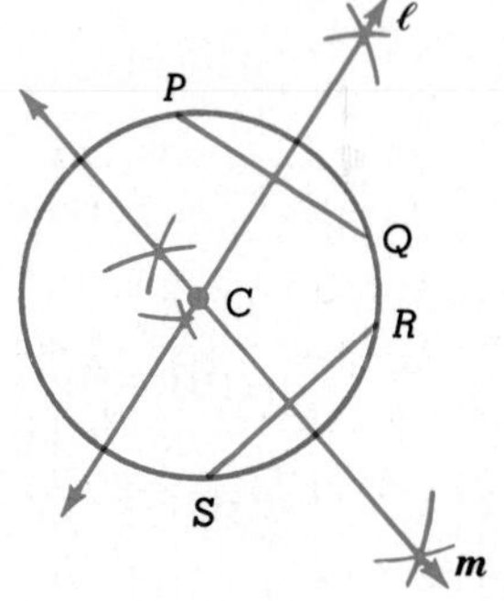

Justification: The perpendicular bisector of a chord contains the center of the circle. Also, two lines intersect in exactly one point. Thus, ℓ and m must intersect at the center of the circle.

Construction 11: Construct a circle circumscribed about a given triangle.

Given: $\triangle ABC$

Construct: $\odot Q$ so that $\odot Q$ is circumscribed about $\triangle ABC$

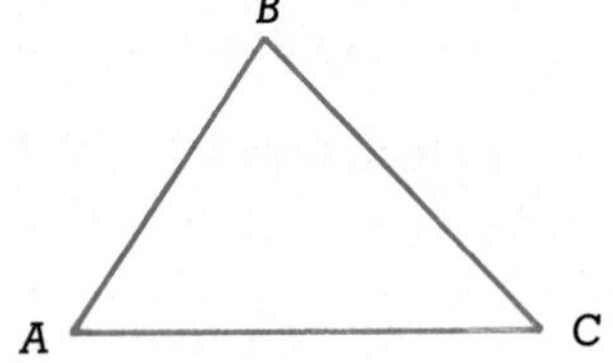

Method:

1. Construct perpendicular bisectors for two sides, $\overline{AB}$ and $\overline{BC}$. Call their intersection Q.
2. Using Q as a center, and QA as the measure of the radius, draw $\odot Q$. Then, $\odot Q$ is circumscribed about $\triangle ABC$.

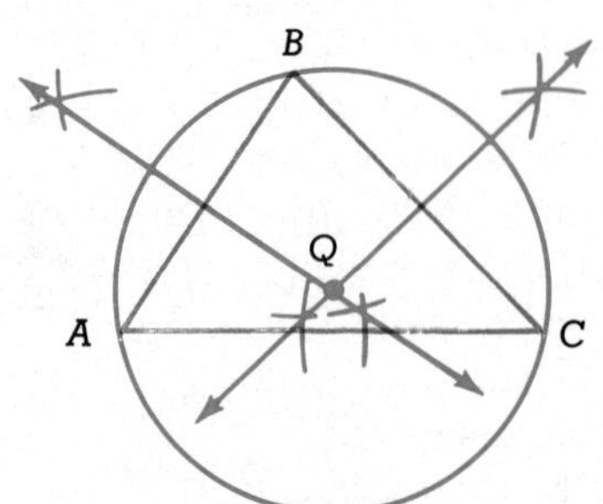

Justification: The perpendicular bisector of a chord contains the center of a circle. Also, each side of a triangle is a chord of a circle circumscribed about the triangle. Thus, Q must be the center of the circle circumscribed about $\triangle ABC$. Point Q is called the **circumcenter.**

The following tells how to inscribe a circle in any triangle ABC.

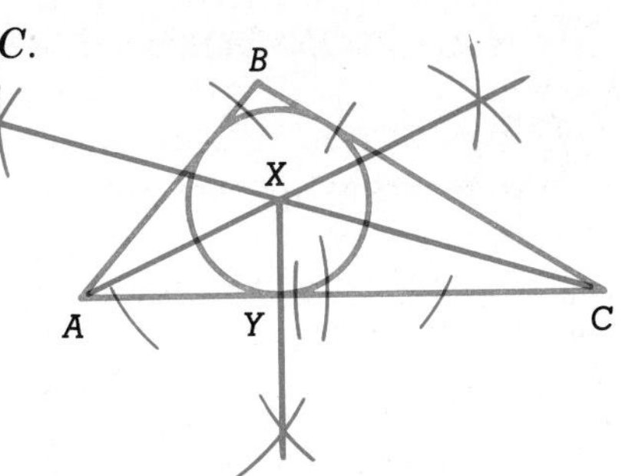

Method:

1. Bisect $\angle A$. Bisect $\angle C$. Call X the intersection of the bisectors.
2. Construct a line through X and perpendicular to $\overline{AC}$. Call the intersection of the perpendicular with $\overline{AC}$, the point Y.
3. Using X as the center, draw a circle with radius measuring XY. Then, $\odot X$ is inscribed within $\triangle ABC$. Point X is called the **incenter.**

EN: Ex: 1-6, Wr: 1-10; AV: Ex: 1-10, Wr: 1-9 odds; p. 450, Wr: 16-19

exercises

FN: Ex: 1-10, Wr: 1-6; p. 450, Wr: 16-19

Exploratory **The figure at the right shows the construction of a line tangent to $\odot C$ through A. Supply reasons for each of the following statements in the justification for the construction.**

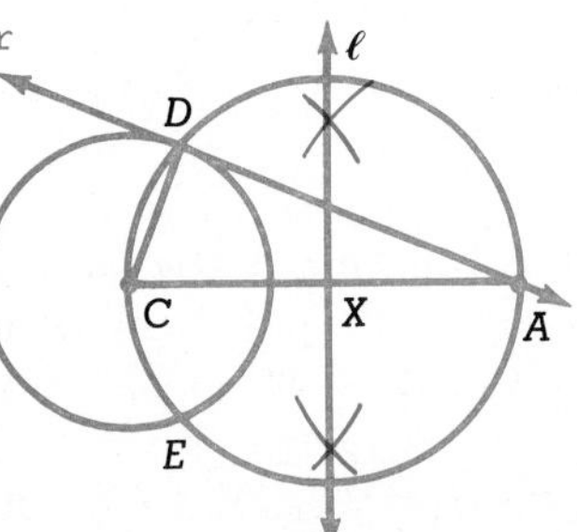

1. $\overline{AC}$ is a diameter of $\odot X$. Def. of Diameter
2. Draw $\overline{CD}$. Postulate 1-1
3. $\widehat{CDA}$ is a semicircle. Def. of Semicircle
4. $\angle CDA$ is a right angle. Theorem 10-8
5. $\overline{CD} \perp \overleftrightarrow{AD}$ Def. of Perpendicular Lines
6. $\overleftrightarrow{AD}$ is tangent to $\odot C$ at D. Theorem 10-11

State *yes* or *no* for each of the following.

7. Suppose a circle is circumscribed about an acute triangle. Can the center of the circle be in the interior of the triangle? Must it be in the interior of the triangle? yes; yes
8. Suppose a circle is circumscribed about an obtuse triangle. Can the center of the circle be in the interior of the triangle? Must it be in the interior of the triangle? no; no

Answer each of the following.

9. Name the type of triangle whose circumcenter lies outside the triangle. obtuse
10. Name the type of triangle whose incenter and circumcenter are the same point. equilateral

Written **Complete each of the following.**

For answers to exercises 1-10, see the Teacher's Guide.

1. Draw a circle. Label the center P. Locate a point on the circle. Label it A. Construct a tangent to $\odot P$ at A.
2. Draw a circle. Label the center Q. Draw a point exterior to the circle. Label it B. Construct a tangent to $\odot Q$ containing B.
3. Draw an acute triangle. Circumscribe a circle about the triangle.
4. Draw an obtuse triangle. Circumscribe a circle about the triangle.
5. Construct a right triangle. Circumscribe a circle about the triangle.
6. Construct a square. Circumscribe a circle about the square.
7. Construct a rectangle. Circumscribe a circle about the rectangle.
8. Construct an equilateral triangle. Inscribe a circle within the triangle.
9. Inscribe a circle within a right triangle.
10. Construct four circles within a square which are tangent to each other and to the sides of the square.

Objectives: to separate a segment into congruent parts, to construct proportional segments, to construct the geometric mean of two segments

13–4 Proportions

It is possible to separate a segment into congruent parts. The following construction shows the method for three congruent parts.

construction

Construction 12: Separate a segment into three congruent parts.
A similar method can be used for any given number of congruent parts.

Given: $\overline{AB}$

Construct: P and Q on $\overline{AB}$ so that $\overline{AP} \cong \overline{PQ} \cong \overline{QB}$

A B

Method:

1. Draw $\overrightarrow{AM}$.
2. With the compass point at A, mark off an arc on $\overline{AM}$ at X. Construct $\overline{XY}$ and $\overline{YZ}$ so that $\overline{AX} \cong \overline{XY} \cong \overline{YZ}$.
3. Draw $\overline{ZB}$. Then, construct lines through Y and X that are parallel to $\overline{ZB}$. Call P and Q the intersection points on $\overline{AB}$. Then $\overline{AP} \cong \overline{PQ} \cong \overline{QB}$.

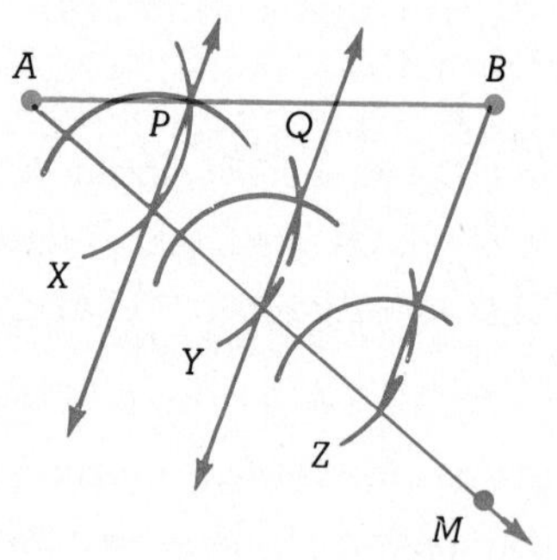

Justification: Since $\overleftrightarrow{PX} \parallel \overleftrightarrow{QY} \parallel \overline{BZ}$ and the lines cut off congruent segments on transversal $\overrightarrow{AZ}$, they cut off congruent segments on transversal $\overline{AB}$.

Encourage students to justify their constructions as shown in the examples.

The following show how to construct proportional segments.

constructions

Construction 13: Given three segments, construct a fourth segment so the measures are proportional.

Given: segments with measures x, y, and z

Construct: a segment with measure a so that $\frac{x}{y} = \frac{z}{a}$

x

y

z

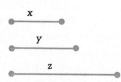

Method:

1. Draw an angle. Call it $\angle P$.
2. With compass setting of x and compass point at P, mark an arc on one side of the angle. Call the intersection point Q.

3. With compass setting of y and point at Q, mark an arc on $\overrightarrow{PQ}$ at R.
4. With compass setting of z and point at P, mark an arc on the other side of the angle at S.
5. Draw $\overline{QS}$. Then, construct a ray parallel to $\overline{QS}$ with endpoint R. The parallel ray intersects $\overrightarrow{PS}$ in a point. Call it T and say $ST = a$. Then, $\frac{x}{y} = \frac{z}{a}$ and $\overline{ST}$ is the required segment.

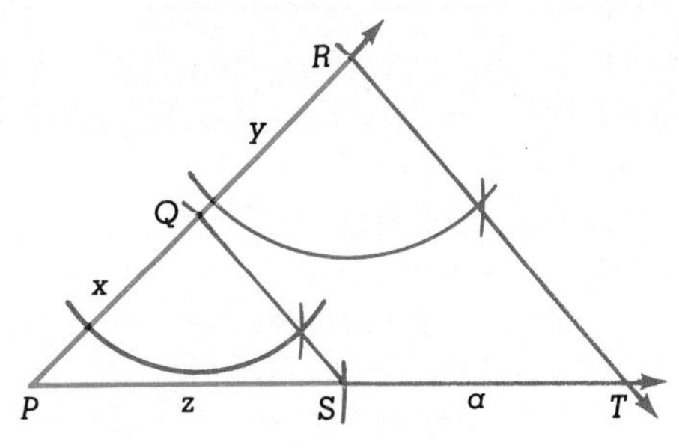

Justification: By Theorem 8–10, if a line is parallel to one side of a triangle and intersects the other two sides, then it separates the sides into segments of proportional lengths.

Construction 14: Construct the geometric mean of two given segments.

Given: $AB = x$ and $CD = y$

Construct: $\overline{PQ}$ so that PQ is the geometric mean of AB and CD

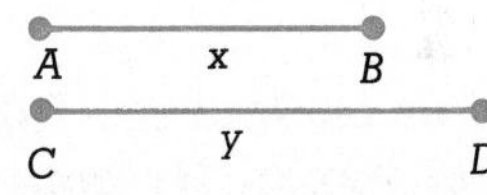

Method:

1. Draw a line. From a point P on the line, mark off segments measuring x and y. Label the endpoints L and M.
2. Construct the perpendicular bisector of $\overline{LM}$. Label the point of intersection S.
3. Using S as a center and LS as a radius, construct a semicircle with endpoints L and M.
4. Construct a line perpendicular to $\overline{LM}$ and containing P. Label the intersection of the line with the semicircle, Q. Then, PQ is the geometric mean of AB and CD.

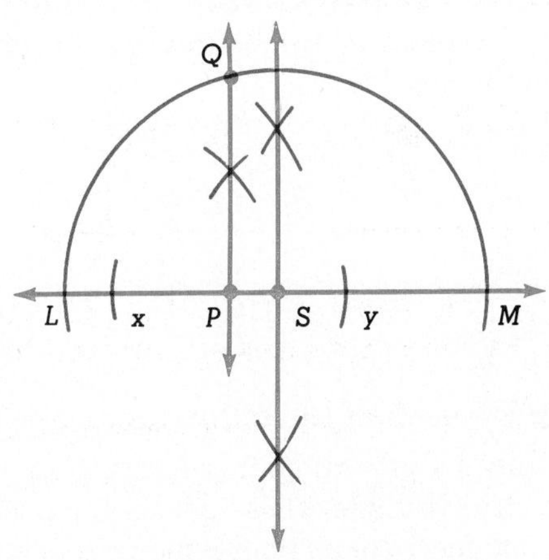

Justification: Draw $\overline{LQ}$ and $\overline{MQ}$. Since $\triangle LMQ$ is inscribed in a semicircle, $\angle LQM$ is a right angle and the triangle is a right triangle. By construction $\overline{PQ}$ is an altitude of $\triangle LQM$. Thus, PQ is the geometric mean between LP and PM. But, $\overline{LP} \cong \overline{AB}$ and $\overline{PM} \cong \overline{CD}$, so PQ is the geometric mean between AB and CD.

EN: Ex: 1-5, Wr: 1-21 odds; p. 457, C: 1-3; AV: Ex: 1-5, Wr: 1-21 odds; p. 453, Wr: 7-10; p. 457, C: 1-3

exercises

FN: Ex: 1-5, Wr: 1-15; p. 453, Wr: 7-10; p. 457, C: 1-3

Exploratory **The figure at the right shows the construction of the geometric mean of *PL* and *PM*. Supply reasons for each of the following statements in the justification for the construction.**

1. Draw $\overline{LQ}$ and $\overline{MQ}$. Postulate 1-1
2. $\widehat{LQM}$ is a semicircle. Definition of Semicircle
3. $\angle LQM$ is a right angle. Theorem 10-8
4. $\overline{PQ}$ is an altitude of $\triangle LQM$. Definition of Altitude
5. PQ is the geometric mean between PL and PM. Theorem 9-2

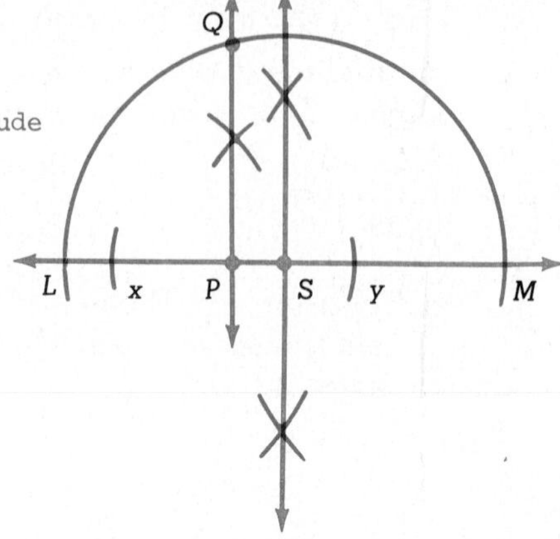

For answers to exercises 1-21, see the Teacher's Guide.

Written **For each of the following, draw a segment that is about 10 centimeters long on a piece of paper. By construction, separate the segment into the given number of congruent parts.**

1. 2 **2.** 3 **3.** 4 **4.** 5 **5.** 6 **6.** 7 **7.** 8

On a piece of paper, draw and label three segments like the segments shown below. Then, for each of the following, construct a segment with measure *x* so that the given proportion holds.

8. $\frac{a}{b} = \frac{c}{x}$ **9.** $\frac{a}{b} = \frac{x}{c}$

10. $\frac{a}{x} = \frac{b}{c}$ **11.** $\frac{x}{a} = \frac{c}{b}$

12. $\frac{a}{2b} = \frac{c}{x}$ **13.** $\frac{x}{2b} = \frac{c}{a}$

14. $\frac{x}{a} = \frac{a}{b}$ **15.** $\frac{x}{b} = \frac{b}{c}$

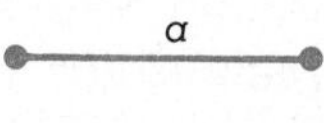

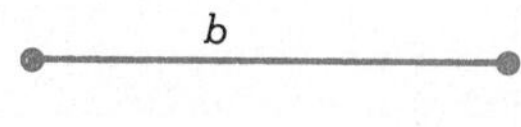

c

Exercises 8–15 and 21

Complete each of the following.

16. Draw a segment. Then, construct an equilateral triangle whose perimeter has the same measure as the segment.

17. Draw a segment. Then, construct a square whose perimeter has the same measure as the segment.

18. Draw a segment. Then, separate the segment into segments whose measures are in the ratio 2 to 3.

19. Draw a segment. Then, separate the segment into segments whose measures are in the ratio 1 to 2.

20. Draw two segments. Then, construct the geometric mean of the two segments.

21. Use the diagram for exercise **8** and construct the geometric mean of segments *a* and *c*.

careers

Carpenter

Joselyn Jedick is a carpenter. She built the house shown at the right. Part of the house is made of equilateral triangles to form what is called a **geodesic dome.**

She also did much of the carpentry work on the interior. Joselyn used her knowledge of geometric concepts and other mathematical skills to help complete the job.

Example A frame for a wall is shown below. Joselyn wants to cut a piece of wood for a brace. Using the information given on the drawing, find the length as represented by x to the nearest tenth of a foot.

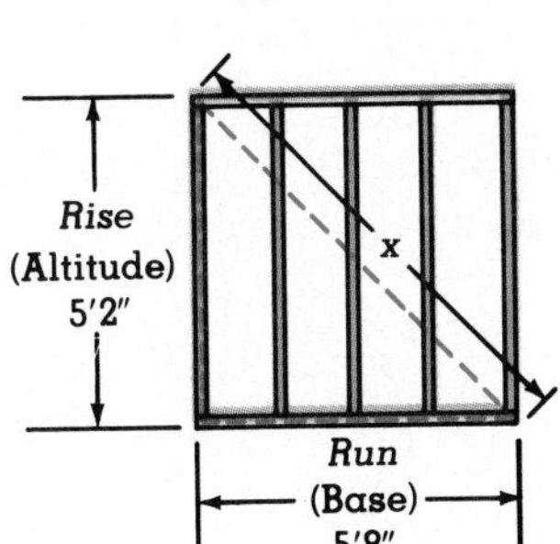

1. The rise, the run, and the base form a right triangle.
2. The Pythagorean Theorem can be applied.
3. Change all units to inches and apply the Pythagorean Theorem.

$$(62)^2 + (68)^2 = x^2$$
$$3844 + 4624 = x^2$$
$$8468 = x^2$$
$$\sqrt{8468} \text{ or } 92.0 \approx x$$

The length is about 92 inches.

4. Divide the number of inches by 12 to find the number of feet.

$$92 \div 12 = 7.\overline{6} \text{ or about } 7.7 \text{ ft.}$$

Exercises Find the value of x to the nearest tenth of a unit.

1.

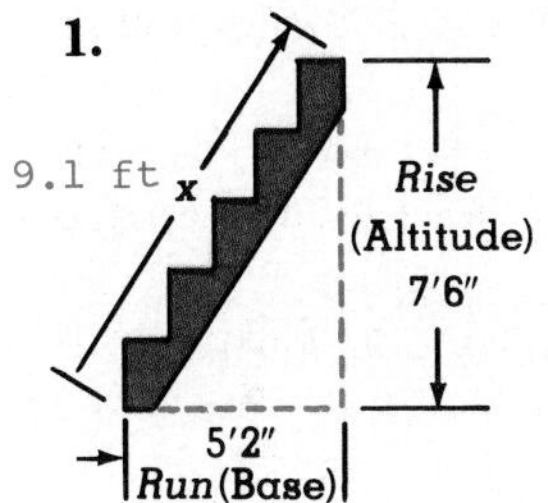

2.

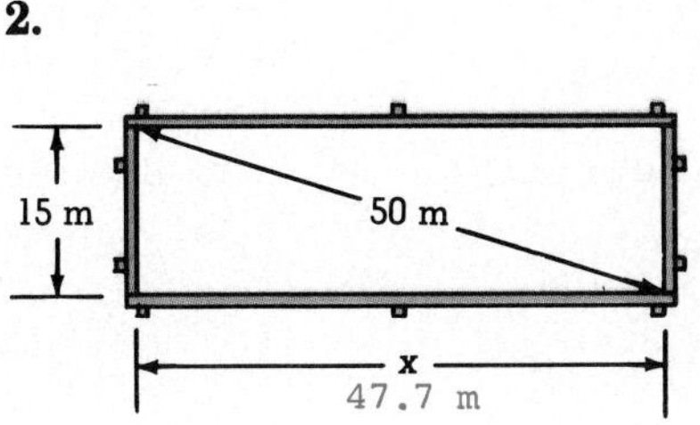

3.

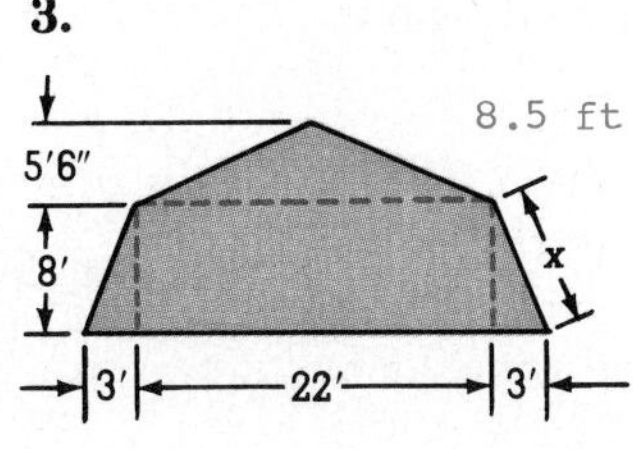

13–5 Loci

Objective: to describe a locus in a plane or in space

In geometry, a figure is a **locus** if and only if it is the set of all points and only those points that satisfy a given condition.

The circle is the locus of all points in the plane of the page that are 2 centimeters from *P*. If a point is in the interior of the circle, it is less than 2 centimeters from *P*. If a point is in the exterior of the circle, it is more than 2 centimeters from *P*.

Suppose you are asked to describe a certain locus. First, you should read the problem carefully and draw the figure.

Find the locus of all points in a plane that are 15 millimeters from a given point, *C*.

The figure is point *C*.

Draw the given figure.

After drawing the given figure, locate several points that satisfy the given conditions.

Draw points that are 15 millimeters from *C*. Locate enough points to suggest the shape of the locus.

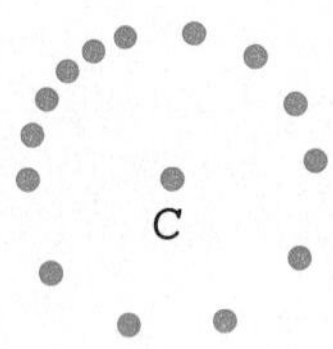

Locate several points.

As soon as the shape of a geometric figure begins to appear, draw a smooth curve or line that contains the points. Then, describe the locus in words.

The points suggest a circle.

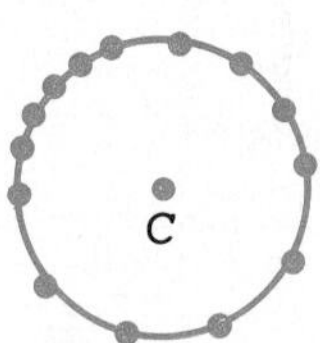

Draw a smooth curve or line.

The locus of all points in a plane that are 15 millimeters from a given point, *C*, is a circle with center *C* and radius measuring 15 millimeters.

Describe the locus.

Procedure for Determining Locus

1. **Draw the given figure.**
2. **Locate several points.**
3. **Draw a smooth curve or line.**
4. **Describe the locus.**

example

1 Determine the locus of all points in a plane that are 2 centimeters from a given line.

The figure is a line. — *Draw the given figure.*

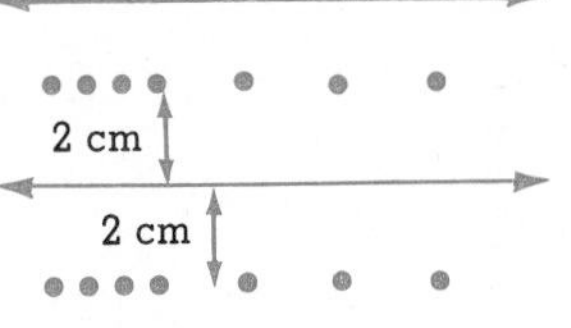

Locate several points.

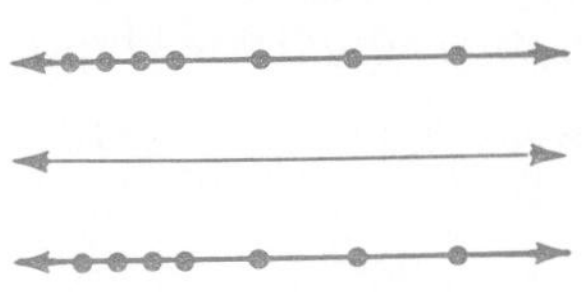

Draw a smooth curve or line.

The locus of all points in a plane that are 2 centimeters from a given line is a pair of lines parallel to the given line and 2 centimeters from the line. — *Describe the locus.*

A locus may differ depending on whether it is *in a plane* or *in space.*

The locus of all points *in a plane* that are equidistant from two parallel lines is a line that is parallel to the given lines and midway between them.

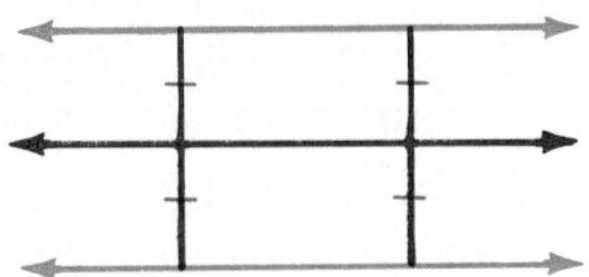

The locus of all points *in space* that are equidistant from two parallel lines is a plane that (1) contains a line parallel to the given lines and midway between them, and (2) is perpendicular to the plane containing the given lines.

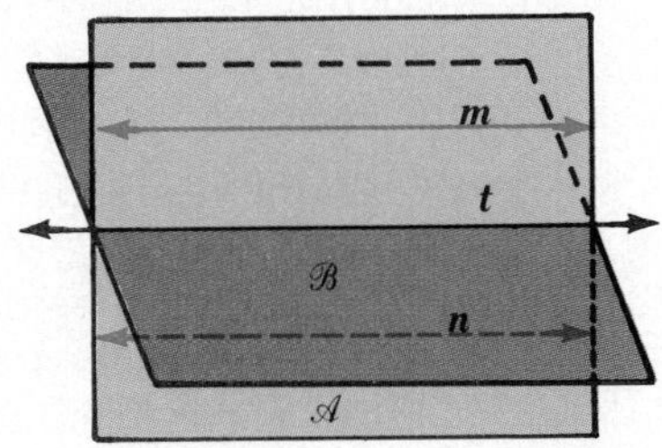

EN: Ex: 1, 2, 13, 14, Wr: 1-20; AV: Ex: 1-15 odds, Wr: 1-19 odds; p. 456, Wr: 6-20 evens

exercises

FN: Wr: 1-16, Wr: 1-19 odds; p. 456, Wr: 16-21; p. 461, TG: 1-4

Exploratory **For each of the following, describe the locus of all points in a plane that are the given distance from a given point *C*. Then describe for all points in space.**

1. 1 mm
2. 2 ft
3. 3 m
4. 4 in.
5. 40 m
6. 100 cm
7. 1000 mm
8. x ft

For answers to exercises 1-16, see the Teacher's Guide.

For each of the following, describe the locus of all points in a plane that are the given distance from a given line ℓ. Then describe it for all points in space.

9. 1 in.
10. 2 mm
11. 3 in.
12. 4 m
13. 40 m
14. 100 ft
15. 1000 cm
16. x in.

Point out, if class needs indicate, that Written exercises 1-16 refer to loci in the plane, and Written exercises 17-20 refer to loci in space.

For answers to exercises 1-20, see the Teacher's Guide.

Written **Describe the locus for each of the following.**

1. all the midpoints of the radii of a circle with radius measuring 10 centimeters
2. all the midpoints of the radii of a circle with radius measuring 12 inches
3. all points in the interior of a 5-inch square that are 2 inches from a side of the square
4. all points in the exterior of a 5-inch square that are 2 inches from a side of the square
5. all points in a plane that are equidistant from the sides of a given angle
6. all points in a plane that are equidistant from two intersecting lines in that plane
7. all the points in a plane that are equidistant from two given points
8. all the points in a plane that are equidistant from the centers of two given circles
9. all the points in a plane that are 5 centimeters from a circle with radius measuring 3 centimeters
10. all the points in a plane that are 3 centimeters from a circle with radius measuring 5 centimeters
11. all the points in a plane that are centers of circles with radii measuring 7 inches and that pass through a given point
12. all points in a plane that are centers of circles tangent to a given line at a given point on the line
13. all the points in a plane that are centers of circles which are tangent to both sides of a given angle
14. all points in a plane that are centers of circles with radii measuring 15 millimeters and tangent to a given line
15. all the points in a plane that are the third vertex of isosceles triangles with a given line segment for a base
16. all points in a plane that are the right angle vertex of right triangles with a given line segment for a hypotenuse
17. all the points in space that are a given distance from a given line
18. all the points in space that are equidistant from two given points
19. all the points in space that are the centers of spheres with radii measuring r units and tangent to a given plane
20. all the points in space that are the centers of spheres that are tangent to a given plane at a given point in the plane

topics in geometry

Vectors

Vectors combine both geometric and algebraic concepts. A *vector* is a quantity with both *magnitude* and *direction*. A directed segment or ray is used to picture a vector.

Both mathematics and physics make frequent use of vectors.

Consider an airplane flying due east at 200 km/h. The directed line segment $\vec{a}$ is a vector that pictures this situation.

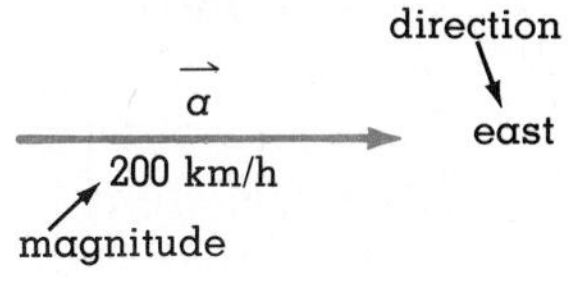

At the same time a wind is blowing due south on the plane at 50 km/h. This can be represented by vector $\vec{b}$.

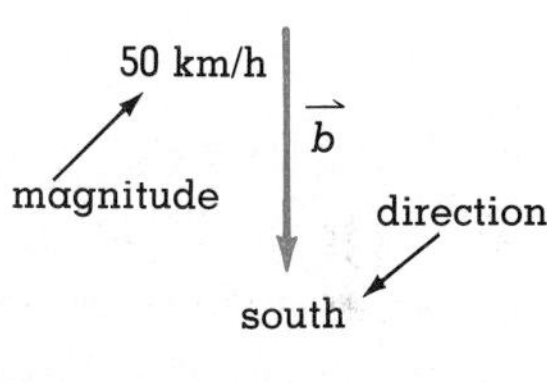

Vector $\vec{c}$ shows the result of combining these two situations. $\vec{c}$ represents the true path and speed of the plane.

The Pythagorean Theorem can be used to find the magnitude of $\vec{c}$ or $|\vec{c}|$. The magnitude is the length of the *resultant velocity*.

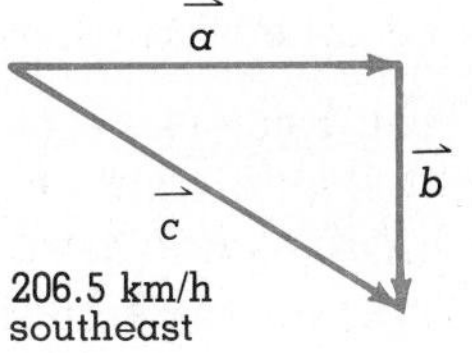

$$|\vec{c}| = \sqrt{200^2 + 50^2}$$
$$= \sqrt{40{,}000 + 2500}$$
$$|\vec{c}| = \sqrt{42{,}500} \text{ or about } 206.2$$

The magnitude of $\vec{c}$ to the nearest tenth is about 206.2 km/h in a southeast direction.

Exercises **Use vectors to solve each of the following.**

1. An airplane flies due west at 240 km/h. At the same time, the wind blows it due south at 70 km/h. What is the plane's resultant velocity? 250 km/h, 16° southwest
2. A boat heads due east across a lake at 8 m/s. It faces a current of 5 m/s moving due south. What is the boat's resultant velocity? 9.4 m/s, 32° southeast
3. Two soccer players kick the ball at the same time. One player's foot exerts a force of 70 newtons west. The other's foot exerts a force of 50 newtons north. What is the magnitude and direction of the resultant force on the ball? 86.0 newtons, 36° northwest
4. An airplane flies at 150 km/h and heads 30° south of east. A 40 km/h wind blows it in the direction 30° west of south. What is the plane's resultant velocity? 155.2 km/h, 45° northeast

13–6 Intersection of Loci

Objective: to solve locus problems that must satisfy several conditions

Some loci must satisfy several conditions. Such loci often can be determined by finding the intersection of loci that meet each condition.

example

1 Determine the locus of all points in a plane that are equidistant from two given points and equidistant from two given parallel lines.

The locus of all points in a plane that are equidistant from two given points is the perpendicular bisector of the segment joining the two points.

Point out that students should consider each condition separately and then focus on the intersection of conditions.

The locus of all points in a plane that are equidistant from two given parallel lines is a line parallel to the given lines and midway between them.

If A and B are the given points, and ℓ and m are the given lines, then C is the only point that is equidistant from A and B, and equidistant from ℓ and m.

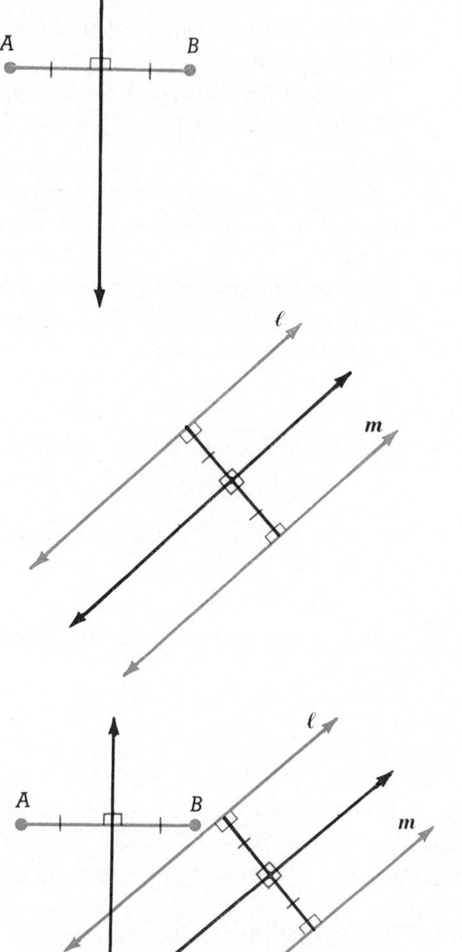

Some construction problems involve finding a point that satisfies several conditions.

example

2 Given $\overline{AB}$, $\overline{AC}$, and $\overline{CD}$, construct $\triangle ABC$ so that $\overline{CD}$ is an altitude.

1. Vertex C of $\triangle ABC$ will lie AC units from A. Thus, the locus of all points that are AC units from A is a circle with center A and radius measuring AC units.

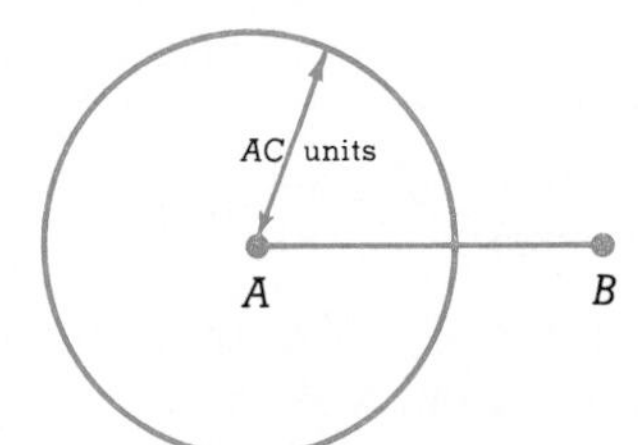

2. Endpoint D of altitude $\overline{CD}$ will lie on side $\overline{AB}$ or on the line containing $\overline{AB}$. Since $\overline{CD}$ is an altitude, then $\overline{CD} \perp \overleftrightarrow{AB}$ and endpoint C will lie on a line parallel to $\overleftrightarrow{AB}$. The locus of all points that are CD units from $\overleftrightarrow{AB}$ are two lines on either side of $\overleftrightarrow{AB}$, parallel to $\overleftrightarrow{AB}$ and CD units away.

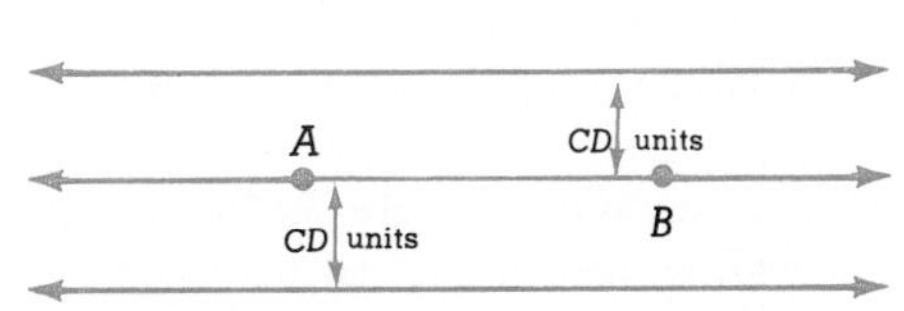

3. Point C must satisfy the conditions for being a vertex, Step 1, and the conditions for being the endpoint of an altitude, Step 2. Only four points satisfy these conditions. Thus, there are four possible ways to draw $\triangle ABC$.

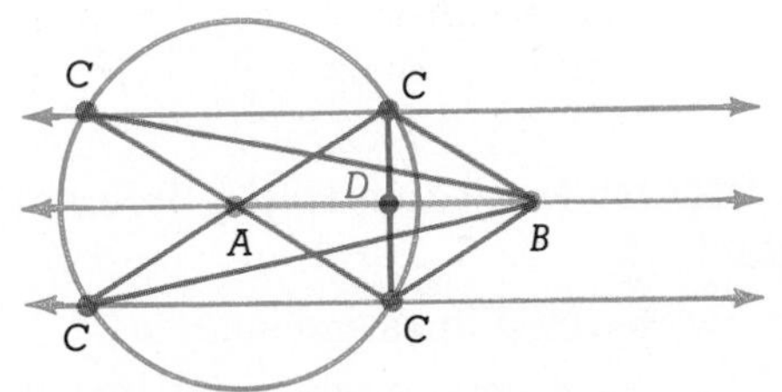

EN: Ex: 1-6, Wr: 1-23 odds; p. 465, Cal: 1-4; AV: Ex: 1-6, Wr: 1-16, 17-23 odds; p. 460, Wr: 6-20 evens; p. 465, Cal: 1-4

exercises

FN: Ex: 1-6, Wr: 1-20, 21, 23; p. 460, Wr: 6-20 evens; p. 465, Cal: 1-2

Exploratory **For each of the following, choose the letter of the best answer.**

1. The locus of points in a plane equidistant from the endpoints of a segment is _____.
   - **a.** a midpoint of the segment
   - **b.** a bisector of the segment
   - **c.** a perpendicular bisector of the segment
   - **d.** two lines parallel to the segment

2. The locus of points in a plane equidistant from the sides of an angle is _____.
   - **a.** a line joining the midpoints of the sides
   - **b.** a bisector of the angle
   - **c.** a circle about the vertex
   - **d.** the angle vertical to the given angle

3. The locus of points in a plane equidistant from two parallel lines is ____.
   a. a line parallel to the lines and midway between them
   b. a line perpendicular to the given lines
   c. a pair of lines parallel to the given lines and at a given distance from them
   d. a circle between the lines and tangent to them

4. The locus of points in a plane equidistant from two intersecting lines is ____.
   a. the intersection of each pair of lines and at a given distance from them
   b. a circle with center at the intersection point and at a given distance from it
   c. a pair of lines perpendicular to the given lines
   d. a pair of lines which bisect the angles formed by the two intersecting lines

5. The locus of points in a plane at a given distance from a given point is ____.
   a. a pair of perpendicular lines that intersect at the given point
   b. a set of circles containing the point with radii of the given distance
   c. a circle whose center is the given point and whose radius measures the given distance
   d. a square whose diagonals intersect at the given point and sides measure the given distance

6. The locus of points in a plane at a given distance from a given line is ____.
   a. a pair of lines parallel to the given line and at a given distance from it
   b. a set of circles whose centers lie on the line and whose radii measure the given distance
   c. a line perpendicular to the given line
   d. a pair of planes parallel to each other and at the given distance from the line

For answers to exercises 1-24, see the Teacher's Guide.

Written **For each of the following, describe all the possible ways the figures can intersect.**

1. two parallel lines and a circle
2. two concentric circles and a line
3. two concentric circles and two parallel lines
4. a sphere and a plane
5. a sphere and two parallel lines
6. two circles
7. two spheres
8. a sphere and two parallel planes
9. a circle and a plane
10. a circle and a sphere

Describe the locus for each of the following.

11. all the points in a plane that are 2 centimeters from a given line and 5 centimeters from a given point on the line
12. all the points in a plane that are 3 centimeters from a given line and 1.5 centimeters from a given point on the line
13. all the points in space that are 2 inches from a given line and 5 inches from a given point on the line
14. all the points in space that are 3 inches from a given line and 2 inches from a given point on the line

15. all the points in a plane that are equidistant from three given points

16. all the points in a plane that are equidistant from a given line and equidistant from two points on the line

17. all the points in a plane that are equidistant from the sides of an angle and 4 inches from the vertex of the angle

18. all the points in a plane that are equidistant from the sides of an angle and a given distance from the vertex of the angle

19. all the points in a plane equidistant from two given parallel lines and a given distance from another line

20. all the points in a plane that are equidistant from two given parallel lines and a given distance from a point *not* on the lines

Complete each of the following.

21. Draw a line, m, and two points, C and D, on one side of the line. Then, construct the locus of points in the plane that are equidistant from C and D.

22. Draw two segments, $\overline{PQ}$ and $\overline{RS}$. Choose a point between P and Q, and label it A. Then, construct a circle tangent to $\overline{PQ}$ at A and whose center lies on $\overline{RS}$.

23. Draw a line, ℓ, and a point, P, on the line. Draw Q *not* on ℓ. Then, construct the locus of the centers of all circles in the plane that contain P and Q.

24. Draw two parallel lines, ℓ and m. Choose a point between ℓ and m, and label it B. Construct a circle tangent to the two lines and containing B.

K or Constant Key

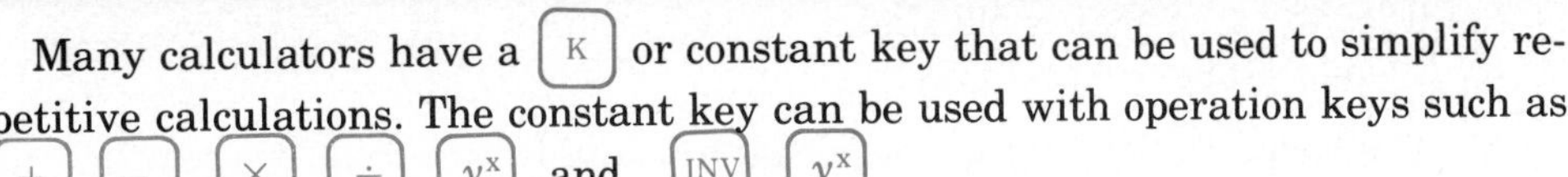

Many calculators have a [K] or constant key that can be used to simplify repetitive calculations. The constant key can be used with operation keys such as [+], [−], [×], [÷], [y^x], and [INV] [y^x]

A number to be used repeatedly must be stored first as the following illustrates.

7 [+] [K] Stores 7 to be added to each following entry

1.8 [−] [K] Stores 1.8 to be subtracted from each following entry

Example **Find $(2)^4$, $(3)^4$, and $(5)^4$.**

Enter:	2 [y^x]	[K]	4	[=]	3	[=]	5	[=]	
Display:	2		4	16	3	81	5	625	

Thus $(2)^4 = 16$, $(3)^4 = 81$, and $(5)^4 = 625$

Exercises **Use the calculator to compute the following.**

1. Add 63 to each of the following: 79, 125, 38.6, and 87.19. 142, 188, 101.6, 150.19

2. Subtract 11.9 from each of the following: 20, 3.4, 126.12, and $^-3.24$. 8.1, -8.5, 114.22, -15.14

3. Multiply 2.4 to each of the following: 22, $^-36$, 4.9, and 93.7. 52.8, -86.4, 11.76, 224.88

4. Find each of the following: $(6)^{2.1}$, $(4)^{2.1}$, $(1.3)^{2.1}$. 43.064323, 18.379174, 1.7349263

Vocabulary

straightedge (443)
compass (443)
construction (443)
locus (458)

Chapter Summary

1. The parts of a construction are: *given, construct statement, diagram, method,* and *justification.* (443)
2. In geometry, a figure is a locus if and only if it is the set of all points and only those points that satisfy a given condition. (458)
3. Procedure for determining a locus: (458)
   1. Draw the given figure.
   2. Locate several points.
   3. Draw a smooth curve or line.
   4. Describe the locus.
4. The locus of all points *in a plane* that are equidistant from two parallel lines is a line that is parallel to the given lines and midway between them. (459)
5. The locus of all points *in space* that are equidistant from two parallel lines is a plane that contains a line parallel to the given lines and midway between them, and is perpendicular to the plane containing the given lines. (459)

Constructions:

Construction 1: Construct a segment congruent to a given segment. (443)

Construction 2: Construct an angle congruent to a given angle.(444)

Construction 3: Construct the bisector of a given angle. (445)

Construction 4: Construct a line perpendicular to a given line and through a given point *not* on the line. (447)

Construction 5: Construct the perpendicular bisector of a given segment. (448)

Construction 6: Construct a line perpendicular to a given line and through a given point on the line. (448)

Construction 7: Construct a line parallel to a given line and through a point *not* on the line. (449)

Construction 8: Construct a line tangent to a given circle at a given point on the circle. (451)

Construction 9: Construct a line tangent to a given circle and through a point *not* on the circle. (451)

Construction 10: Locate the center of a given circle. (452)

Construction 11: Construct a circle circumscribed about a given triangle. (452)

Construction 12: Separate a segment into three congruent parts.(454)

Construction 13: Given three segments, construct a fourth segment so the measures are proportional. (454)

Construction 14: Construct the geometric mean of two given segments. (455)

Chapter Review

For answers to exercises 1-28, see the Teacher's Guide.

13–1 On a piece of paper, draw and label two segments like the segments shown at the right. Then, construct segments for each of the following measures.

1. $XY + WZ$
2. $WZ - XY$
3. $4WZ$
4. $2XY - WZ$

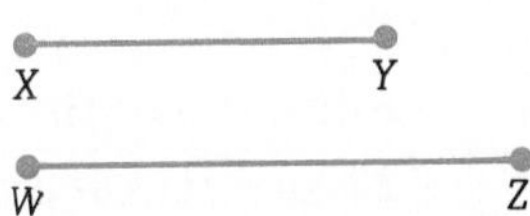

On a piece of paper, draw and label two angles like the angles shown at the right. Then, construct angles with each of the following degree measures.

5. $a + b$
6. $a - b$
7. $\frac{1}{2}a$
8. $a - \frac{1}{2}b$

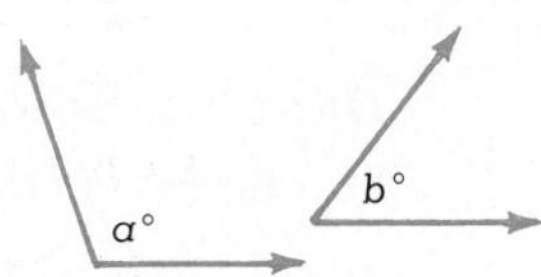

13–2 Complete each of the following.

9. Draw a segment. Label it $\overline{AB}$. Construct a line perpendicular to $\overline{AB}$.
10. Draw a line and a point *not* on the line. Label them ℓ and Q. Construct a line parallel to ℓ and containing Q.

13–3 Complete each of the following.

11. Draw a circle. Label the center C. Draw a point exterior to the circle. Label it A. Construct a tangent to $\odot C$ containing A.

12. Draw a triangle. Circumscribe a circle about the triangle.

13–4 On a piece of paper, draw and label three segments like the segments shown at the right. Then, for each of the following, construct a segment with measure x so that the given proportion holds.

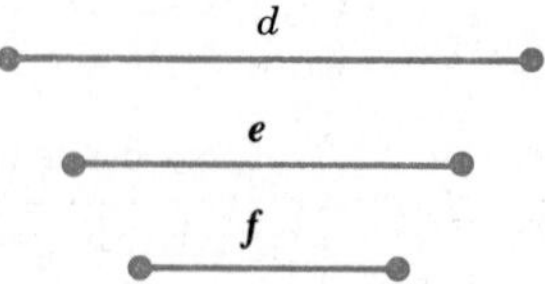

13. $\frac{d}{e} = \frac{f}{x}$

14. $\frac{d}{f} = \frac{x}{e}$

15. $\frac{x}{d} = \frac{d}{e}$

16. $\frac{f}{x} = \frac{2e}{d}$

17. Draw a segment. Then, construct a rhombus whose perimeter has the same measure as the segment.

13–5 Describe the locus for each of the following.

18. all the points in a plane that are 1 foot from a given point C

19. all the points in space that are 1 inch from a given point A

20. all the midpoints of the diameters of a circle

21. all the points in a plane that are centers of circles with radii measuring 11 centimeters and that pass through a given point

13–6 For each of the following, describe all the possible ways the figures can intersect.

22. a circle and a plane

23. a sphere and a line

24. two concentric circles and a plane

25. two parallel planes and a circle

Describe the locus for each of the following.

26. the perpendicular bisector of a segment

27. a plane parallel to two given planes and midway between them

Complete the following.

28. Draw a line, ℓ, and two points, E and F, on one side of the line. Then, construct the locus of points in the plane that are equidistant from E and F.

Chapter Test

For answers to exercises 1-19, see the Teacher's Guide.

On a piece of paper, draw and label two segments like the segments shown at the right. Then, construct segments for each of the following measures.

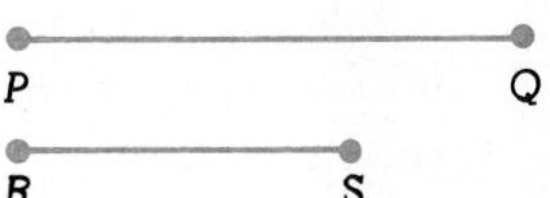

1. $PQ - RS$
2. $3PQ$
3. $3RS - PQ$
4. $2(RS + PQ)$
5. Draw two angles with degree measures c and d. Then, construct an angle having degree measure $c + d$.

Complete each of the following.

6. Draw a line and a point *not* on the line. Label them m and T. Construct a line perpendicular to m and containing T.
7. Draw an obtuse triangle. Construct the medians of the triangle.
8. Draw a circle. Label the center H and a point on the circle T. Construct a tangent to $\odot H$ at T.
9. Construct a 30°–60°–90° triangle. Circumscribe a circle about the triangle.
10. On a piece of paper, draw and label three segments with measures r, s, and t. Then, construct a segment with measure x so that the proportion $\frac{r}{s} = \frac{x}{t}$ holds.
11. Draw a segment. Then, separate the segment into segments whose measures are in the ratio of 1 to 3.

Describe the locus for each of the following.

12. all the points in a plane that are 5 inches from a given line ℓ
13. all the points in a plane that are 4 centimeters from a given point A
14. all the points in space that are 3 meters from a given point C
15. all the points in space that are 10 feet from a given line n

For each of the following, describe all the possible ways the figures can intersect.

16. two concentric spheres and a line
17. two parallel planes and a sphere

Describe the locus for each of the following.

18. the intersection of two planes
19. all the points in space that are 6 millimeters from a given line and 10 millimeters from a given point on the line

chapter 14 Transformations

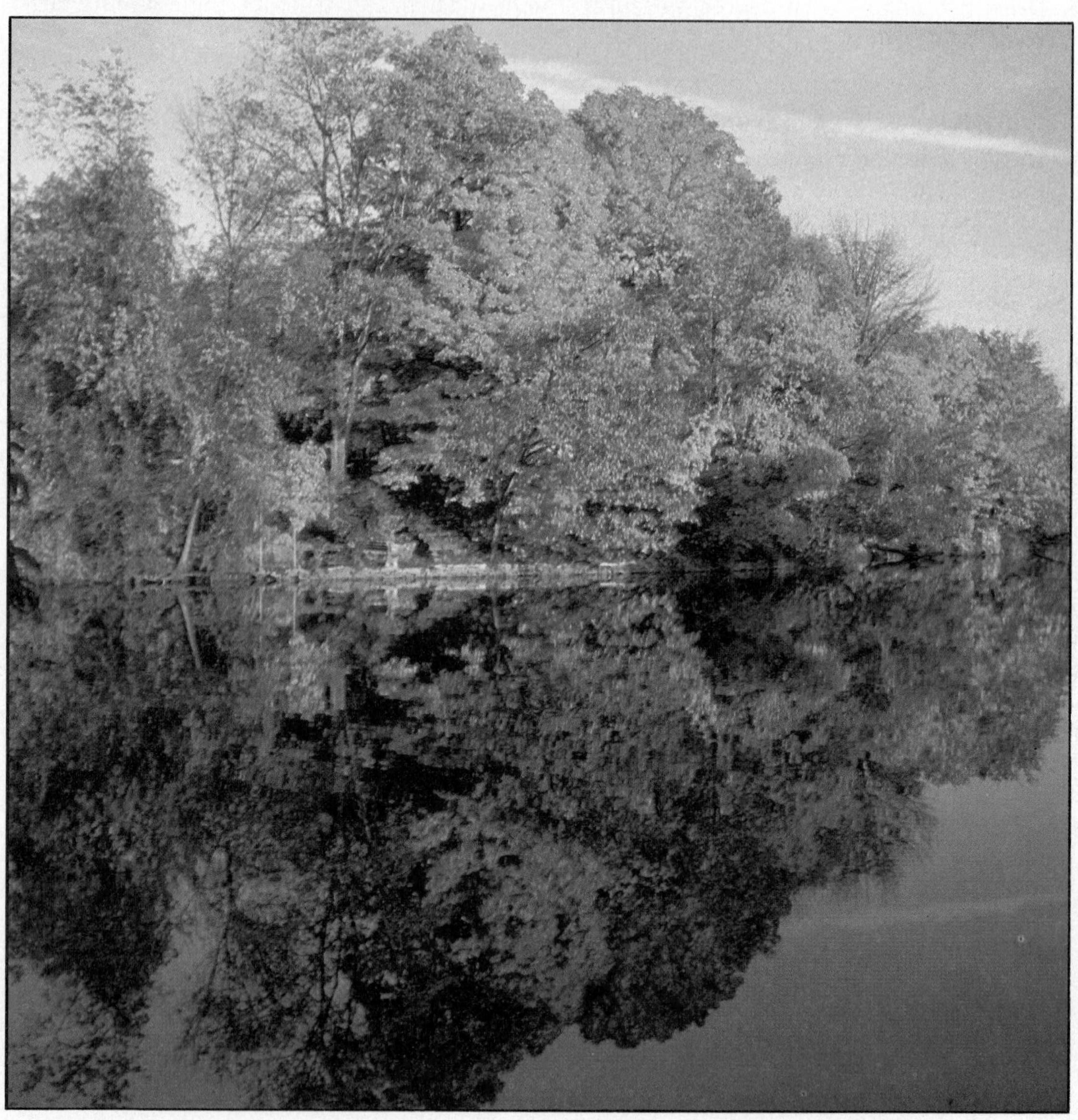

Reflections are one kind of transformation. The photograph above was created by using a reflection on a pond.

14–1 Mappings

Objectives: to name the image and the preimage of a mapping, to recognize isometry or congruence transformations

Figures can be changed in many ways. Some are shown below.

A figure can be reflected.

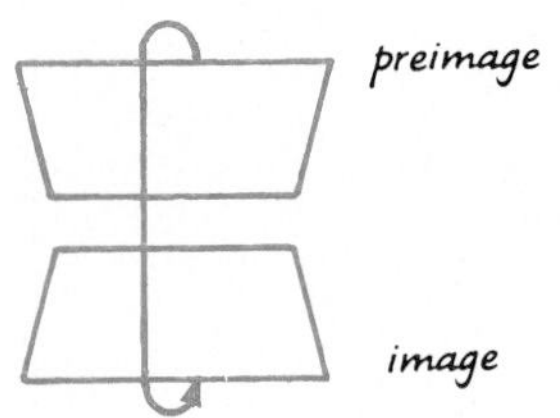

A figure can be rotated.

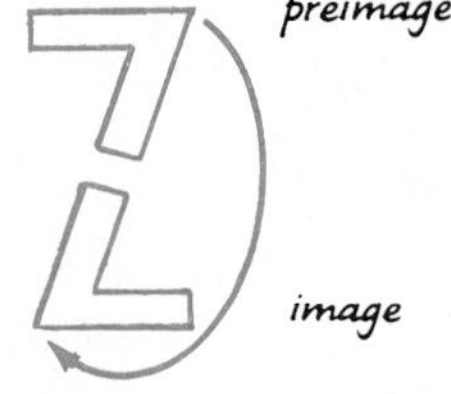

A figure can be slid.

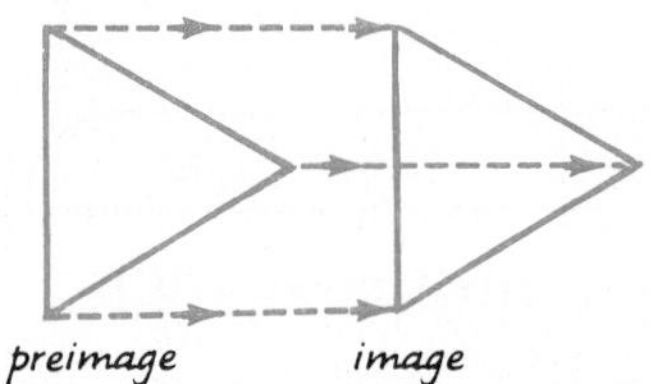

A figure can be enlarged.

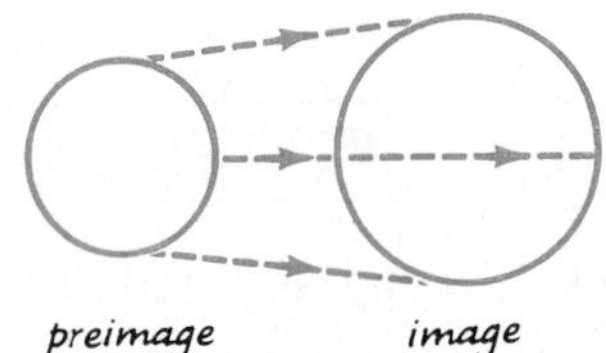

Emphasize the concept of mapping. Students may recall the use of this term with regard to the study of functions in algebra.

The mappings shown above are called **transformations.** A transformation maps a *preimage* onto an *image.*

Definition of Transformation

In a plane, a mapping is a transformation if and only if each point has exactly one image point and each image point has exactly one preimage point.

The symbol $\rightarrow$ is used to indicate mapping. For example, $\triangle ABC \rightarrow \triangle PQR$ means $\triangle ABC$ *is mapped onto* $\triangle PQR$. The order of the letters indicates the correspondence of the preimage to the image. The first vertices, A and P, are corresponding vertices. The second vertices, B and Q, are corresponding vertices. The third vertices, C and R, are corresponding vertices.

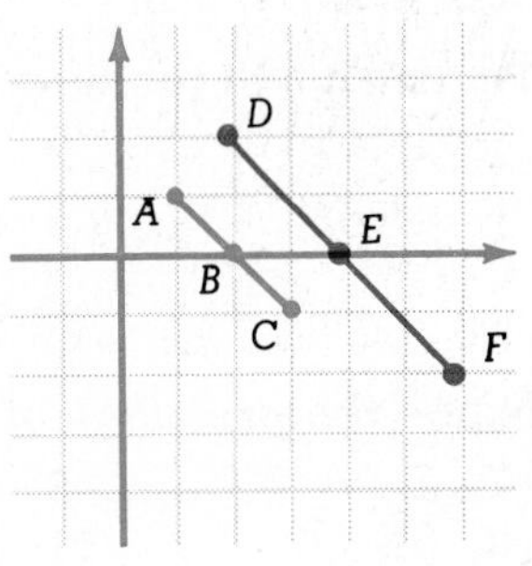

In the figure $\overline{AC} \rightarrow \overline{DF}$, A and D are corresponding points. C and F are corresponding points. B and E are corresponding points. Every point on $\overline{AC}$ corresponds to a point on $\overline{DF}$, and every point on $\overline{DF}$ corresponds to a point on $\overline{AC}$. Thus, the mapping is a transformation.

When a geometric figure and its transformation image are congruent, the mapping is called an *isometry* or a **congruence transformation.** Other mappings are called **similarity transformations.**

example

1 Suppose $\triangle ABC \to \triangle PQR$. Show that this mapping is an isometry.

$\overline{AB} \cong \overline{PQ}$, $\overline{BC} \cong \overline{QR}$, $\overline{AC} \cong \overline{PR}$

$\triangle ABC \cong \triangle PQR$ by SSS

$\triangle ABC$ is the preimage.

$\triangle PQR$ is the image.

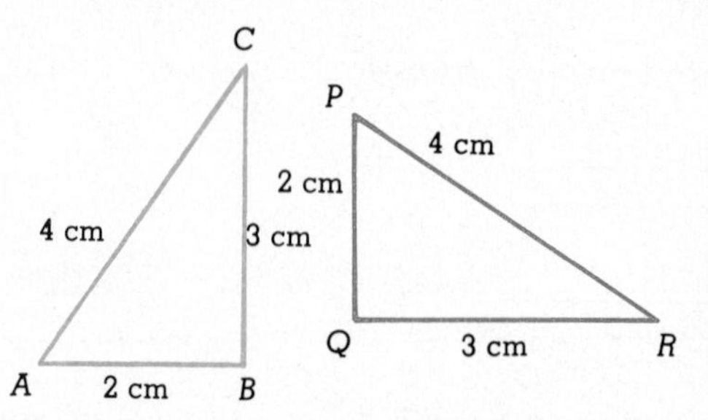

EN: Ex: 1-5, Wr: 1-16, 21-26; AV: Ex: 1-10, Wr: 1-23; FN: Ex: 1-10, Wr: 1-23

exercises

Exploratory **Answer the following, if quadrilateral *RSTU* → quadrilateral *ABCD*.**

1. Name the image of $\overline{UT}$. $\overline{DC}$
2. Name the preimage of *D*. U
3. Name the preimage of $\angle B$. $\angle S$
4. Name the image of $\angle T$. $\angle C$
5. Name the preimage of $\overline{AB}$. $\overline{RS}$

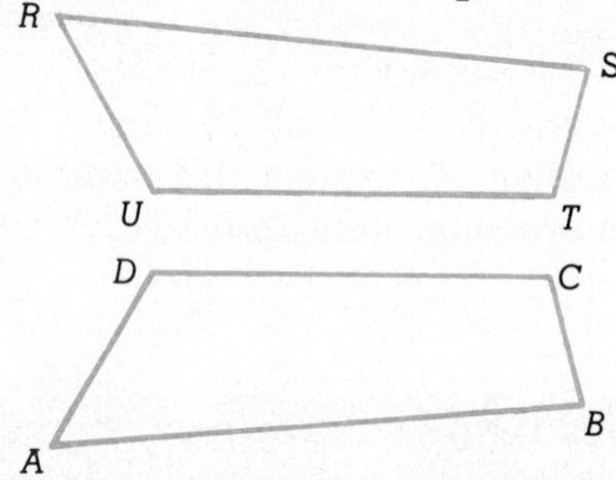

Answer each of the following, if pentagon *ABCDE* → pentagon *PQRST*.

6. Name the image of $\overline{CD}$. $\overline{RS}$
7. Name the image of $\angle E$. $\angle T$
8. Name the preimage of $\overline{PT}$. $\overline{AE}$
9. Name the preimage of $\angle Q$. $\angle B$
10. Name the image of $\overline{BC}$. $\overline{QR}$

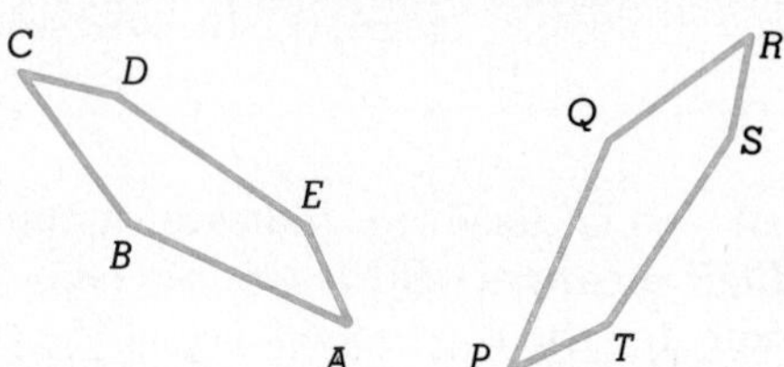

Written **In the figure, $\triangle ABC \to \triangle EBD$. Name the image of each of the following.**

1. *A* E
2. *B* B
3. *C* D
4. $\angle CAB$ $\angle DEB$
5. $\angle BCA$ $\angle BDE$
6. $\overline{AC}$ $\overline{ED}$

Name the preimage of each of the following.

7. *E* A
8. *B* B
9. *D* C
10. $\overline{BE}$ $\overline{BA}$
11. $\overline{DE}$ $\overline{CA}$
12. $\angle DBE$ $\angle CBA$

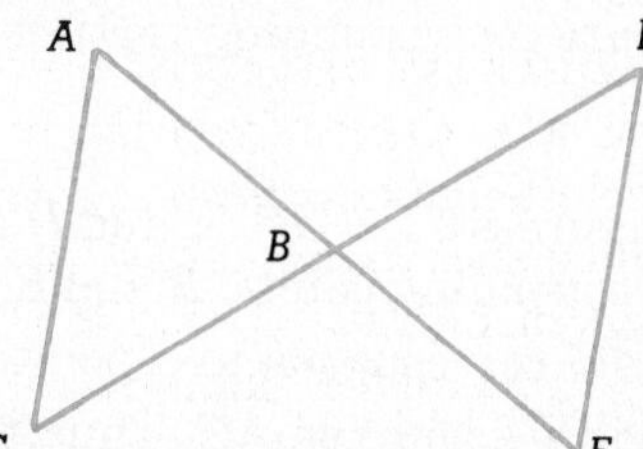

If the mapping is an isometry, use the figures below to find the image of the preimage given in exercises 13–20.

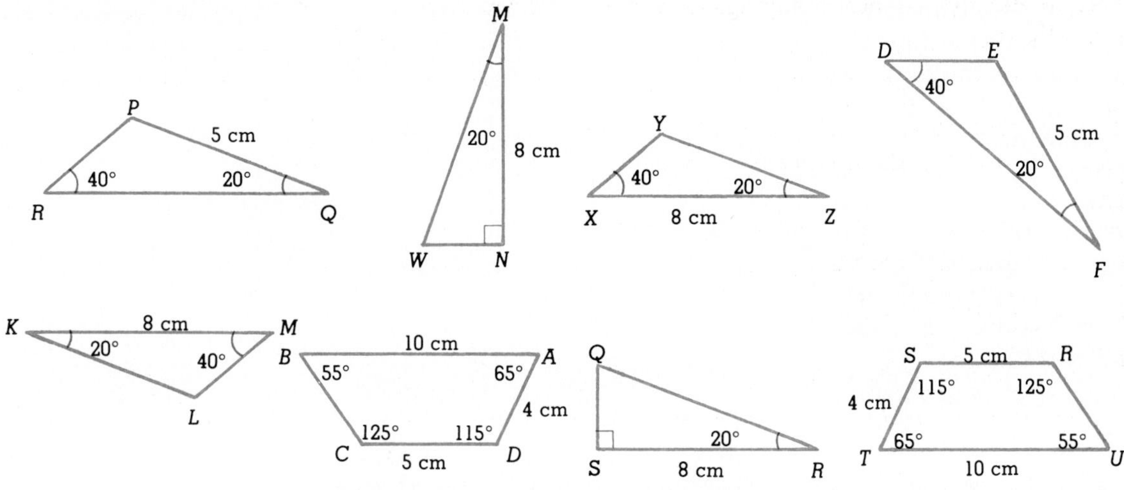

13. $\triangle MWN$ △ RQS
14. $\triangle PQR$ △ EFD
15. $\triangle SRQ$ △ NMW
16. $\triangle MKL$ △ XZY
17. $\triangle LMK$ △ YXZ
18. quadrilateral *RSTU* quad. CDAB
19. quadrilateral *BADC* quad. UTSR
20. $\triangle ZYX$ △ KLM

In the figure at the right, $\triangle XYW \cong \triangle ZYW$.

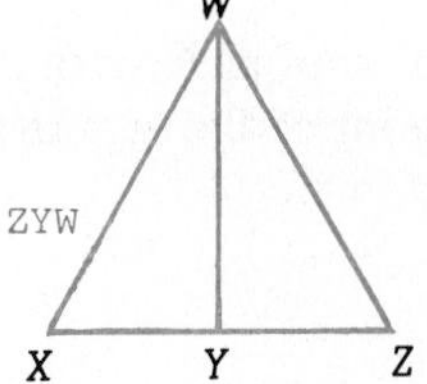

21. Name a segment that is its own preimage. $\overline{WY}$
22. Name two points that are their own preimages. W, Y
23. Name a mapping that describes the congruence. △ XYW⟶ △ ZYW

The L-shaped tile at the left is gray on top and blue underneath. Suppose two of these L-shaped tiles are used to form each of the following. Name the colors for figure *A* and figure *B*.

24. A gray; B gray

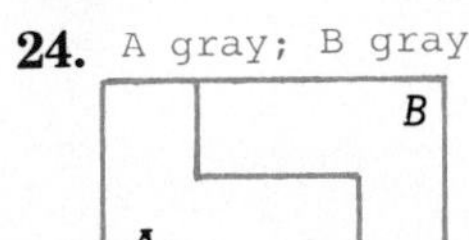

25. A gray; B gray

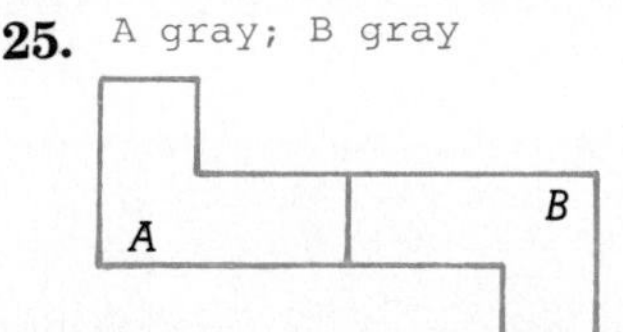

26. A blue; B gray

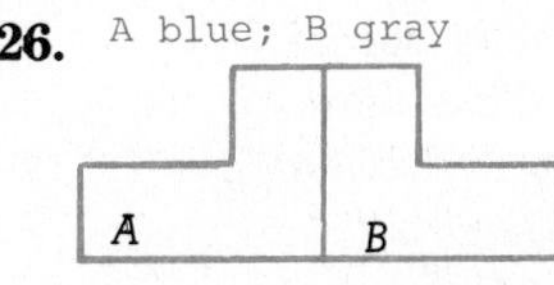

Futurists — computers

Futurists are individuals who study and plan for the future. Their work includes the study of the impact of computers on society. Benefits of computers include advances in banking, shopping, medical care, building design, etc. Some shortcomings include possible large-scale unemployment, computer crime, depersonalization, and rapid social change. Thus, all people need to learn to understand and live with computers.

Objectives: to name a reflection image with respect to a line, to recognize line symmetry and point symmetry, to draw reflection images, lines of symmetry, and points of symmetry

14–2 Reflections

One type of transformation is a **reflection.** For example, in the figure at the right, A is the reflection image of X with respect to ℓ. The *line of reflection,* ℓ, is a perpendicular bisector of the segment drawn from X to A. Since P is on the line of reflection, its image is P itself.

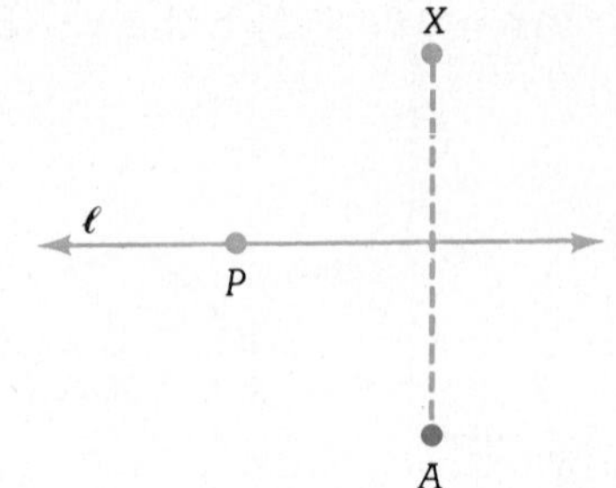

A line that is perpendicular to a segment and bisects the segment is a perpendicular bisector of the segment.

It is also possible to have a reflection image with respect to a point.

S is the reflection of R with respect to Q. The *point of reflection,* Q, is the midpoint of the segment drawn from R to S.

The reflection images of collinear points are collinear. The images of collinear points A, B, and C are the collinear points P, Q, and R. Therefore, it is said that *reflections preserve collinearity.*

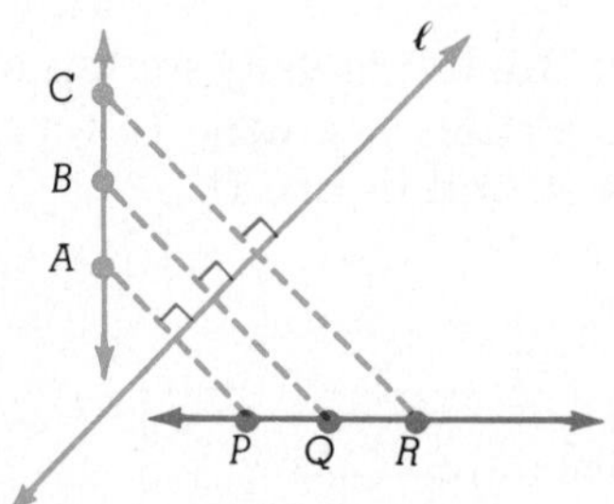

Points are collinear if and only if they lie on the same line.

Point out to students the properties preserved by reflections as noted on this page and on page 475. Subsequent lessons include references to properties that are preserved by different transformations.

The reflection image of Y is between the image of X and Z if and only if Y is between X and Z. Thus, *reflections preserve betweenness of points.*

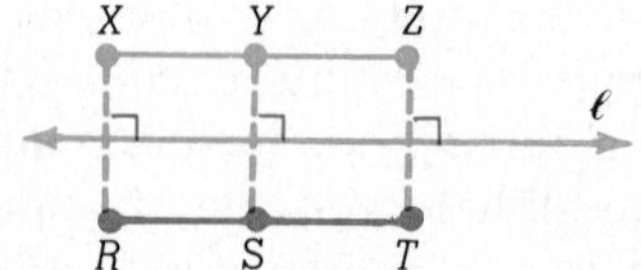

Reflections also *preserve angle measure* and *distance measure.* $\triangle XYZ$ is the reflection image of $\triangle ABC$. By measuring the corresponding parts of $\triangle ABC$ and $\triangle XYZ$ it can be shown that $\triangle ABC$ is congruent to $\triangle XYZ$.

Points A, B, and C can be read in a clockwise fashion. $\triangle ABC$ is said to have a clockwise orientation.

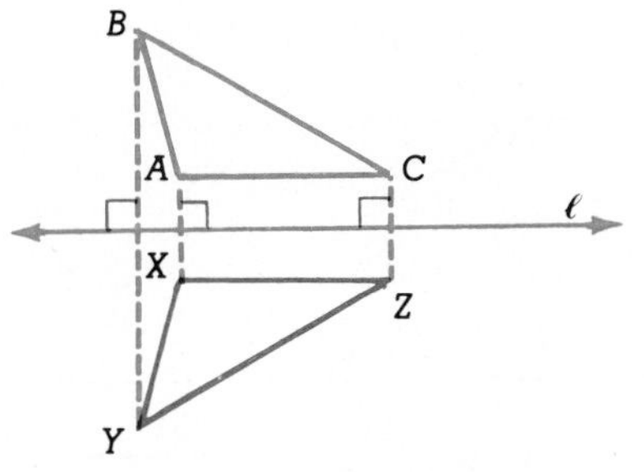

Corresponding points, X, Y, and Z are then in a counterclockwise position. $\triangle XYZ$ is said to have a counterclockwise orientation.

Point out the concept of orientation in terms of the corresponding parts of a figure and its image.

Suppose $\triangle CAB$ has a counterclockwise orientation, then what is the orientation of the reflection image? counterclockwise

Because only the orientation of a geometric figure is changed, *a reflection is an isometry.*

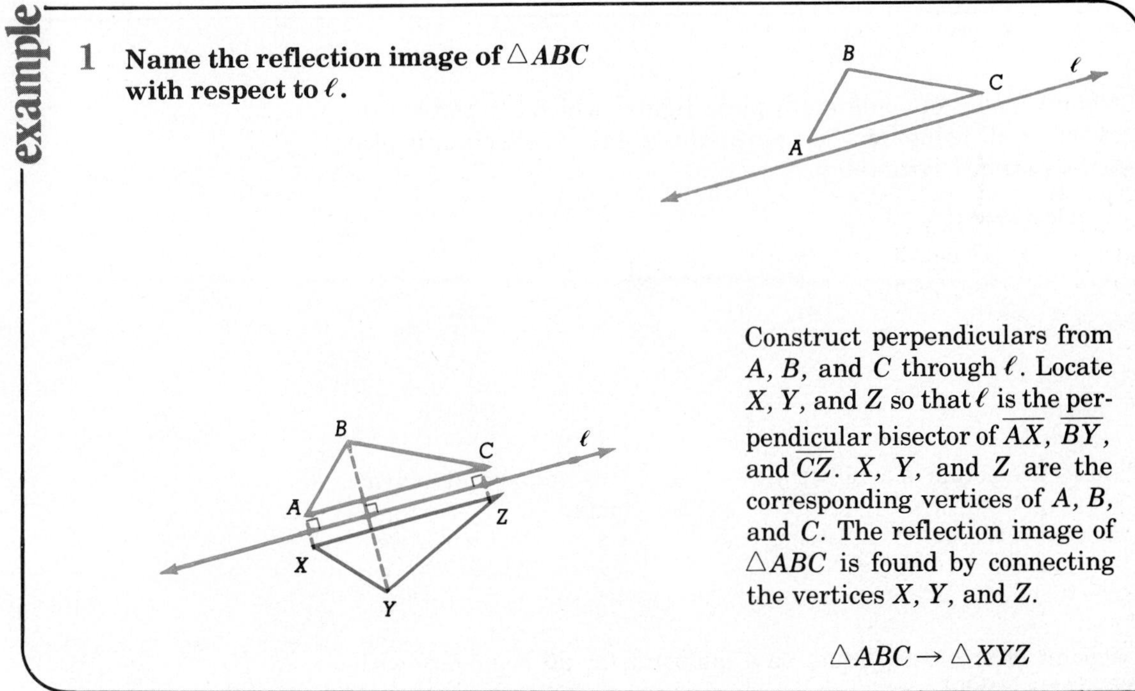

1 Name the reflection image of $\triangle ABC$ with respect to ℓ.

Construct perpendiculars from A, B, and C through ℓ. Locate X, Y, and Z so that ℓ is the perpendicular bisector of $\overline{AX}$, $\overline{BY}$, and $\overline{CZ}$. X, Y, and Z are the corresponding vertices of A, B, and C. The reflection image of $\triangle ABC$ is found by connecting the vertices X, Y, and Z.

$\triangle ABC \rightarrow \triangle XYZ$

A line can be drawn through many plane figures so that the figure on one side is a reflection image of the figure on the opposite side. In such a case, the line of reflection is called a **line of symmetry.**

Note that the term "axis of symmetry" is sometimes used in place of "line of symmetry".

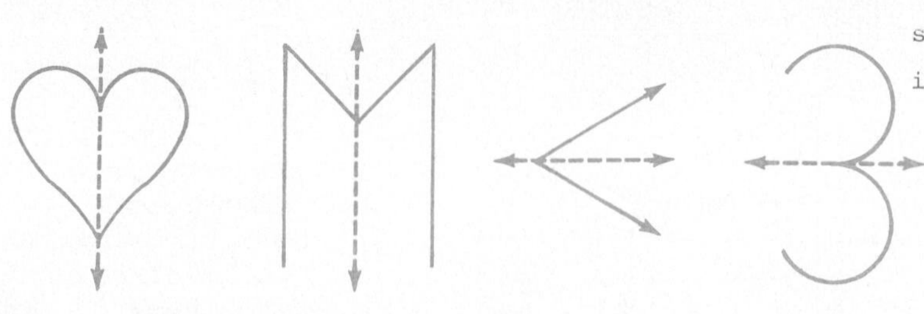

example

2 Test the given lines to see if they are lines of symmetry for rectangle *ABCD*.

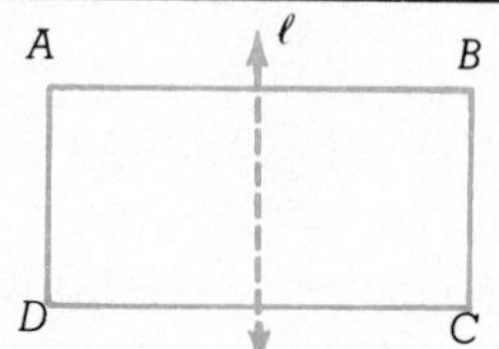

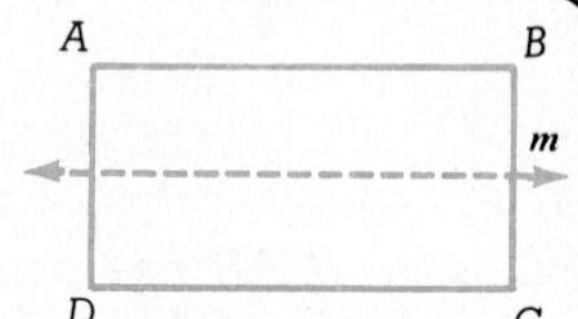

By measuring, it can be seen that ℓ is the perpendicular bisector of both $\overline{AB}$ and $\overline{CD}$. Any point to the left of ℓ has its reflection image to the right of ℓ. Likewise, by measuring, it can be seen that m is the perpendicular bisector of $\overline{AD}$ and $\overline{BC}$. Also, any point above m has its reflection image below m. Therefore, ℓ and m are lines of symmetry for rectangle *ABCD*.

A point can be found for many plane figures which is a point of reflection for all points on the figure. This point of reflection is also called a **point of symmetry.**

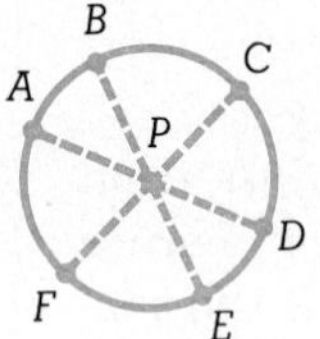

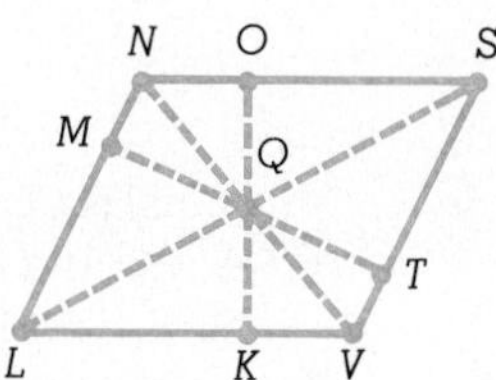

P and *Q* are points of symmetry.

P and Q are midpoints of the segments drawn.

R is *not* a point of symmetry.

R is not a midpoint of the segment drawn.

A point of symmetry must be a midpoint for all segments with endpoints on the figure.

EN: Ex: 1-15, Wr: 1-33; AV: Ex: 1-15, Wr: 1-12, 13-33 odds; p. 473, Wr: 24-26

exercises

FN: Ex: 1-15; Wr: 1-20; p. 473, Wr: 24-26

Exploratory **For each of the following figures, name the reflection image with respect to ℓ.**

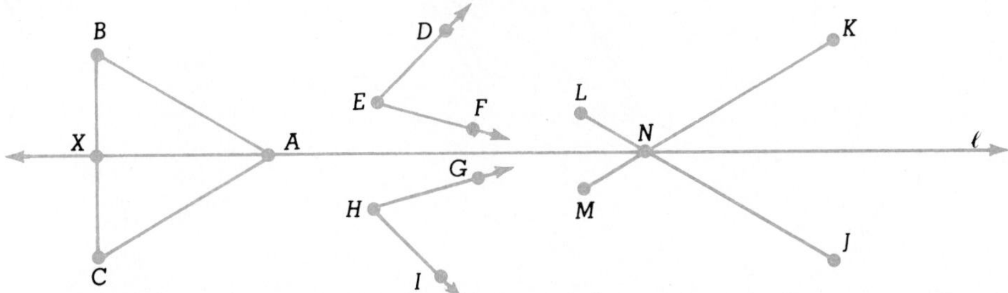

1. A A
2. B C
3. $\overline{AB}$ $\overline{AC}$
4. F G
5. M L
6. K J
7. $\overline{KM}$ $\overline{JL}$
8. $\angle DEF$ $\angle$ IHG
9. $\overline{EF}$ $\overline{HG}$
10. $\triangle BXA$ $\triangle$ CXA
11. N N
12. $\overline{DE}$ $\overline{IH}$

For each of the following, indicate if the figure has line symmetry, point symmetry, or both.

13. both

14. both

15. point

Written **Copy each figure below. Then draw the reflection image of each figure with respect to *m*.** For answers to exercises 1-6, see the Teacher's Guide.

1.

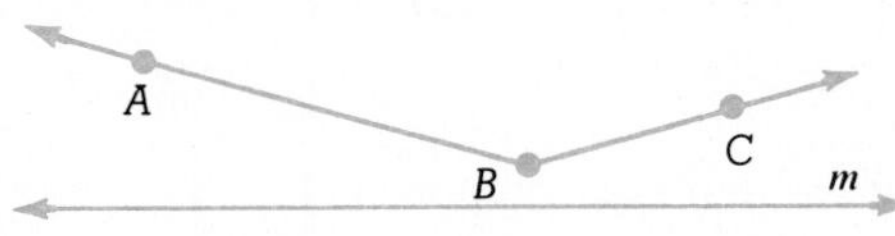

2.

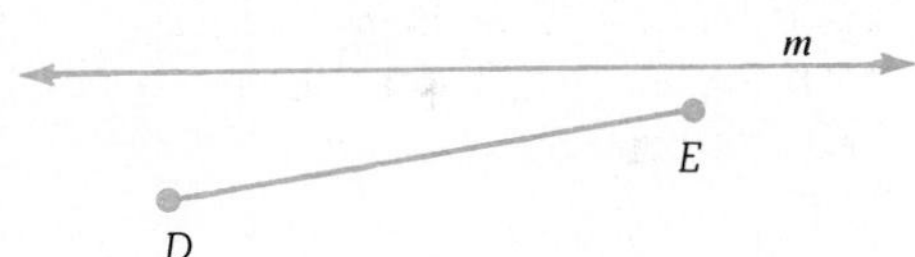

3.

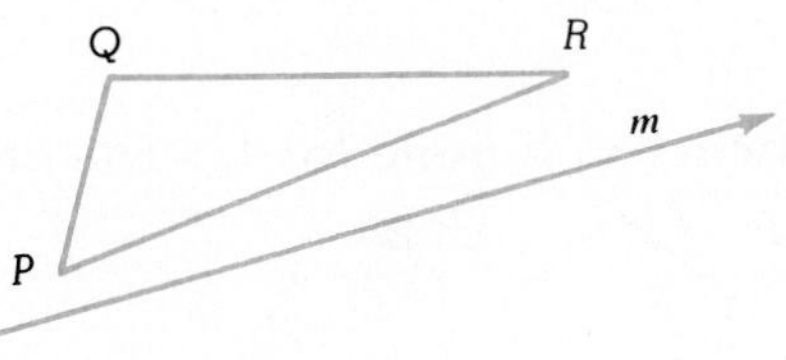

4.

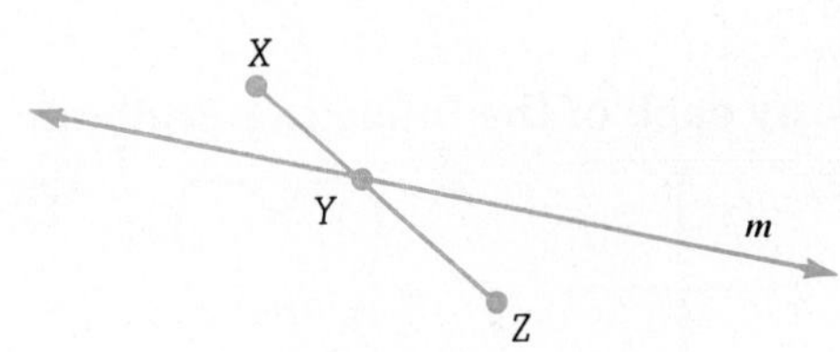

5.

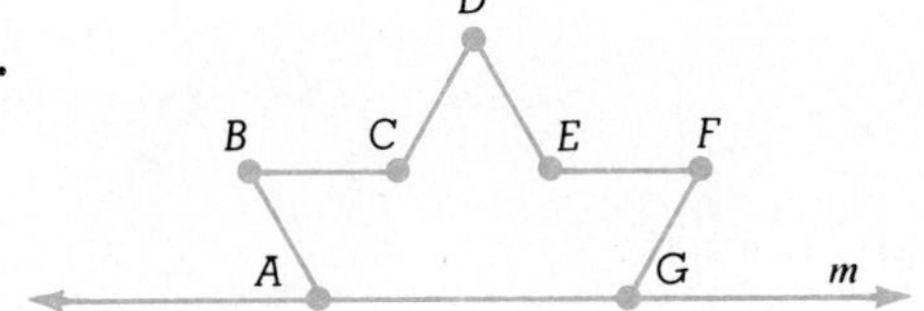

6.

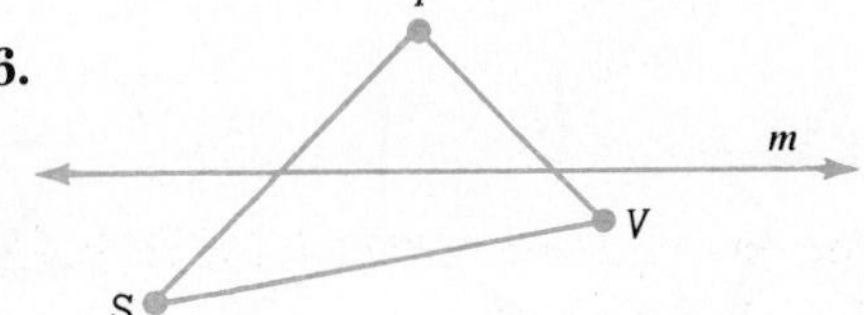

For each of the following, determine whether or *not* ℓ is a line of symmetry. Write *yes* or *no*. Then, explain your answer.

7. No, not all points are the same distance from ℓ.

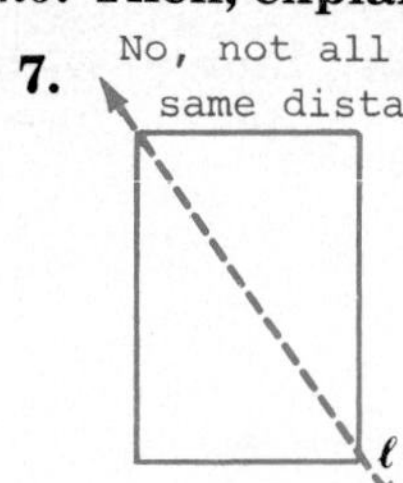

8. yes

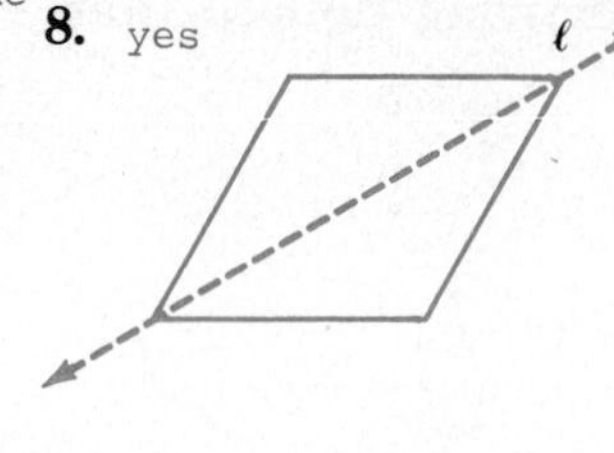

9. yes

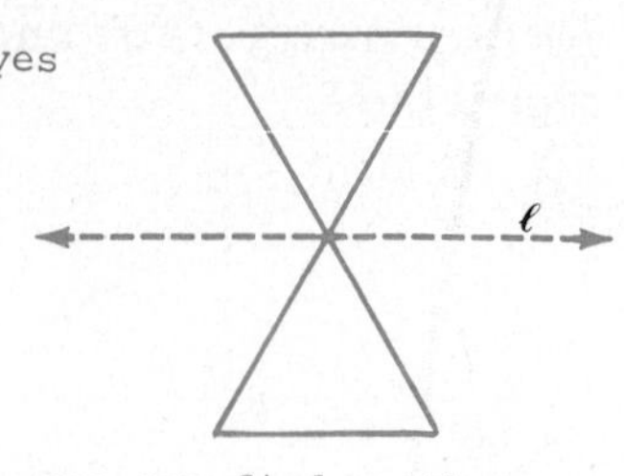

In exercises 8-12, for any point A on the figure, one can find another point B on the figure so that ℓ is the $\perp$ bisector of $\overline{AB}$.

10. yes

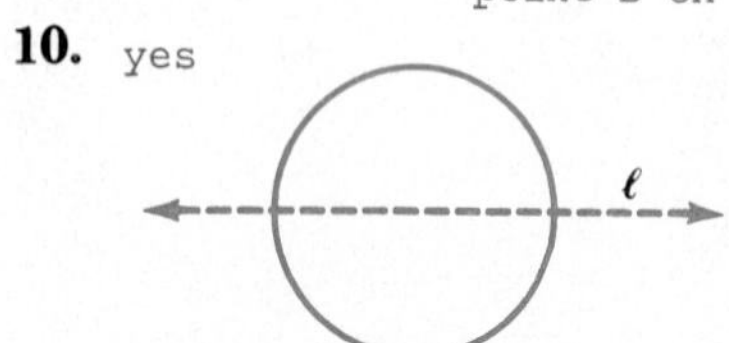

11. yes

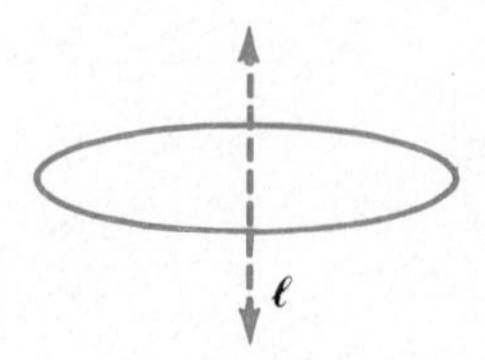

12. yes

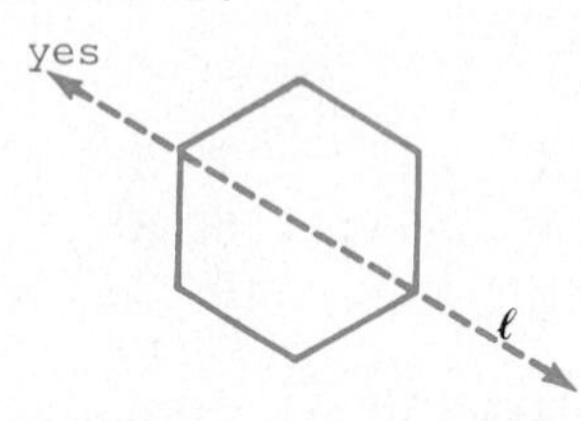

Copy each of the following. Draw the reflection image if *R* is the point of reflection.

For answers to exercises 13-21, 24, 25, 27, 32, 34, see the Teacher's Guide.

13.

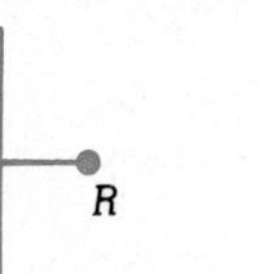

14.

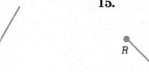

15.

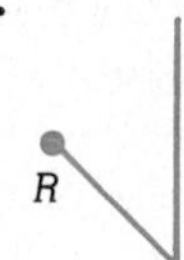

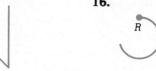

16.

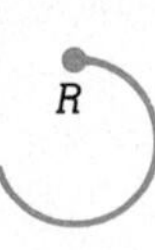

Copy the following letters. Draw all possible lines of symmetry for each. If none exist, write none.

17.

18.

19.

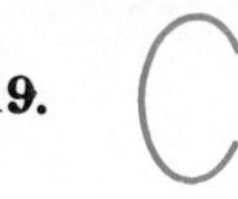

20.

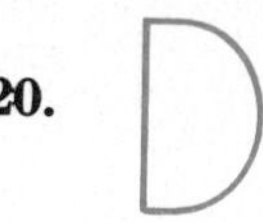

21.

22. none

23. none

24.

Copy each of the following. Indicate any point of symmetry. If none exist, write none.

25.

26. none

27.

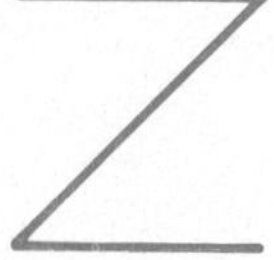

28. none

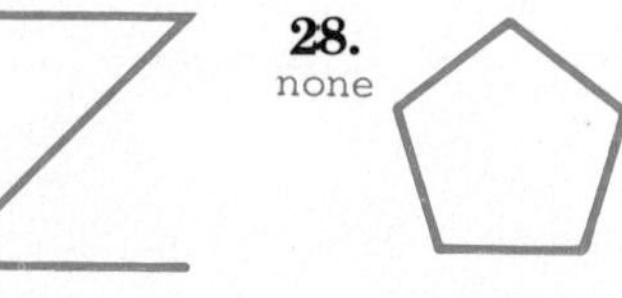

29. none

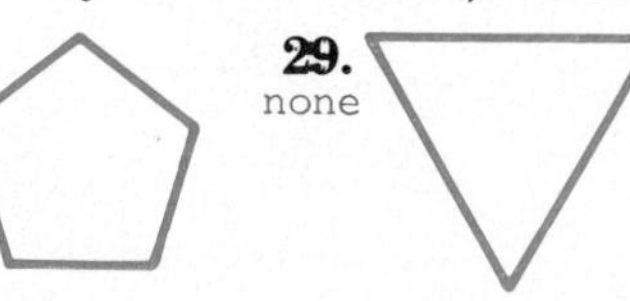

30. none

31. none

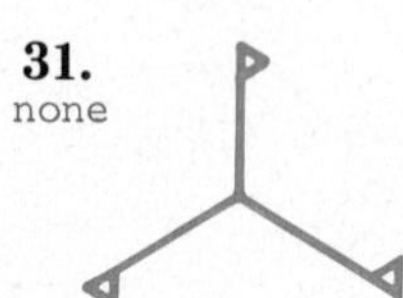

32.

33. none

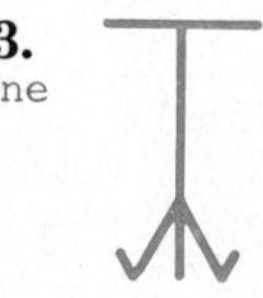

34.

14–3 Translations

Objective: to name and draw translation images of figures with respect to parallel lines

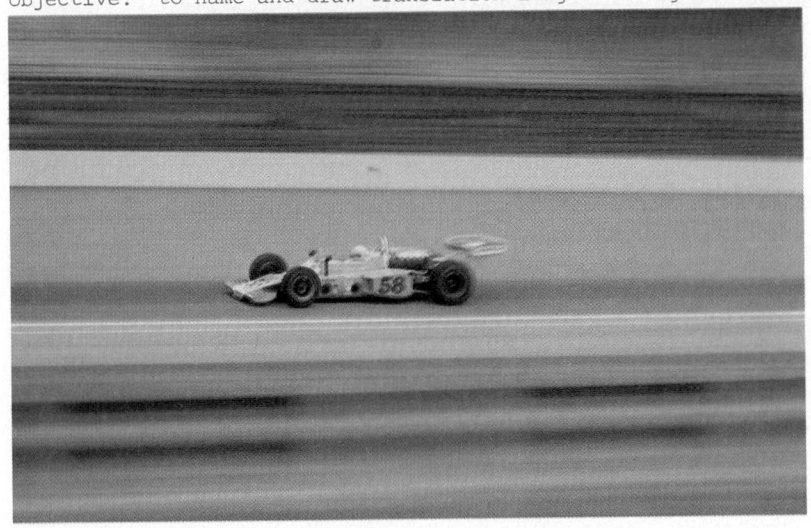

Two successive reflections together are called a composite of reflections.

A racing car speeds along a track to the finish line. The result of a movement in one direction is a transformation called a **translation.**

To find a translation image, perform two reflections in a row with respect to two parallel lines. For example, the translation image of the blue figure with respect to the parallel lines, ***s*** and ***t***, is the red figure. First the blue figure is reflected onto the green figure with respect to ***s***. Then, the green figure is reflected onto the red figure with respect to ***t***.

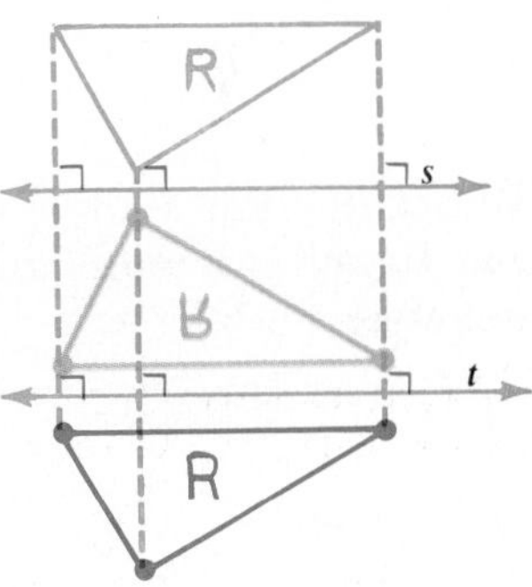

example

1 Draw the translation image of $\triangle ABC$ with respect to the parallel lines *s* and *t*.

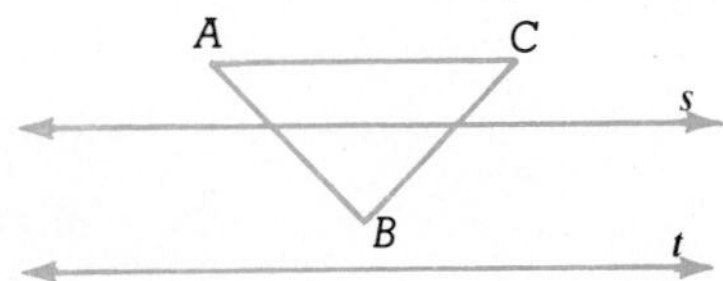

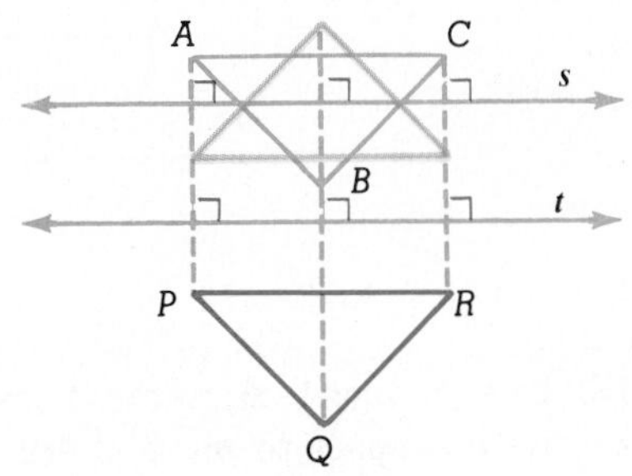

First draw the reflection image of $\triangle ABC$ with respect to ***s***. Then draw the reflection image of that figure with respect to ***t***. Thus, $\triangle PQR$ is the translation image of $\triangle ABC$.

Since translations are composites of two reflections, all properties preserved by reflections are preserved by translations. The properties preserved are collinearity, angle and distance measure, and betweenness of points.

A translation is an isometry.

Emphasize the properties preserved by translations.

EN: Ex: 1-11 odds, Wr: 2-24 evens, 25-32; AV: Ex: 1-12, Wr: 1-21; p. 478, Wr: 14-32 evens

exercises

FN: Ex: 1-12, Wr: 1-21; p. 478, Wr: 21-33

Exploratory **In the figure below *m* and *n* are parallel. For each of the following, name the reflection image with respect to the given line.**

1. A, m B
2. F, m F
3. E, m G
4. B, n C
5. H, n H
6. G, n P
7. A, n D
8. F, n Q
9. E, n R

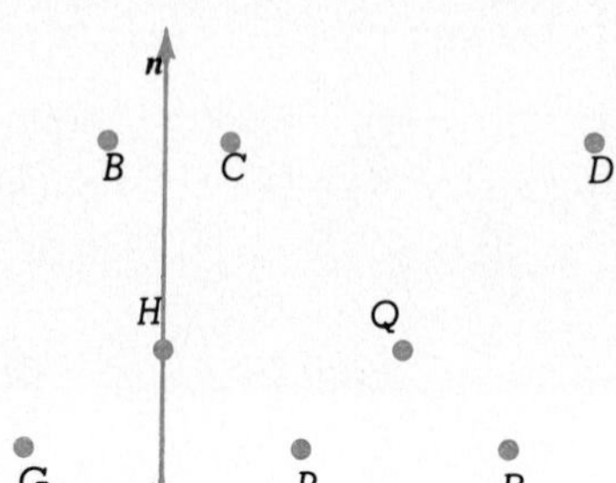

For each of the following, name the translation image with respect to *m*, then *n*.

10. A C
11. F Q
12. E P

Written **For each of the following ℓ and *m* are parallel. Determine whether or *not* each red figure is a translation image of the blue figure. Write *yes* or *no*. Then, explain your answer.**

1. yes

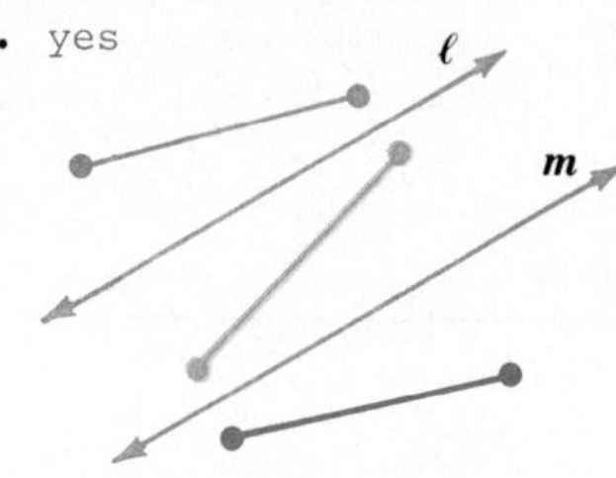

2. No, the green reflection image is incorrect.

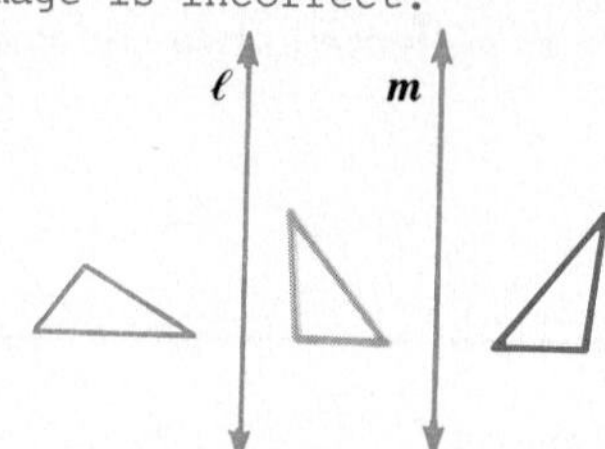

3. yes

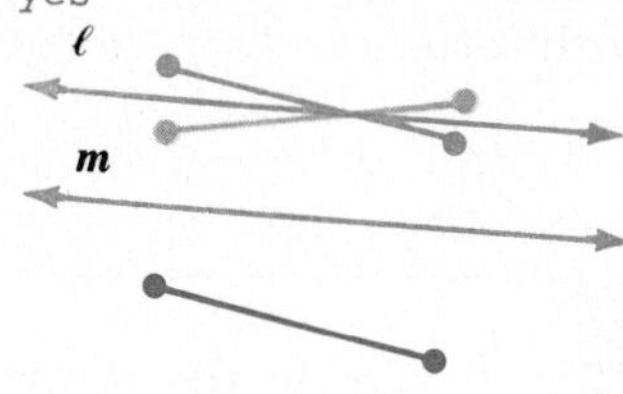

4. yes

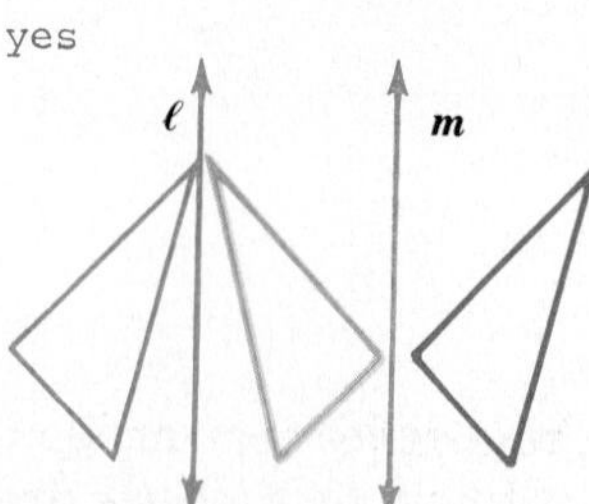

5. No, the green and red reflection images are incorrect.

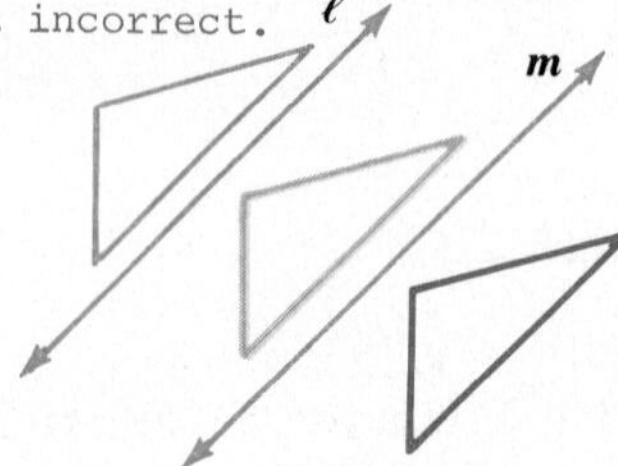

6. yes

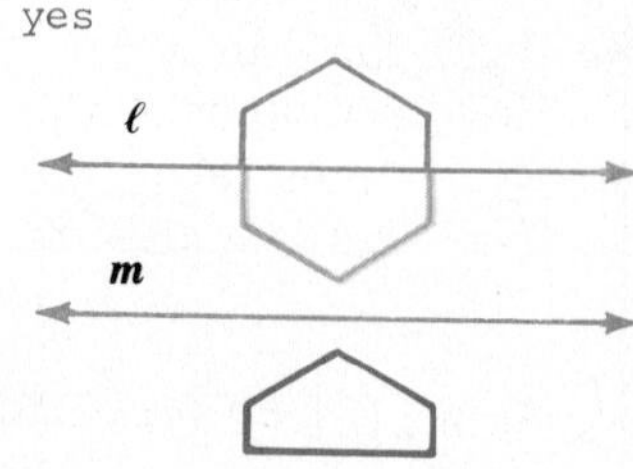

For answers to exercises 7-18, see the Teacher's Guide.

7–12. In exercises **1–6**, name the reflections with respect to ℓ. If there are none, write none.

13–18. In exercises **1–6**, name the reflections with respect to ***m***. If there are none, write none.

For answers to exercises 19-24, see the Teacher's Guide.

Copy each of the following. Then find the translation image of each geometric figure with respect to the parallel lines *s* and *t*.

19.

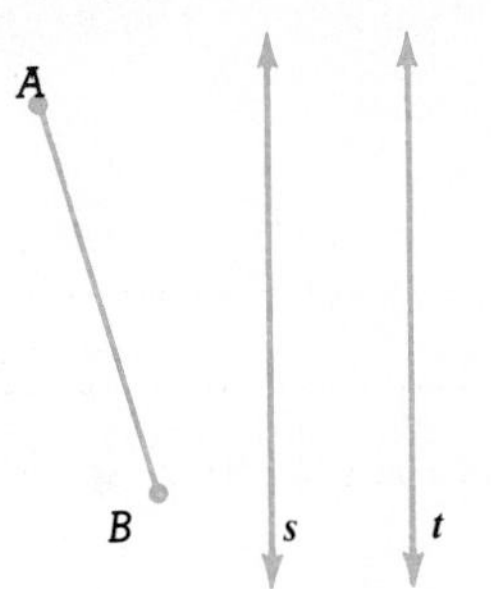

20.

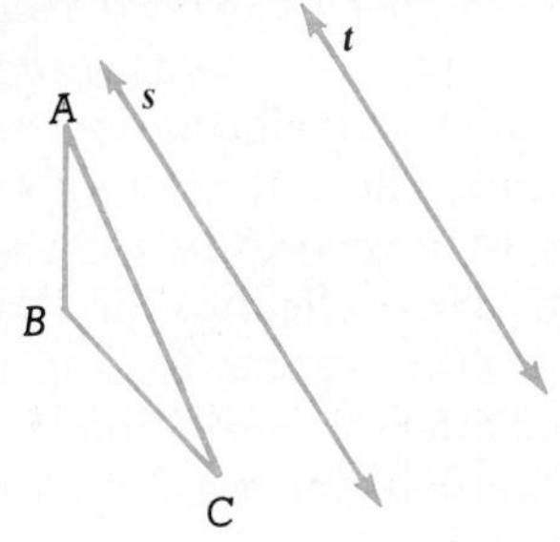

21.

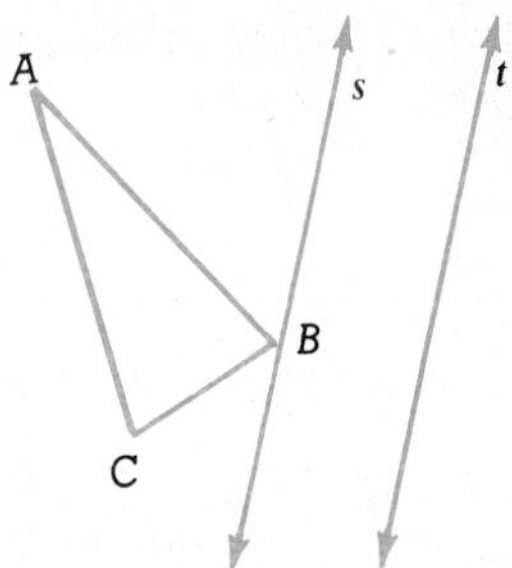

22.

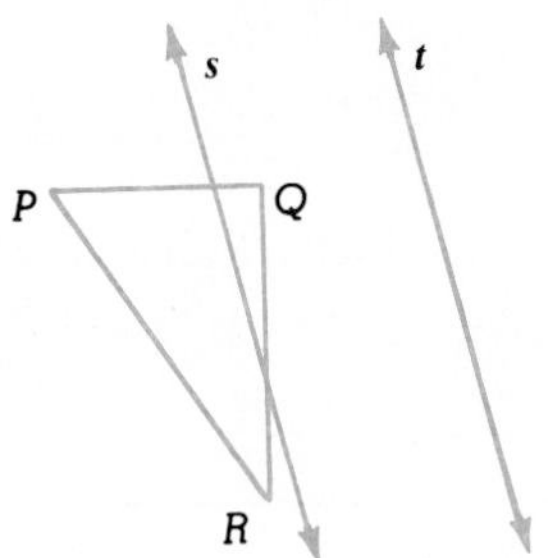

23.

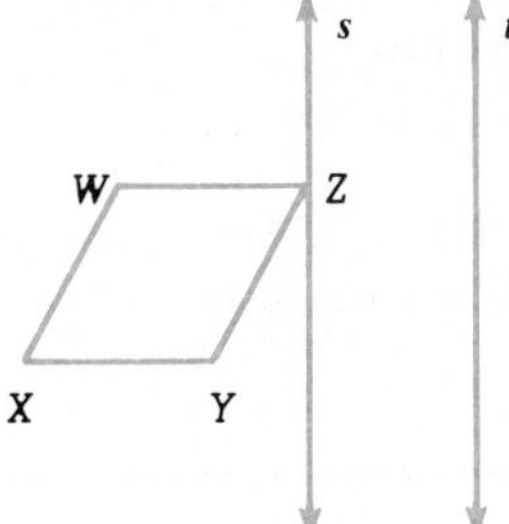

24.

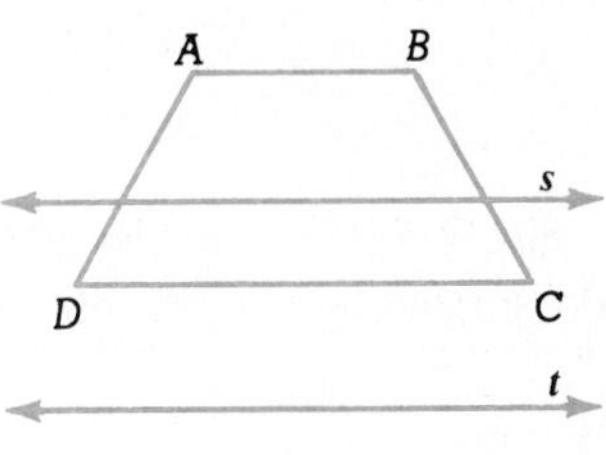

Use the figures below to name each of the following triangles. Assume $s \parallel t$.

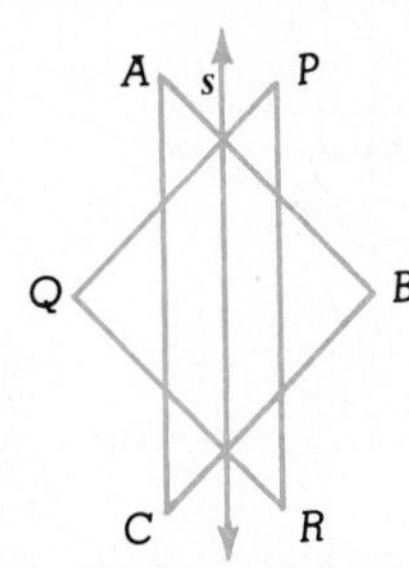

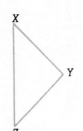

25. Reflection image of $\triangle ABC$ with respect to ***s*** △ PQR

26. Reflection image of $\triangle XYZ$ with respect to ***s*** △ STU

27. Reflection image of $\triangle PQR$ with respect to ***t*** △ LMN

28. Translation image of $\triangle ABC$ with respect to ***s*** and ***t*** △ LMN

29. Translation image of $\triangle PQR$ with respect to ***s*** and ***t*** △ STU

For answers to exercises 30-32, see the Teacher's Guide.

30. Plan a proof to show that the translation image of $\triangle ABC$ with respect to the parallel lines ℓ and ***m*** preserves collinearity.

31. Plan a proof to show that the translation image of $\triangle ABC$ with respect to the parallel lines ℓ and ***m*** preserves betweenness of points.

32. Plan a proof to show that the translation image of $\triangle ABC$ with respect to the parallel lines ℓ and ***m*** preserves angle and distance measure.

Objectives: to recognize whether or not a composite of two reflections is a rotation, to find the measurement of the angle of rotation, to find the reflection image of figures with respect to two intersecting lines

14–4 Rotations

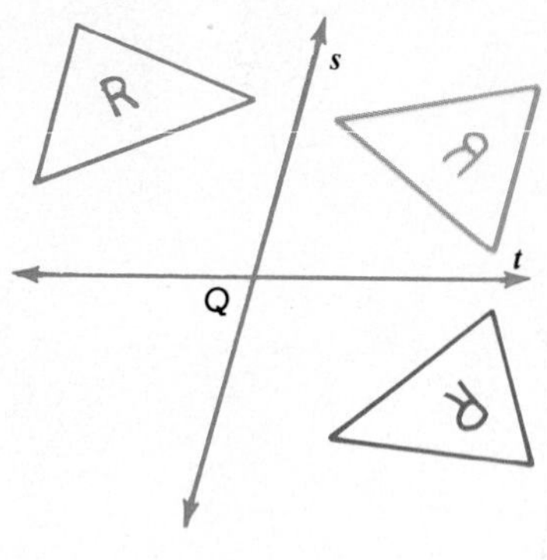

The composite of two reflections with respect to two intersecting lines is a transformation called a **rotation.** The reflection of the blue figure with respect to s is the green figure. The reflection of the green figure with respect to t is the red figure. Since s and t intersect, the red figure is the rotation image of the blue figure. Q, the intersection of the two lines, is called the **center of rotation.**

Since rotations are composites of two reflections, all properties preserved by reflections are preserved by rotations. Make note of the properties preserved.

A rotation is an isometry.

example

1 Suppose t and s intersect and $\triangle ABC$ is on one side of t and s. Construct the rotation image of $\triangle ABC$ with respect to s and then t.

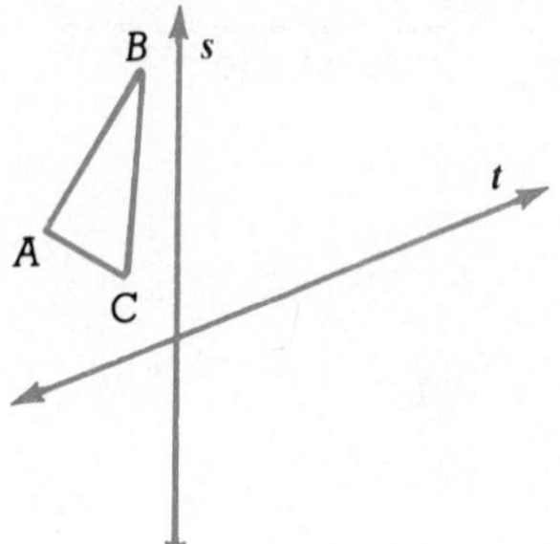

$\triangle ABC$ is on one side of t and s.

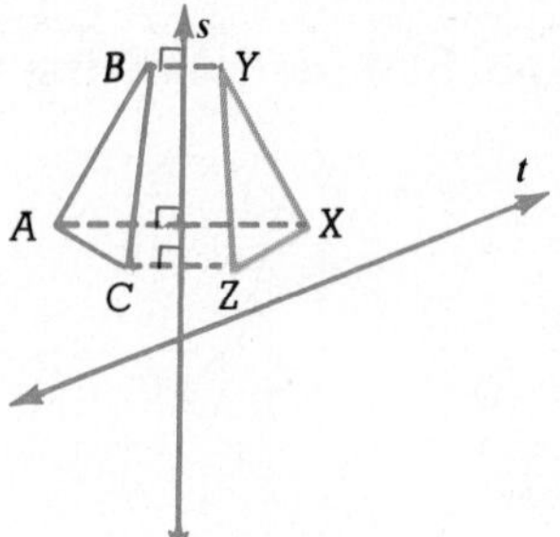

First, reflect $\triangle ABC$ with respect to s. The image is $\triangle XYZ$.

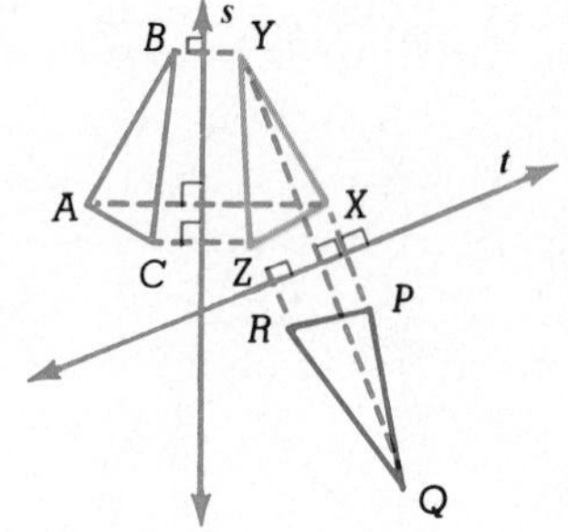

Then, reflect $\triangle XYZ$ with respect to t. The image is $\triangle PQR$.

The figure at the right shows how two reflections can be used to find the rotation image of $\overline{AB}$ with respect to ℓ and m. The image is $\overline{PQ}$.

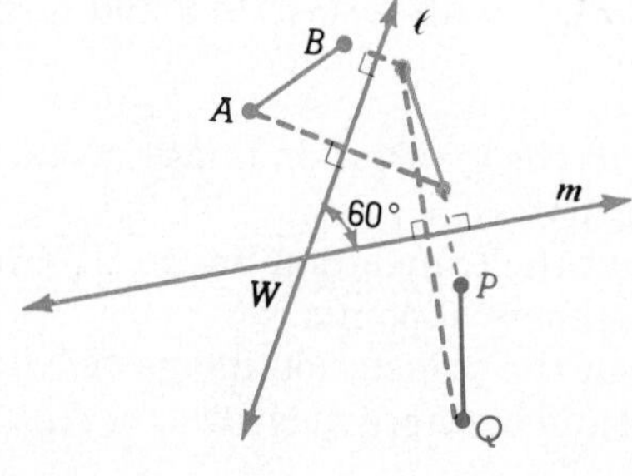

The same rotation image can be determined by using angles. Notice that ℓ and m form a 60° angle. It can be shown that $\angle AWP = 2(60)$ or 120. Also, $\overline{AW} \cong \overline{WP}$. Likewise, it can be shown that if segments are drawn from B to W and from Q to W, then $m\angle BWQ = 120$ and $\overline{BW} \cong \overline{WQ}$.

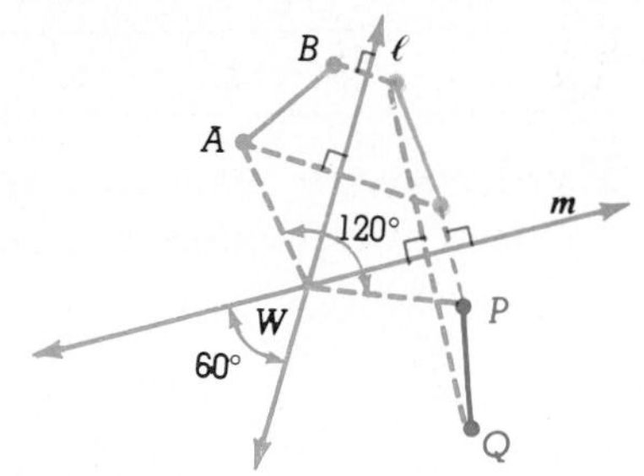

The angles, $\angle AWP$ and $\angle BWQ$, are called **angles of rotation.** In both cases, the degree measure of the angles is 2(60) or 120.

$\angle AWP$ is determined by A, the center of rotation, W, and the rotation image, P.

In a given rotation, if A is the preimage, P is the image, and W is the center of rotation, then the measure of the angle of rotation, $\angle AWP$, equals twice the measure of the angle between the intersecting lines of reflection.

Postulate 14–1

The following example shows how to find a rotation image using the angles of rotation.

example

2 **The intersection of ℓ and m at P forms a 40° angle. Use the angles of rotation to find the rotation image of $\overline{XY}$.**

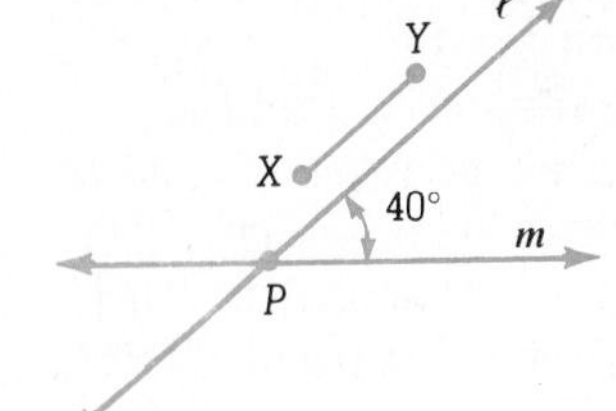

The angle of rotation has a degree measure of 2(40), or 80.

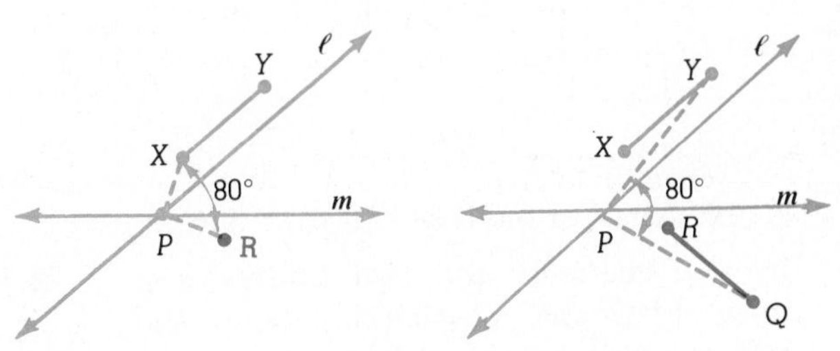

Construct $\angle XPR$ so that its degree measure is 80, and $\overline{XP} \cong \overline{PR}$. Then, construct $\angle YPQ$ so that its degree measure is 80, and $\overline{YP} \cong \overline{PQ}$. The rotation image of $\overline{XY}$ is $\overline{RQ}$.

EN: Ex: 1,2,3-13 odds, Wr: 1-16; p. 485, AR: 2,4; AV: Ex: 1-13, Wr: 1-15 odds; p. 485, AR: 1-4; p. 481, Wr: 22-32 evens

exercises

FN: Ex: 1-13, Wr: 1-10; p. 485, AR: 1-4; p. 481, Wr: 22-30

Exploratory **For each of the following, determine whether or *not* the indicated composition of reflections is a rotation. Explain your answer.**

In both cases, there are proper successive reflections with respect to two intersecting lines.

1. yes

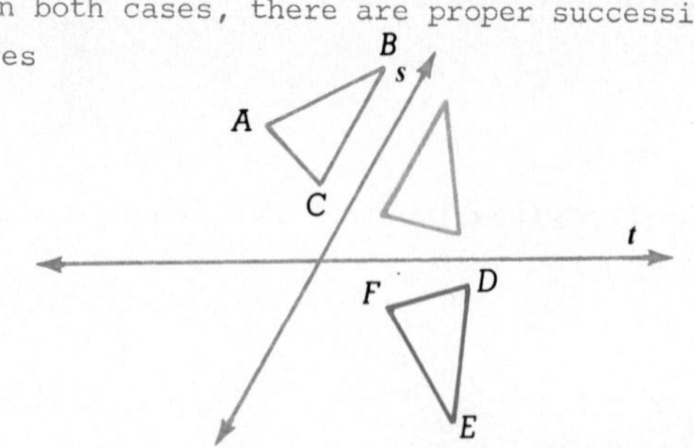

2. yes

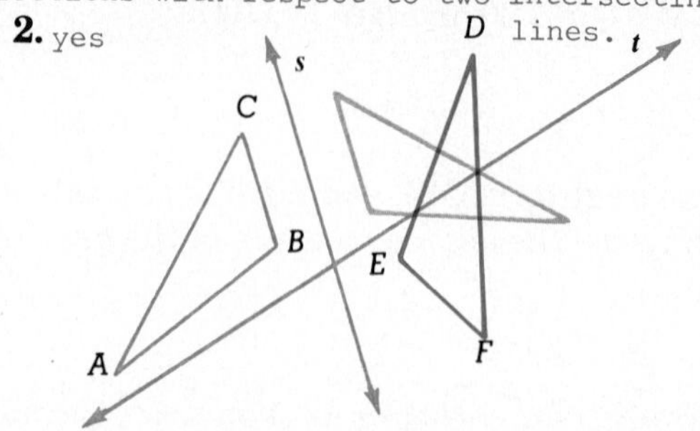

Use the figure to answer each problem.

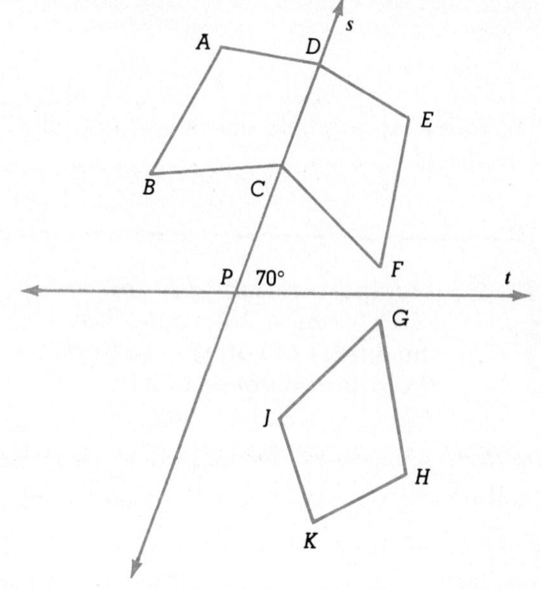

3. Find the reflection image of quadrilateral *ABCD* with respect to ***s***. quad. EFCD
4. Find the reflection image of quadrilateral *CDEF* with respect to ***t***. quad. JKHG
5. Find the rotation image of quadrilateral *ABCD* with respect to *s* and ***t***. quad. HGJK
6. Find the reflection image of quadrilateral *JKHG* with respect to ***t***. quad. CDEF
7. Find the rotation image of quadrilateral *JKHG* with respect to *t* and ***s***. quad. CDAB
8. Find the degree measure of $\angle APH$. 140
9. Find the degree measure of $\angle BPG$. 140
10. Find the degree measure of $\angle CPK$. 140
11. Find the degree measure of $\angle DPJ$. 140
12. Find the reflection image of *C* with respect to ***s***. C
13. Find the rotation image of $\overline{BD}$ with respect to *s* and ***t***. $\overline{GK}$

For answers to exercises 1-2, see the Teacher's Guide.

Written **Answer each of the following.**

1. Draw a segment and two intersecting lines. Find the rotation image of the segment with respect to the two intersecting lines.
2. Draw a triangle and two intersecting lines. Find the rotation image of the triangle with respect to the two intersecting lines.

Two lines intersect to form the angle with the following measurements. Find the measurement of each angle of rotation.

3. 30° 60°
4. 45° 90°
5. 60° 120°
6. 37° 74°

For answers to exercises 7-12, see the Teacher's Guide.

Copy each of the following. Then, use the angles of rotation to find the rotation image of each geometric figure with respect to *s* and *t*.

7.

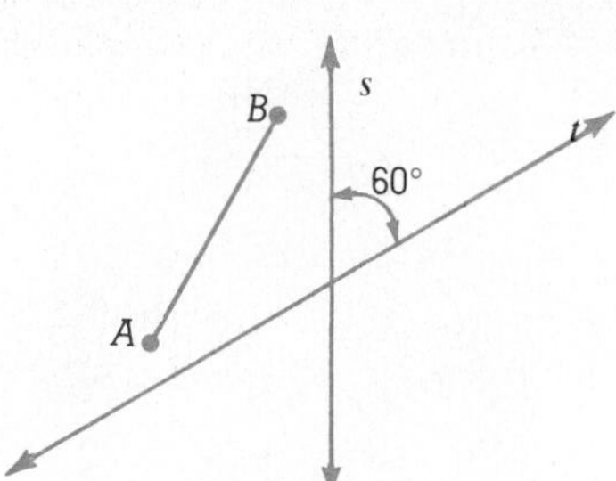

8.

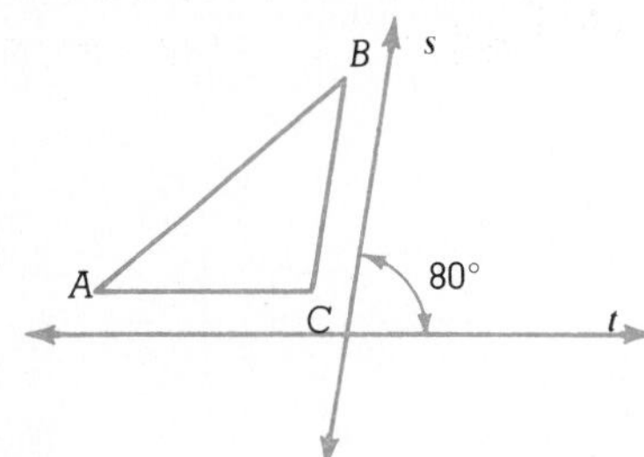

9.

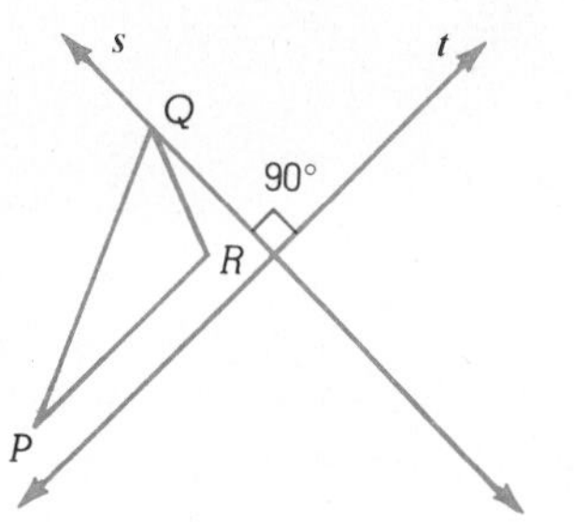

10.

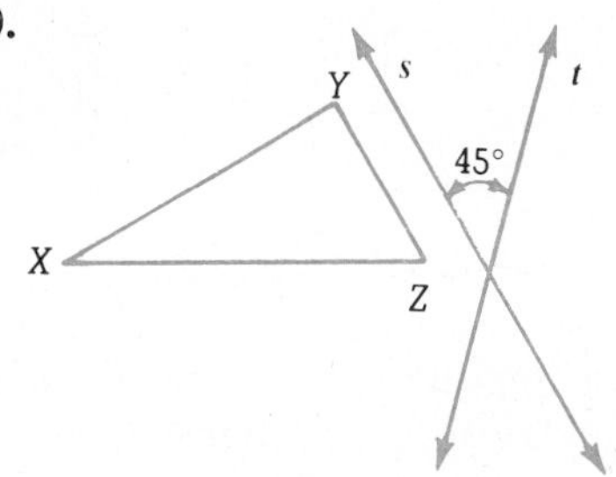

11.

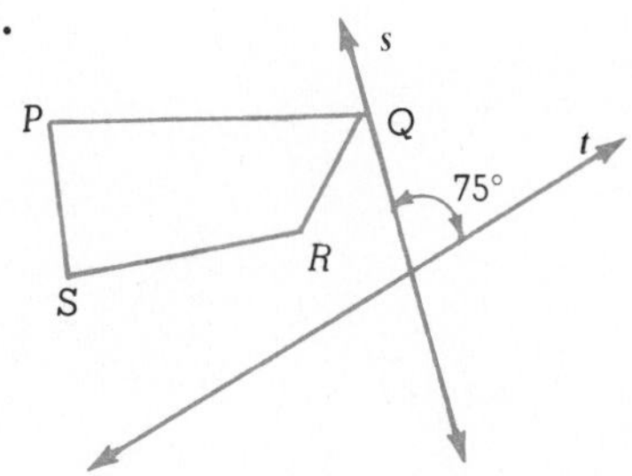

12.

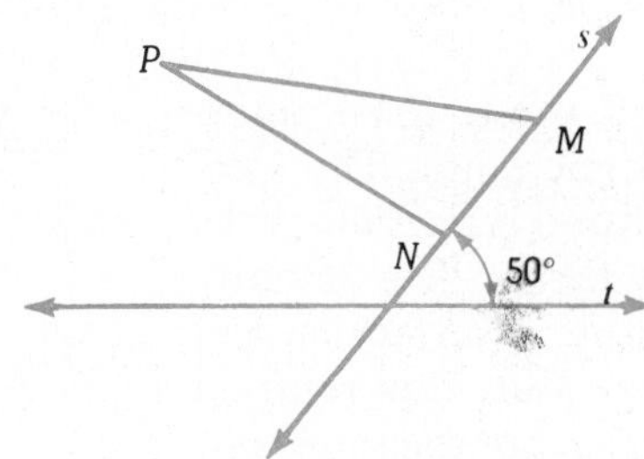

Determine whether or *not* each of the following is preserved by a rotation. Write *yes* or *no*.

13. collinearity yes **14.** betweenness of points yes **15.** angle measure yes **16.** distance measure yes

Solving Rational Equations — algebra review

Example Solve $\frac{3}{2x} - \frac{2x}{x+1} = {}^-2$.

$$2x(x+1)\left(\frac{3}{2x} - \frac{2x}{x+1}\right) = 2x(x+1)({}^-2)$$

$$3x + 3 - 4x^2 = {}^-4x^2 - 4x$$

$$x = \frac{{}^-3}{7}$$

Exercises Solve each equation.

1. $\frac{3}{5x} + \frac{7}{2x} = 1$ x = 41/10 **2.** $\frac{5}{6} - \frac{2m}{2m+3} = \frac{19}{6}$ m = -21/20 **3.** $\frac{4x}{2x+3} - \frac{2x}{2x-3} = 1$ x = 1/2 **4.** $\frac{z+3}{z-1} + \frac{z+1}{z-3} = 2$ z = 2

14–5 Composites

The picture at the left was taken using mirror reflections. How many reflections do you see? 1 to 4

Objectives: to recognize reflection images that result from composition of reflections, rotations, and/or translations, to name the type of isometry that maps one figure into another, to construct composite images and/or lines of reflection

You may want students to use mirrors to help them develop an understanding of reflections.

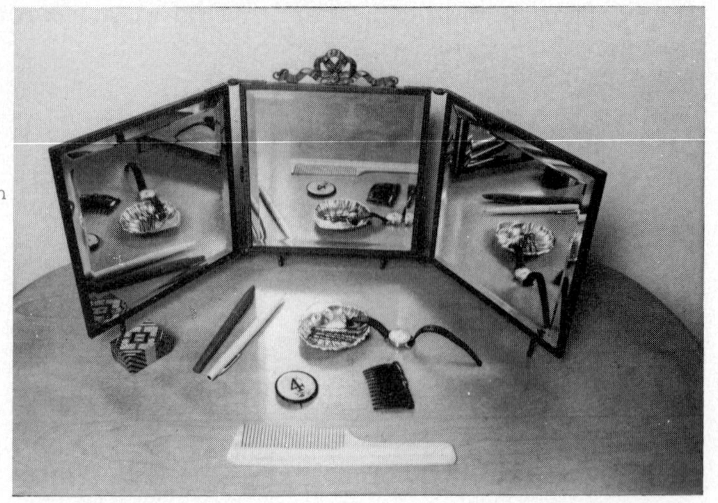

Recall that composites of two reflections, rotations and translations, are isometries. Also, other composites of reflections also can be described as isometries. The number of reflections and the relationship of the lines of reflections determine the kind of isometry.

Isometries is the plural of isometry.

Consider three lines intersecting at one point. The composite of three reflections with respect to these lines actually is a composite of a rotation and a reflection. But, this rotation and reflection are the same as a single reflection with respect to a line.

In the figure at the right, $\triangle ABC$ is transformed to $\triangle GHF$. This transformation can be described in the following three ways.

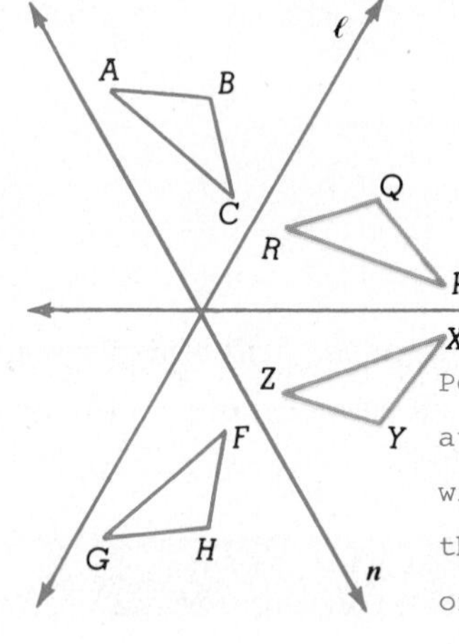

Point out that the transformation at the left changes the clockwise orientation of △ ABC into the counterclockwise orientation of △ GHF. Thus the property of orientation is not preserved.

first way

$$\triangle ABC \xrightarrow{\text{reflection}} \triangle PQR \xrightarrow{\text{reflection}} \triangle XYZ \xrightarrow{\text{reflection}} \triangle GHF$$

second way

$$\triangle ABC \xrightarrow{\text{rotation}} \triangle XYZ \xrightarrow{\text{reflection}} \triangle GHF$$

third way

$$\triangle ABC \xrightarrow{\text{reflection}} \triangle GHF$$

△ABC *has a clockwise orientation.*

△GHF *has a counterclockwise orientation.*

examples

1 **Construct the composite of three reflections of $\overline{AB}$ with respect to the three parallel lines ℓ, *m*, and *n*.**

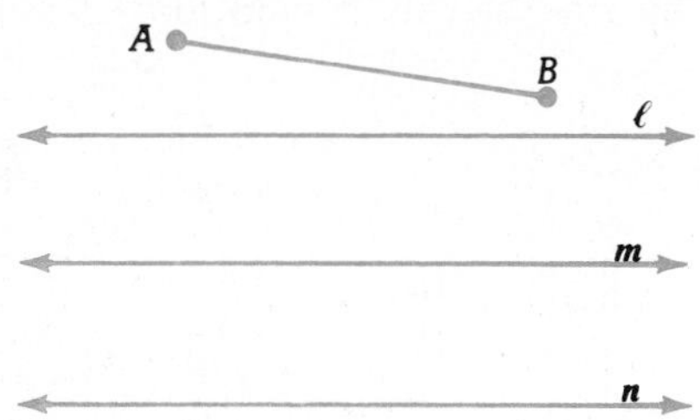

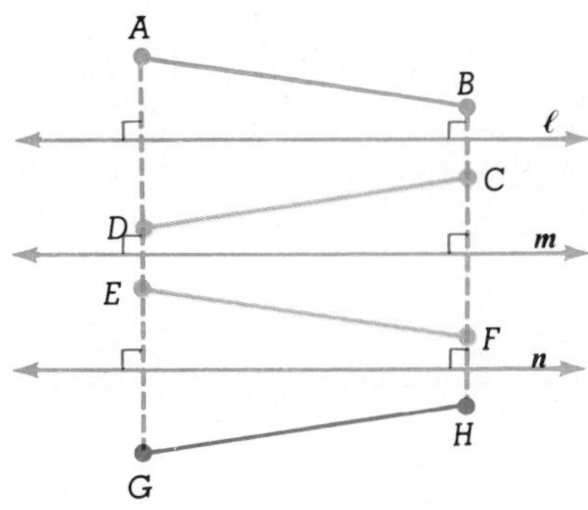

Construct perpendicular lines from A and B through ℓ, *m,* and *n.* Locate D and C so that ℓ bisects $\overline{AD}$ and $\overline{BC}$. Likewise, locate E, F, G, and H. Notice $\overline{GH}$ is the reflection image of $\overline{AB}$ with respect to the parallel lines ℓ, *m,* and *n.*

2 **Describe the single isometry that can be used to map $\overline{PQ}$ onto $\overline{VW}$.**

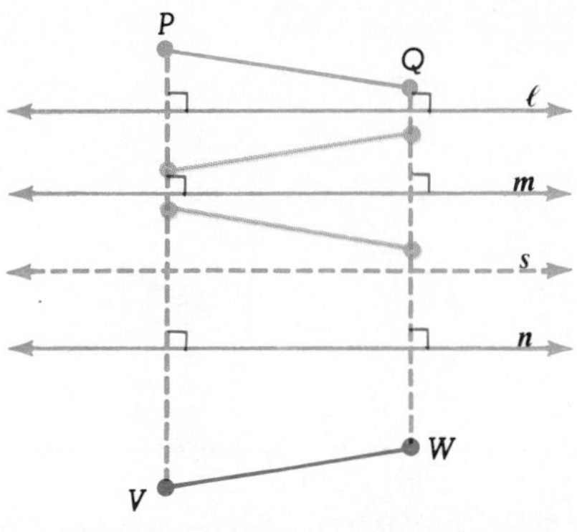

Draw $\overline{PV}$ and $\overline{QW}$ perpendicular to ℓ, *m,* and *n.* Locate *s,* the perpendicular bisector of $\overline{PV}$ and $\overline{QW}$. Thus, $\overline{PQ}$ maps onto $\overline{VW}$ by a single reflection of $\overline{PQ}$ with respect to *s.*

The figure at the right shows a composite of four reflections with respect to the parallel lines ℓ, *m, n,* and *t.* A composite of two translations with respect to ℓ. *m, n,* and *t* will also map $\triangle ABC$ onto $\triangle PQR$. But a single translation also can map $\triangle ABC$ onto $\triangle PQR$.

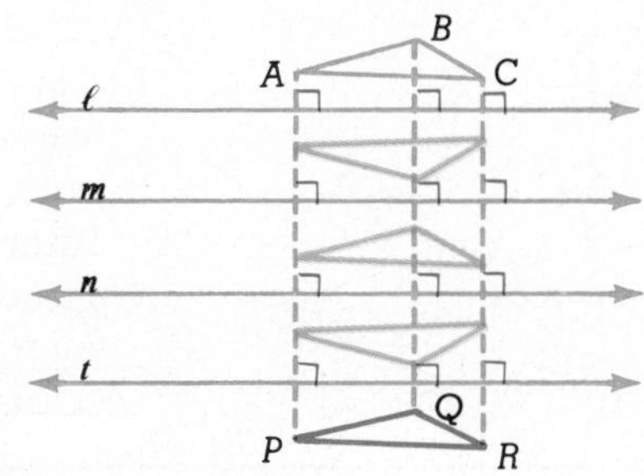

Using only ℓ, m, n, or t as the possible lines of reflection, there are two choices for finding the translation.

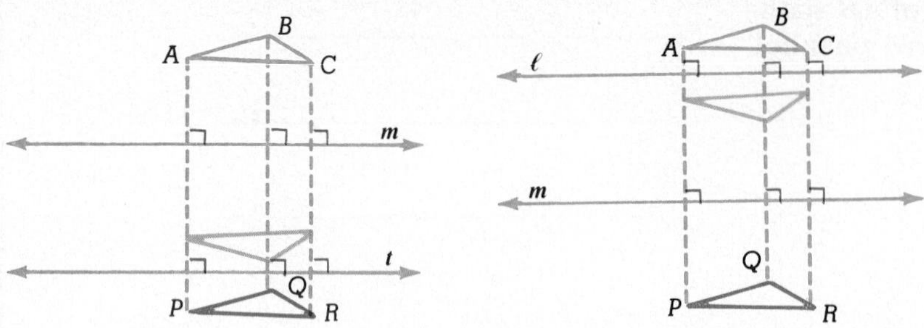

$\triangle ABC$ is mapped onto $\triangle PQR$ by a single translation with respect to either m parallel to t or ℓ parallel to n.

example

3 Suppose $\triangle PQR \cong \triangle ABC$. Name an isometry that maps $\triangle PQR$ onto $\triangle ABC$. Construct the necessary lines of reflection.

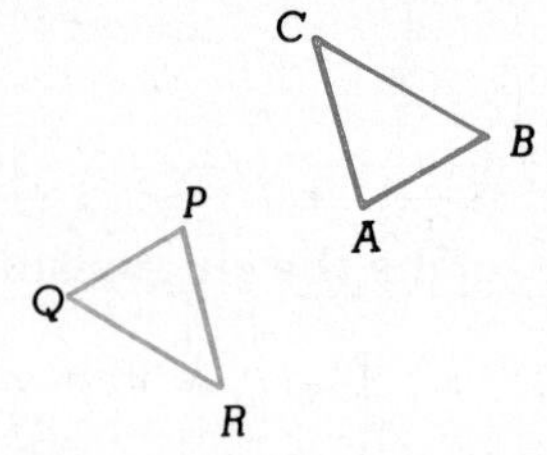

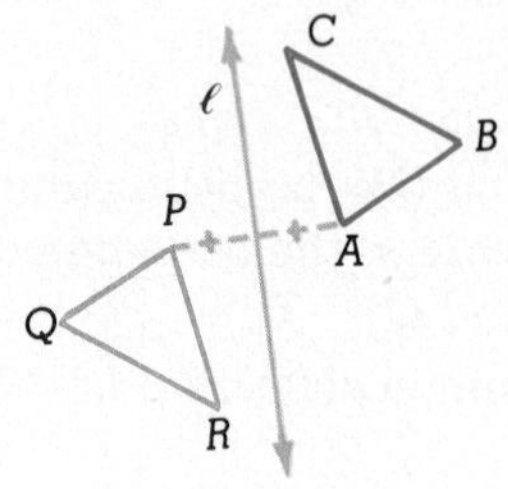

Construct ℓ, the perpendicular bisector of $\overline{PA}$.

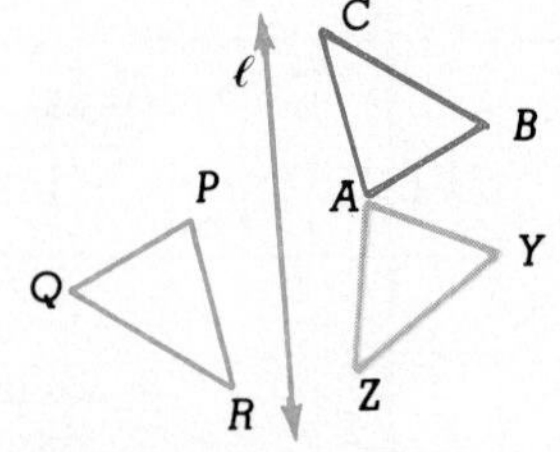

Reflect $\triangle PQR$ with respect to ℓ. Call this image $\triangle AYZ$.

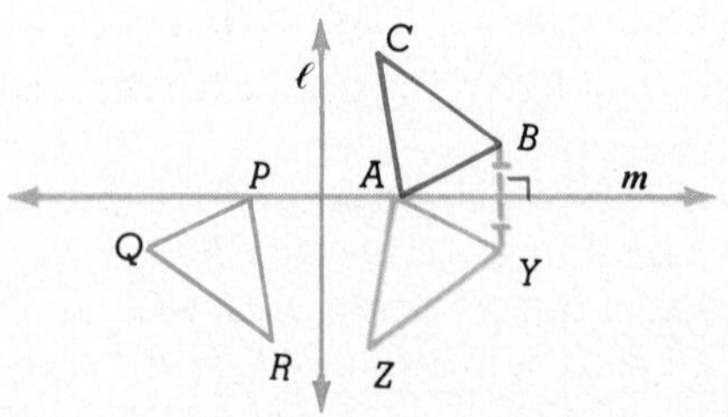

Construct m, the perpendicular bisector of $\overline{YB}$. The reflection of $\triangle AYZ$ with respect to m is $\triangle ABC$. Since ℓ intersects m, and $\triangle ABC$ is a composite of two reflections, $\triangle PQR$ maps onto $\triangle ABC$ by a rotation transformation.

Sometimes, the result of a composition of three reflections is *not* a single reflection, translation, or rotation. The result is an isometry called a **glide reflection,** which is a composition of a reflection and a translation.

In the figure, $\triangle ABC$ is reflected onto $\triangle GHK$ with respect to the parallel lines ℓ and m and the transversal n. The result is a glide reflection.

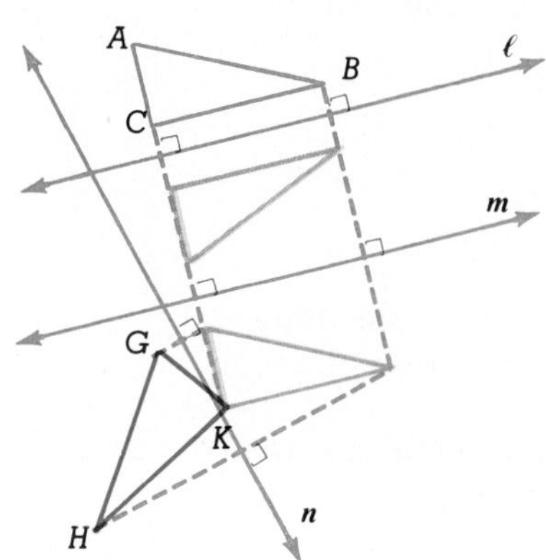

EN: Ex: 1-9, Wr: 1-12; p. 491, C: 1-4; AV: Ex: 1-9, Wr: 1-9; p. 491, C: 1-4; pp. 484-5, Wr: 2-16 evens

exercises

FN: Ex: 1-9, Wr: 1-11 odds; p. 491, C: 1-4; p. 485, Wr: 11-16

Exploratory **Answer each of the following for the figures labeled *A, B, C, D, E, F, G,* and *H*. Assume, ℓ, *m, n, p, q, r,* and *s* are parallel.**

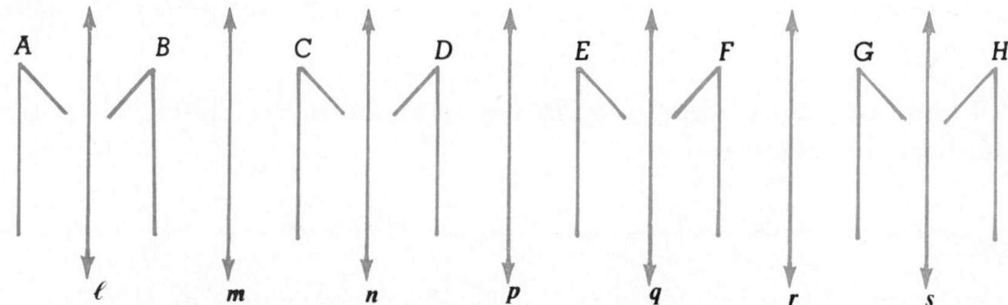

1. Name the reflection image of figure A with respect to n. F
2. Name the image of figure A as a composite of three reflections with respect to ℓ, n, and q. F
3. Name the reflection image of figure C as a composite of five reflections with respect to n, p, q, r, and s. H
4. Name the reflection image of figure G as a composite of two reflections with respect to q and m. A
5. Name the one reflection line that can be used to map figure A onto figure H. p
6. Name the two reflection lines that can be used to map figure A onto figure G.
7. Name the three reflection lines that can be used to map figure A onto figure F.
8. Name the single isometry that maps figure A onto figure E.
9. Name the single isometry that maps figure A onto figure F. reflection with respect to n

6. any of the following: m, q; ℓ, p; n, r
7. any of the following: ℓ, m, p; ℓ, n, q; m, p, q
8. translation with respect to ℓ, n or m, p

Written **For each of the following, copy the diagram. Then, answer.**

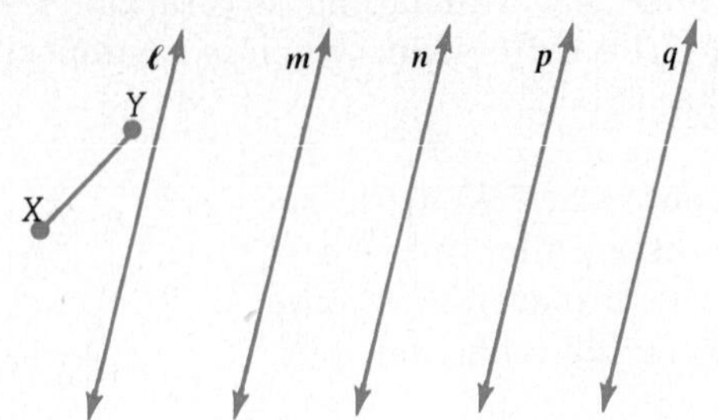

1. Construct the composite of five reflections with respect to the parallel lines ℓ, ***m***, ***n***, ***p***, and ***q***. See the Teacher's Guide.
2. Describe the single isometry that can be used to map $\overline{XY}$ onto its image. reflection with respect to n

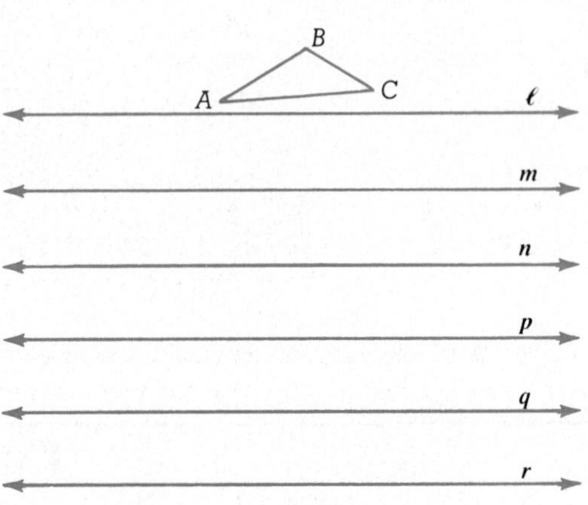

3. Construct the composite of six reflections of $\triangle ABC$ with respect to the parallel lines ℓ, ***m***, ***n***, ***p***, ***q***, and ***r***. See the Teacher's Guide.
4. Describe the single isometry that can be used to map $\triangle ABC$ onto its image with respect to ***n*** and ***r***. translation
5. Find another pair of lines that can be used to form a single isometry that maps $\triangle ABC$ onto its image. ℓ, p
6. Name the different ways a composite of two or more reflections, with respect to parallel lines, can be described.
An odd number of reflections can be called a single reflection. An even number of reflections is a translation.

Name the kind of isometry that maps one figure onto the other. Then, copy each figure and construct the lines of reflection. For answers to exercises 7-12, see the Teacher's Guide.

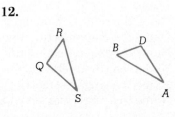

7. A B C P Q R

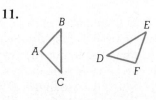

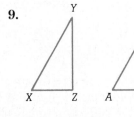

8. T Q R S P

9. Y X Z

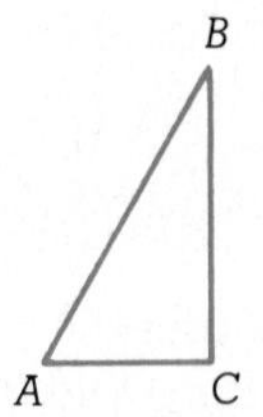

10. R S L T M N

11. B E A D F C

12. R D B Q S A

careers

Urban Designers

Chris Yessios is an urban designer. Dr. Yessios uses a computer to generate visual models, computer graphics, of a building or of a group of buildings. The designer can study alternate points of view by using geometric transformations. Computer programs are written to activate the various transformations.

These alternative designs can be made as line drawings whether on a CRT (cathode ray tube) screen or as line drawings on paper using a pen-and-ink plotter.

The figure shown at the right illustrates a rotation generated by computer graphics.

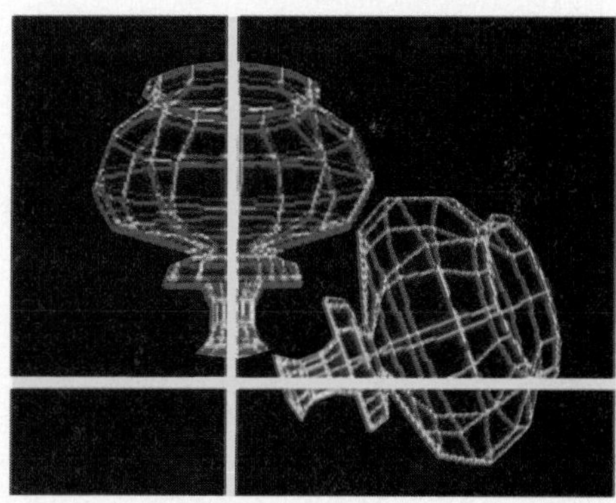

Exercises **Determine the geometric transformation(s) illustrated by each of the following.**

1. rotation

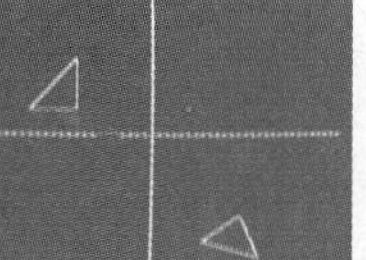

2. reflection

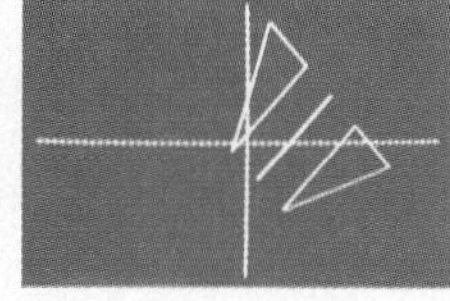

3. dilation

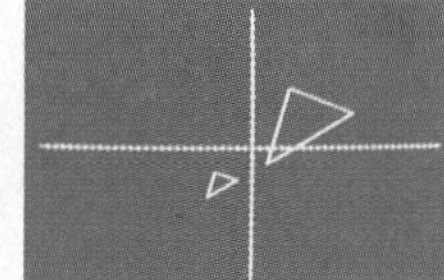

4. translation

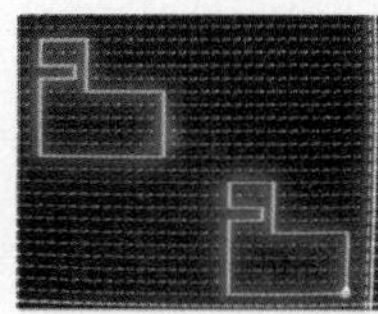

5. rotation

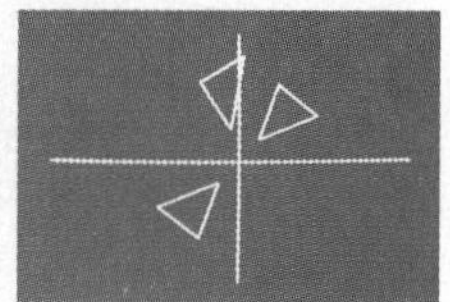

Objectives: to use scale factors to determine if a dilation is an enlargement, reduction, or a congruence transformation, to find the scale factor for a given dilation, to find the dilation image for a given center and scale factor

14–6 Dilations

A geometric figure can be altered in size. Enlarging or reducing the figure will *not* change its shape. This type of transformation is called a **dilation** or a similarity transformation.

Point out that a zoom lens on a 35 mm camera functions like a dilation.

In the figure, $\triangle XYZ$ is the dilation image of $\triangle PQR$. The measure of the distance from C to a point on $\triangle XYZ$ is twice the measure of the distance from C to a point on $\triangle PQR$. For example, the following equations hold.

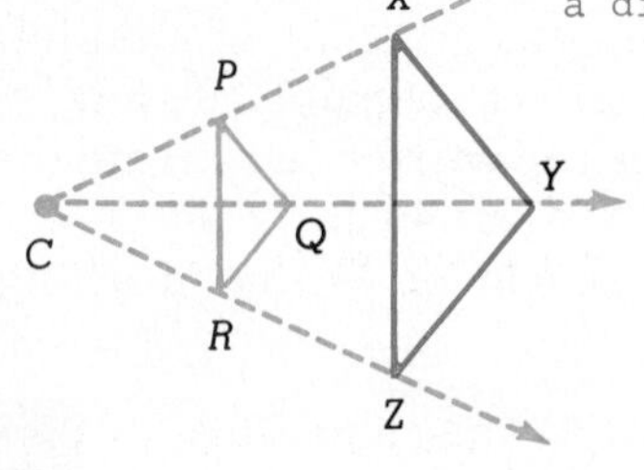

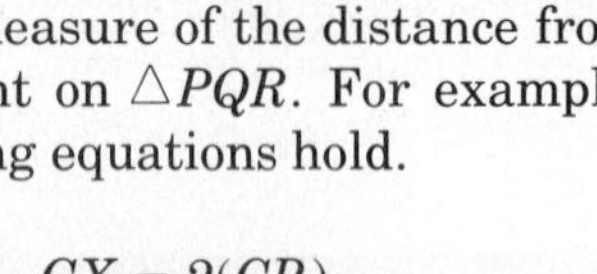

$$CX = 2(CP)$$
$$CY = 2(CQ)$$
$$CZ = 2(CR)$$

In this transformation, $\triangle PQR$, with **center** C and a **scale factor** of 2, is enlarged to $\triangle XYZ$.

The figure shows a dilation where the preimage $\overline{AB}$ is reduced to $\overline{ED}$ by a scale factor of $\frac{1}{3}$. Thus, $CE = \frac{1}{3}(CA)$. Therefore, $\frac{CE}{CA} = \frac{1}{3}$ and $\frac{CD}{CB} = \frac{1}{3}$. By proving $\triangle CAB \sim \triangle CED$, it can be shown that $ED = \frac{1}{3}(AB)$.

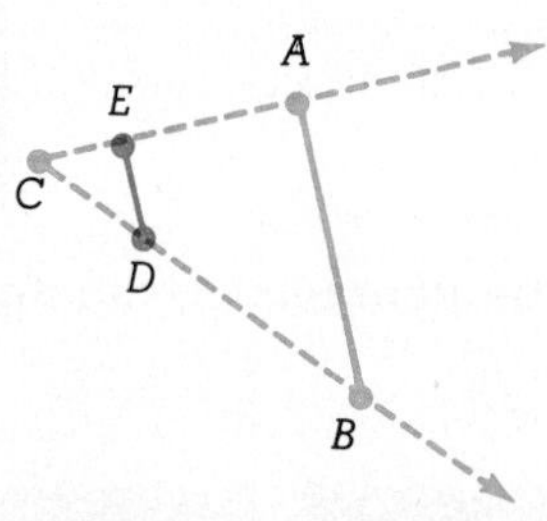

If a dilation with center C and a scale factor k maps A onto E and B onto D, then $ED = k(AB)$.

Theorem 14–1

Notice that when the scale factor is 3, the figure is enlarged. When the scale factor is $\frac{1}{3}$, the figure is reduced. In general, if k is the scale factor for a dilation, then the following is true.

If $k > 1$, the dilation is an *enlargement.*
If $0 < k < 1$, the dilation is a *reduction.*
If $k = 1$, the dilation is a *congruence transformation.*

The first two cases represent dilations that are not isometries.

example

1 Given center C and a scale factor of $\frac{3}{4}$, find the dilation image of $\triangle PQR$.

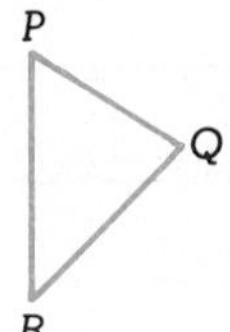

Since the scale factor is less than 1, the dilation is a reduction.

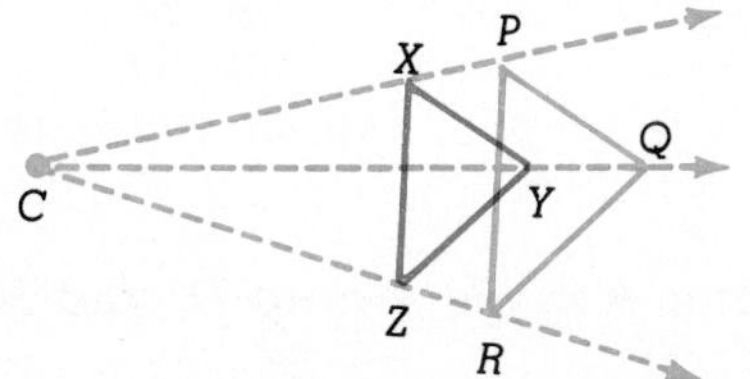

Draw $\overrightarrow{CP}$, $\overrightarrow{CQ}$, and $\overrightarrow{CR}$. Find X, Y, and Z so that $CX = \frac{3}{4}(CP)$, $CZ = \frac{3}{4}(CR)$, and $CY = \frac{3}{4}(CQ)$. $\triangle XYZ$ is the dilation image of $\triangle PQR$.

The following examples illustrate some of the basic properties of dilations.

example

2 Given center C, $\angle EFG$, and its dilation image $\angle QRS$, examine $\overline{EF}$ and $\overline{QR}$ and $m\angle EFG$ and $m\angle QRS$. Determine whether the measures are enlarged reduced or congruent.

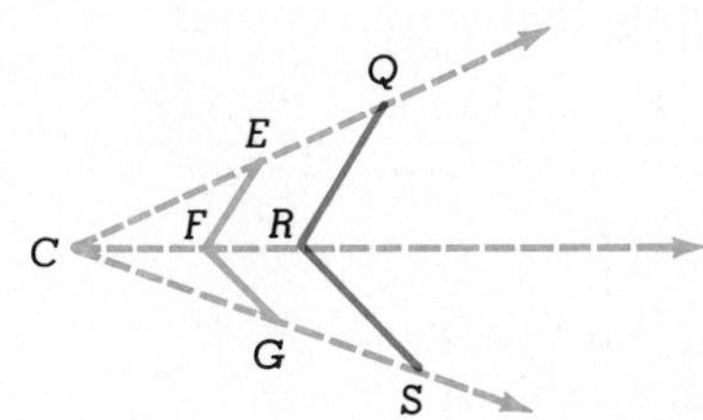

$\overline{EF}$ is enlarged to $\overline{QR}$.
$EF < QR$
$\angle EFG \cong \angle QRS$.

The dilation preserves angle measure but *not* the measure of a segment unless the scale factor is 1.

example

3 Given center C, $\triangle ABE$, and its dilation image $\triangle RFD$, describe the orientation of the two triangles.

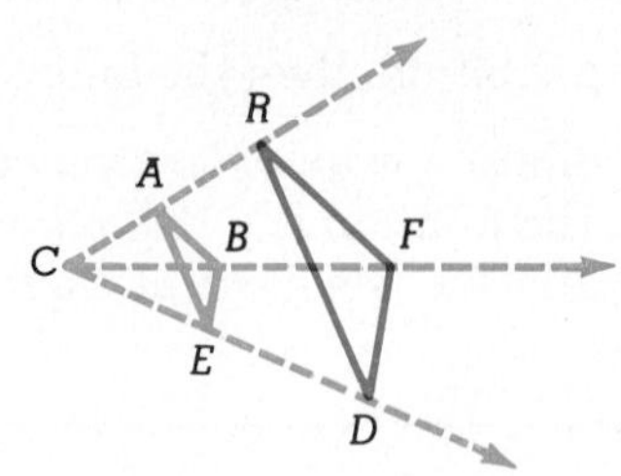

$\triangle ABE$ has a clockwise orientation and its dilation image also has a clockwise orientation. Dilation is said to preserve orientation.

EN: Ex: 1-7 odds, Wr: 1-19 odds, 22-50 evens; p. 495, E: 1-3; AV: Ex: 1-9, Wr: 1-23 odds, 24-50 evens; p. 495, E: 1-3; p. 490, Wr: 10-12

exercises

FN: Ex: 1-9, Wr: 1-19 odds, 21-38, 43-49 odds; p. 490, Wr: 2-12 evens

Exploratory **For each of the following scale factors, determine whether the dilation is an enlargement, reduction, or a congruence transformation.**

1. $4\frac{2}{5}$ enlargement
2. $\frac{3}{8}$ reduction
3. $\frac{1}{6}$ reduction
4. $\frac{3}{2}$ enlargement
5. 0.61 reduction
6. 7 enlargement
7. 1 congruence
8. 2.5 enlargement
9. Determine whether or *not* it is possible to have a scale factor of 0. Explain your answer.
No, all figures would have a single point as dilation images.

Written **A dilation with center C and a scale factor k maps A onto D, and B onto E. Find k for each of the following conditions.**

1. $CD = 10$, $CA = 5$ 2
2. $CE = 18$, $CB = 9$ 2
3. $CD = 6$, $CA = 4$ 3/2
4. $CA = 2$, $CD = 10$ 5
5. $AB = 3$, $DE = 1$ 1/3
6. $AB = 3$, $DE = 4$ 4/3
7. $CD = 3$, $CA = 6$ 1/2
8. $CB = 28$, $CE = 7$ 1/4
9. $DE = 12$, $AB = 4$ 3
10. $AB = 16$, $DE = 4$ 1/4
11–20. Determine whether the dilation is an enlargement, reduction, or congruence transformation for each of the conditions in exercises **1–10.** enlargements are: 11, 12, 13, 14, 16, 19; reductions are: 15, 17, 18, 20

Draw and label a figure like the one shown below. Then, find the dilation image of $\triangle ABC$ for the given scale factor and center.

For answers to exercises 21-24, see the Teacher's Guide.

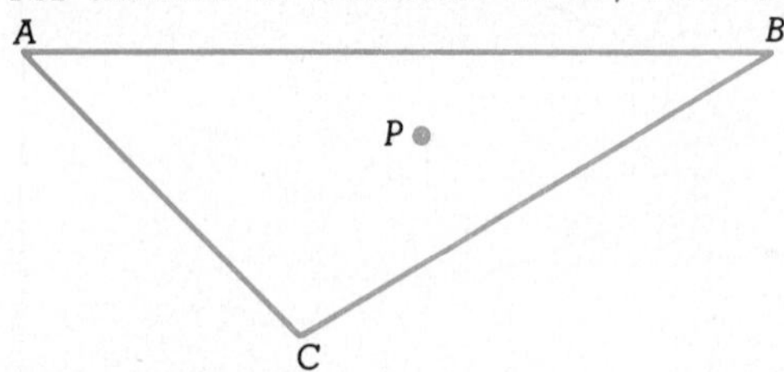

21. 3, center E
22. $\frac{1}{3}$, center E
23. 2, center P
24. $\frac{1}{2}$, center P

For each of the following scale factors, find the image of A with respect to a dilation with center P.

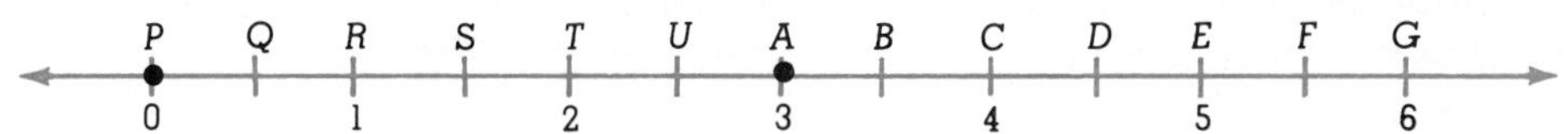

25. 1 A **26.** 2 G **27.** $\frac{2}{3}$ T **28.** $1\frac{1}{3}$ C

29. $\frac{1}{2}$ S **30.** $1\frac{1}{6}$ B **31.** $1\frac{5}{6}$ F **32.** $1\frac{1}{2}$ D

Graph each of the following ordered pairs. Then, connect the graphs in order. Using (0, 0) as the center of dilation and a scale factor of 2, draw the dilation image. Then repeat this using a scale factor of $\frac{1}{2}$. For answers to exercises 33-42, see the Teacher's Guide.

33. (0, 2), (4, 0)
34. (3, ⁻3), (⁻2, ⁻2)
35. (⁻2, ⁻1), (⁻2, ⁻2)
36. (3, 4), (6, 2)
37. (3, 4), (6, 10), (⁻3, 5)
38. (6, 5), (4, 5), (3, 7)
39. (⁻1, 4), (0, 1), (2, 3)
40. (1, ⁻2), (4, ⁻3), (6, ⁻1)
41. (1, 2), (3, 3), (3, 5), (1, 4)
42. (4, 2), (⁻4, 6), (⁻6, ⁻8), (6, ⁻10)

Find the measure of the image of $\overline{AB}$ with respect to a dilation with the given scale factors.

43. $AB = 5$ in., $k = 6$ 30 in.
44. $AB = \frac{2}{3}$ cm, $k = \frac{1}{2}$ $\frac{1}{3}$ cm
45. $AB = 16$ ft, $k = 1\frac{1}{2}$ 24 ft
46. $AB = 3.1$ m, $k = 5$ 15.5 m
47. $AB = 12$ cm, $k = \frac{1}{4}$ 3 cm
48. $AB = 3\frac{1}{3}$ in., $k = 9$ 30 in.

49. Plan a proof to show that a dilation with center C and scale factor $\frac{1}{2}$ maps $\overline{AB}$ onto $\overline{ED}$ such that $ED = \frac{1}{2}(AB)$.

50. Plan a proof to show that a dilation with center C and scale factor k maps $\overline{AB}$ onto $\overline{ED}$ such that $ED = k(AB)$.

For answers to exercises 49-50, see the Teacher's Guide.

Transformations in Art and Nature

excursions in geometry

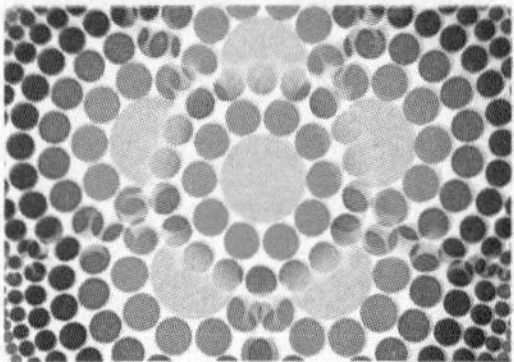

Reflections, rotations, translations, lines of symmetry, and so on often appear in art and nature. The kaleidoscope illustrates rotations, reflections, point and line symmetry.

See the Teacher's Guide.

Exercises **List all possible kinds of transformations in the following.**

1. reflection

2. line symmetry

3. line symmetry

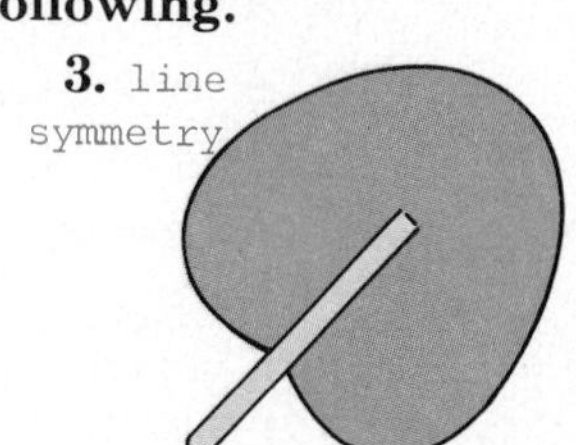

Vocabulary

transformation (471)
image (471)
preimage (471)
isometry (472)
congruence transformation (472)
similarity transformation (472)
reflection (474)
line of reflection (474)
point of reflection (474)
line of symmetry (476)
point of symmetry (476)
composite of reflections (479)
translation (479)
rotation (482)
center of rotation (482)
angle of rotation (483)
glide reflection (489)
dilation (492)
scale factor (492)
enlargement (493)
reduction (493)

Chapter Summary

1. Moving a geometric figure to show that it coincides with another geometric figure is called a mapping. The second figure is called the image of the first figure. The first figure is called the preimage of the second figure. (471)
2. Definition of a transformation: In a plane, a mapping is a transformation if and only if each point has exactly one image point and each image point has exactly one preimage point. (471)
3. When a geometric figure and its transformation image are congruent, the mapping is called an isometry. (472)
4. A reflection with respect to ℓ is a transformation such that if A is on ℓ then A and its image B are the same point. If A is not on ℓ, then ℓ is the perpendicular bisector of $\overline{AB}$. (474)
5. Reflections preserve collinearity, betweenness of points, angle measure, and distance measure. (474)
6. A line of symmetry is a line of reflection. (476)
7. A translation is a composite of two reflections with respect to two parallel lines. (479)
8. All properties preserved by reflections are preserved by translations. (480)
9. A rotation is the composite of two reflections with respect to two intersecting lines. The point of intersection is called the center of rotation. (482)

10. All properties preserved by reflections are preserved by rotations. (482)

11. Postulate 14–1: In a given rotation, if A is the preimage, P is the image, and W is the center of rotation, then the measure of the angle of rotation, $\angle AWP$, equals twice the measure of the angle between the intersecting lines of reflection. (483)

12. A composite of more than two reflections can be described as a single isometry or a congruence transformation. (486)

13. A composite of three reflections that does not result in a reflection, translation, or a rotation is an isometry called a glide reflection. A glide reflection consists of a reflection and a translation. (489)

14. A dilation is a similarity transformation. (492)

15. Theorem 14–1: If a dilation with center C and a scale factor k maps A onto E and B onto D then $ED = k(AB)$. (492)

16. A dilation with center C and a scale factor k changes the size of the figure but not its shape. If $k > 1$, then the dilation is an enlargement. If $0 < k < 1$, then the dilation is a reduction. If $k = 1$, then the dilation is a congruence transformation. (493)

Chapter Review

14–1 Suppose $\triangle ABE \rightarrow \triangle CBD$ and is an isometry. Name the preimage for each of the following.

1. D E 2. $\angle CBD$ $\angle$ ABE 3. B B 4. $\triangle CBD$ $\triangle$ ABE

For each of the following, name a part congruent to the given part.

5. $\angle A$ $\angle$ C 6. $\overline{BE}$ $\overline{\text{BD}}$ 7. $\overline{AB}$ $\overline{\text{CB}}$ 8. $\triangle BDC$ $\triangle$ BEA

14–2 9. Draw an equilateral triangle. Then, draw all the lines of symmetry and any point of symmetry. For answers to exercises 9-13, see the Teacher's Guide.

Copy each of the following. Then draw the reflection image of each figure with respect to ℓ.

10. 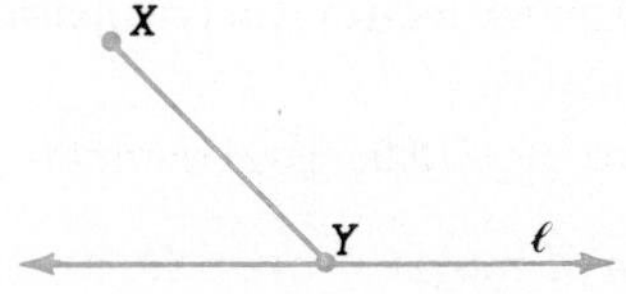

11. 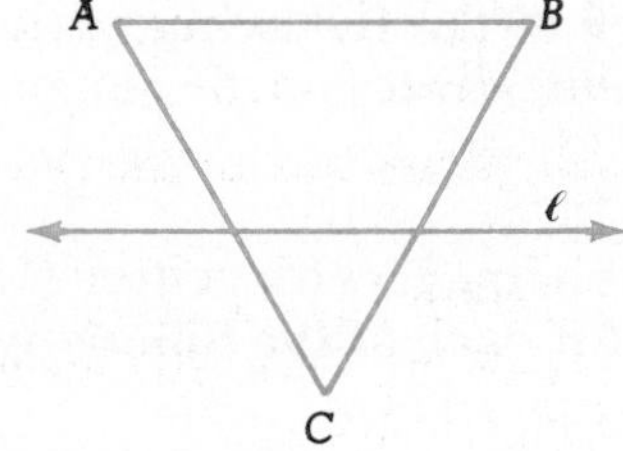

14–3 **Copy each of the following. Then, draw the translation image of each figure with respect to the parallel lines s and t.**

12.

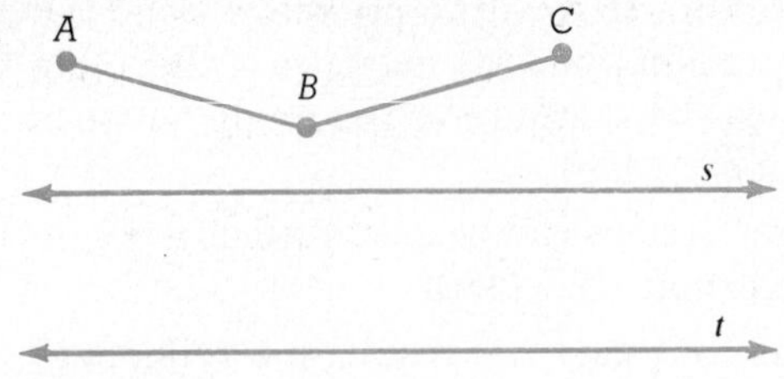

13.

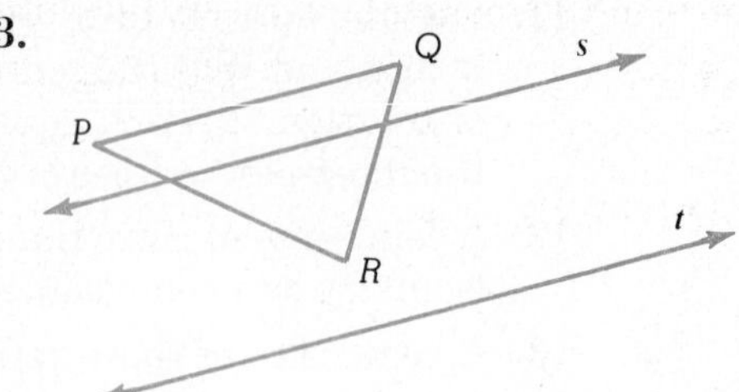

14–4 **Use the figure to solve each of the following.**

14. Find the degree measure of the angle of rotation. 140

15. Copy the figure at the right. Then, draw the rotation image with respect to ℓ and m. See the Teacher's Guide.

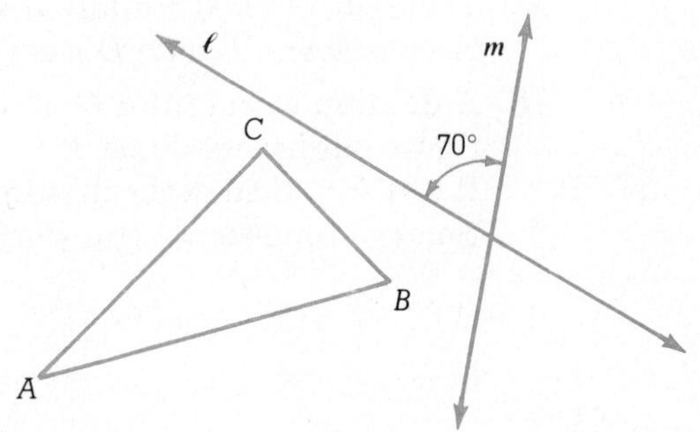

14–5 **For each of the following, name a single isometry that can be used to map $\triangle ABC$ onto $\triangle PQR$.**

16. reflection with respect to m

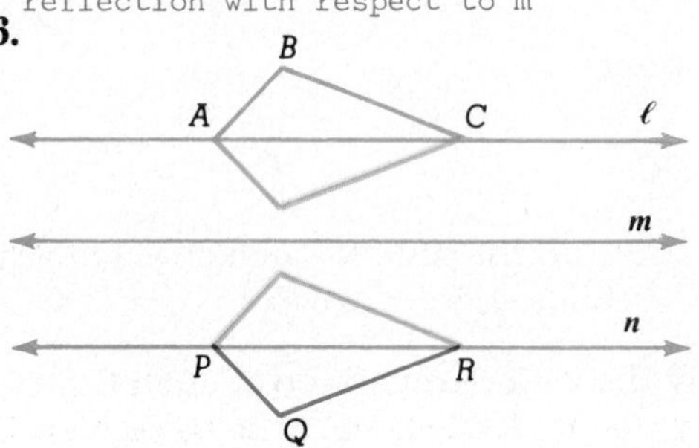

17. reflection with respect to m

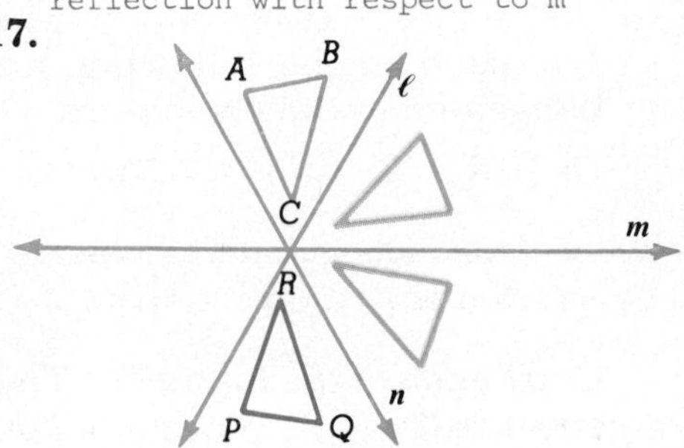

14–6 **For each of the following scale factors, determine whether the dilation is an enlargement, reduction, or congruence transformation.**

18. 5 enlargement

19. $\frac{1}{4}$ reduction

20. 1 congruence transformation

A dilation image with center C and a scale factor k maps A onto D, and B onto E. Find k for each of the following conditions.

21. $CD = 8, CA = 2$ 4

22. $CB = 3, CE = 9$ 3

Chapter Test

Determine whether or *not* each of the following are isometries. Write *yes* or *no*.

1. reflection yes **2.** translation yes **3.** rotation yes **4.** glide reflection yes

5–8. Name the properties preserved by each of the transformations in exercises **1–4**.
5. collinearity, angle measure, distance, betweeness 6.- 8. same as reflection

Describe each of the following as a *reflection*, a *rotation*, a *translation*, or a *glide reflection*.

9. translation

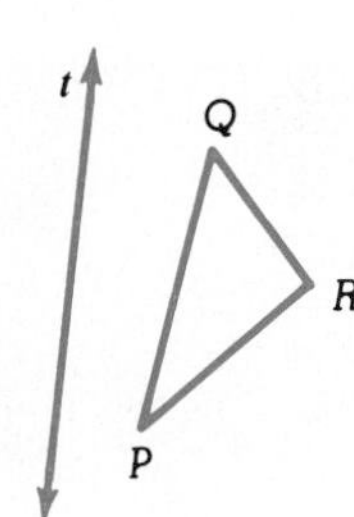

10. reflection

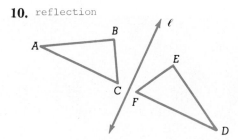

11. rotation

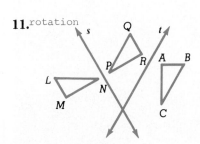

12. glide reflection

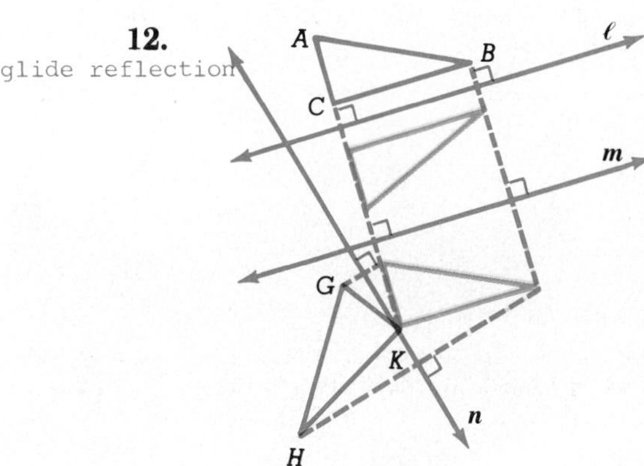

For answers to exercises 13-14, see the Teacher's Guide.

13. Copy, then draw all possible lines of symmetry for the figure at the right.

14. Draw a triangle and four parallel lines. Reflect the triangle with respect to the four lines.

15. Name the single isometry that can be used in exercise **14.** translation

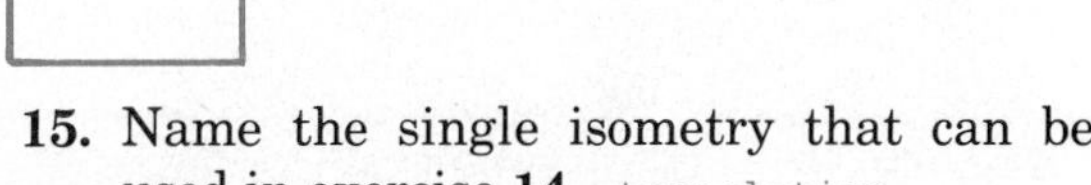

Determine whether the dilation is an enlargement, reduction, or congruence transformation for each of the following scale factors.

16. $1\frac{1}{3}$ enlargement **17.** 1 congruence transformation **18.** 0.3 reduction **19.** 8 enlargement

Copy, then draw the dilation image of the figure at the right for the given conditions.

20. center C, $k = 3$

21. center C, $k = \frac{1}{3}$

22. center C, $k = 1$

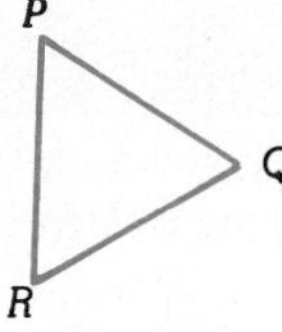

For answers to exercises 20-22, see the Teacher's Guide.

Appendix: BASIC

Microcomputers are used by many people. One of the languages used to communicate with such computers is called BASIC.

The exercises in each section of the Appendix incorporate geometric concepts developed in chapters throughout the entire book.

Objectives: to evaluate BASIC expressions using the order of operations, to write correct BASIC expressions, to write simple computer programs in BASIC, to use READ/DATA statements in programs

The Language of BASIC

BASIC is a frequently used computer language. BASIC is an abbreviation for **B**eginner's **A**ll-purpose **S**ymbolic **I**nstruction **C**ode. In BASIC, some operation symbols are the same as those in algebra.

Algebra	BASIC	Algebra	BASIC
+	+	÷	/
−	−	=	=
×	*	5^2	5 ↑ 2

In BASIC, raising to a power is usually indicated by ↑.

Variables may be represented by a letter or by a letter and a numeral. A, B, X, C1, D2, and M5 are examples of variables in BASIC. *Check your manual to see if your computer allows other variable names.*

Note that some computers print out 5↑2 in the form 5^2.

In BASIC an operation symbol *cannot* be omitted. For example, A times B must be written A * B, *not* AB as allowed in algebra.

The computer performs operations in the same order as in algebra.

In BASIC, leading zeros are ignored. For instance, 0.04 is written as .04.

Order of Operations in BASIC

1. **Do all operations in parentheses, from the innermost parentheses outward.**
2. **Evaluate all powers from left to right.**
3. **Do all multiplications and/or divisions from left to right.**
4. **Do all additions and/or subtractions from left to right.**

The order of operations is shown in the following example.

example

1 Evaluate 18/3 − (6 + 2) * 3 ↑ 2 + 4.

18/3 − (6 + 2) * 3 ↑ 2 + 4 = 18/3 − 8 * 3 ↑ 2 + 4 — *Do operations in parentheses.*
= 18/3 − 8 * 9 + 4 — *Evaluate powers.*
= 6 − 72 + 4 — *Do the division and multiplication.*
= ⁻62 — *Do the addition and subtraction.*

The value of the expression is ⁻62.

A computer program is a sequence of statements which gives directions to the computer. The purpose of a computer program is to put information into the computer (*input*), have the computer do calculations (*execution*), and get results out of the computer (*output*). Here is a sample program.

```
10 PRINT 7.8 + 2.5
20 END
```

line numbers (10, 20) — *statements* (PRINT 7.8 + 2.5, END)

In a BASIC program each statement must have a line number. Integers from 1 to 9999 are commonly used as line numbers. The computer executes the instructions in the order in which the statements are numbered. The last statement should be an END statement. Other statements used in programs are READ/DATA statements.

Refer to your manual to determine the maximum line number allowed on your system.

Point out that line numbers are usually multiples of 10. This allows another statement to be inserted between two others.

example

The END statement is not required by all computers.

2 Write a program to find the sum and product of two numbers.

```
10  READ A, B
20  DATA 16, 5
30  PRINT A + B
40  PRINT A * B
50  END
RUN
21
80
```

The computer assigns the numbers from the DATA statement in line 20 to the variables A and B in order.
A = 16   B = 5

21 = A + B
*80 = A * B*

The sum and product of any two numbers may be found by changing the numbers in the DATA statement.

```
10  READ A, B
20  DATA 6, 4
30  PRINT A + B
40  PRINT A * B
50  END
RUN
10
24
```

The computer assigns 6 to A and 4 to B.

RUN tells the computer to execute the program.

3 Write a BASIC program to compute and print the perimeter and area of a rectangle with length 2.6 centimeters and width 1.7 centimeters.

```
10  READ L, W
20  DATA 2.6, 1.7
30  PRINT 2 * L + 2 * W, L * W
40  END
RUN
8.6      4.42
```

The comma in line 30 tells the computer to print the output on one line in zones.

exercises

Written **Write an expression in BASIC for each of the following.**

1. $5a + 2$ 5*A + 2
2. $xyz + 7$ X*Y*Z + 7
3. $9x + 4y - 3$ 9*X + 4*Y - 3
4. $(3x - 4y)^2$ (3*X - 4*Y)↑2
5. $\frac{m + 6}{b}$ (M + 6)/B
6. $\frac{2x + 5}{3y}$ (2*X + 5)/(3*Y)
7. $4a^2 + 6a - 7$ 4*A↑2 + 6*A - 7
8. 7^{y+4} 7↑(Y + 4)
9. $\frac{5x + 2}{3y - 7}$ (5*X + 2)/(3*Y - 7)
10. $\left(\frac{x}{y} + w\right)^2$ (X/Y + W)↑2

Evaluate each of the following expressions.

11. 7 * 3 ↑ 2 63
12. (4 + 78)/2 + 5 46
13. ((13 + 11)/4)/6 1
14. (4 * (4 + 8))/16 3
15. 4 * 3 ↑ 2 36
16. (4 * 3) ↑ 2 144

Evaluate each of the following. Use A = 10, B = 5, and C = 2.

17. A * B + 3 53
18. A * (B + 3) 80
19. C − B + 5 2
20. A * B ↑ C 250
21. (A/B) ↑ 2 4
22. A/B ↑ 2 0.4

Write programs in BASIC to solve each of the following problems. Use READ/DATA statements. For answers to exercises 23-32, see the Teacher's Guide.

23. Find the value of $A^2 - B^2$, $(A - B)^2$, $A^2 + B^2$, and $(A + B)^2$ when A = 5 and B = 2.
24. Find the circumference and area of a circle with radius 2.58 cm. Use $\pi = 3.14159$.
25. Find the area of a triangle with base 7.3 cm and height 4.8 cm.
26. Find the volume and surface area of a cube with each edge 5.5 cm.
27. Find the complement and supplement of an angle which has a degree measure of 68.
28. Two angles of a triangle have degree measures of 48 and 30. Find the degree measure of the third angle.
29. Find the sum of the degree measures of the angles of a regular polygon with 40 sides.
30. Find the number of sides of a regular polygon if the degree measure of one of its angles is 168.
31. The sides of a pentagon have lengths of 16 cm, 8.2 cm, 4.3 cm, 4.2 cm, and 4.1 cm. Find the perimeter of the pentagon.
32. The bases of a trapezoid have lengths of 10 inches and 20 inches, and the height of the trapezoid is 6 inches. Find the area of the trapezoid.

Objectives: to write statements that assign values to variables in a BASIC program, to express numerals using E notation, to correct errors in BASIC expressions, to use LET statements in programs

Assignment of Variables

In BASIC, the left side of an equation can have *only one* variable. The equals sign tells the computer to assign the value of the expression on the right to the variable on the left. An equals sign is used in a LET statement.

Note that with IF-THEN statements, considered in the next section, more than one variable may appear on the left side of an equation.

```
10  LET X = 5              5 is assigned to X.
20  LET Y = 2              2 is assigned to Y.
30  LET A = 5 * Y + 20/X   The value of A is computed and assigned.
40  PRINT A                The value of A is printed.
50  END
RUN
14                         The output is 14.
```

With some computers, LET may be omitted from a LET statement. For example, line 10 could be entered as 10 X = 5.

A different program may be written for the same problem.

```
10  READ X, Y
20  DATA 5, 2
30  LET A = 5 * Y + 20/X
40  PRINT A
50  END
RUN
14
```

*In this program, the data are assigned as follows. X = 5, Y = 2. The value of 5 * Y + 20/X is then computed and assigned to A in line 30. This value is then printed.*

In the DATA statement, the value of a variable cannot be entered as a fraction. For example, the value $\frac{1}{2}$ is entered as .5 rather than $\frac{1}{2}$.

LET statements also can be used to assign a new value to a variable as shown in the following example.

example

1 Write a program using BASIC to compute the volumes of three cubes with sides measuring 2 centimeters, 3 centimeters, and 4 centimeters.

```
10  LET M = 2         The value of 2 is assigned to M.
20  PRINT M, M ↑ 3    Output   2   8
30  LET M = M + 1     Now the value of 3 is assigned to M.
40  PRINT M, M ↑ 3    Output   3   27
50  LET M = M + 1     Now what value is assigned to M?  4
60  PRINT M, M ↑ 3    What is the output?  4, 64
70  END
```

The PRINT statement can be used to print words as well as the results of calculations. The computer will print the symbols that are placed between quotation marks.

example

2 Write a program using BASIC to compute the perimeter and area of an equilateral triangle with each side 6 inches and an altitude approximately 5.2 inches.

```
10  LET S = 6
20  LET H = 5.2
30  LET P = S + S + S
40  LET A = 1/2 * S * H
50  PRINT "PERIMETER IS  "; P; "  INCHES"
60  PRINT "AREA IS APPROXIMATELY  "; A; "  SQ INCHES"
70  END
RUN
PERIMETER IS 18 INCHES
AREA IS APPROXIMATELY 15.6 SQ INCHES
```

The semicolon tells the computer to print the output close together.

When the output is more than six significant digits, some computers will use **E notation.** This is the computer equivalent of scientific notation. For example, 5.15076E + 07 means 5.15076×10^7 or 51,507,600.

Refer to your manual to determine the number of significant digits at which your system will use E notation.

Output	Scientific Notation	E Notation
17161308	1.7161308×10^7	1.71613E + 07
0.009514	9.514×10^{-3}	9.514E − 03

exercises

Written **Express each of the following using scientific notation. Then, express each using E notation.**

1. 7,437,600 7.4376×10^6, 7.4376E + 06
2. 0.000002827381 2.827381×10^{-6}, 2.827381E - 06
3. 0.002987 2.987×10^{-3}, 2.987E - 03
4. 14,630,040,000 1.463004×10^{10}, 1.463004E + 10

Express the value of each expression without using scientific notation.

5. 7.063E + 10 70,630,000,000
6. 3.33127E − 05 0.0000333127
7. 2.322E − 07 0.0000002322
8. 2.8062E + 06 2,806,200

Find the value of X in each BASIC statement. Let A = 5, B = 2, and Cl = 9.

9. 10 LET X = B * A + Cl 19
10. 10 LET X = A * B + 6 16
11. 10 LET X = A/B + 9 11.5
12. 10 LET X = Cl + A + 6 20

Correct the error in each expression or statement below.

13. (7 + 8/2 (7 + 8)/2
14. 4 * X↑2 − 2Y 4*X↑2 - 2*Y
15. 10 LET 2 * Y = 4 + A
    10 LET Y = (4 + A)/2
16. 10 LET A + B = C + D
    10 LET A = C + D - B

Each mathematical expression is followed by an incorrect BASIC expression. Write the correct BASIC expression.

17. $\frac{m+2}{r-3}$, M + 2/(R − 3) (M + 2)/(R - 3)

18. $\frac{ab}{y+3}$, (A * B)Y + 3 A*B/(Y + 3)

19. $\frac{(x+a)^2}{2z}$, X + A ↑ 2/2Z (X + A)↑2/(2*Z)

20. $\left(\frac{x}{y}\right)^{n-1}$, X/Y ↑ N − 1 (X/Y)↑(N - 1)

Write each formula using a LET statement.

21. $A = \frac{1}{2}bh$ 10 LET A = 1/2*B*H

22. $V = \ell wh$ 10 LET V = L*W*H

23. $A = \frac{1}{2}h(b_1 + b_2)$ 10 LET A = 1/2*H*(B1 + B2)

24. $m = \frac{y_2 - y_1}{x_2 - x_1}$ 10 LET M = (Y2 - Y1)/(X2 - X1)

For answers to exercises 25-44, see the Teacher's Guide.

For each of the following problems, write a BASIC program using the given values of A, B, and C to compute and print the value of X. Use LET statements.

25. A = 5, B = 10, C = 4
X = 3A + 5B − 6C

26. A = 10, B = 2, C = 13
X = $3A^2$ − 4(B + C)

27. A = 2, B = ⁻3, C = 11
X = A^2 − 4B + C

28. A = ⁻1, B = 15, C = ⁻4
X = $(A \cdot B)^2$ − 5C

Write programs using BASIC to solve each of the following problems.

29. Change 1 meter, 2 meters, and 3 meters to centimeters.

30. Find the average of the numbers 12, 254, 618, 29, and 73.

31. Find the perimeter of a rectangle whose length is 16 cm and whose width is 6 cm.

32. Find the area of a square whose side has a measurement of 7.5 mm.

33. Find the area of a parallelogram whose base has a measurement of 12 inches and whose altitude has a measurement of $5\frac{1}{2}$ inches. Remind students that $5\frac{1}{2}$ must be entered as 5.5.

34. Find the circumference of a circle with a diameter of 14 mm. Use 3.14 for π.

35. Find the coordinates of the midpoint of the segment whose endpoints have coordinates (3, ⁻6) and (11, 5).

36. Find the slope of the line passing through the points with coordinates (⁻4, 7) and (⁻1, ⁻2).

37. Find the degree measure of the two congruent angles of an isosceles triangle if the third angle has a degree measure of 110.

38. Find the degree measure of the exterior angle of a triangle if the two remote interior angles have degree measures of 36 and 98.

39. Find the degree measure of a central angle of a regular polygon with 35 sides.

40. Find the sum of the degree measures of the angles of a triangle and convex quadrilateral.

41. Find the approximate area of a regular hexagon whose side has a measurement of 4 cm and apothem has a measurement of approximately 3.5 cm.

42. Find the volume of a rectangular solid whose length is 7.5 cm, width is 4 cm, and height is 2.5 cm.

43. Find the total surface area of a right prism whose bases each have an area of 6 square inches and a perimeter of 10 inches, and whose height is 10 inches.

44. Find the total surface area of a right cylinder whose height is 14 cm and whose bases have radii of 8 cm. Use 3.14 for π.

IF-THEN Statements

Objective: to write BASIC programs using IF-THEN statements

The IF-THEN statement is used to compare two numbers. It tells the computer what to do based on the results of the comparison.

A general form of the IF-THEN statement is as follows.

IF algebraic sentence THEN line number

If the algebraic sentence is true, then control goes to the line whose number follows THEN. If the algebraic sentence is false, then the computer executes the next line in sequence.

The algebraic sentence in the IF-THEN statement uses one of the following symbols.

Help students recognize the true-false tests provided by IF-THEN statements in a program. Students may need some guidance in following the sequences of steps for examples 1 and 2.

BASIC symbol	Meaning
=	is equal to
<	is less than
< =	is less than or equal to
>	is greater than
> =	is greater than or equal to
< >	is not equal to

example

1 Write a program to compute and print integers whose fourth powers are less than 1000.

```
10  LET N = 0              Assign a value of zero to N. Why?
20  LET N = N + 1          Increase the value of N by one.
30  LET F = N ↑ 4          Assign the value of N ↑ 4 to F.
40  IF F > = 1000 THEN 70  Test line.
        No          Yes
50  PRINT N, F
60  GO TO 20               Return to line 20 of the program.
70  END
```

The variable N may have been assigned some value by a previous program.

When the computer executes line 40, it tests the value of F. If F is less than 1000, then control goes to line 50 and the values of N and F are printed. Next, line 60 sends control to line 20 to compute the next integer. If F is greater than or equal to 1000, control goes to line 70.

Sometimes a programmer needs to count how many times an operation is performed. In the program below, line 40 keeps the count. Each time the computer comes back to statement 40, the count is increased by one.

example

2 Write a program to count the number of powers of five between 100 and 1,000,000 and print each one. Express each both as a number with no exponent, and as a power of five.

```
10  LET K = 1                      The counter K starts at 1.
20  LET X = 125                    5^3 = 125 is the first power of 5 greater than 100.
30  PRINT K, X, "5 ↑ "; (K + 2)
40  LET K = K + 1                  The counter increases by one.
50  LET X = X * 5                  The next power of 5 is calculated.
60  IF X > = 1000000 THEN 80       The test line checks to see if that power
70  GO TO 30                       of 5 is greater than or equal to 1,000,000.
80  END
```

In line 30, why is K + 2 used for the exponent? So that the first power printed is 5^3.

exercises

Written **Let A = 5, B = 8, and X = 10. State the line number of the statement that control will go to after the IF-THEN statement is executed.**

1.
```
10  IF A > = −4 THEN 90
20  PRINT 2 * A
```
90

2.
```
10  IF A < > B THEN 50
20  PRINT X
```
50

3.
```
41  IF A − B > X THEN 75
44  PRINT B − A
```
44

4.
```
45  IF B * X < A ↑ 3 THEN 10
50  PRINT B * X
```
10

5.
```
20  IF A * B = X THEN 100
25  PRINT A * B
```
25

6.
```
35  IF X − A ↑ 2 < 0 THEN 52
45  PRINT B
```
52

Use the program at the right to determine whether A, B, or both A and B will be printed. Give the value of any variable printed.

7. A = 12, B = 12   B, 12
8. A = 14, B = 19   B, 19
9. A = 9, B = 21   A, 19; B, 21
10. A = 21, B = 5   A, 21; B, 5
11. A = 28, B = 38   B, 38

```
10  IF A > B THEN 40
20  LET A = A + 10
30  IF A > = B THEN 50
40  PRINT A
50  PRINT B
60  END
```

Write programs in BASIC to solve each of the following problems. Use IF-THEN statements. For answers to exercises 12-25, see the Teacher's Guide.

12. Print the integers from 10 to 1 in descending order.

13. Print the even integers from 1 to 20 in ascending order.

14. Determine if a triangle exists given the measures of its sides. Use the following sets of data: 4, 4, 4; 2, 5, 1; 4,7, 9; 6, 7, 20.

See the Teacher's Guide sample program for exercise 14 to see how data is entered to avoid OUT OF DATA error.

15. Print the degree measure of an angle and determine whether or not the angle is acute, obtuse, or right. Use the following data: 17, 164, 39, 90, 111, 85, 127, 45, 63.

16. Classify a triangle as acute, obtuse, or right, given the degree measures of two angles of the triangle. Use the following sets of data: 45, 60; 95, 20; 37, 53; 124, 46; 90, 45; 23, 49.

17. Determine if a triangle is a right triangle given the measures of its sides. Use the following sets of data: 3, 4, 5; 15, 20, 30; 27, 36, 45; 2, 7, 9; 9, 40, 41; 21, 28, 35.

18. Determine if a given number is a multiple of 17. Use the following data: 102, 43, 117, 204, 89, 85, 155.

19. Print the multiples of seven less than 500.

20. Count the number of powers of six less than 900,000. Express each power as a number without using an exponent.

21. Determine if a point with given coordinates lies on the graph of $3x + 6y = 15$. Use the following ordered pairs: (1, 7), (3, 1), ($^-1$, 6), ($^-4$, $^-2$), (1, 2), $\left(4, \frac{1}{2}\right)$.

22. Determine if the slope of a line is undefined given the coordinates of two points that lie on the line. Use the following sets of ordered pairs: (3, 5), (7, 6); (2, 1), (2, 6); ($^-3$, 4), (3, 8); ($^-1$, 7), (7, 7); ($^-2$, $^-10$), (2, 10).

23. Read a number and determine if it is greater than 10 or less than $^-10$. If it is greater than 10, print the number and its square. If it is less than $^-10$, print the number and its cube. If it is neither greater than 10 nor less than $^-10$, print the number. Use the following data: 16, $^-90$, 45, 6, 13, $^-42$, $^-8$.

24. Read four integers given in any order and print the greatest integer. Use the following sets of data: 3, $^-7$, 8, 5; $^-10$, 25, 0, 6; $^-1$, $^-6$, $^-11$, $^-2$; $^-5$, 8, 4, 13.

25. Read three integers given in any order and print them from least to greatest. Use the following sets of data: 2, 1, 5; $^-3$, 6, $^-7$; 0, 10, 6; 25, $^-4$, 13; 21, $^-30$, 2.

Due to the way in which values are stored in a computer, an expression such as 7^2 (7↑2) may be given a value of 49.0000001 rather than 49. This may affect the execution of some programs, as in exercise 17.

Objectives: to write BASIC programs using FOR-NEXT statements, to find the output of programs with nested and/or independent loops, to locate errors in programs

FOR-NEXT Loops

Sometimes an operation needs to be used on different sets of data. FOR-NEXT statements allow the computer to loop through the same operation several times.

The following program uses an IF-THEN statement to print the multiples of two up to six.

```
10  LET M = 1
20  IF M > 3 THEN 60
30  PRINT M, M * 2
40  LET M = M + 1
50  GO TO 20
60  END
RUN
1    2
2    4
3    6
```

A simpler way to write the program involves the use of a FOR-NEXT statement. Emphasize how FOR-NEXT statements can simplify a program.

```
10  FOR M = 1 TO 3 STEP 1
20      PRINT M, M * 2
30  NEXT M
40  END
```

The phrase STEP 1 tells the computer to increase M by one each time.

The computer continues until the value of M is greater than 3.

Point out that when the computer reads line 30 in this program, it goes back to line 10 and increases the value of M by 1.

A general form of the FOR statement is as follows:

FOR Variable = Number TO Number STEP Number

If the step is not indicated, most computers will automatically use a step of one. Emphasize this point of the student annotation.

Every time a FOR statement is used, there must be a NEXT statement.

example

1 Write a program using BASIC to compute and print the sum of the squares of all even integers from 2 to 100.

```
10  LET S = 0
20  FOR N = 2 TO 100 STEP 2
30      LET Y = N ↑ 2
40      LET S = S + Y
50  NEXT N
60  PRINT "SUM = "; S
70  END
RUN
SUM = 171700
```

The variable S represents the sum of all values of Y up to this point.

What would be different about the output if line 60 were given the line number 45? The partial sums would be printed.

Review the use of the semicolon in printing outputs. See student annotation in example 2, page 505, for the explanation.

Headings can help make output easier to read. The following example shows how headings may be included in the output.

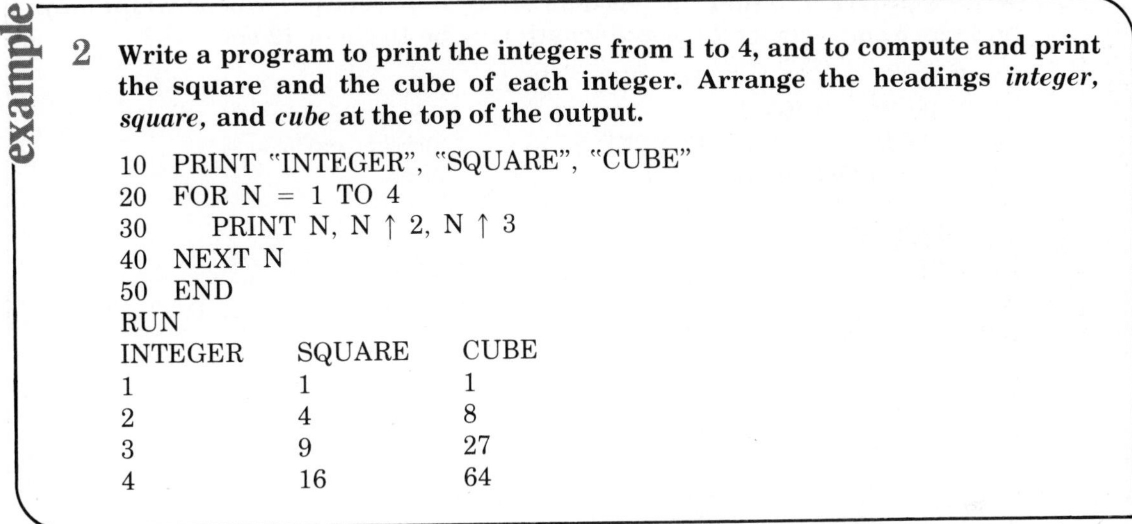

example

2 Write a program to print the integers from 1 to 4, and to compute and print the square and the cube of each integer. Arrange the headings *integer*, *square*, and *cube* at the top of the output.

```
10 PRINT "INTEGER", "SQUARE", "CUBE"
20 FOR N = 1 TO 4
30     PRINT N, N ↑ 2, N ↑ 3
40 NEXT N
50 END
RUN
INTEGER     SQUARE    CUBE
1           1         1
2           4         8
3           9         27
4           16        64
```

It often is useful to have more than one loop. There are only two ways that loops can appear in a program.

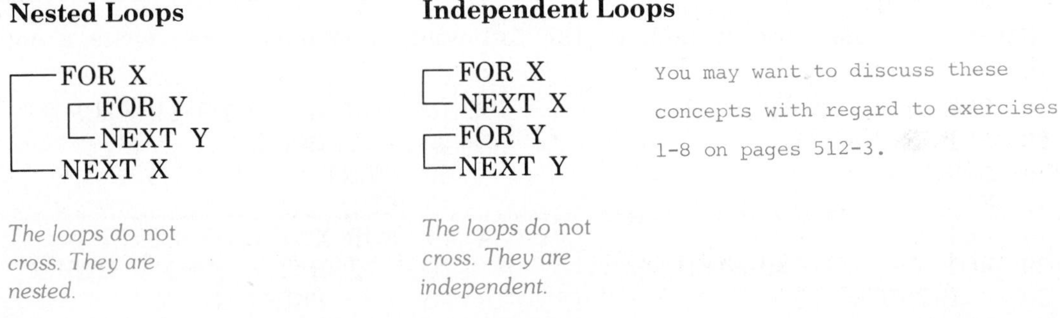

Nested Loops
FOR X
FOR Y
NEXT Y
NEXT X
Independent Loops
FOR X
NEXT X
FOR Y
NEXT Y

The loops do not cross. They are nested.

The loops do not cross. They are independent.

You may want to discuss these concepts with regard to exercises 1-8 on pages 512-3.

Loops cannot be used as shown below.

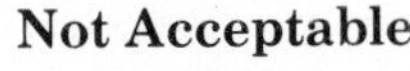

Not Acceptable

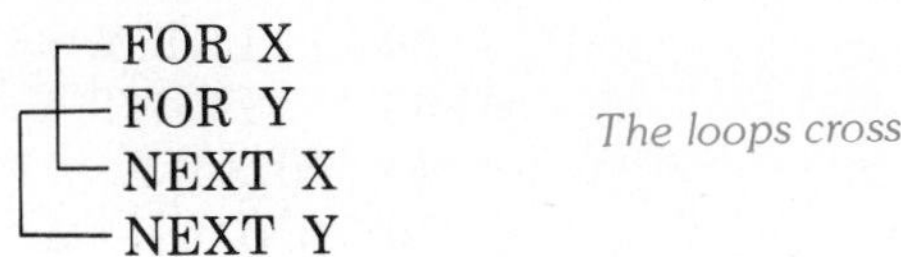

FOR X
FOR Y
NEXT X
NEXT Y

The loops cross.

The following example shows the correct use of nested loops.

example

3 Write a program to find the possible areas of a rectangle whose width may be 4 cm, 5 cm, 6 cm, or 7 cm and length may be 10 cm or 12 cm.

```
10 PRINT "WIDTH", "LENGTH", "AREA"
20 FOR W = 4 TO 7
30    FOR L = 10 TO 12 STEP 2
40       PRINT W, L, W * L
50    NEXT L
60 NEXT W
70 END
RUN
WIDTH     LENGTH     AREA
4         10         40
4         12         48
5         10         50
5         12         60
6         10         60
6         12         72
7         10         70
7         12         84
```

This is an example of nested loops. W has the same value while L goes through its loop.

exercises

Written Find the error in each of the following programs. Then write a correct program. For correct programs to exercises 1-8, see the Teacher's Guide.

1.
```
10 FOR K = 1 TO 16 STEP 0
20    PRINT K
30 NEXT K
40 END
```
The number after STEP cannot be 0.

2.
```
10 FOR M = 3 TO 25, STEP 2
20    PRINT M
30 NEXT M
40 END
```
A comma should not appear after 25.

3.
```
10 LET X = 4
20 FOR T = 1 TO 40 STEP 3
30    PRINT T
40 NEXT X
50 END
```
The variable in the NEXT statement should be T not X.

4.
```
10 FOR X = 1 TO 6 STEP 3
20    FOR Y = 2 TO 4 STEP 2
30       PRINT X * Y
40    NEXT X
50 NEXT Y
60 END
```
The variables in statements 40 and 50 are reversed.

Write the output of each program. The output to exercises 5-7 will print out in a vertical column.

5.
```
10 FOR N = 4 TO 31 STEP 3
20    PRINT N
30 NEXT N
40 END
```
4 7 10 13 16 19 22 25 28 31

6.
```
10 FOR X = 1 TO 10
20    LET Y = 11 - X
30    PRINT Y
40 NEXT X
50 END
```
10 9 8 7 6 5 4 3 2 1

7.
```
10 FOR I = 1 TO 3 STEP 1
20     LET A = 8
30     PRINT A
40 NEXT I
50 END
```
8 8 8

8.
```
10 FOR L = 10 TO 100 STEP 10
20     LET M = L ↑ 2
30     PRINT "INTEGER"; L,
       "SQUARE"; M
40 NEXT L
50 END
```
See the Teacher's Guide for output.

Write a program using BASIC to solve each of the following problems. Use FOR-NEXT loops. For answers to exercises 9-17, see the Teacher's Guide.

9. Find and print the sum of the cubes of the integers from 1 to 20 inclusive.

10. Find and print the complements of angles with degree measures from 0 to 90 in steps of five.

11. Find and print the values of y for the equation $y = x^2 - x + 6$ when $x = {}^-3, {}^-2, {}^-1, 0, 1, 2$, and 3.

12. The formula for Fahrenheit to Celsius conversion is $C = \frac{5}{9}(F - 32)$. Find the Celsius temperatures for Fahrenheit temperatures from 0° to 100° in steps of two.

13. The measures of the lengths and widths of three rectangles are 8 by 5, 9.2 by 3.4, and 17 by 18. Compute and print both the perimeter and area for each rectangle. Arrange the headings, length, width, perimeter, and area at the top.

14. Given the sets of ordered pairs (2, 5), (4, ⁻6); (7, 8), (⁻9, 5); and (4, 2.8), (3.6, ⁻2.1), find the slope of each line joining each pair of points.

15. Find and print the number of diagonals of every polygon from a triangle to a 25-gon. Arrange the headings *sides* and *diagonals* at the top of the output.

16. Find and print the sum of the interior angles of every regular polygon from a triangle to a 50-gon. Arrange the headings *sides* and *sum of angles* at the top of the output.

17. A right cylinder with a height of $2a$ is inscribed in a sphere whose radius has a measure of 20. Using the formula for the volume of a right cylinder ($V = \pi r^2 h$), and the figure at the right, we can derive a formula for the volume of this cylinder. This formula is $2\pi a(400 - a^2)$. Use this formula to find the volume of this cylinder for values of a from 1 to 20.

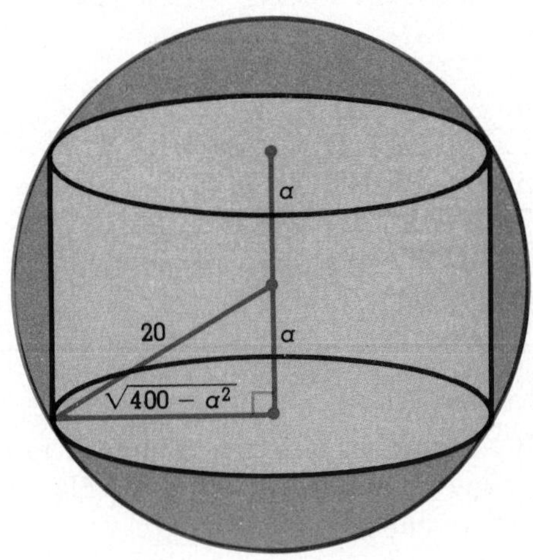

Some computers only allow three columns to be arranged by commas in a PRINT statement. In order to create four or more columns, as in exercise 13, it may be necessary to use the TAB function.

BASIC Functions

Objective: to write BASIC programs using the ABS(X), SQR(X), and INT(X) functions

BASIC functions are subprograms stored in the computer which may be used to simplify a program. For example, programmers may need to find the absolute value of a number. Instead of writing a program to find the absolute value, they can use a function to have this done automatically by the computer.

Some common BASIC functions are listed below.

ABS(X)	*absolute value of X*
SQR(X)	*square root of X*
INT(X)	*greatest integer less than or equal to X*

The absolute value function, ABS(X), gives the absolute value of X as illustrated in the following examples.

ABS(3) = 3 ABS(0) = 0 ABS(−4.8) = 4.8

example

1 Write a program using BASIC to find the distance between points *A* and *B*, *A* and *C*, *A* and *D*, *B* and *C*, *B* and *D*, and *C* and *D* on the number line.

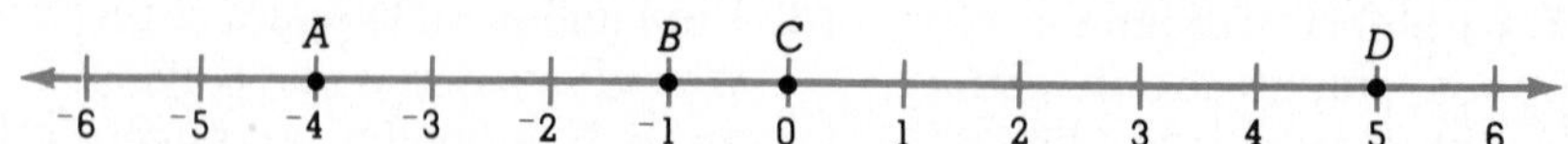


```
10 PRINT "POINT 1", "POINT 2", "DISTANCE"
20 PRINT                              A blank line will appear in the output.
30 FOR L = 1 TO 6
40    READ X, Y
50    LET D = ABS(X - Y)              The computer will assign the
60    PRINT X, Y, D                   absolute value of (X - Y) to D.
70 NEXT L
80 DATA -4, -1, -4, 0, -4, 5, -1, 0, -1, 5, 0, 5
90 END
```

The SQR(X) function tells the computer to calculate the square root of X. Some examples of valid BASIC statements using the SQR(X) function follow.

```
10 LET A = SQR(144)                   Since SQR(X) represents a
10 IF B = SQR(X) THEN 80              number, it can be used in
10 FOR I = 1 TO SQR(X) STEP 4         IF-THEN and FOR-NEXT
                                      statements.
```

example

2 Write a program using BASIC to find the square roots of the integers from 1 to 10.

```
10  FOR I = 1 TO 10
20     PRINT "THE SQUARE ROOT OF ";I;" IS ";SQR(I)
30  NEXT I
40  END
```

The INT(X) function is called the greatest integer function. After computing or reading the value of X, it finds the greatest integer less than or equal to X. Here are some examples.

It may be helpful to show the student a graph of the greatest integer function as you review this concept with students.

INT(8.02) = 8   INT(−5.6) = −6
INT(15) = 15   INT(72.99) = 72

example

3 Write a program using BASIC to find the factors of a given positive integer.

```
10  READ N
20  DATA 20, 48, 90, 0
25  IF N = 0 THEN 80
30  FOR X = 1 TO N
40     IF N/X < > INT(N/X) THEN 60
50     PRINT X;" IS A FACTOR OF ";N
60  NEXT X
70  GO TO 10
80  END
```

If N/X = INT(N/X), then N/X must be an integer. Therefore, X divides N evenly or X is a factor of N.

Pythagorean triples are sets of positive integers {A, B, C} such that $A^2 + B^2 = C^2$. A, B, and C represent the measures of the sides of a right triangle. The following program finds and prints all Pythagorean triples when A and B are less than or equal to 15.

```
10  FOR A = 1 TO 15
20     FOR B = A TO 15
30        LET C = SQR(A ↑ 2 + B ↑ 2)
40        IF C < > INT(C) THEN 60
50        PRINT A, B, C
60     NEXT B
70  NEXT A
80  END
```

Why does B go from A to 15?

Output

3	4	5
5	12	13
6	8	10
8	15	17
9	12	15

See the comment regarding rounding errors at the bottom of page 509.

exercises

Written **Write the output of each of the following PRINT statements. Let A = ⁻3, B = 16, C = 4.2, and D = 1.**

1. PRINT ABS (A) 3
2. PRINT ABS (B ↑ D) 16
3. PRINT SQR (B) 4
4. PRINT INT (C) 4
5. PRINT SQR (B) − SQR (D) 3
6. PRINT INT (SQR(C)) 2
7. PRINT 12 * INT (C) 48
8. PRINT INT (ABS(A)) 3

Write programs using BASIC to solve each of the following problems. Use BASIC functions. For answers to exercises 9-16, see the Teacher's Guide.

9. Find the absolute value of a given number. Print both the number and its absolute value. Use the following data: ⁻2, 4.761, 0, ⁻0.011, 7.999.
10. Find the square root of a number. Print both the number and its square root if it exists. Use the following data: 2, 4.761, 0, ⁻3, 8.
11. Find and print the sum of the greatest integers of the square roots of all integers from 1 to 10.
12. Find and print the greatest integer of the sum of the square roots of all integers from 1 to 10.
13. Print an integer and state whether it is odd or even. Use the INT(X) function in your program. Use the following data: ⁻6, ⁻5, ⁻1, 0, 2, 9.
14. Use the Pythagorean Theorem to find the measure of the hypotenuse of a right triangle given the measures of the legs of the right triangle. Print the measures of all sides of the triangle. Use the following data: 3, 4; 8, 15; 4, 4; 9, 10.
15. Find and print the distance between the following pairs of points: (1, 5), (⁻7, 2); (2, ⁻2.5), (⁻11.7, ⁻1). Recall that the distance between two points (x_1, y_1) and (x_2, y_2) is $\sqrt{(x_2 - x_1)^2 + (y_2 - y_1)^2}$.
16. Given three measures of the sides of a triangle, determine whether or not the triangle is a right triangle. Use the following sets of data: 4, 5, 7; 9, 40, 41; 20, 21, 29.

In regard to exercise 16, refer to the comment on rounding errors at the bottom of page 509.

Diagnostic Skills Review

Integer Equations: Addition and Subtraction 518
Integer Equations: Multiplication and Division .. 519
Fraction Equations: Addition and Subtraction ... 520
Fraction Equations: Multiplication and Division . 521
Decimals: Addition and Subtraction 522
Decimals: Multiplication and Division 523
Forms of Real Numbers 524
Scientific Notation 525
Evaluating Expressions 526
Solving Linear Equations 527
Solving Linear Inequalities 528
Proportions and Percents 529
Absolute Value 530
Factoring 531
Simplifying Radicals 532
Operations with Radicals 533
Solving Radical and Quadratic Equations 534

Integer Equations: Addition and Subtraction

Solve each equation.

1. $7 + 5 = x$ 12
2. $6 + 4 = x$ 10
3. $8 + 9 = x$ 17
4. $19 + 20 = x$ 39
5. $13 + 15 = x$ 28
6. $45 + 24 = x$ 69
7. $38 + 16 = x$ 54
8. $96 + 52 = x$ 148
9. $77 + 9 = x$ 86
10. $104 + 47 = x$ 151
11. $83 + 86 = x$ 169
12. $27 + 34 = x$ 61
13. $636 + 104 = x$ 740
14. $108 + 597 = x$ 705
15. $302 + 969 = x$ 1271
16. $47 + 38 + 76 = x$ 161
17. $29 + 62 + 35 = x$ 126
18. $51 + 89 + 96 = x$ 236
19. $20 + 63 + 57 = x$ 140
20. $34 + 49 + 72 = x$ 155
21. $66 + 28 + 92 = x$ 186
22. ${}^-8 + {}^-5 = x$ ${}^-13$
23. ${}^-7 + {}^-9 = x$ ${}^-16$
24. ${}^-10 + {}^-12 = x$ ${}^-22$
25. $0 + {}^-6 = x$ ${}^-6$
26. ${}^-4 + {}^-3 = x$ ${}^-7$
27. ${}^-10 + 0 = x$ ${}^-10$
28. ${}^-40 + {}^-30 = x$ ${}^-70$
29. ${}^-25 + {}^-71 = x$ ${}^-96$
30. $0 + {}^-62 = x$ ${}^-62$
31. ${}^-66 + {}^-33 = x$ ${}^-99$
32. ${}^-36 + {}^-42 = x$ ${}^-78$
33. ${}^-86 + {}^-200 = x$ ${}^-286$
34. ${}^-152 + {}^-18 = x$ ${}^-170$
35. ${}^-206 + {}^-606 = x$ ${}^-812$
36. ${}^-829 + {}^-91 = x$ ${}^-920$
37. ${}^-709 + {}^-196 = x$ ${}^-905$
38. ${}^-643 + {}^-167 = x$ ${}^-810$
39. ${}^-229 + {}^-280 = x$ ${}^-509$
40. ${}^-7468 + {}^-4923 = x$ ${}^-12{,}391$
41. ${}^-25{,}406 + {}^-9{,}329 = x$
42. ${}^-2397 + {}^-4945 = x$ ${}^-7342$
43. ${}^-11 + 11 = x$ 0
44. ${}^-1 + 12 = x$ 11
45. $5 + {}^-5 = x$ 0
46. ${}^-10 + 7 = x$ ${}^-3$
47. $10 + {}^-4 = x$ 6
48. $56 + {}^-10 = x$ 46
49. ${}^-8 + 13 = x$ 5
50. $12 + {}^-19 = x$ ${}^-7$
51. ${}^-15 + 14 = x$ ${}^-1$
52. $24 + {}^-36 = x$ ${}^-12$
53. $52 + {}^-48 = x$ 4
54. ${}^-24 + 30 = x$ 6
55. $40 + {}^-27 = x$ 13
56. ${}^-54 + 46 = x$ ${}^-8$
57. $38 + {}^-50 = x$ ${}^-12$
58. ${}^-16 + 31 = x$ 15
59. $75 + {}^-92 = x$ ${}^-17$
60. $123 + {}^-106 = x$ 17
61. ${}^-2046 + 8752 = x$ 6706
62. ${}^-104 + 96 = x$ ${}^-8$
63. $728 + {}^-469 = x$ 259

41. ${}^-34{,}735$

Solve each equation.

64. $47 - 41 = x$ 6
65. $13 - 5 = x$ 8
66. $21 - 17 = x$ 4
67. $39 - 0 = x$ 39
68. $85 - 72 = x$ 13
69. $65 - 0 = x$ 65
70. $165 - 141 = x$ 24
71. $236 - 125 = x$ 111
72. $387 - 281 = x$ 106
73. $603 - 591 = x$ 12
74. $409 - 268 = x$ 141
75. $506 - 152 = x$ 354
76. $792 - 237 = x$ 555
77. $176 - 59 = x$ 117
78. $321 - 218 = x$ 103
79. $226 - 177 = x$ 49
80. $833 - 546 = x$ 287
81. $920 - 639 = x$ 281
82. $1072 - 295 = x$ 777
83. $2510 - 88 = x$ 2422
84. $6302 - 2567 = x$ 3735
85. $9 - 5 = x$ 4
86. $5 - 9 = x$ ${}^-4$
87. $6 - 10 = x$ ${}^-4$
88. $13 - 10 = x$ 3
89. $10 - 13 = x$ ${}^-3$
90. $2 - 7 = x$ ${}^-5$
91. $21 - 38 = x$ ${}^-17$
92. $15 - 11 = x$ 4
93. $42 - 50 = x$ ${}^-8$
94. $9 - {}^-6 = x$ 15
95. $18 - {}^-2 = x$ 20
96. $4 - {}^-5 = x$ 9
97. $22 - {}^-11 = x$ 33
98. $40 - {}^-32 = x$ 72
99. $25 - {}^-8 = x$ 33
100. $34 - {}^-6 = x$ 40
101. $75 - {}^-24 = x$ 99
102. $67 - {}^-40 = x$ 107
103. ${}^-6 - {}^-2 = x$ ${}^-4$
104. ${}^-8 - {}^-7 = x$ ${}^-1$
105. ${}^-10 - {}^-6 = x$ ${}^-4$
106. ${}^-31 - {}^-40 = x$ 9
107. ${}^-23 - {}^-28 = x$ 5
108. ${}^-15 - {}^-35 = x$ 20
109. ${}^-23 - 5 = x$ ${}^-28$
110. ${}^-31 - 18 = x$ ${}^-49$
111. ${}^-68 - 30 = x$ ${}^-98$
112. ${}^-5 - 7 = x$ ${}^-12$
113. ${}^-84 - 6 = x$ ${}^-90$
114. ${}^-92 - 7 = x$ ${}^-99$

Integer Equations: Multiplication and Division

Solve each equation.

1. $20 \cdot 5 = x$ 100
2. $10 \cdot 100 = x$ 1000
3. $6 \cdot 40 = x$ 240
4. $100 \cdot 1000 = x$ 100,000
5. $204 \cdot 7 = x$ 1428
6. $505 \cdot 6 = x$ 3030
7. $32 \cdot 9 = x$ 288
8. $68 \cdot 8 = x$ 544
9. $43 \cdot 4 = x$ 172
10. $28 \cdot 10 = x$ 280
11. $46 \cdot 100 = x$ 4600
12. $1000 \cdot 97 = x$ 97,000
13. $43 \cdot 36 = x$ 1548
14. $86 \cdot 57 = x$ 4902
15. $62 \cdot 79 = x$ 4898
16. $709 \cdot 16 = x$ 11,344
17. $32 \cdot 603 = x$ 19,296
18. $204 \cdot 38 = x$ 7752
19. $840 \cdot 603 = x$ 506,520
20. $958 \cdot 643 = x$ 615,994
21. $657 \cdot 399 = x$ 262,143
22. $^-5 \cdot {^-3} = x$ 15
23. $^-6 \cdot {^-7} = x$ 42
24. $^-9 \cdot {^-6} = x$ 54
25. $^-11 \cdot {^-12} = x$ 132
26. $^-2 \cdot {^-1000} = x$ 2000
27. $^-1 \cdot {^-576} = x$ 576
28. $^-100 \cdot {^-341} = x$ 34,100
29. $^-907 \cdot {^-700} = x$ 634,900
30. $^-87 \cdot {^-10} = x$ 870
31. $^-74 \cdot {^-6} = x$ 444
32. $^-89 \cdot {^-5} = x$ 445
33. $^-21 \cdot {^-9} = x$ 189
34. $^-308 \cdot {^-92} = x$ 28,336
35. $^-403 \cdot {^-37} = x$ 14,911
36. $^-36 \cdot {^-605} = x$ 21,780
37. $^-58 \cdot {^-91} = x$ 5278
38. $^-26 \cdot {^-19} = x$ 494
39. $^-49 \cdot {^-68} = x$ 3332
40. $^-6072 \cdot {^-52} = x$ 315,744
41. $^-5416 \cdot {^-31} = x$ 167,896
42. $^-62 \cdot {^-9557} = x$ 592,534
43. $^-8 \cdot 0 = x$ 0
44. $1 \cdot {^-17} = x$ $^-17$
45. $0 \cdot {^-6} = x$ 0
46. $100 \cdot {^-9} = x$ $^-900$
47. $45 \cdot {^-1000} = x$ $^-45{,}000$
48. $2 \cdot {^-1} = x$ $^-2$
49. $^-106 \cdot 5 = x$ $^-530$
50. $^-3 \cdot 406 = x$ $^-1218$
51. $^-309 \cdot 7 = x$ $^-2163$
52. $^-26 \cdot 32 = x$ $^-832$
53. $85 \cdot {^-19} = x$ $^-1615$
54. $66 \cdot {^-58} = x$ $^-3828$
55. $^-7 \cdot {^-6} \cdot 4 = x$ 168
56. $^-8 \cdot 6 \cdot {^-7} = x$ 336
57. $10 \cdot {^-11} \cdot {^-9} = x$ 990
58. $^-5 \cdot {^-3} \cdot {^-2} = x$ $^-30$
59. $^-9 \cdot 0 \cdot {^-11} = x$ 0
60. $^-5 \cdot {^-6} \cdot {^-4} = x$ $^-120$
61. $^-2 \cdot {^-1} \cdot 5 \cdot {^-4} = x$ $^-40$
62. $3 \cdot 4 \cdot {^-7} \cdot 8 = x$ $^-672$
63. $^-3 \cdot {^-1} \cdot {^-8} \cdot {^-6} = x$ 144

Solve each equation.

64. $40 \div 5 = x$ 8
65. $24 \div 6 = x$ 4
66. $38 \div 1 = x$ 38
67. $144 \div 12 = x$ 12
68. $169 \div 13 = x$ 13
69. $56 \div 7 = x$ 8
70. $912 \div 16 = x$ 57
71. $928 \div 29 = x$ 32
72. $5644 \div 83 = x$ 68
73. $1441 \div 131 = x$ 11
74. $4080 \div 255 = x$ 16
75. $6408 \div 712 = x$ 9
76. $35{,}288 \div 88 = x$ 401
77. $11{,}495 \div 55 = x$ 209
78. $77{,}478 \div 37 = x$ 2094
79. $^-55 \div {^-11} = x$ 5
80. $^-84 \div {^-12} = x$ 7
81. $^-51 \div {^-17} = x$ 3
82. $^-206 \div {^-1} = x$ 206
83. $^-175 \div {^-25} = x$ 7
84. $^-78 \div {^-13} = x$ 6
85. $^-720 \div {^-18} = x$ 40
86. $^-3600 \div {^-60} = x$ 60
87. $^-1950 \div {^-65} = x$ 30
88. $^-6570 \div {^-365} = x$ 18
89. $^-5280 \div {^-220} = x$ 24
90. $^-1728 \div {^-12} = x$ 144
91. $48 \div {^-6} = x$ $^-8$
92. $^-28 \div 4 = x$ $^-7$
93. $^-18 \div 9 = x$ $^-2$
94. $63 \div {^-9} = x$ $^-7$
95. $64 \div {^-16} = x$ $^-4$
96. $^-42 \div 14 = x$ $^-3$
97. $^-968 \div 8 = x$ $^-121$
98. $^-6054 \div 6 = x$ $^-1009$
99. $5810 \div {^-83} = x$ $^-70$
100. $1950 \div {^-65} = x$ $^-30$
101. $1116 \div {^-31} = x$ $^-36$
102. $^-1441 \div 131 = x$ $^-11$
103. $^-3784 \div 172 = x$ $^-22$
104. $4500 \div {^-50} = x$ $^-90$
105. $920 \div {^-23} = x$ 40

Solve each equation.

106. $8 + 5 + 6 \div 3 - 2 = x$ 13
107. $7 + 4 + 3 - 1 = x$ 13
108. $7 + 6 - 4 + 3 = x$ 12
109. $8 - 5 + 3 - 2 = x$ 4
110. $12 \cdot 8 + 12 \div 2 = x$ 102
111. $8 \div 2 + 5 \cdot 6 - 20 \div 4 = x$ 29

Fraction Equations: Addition and Subtraction

Solve each equation and express answers in simplest form.

1. $\frac{1}{3} + \frac{1}{3} = x$ $\frac{2}{3}$
2. $\frac{2}{9} + \frac{5}{9} = x$ $\frac{7}{9}$
3. $\frac{4}{11} + \frac{6}{11} = x$ $\frac{10}{11}$
4. $\frac{8}{15} + \frac{11}{15} = x$ $1\frac{4}{15}$
5. $\frac{2}{3} + \frac{2}{3} = x$ $1\frac{1}{3}$
6. $\frac{11}{18} + \frac{17}{18} = x$ $1\frac{5}{9}$
7. $1\frac{1}{5} + \frac{2}{5} = x$ $1\frac{3}{5}$
8. $4\frac{1}{4} + 3\frac{3}{4} = x$ 8
9. $5\frac{1}{12} + 11\frac{7}{12} = x$ $16\frac{2}{3}$
10. $\frac{1}{2} + \frac{3}{4} = x$ $1\frac{1}{4}$
11. $\frac{1}{3} + \frac{2}{9} = x$ $\frac{5}{9}$
12. $\frac{5}{12} + \frac{1}{6} = x$ $\frac{7}{12}$
13. $7\frac{5}{6} + 4\frac{5}{9} = x$ $12\frac{7}{18}$
14. $2\frac{9}{10} + 1\frac{11}{12} = x$ $4\frac{49}{60}$
15. $3\frac{7}{20} + 1\frac{11}{12} = x$ $5\frac{4}{15}$
16. $-\frac{1}{6} + -\frac{2}{6} = x$ $-\frac{1}{2}$
17. $-\frac{3}{4} + -\frac{1}{4} = x$ $^{-}1$
18. $-\frac{5}{7} + -\frac{1}{7} = x$ $-\frac{6}{7}$
19. $-\frac{5}{6} + -\frac{5}{6} = x$ $^{-}1\frac{2}{3}$
20. $-\frac{3}{5} + -\frac{4}{5} = x$ $^{-}1\frac{2}{5}$
21. $-\frac{2}{13} + -\frac{12}{13} = x$ $^{-}1\frac{1}{13}$
22. $^{-}1\frac{1}{4} + {}^{-}3\frac{1}{4} = x$ $^{-}4\frac{1}{2}$
23. $^{-}2\frac{10}{21} + {}^{-}8\frac{17}{21} = x$ $^{-}11\frac{2}{7}$
24. $^{-}5\frac{7}{10} + {}^{-}3\frac{3}{10} = x$ $^{-}9$
25. $^{-}6\frac{5}{8} + -\frac{1}{4} = x$ $^{-}6\frac{7}{8}$
26. $^{-}3\frac{1}{4} + {}^{-}2\frac{1}{2} = x$ $^{-}5\frac{3}{4}$
27. $^{-}4\frac{1}{7} + {}^{-}2\frac{2}{21} = x$ $^{-}6\frac{5}{21}$
28. $\frac{5}{7} + -\frac{1}{7} = x$ $\frac{4}{7}$
29. $-\frac{14}{15} + \frac{1}{15} = x$ $-\frac{13}{15}$
30. $-\frac{4}{5} + \frac{3}{5} = x$ $-\frac{1}{5}$
31. $-\frac{2}{3} + \frac{1}{3} = x$ $-\frac{1}{3}$
32. $\frac{3}{8} + -\frac{1}{8} = x$ $\frac{1}{4}$
33. $-\frac{3}{7} + \frac{5}{7} = x$ $\frac{2}{7}$
34. $\frac{1}{4} + -\frac{2}{3} = x$ $-\frac{5}{12}$
35. $-\frac{4}{5} + \frac{5}{6} = x$ $\frac{1}{30}$
36. $-\frac{3}{8} + \frac{4}{7} = x$ $\frac{11}{56}$
37. $^{-}2\frac{1}{10} + 3\frac{4}{5} = x$ $1\frac{7}{10}$
38. $1\frac{4}{9} + {}^{-}2\frac{5}{6} = x$ $^{-}1\frac{7}{18}$
39. $^{-}4\frac{1}{4} + 5\frac{3}{20} = x$ $\frac{9}{10}$

Solve each equation and express answers in simplest form.

40. $\frac{3}{5} - \frac{2}{5} = x$ $\frac{1}{5}$
41. $\frac{7}{9} - \frac{2}{9} = x$ $\frac{5}{9}$
42. $\frac{9}{11} - \frac{4}{11} = x$ $\frac{5}{11}$
43. $\frac{1}{2} - \frac{3}{8} = x$ $\frac{1}{8}$
44. $\frac{8}{9} - \frac{1}{6} = x$ $\frac{13}{18}$
45. $\frac{11}{12} - \frac{2}{3} = x$ $\frac{1}{4}$
46. $4\frac{3}{5} - 3\frac{1}{5} = x$ $1\frac{2}{5}$
47. $1 - \frac{2}{5} = x$ $\frac{3}{5}$
48. $1\frac{1}{9} - \frac{4}{9} = x$ $\frac{2}{3}$
49. $4 - \frac{7}{8} = x$ $3\frac{1}{8}$
50. $5\frac{1}{2} - 3\frac{1}{4} = x$ $2\frac{1}{4}$
51. $3\frac{11}{12} - 1\frac{2}{3} = x$ $2\frac{1}{4}$
52. $-\frac{2}{3} - -\frac{1}{3} = x$ $-\frac{1}{3}$
53. $-\frac{4}{11} - -\frac{3}{11} = x$ $-\frac{1}{11}$
54. $-\frac{8}{15} - -\frac{4}{15} = x$ $-\frac{4}{15}$
55. $-\frac{15}{17} - -\frac{7}{17} = x$ $-\frac{8}{17}$
56. $-\frac{1}{2} - -\frac{1}{4} = x$ $-\frac{1}{4}$
57. $-\frac{3}{4} - -\frac{3}{8} = x$ $-\frac{3}{8}$
58. $^{-}5\frac{6}{7} - {}^{-}2\frac{4}{7} = x$ $^{-}3\frac{2}{7}$
59. $^{-}5\frac{3}{5} - {}^{-}2\frac{3}{10} = x$ $^{-}3\frac{3}{10}$
60. $^{-}8\frac{7}{8} - {}^{-}4\frac{5}{12} = x$ $^{-}4\frac{11}{24}$
61. $^{-}1\frac{7}{8} - -\frac{5}{8} = x$ $^{-}1\frac{1}{4}$
62. $^{-}2\frac{3}{10} - {}^{-}1\frac{1}{10} = x$ $^{-}1\frac{1}{5}$
63. $^{-}3\frac{5}{6} - {}^{-}1\frac{1}{6} = x$ $^{-}2\frac{2}{3}$
64. $2 - -\frac{3}{4} = x$ $2\frac{3}{4}$
65. $^{-}3 - \frac{5}{6} = x$ $^{-}3\frac{5}{6}$
66. $1\frac{1}{5} - -\frac{3}{5} = x$ $1\frac{4}{5}$
67. $^{-}1\frac{1}{6} - \frac{5}{6} = x$ $^{-}2$
68. $^{-}8\frac{1}{12} - 5\frac{5}{12} = x$ $^{-}13\frac{1}{2}$
69. $2\frac{7}{15} - {}^{-}6\frac{13}{15} = x$ $9\frac{1}{3}$
70. $-\frac{5}{6} - \frac{1}{3} = x$ $^{-}1\frac{1}{6}$
71. $\frac{3}{5} - -\frac{9}{10} = x$ $1\frac{1}{2}$
72. $-\frac{5}{8} - \frac{17}{24} = x$ $^{-}1\frac{1}{3}$
73. $\frac{3}{5} - {}^{-}3\frac{1}{4} = x$ $3\frac{17}{20}$
74. $^{-}4\frac{2}{3} - 8\frac{1}{5} = x$ $^{-}12\frac{13}{15}$
75. $^{-}5\frac{1}{2} - 2\frac{1}{3} = x$ $^{-}7\frac{5}{6}$
76. $1\frac{1}{2} - -\frac{3}{4} = x$ $2\frac{1}{4}$
77. $1\frac{1}{12} - -\frac{2}{3} = x$ $1\frac{3}{4}$
78. $7\frac{1}{6} - {}^{-}5\frac{2}{3} = x$ $12\frac{5}{6}$

Fraction Equations: Multiplication and Division

Solve each equation and express answers in simplest form.

1. $\frac{1}{3} \cdot \frac{2}{3} = x$ $\frac{2}{9}$
2. $\frac{3}{4} \cdot \frac{4}{3} = x$ 1
3. $\frac{5}{6} \cdot \frac{3}{6} = x$ $\frac{5}{12}$
4. $\frac{3}{5} \cdot \frac{3}{7} = x$ $\frac{9}{35}$
5. $\frac{5}{7} \cdot \frac{2}{13} = x$ $\frac{10}{91}$
6. $\frac{8}{11} \cdot \frac{9}{10} = x$ $\frac{36}{55}$
7. $\frac{2}{3} \cdot \frac{9}{16} = x$ $\frac{3}{8}$
8. $\frac{10}{9} \cdot \frac{15}{8} = x$ $2\frac{1}{12}$
9. $\frac{25}{24} \cdot \frac{21}{10} = x$ $2\frac{3}{16}$
10. $3 \cdot \frac{1}{2} = x$ $1\frac{1}{2}$
11. $\frac{2}{3} \cdot 9 = x$ 6
12. $\frac{3}{5} \cdot 5\frac{1}{6} = x$ $3\frac{1}{10}$
13. $4\frac{1}{11} \cdot \frac{3}{5} = x$ $2\frac{5}{11}$
14. $2\frac{1}{2} \cdot 3\frac{2}{7} = x$ $8\frac{3}{14}$
15. $3\frac{1}{8} \cdot 2\frac{4}{5} \cdot \frac{5}{7} = x$ $6\frac{1}{4}$
16. $-\frac{3}{4} \cdot -\frac{1}{2} = x$ $\frac{3}{8}$
17. $-\frac{1}{4} \cdot -\frac{3}{5} = x$ $\frac{3}{20}$
18. $-\frac{1}{7} \cdot -\frac{5}{8} = x$ $\frac{5}{56}$
19. $-\frac{9}{15} \cdot -\frac{15}{9} = x$ 1
20. $-\frac{9}{16} \cdot {}^-64 = x$ 36
21. ${}^-16 \cdot -\frac{5}{24} = x$ $3\frac{1}{3}$
22. ${}^-3\frac{2}{3} \cdot -\frac{1}{8} = x$ $\frac{11}{24}$
23. $-\frac{4}{9} \cdot {}^-3\frac{1}{8} = x$ $1\frac{7}{18}$
24. ${}^-3\frac{2}{3} \cdot {}^-2\frac{3}{5} = x$ $9\frac{8}{15}$
25. ${}^-5\frac{1}{7} \cdot {}^-4\frac{4}{5} = x$ $24\frac{24}{35}$
26. ${}^-1\frac{3}{8} \cdot {}^-2\frac{1}{7} \cdot -\frac{1}{11} = x$ $-\frac{15}{56}$
27. ${}^-2\frac{1}{9} \cdot -\frac{5}{7} \cdot {}^-4\frac{2}{3} = x$ ${}^-7\frac{1}{27}$
28. $-\frac{1}{2} \cdot \frac{3}{5} = x$ $-\frac{3}{10}$
29. $\frac{6}{7} \cdot -\frac{5}{8} = x$ $-\frac{15}{28}$
30. $\frac{2}{3} \cdot -\frac{4}{9} = x$ $-\frac{8}{27}$
31. $\frac{7}{10} \cdot -\frac{5}{28} = x$ $-\frac{1}{8}$
32. $-\frac{4}{5} \cdot 30 = x$ ${}^-24$
33. ${}^-6 \cdot \frac{5}{11} = x$ ${}^-2\frac{8}{11}$
34. $-\frac{5}{9} \cdot 4\frac{2}{5} = x$ ${}^-2\frac{4}{9}$
35. $\frac{3}{10} \cdot {}^-2\frac{3}{5} = x$ $-\frac{39}{50}$
36. $-\frac{1}{3} \cdot 3\frac{3}{7} = x$ ${}^-1\frac{1}{7}$
37. $3\frac{1}{3} \cdot {}^-1\frac{3}{5} = x$ ${}^-5\frac{1}{3}$
38. $2\frac{1}{6} \cdot {}^-2\frac{4}{7} = x$ ${}^-5\frac{4}{7}$
39. $1\frac{5}{6} \cdot {}^-5\frac{1}{2} = x$ ${}^-10\frac{1}{12}$

Solve each equation and express answers in simplest form.

40. $\frac{2}{5} \div \frac{3}{7} = x$ $\frac{14}{15}$
41. $\frac{4}{9} \div \frac{5}{7} = x$ $\frac{28}{45}$
42. $\frac{6}{13} \div \frac{5}{7} = x$ $\frac{42}{65}$
43. $\frac{8}{17} \div \frac{15}{13} = x$ $\frac{104}{255}$
44. $\frac{1}{2} \div \frac{4}{5} = x$ $\frac{5}{8}$
45. $\frac{8}{15} \div \frac{4}{5} = x$ $\frac{2}{3}$
46. $3 \div 2\frac{3}{4} = x$ $1\frac{1}{11}$
47. $2\frac{3}{5} \div 2 = x$ $1\frac{3}{10}$
48. $\frac{2}{5} \div 2\frac{1}{3} = x$ $\frac{6}{35}$
49. $7 \div \frac{7}{8} = x$ 8
50. $3\frac{1}{8} \div 3\frac{3}{4} = x$ $\frac{5}{6}$
51. $5\frac{3}{5} \div 4\frac{1}{5} = x$ $1\frac{1}{3}$
52. $-\frac{5}{8} \div -\frac{8}{5} = x$ $\frac{25}{64}$
53. $-\frac{7}{16} \div -\frac{7}{11} = x$ $\frac{11}{16}$
54. $-\frac{9}{14} \div -\frac{3}{7} = x$ $1\frac{1}{2}$
55. ${}^-8 \div {}^-3\frac{2}{3} = x$ $2\frac{2}{11}$
56. ${}^-1\frac{4}{7} \div {}^-3 = x$ $\frac{11}{21}$
57. ${}^-3\frac{2}{5} \div -\frac{3}{4} = x$ $4\frac{8}{15}$
58. $-\frac{5}{2} \div {}^-2\frac{1}{3} = x$ $1\frac{1}{14}$
59. ${}^-4\frac{5}{8} \div {}^-3\frac{4}{7} = x$ $1\frac{59}{200}$
60. ${}^-4\frac{4}{7} \div -\frac{8}{9} = x$ $5\frac{1}{7}$
61. $-\frac{6}{7} \div {}^-5\frac{2}{5} = x$ $\frac{10}{63}$
62. ${}^-5\frac{1}{5} \div {}^-2\frac{1}{6} = x$ $2\frac{2}{5}$
63. ${}^-2\frac{4}{7} \div {}^-1\frac{1}{2} = x$ $1\frac{5}{7}$
64. $\frac{3}{8} \div -\frac{5}{7} = x$ $-\frac{21}{40}$
65. $-\frac{2}{3} \div \frac{1}{2} = x$ ${}^-1\frac{1}{3}$
66. $\frac{1}{9} \div -\frac{1}{9} = x$ ${}^-1$
67. $-\frac{2}{5} \div 7 = x$ $-\frac{2}{35}$
68. $4 \div -\frac{2}{3} = x$ ${}^-6$
69. ${}^-7 \div 4 = x$ ${}^-1\frac{3}{4}$
70. $2 \div {}^-2\frac{2}{3} = x$ $-\frac{3}{4}$
71. ${}^-2\frac{8}{9} \div 4 = x$ $-\frac{13}{18}$
72. $1\frac{3}{4} \div -\frac{7}{12} = x$ ${}^-3$
73. $4\frac{2}{5} \div -\frac{11}{15} = x$ ${}^-6$
74. ${}^-2 \div 2\frac{1}{7} = x$ $-\frac{14}{15}$
75. ${}^-2\frac{5}{8} \div 7\frac{1}{2} = x$ $-\frac{7}{20}$
76. ${}^-1\frac{3}{5} \div 2\frac{2}{5} = x$ $-\frac{2}{3}$
77. $3\frac{1}{8} \div {}^-1\frac{3}{8} = x$ ${}^-2\frac{3}{11}$
78. ${}^-3\frac{1}{21} \div 1\frac{21}{35} = x$ ${}^-1\frac{19}{21}$

Decimals: Addition and Subtraction

Find each sum.

1. $0.17 0.29 0.54 $1.00	**2.** 7 8.49 0.78 16.27	**3.** 4.03 0.95 13.98 18.96	**4.** 0.95 4.1 15 20.05
5. 1.68 0.93 2.75 5.36	**6.** 9.74 0.05 3.764 13.554	**7.** 1.5 70.081 68.499 140.080	**8.** 142.7 0.02 82.6 1.584 226.904
9. 58.27 3.1 0.045 61.415	**10.** $18.93 45.27 23.84 $88.04	**11.** 752.95 17.461 0.3 8.77 779.481	**12.** $1375.34 503.19 594.19 65.04 $2537.76

13. $6 + 4.2 + 9$ 19.2
14. $0.42 + 0.06 + 1.11$ 1.59
15. $0.2 + 6.51 + 2.03$ 8.74
16. $0.006 + 2 + 10.01$ 12.016
17. $4.4 + 30.6 + 11.2$ 46.2
18. $6.501 + 1.1 + 1$ 8.601
19. ${}^{-}28 + {}^{-}45.50$ ${}^{-}73.50$
20. ${}^{-}22.49 + {}^{-}83$ ${}^{-}105.49$
21. ${}^{-}10.04 + {}^{-}0.18$ ${}^{-}10.22$
22. ${}^{-}5.9 + 18.1$ 12.2
23. $7.11 + {}^{-}1.02$ 6.09
24. ${}^{-}6.51 + 2.03$ ${}^{-}4.48$
25. $3.75 + {}^{-}6.8$ ${}^{-}3.05$
26. ${}^{-}65 + 15.64$ ${}^{-}49.36$
27. $0.046 + {}^{-}0.567$ ${}^{-}0.521$

Find each difference.

28. 7.8 − 5.3 2.5	**29.** 57.96 − 23.71 34.25	**30.** 4.01 − 3.92 0.09	**31.** 6.0437 − 1.9864 4.0573
32. 8.00 − 7.87 0.13	**33.** $4 − 1.34 $2.66	**34.** 11.000 − 9.741 1.259	**35.** 5 − 2.896 2.104
36. 20.48 − 16.8 3.68	**37.** 28.05 − 9.95 18.1	**38.** 8 − 3.49 4.51	**39.** 932 − 0.003 931.997
40. 26.706 − 6.897 19.809	**41.** 1.7 − 0.846 0.854	**42.** 86.4 − 75.92 10.48	**43.** 86.4 − 75.92 10.48

44. ${}^{-}8.4 - {}^{-}2.3$ ${}^{-}6.1$
45. ${}^{-}0.41 - {}^{-}65$ 64.59
46. ${}^{-}3.1 - {}^{-}7.5$ 4.4
47. ${}^{-}11.0 - {}^{-}6.9$ ${}^{-}4.1$
48. ${}^{-}5 - {}^{-}1.3$ ${}^{-}3.7$
49. ${}^{-}6.8 - {}^{-}9.9$ 3.1
50. ${}^{-}7.25 - {}^{-}15.86$ 8.61
51. ${}^{-}27.2 - {}^{-}6.4$ ${}^{-}20.8$
52. ${}^{-}6 - {}^{-}1.4$ ${}^{-}4.6$
53. $0.8 - {}^{-}0.76$ 1.56
54. ${}^{-}6.51 - 4.3$ ${}^{-}10.81$
55. $4.5 - {}^{-}2.1$ 6.6
56. ${}^{-}29.3 - 14.22$ ${}^{-}43.52$
57. $16 - {}^{-}2.9$ 18.9
58. ${}^{-}7 - 35.8$ ${}^{-}42.8$
59. $101 - {}^{-}76.4$ 177.4
60. ${}^{-}3.2 - 18.42$ ${}^{-}21.62$
61. ${}^{-}13.0 - 6.8$ ${}^{-}19.8$

Decimal Equations: Multiplication and Division

Solve each equation.

1. $x = 68 \cdot 0.7$ 47.6
2. $406 \cdot 0.9 = x$ 365.4
3. $4065 \cdot 0.7 = y$ 2845.5
4. $y = 11.5 \cdot 22$ 253
5. $a = 4.68 \cdot 47$ 219.96
6. $b = 0.09 \cdot 18$ 1.62
7. $12.5 \cdot 0.5 = a$ 6.25
8. $11.54 \cdot 4.3 = c$ 49.622
9. $a = 32.1 \cdot 2.5$ 80.25
10. $c = {}^-22.6 \cdot 7.4$ $^-167.24$
11. $7.52 \cdot {}^-1.8 = x$ $^-13.536$
12. $20.07 \cdot {}^-9.5 = y$ $^-190.665$
13. ${}^-16.8 \cdot 0.55 = a$ $^-9.24$
14. ${}^-4.65 \cdot 1.58 = c$ $^-7.347$
15. $x = {}^-25.06 \cdot 1.05$ $^-26.313$
16. ${}^-47.5 \cdot {}^-3.19 = m$ 151.525
17. $y = {}^-24.2 \cdot {}^-0.25$ 6.05
18. ${}^-7.24 \cdot {}^-0.36 = p$ 2.6064
19. $y = {}^-6.15 \cdot {}^-0.51$ 3.1365
20. ${}^-31.24 \cdot {}^-8.61 = c$ 268.9764
21. ${}^-452.2 \cdot {}^-0.08 = a$ 36.176
22. $9.06 \cdot {}^-0.53 = y$ $^-4.8018$
23. $a = {}^-12.08 \cdot 4.25$ $^-51.34$
24. $8.94 \cdot 0.005 = y$ 0.0447
25. $m = 32.7 \cdot 2.29$ 74.883
26. ${}^-4.88 \cdot 1.25 = r$ $^-6.1$
27. ${}^-4.48 \cdot {}^-6.25 = m$ 28
28. $a = 216.17 \cdot 9.63$ 2081.7171
29. $m = {}^-0.4082 \cdot 11.85$ $^-4.83717$
30. ${}^-140.15 \cdot {}^-0.186 = t$ 26.0679
31. $q = 19.042 \cdot 8.54$ 162.61868
32. $4.007 \cdot 1.95 = n$ 7.81365
33. $0.0645 \cdot 0.81 = x$ 0.052245
34. $a = 8.265 \cdot {}^-3.32$ $^-27.4398$
35. $x = {}^-2.508 \cdot {}^-0.975$ 2.4453
36. $m = 43.616 \cdot 2.405$ 104.89648
37. $0.0182 \cdot 0.007 = y$ 0.0001274
38. $r = 0.0615 \cdot 0.13$ 0.007995
39. $z = {}^-0.0036 \cdot {}^-0.28$ 0.001008
40. $y = {}^-723 \cdot {}^-0.0068$ 4.9164
41. $462.1 \cdot 0.0094 = q$ 4.34374
42. $a = 87.061 \cdot 0.0016$ 0.1392976
43. $0.0074 \cdot {}^-61.3 = a$ $^-0.45362$
44. $0.0076 \cdot 0.00821 = b$ 0.000062396
45. $0.0086 \cdot 0.00909 = c$ 0.000078174
46. $x = 1249.867 \cdot 0.069$ 86.240823
47. $n = 187.411 \cdot 0.0098$ 1.8366278
48. $t = 9.16739 \cdot 8.721$ 79.94880819
49. $0.00886 \cdot 0.0708 = b$ 0.000627288
50. $y = 0.007201 \cdot 0.00899$ 0.00006473699
51. $0.06121 \cdot 0.000619 = x$ 0.00003788899

52. $m = 2.7 \div 3$ 0.9
53. $z = 4.8 \div 8$ 0.6
54. $11.4 \div 6 = q$ 1.9
55. $z = 68 \div 8$ 8.5
56. $41 \div 5 = n$ 8.2
57. $79 \div 5 = p$ 15.8
58. $m = {}^-8 \div 20$ $^-0.4$
59. $12 \div {}^-30 = a$ $^-0.4$
60. $b = 98 \div {}^-8$ $^-12.25$
61. $p = 2.92 \div {}^-4$ $^-0.73$
62. $52.8 \div {}^-24 = b$ $^-2.2$
63. ${}^-164.97 \div 47 = z$ $^-3.51$
64. ${}^-0.451 \div {}^-11 = q$ 0.041
65. $r = {}^-1.881 \div {}^-19$ 0.099
66. ${}^-1.681 \div {}^-41 = h$ 0.041
67. $m = {}^-3.286 \div {}^-62$ 0.053
68. ${}^-1.953 \div {}^-63 = a$ 0.031
69. ${}^-1.892 \div {}^-43 = b$ 0.044
70. $63 \div {}^-0.9 = p$ $^-70$
71. $c = 86 \div {}^-4.3$ $^-20$
72. $d = 105 \div 2.1$ 50
73. $81 \div 0.27 = q$ 300
74. $d = 54 \div 0.18$ 300
75. $m = {}^-33 \div 0.66$ $^-50$
76. $x = 30.1 \div 0.7$ 43
77. $82.8 \div 0.4 = m$ 207
78. ${}^-565.6 \div {}^-0.7 = y$ 808
79. $19.5 \div 1.5 = q$ 13
80. ${}^-18.53 \div {}^-1.7 = d$ 10.9
81. $0.0418 \div 0.19 = m$ 0.22
82. $1.781 \div 0.13 = r$ 13.7
83. $0.1804 \div 4.4 = m$ 0.041
84. $0.1696 \div 3.2 = s$ 0.053
85. $b = 0.2808 \div 0.078$ 3.6
86. $x = 0.1001 \div {}^-0.77$ $^-0.13$
87. $p = 0.5805 \div 2.15$ 0.27
88. $c = 19.317 \div 0.94$ 20.55
89. $y = 9.557 \div 1.9$ 5.03
90. $m = 15.33 \div {}^-14.6$ $^-1.05$
91. $2.006 \div 0.118 = p$ 17
92. $0.4484 \div 1.18 = n$ 0.38
93. $a = 29.45 \div 6.2$ 4.75
94. $x = 0.24102 \div 0.117$ 2.06
95. $q = {}^-9.8049 \div {}^-0.966$ 10.15
96. $0.1107 \div 2.25 = r$ 0.0492
97. $m = 0.32539 \div 5.006$ 0.065
98. $0.046626 \div 8.18 = z$ 0.0057
99. $n = 21.99256 \div 3.14$ 7.004
100. $8.9238 \div {}^-83.4 = a$ $^-0.107$
101. $1.573 \div {}^-6.05 = b$ $^-0.26$
102. ${}^-2800 \div {}^-625 = d$ 4.48
103. $21.5025 \div 7.05 = p$ 3.05

Forms of Real Numbers

Write each fraction as a decimal.

1. $\frac{2}{5}$ 0.4 2. $-\frac{1}{4}$ $^{-}0.25$ 3. $-\frac{7}{10}$ $^{-}0.7$ 4. $\frac{3}{20}$ 0.15

5. $-\frac{4}{5}$ $^{-}0.8$ 6. $-\frac{17}{20}$ $^{-}0.85$ 7. $\frac{1}{3}$ $0.\overline{3}$ 8. $-\frac{1}{6}$ $^{-}0.1\overline{6}$

9. $-\frac{2}{3}$ $^{-}0.\overline{6}$ 10. $\frac{1}{9}$ $0.\overline{1}$ 11. $-\frac{5}{6}$ $^{-}0.8\overline{3}$ 12. $\frac{2}{9}$ $0.\overline{2}$

13. $\frac{3}{7}$ $^{-}0.\overline{428571}$ 14. $-\frac{1}{12}$ $^{-}0.08\overline{3}$ 15. $\frac{5}{7}$ $0.\overline{714285}$ 16. $-\frac{7}{12}$ $^{-}0.58\overline{3}$

17. $-\frac{8}{9}$ $^{-}0.\overline{8}$ 18. $\frac{4}{25}$ 0.16 19. $\frac{3}{11}$ $0.\overline{27}$ 20. $-\frac{9}{16}$ $^{-}0.5625$

Write each mixed numeral as a decimal.

21. $1\frac{3}{4}$ 1.75 22. $2\frac{1}{2}$ 2.5 23. $^{-}5\frac{9}{10}$ $^{-}5.9$ 24. $^{-}6\frac{3}{5}$ $^{-}6.6$

25. $4\frac{1}{3}$ $4.\overline{3}$ 26. $^{-}1\frac{5}{6}$ $^{-}1.8\overline{3}$ 27. $7\frac{3}{16}$ 7.1875 28. $2\frac{5}{7}$ $2.\overline{714285}$

29. $^{-}2\frac{7}{11}$ $^{-}2.\overline{63}$ 30. $8\frac{2}{3}$ $8.\overline{6}$ 31. $^{-}9\frac{5}{9}$ $^{-}9.\overline{5}$ 32. $11\frac{1}{6}$ $11.1\overline{6}$

33. $75\frac{1}{4}$ 75.25 34. $^{-}101\frac{4}{5}$ $^{-}101.8$ 35. $3\frac{5}{8}$ 3.625 36. $^{-}52\frac{7}{12}$ $^{-}52.58\overline{3}$

37. $32\frac{1}{8}$ 32.125 38. $73\frac{3}{10}$ 73.3 39. $^{-}18\frac{11}{12}$ $^{-}18.91\overline{6}$ 40. $16\frac{6}{7}$ $16.\overline{857142}$

For each of the following, write an equivalent fraction with a denominator of 100.

41. $-\frac{1}{2}$ $-\frac{50}{100}$ 42. $-\frac{1}{5}$ $-\frac{20}{100}$ 43. $\frac{1}{4}$ $\frac{25}{100}$ 44. $-\frac{1}{10}$ $-\frac{10}{100}$

45. $\frac{1}{20}$ $\frac{5}{100}$ 46. $-\frac{3}{4}$ $-\frac{75}{100}$ 47. $-\frac{4}{5}$ $-\frac{80}{100}$ 48. $\frac{7}{25}$ $\frac{28}{100}$

49. $-\frac{7}{4}$ $-\frac{175}{100}$ 50. $-\frac{9}{20}$ $-\frac{45}{100}$ 51. $\frac{9}{50}$ $\frac{18}{100}$ 52. $-\frac{67}{10}$ $-\frac{670}{100}$

53. $\frac{49}{25}$ $\frac{196}{100}$ 54. $-\frac{27}{5}$ $-\frac{540}{100}$ 55. $\frac{19}{4}$ $\frac{475}{100}$ 56. $-\frac{25}{20}$ $-\frac{125}{100}$

57. $\frac{13}{10}$ $\frac{130}{100}$ 58. $-\frac{4320}{1000}$ $-\frac{432}{100}$ 59. $\frac{14}{5}$ $\frac{280}{100}$ 60. $\frac{21}{20}$ $\frac{105}{100}$

Write each decimal as a fraction in simplest form.

61. 0.7 $\frac{7}{10}$ 62. $^{-}0.25$ $-\frac{1}{4}$ 63. $^{-}0.6$ $\frac{3}{5}$ 64. $^{-}0.15$ $-\frac{3}{20}$

65. $^{-}0.625$ $-\frac{5}{8}$ 66. 0.85 $\frac{17}{20}$ 67. $^{-}0.875$ $-\frac{7}{8}$ 68. $0.\overline{3}$ $\frac{1}{3}$

69. $^{-}9.50$ $^{-}9\frac{1}{2}$ 70. $^{-}2.75$ $^{-}2\frac{3}{4}$ 71. 3.125 $3\frac{1}{8}$ 72. $^{-}1.34$ $^{-}1\frac{17}{50}$

73. $11.\overline{6}$ $11\frac{2}{3}$ 74. $^{-}9.\overline{3}$ $^{-}9\frac{1}{3}$ 75. 25.25 $25\frac{1}{4}$ 76. $^{-}2.75$ $^{-}2\frac{3}{4}$

77. $^{-}13.125$ $^{-}13\frac{1}{8}$ 78. 4.15 $4\frac{3}{20}$ 79. $^{-}8.\overline{3}$ $^{-}8\frac{1}{3}$ 80. 22.875 $22\frac{7}{8}$

81. 1.375 $1\frac{3}{8}$ 82. $^{-}2.25$ $^{-}2\frac{1}{4}$ 83. $9.\overline{6}$ $9\frac{2}{3}$ 84. 7.24 $7\frac{6}{25}$

85. $0.\overline{4}$ $\frac{4}{9}$ 86. $0.\overline{37}$ $\frac{37}{99}$ 87. $0.\overline{524}$ $\frac{524}{999}$ 88. $0.\overline{163}$ $\frac{163}{999}$

89. $2.\overline{3}$ $2\frac{1}{3}$ 90. $^{-}1.\overline{26}$ $^{-}1\frac{26}{99}$ 91. $^{-}0.3\overline{27}$ $-\frac{18}{55}$ 92. $5.\overline{371}$ $5\frac{371}{999}$

Scientific Notation

Express each of the following using scientific notation.

1. 40 4×10
2. 400 4×10^2
3. 4,000 4×10^3
4. 40,000 4×10^4
5. 20,691 2.0691×10^4
6. 2069.1 2.0691×10^3
7. 206.91 2.0691×10^2
8. 20.691 2.0691×10
9. $^-42.3$ $^-4.23 \times 10$
10. $^-8{,}200{,}000$ $^-8.2 \times 10^6$
11. 36.241 3.6241×10
12. 95,236 9.5236×10^4
13. 300,000 3×10^5
14. 0.00015 1.5×10^{-4}
15. 0.0015 1.5×10^{-3}
16. 0.015 1.5×10^{-2}
17. 0.15 1.5×10^{-1}
18. 0.0692 6.92×10^{-2}
19. 0.00000308 3.08×10^{-6}
20. 0.007 7×10^{-3}
21. $^-0.029$ $^-2.9 \times 10^{-2}$
22. 0.0009 9×10^{-4}
23. $^-325{,}000{,}000$ $^-3.25 \times 10^8$
24. 1,200,000 1.2×10^6

Express each of the following using decimal notation.

25. 5×10^2 500
26. 5×10^3 5000
27. 5×10^4 50,000
28. 5×10^5 500,000
29. $^-2.1 \times 10^3$ $^-2100$
30. 1.05×10^5 105,000
31. $^-5.704 \times 10^3$ $^-5704$
32. 3.157×10^2 315.7
33. $^-9.5 \times 10^6$ $^-9{,}500{,}000$
34. 6.33×10^8 633,000,000
35. $^-7.2 \times 10^7$ $^-72{,}000{,}000$
36. $^-5.402 \times 10^3$ $^-5402$
37. $^-62.1 \times 10^7$ $^-621{,}000{,}000$
38. 9×10^{-1} 0.9
39. 9×10^{-2} 0.09
40. 9×10^{-3} 0.009
41. 9×10^{-4} 0.0009
42. 4.8×10^{-1} 0.48
43. $^-3.6 \times 10^{-3}$ $^-0.0036$
44. $^-7.7 \times 10^{-4}$ $^-0.00077$
45. $^-8 \times 10^{-7}$ $^-0.0000008$
46. $^-6.4 \times 10^{-8}$ $^-0.000000064$
47. $^-1.002 \times 10^{-3}$ $^-0.001002$
48. $^-1.6 \times 10^{-4}$ $^-0.00016$

Evaluate. Express each answer in scientific notation.

49. $(4.3 \times 10^3)(2.0 \times 10^2)$ 8.6×10^5
50. $(3.6 \times 10^5)(7.5 \times 10^3)$ 2.7×10^9
51. $(1.5 \times 10)(3.4 \times 10^6)$ 5.1×10^7
52. $(7.22 \times 10^4)(5.1 \times 10^7)$ 3.6822×10^{12}
53. $(^-45 \times 10^2)(^-5 \times 10^4)$ 2.25×10^8
54. $(^-4.8 \times 10)(^-9.6 \times 10^8)$ 4.608×10^{10}
55. $(^-6 \times 10^7)(^-8.2 \times 10^5)$ 4.92×10^{13}
56. $(^-12.1 \times 10^3)(^-3.4 \times 10^2)$ 4.114×10^6
57. $(8 \times 10^3)(^-5 \times 10^9)$ $^-4 \times 10^{13}$
58. $(^-24 \times 10^6)(3 \times 10^9)$ $^-7.2 \times 10^{16}$
59. $(7.01 \times 10^8)(^-9.1 \times 10)$ $^-6.3791 \times 10^{10}$
60. $(^-3 \times 10^4)(7 \times 10^4)$ $^-2.1 \times 10^9$
61. $(5 \times 10^{-4})(6 \times 10^{-6})$ 3×10^{-9}
62. $(2 \times 10^{-3})(4 \times 10^{-2})$ 8×10^{-5}
63. $(2.3 \times 10^{-1})(9.2 \times 10^{-5})$ 2.116×10^{-5}
64. $(34.01 \times 10^{-7})(6 \times 10^{-8})$ 2.0406×10^{-13}
65. $(7 \times 10^2)(6 \times 10^{-2})$ 4.2×10
66. $(4 \times 10^{-3})(8 \times 10^5)$ 3.2×10^3
67. $(8.8 \times 10^{-7})(1.1 \times 10^4)$ 9.68×10^{-3}
68. $(12 \times 10^{10})(12 \times 10^{-6})$ 1.44×10^6
69. $(^-2 \times 10^{-5})(9 \times 10^3)$ $^-1.8 \times 10^{-1}$
70. $(7 \times 10^{-8})(^-4 \times 10^6)$ $^-2.8 \times 10^{-1}$
71. $\dfrac{24 \times 10^6}{3 \times 10^2}$ 8×10^4
72. $\dfrac{45 \times 10^3}{9 \times 10^5}$ 5×10^{-2}
73. $\dfrac{12 \times 10^{12}}{4 \times 10^6}$ 3×10^6
74. $\dfrac{8 \times 10^{-5}}{2 \times 10^{-3}}$ 4×10^{-2}
75. $\dfrac{33 \times 10^{-4}}{11 \times 10^{-5}}$ 3×10
76. $\dfrac{63 \times 10^{-4}}{7 \times 10^{-4}}$ 9×10^0
77. $\dfrac{10 \times 10^8}{5 \times 10^{-3}}$ 2×10^{11}
78. $\dfrac{169 \times 10^{-4}}{13 \times 10^6}$ 1.3×10^{-9}
79. $\dfrac{6 \times 10}{2 \times 10^{-2}}$ 3×10^3
80. $\dfrac{^-2.5 \times 10^2}{5 \times 10^{-3}}$ $^-5 \times 10^4$
81. $\dfrac{^-48 \times 10^5}{^-2 \times 10^{-4}}$ 2.4×10^{10}
82. $\dfrac{9 \times 10^{-1}}{^-3 \times 10^{-1}}$ $^-3 \times 10^0$

Evaluating Expressions

Evaluate.

1. $t \div 4$ if $t = {}^-16$ $\quad {}^-4$
2. $k \div 3$ if $k = 15$ $\quad 5$
3. ${}^-96 \div q$ if $q = 12$ $\quad {}^-8$
4. ${}^-76 \div m$ if $m = {}^-19$ $\quad 4$
5. $\frac{x}{15}$ if $x = 60$ $\quad 4$
6. $\frac{y}{{}^-9}$ if $y = 36$ $\quad {}^-4$
7. $\frac{{}^-54}{p}$ if $p = {}^-9$ $\quad 6$
8. $\frac{8}{n}$ if $n = {}^-40$ $\quad -\frac{1}{5}$
9. $\frac{z}{32}$ if $z = {}^-8$ $\quad -\frac{1}{4}$
10. $\frac{t}{{}^-7}$ if $t = {}^-84$ $\quad 12$
11. $\frac{2x}{{}^-15}$ if $x = {}^-30$ $\quad 4$
12. $\frac{{}^-112}{{}^-4n}$ if $n = {}^-7$ $\quad {}^-4$
13. $2y + 3$ if $y = {}^-5$ $\quad {}^-7$
14. $3(x - 9)$ if $x = 7$ $\quad {}^-6$
15. $t(t + 4)$ if $t = {}^-8$ $\quad 32$
16. $r^2 - 2r$ if $r = {}^-3$ $\quad 15$
17. $q^2(q - 8)$ if $q = 4$ $\quad {}^-64$
18. $\frac{5a^2 + a}{2a}$ if $a = {}^-2$ $\quad {}^-4\frac{1}{2}$

Evaluate if $a = 6$, $b = 4$, and $c = {}^-3$.

19. $a + (b + c)$ $\quad 7$
20. $a + (b - c)$ $\quad 13$
21. $6(a + b)$ $\quad 60$
22. $a - (b - c)$ $\quad {}^-1$
23. $a - b - c$ $\quad 5$
24. $a(b + |c|)$ $\quad 42$
25. $ab|c|$ $\quad 72$
26. $ab + ac$ $\quad 6$
27. $a^2 + b^2 + c^2$ $\quad 61$
28. $7a - (2b + c)$ $\quad 37$
29. $a^2 - c^2$ $\quad 27$
30. $36 - 4c^2$ $\quad 0$
31. $\frac{4(a - b)}{|c - 1|}$ $\quad 2$
32. $\frac{3(4b + 5a)}{23}$ $\quad 6$
33. $\frac{(a - b)(a + b)}{2c}$ $\quad {}^-3\frac{1}{3}$
34. $\frac{3ab}{2a + |c|}$ $\quad 4\frac{4}{5}$
35. $\frac{5a + 3c}{3b}$ $\quad 1\frac{3}{4}$
36. $\frac{3ab^2 - c^3}{a}$ $\quad 52\frac{1}{2}$

The relationship between Celsius temperature (C) and Fahrenheit temperature (F) is given by $C = \frac{5(F - 32)}{9}$. Find the Celsius temperature for the given temperatures.

37. 68°F $\quad$ 20°C
38. 86°F $\quad$ 30°C
39. ${}^-22$°F $\quad$ ${}^-30$°C
40. 32°F $\quad$ 0°C
41. 23°F $\quad$ ${}^-5$°C
42. ${}^-4$°F $\quad$ ${}^-20$°C

The formula for the area of a trapezoid is $A = \frac{h}{2}(b + B)$

A stands for the area, h stands for the altitude, and b and B stand for the bases. Calculate the area of the trapezoid given the following.

43. $b = 16$, $B = 30$, and $h = 18$ $\quad 414$
44. $b = 7$, $B = 12$, and $h = 9$ $\quad 85.5$
45. $b = 20$, $B = 25$, and $h = 22$ $\quad 495$
46. $b = 5$, $B = 11$, and $h = 8$ $\quad 64$

The formula for the volume of a sphere is $V = \frac{4}{3}\pi r^3$. V stands for the volume and r for the radius. Calculate the volume of the sphere given the following.

47. $\pi = \frac{22}{7}$, $r = \frac{1}{4}$ $\quad \frac{11}{168}$
48. $\pi = \frac{22}{7}$, $r = 2\frac{1}{2}$ $\quad 65\frac{10}{21}$
49. $\pi = 3.14$, $r = 3$ $\quad 113.04$
50. $\pi = 3.14$, $r = 6$ $\quad 904.32$

Solving Linear Equations

Solve each equation.

1. $5 + x = 9$ $\quad x = 4$
2. ${}^{-}14 + y = 10$ $\quad y = 24$
3. $56 + z = {}^{-}3$ $\quad z = {}^{-}59$
4. $38 = t + 21$ $\quad t = 17$
5. $72 = p + {}^{-}8$ $\quad p = 80$
6. ${}^{-}19 = q + {}^{-}4$ $\quad q = {}^{-}15$
7. ${}^{-}25 + h = {}^{-}33$ $\quad h = {}^{-}8$
8. $m + {}^{-}14 = 6$ $\quad m = 20$
9. $d + 40 = 27$ $\quad d = {}^{-}13$
10. ${}^{-}x + 9 = 15$ $\quad x = {}^{-}6$
11. ${}^{-}y + {}^{-}2 = {}^{-}85$ $\quad y = 83$
12. ${}^{-}f + {}^{-}7 = 1$ $\quad f = {}^{-}8$
13. $a - 4 = 72$ $\quad a = 76$
14. $b - 9 = {}^{-}23$ $\quad b = {}^{-}14$
15. $c - 11 = 6$ $\quad c = 17$
16. ${}^{-}102 = w - 99$ $\quad w = {}^{-}3$
17. $61 = s - 71$ $\quad s = 132$
18. ${}^{-}28 = k - 80$ $\quad k = 52$
19. $z - {}^{-}15 = 36$ $\quad z = 21$
20. $x - {}^{-}40 = {}^{-}58$ $\quad x = {}^{-}98$
21. $y - {}^{-}16 = 59$ $\quad y = 43$
22. ${}^{-}66 = a - {}^{-}1$ $\quad a = {}^{-}67$
23. $524 = m - {}^{-}300$ $\quad m = 224$
24. ${}^{-}75 = q - {}^{-}24$ $\quad q = {}^{-}99$
25. $6x = 18$ $\quad x = 3$
26. $8y = 64$ $\quad y = 8$
27. $10z = 5$ $\quad z = 1/2$
28. ${}^{-}20 = {}^{-}4a$ $\quad a = 5$
29. ${}^{-}8 = 8c$ $\quad c = {}^{-}1$
30. $35 = {}^{-}5d$ $\quad d = {}^{-}7$
31. $\frac{1y}{2} = 12$ $\quad y = 24$
32. $\frac{x}{7} = 9$ $\quad x = 63$
33. $\frac{z}{{}^{-}5} = 3$ $\quad z = {}^{-}15$
34. ${}^{-}13 = \frac{h}{7}$ $\quad h = {}^{-}91$
35. ${}^{-}32 = \frac{t}{{}^{-}14}$ $\quad t = 448$
36. $25 = \frac{n}{{}^{-}11}$ $\quad n = {}^{-}275$
37. $\frac{2r}{3} = {}^{-}24$ $\quad r = {}^{-}36$
38. $\frac{{}^{-}5s}{7} = {}^{-}20$ $\quad s = 28$
39. $\frac{6p}{{}^{-}11} = 54$ $\quad p = {}^{-}99$
40. ${}^{-}21 = \frac{{}^{-}7y}{10}$ $\quad y = 30$
41. $36 = \frac{9x}{{}^{-}15}$ $\quad x = {}^{-}60$
42. ${}^{-}42 = \frac{{}^{-}4z}{{}^{-}5}$ $\quad z = {}^{-}52\frac{1}{2}$
43. $4x + 8 = 20$ $\quad x = 3$
44. $6y - 8 = 22$ $\quad y = 5$
45. $9z - 30 = 6$ $\quad z = 4$
46. $3m + 4 = {}^{-}11$ $\quad m = {}^{-}5$
47. ${}^{-}5r + 6 = {}^{-}14$ $\quad x = 4$
48. $3 + {}^{-}4m = 7$ $\quad m = {}^{-}1$
49. $13 = 2x - 7$ $\quad x = 10$
50. $47 = 3k - 7$ $\quad k = 18$
51. ${}^{-}50 = 6m - 8$ $\quad m = {}^{-}7$
52. $8a - 10 = {}^{-}90$ $\quad a = {}^{-}10$
53. $25 = 4g + 5$ $\quad g = 5$
54. ${}^{-}3z - 18 = 9$ $\quad z = {}^{-}9$
55. $\frac{x}{5} + 2 = 7$ $\quad x = 25$
56. $\frac{m}{3} + 6 = 14$ $\quad m = 24$
57. $\frac{y}{3} + 6 = {}^{-}9$ $\quad y = {}^{-}45$
58. $\frac{b}{7} - 8 = {}^{-}12$ $\quad b = {}^{-}28$
59. $\frac{d}{10} - 3 = {}^{-}5$ $\quad d = {}^{-}20$
60. $\frac{r}{{}^{-}6} - 4 = 7$ $\quad r = {}^{-}66$
61. $\frac{d + 5}{3} = {}^{-}9$ $\quad d = {}^{-}32$
62. $\frac{3 + f}{7} = {}^{-}5$ $\quad f = {}^{-}38$
63. $\frac{m - 5}{4} = 5$ $\quad m = 25$
64. $\frac{4r + 8}{16} = 7$ $\quad r = 26$
65. $\frac{3d - 4}{5} = 4$ $\quad d = 8$
66. $\frac{7n - {}^{-}1}{8} = 8$ $\quad n = 9$
67. $5y + 9 = 8y$ $\quad y = 3$
68. $6a - 10 = 4a$ $\quad a = 5$
69. $4c + 15 = 9c$ $\quad c = 3$
70. $7p - 12 = 4p + 6$ $\quad p = 6$
71. $7m + 56 = 3m + 36$ $\quad m = {}^{-}5$
72. ${}^{-}3x + 6 = 12 - 2x$ $\quad x = {}^{-}6$
73. $2(x + 2) = {}^{-}32$ $\quad x = {}^{-}18$
74. ${}^{-}52 = 2(3z - 8)$ $\quad z = {}^{-}6$
75. ${}^{-}4(x + 1) = {}^{-}12$ $\quad x = 2$
76. $2(n + 4) = n + 10$ $\quad n = 2$
77. $7x - 2 = 3(3x + 3)$ $\quad x = -11/2$
78. $4y - 3(y - 2) = 41$ $\quad y = 35$

Solve each equation for the variable indicated.

79. $P = 2l + 2w$, for l
80. $A = bh$, for h
81. $d = rt$, for r
82. $C = 2\pi r$, for r
83. $a = (b - c)p$, for c
84. $x(y + z) = t$, for y
85. $\frac{e}{f} = g + h$, for f
86. $A = \frac{1}{2}bh$ for b
87. $A = \frac{h}{2}(b + B)$, for B

79. $l = (1/2)P - w$ 80. $h = A/b$ 81. $r = d/t$ 82. $r = C/2\pi$
83. $c = b - (a/p)$ 84. $y = (t/x) - z$ 85. $f = e/(g + h)$
86. $b = 2A/h$ 87. $B = (2A/h) - b$

Solving Linear Inequalities

Solve each inequality.

1. $y + 3 < 6$ $y < 3$
2. $n + 2 < 5$ $n < 3$
3. $x + 6 \geq {}^-14$ $x \geq {}^-20$
4. $a + 4 > 2$ $a > {}^-2$
5. $b - 3 > 8$ $b > 11$
6. $c - 5 < 3$ $c < 8$
7. $4y \leq 3y + 4$ $y \leq 4$
8. $3y < 2y + 6$ $y < 6$
9. $6a > 5a - 2$ $a > {}^-2$
10. $5n > 4n - 3$ $n > {}^-3$
11. $11 \geq y - 5$ $y \leq 16$
12. $16 > n - 5$ $n < 21$
13. $13 < b + 6$ $b > 7$
14. $4 < c + 16$ $c > {}^-12$
15. $f - {}^-3 \leq {}^-6$ $f \leq {}^-9$
16. $r - {}^-4 \geq 12$ $r \geq 8$
17. ${}^-20 + 5y \geq 6y$ $y \leq {}^-20$
18. $12d - 18 < 11d$ $d < 18$
19. ${}^-7 + 6x < 7x + 2$ $x > {}^-9$
20. $14z - {}^-3 \leq 15z + 6$ $z \geq {}^-3$
21. $9y - 4 > 10y + {}^-12$ $y < 8$
22. $\frac{x}{4} < 9$ $x < 36$
23. $\frac{y}{5} < 3$ $y < 15$
24. $\frac{z}{4} > {}^-5$ $z > {}^-20$
25. $\frac{r}{{}^-2} < 4$ $r > {}^-8$
26. $\frac{s}{{}^-8} \geq {}^-7$ $s \leq 56$
27. $\frac{k}{{}^-9} < {}^-6$ $k > 54$
28. $\frac{h}{12} \leq {}^-40$ $h \leq {}^-480$
29. $\frac{m}{{}^-10} > 11$ $m < {}^-110$
30. $\frac{y}{15} < 12$ $y < 180$
31. $2 < \frac{x}{8}$ $x > 16$
32. ${}^-3 \leq \frac{d}{7}$ $d \geq {}^-21$
33. $20 > \frac{g}{4}$ $g < 80$
34. $38 > \frac{t}{{}^-2}$ $t > {}^-76$
35. $9 < \frac{z}{{}^-6}$ $z < {}^-54$
36. ${}^-13 \geq \frac{s}{{}^-12}$ $s \geq 156$
37. $5x \geq 20$ $x \geq 4$
38. $6y < {}^-12$ $y < {}^-2$
39. $14z > {}^-70$ $z > {}^-5$
40. ${}^-21 \leq 7a$ $a \geq {}^-3$
41. $46 > 2c$ $c < 23$
42. ${}^-84 < 4b$ $b > {}^-21$
43. ${}^-2f > 26$ $f < {}^-13$
44. ${}^-15x > {}^-105$ $x < 7$
45. ${}^-3z \geq 27$ $z \leq {}^-9$
46. ${}^-8r \leq {}^-48$ $r \geq 6$
47. ${}^-9s < 63$ $s > {}^-7$
48. ${}^-31t < {}^-651$ $t > 21$
49. $1600 > {}^-50k$ $k > {}^-32$
50. ${}^-925 < 37p$ $p > {}^-25$
51. $72 \geq {}^-8y$ $y \geq {}^-9$
52. ${}^-85x \leq {}^-255$ $x \geq 3$
53. ${}^-33w > 297$ $w < {}^-9$
54. ${}^-18 < 3z$ $z > {}^-6$
55. $3a + 4 > 16$ $a > 4$
56. $5t + 40 \leq 55$ $t \leq 3$
57. $7 + 6z > 19$ $z > 2$
58. $12b - 32 < {}^-6$ $b < 2\,1/6$
59. $9y - 5 \geq {}^-50$ $y \geq {}^-5$
60. $8m - 13 < {}^-37$ $m < {}^-3$
61. $16 - 5x > 31$ $x < {}^-3$
62. ${}^-4c + 3 < {}^-21$ $c > 6$
63. ${}^-24 \leq 8 - 16q$ $q \leq 2$
64. ${}^-7k - 12 \geq 37$ $k \leq {}^-7$
65. ${}^-20 - 3w > {}^-32$ $w < 4$
66. ${}^-13y - 11 < 54$ $y > {}^-5$
67. $13x - 5 \leq 10x + 4$ $x \leq 3$
68. $2y + 8 > 5y - 7$ $y < 5$
69. $z - 6 > 3z + 2$ $z < {}^-4$
70. $16s - 15 \geq 12s - 3$ $s \geq 3$
71. $9r + 3 < 6r + 3$ $r < 0$
72. $4t - 18 < t + 9$ $t < 9$
73. $2(n + 4) > n + 10$ $n > 2$
74. $3(x + 6) > 2x + 12$ $x > {}^-6$
75. $3y + 7 \leq 4(y + 2)$ $y \geq {}^-1$
76. $7(m + 8) \leq 3m + 36$ $m \leq {}^-5$
77. ${}^-7({}^-x + 4) > 14$ $x > 6$
78. $9 > {}^-3b + 6(b - 4)$ $b < 11$
79. $\frac{3a - 5}{2} > 2a + 1$ $a < {}^-7$
80. $\frac{3c}{4} - \frac{5}{8} < 0$ $c < \frac{5}{6}$
81. $\frac{5 - 2k}{3} \leq {}^-7$ $k \geq 13$

Find the set of all integers, x, satisfying the given conditions.

82. $x > {}^-5$ and $x < 4$ $\{{}^-4, {}^-3, \ldots, 2, 3\}$
83. $x \geq {}^-2$ and $x \leq 2$ $\{{}^-2, {}^-1, 0, 1, 2\}$
84. $x \leq 10$ and $x < {}^-1$ $\{{}^-2, {}^-3, {}^-4, \ldots\}$
85. $x < 9$ and $x \geq {}^-3$ $\{{}^-3, {}^-2, \ldots, 7, 8\}$
86. $x > 0$ or $x \geq 3$ $\{1, 2, 3, \ldots\}$
87. $x > 25$ or $x < 30$ all integers
88. $2 < 3x + 2$ and $3x + 2 < 14$ $\{1, 2, 3\}$
89. $9 - 2x > 11$ and $5x < 2x + 9$ $\{{}^-2, {}^-3, {}^-4, \ldots\}$
90. $x + 4 > {}^-2$ and $x - 5 < {}^-1$ $\{{}^-5, {}^-4, \ldots, 2, 3\}$
91. $2x < 30$ or $3x > 60$ $\{\ldots 13, 14, 21, 22, \ldots\}$

Proportions and Percents

Cross multiply to determine whether or not the ratios are equivalent. Write yes or no.

1. $\frac{1}{2}, \frac{2}{4}$ yes
2. $\frac{1}{3}, \frac{2}{6}$ yes
3. $\frac{1}{5}, \frac{2}{11}$ no
4. $\frac{1}{10}, \frac{2}{5}$ no
5. $\frac{1}{8}, \frac{3}{24}$ yes
6. $\frac{1}{7}, \frac{4}{28}$ yes
7. $\frac{2}{5}, \frac{4}{9}$ no
8. $\frac{3}{4}, \frac{6}{8}$ yes
9. $\frac{2}{3}, \frac{3}{9}$ no
10. $\frac{2}{7}, \frac{6}{21}$ yes
11. $\frac{4}{5}, \frac{15}{20}$ no
12. $\frac{5}{6}, \frac{15}{18}$ yes
13. $\frac{4}{9}, \frac{12}{27}$ yes
14. $\frac{6}{15}, \frac{12}{45}$ no
15. $\frac{8}{21}, \frac{4}{10}$ no
16. $\frac{11}{24}, \frac{33}{72}$ yes

Solve each proportion.

17. $\frac{2}{5} = \frac{4}{c}$ $c = 10$
18. $\frac{5}{12} = \frac{10}{y}$ $y = 24$
19. $\frac{8}{12} = \frac{2}{e}$ $e = 3$
20. $\frac{18}{24} = \frac{3}{k}$ $k = 4$
21. $\frac{3}{4} = \frac{m}{12}$ $m = 9$
22. $\frac{4}{7} = \frac{x}{14}$ $x = 8$
23. $\frac{2}{9} = \frac{z}{27}$ $z = 6$
24. $\frac{3}{10} = \frac{b}{30}$ $b = 9$
25. $\frac{h}{6} = \frac{2}{12}$ $h = 1$
26. $\frac{u}{12} = \frac{3}{36}$ $u = 1$
27. $\frac{x}{22} = \frac{15}{11}$ $x = 30$
28. $\frac{h}{30} = \frac{102}{60}$ $h = 51$
29. $\frac{1}{v} = \frac{9}{27}$ $v = 3$
30. $\frac{84}{d} = \frac{28}{5}$ $d = 15$
31. $\frac{7}{r} = \frac{21}{28}$ $r = 9\frac{1}{3}$
32. $\frac{7}{q} = \frac{28}{16}$ $q = 4$
33. $\frac{p}{84} = \frac{25}{100}$ $p = 21$
34. $\frac{p}{50} = \frac{115}{100}$ $p = 57.5$
35. $\frac{11}{44} = \frac{r}{100}$ $r = 25$
36. $\frac{12}{60} = \frac{r}{100}$ $r = 20$
37. $\frac{5}{B} = \frac{10}{100}$ $B = 50$
38. $\frac{75}{B} = \frac{50}{100}$ $B = 150$
39. $\frac{135}{B} = \frac{675}{100}$ $B = 20$
40. $\frac{90}{40} = \frac{r}{100}$ $r = 225$

Solve each of the following.

41. 10% of 60 is 6.
42. 25% of 84 is 21.
43. 6% of 150 is 9.
44. 485% of 180 is 873.
45. 205% of 22 is 45.1.
46. 110% of 40 is 44.
47. 8.2 is 4.1% of 200.
48. 49.5 is 16.5% of 300.
49. 64.2 is 42.8% of 150.
50. 8 is $16\frac{2}{3}$% of 48.
51. 603 is $112\frac{1}{2}$% of 536.
52. 90 is $11\frac{1}{4}$% of 800.
53. 32.3 is 19% of 170.
54. 10.8% of 20 is 2.16.
55. 40.5% of 120 is 48.6.
56. $13\frac{3}{4}$% of 4000 is 550.
57. $83\frac{1}{3}$% of 150 is 125.
58. 45.76 is 20.8% of 220.
59. 8 is 25 % of 32.
60. 9 is 20 % of 45.
61. 11 is 50 % of 22.
62. 120 is 15 % of 800.
63. 57 is 60 % of 95.
64. 713 is 23 % of 3100.
65. 40 % of 40 is 16.
66. 11 % of 500 is 55.
67. 24 % of 71 is 17.04.
68. 120 % of 85 is 102.
69. 360 % of 705 is 2538.
70. 200 % of 45 is 90.
71. 12 is 12 1/2 % of 96.
72. 25 is 62 1/2 % of 40.
73. 56 is 350 % of 16.
74. 20% of 60 is 12.
75. 30% of 70 is 21.
76. 25% of 300 is 75.
77. 3% of 600 is 18.
78. 65% of 40 is 26.
79. 44% of 85 is 37.4.
80. 85 is 68% of 125.
81. 117 is 26% of 450.
82. 738 is 72% of 1025.
83. 770 is $87\frac{1}{2}$% of 880.
84. 32 is $66\frac{2}{3}$% of 48.
85. 135 is 675% of 20.

Absolute Value

Solve each equation.

1. $|^-5| = x$ 5
2. $|^-9| = x$ 9
3. $|^-3.7| = y$ 3.7
4. $y = |105.2|$ 105.2
5. $z = |9.7|$ 9.7
6. $r = |0.18|$ 0.18
7. $t = |5 - 12|$ 7
8. $m = |^-3 + ^-4|$ 7
9. $k = |51 + ^-48|$ 3
10. $|^-30 - ^-5| = s$ 25
11. $|^-60 - 25| = q$ 85
12. $|24 + ^-16| = x$ 8
13. $|2 \cdot 3 - 7| = f$ 1
14. $|32 - 4 \cdot 8| = k$ 0
15. $|^-11 \cdot 9 + ^-5 \cdot 10| = y$ 149
16. $|^-5| + 4 = x$ 9
17. $^-8 + |12| = z$ 4
18. $7 - |^-24| = l$ $^-17$
19. $a = |11.4| - |^-12|$ $^-0.6$
20. $r = ^-|3| + ^-29$ $^-32$
21. $c = |45 - 10| - 37$ $^-2$
22. $x + |^-72| = 91 - |38|$ $^-19$
23. $^-62 + |56| = b - |47|$ 41
24. $^-|84| - |100| = 12 - y$ 196

Evaluate if $a = ^-3$.

25. $|a|$ 3
26. $|^-7a|$ 21
27. $|11a|$ 33
28. $|a - 4|$ 7
29. $|3a + 6|$ 3
30. $|3 - a|$ 6
31. $a - |a|$ $^-6$
32. $a + |a|$ 0
33. $|^-5a - 9|$ 6
34. $25 - |2a + 7|$ 24
35. $2|4a - 9|$ 42
36. $^-3|a + 1| + 2|a - 6|$ 12
37. $5|a + 4| - |6a|$ $^-13$
38. $|^-8a| + ^-|12a + 3|$ $^-9$
39. $^-4|7a| + 3|a|$ $^-75$
40. $|a - 8| - 10|3a + 10|$ 1
41. $|^-a + 56| + 53$ 112
42. $^-6|7 - a| + |20a|$ 0

Solve each of the following open sentences.

43. $|y + 3| = 2$ $^-1, ^-5$
44. $|x + 10| = 6$ $^-4, ^-16$
45. $|m - 7| = 8$ 15, $^-1$
46. $|t - 2| = 5$ 7, $^-3$
47. $|r - 6| = ^-3$ no solutions
48. $|k - 9| = 4$ 13, 5
49. $|2x + 1| = 7$ 3, $^-4$
50. $|3x + 7| = ^-21$ no solutions
51. $|4a - 6| = 10$ 4, $^-1$
52. $|5s - 5| = 20$ 5, $^-3$
53. $8|p - 3| = 88$ $^-8$, 14
54. $5|y + 4| = 45$ 5, $^-13$
55. $2|3d + 3| = 18$ $^-4$, 2
56. $4|2b + 6| = 32$ 1, $^-7$
57. $^-6|2x - 14| = ^-42$ 21/2, 7/2
58. $4|6r - 1| = 29$ $^-25/24$, 11/8
59. $3|p + 9| + 6 = 0$ no solutions
60. $9|3 - 2a| = 15$ 2/3, 7/3
61. $2|7 - 3f| = 3$ 11/6, 17/6
62. $3|y + 5| = y - 7$ no solutions
63. $|4r + 6| = r - 5$ no solutions
64. $|7 + 4s| = 12 - s$ 1, $^-19/3$
65. $5|3t - 4| = t + 1$ 3/2, 19/16
66. $42 + |3z - 8| = 10$ no solutions
67. $|a| > 3$ $a > 3$ or $a < ^-3$
68. $|b| > 4$ $b > 4$ or $b < ^-4$
69. $|z| \leq 9$ $z \geq ^-9$ and $z \leq 9$
70. $|f| \geq 2$ $f \geq 2$ or $f \leq ^-2$
71. $|r| \leq 6$ $r \leq 6$ and $r \geq ^-6$
72. $|s| \leq 7$ $s \leq 7$ and $s \geq ^-7$
73. $|m| > ^-5$ all reals
74. $|t| < 0$ no solution
75. $|x + 1| \geq 3$ $x \geq 2$ or $x \leq ^-4$
76. $|r + 2| \geq 0$ all reals
77. $|p - 5| < 0$ no solution
78. $|c| - 5 < 0$ $c > ^-5$ and $c < 5$
79. $|6 - s| \leq 2$ $s \geq 4$ and $s \leq 8$
80. $|2 - y| \geq 1$ $y \leq 1$ or $y \geq 3$
81. $|a + 4| > ^-2$ all reals
82. $|8 + b| < 2$ $b > ^-10$ and $b < ^-6$
83. $|7y| \geq 21$ $y \leq ^-3$ or $y \geq 3$
84. $|5x| < 35$ $x > ^-7$ and $x < 7$
85. $|2m| < 26$ $m \geq ^-13$ and $m \leq 13$
86. $|2s - 9| \leq 27$ $s \geq ^-9$ and $s \leq 18$
87. $|3x + 11| > 42$ $x > 10\ 1/3$ or $x < 17\ 2/3$
88. $|4x - 3| \geq 12$ $x \geq 15/4$ or $x \leq ^-9/4$

Factoring

Find the prime factorization of each integer. Write each negative integer as the product of $^-1$ and its prime factors.

1. 21 $3 \cdot 7$
2. 18 $2 \cdot 3^2$
3. 36 $2^2 \cdot 3^2$
4. 60 $2^2 \cdot 3 \cdot 5$
5. $^-24$ $^-1 \cdot 2^3 \cdot 3$
6. $^-36$ $^-1 \cdot 2^2 \cdot 3^2$
7. $^-95$ $^-1 \cdot 5 \cdot 19$
8. $^-48$ $^-1 \cdot 2^4 \cdot 3$
9. 16 2^4
10. $^-27$ $^-1 \cdot 3^3$
11. $^-55$ $^-1 \cdot 5 \cdot 11$
12. 72 $2^3 \cdot 3^2$
13. $^-450$ $^-1 \cdot 2 \cdot 3^2 \cdot 5^2$
14. 200 $2^3 \cdot 5^2$
15. 372 $2^2 \cdot 3 \cdot 31$
16. $^-163$ $^-1 \cdot 163$

Factor each expression.

17. $16y - 8$ $8(2y - 1)$
18. $3z + 9$ $3(z + 3)$
19. $13a^2 + 39$ $13(a^2 + 3)$
20. $42r^2 - 6$ $6(7r^2 - 1)$
21. $^-2x + 5ax$ $x(^-2 + 5a)$
22. $z - 2az$ $z(1 - 2a)$
23. $qx - 5x$ $x(q - 5)$
24. $^-20xy - 16xz$ $^-4x(5y + 4z)$
25. $x + 7x^2$ $x(1 + 7x)$
26. $85m - 6m^2$ $m(85 - 6m)$
27. $^-17y^2 + 11y^4$ $y^2(^-17 + 11y^2)$
28. $5c^5 - 3c^9$ $c^5(5 - 3c^4)$
29. $2x^6 + 8x^7$ $2x^6(1 + 4x)$
30. $^-7p^3 + 56p^4$ $7p^3(^-1 + 8p)$
31. $y^2 - 8y + 16$ $(y - 4)^2$
32. $a^2 - 16a + 64$ $(a - 8)^2$
33. $p^2 - 2p + 1$ $(p - 1)^2$
34. $n^2 + 10n + 25$ $(n + 5)^2$
35. $9a^2 - 12ab + 4b^2$ $(3a - 2b)^2$
36. $9x^2 - 24xy + 16y^2$ $(3x - 4y)^2$
37. $x^2 - 2xy + y^2$ $(x - y)^2$
38. $49p^2 - 14p + 1$ $(7p - 1)^2$
39. $64b^2 + 48bc + 9c^2$ $(8b + 3c)^2$
40. $36 - 24x + 4x^2$ $(6 - 2x)^2$
41. $9x^2 + 48xy + 64y^2$ $(3x + 8y)^2$
42. $4m^2 + 12m + 9$ $(2m + 3)^2$
43. $4a^4 + 4a^2 + 1$ $(2a^2 + 1)^2$
44. $49 - 28x^2 + 4x^4$ $(7 - 2x^2)^2$
45. $1 - 14p^4 + 49p^8$ $(1 - 7p^4)^2$
46. $4x^6 - 12x^3y^3 + 9y^6$ $(2x^3 - 3y^3)^2$
47. $y^2 - 81$ $(y + 9)(y - 9)$
48. $m^2 - 100$ $(m + 10)(m - 10)$
49. $r^2 - 4x^2$ $(r + 2x)(r - 2x)$
50. $c^2 - 49b^2$ $(c + 7b)(c - 7b)$
51. $25a^2 - b^2$ $(5a + b)(5a - b)$
52. $4x^2 - 9$ $(2x + 3)(2x - 3)$
53. $36s^2 - 100$ $(6s + 10)(6s - 10)$
54. $1 - 64y^2$ $(1 + 8y)(1 - 8y)$
55. $^-49 + 16t^2$ $(4t + 7)(4t - 7)$
56. $^-121 + 9x^2$ $(3x + 11)(3x - 11)$
57. $4x^2 - 9y^2$ $(2x + 3y)(2x - 3y)$
58. $a^8 - b^{10}$ $(a^4 + b^5)(a^4 - b^5)$
59. $12c^2 - 12$ $12(c + 1)(c - 1)$
60. $81 - 9x^2$ $9(3 + x)(3 - x)$
61. $(a + b)^2 - m^2$ $(a + b + m)(a + b - m)$
62. $(x - y)^2 - z^2$ $(x - y + z)(x - y - z)$
63. $y^4 - x^4$ $(y^2 + x^2)(y + x)(y - x)$
64. $4y^6 - 9x^4$ $(2y^3 + 3x^2)(2y^3 - 3x^2)$
65. $x^2 + 9x + 18$ $(x + 3)(x + 6)$
66. $a^2 + 20a + 36$ $(a + 2)(a + 18)$
67. $r^2 + 11r + 10$ $(r + 10)(r + 1)$
68. $p^2 + 13p + 30$ $(p + 10)(p + 3)$
69. $y^2 - 10y + 16$ $(y - 8)(y - 2)$
70. $t^2 - 11t + 28$ $(t - 4)(t - 7)$
71. $k^2 - 16k + 15$ $(k - 15)(k - 1)$
72. $m^2 - 17m + 72$ $(m - 9)(m - 8)$
73. $d^2 + 4d - 21$ $(d + 7)(d - 3)$
74. $x^2 + 8x - 20$ $(x + 10)(x - 2)$
75. $a^2 + 12a - 45$ $(a + 15)(a - 3)$
76. $h^2 + 6h - 16$ $(h + 8)(h - 2)$
77. $c^2 - 5c - 36$ $(c - 9)(c + 4)$
78. $y^2 - 2y - 48$ $(y - 8)(y + 6)$
79. $2s^2 + 7s + 3$ $(2s + 1)(s + 3)$
80. $b^2 - 2b - 63$ $(b - 9)(b + 7)$
81. $3f^2 + 13f + 12$ $(3f + 4)(f + 3)$
82. $2h^3 - 8h^2 - 42h$ $2h(h - 7)(h + 3)$

Simplifying Radicals

Simplify. See bottom of page for answers to problems 58–62 and 90.

1. $-\sqrt{4}$ $^-2$
2. $\sqrt{25}$ 5
3. $\pm\sqrt{9}$ ± 3
4. $-\sqrt{36}$ $^-6$
5. $\sqrt{81}$ 9
6. $\pm\sqrt{49}$ ± 7
7. $-\sqrt{64}$ $^-8$
8. $\sqrt{121}$ 11
9. $\pm\sqrt{169}$ ± 13
10. $-\sqrt{225}$ $^-15$
11. $\sqrt{144}$ 12
12. $\pm\sqrt{100}$ ± 10
13. $\sqrt{0.0036}$ 0.06
14. $\sqrt{0.16}$ 0.4
15. $\sqrt{0.64}$ 0.8
16. $\sqrt{1.44}$ 1.2
17. $\sqrt{8}$ $2\sqrt{2}$
18. $\sqrt{27}$ $3\sqrt{3}$
19. $\sqrt{12}$ $2\sqrt{3}$
20. $\sqrt{32}$ $4\sqrt{2}$
21. $-\sqrt{75}$ $^-5\sqrt{3}$
22. $\pm\sqrt{72}$ $\pm 6\sqrt{2}$
23. $\sqrt{240}$ $4\sqrt{15}$
24. $-\sqrt{180}$ $^-6\sqrt{5}$
25. $\sqrt{128}$ $8\sqrt{2}$
26. $-\sqrt{125}$ $^-5\sqrt{5}$
27. $\sqrt{147}$ $7\sqrt{3}$
28. $\pm\sqrt{108}$ $\pm 6\sqrt{3}$
29. $-\sqrt{112}$ $^-4\sqrt{7}$
30. $-\sqrt{44}$ $^-2\sqrt{11}$
31. $\pm\sqrt{45}$ $\pm 3\sqrt{5}$
32. $\sqrt{162}$ $9\sqrt{2}$
33. $\sqrt{x^2}$ $|x|$
34. $\sqrt{y^4}$ y^2
35. $\sqrt{a^6}$ $|a^3|$
36. $\sqrt{t^{10}}$ $|t^5|$
37. $\sqrt{m^8}$ m^4
38. $\sqrt{a^2}$ $|a|$
39. $\sqrt{x}$ $\sqrt{x}$
40. $\sqrt{z^{12}}$ z^6
41. $\sqrt{x^{30}}$ $|x^{15}|$
42. $\sqrt{y^{64}}$ y^{32}
43. $\sqrt{a^{150}}$ $|a^{75}|$
44. $\sqrt{c^{90}}$ $|c^{45}|$
45. $\sqrt{t^5}$ $t^2\sqrt{t}$
46. $\sqrt{k^7}$ $|k^3|\sqrt{k}$
47. $\sqrt{p^{11}}$ $|p^3|\sqrt{p}$
48. $\sqrt{s^{21}}$ $s^{10}\sqrt{s}$
49. $\sqrt{ab^2}$ $|b|\sqrt{a}$
50. $\sqrt{r^2t^4z}$ $|r|t^2\sqrt{z}$
51. $\sqrt{3c^2}$ $|c|\sqrt{3}$
52. $\sqrt{5a^4}$ $a^2\sqrt{5}$
53. $\sqrt{4m^2}$ $2|m|$
54. $\sqrt{9x^2z}$ $3|x|\sqrt{z}$
55. $\sqrt{40k^8}$ $2k^4\sqrt{10}$
56. $\sqrt{11x^6}$ $|x^3|\sqrt{11}$
57. $\sqrt{1600x^3}$ $40|x|\sqrt{x}$
58. $\sqrt{4x^5y^7}$
59. $\sqrt{0.16a^{10}b^8}$
60. $\sqrt{m^4r^3t}$ $m^2|r|\sqrt{rt}$
61. $\frac{1}{5}\sqrt{54x^2y^4}$
62. $\frac{2}{3}\sqrt{24a^2b^2}$
63. $\sqrt{3ab^5}$ $b^2\sqrt{3ab}$
64. $\frac{1}{6}\sqrt{45x^2z}$ $\frac{1}{2}|x|\sqrt{5z}$
65. $-\sqrt{\frac{4}{9}}$ $-\frac{2}{3}$
66. $\pm\sqrt{\frac{25a^2}{4b^2}}$ $\pm\frac{5|a|}{2|b|}$
67. $\sqrt{\frac{49x^4}{36y^2}}$ $\frac{7x^2}{6|y|}$
68. $\sqrt{\frac{100a^2b^6}{81c^{10}}}$ $\frac{10|a|b^3}{9|c^5|}$
69. $\sqrt{\frac{27}{x^3}}$ $\frac{3\sqrt{3}}{|x|\sqrt{x}}$
70. $\sqrt{\frac{y^4}{16y^2}}$ $\frac{|y|}{4}$
71. $\sqrt{\frac{64r^2t^{14}}{25s^6}}$ $\frac{8|rt^7|}{5|s^3|}$
72. $\sqrt{\frac{9k^{12}}{25l^{10}}}$ $\frac{3k^6}{5|l^5|}$

Rationalize the denominators of the following.

73. $\frac{1}{\sqrt{5}}$ $\frac{\sqrt{5}}{5}$
74. $\frac{3}{\sqrt{7}}$ $\frac{3\sqrt{7}}{7}$
75. $\frac{^-8}{\sqrt{11}}$ $-\frac{8\sqrt{11}}{11}$
76. $\frac{^-8y}{\sqrt{15}}$ $-\frac{8y\sqrt{15}}{15}$
77. $\frac{3}{2\sqrt{5}}$ $\frac{3\sqrt{5}}{10}$
78. $\sqrt{\frac{a}{3}}$ $\frac{\sqrt{3a}}{3}$
79. $\frac{5\sqrt{21}}{\sqrt{5}}$ $\sqrt{105}$
80. $\sqrt{\frac{10}{7}}$ $\frac{\sqrt{70}}{7}$
81. $\sqrt{\frac{45}{2}}$ $\frac{3\sqrt{10}}{2}$
82. $-\sqrt{\frac{50}{3}}$ $-\frac{5\sqrt{6}}{3}$
83. $-\frac{\sqrt{48}}{\sqrt{3}}$ $^-4$
84. $\sqrt{\frac{7}{8}}$ $\frac{\sqrt{14}}{4}$
85. $-\sqrt{\frac{54}{r}}$ $-\frac{3\sqrt{6r}}{r}$
86. $\frac{\sqrt{8}}{\sqrt{9x}}$ $\frac{2\sqrt{2x}}{3x}$
87. $\pm\sqrt{\frac{7x^2}{4y}}$ $\pm\frac{x\sqrt{7y}}{2y}$
88. $\frac{\sqrt{22a}}{\sqrt{8y^2}}$ $\frac{\sqrt{11a}}{2y}$
89. $\sqrt{\frac{20m}{3}}$ $\frac{2\sqrt{15m}}{3}$
90. $\pm\sqrt{\frac{2k}{11m}}$
91. $\frac{\sqrt{18s}}{\sqrt{3}}$ $\sqrt{6s}$
92. $-\sqrt{\frac{b}{6}}$ $-\frac{\sqrt{6b}}{6}$
93. $\frac{^-5\sqrt{21}}{\sqrt{5}}$ $-\sqrt{105}$
94. $\frac{3\sqrt{7}}{\sqrt{2}}$ $\frac{3\sqrt{14}}{2}$
95. $\frac{6\sqrt{36}}{\sqrt{2}}$ $18\sqrt{2}$
96. $\frac{^-2\sqrt{27}}{\sqrt{3}}$ $^-6$
97. $\frac{11}{4\sqrt{6}}$ $\frac{11\sqrt{6}}{24}$
98. $\frac{^-3}{10\sqrt{15}}$ $-\frac{\sqrt{15}}{50}$
99. $\frac{20}{^-5\sqrt{2}}$ $^-2\sqrt{2}$
100. $\frac{4}{7\sqrt{8}}$ $\frac{\sqrt{2}}{7}$
101. $\frac{^-6\sqrt{56}}{2\sqrt{10}}$ $\frac{^-6\sqrt{35}}{5}$
102. $\frac{9\sqrt{20}}{3\sqrt{11}}$ $\frac{6\sqrt{55}}{11}$
103. $\frac{^-4\sqrt{24}}{12\sqrt{27}}$ $\frac{^-2\sqrt{2}}{9}$
104. $\frac{16\sqrt{40}}{8\sqrt{32}}$ $\sqrt{5}$

58. $2x^2|y^3|\sqrt{xy}$ 59. $0.4|a^5|b^4$ 61. $\frac{3}{5}|x|y^2\sqrt{6}$ 62. $\frac{4}{3}|ab|\sqrt{6}$

90. $\pm\frac{\sqrt{22km}}{11m}$

Operations With Radicals

Simplify.

1. $3\sqrt{5} + 2\sqrt{5}$ $5\sqrt{5}$
2. $8\sqrt{3} + {}^-2\sqrt{3}$ $6\sqrt{3}$
3. ${}^-6\sqrt{7} + 4\sqrt{7}$ ${}^-2\sqrt{7}$
4. ${}^-8\sqrt{6} + {}^-2\sqrt{6}$ ${}^-10\sqrt{6}$
5. $4\sqrt{x} + {}^-9\sqrt{x}$ ${}^-5\sqrt{x}$
6. ${}^-2\sqrt{y} + 11\sqrt{y}$ $9\sqrt{y}$
7. $\frac{1}{4}\sqrt{xy} + \frac{3}{4}\sqrt{xy}$ $\sqrt{xy}$
8. $\frac{2}{3}\sqrt{11} + -\frac{1}{3}\sqrt{11}$ $\frac{1}{3}\sqrt{11}$
9. $-\frac{5}{8}\sqrt{3} + -\frac{1}{8}\sqrt{3}$ $-\frac{3}{4}\sqrt{3}$
10. $3\sqrt{21} - 11\sqrt{21}$ ${}^-8\sqrt{21}$
11. $18\sqrt{z} - 5\sqrt{z}$ $13\sqrt{z}$
12. $4\sqrt{t} - 10\sqrt{t}$ ${}^-6\sqrt{t}$
13. $84\sqrt{m} - 56\sqrt{m}$ $28\sqrt{m}$
14. ${}^-7\sqrt{3} - 11\sqrt{3}$ ${}^-18\sqrt{3}$
15. ${}^-2\sqrt{k} - {}^-5\sqrt{k}$ $3\sqrt{k}$
16. $2\sqrt{3} + \sqrt{27}$ $5\sqrt{3}$
17. $\sqrt{8} + 3\sqrt{2}$ $5\sqrt{2}$
18. $5\sqrt{5} + \sqrt{20}$ $7\sqrt{5}$
19. $\sqrt{8} + \sqrt{50}$ $7\sqrt{2}$
20. $\sqrt{27} - \sqrt{12}$ $\sqrt{3}$
21. $\sqrt{32} - \sqrt{18}$ $\sqrt{2}$
22. ${}^-\sqrt{44a} + \sqrt{99a}$ $\sqrt{11a}$
23. ${}^-\sqrt{50c} + {}^-\sqrt{32c}$ ${}^-9\sqrt{2c}$
24. $\sqrt{20} - \sqrt{80}$ ${}^-2\sqrt{5}$
25. $\sqrt{24x} + {}^-\sqrt{54x}$ ${}^-\sqrt{6x}$
26. ${}^-\sqrt{18y} + \sqrt{50y}$ $2\sqrt{2y}$
27. ${}^-\sqrt{45t} + {}^-\sqrt{125t}$ ${}^-8\sqrt{5t}$
28. $\sqrt{18} + \sqrt{72} - \sqrt{50}$ $4\sqrt{2}$
29. $2\sqrt{40} - \sqrt{160} + \sqrt{72}$ $6\sqrt{2}$
30. $\sqrt{3} - 2\sqrt{12} - \sqrt{27}$ ${}^-6\sqrt{3}$
31. $3\sqrt{18} - \sqrt{8} + 2\sqrt{32}$ $15\sqrt{2}$
32. $3\sqrt{5} + 2\sqrt{20} - \sqrt{125}$ $2\sqrt{5}$
33. $2\sqrt{20} - 3\sqrt{80} + \sqrt{45}$ ${}^-5\sqrt{5}$
34. $7\sqrt{5x^2} + x\sqrt{20}$ $9x\sqrt{5}$
35. $\sqrt{a^2b} - 2|a|\sqrt{b} + 9\sqrt{a^2b}$
36. $|y|\sqrt{x^2yz} - \sqrt{x^2y^3z}$ 0

35. $8|a|\sqrt{b}$

37. $\sqrt{3}\sqrt{2}$ $\sqrt{6}$
38. $\sqrt{12}\sqrt{3}$ 6
39. $\sqrt{18}\sqrt{6}$ $6\sqrt{3}$
40. $\sqrt{2}\sqrt{24}\sqrt{3}$ 12
41. $\sqrt{a}\sqrt{a^3}$ a^2
42. $\sqrt{y^5}\sqrt{y^7}$ y^6
43. $\sqrt{5x}\sqrt{8x}$ $2|x|\sqrt{10}$
44. $4\sqrt{2}\sqrt{10}$ $8\sqrt{5}$
45. $3\sqrt{5}\sqrt{18}$ $9\sqrt{10}$
46. $(\sqrt{7})^2$ 7
47. $(2\sqrt{3})^2$ 12
48. $(2\sqrt{32})^2$ 128
49. $\sqrt{8}\sqrt{\frac{1}{2}}$ 2
50. $\sqrt{\frac{1}{3}}\sqrt{9}$ $\sqrt{3}$
51. $\sqrt{\frac{10}{4}}\sqrt{\frac{8}{5}}$ 2
52. $2\sqrt{2} \cdot 4\sqrt{8}$ 32
53. $5\sqrt{3} \cdot 7\sqrt{2}$ $35\sqrt{6}$
54. $2\sqrt{5} \cdot \sqrt{125}$ 50
55. $\sqrt{5}(\sqrt{5} + \sqrt{3})$ $5 + \sqrt{15}$
56. $\sqrt{3}(\sqrt{3} + \sqrt{5})$ $3 + \sqrt{15}$
57. $\sqrt{2}(\sqrt{2} - \sqrt{6})$ $2 - 2\sqrt{3}$
58. $(3 - \sqrt{7})(3 + \sqrt{7})$ 2
59. $(5 - \sqrt{5})(5 + \sqrt{5})$ 20
60. $(\sqrt{2} - 3)(\sqrt{2} + 3)$ ${}^-7$
61. $(\sqrt{10} + \sqrt{3})(\sqrt{10} - \sqrt{3})$ 7
62. $(\sqrt{7} - \sqrt{2})(\sqrt{7} + \sqrt{2})$ 5
63. $(\sqrt{3} + 2\sqrt{5})(\sqrt{3} - 2\sqrt{5})$ ${}^-17$
64. $(\sqrt{a + b})(\sqrt{a + b})$ $a + b$
65. $(\sqrt{a} - \sqrt{b})(\sqrt{a} + \sqrt{b})$
66. $\sqrt{x - y} \cdot \sqrt{4x - 4y}$ $2x - 2y$
67. $\frac{\sqrt{15}}{\sqrt{3}}$ $\sqrt{5}$
68. $\frac{\sqrt{21}}{\sqrt{7}}$ $\sqrt{3}$

65. $a - b$

69. $\frac{\sqrt{93}}{\sqrt{3}}$ $\sqrt{31}$
70. $\frac{\sqrt{54}}{\sqrt{6}}$ 3
71. $\frac{\sqrt{72}}{\sqrt{8}}$ 3
72. $\frac{\sqrt{144}}{\sqrt{8}}$ $3\sqrt{2}$
73. $\frac{\sqrt{100}}{\sqrt{4}}$ 5
74. $\frac{\sqrt{36}}{\sqrt{9}}$ 2
75. $\frac{\sqrt{16x^4}}{\sqrt{4x^2}}$ $2x$
76. $\frac{8\sqrt{x^5}}{3\sqrt{x}}$ $\frac{8}{3}x^2$
77. $\frac{\sqrt{28}}{\sqrt{7}}$ 2
78. $\frac{\sqrt{7}}{\sqrt{3}}$ $\frac{\sqrt{21}}{3}$
79. $\frac{5\sqrt{21}}{\sqrt{5}}$ $\sqrt{105}$
80. $\sqrt{\frac{3}{7}}$ $\frac{\sqrt{21}}{7}$
81. $\sqrt{\frac{b}{6}}$ $\frac{\sqrt{6b}}{6}$
82. $\sqrt{\frac{x^4}{11}}$ $\frac{x^2\sqrt{11}}{11}$
83. $\sqrt{\frac{27}{y}}$ $\frac{3\sqrt{3y}}{y}$
84. $\sqrt{\frac{54}{z}}$ $\frac{3\sqrt{6z}}{z}$
85. $\frac{\sqrt{18y^2}}{\sqrt{3}}$ $|y|\sqrt{6}$
86. $\frac{\sqrt{24x}}{8\sqrt{x^3}}$ $\frac{\sqrt{6}}{4x}$
87. $\frac{a^3\sqrt{ab^3}}{\sqrt{a^3b}}$ a^2b

Solving Radical and Quadratic Equations

Solve each equation.

1. $\sqrt{x} = 2$ 4
2. $\sqrt{y} = 9$ 81
3. $-\sqrt{r} = {}^{-}6$ 36
4. $-\sqrt{m} = {}^{-}5$ 25
5. $\sqrt{5y} = 5$ 5
6. $\sqrt{x} - 9 = 0$ 81
7. $\sqrt{4a} = 1$ 1/4
8. $3 + \sqrt{m} = 5$ 4
9. $2 + \sqrt{r} = 10$ 64
10. $\sqrt{4b + 1} = 3$ 2
11. $\sqrt{2c + 7} = 5$ 9
12. $\sqrt{8y + 1} = 5$ 3
13. $\sqrt{3b - 5} - 4 = 0$ 7
14. $\sqrt{3x + 7} - 7 = 0$ 14
15. $\sqrt{2x + 7} - 3 = 0$ 1
16. $\sqrt{r} = 3\sqrt{5}$ 45
17. $3\sqrt{7} = \sqrt{x}$ 63
18. $\sqrt{y} = 2\sqrt{8}$ 32
19. $\sqrt{m} = 4\sqrt{7}$ 112
20. $5\sqrt{10} = \sqrt{x}$ 250
21. $5\sqrt{5} = \sqrt{c}$ 125
22. $\sqrt{\frac{p}{3}} = 5$ 75
23. $\sqrt{\frac{4a}{3}} - 2 = 0$ 3
24. $\sqrt{\frac{2x}{3}} - 4 = 0$ 24
25. $\frac{8}{\sqrt{x + 3}} = 2$ 13
26. $\frac{\sqrt{x}}{\sqrt{2}} = \sqrt{5}$ 10
27. $\frac{\sqrt{2x + 1}}{3} + 2 = 5$ 40
28. $\sqrt{2x^2 - 121} = x$ 11
29. $\sqrt{x + 2} = x - 4$ 7
30. $\sqrt{1 - 2y} = 1 + y$ 0
31. $\sqrt{5a + 1} + 6 = 10$ 3
32. $n + \sqrt{n^2 + 3} = 3n$ 1
33. $\sqrt{10 + x} - \sqrt{10 - x} = 2$ 6

Solve each equation.

34. $(x - 4)(x + 5) = 0$ 4, ⁻5
35. $y(y - 6) = 0$ 0, 6
36. $(3x + 4)(2x - 5) = 0$ ⁻4/3, 5/2
37. $(x - 7)^2 = 0$ 7
38. $x^2 + 2x + 1 = 0$ ⁻1
39. $x^2 - 36 = 0$ ±6
40. $x^2 + 2x - 48 = 0$ ⁻8, 6
41. $x^2 - 12x + 35 = 0$ 5, 7
42. $y^2 - 7y = 0$ 0, 7
43. $y^2 + 17y + 72 = 0$ ⁻9, ⁻8
44. $2x^2 + 12x + 16 = 0$ ⁻4, ⁻2
45. $3y^2 - 21y + 36 = 0$ 3, 4
46. $9a^2 - 64 = 0$ 8/3, ⁻8/3
47. $25b^2 - 16 = 0$ 4/5, ⁻4/5
48. $3y^2 - 15y = 0$ 0, 5
49. $9x^2 + 6x + 1 = 0$ ⁻1/3
50. $4x^2 - 12x + 9 = 0$ 3/2
51. $x^2 = 121$ ±121
52. $17x^2 = 68x$ 0, 4
53. $2y^2 + 24y = {}^{-}40$ ⁻10, ⁻2
54. $y^2 + 3y = 40$ ⁻8, 5
55. $2a^2 - 3a = 9$ ⁻3/2, 3
56. $10b^2 + 33b = 7$ 1/5, ⁻7/2
57. $18y^2 - 3y = 15$ 1, ⁻5/6

Use the quadratic formula to solve each equation. The quadratic formula is $\frac{{}^{-}b \pm \sqrt{b^2 - 4ac}}{2a}$.

58. $x^2 + 7x + 6 = 0$ ⁻1, ⁻6
59. $a^2 + 8a + 15 = 0$ ⁻3, ⁻5
60. $2a^2 + a - 15 = 0$ ⁻3, 5/2
61. $2y^2 + 7y + 3 = 0$ ⁻3, ⁻1/2
62. $3m^2 + 5m + 2 = 0$ ⁻1, ⁻2/3
63. $3x^2 + 23x + 14 = 0$ ⁻7, ⁻2/3
64. $3x^2 + 14x = 5$ ⁻5, 1/3
65. $m^2 - 2m = 8$ 4, ⁻2
66. $r^2 + 9 = 10r$ 9, 1
67. $m^2 + 36 = 13m$ 4, 9
68. $4x^2 - 8x = {}^{-}3$ 1/2, 3/2
69. $4b^2 = 20b$ 0, 5
70. $2x^2 = 3 + x$ ⁻1, 3/2
71. $3y^2 + 2 = 5y$ 1, 2/3
72. $b^2 - b - 3 = 0$ $(1 \pm \sqrt{13})/2$
73. $y^2 - 27 = 0$ $\pm 3\sqrt{3}$
74. $x^2 - 125 = 0$ $\pm 5\sqrt{5}$
75. $m^2 = 32$ $\pm 4\sqrt{2}$
76. $x^2 - 6x - 2 = 0$ $3 \pm \sqrt{11}$
77. $y^2 - 2y = 1$ $1 \pm \sqrt{2}$
78. $y^2 + 4y = 3$ ${}^{-}2 \pm \sqrt{7}$
79. $2a^2 - 5a + 1 = 0$ $(5 \pm \sqrt{17})/4$
80. $3b^2 - 5b + 1 = 0$ $(5 \pm \sqrt{13})/6$
81. $x^2 + 3x = 1$ $({}^{-}3 \pm \sqrt{13})/2$
82. $3y^2 + y - 1 = 0$ $({}^{-}1 \pm \sqrt{13})/6$
83. $x^2 + 2x + 5 = 0$ no real solution

Symbols

h	altitude (367)
$\angle$	angle (68)
a	apothem (372)
$\approx$	approximately equal to (249)
$\widehat{AB}$	arc with endpoints A and B (327)
B	area of base of a prism (382)
b	base (368)
BASIC	**B**eginner's **A**ll-purpose **S**ymbolic **I**nstructional **C**ode (501)
cm	centimeter (363)
$\odot P$	circle with center P (323)
C	circumference (377)
$\cong$	congruent, is congruent to (54)
cos	cosine (303)
cm^3	cubic centimeters (392)
m^3	cubic meters (397)
$^\circ$	degree (71)
d	diagonal of a square (299), diameter (323) distance (410)
AB	distance between points A and B (39)
$=$	equals, is equal to (36)
km	kilometer (365)
L	lateral area (382)
$\overleftrightarrow{DE}$	line containing points D and E (2)
$\rightarrow$	mapping, is mapped onto (471)
$m\angle A$	measure of angle A (71)
$m\widehat{AB}$	measure of arc AB (327)
m	meter (364)
mm	millimeter (369)
$\sqrt{}$	nonnegative square root (287)
(4, 2)	ordered pair (405)
(x, y, z)	ordered triple (431)
$\parallel$	parallel, is parallel to (171)
$\square$	parallelogram (216)
P	perimeter (236)
$\perp$	perpendicular, is perpendicular to (86)
π	pi (37)
n-gon	polygon with n sides (208)
r	radius (377)
$\overrightarrow{PQ}$	ray with endpoint P passing through Q (67)
k	scale factor for a dilation (492)
$\overline{PQ}$	segment with endpoints P and Q (44)
s	side of a regular polygon (237)
$\sim$	similar, is similar to (258)
sin	sine (303)
l	slant height (387)
m	slope (413)
cm^2	square centimeter (363)
m^2	square meter (364)
S	sum of the degree measure of a convex polygon (211)
tan	tangent (304)
T	total surface area (382)
$\triangle$	triangle (103)
V	volume (392)

Postulates and Theorems

Chapter 1: Points, Lines, and Planes

Postulate 1–1 Through any two points there is exactly one line. (14)

Postulate 1–2 Through any three points not on the same line there is exactly one plane. (14)

Postulate 1–3 A line contains at least two points. (15)

Postulate 1–4 A plane contains at least three points not on the same line. (15)

Postulate 1–5 If two points lie in a plane, then the entire line containing those two points lies in that plane. (15)

Postulate 1–6 If two planes intersect, then their intersection is a line. (15)

Theorem 1–1 If there is a line and a point not on the line, then there is exactly one plane that contains them. (19)

Theorem 1–2 If two lines intersect, then exactly one plane contains both lines. (23)

Chapter 2: Measure

Postulate 2–1
Number Line Postulate
Each real number corresponds to exactly one point on a number line. Each point on a number line corresponds to exactly one real number. (37)

Postulate 2–2
Ruler Postulate
The points on any line can be paired with the real numbers so that, given any two points P and Q on the line, P corresponds to zero, and Q corresponds to a positive number. (39)

Postulate 2–3
Distance Postulate
For any two points on a line and a given unit of measure, there is a unique positive number called the measure of the distance between the two points. (40)

Properties of equality:

		For any numbers a, b, and c
Postulate 2–4	reflexive	$a = a$ (48)
Postulate 2–5	symmetric	If $a = b$, then $b = a$. (48)
Postulate 2–6	transitive	If $a = b$ and $b = c$, then $a = c$. (48)
Postulate 2–7	addition and subtraction	If $a = b$, then $a + c = b + c$, and $a - c = b - c$. (48)
Postulate 2–8	multiplication and division	If $a = b$, then $a \cdot c = b \cdot c$, and if c is not zero, $\frac{a}{c} = \frac{b}{c}$. (48)
Postulate 2–9	substitution	If $a = b$, then a may be replaced by b. (49)

Properties of operations: (49)

	For any numbers a, b, and c		
		Addition	Multiplication
Postulate 2–10	Commutative	$a + b = b + a$	$a \cdot b = b \cdot a$
Postulate 2–11	Associative	$(a + b) + c = a + (b + c)$	$(a \cdot b) \cdot c = a \cdot (b \cdot c)$
Postulate 2–12	Identity	$a + 0 = a = 0 + a$	$a \cdot 1 = a = 1 \cdot a$
Postulate 2–13	Inverse	$a + {}^{-}a = 0 = {}^{-}a + a$	If a is not zero, then $a \cdot \frac{1}{a} = 1 = \frac{1}{a} \cdot a$.
Postulate 2–14	Distributive of multiplication over addition: $a(b + c) = ab + ac$ and $(b + c)a = ba + ca$		

Properties of inequality:

	For any numbers a, b, and c	
Postulate 2–15	Comparison	$a < b$, or $a = b$, or $a > b$ (58)
Postulate 2–16	addition and subtraction (58)	1. If $a > b$, then $a + c > b + c$ and $a - c > b - c$. 2. If $a < b$, then $a + c < b + c$ and $a - c < b - c$.
Postulate 2–17	multiplication and division (58)	1. If $c > 0$ and $a < b$, then $ac < bc$ and $\frac{a}{c} < \frac{b}{c}$. 2. If $c > 0$ and $a > b$, then $ac > bc$ and $\frac{a}{c} > \frac{b}{c}$. 3. If $c < 0$ and $a < b$, then $ac > bc$ and $\frac{a}{c} > \frac{b}{c}$. 4. If $c < 0$ and $a > b$, then $ac < bc$ and $\frac{a}{c} < \frac{b}{c}$.
Postulate 2–18	transitive	1. If $a < b$ and $b < c$, then $a < c$. 2. If $a > b$ and $b > c$, then $a > c$. (59)

Theorem 2–1 If a segment is given, then it has exactly one midpoint. (45)

Theorem 2–2 Congruence of segments is reflexive. (54)

Theorem 2–3 Congruence of segments is symmetric. (54)

Theorem 2–4 Congruence of segments is transitive. (54)

Theorem 2–5 Midpoint Theorem — If M is the midpoint of $\overline{PQ}$, then $\overline{PM} \cong \overline{MQ}$. (55)

Theorem 2–6 Bisector Theorem — If $\overline{PQ}$ is bisected at point M, then $\overline{PM} \cong \overline{MQ}$. (56)

Chapter 3: Angles and Perpendiculars

Postulate 3–1 Angle Measure Postulate — For every angle there is a unique positive number between 0 and 180 called the degree measure of the angle. (71)

Postulate 3–2 Protractor Postulate — Given a ray on the edge of a half plane, for every positive number r between 0 and 180 there is exactly one ray in the half plane such that the degree measure of the angle formed by the two rays is r. (71)

Postulate 3–3 Angle Addition Postulate — If R is in the interior of $\angle PQS$, then $m\angle PQR + m\angle RQS = m\angle PQS$. (73)

Postulate 3–4 Supplement Postulate — If two angles form a linear pair, then they are supplementary angles. (76)

Theorem 3–1 — Congruence of angles is reflexive, symmetric, and transitive. (73)

Theorem 3–2 — If two angles are supplementary to the same angle, then they are congruent. (77)

Theorem 3–3 — If two angles are supplementary to two congruent angles, then the two angles are congruent to each other. (78)

Theorem 3–4 — If two angles are complementary to the same angle, then they are congruent to each other. (78)

Theorem 3–5 — If two angles are complementary to two congruent angles, then the two angles are congruent to each other. (78)

Theorem 3–6 — If two angles are right angles, then the angles are congruent. (81)

Theorem 3–7 — If one angle in a linear pair is a right angle, then the other angle is also a right angle. (81)

Theorem 3–8 — If two angles are congruent and supplementary, then each angle is a right angle. (81)

Theorem 3–9 — If two intersecting lines form one right angle, then they form four right angles. (82)

Theorem 3–10 — If two angles are vertical, then they are congruent. (82)

Theorem 3–11 — If two lines are perpendicular, then they form four right angles. (87)

Theorem 3–12 — If a point is on a line in a plane, then there is exactly one line in that plane perpendicular to the given line. (87)

Theorem 3–13 — If two lines are perpendicular, then they form congruent adjacent angles. (87)

Theorem 3–14 — If two intersecting lines form congruent adjacent angles, then they are perpendicular. (87)

Theorem 3–15 — If a line is perpendicular to two intersecting lines at their point of intersection, then it is perpendicular to the plane that contains the two lines. (90)

Theorem 3–16 — Two planes are perpendicular if and only if they intersect to form a right dihedral angle. (92)

Chapter 4: Congruent Triangles

Postulate 4–1 SSS — If each side of one triangle is congruent to the corresponding side of another triangle, then the triangles are congruent. (116)

Postulate 4–2 SAS — If two sides and the included angle of one triangle are congruent to the corresponding sides and included angle of another triangle, then the triangles are congruent. (116)

Postulate 4–3 ASA — If two angles and the included side of one triangle are congruent to the corresponding angles and included side of another triangle, then the triangles are congruent. (117)

Postulate 4–4 HL	If the hypotenuse and a leg of one right triangle are congruent to the corresponding sides of another right triangle, then the triangles are congruent. (135)
Theorem 4–1 Angle Sum Theorem	The sum of the degree measures of the angles of a triangle is 180. (107)
Theorem 4–2	If a triangle is equiangular, then the degree measure of each angle is 60. (108)
Theorem 4–3	If a triangle is a right triangle, then the acute angles are complementary. (108)
Theorem 4–4	Congruence of triangles is reflexive, symmetric, and transitive. (114)
Theorem 4–5 AAS	If two angles and a nonincluded side of one triangle are congruent to the corresponding angles and nonincluded side of another triangle, then the triangles are congruent. (121)
Theorem 4–6 Isosceles Triangle Theorem	If two sides of a triangle are congruent, then the angles opposite those sides are congruent. (129)
Theorem 4–7	If a triangle is equilateral, then the triangle is equiangular. (129)
Theorem 4–8	If a triangle is equilateral, then each angle has degree measure of 60. (129)
Theorem 4–9	If two angles of a triangle are congruent, then the sides opposite those angles are congruent. (130)
Theorem 4–10	If a triangle is equiangular, then the triangle is equilateral. (130)
Theorem 4–11 HA	If the hypotenuse and an acute angle of one right triangle are congruent to the corresponding hypotenuse and acute angle of another right triangle, then the triangles are congruent. (133)
Theorem 4–12 LL	If the legs of one right triangle are congruent to the corresponding legs of another right triangle, then the triangles are congruent. (133)
Theorem 4–13 LA	If one leg and an acute angle of one right triangle are congruent to the corresponding leg and acute angle of another right triangle, then the triangles are congruent. (134)

Chapter 5: Triangle Inequalities

Theorem 5–1 Exterior Angle Theorem	If an angle is an exterior angle of a triangle, then its measure is equal to the sum of the measures of the two remote interior angles. (142)
Theorem 5–2 Inequality Theorem	For any numbers a and b, $a > b$ if and only if there is a positive number c such that $a = b + c$. (142)
Theorem 5–3	If an angle is an exterior angle of a triangle, then its measure is greater than the measure of either remote interior angle. (142)
Theorem 5–4	If the measures of two sides of a triangle are unequal, then the measure of the angles opposite those sides are unequal in the same order. (152)

Theorem 5–5	If the measures of two angles of a triangle are unequal, then the measures of the sides opposite those angles are unequal in the same order. (153)
Theorem 5–6	A segment is the shortest segment from a point to a line if and only if it is the segment perpendicular to the line. (154)
Theorem 5–7	A segment is the shortest segment from a point to a plane if and only if it is the segment perpendicular to the plane. (154)
Theorem 5–8 Triangle Inequality	The sum of the measures of any two sides of a triangle is greater than the measure of the third side. (156)
Theorem 5–9 Hinge Theorem	If two sides of one triangle are congruent to two sides of another triangle and the measures of the included angles are unequal, then the measures of the third sides are unequal in the same order. (160)
Theorem 5–10 Converse of the Hinge Theorem	If two sides of one triangle are congruent to two sides of another triangle and the measures of the third sides are unequal, then the measures of the angles included between the pairs of congruent sides are unequal in the same order. (160)

Chapter 6: Parallels

Postulate 6–1 Parallel Postulate	If there is a line and a point not on the line, then there is exactly one line through the point that is parallel to the given line. (186)
Theorem 6–1	If two lines are cut by a transversal and one pair of alternate interior angles are congruent, then the other pair of alternate interior angles also are congruent. (173)
Theorem 6–2	If two lines are cut by a transversal and one pair of corresponding angles are congruent, then all pairs of corresponding angles are congruent. (173)
Theorem 6–3	If a triangle is a right triangle, then it has no more than one right angle. (177)
Theorem 6–4	In a plane, if two lines are cut by a transversal so that a pair of alternate interior angles are congruent, then the two lines are parallel. (178)
Theorem 6–5	In a plane, if two lines are cut by a transversal so that a pair of corresponding angles are congruent, then the two lines are parallel. (181)
Theorem 6–6	If two lines are cut by a transversal so that a pair of consecutive interior angles are supplementary, then the lines are parallel. (182)
Theorem 6–7	In a plane, if two lines are cut by a transversal so that a pair of alternate exterior angles are congruent, then the lines are parallel. (182)
Theorem 6–8	In a plane, if two lines are perpendicular to the same line, then the two lines are parallel. (182)
Theorem 6–9	If two parallel lines are cut by a transversal, then each pair of corresponding angles are congruent. (186)
Theorem 6–10	If two parallel lines are cut by a transversal, then each pair of alternate interior angles are congruent. (186)

Theorem 6–11	If two parallel lines are cut by a transversal, then each pair of consecutive interior angles are supplementary. (186)
Theorem 6–12	If two parallel lines are cut by a transversal, then each pair of alternate exterior angles are congruent. (186)
Theorem 6–13	In a plane, if a line is perpendicular to one of two parallel lines, then it is perpendicular to the other. (191)
Theorem 6–14	Given a line and a point not on the line, there is exactly one line through the point that is perpendicular to the given line. (195)
Theorem 6–15	In a plane, two lines are parallel if and only if they are everywhere equidistant. (195)

Chapter 7: Polygons

Theorem 7–1	If a convex polygon has n sides, and S is the sum of the degree measures of its angles, then $S = (n - 2)180$. (211)
Theorem 7–2	If a polygon is convex, then the sum of the degree measures of the exterior angles, one at each vertex, is 360. (213)
Theorem 7–3	If a quadrilateral is a parallelogram, then a diagonal separates it into two congruent triangles. (216)
Theorem 7–4	If a quadrilateral is a parallelogram, then its opposite angles are congruent. (217)
Theorem 7–5	If a quadrilateral is a parallelogram, then its opposite sides are congruent. (217)
Theorem 7–6	If a quadrilateral is a parallelogram, then its diagonals bisect each other. (217)
Theorem 7–7	If both pairs of opposite sides of a quadrilateral are congruent, then the quadrilateral is a parallelogram. (220)
Theorem 7–8	If two sides of a quadrilateral are parallel and congruent, then the quadrilateral is a parallelogram. (221)
Theorem 7–9	If the diagonals of a quadrilateral bisect each other, then the quadrilateral is a parallelogram. (221)
Theorem 7–10	If a quadrilateral is a rectangle, then its diagonals are congruent. (224)
Theorem 7–11	If a quadrilateral is a rhombus, then each diagonal bisects a pair of opposite angles. (225)
Theorem 7–12	If a quadrilateral is a rhombus, then its diagonals are perpendicular. (226)
Theorem 7–13	If a trapezoid is isosceles, then each pair of base angles is congruent. (230)
Theorem 7–14	If a trapezoid is isosceles, then its diagonals are congruent. (231)
Theorem 7–15	If a quadrilateral is a trapezoid, then the median is parallel to the bases, and its measure is one-half the sum of the measures of the bases. (232)
Theorem 7–16 Perimeter of a Rectangle	If a rectangle has perimeter P units, a length of ℓ units, and a width of w units, then $P = 2(\ell + w)$. (236)

Theorem 7–17 Perimeter of a Regular Polygon	If a regular n-gon has a perimeter of P units, and a side measures s units, then $P = ns$. (237)

Chapter 8: Similarity

Postulate 8–1 AA Similarity	If two angles of one triangle are congruent to two corresponding angles of another triangle, then the triangles are similar. (263)
Theorem 8–1 Equality of Cross Products	For any numbers a and c, and any nonzero numbers b and d, $\frac{a}{b} = \frac{c}{d}$ if and only if $ad = bc$. (250)

For any numbers a, b, c, and d, the following properties hold whenever all denominators are nonzero.

Theorem 8–2	If $\frac{a}{b} = \frac{c}{d}$, then $\frac{a}{c} = \frac{b}{d}$. (254)
Theorem 8–3	If $\frac{a}{b} = \frac{c}{d}$, then $\frac{b}{a} = \frac{d}{c}$. (254)
Theorem 8–4 Addition Property of Proportions	$\frac{a}{b} = \frac{c}{d}$ if and only if $\frac{a+b}{b} = \frac{c+d}{d}$. (254)
Theorem 8–5 Subtraction Property of Proportions	$\frac{a}{b} = \frac{c}{d}$ if and only if $\frac{a-b}{b} = \frac{c-d}{d}$. (254)
Theorem 8–6 Summation Property of Proportions	$\frac{a}{b} = \frac{c}{d}$ if and only if $\frac{a}{b} = \frac{a+c}{b+d}$ or $\frac{c}{d} = \frac{a+c}{b+d}$. (254)
Theorem 8–7 SSS Similarity	If there is a correspondence between the two triangles so that the measures of their corresponding sides are proportional, then the two triangles are similar. (264)
Theorem 8–8 SAS Similarity	If the measures of two sides of a triangle are proportional to the measures of two corresponding sides of another triangle, and the included angles are congruent, then the triangles are similar. (265)
Theorem 8–9	If a line intersects two sides of a triangle, and separates the sides into segments of proportional lengths, then the line is parallel to the third side. (267)
Theorem 8–10	If a line is parallel to one side of a triangle and intersects the other two sides, then it separates the sides into segments of proportional lengths. (268)
Theorem 8–11	If a segment has as its endpoints the midpoints of two sides of a triangle, then it is parallel to the third side and its length is one-half the length of the third side. (269)
Theorem 8–12	If three parallel lines intersect two transversals, then they divide the transversals proportionally. (269)

Theorem 8–13 If three parallel lines cut off congruent segments on one transversal, then they cut off congruent segments on any transversal. (269)

Theorem 8–14 If two triangles are similar, then the measures of corresponding perimeters are proportional to the measures of corresponding sides. (272)

Theorem 8–15 If two triangles are similar, then the measures of corresponding altitudes are proportional to the measures of corresponding sides. (273)

Theorem 8–16 If two triangles are similar, then the measures of corresponding angle bisectors of the triangles are proportional to the measures of corresponding sides. (273)

Theorem 8–17 If two triangles are similar, then the measures of corresponding medians are proportional to the measures of corresponding sides. (274)

Chapter 9: Right Triangles

Postulate 9–1
Product Property of Square Roots
For any nonnegative numbers a and b, $\sqrt{ab} = \sqrt{a} \cdot \sqrt{b}$. (288)

Postulate 9–2
Quotient Property of Square Roots
For any nonnegative numbers a and b with $b \neq 0$, $\sqrt{\frac{a}{b}} = \frac{\sqrt{a}}{\sqrt{b}}$. (288)

Theorem 9–1 If the altitude is drawn from the vertex of the right angle to the hypotenuse of a right triangle, then the two triangles formed are similar to the given triangle and to each other. (291)

Theorem 9–2 The measure of the altitude drawn from the right angle to the hypotenuse of a right triangle is the geometric mean between the measure of the two segments of the hypotenuse. (292)

Theorem 9–3 If the altitude is drawn to the hypotenuse of a right triangle, then the measure of a leg of the triangle is the geometric mean between the measure of the hypotenuse and the measure of the segment of the hypotenuse adjacent to that leg. (293)

Theorem 9–4
The Pythagorean Theorem
If a triangle is a right triangle, then the sum of the squares of the measures of the legs equals the square of the measure of the hypotenuse. (295)

Theorem 9–5
Converse of the Pythagorean Theorem
If the sum of the squares of the measures of two sides of a triangle equals the square of the measure of the longest side, then the triangle is a right triangle. (296)

Theorem 9–6 If each acute angle of a right triangle a has degree of measure 45, then the hypotenuse measures $\sqrt{2}$ times the measure of a leg. (299)

Theorem 9–7 If the acute angles of a right triangle have degree measures of 30 and 60, then the measure of the hypotenuse is 2 times the measure of the shorter leg and the measure of the longer leg is $\sqrt{3}$ times the measure of the shorter leg. (300)

Chapter 10: Circles and Spheres

Postulate 10–1 Arc Addition Postulate — If Q is a point on $\widehat{PQR}$, then $m\widehat{PQ} + m\widehat{QR} = m\widehat{PQR}$. (328)

Theorem 10–1 In a plane, if a line contains a point in the interior of a circle, then the line intersects the circle in exactly two points. (324)

Theorem 10–2 In a circle or in congruent circles, two central angles are congruent if and only if their minor arcs are congruent. (329)

Theorem 10–3 In a circle or in congruent circles, two minor arcs are congruent if and only if their corresponding chords are congruent. (331)

Theorem 10–4 In a circle, if a diameter is perpendicular to a chord, then it bisects the chord and its arcs. (332)

Theorem 10–5 In a circle or in congruent circles, two chords are congruent if and only if they are equidistant from the center. (332)

Theorem 10–6 If an angle is inscribed in a circle, then the measure of the angle equals one-half the measure of its intercepted arc. (336)

Theorem 10–7 If two inscribed angles of a circle or congruent circles intercept congruent arcs, then the angles are congruent. (337)

Theorem 10–8 If an angle is inscribed in a semicircle, then the angle is a right angle. (337)

Theorem 10–9 If the angles of a quadrilateral are inscribed in a circle, then each pair of opposite angles are supplementary. (337)

Theorem 10–10 If a line is tangent to a circle, then it is perpendicular to the radius drawn to the point of tangency. (340)

Theorem 10–11 In a plane, if a line is perpendicular to a radius of a circle at its endpoint on the circle, then the line is a tangent. (341)

Theorem 10–12 If two segments from the same exterior point are tangent to a circle, then they are congruent. (341)

Theorem 10–13 If two secants intersect in the interior of a circle, then the measure of an angle formed is one-half the sum of the measures of the arcs intercepted by the angle and its vertical angle. (344)

Theorem 10–14 If two secants intersect in the exterior of a circle, then the measure of an angle formed is one-half the positive difference of the measures of the intercepted arcs. (344)

Theorem 10–15 If a secant and a tangent intersect at the point of tangency, then the measure of each angle formed is one-half the measure of its intercepted arc. (345)

Theorem 10–16 If a secant and a tangent, or two tangents, intersect in the exterior of a circle, then the measure of the angle formed is one-half the positive difference of the measures of the intercepted arcs. (346)

Theorem 10–17 If two chords intersect in a circle, then the product of the measures of the segments of one chord equals the product of the measures of the segments of the other chord. (348)

Theorem 10–18 If two secant segments are drawn to a circle from an exterior point, then the product of the measures of one secant segment and its external secant segment equals the product of the measures of the other secant segment and its external secant segment. (349)

Theorem 10–19 If a tangent segment and a secant segment are drawn to a circle from an exterior point, then the square of the measure of the tangent segment equals the product of the measures of the secant segment and its external secant segment. (349)

Theorem 10–20 If a plane intersects a sphere in more than one point, then the intersection is a circle. (354)

Chapter 11: Area and Volume

Postulate 11–1 Area Postulate — For any polygonal region and a given unit of measure, there is a unique positive number called the measure of the area of the region. (363)

Postulate 11–2 If two figures are congruent, then they have exactly the same area. (364)

Postulate 11–3 Area Addition Postulate — If a polygonal region is separated into nonoverlapping regions, then the sum of the areas of these regions equals the area of the entire region. (364)

Postulate 11–4 Area of a Rectangle — If a rectangle has an area of A square units, a length of ℓ units, and a width of w units, then $A = \ell w$. (364)

Postulate 11–5 Volume Postulate — For any solid region and a given unit of measure, there is a unique positive number called the measure of the volume of the region. (391)

Postulate 11–6 If two solids are congruent, then they have exactly the same volume. (392)

Postulate 11–7 Volume Addition Postulate — If a solid region is separated into nonoverlapping regions, then the sum of the volumes of these regions equals the volume of the given region. (392)

Postulate 11–8 If a right prism has a volume of V cubic units, a base with an area of B square units, and a height of h units, then $V = Bh$. (392)

Postulate 11–9 Cavaleri's Principle — If two solids have the same cross-sectional area at every level, and the same height, then they have the same volume. (396)

Theorem 11–1 Area of a Square — If a square has an area of A square units, and each side is s units long, then $A = s^2$. (364)

Theorem 11–2 Area of a Parallelogram — If a parallelogram has an area of A square units, a base of b units, and a corresponding altitude of h units, then $A = bh$. (367)

Theorem 11–3 Area of a Triangle — If a triangle has an area of A square units, a base of b units, and a corresponding altitude of h units, then $A = \frac{1}{2}bh$. (368)

Theorem 11–4 Area of a Trapezoid — If a trapezoid has an area of A square units, bases of b_1 units and b_2 units, and an altitude of h units, then $A = \frac{1}{2}h(b_1 + b_2)$. (368)

Theorem 11–5 A polygon is regular if and only if a circle inscribed in the polygon and a circle circumscribed about the polygon have the same center. (371)

Theorem 11–6 If a segment is an apothem of a regular polygon, then it is perpendicular to a side of the polygon at the point of tangency with the inscribed circle. (372)

Theorem 11–7 Area of a Regular Polygon: If a regular polygon has an area of A square units, a perimeter of p units, and an apothem of a units, then $A = \frac{1}{2}ap$. (372)

Theorem 11–8 If a regular polygon has n sides, then the degree measure of each central angle is $\frac{360}{n}$. (373)

Theorem 11–9 Circumference of a Circle: If a circle has a circumference of C units and a radius of r units, then $C = 2\pi r$. (377)

Theorem 11–10 Area of a Circle: If a circle has an area of A square units and a radius of r units, then $A = \pi r^2$. (377)

Theorem 11–11 Lateral Area of a Right Prism: If a right prism has a lateral area of L square units, a height of h units, and each base has a perimeter of p units, then $L = ph$. (382)

Theorem 11–12 Total Surface Area of a Right Prism: If the total surface area of a right prism is T square units, each base has an area of B square units, a perimeter of p units, and the height is h units, then $T = ph + 2B$. (382)

Theorem 11–13 Lateral Area of a Right Cylinder: If a right cylinder has a lateral area of L square units, a height of h units, and the bases have radii of r units, then $L = 2\pi rh$. (383)

Theorem 11–14 Total Surface Area of a Right Cylinder: If a right cylinder has a total surface area of T square units, height of h units, and the bases have radii of r units, then $T = 2\pi rh + 2\pi r^2$. (383)

Theorem 11–15 Lateral Area for a Regular Pyramid: If a regular pyramid has a lateral area of L square units, a slant height of ℓ units, and its base has perimeter p units, then $L = \frac{1}{2}p\ell$. (387)

Theorem 11–16 Lateral and Total Surface Area of a Right Circular Cone: If a right circular cone has a lateral area of L square units, a total surface area of T square units, a slant height of ℓ units, and the radius of the base is r units, then $L = \pi r\ell$ and $T = \pi r\ell + \pi r^2$. (388)

Theorem 11–17 Surface Area of a Sphere: If a sphere has a surface area of A square units and a radius of r units, then $A = 4\pi r^2$. (389)

Theorem 11–18 Volume of a Right Cylinder: If a right cylinder has a volume of V cubic units, a height of h units, and a radius of r units, then $V = \pi r^2 h$. (393)

Theorem 11–19 Volume of a Right Pyramid: If a right pyramid has a volume of V cubic units, a height of h units, and the area of the base is B square units, then $V = \frac{1}{3}Bh$. (395)

Theorem 11–20 Volume of a Right Circular Cone: If a right circular cone has a volume of V cubic units, a height of h units, and the area of the base is B square units, then $V = \frac{1}{3}Bh$. (395)

Theorem 11–21 Volume of a Sphere: If a sphere has a volume of V cubic units and a radius of r units, then $V = \frac{4}{3}\pi r^3$. (396)

Chapter 12: Coordinates

Postulate 12–1 Each point in a coordinate plane corresponds to exactly one ordered pair of numbers. Each ordered pair of numbers corresponds to exactly one point in a coordinate plane. (405)

Theorem 12–1 Distance Formula — The distance between two points with coordinates (x_1, y_1) and (x_2, y_2) is given by the following formula. (410)

$$d = \sqrt{(x_2 - x_1)^2 + (y_2 - y_1)^2}$$

Theorem 12–2 Midpoint Formula — If the coordinates of A and B are (x_1, y_1) and (x_2, y_2) respectively, then the midpoint M of $\overline{AB}$ has coordinates $\left(\frac{x_1 + x_2}{2}, \frac{y_1 + y_2}{2}\right)$. (411)

Theorem 12–3 Two lines have the same slope if and only if they are parallel and nonvertical. (415)

Theorem 12–4 Two nonvertical lines are perpendicular if and only if the product of their slopes is $^-1$. (415)

Theorem 12–5 Slope-Intercept Form — The equation of the line having a slope m and y-intercept b is $y = mx + b$. (417)

Theorem 12–6 Point-Slope Form — The equation of the line passing through the point whose coordinates are (x_1, y_1) and which has a slope m is $y - y_1 = m(x - x_1)$. (418)

Theorem 12–7 General Equation of a Circle — The equation of a circle with center at (h, k) and radius measuring r units is $(x - h)^2 + (y - k)^2 = r^2$. (423)

Theorem 12–8 Given two points $A(x_1, y_1, z_1)$ and $B(x_2, y_2, z_2)$ in space, the distance between A and B is given by the following equation. (431)

$$AB = \sqrt{(x_2 - x_1)^2 + (y_2 - y_1)^2 + (z_2 - z_1)^2}$$

Chapter 14: Transformations

Postulate 14–1 In a given rotation, if A is the preimage, P is the image, and W is the center of rotation, then the measure of the angle of rotation, $\angle AWP$, equals twice the measure of the angle between the intersecting lines of reflection. (483)

Theorem 14–1 If a dilation with center C and a scale factor k maps A onto E and B onto D, then $ED = k(AB)$. (492)

SQUARES AND APPROXIMATE SQUARE ROOTS

n	n^2	$\sqrt{n}$	n	n^2	$\sqrt{n}$
1	1	1.000	51	2601	7.141
2	4	1.414	52	2704	7.211
3	9	1.732	53	2809	7.280
4	16	2.000	54	2916	7.348
5	25	2.236	55	3025	7.416
6	36	2.449	56	3136	7.483
7	49	2.646	57	3249	7.550
8	64	2.828	58	3364	7.616
9	81	3.000	59	3481	7.681
10	100	3.162	60	3600	7.746
11	121	3.317	61	3721	7.810
12	144	3.464	62	3844	7.874
13	169	3.606	63	3969	7.937
14	196	3.742	64	4096	8.000
15	225	3.873	65	4225	8.062
16	256	4.000	66	4356	8.124
17	289	4.123	67	4489	8.185
18	324	4.243	68	4624	8.246
19	361	4.359	69	4761	8.307
20	400	4.472	70	4900	8.367
21	441	4.583	71	5041	8.426
22	484	4.690	72	5184	8.485
23	529	4.796	73	5329	8.544
24	576	4.899	74	5476	8.602
25	625	5.000	75	5625	8.660
26	676	5.099	76	5776	8.718
27	729	5.196	77	5929	8.775
28	784	5.292	78	6084	8.832
29	841	5.385	79	6241	8.888
30	900	5.477	80	6400	8.944
31	961	5.568	81	6561	9.000
32	1024	5.657	82	6724	9.055
33	1089	5.745	83	6889	9.110
34	1156	5.831	84	7056	9.165
35	1225	5.916	85	7225	9.220
36	1296	6.000	86	7396	9.274
37	1369	6.083	87	7569	9.327
38	1444	6.164	88	7744	9.381
39	1521	6.245	89	7921	9.434
40	1600	6.325	90	8100	9.487
41	1681	6.403	91	8281	9.539
42	1764	6.481	92	8464	9.592
43	1849	6.557	93	8649	9.644
44	1936	6.633	94	8836	9.695
45	2025	6.708	95	9025	9.747
46	2116	6.782	96	9216	9.798
47	2209	6.856	97	9409	9.849
48	2304	6.928	98	9604	9.899
49	2401	7.000	99	9801	9.950
50	2500	7.071	100	10000	10.000

TRIGONOMETRIC RATIOS

Angle	sin	cos	tan	Angle	sin	cos	tan
0°	0.0000	1.0000	0.0000	45°	0.7071	0.7071	1.0000
1°	0.0175	0.9998	0.0175	46°	0.7193	0.6947	1.0355
2°	0.0349	0.9994	0.0349	47°	0.7314	0.6820	1.0724
3°	0.0523	0.9986	0.0524	48°	0.7431	0.6691	1.1106
4°	0.0698	0.9976	0.0699	49°	0.7547	0.6561	1.1504
5°	0.0872	0.9962	0.0875	50°	0.7660	0.6428	1.1918
6°	0.1045	0.9945	0.1051	51°	0.7771	0.6293	1.2349
7°	0.1219	0.9925	0.1228	52°	0.7880	0.6157	1.2799
8°	0.1392	0.9903	0.1405	53°	0.7986	0.6018	1.3270
9°	0.1564	0.9877	0.1584	54°	0.8090	0.5878	1.3764
10°	0.1736	0.9848	0.1763	55°	0.8192	0.5736	1.4281
11°	0.1908	0.9816	0.1944	56°	0.8290	0.5592	1.4826
12°	0.2079	0.9781	0.2126	57°	0.8387	0.5446	1.5399
13°	0.2250	0.9744	0.2309	58°	0.8480	0.5299	1.6003
14°	0.2419	0.9703	0.2493	59°	0.8572	0.5150	1.6643
15°	0.2588	0.9659	0.2679	60°	0.8660	0.5000	1.7321
16°	0.2756	0.9613	0.2867	61°	0.8746	0.4848	1.8040
17°	0.2924	0.9563	0.3057	62°	0.8829	0.4695	1.8807
18°	0.3090	0.9511	0.3249	63°	0.8910	0.4540	1.9626
19°	0.3256	0.9455	0.3443	64°	0.8988	0.4384	2.0503
20°	0.3420	0.9397	0.3640	65°	0.9063	0.4226	2.1445
21°	0.3584	0.9336	0.3839	66°	0.9135	0.4067	2.2460
22°	0.3746	0.9272	0.4040	67°	0.9205	0.3907	2.3559
23°	0.3907	0.9205	0.4245	68°	0.9272	0.3746	2.4751
24°	0.4067	0.9135	0.4452	69°	0.9336	0.3584	2.6051
25°	0.4226	0.9063	0.4663	70°	0.9397	0.3420	2.7475
26°	0.4384	0.8988	0.4877	71°	0.9455	0.3256	2.9042
27°	0.4540	0.8910	0.5095	72°	0.9511	0.3090	3.0777
28°	0.4695	0.8829	0.5317	73°	0.9563	0.2924	3.2709
29°	0.4848	0.8746	0.5543	74°	0.9613	0.2756	3.4874
30°	0.5000	0.8660	0.5774	75°	0.9659	0.2588	3.7321
31°	0.5150	0.8572	0.6009	76°	0.9703	0.2419	4.0108
32°	0.5299	0.8480	0.6249	77°	0.9744	0.2250	4.3315
33°	0.5446	0.8387	0.6494	78°	0.9781	0.2079	4.7046
34°	0.5592	0.8290	0.6745	79°	0.9816	0.1908	5.1446
35°	0.5736	0.8192	0.7002	80°	0.9848	0.1736	5.6713
36°	0.5878	0.8090	0.7265	81°	0.9877	0.1564	6.3138
37°	0.6018	0.7986	0.7536	82°	0.9903	0.1392	7.1154
38°	0.6157	0.7880	0.7813	83°	0.9925	0.1219	8.1443
39°	0.6293	0.7771	0.8098	84°	0.9945	0.1045	9.5144
40°	0.6428	0.7660	0.8391	85°	0.9962	0.0872	11.4301
41°	0.6561	0.7547	0.8693	86°	0.9976	0.0698	14.3007
42°	0.6691	0.7431	0.9004	87°	0.9986	0.0523	19.0811
43°	0.6820	0.7314	0.9325	88°	0.9994	0.0349	28.6363
44°	0.6947	0.7193	0.9657	89°	0.9998	0.0175	57.2900
45°	0.7071	0.7071	1.0000	90°	1.0000	0.0000	∞

Glossary

ABS function The absolute value function, ABS(X), tells the computer to find the absolute value of X. (514)

acute angle An acute angle is one whose degree measure is less than 90. (81)

acute triangle An acute triangle is a triangle with all acute angles. (104)

adjacent angles Two angles in the same plane are adjacent if and only if they have a common side and a common vertex, but no interior points in common. (73)

alternate exterior angles In the figure, transversal t intersects lines ℓ and m. $\angle 5$ and $\angle 3$, and $\angle 6$ and $\angle 4$ are alternate exterior angles. (172)

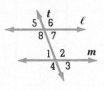

alternate interior angles In the figure, transversal t intersects lines ℓ and m. $\angle 1$ and $\angle 7$, and $\angle 2$ and $\angle 8$ are alternate interior angles. (172)

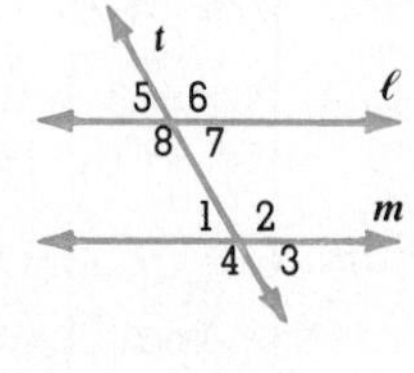

altitude of a prism An altitude of a prism is a segment perpendicular to the base planes with an endpoint in each plane. The length of an altitude is called the *height* of the prism. (381)

altitude of a triangle A segment is an altitude of a triangle if and only if the following conditions hold.

1. Its endpoints are a vertex of a triangle and a point on the line containing the opposite side.
2. It is perpendicular to the line containing the opposite side. (125)

angle A figure is an angle if and only if it consists of two noncollinear rays with a common endpoint. The rays are the *sides* of the angle. The endpoint is the *vertex* of the angle. An angle separates a plane into three parts, the *interior* of the angle, the *exterior* of the angle, and the angle itself. (68)

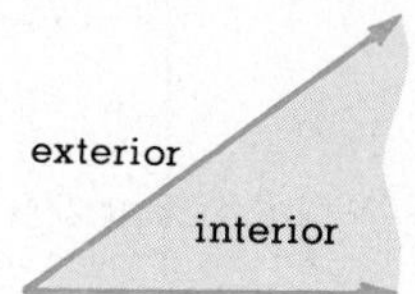

angle bisector A ray, $\overrightarrow{QS}$, is a bisector of $\angle PQR$ if and only if S is in the interior of the angle and $\angle PQS \cong \angle RQS$. (126)

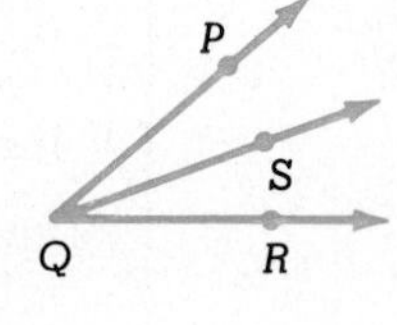

angle of rotation The angle of rotation, $\angle ABC$, is determined by A, the preimage, B, the center of rotation, and C, the rotation image. (483)

apothem A segment is an apothem of a regular polygon if and only if it is a radius of a circle inscribed in the polygon . (371)

arc See major arc and minor arc. (327)

arc measure The degree measure of a minor arc is the degree measure of its central angle. The degree measure of a major arc is 360 minus the degree measure of its central angle. The degree measure of a semicircle is 180. (327)

area The area of a polygonal region is the measure of the region formed by the polygon and its interior. (363)

area of a circle The area of a circle is the limit of the area of the inscribed polygons as the number of sides increases. (376)

area of a sector of a circle If a sector of a circle has an area of A square units, a central angle measurement of N degrees, and a radius of r units, then $A = \frac{N}{360}\pi r^2$. (378)

auxiliary figure An auxiliary figure is included on a geometric figure in order to prove a given theorem. (129)

axis In a coordinate plane, the *x-axis* is the horizontal number line and the *y-axis* is the vertical number line. (405)

axis of a cylinder See cylinder. (383)

base of a prism See prism. (381)

BASIC BASIC, an abbreviation for **B**eginner's **A**ll-purpose **S**ymbolic **I**nstruction **C**ode, is a frequently used computer language. (501)

bases of a trapezoid See trapezoid. (230)

between A point Q is between points P and R if and only if each of the following conditions hold.
1. P, Q, and R are collinear.
2. $PQ + QR = PR$. (44)

biconditional statement A biconditional statement is a statement that can be written in *if and only if form*. All definitions are biconditional statements because they are reversible. (12)

center of a regular polygon A point is a center of a regular polygon if and only if it is the common center of its inscribed and circumscribed circles. (371)

center of rotation See rotation. (482)

central angle A central angle of a circle is an angle formed by two rays coplanar with the circle. The vertex of the angle is the center of the circle. (327)

chord A chord of a circle is a segment whose endpoints are points on the circle. (323)

circle A figure is a circle if and only if it is the set of all points in a plane that are a given distance from a given point in the plane, called the *center*. A circle separates a plane into three parts, the *interior*, the *exterior*, and the circle itself. (323)

circumference The circumference of a circle is the limit of the perimeter of the inscribed regular polygons as the number of sides increases. (376)

circumscribed polygon A polygon is circumscribed about a circle if and only if each side of the polygon is tangent to the circle. (342)

collinear points Points are collinear if and only if they lie on the same line. (5)

common tangent A line that is tangent to two circles that are in the same plane is called a common tangent of the two circles. A common tangent that does not intersect the segment whose endpoints are the centers of the circles is a *common external tangent*. A common tangent that intersects the segment whose endpoints are the centers of the circles is a *common internal tangent*. (325)

common external tangent See common tangent. (325)

common internal tangent See common tangent. (325)

compass A compass is an instrument used to draw circles and arcs of circles. (443)

complementary angles Two angles are complementary if and only if the sum of their degree measures is 90. (76)

composite of reflections Two successive reflections are called a composite of reflections. (479)

concave polygon A polygon is concave if and only if it is not a convex polygon. (208)

concentric circles Concentric circles are circles that lie in the same plane and have the same center. (328)

conclusion See conditional statement. (11)

conditional statement A conditional statement is a statement that can be written in *if-then form.* The part following *if* is called the *hypothesis.* The part following *then* is called the *conclusion.* Conditional statements may be true or false. (10)

congruence transformation If k is the scale factor for a dilation and $k = 1$, then the dilation is a congruence transformation. (472, 493)

congruent angles Two angles are congruent if and only if they have the same measurement. (72)

congruent circles Two circles are congruent if and only if their radii are congruent. (328)

congruent segments Two segments are congruent if and only if they have exactly the same length. (54)

congruent triangles Two triangles are congruent if and only if there is a correspondence such that their corresponding parts are congruent. (113)

consecutive interior angles In the figure, transversal t intersects lines ℓ and m. $\angle 7$ and $\angle 2$, and $\angle 8$ and $\angle 1$ are consecutive interior angles. (172)

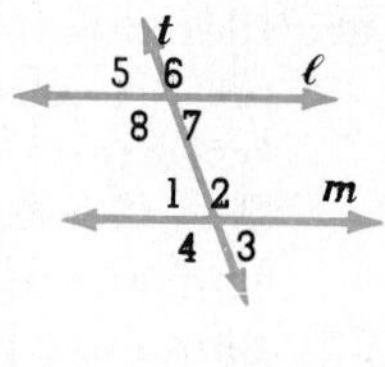

construction The process of drawing a figure that will satisfy certain given conditions, using only a compass and a straightedge, is a construction. (443)

contrapositive The contrapositive of a conditional statement is formed by interchanging the hypothesis and conclusion, and negating both. The contrapositive of a true statement is always a true statement. The contrapositive of a false statement is always a false statement. (28)

converse The converse of a conditional statement is formed by interchanging the hypothesis and conclusion. (11)

convex polygon A polygon is convex if and only if any line containing a side of the polygon does not contain a point in the interior of the polygon. (208)

coordinate **1.** A number associated with a point on a number line is called the coordinate of the point. (37) **2.** In an ordered pair, the first component is called the x-coordinate and the second component is called the y-coordinate. (405)

coplanar points Points are coplanar if and only if they lie in the same plane. (5)

corresponding angles In the figure, transversal t intersects lines ℓ and m. $\angle 5$ and $\angle 1$, $\angle 8$ and $\angle 4$, $\angle 6$ and $\angle 2$, and $\angle 7$ and $\angle 3$ are corresponding angles. (172)

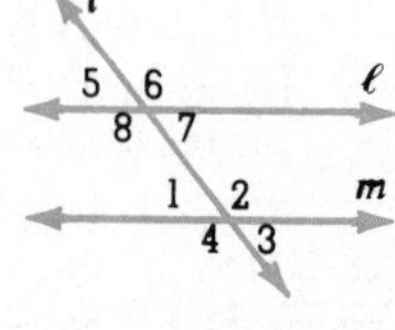

cosine A ratio is the cosine of an acute angle of a right triangle if and only if it is the ratio of the measure of the leg adjacent to the acute angle to the measure of the hypotenuse. (303)

cross products Every proportion has two cross products. In the proportion $\frac{a}{b} = \frac{c}{d}$, where $b \neq 0$ and $d \neq 0$, the cross products are ad and bc. The cross products of a proportion are equal. (250)

cross section A cross section of a solid is the intersection of the solid with a plane that is parallel to the base of the solid. (396)

cylinder A solid figure whose bases are formed by congruent circles in parallel planes. The segment whose endpoints are the centers of the circles is called the *axis* of the cylinder. The *altitude* is a segment perpendicular to the base planes with an endpoint in each plane. (383)

definition A definition is an explanation of how a word is to be used. (19)

degree A degree is one of the units of measure used in measuring angles. (71)

diagonal A segment joining two nonconsecutive vertices of a polygon is called a diagonal of the polygon. (211)

diameter A diameter of a circle is a chord which contains the center of the circle. (323)

dihedral angle An angle is dihedral if and only if it consists of two noncoplanar half planes with a common edge. Each half plane is called a *face*. (91)

dilation A dilation is a transformation in which size is altered based on a center, C, and a scale factor, k. This is also called a *similarity transformation*. (492)

distance The absolute value of the difference of the coordinates of two points on a number line represents the measure of the distance between the two points. (40)

distance between a point and a line The distance between a point and a line is the length of the segment perpendicular to the line from the point. The measure of the distance between a line and point on the line is zero. (195)

distance formula The distance between two points with coordinates (x_1, y_1) and (x_2, y_2) is given by the following formula.

$$d = \sqrt{(x_2 - x_1)^2 + (y_2 - y_1)^2} \quad (410)$$

edge of a half plane A line that separates a plane into two half planes is called the edge of each half plane. (71)

endpoints See segment. (44)

END statement The last statement in a computer program is usually the END statement. (502)

enlargement If k is the scale factor for a dilation, and $k > 1$, then the dilation is an enlargement. (493)

E notation E notation is the computer equivalent of scientific notation. (505)

equation of a circle The equation of a circle with center at (h, k) and radius measuring r units is $(x - h)^2 + (y - k)^2 = r^2$. (423)

equation of a sphere The equation of a sphere whose center is at (i, j, k) and that has a radius measuring r units is $(x - i)^2 + (y - j)^2 + (z - k)^2 = r^2$. (433)

equiangular triangle An equiangular triangle is a triangle with all angles congruent. (104)

equidistant Equidistant means at the same distance. (195)

equilateral triangle An equilateral triangle is a triangle with all sides congruent. (104)

exactly one Exactly one means at least one and no more than one. (186)

exterior angle An angle is an exterior angle of a polygon if and only if it forms a linear pair with one of the angles of the polygon. In the figure, $\angle 2$ is an exterior angle. (141, 213)

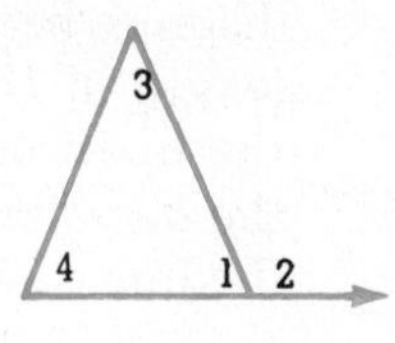

exterior angles In the figure, transversal t intersects lines ℓ and m. $\angle 3$, $\angle 4$, $\angle 5$, and $\angle 6$ are exterior angles. (172)

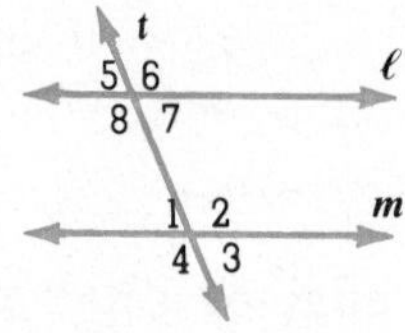

external secant segment See secant segment. (349)

exterior of a circle See circle. (324)

exterior of an angle See angle. (69)

exterior of a triangle See triangle. (105)

face of a dihedral angle See dihedral angle. (91)

formal proof A formal proof is a proof that has five main parts, namely, the theorem, the given, the prove statement, a diagram, and the proof with statements and reasons. (19)

FOR-NEXT statements FOR-NEXT statements are used to loop through the same set of statements several times. (510)

geometric mean For any positive numbers a and b, x is the geometric mean between a and b if and only if $\frac{a}{x} = \frac{x}{b}$ and x is positive. (292)

glide reflection The composition of a translation and a line reflection is a glide reflection. (489)

golden rectangles Golden rectangles are rectangles whose measures of their adjacent sides are always in the ratio of about 1 to 1.618. (255)

great circle If a plane intersects a sphere in more than one point and contains the center of the sphere, the intersection of the plane and the sphere is called a great circle. (355)

half plane The part of a plane on one side of a line in the plane is a half plane. (71)

hypotenuse In a right triangle, the side opposite the right angle is called the hypotenuse. (133)

hypothesis See conditional statement. (11)

if and only if form See biconditional statement. (12)

if-then form See conditional statement. (10)

IF-THEN statement An IF-THEN statement is used to compare two numbers. It tells the computer what to do based on the results of the comparison. (507)

image If A is mapped onto A', then A' is called the image of A. The *preimage* of A is A'. (471)

indirect reasoning In indirect reasoning, you assume the opposite of what you want to prove. Then, show that this assumption leads to a contradiction. (176)

inscribed angle An angle is an inscribed angle if and only if its vertex lies on a circle and its sides contain chords of the circle. (335)

inscribed polygon A polygon is inscribed in a circle if and only if each of its vertices lie on the circle. (337)

integers The integers consist of the set of numbers $\{\ldots, {}^-3, {}^-2, {}^-1, 0, 1, 2, 3, \ldots\}$. (35)

intercepted arc An angle intercepts an arc if and only if each of the following conditions hold.

1. The endpoints of the arc lie on the angle.
2. All points of the arc, except the endpoints, are in the interior of the angle.
3. Each side of the angle contains an endpoint of the arc. (335)

interior angles In the figure, transversal t intersects lines ℓ and m. $\angle 1$, $\angle 2$, $\angle 7$, and $\angle 8$ are interior angles. (172)

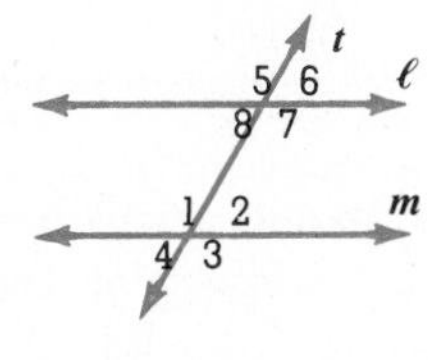

interior of a circle See circle. (324)

interior of an angle See angle. (69)

interior of a triangle See triangle. (105)

intersect Two lines, or lines and planes, intersect if they have points in common. (2)

INT function The greatest integer function, INT(X), tells the computer to find the greatest integer less than or equal to X. (514)

inverse The inverse of a conditional statement is formed by negating both the hypothesis and conclusion. (27)

irrational number An irrational number is a decimal number that is nonterminating and nonrepeating. An example is π. $\pi \approx 3.14159265358979323846264338\ldots$ (37)

isometry When a geometric figure and its transformation image are congruent, the mapping is called an isometry or congruence transformation. (472)

isosceles trapezoid An isosceles trapezoid is a trapezoid in which the legs are congruent. (230)

isosceles triangle An isosceles triangle is a triangle with at least two sides congruent. (104)

lateral area The lateral area of a prism is the area of all the lateral faces. (382)

lateral edges See prism. (381)

lateral faces See prism. (381)

legs of a right triangle In a right triangle, the two sides that are not opposite the right angle are called the legs. (133)

legs of a trapezoid See trapezoid. (230)

length The length of a segment is the distance between the two endpoints of the segment. The length of a segment is the same as the measurement of a segment. (44)

LET statement The LET statement uses an equals sign to assign the value of the expression on the right to the variable on the left. (504)

line Line is one of the basic undefined terms of geometry. Lines extend indefinitely and have no thickness or width. Lines are represented by double arrows and named by lower case letters. A line also can be named using double arrows over capital letters representing two points on the line. (1)

linear equation An equation is linear if and only if it can be written in the form $Ax + By = C$, where A, B, and C are any real numbers, and A and B are not both 0. (406)

line of reflection Line ℓ is a line of reflection if it is the perpendicular bisector of the segment drawn from point X to its reflection image point A. (474)

line of symmetry A line of symmetry is a line that can be drawn through a plane figure so that the figure on one side is the reflection image of the figure on the opposite side. (476)

linear pair Two angles form a linear pair if and only if they are adjacent and their noncommon sides are opposite rays. (76)

line perpendicular to a plane A line is perpendicular to a plane if and only if the given line is perpendicular to every line in the plane that intersects it. (90)

locus In geometry, a figure is a locus if and only if it is the set of all points and only those points that satisfy a given condition. (458)

major arc If $\angle APB$ is a central angle of circle P, and C is any point on the circle and in the exterior of the angle, then points A and B and all points of the circle exterior to $\angle APB$ form a major arc called $\widehat{ACB}$. Three letters are needed to name a major arc. (327)

measure See measurement. (39)

measurement A measurement consists of a number called the *measure* and a *unit of measure.* In the measurement 3 meters, 3 is the measure and meter is the unit of measure. (39)

median of a trapezoid See trapezoid. (231)

median of a triangle A segment is a median of a triangle if and only if its endpoints are a vertex of the triangle and the midpoint of the side opposite the vertex. (125)

midpoint A point M is the midpoint of a segment, $\overline{PQ}$, if and only if M is between P and Q, and $PM = MQ$. (44)

midpoint formula If the coordinates of A and B are (x_1, y_1) and (x_2, y_2) respectively, then the midpoint M of $\overline{AB}$ has coordinates $\left(\frac{x_1 + x_2}{2}, \frac{y_1 + y_2}{2}\right)$. (411)

minor arc If $\angle APB$ is a central angle of circle P, then points A and B and all points of the circle interior to the angle form a minor arc called $\widehat{AB}$. (327)

natural numbers The natural numbers consist of the set of numbers $\{1, 2, 3, \ldots\}$. (35)

negation A negation is a statement formed by denying another statement. (27)

***n*-gon** A polygon with n sides is called an n-gon. (208)

noncollinear points Points are noncollinear if and only if they do not lie on the same line. (6)

noncoplanar points Points are noncoplanar if and only if they do not lie in the same plane. (8)

number line A number line is a line on which each point corresponds to exactly one real number. (35)

oblique prism A prism that is not a right prism is called an oblique prism. (381)

obtuse angle An obtuse angle is one whose degree measure is greater than 90. (81)

obtuse triangle An obtuse triangle is a triangle with one obtuse angle. (104)

opposite rays $\overrightarrow{PQ}$ and $\overrightarrow{PR}$ are opposite rays if and only if P is between Q and R. (67)

R P Q

ordered pair An ordered pair is a pair of numbers in which the order is specified. An ordered pair is used to locate points in a plane. (405)

origin The point of intersection of the x-axis and y-axis in a coordinate plane is called the origin and names O. (405)

parallel lines Two lines are parallel if and only if they lie in the same plane and do not intersect. (171)

parallelogram A quadrilateral is a parallelogram if and only if both pair of opposite sides are parallel. Any side of a parallelogram may be called a *base*. For each base there is a corresponding segment called the *altitude* that is perpendicular to the base and has its endpoints on the lines containing the base and the opposite side. (216, 367)

perimeter The sum of the measures of the sides of a polygon is the measure of the perimeter of the polygon. (236)

perpendicular lines Two lines are perpendicular if and only if they intersect to form a right angle. (86)

perpendicular planes Two planes are perpendicular if and only if any line in one of them that is perpendicular to their line of intersection is also perpendicular to the other plane. (91)

plane Plane is one of the basic undefined terms of geometry. Planes extend indefinitely in all directions and have no thickness. A plane is represented by a four-sided figure and is named by a capital script letter or by three points of the plane that are not on the same line. (1)

plane angle A plane angle of a dihedral angle is the intersection of the dihedral angle and a plane perpendicular to its edge. (92)

plane perpendicular to a line A plane is perpendicular to a line if and only if every line in the plane that intersects the given line is perpendicular to it. (90)

Platonic solid A Platonic solid is any one of the five regular polyhedrons: tetrahedron, hexahedron, octahedron, dodecahedron, or icosohedron. (241)

point Point is one of the basic undefined terms of geometry. Points have no dimensions, are represented by dots, and are named by capital letters. (1)

point of reflection Point S is the reflection of point R with respect to point Q, the point of reflection, if Q is the midpoint of the segment drawn from R to S. (474)

point of symmetry A point of symmetry is a point that can be placed in the interior of a plane figure so that it is the midpoint of all segments that contain it and have endpoints on the figure. (476)

point of tangency See tangent. (324)

point-slope form The equation of a line passing through a point whose coordinates are (x_1, y_1) and which has a slope m is $y - y_1 = m(x - x_1)$. (418)

polygon A figure is a polygon if and only if it meets each of the following conditions.
1. It is formed by three or more coplanar segments called *sides*.
2. Sides that have a common endpoint are noncollinear.
3. Each side intersects exactly two other sides, but only at their endpoints. (207)

polygonal region A polygon and its interior form a polygonal region. (363)

polyhedron A solid with flat surfaces that form polygons is called a polyhedron. The flat surfaces formed by the polygons and their interiors are called *faces*. Pairs of faces intersect at *edges*. Three or more edges intersect at a *vertex*. (240)

postulate A postulate in geometry is a statement that describes a fundamental property of the basic terms. Postulates are accepted as being true. (14)

preimage See image. (471)

principal square root The principal square root of a nonnegative number is the nonnegative square root. (287)

PRINT statement A PRINT statement tells the computer what to print as output. (502)

prism A solid with the following characteristics is a prism.
1. Two faces, called *bases,* are formed by congruent polygons that lie in parallel planes.
2. The faces that are not bases, called *lateral faces,* are formed by parallelograms.
3. The intersections of two adjacent lateral faces are called *lateral edges* and are parallel segments. (381)

proportion A proportion is an equation of the form $\frac{a}{b} = \frac{c}{d}$ that states that two ratios are equivalent. (249)

protractor A protractor is a tool used to find the degree measure of a given angle. (71)

pyramid A solid with the following characteristics is a pyramid.
1. All the faces, except one face, intersect at a point called the *vertex*.
2. The face that does not intersect at the vertex is called the *base* and forms a polygon.
3. The faces meeting at the vertex are called *lateral faces* and form triangles. (387)

quadrant One of the four regions into which two perpendicular number lines separate the plane is a quadrant. (405)

radical sign The symbol $\sqrt{\quad}$ is called a radical sign. It indicates a nonnegative square root. (287)

radicand The expression under a radical sign is called the radicand. (287)

radius of a circle A radius of a circle is a segment whose endpoints are the center of the circle and a point on the circle. (323)

radius of a regular polygon A segment is a radius of a regular polygon if and only if it is a radius of a circle circumscribed about the polygon. (371)

ratio A ratio is a comparison of two numbers using division. (249)

rationalizing the denominator The method used to simplify a radical fraction so that the denominator of the fraction becomes a rational number is called rationalizing the denominator. (289)

rational number A rational number is any number that can be expressed in the form $\frac{a}{b}$, where a and b denote integers and b is not zero. (35)

ray $\overrightarrow{PQ}$ is a ray if and only if it is the set of points $\overline{PQ}$ and all points S for which Q is between P and S. (67)

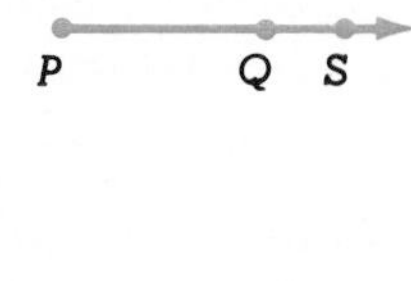

READ/DATA statements The READ statement tells the computer the variables to which the values in the DATA statement are to be assigned. (502)

real numbers The rational and irrational numbers make up the real numbers. Each point on a number line can be named by a real number. (37)

rectangle A quadrilateral is a rectangle if and only if it is a parallelogram with four right angles. (224)

reduction If k is the scale factor for a dilation, and $0 < k < 1$, then the dilation is a reduction. (493)

reflection See line of reflection or point of reflection. (474)

regular polygon A polygon is regular if and only if it is a convex polygon with all sides congruent and all angles congruent. (208)

regular polyhedron Each face of a regular polyhedron forms a regular polygon and each edge of a regular polyhedron has the same measure. (241)

regular pyramid A pyramid is a regular pyramid if and only if its base is regular and the segment is the center of the base and the vertex is perpendicular to the base. This segment is called the *altitude*. (387)

remote interior angles The angles in a triangle that are not adjacent to a given exterior angle are called remote interior angles. (141)

repeating decimal A repeating decimal is a decimal number in which a nonzero digit or group of digits repeat. A bar over the repeating digit or digits indicates a repeating decimal. Examples are $0.\overline{3}$ and $0.\overline{421}$. (36)

rhombus A quadrilateral is a rhombus if and only if it is a parallelogram with all four sides congruent. (225)

right angle A right angle is an angle whose degree measure is 90. (81)

right circular cone A solid figure that has a circular base and an axis from the vertex that is perpendicular to the base is a right circular cone. (388)

right cylinder A cylinder whose axis is also an altitude of the figure is a right cylinder. (383)

right dihedral angle A dihedral angle is a right dihedral angle if and only if its plane angles are right angles. (91)

right prism If the lateral edges of a prism are also altitudes, then the prism is a right prism. (381)

right triangle A right triangle is a triangle with one right angle. (104)

rotation The composite of two reflections with respect to two intersecting lines is a transformation called a rotation. The intersection of the two lines is called the *center of rotation*. (482)

RUN RUN tells the computer to execute the program. (502)

scalene triangle A scalene triangle is a triangle with no two sides congruent. (104)

secant A secant is a line that intersects a circle in exactly two points. (324)

secant segment A secant segment is a segment that contains a chord of a circle. The part or parts of a secant segment that are exterior to the circle are called *external secant segments*. (349)

sector A sector of a circle is a region bounded by a central angle and the intercepted arc. (378)

segment A segment is a part of a line that consists of two points, called *endpoints*, and all the points between them. (44)

segment bisector A segment bisector is a segment, line, or plane that intersects a segment at its midpoint. (55)

semicircle A line containing the diameter of a circle separates the circle into two semicircles. (327)

sides of an angle See angle. (68)

similar figures Figures that have the same shape but which may differ in size are called similar figures. (258)

similarity transformation See dilation. (472)

similar polygons Two polygons are similar if and only if there is a correspondence such that their corresponding angles are congruent and the measures of their corresponding sides are proportional. (258)

sine A ratio is the sine of an acute angle of a right triangle if and only if it is the ratio of the measure of the leg opposite the acute angle to the measure of the hypotenuse. (303)

skew lines Two lines are skew if and only if they do not intersect and are not in the same plane. (171)

slant height The height of each lateral face of a regular pyramid is called the slant height. (387)

slope The slope of a line containing two points with coordinates (x_1, y_1) and (x_2, y_2) is given by the following formula.

$m = \frac{y_2 - y_1}{x_2 - x_1}$ **where** $x_2 \neq x_1$ (413)

slope-intercept form The equation of the line having a slope m and y-intercept b is $y = mx + b$. (417)

sphere In space, a figure is a sphere if and only if it is the set of all points that are a given distance from a given point, called the *center*. (353)

square A quadrilateral is a square if and only if it is a rectangle and all four sides are congruent. (226)

square root For any numbers a and b, if $a^2 = b$, then a is a square root of b. (287)

SQR function The square root function, SQR(X), tells the computer to calculate the square root of X. (514)

straightedge Any instrument used as a guide to draw a line is a straightedge. (443)

supplementary angles Two angles are supplementary if and only if the sum of their degree measures is 180. (76)

surface area The sum of the areas of the faces of a solid figure is the surface area. (381)

tangent **1.** A ratio is the tangent of an acute angle of a right triangle if and only if it is the ratio of the measure of the leg opposite the acute angle to the measure of the leg adjacent to the acute angle. (304) **2.** A tangent is a line in a plane that intersects a circle in the plane in exactly one point. The point of intersection is the *point of tangency.* (324)

tangent segment A tangent segment is a segment that intersects a circle in exactly one point and lies on a tangent. (341)

terminating decimal A terminating decimal is a decimal number in which the division process stops or terminates because a remainder of zero has been reached. An example is 0.35. (36)

theorem A theorem is a statement that must be proven before accepted. (19)

transformation In a plane, a mapping is a transformation if and only if each point has exactly one image point and each image point has exactly one preimage point. (471)

translation A composite of two reflections over two parallel lines is a translation. (479)

transversal In a plane, a line is a transversal if and only if it intersects two other lines in two different points. (172)

trapezoid A quadrilateral is a trapezoid if and only if it has exactly one pair of parallel sides. The parallel sides of a trapezoid are called *bases.* The nonparallel sides are called *legs.* The line segment joining the midpoints of the legs of a trapezoid is called the *median.* The *altitude* is a segment perpendicular to both bases with its endpoints on the bases. (230, 368)

triangle A triangle is a figure formed by three noncollinear segments called sides. Each endpoint of a side is an endpoint of exactly one other side. The endpoints are the *vertices* of the triangle. A triangle separates a plane into three parts, the triangle, its *interior,* and its *exterior.* (103)

trigonometric ratio A ratio of the measures of two sides of a right triangle is called a trigonometric ratio. (303)

undefined term An undefined term is a word which has a meaning that is readily understood. The basic undefined terms of geometry are point, line, and plane. (5)

unit of measure See measurement. (39)

vertex of an angle See angle. (68)

vertical angles Two angles are vertical if and only if they are two nonadjacent angles formed by two intersecting lines. (82)

volume The measure of the amount of space a figure encloses is the volume of the figure. (391)

whole numbers The whole numbers consist of the set of numbers $\{0, 1, 2, 3, \ldots\}$. (35)

***x*-axis** See axis. (405)

***y*-axis** See axis. (405)

Index

A

AAS, 121
AA similarity, 263
ABS(X), 514
Acute angle, 81
Acute triangle, 104
Addition, properties, 49
    proportions, 254
Addition and subtraction properties
    equality, 48
    inequality, 58
Adjacent angles, 73
Algebraic review
    factoring, 175
    factoring equations, 252
    percents, 42
    prime factorization, 124
    quadratic formula, 422
    radical equations, 330
    solving rational equations, 485
Alternate exterior angles, 172
Alternate interior angles, 172
Altitude
    cylinder, 383
    parallelogram, 367
    prisms, 381
    regular pyramid, 387
    triangle, 125
Angles, 68
    acute, 81
    adjacent, 73
    base, 230
    bisector, 126
    central, 327
    complementary, 76
    congruent, 72
    constructions, 444–445
    corresponding, 172
    dihedral, 91
    exterior, 172
    exterior of, 69
    exterior, polygon, 213
    exterior, triangle, 141
    inscribed, 335
    interior, 172
    interior of, 69
    linear pair, 76
    measuring, 344
        degrees, 71
        radians, 75
    obtuse, 81
    opposites, 217
    plane, 92
    polygon, 211
    remote interior, 141
    right, 81
    right dihedral, 92
    of rotation, 483
    sides, 68
    supplementary, 76
    vertex, 68
    vertical, 82
Angle Addition Postulate, 73
Angle of depression, 312
Angle of elevation, 312
Angle Measure Postulate, 71
Angle Sum Theorem, 107
Apothems
    regular polygon, 371
Arcs
    of the chord, 331
    intercepted, 335
    major and minor, 327
    measure of, 327
Arc Addition Postulate, 328
Area, 363
    circle, 376, 377
    lateral, 382
        regular pyramid, 387
        right circular cone, 388
        right cylinder, 383
    parallelogram, 367
    rectangle, 364
    regular polygons, 372
    sector of a circle, 378
    square, 364
    surface, 381
        right circular cone, 388
        sphere, 389
    trapezoid, 368
    triangles, 368
Area Addition Postulate, 364
Area Postulate, 363
ASA, 117
Associative properties, 49
Auxiliary segment, 129
Axis
    cone, 388
    cylinder, 383

B

Base angles, 230
Bases
    cone, 388
    parallelogram, 367
    prism, 381
    pyramid, 387
    trapezoid, 230
BASIC, 501
    E notation, 505
    FOR-NEXT statements, 510
    functions, 514

IF-THEN statement, 508
LET statement, 504
order of operations, 501
PRINT statement, 504
READ/DATA statements, 502
Between, 44
Biconditional statement, 12
Bisector
angle, 126
perpendicular, 125, 448
segment, 55
theorem, 56

C

Calculators, 17, 85, 159, 215, 310, 375, 465
Careers
advertising designer, 253
architect, 151
carpenter, 457
carpet installer, 53
drafter, 430
mineralogist, 229
navigator, 111
paralegal aide, 9
recreation supervisor, 306
rescuer, 94
scuba diving, 399
seismologist, 352
soil scientist, 185
urban designer, 491
Cavalieri's Principle, 396
Center
circles, 326
dilation, 492
regular polygon, 371
of rotation, 482
spheres, 353
Central angle, 327
Chapter Review, 31, 63, 97, 138, 167, 201, 245, 283, 317, 359, 401, 436, 467, 497
Chapter Summary, 30, 61, 95, 136, 166, 200, 243, 281, 316, 357, 400, 435, 466, 496
Chapter Test, 33, 65, 99, 139, 169, 203, 247, 285, 319, 361, 403, 439, 469, 499
Chord, 323
arc of, 331
sphere, 353
Circles, 323
arcs, 327
area, 376, 377
center, 326
central angle, 327
chord, 323
circumference, 376
circumscribed, 452
polygon, 342
concentric, 328
congruent, 328
constructions, 451
diameter, 323
equation, 423
exterior and interior, 324
great, 355
inscribed angle, 453
angle, 335
polygon, 337
measuring angles, 344
radius, 323
secant, 324
sector, 378
segments, 348–350
tangent, 324, 340
tangent
common, 325
Circumcenter, 452
Circumference, 376
Circumscribed
circle, 452
polygon, 342
Collinear points, 5
Common tangent, 325
external and internal, 325
Commutative properties, 49
Comparison property, 58
Compass, 443
Complementary angles, 76
Composite
of reflections, 479
transformation, 486
Composite numbers, 124
Computer program, 501
Computers, 43, 128, 190, 339, 412, 473
Concave polygon, 208
Concentric circles, 328
Conclusion, 11
Conditional statement, 10
conclusion, 11
contrapositive, 28
converse, 11
hypothesis, 11
inverse, 27
negation, 27
Cone
axis, 388
base, 388
vertex, 388
see right circular cone
Congruence
angles, 72
circles, 328
segments, 54
triangles, 112
tests for, 116–117, 121–122
Congruence transformation, 472
Constructions, 443
angle bisector, 445
center, circle, 452
circumscribed circle, 452
congruent angle, 444
congruent parts, 454
congruent segment, 443
geometric mean, 455
parallel line, 449
perpendicular bisector, 448
perpendicular line, 447, 448
proportional segments, 454
proportions, 454–455
tangents, 451
Contradictions, 199
Contrapositive, 28
Converse, 11
Pythagorean Theorem, 296
Convex polygon, 208
Coordinates, 405
in space, 431
number line, 37
Coordinate plane
distance, 409
ordered pairs, 405
quadrant, 405
Coordinate proofs, 426
Coplanar points, 5

Corresponding angles, 172
Corresponding parts, 112
    proportional sides, 255
Cosine, 303
Cross products, 250
Cross products
    equality, 250
Cross section, 396
Cumulative Review, 100–101, 204–205, 320–321, 440–441
Cylinders
    altitude, 383
    axis, 383
    right, 383
    see right cylinder

D

Decagons, 208
Decimals, 36
Definitions, guidelines, 5
Degrees, 71
Depression, angle of, 312
Diagonals, 211
Diagrams, using, 146
Diameter
    circle, 323
    sphere, 353
Dihedral angle, 91
    face, 91
    right, 92
Dilations
    center, 492
    scale factor, 492
Distance, 39
    between parallel lines, 196
    between a point and a line, 195
    postulate, 40
Distance Formula, 410
Distributive property, 49
Dodecagons, 208
Dodecahedron, 241

E

Edges
    half planes, 71
    lateral, 381
    polyhedrons, 240
Elevation, angle of, 312
Elimination method, 420
Elliptic geometry, 315
Endpoints, 44
E notation, 505
Equality, properties, 48–49
Equations
    circle, 423
    linear, 406, 417
    rational, 485
Equiangular triangle, 104
Equidistant, 195
Equilateral triangle, 104
Euler's Formula, 242
Excursions in Geometry, 4, 47, 57, 75, 120, 155, 164, 180, 199, 219, 242, 257, 302, 326, 366, 380, 408, 495
Exterior
    circles, 324
    triangle, 105
Exterior angles, 69, 213
    alternate, 172
    triangle, 141
Exterior Angle Theorem, 142
External secant segments, 349

F

Faces
    dihedral angle, 91
    lateral, 381, 387
    polyhedrons, 240
Factoring, 175
Finite geometry, 26
Flow proofs, 80
Formal proofs, 19
Formulas
    area
        circle, 377
        parallelogram, 367
        rectangle, 364
        regular polygons, 372
        sectors of a circle, 378
        square, 364
        trapezoids, 368
        triangles, 368
    circumference, circle, 377
    distance, 410
    Euler's, 242
    Heron's, 302
    lateral area
        regular pyramid, 387
        right circular cone, 388
        right cylinder, 383
        right prism, 382
    midpoint, 411
    perimeter
        rectangle, 236
        regular polygon, 237
    quadratic, 422
    slope, 413
    surface area
        right circular cone, 388
        right cylinder, 383
        right prism, 382
        sphere, 389
    volume
        right circular cone, 395
        right cylinder, 393
        right prism, 392
        right pyramid, 395
        sphere, 396
FOR-NEXT loops, 510
FOR-NEXT statements, 510
Functions
    BASIC, 514
    trigonometric, 375

G

Geodesic dome, 457
Geometric mean, 292
    constructions, 455

Geometry, Topics in
- elliptic, 315
- finite, 26
- flowproof, 80
- hyperbolic, 235
- projective, 165
- spherical, 315
- topology, 386

Glide reflection, 489
Golden ratio, 255
Golden rectangles, 255
Graphing
- circles, 423
- linear equation, 406, 417
- ordered pairs, 405
- slope, 413
- systems of equations, 420

Great circle, 355

H

HA, 133
Half planes, 71
- edge, 71

Hemispheres, 355
Heptagons, 208
Heron's Formula, 302
Hexagons, 208
Hexahedron, 241
Hinge Theorem, 160
- converse, 160

HL, 135
Hyperbolic geometry, 235
Hypotenuse, 133
Hypothesis, 11

I

Icosahedron, 241
Identity properties, 49
If-then form, 10
IF-THEN statement, 508
Image, 471
Incenter, 453
Independent loops, 511
Indirect proof, 176
- writing, 177

Indirect reasoning, 176
Inequality, properties, 58–59
Inequality Theorem, 142
Inscribed angle, 335
Inscribed circle, 453
Inscribed polygon, 337
Integers, 35
Intercepted arcs, 335
Interior, angles, 69
- alternate, 172
- consecutive, 172
- remote, 141

Interior
- circles, 324
- triangle, 105

Intersection, 2
- of loci, 462

INT(X), 514
Inverse, 27
Inverse properties, 49
Irrational numbers, 37, 289
Isometry, 472
- reflection, 475
- rotation, 482
- translation, 480

Isosceles trapezoid, 230
Isosceles triangle, 104
- theorem, 129

L

LA, 134
Lateral area, 382
- regular pyramid, 387
- right circular cone, 388
- right cylinder, 383

Lateral faces, 381
- pyramid, 387

Legs
- right triangle, 133
- trapezoid, 230

LET statement, 504
Linear equations, 406
- point-slope form, 418
- slope-intercept form, 417
- systems, 420

Linear pair, 76
Lines, 1
- distance to a point, 195
- intersection, 2
- parallel, 171
- perpendicular, 86
- of reflection, 474
- skew, 171
- slope, 413
- of symmetry, 476
- transversal, 172
- y-intercept, 417

LL, 133
Loci, 458
- intersection, 462

Loops, 511

M

Magnitude, 461
Major arc, 327
Mappings, 471
Mean
- geometric, 292

Measure, 39
- angles, circles, 344
- of arcs, 327

Median
- trapezoid, 232
- triangle, 125

Metric system, 47
Midpoint, 44
- formula, 411
- theorem, 54

Minor arc, 327
Multiplication and division properties
  equality, 48
  inequality, 58
Multiplication, properties, 49

N

Negation, 27
Nested loops, 511
n-gon, 208
Nonagons, 208
Number line, 35
  coordinates, 37
  postulate, 37
Numbers
  composite, 124
  integers, 35
  irrational, 37, 289
  prime, 124
  rational, 35
  real, 37
  whole, 35

O

Oblique prism, 381
Obtuse angles, 81
Obtuse triangle, 104
Octagons, 208
Octahedron, 241
Opposite angles, 217
Opposite rays, 67
Opposite sides, 217
Ordered pairs, 405
Ordered triple, 431
Order of operations, 501
Origin, 405

P

Parallel lines, 171
  constructions, 449
  distance, 196
  tests, 181
  using, 191
Parallel Postulate, 186
Parallelograms, 216
  altitude, 367
  area, 367
  base, 367
  opposite angles, sides, 217
  rectangles, 224
  rhombus, 225
  square, 226
  tests, 220
Pentagon, 208
Pentagram, 257
Perimeter, 236
  rectangle, 236
  regular polygon, 237
Perpendicular bisector, 125, 448
Perpendicular lines, 86
  constructions, 447–448
Perpendicular planes, 90
π(pi), 377
Pick's Theorem, 366
Plane angle, 92
Planes, 1
  half, 71
  perpendicular, 90
  see coordinate plane
Platonic solids, 241
Points, 1
  collinear, 5
  coplanar, 5
  distance to a line, 195
  of reflection, 474
  of symmetry, 476
  of tangency, 324, 340
Point-slope form, 418
Polygonal region, 363
Polygons, 207
  angles, 211
  circumscribed, 342
  concave and convex, 208
  diagonals, 211
  exterior angles, 213
  inscribed, 337
  perimeter, 236
  problem solving, 212
  regular, 208
  similar, 258
  vertices, 207
Polyhedrons, 240
  edges, 240
  faces, 240
  platonic solids, 241
  regular, 241
  vertices, 240
Preimage, 471
Prime factorization, 124
Prime numbers, 124
PRINT statement, 504
Prisms, 381
  bases, 381
  lateral, 381
  lateral edges, 381
  lateral faces, 381
  oblique, 381
  right, 381
  see right prism
Problem solving
  procedure, 212
    proportions, 277
  Pythagorean Theorem, 297
  similar figures, 276
Product property, square roots, 288
Projective geometry, 165
Proofs
  coordinate, 426
  flow, 80
  formal, 19
  indirect, 176
  writing, 22
Proportional parts, 267
Proportions, 249
  constructions, 454–455
  corresponding sides, 255
  cross products, 250
  geometric mean, 292

problem solving procedure, 277
properties, 254
Protractor Postulate, 71
Pyramids
bases, 387
lateral faces, 387
regular, 387
vertex, 387
Pythagorean Theorem, 295
converse, 296
problem solving, 297
Pythagorean triples, 515

Q

Quadrants, 405
Quadratic formula, 422
Quadrilaterals, 208
parallelogram, 216
rectangle, 224
rhombus, 225
square, 226
trapezoid, 230
Quotient property, square roots, 288

R

Radians, 75
Radical sign, 287
Radicand, 287
Radius
circle, 323
regular polygons, 371
sphere, 353
Rational equations, 485
Rational numbers, 35
Rationalizing the denominator, 289
Ratios, 249
golden, 255
trigonometric, 303
Rays, 67
opposite, 67
READ/DATA statements, 502
Real numbers, 37
properties, 48–49
Reasoning, indirect, 176
Rectangles, 224
area, 364
golden, 255
perimeter, 236
Reflections, 474
composite, 479
glide, 489
line of, 474
point of, 474
Reflexive property
equality, 48
Regular polygons, 208
apothem, 371
area, 372
center, 371
perimeter, 237
radii, 371
Regular polyhedrons, 241
Regular pyramid, 387
altitude, 387
lateral area, 387
slant height, 387
Repeating decimal, 36
Resultant, 461
Rhombus, 225
Riemannian geometry, 315
Right angles, 81
Right circular cone
surface area, 388
volume, 395
Right cylinders, 383
lateral area, 383
surface area, 383
volume, 393
Right dihedral angles, 92
Right prisms, 381
volume, 392
Right pyramids
volume, 395
Right triangles, 104
special, 299
theorems, 133–135
Rotations, 482
angles of, 483
center of, 482
Ruler Postulate, 39

S

SAS, 116
SAS Similarity, 265
Scale factor, 492
Scalene triangle, 104
Scientific notation, see E notation
Secant, circle, 324
Secant segments, 349
external, 349
Sectors
area, 378
circle, 378
Segment, 44
bisector, 55
congruent, 54
constructions, 443, 448
endpoints, 44
external secant, 349
midpoint, 44
secant, 349
tangent, 341
Semicircles, 327
Sides
angles, 68
opposite, 217
triangle, 103
Significant digits, 57
Similar figures, 258
problem solving, 276
Similar polygons, 258
parts, 272
Similar triangles, 263
Similarity transformation, 472
Simple closed curve, 155
Sine, 303

Skew lines, 171
Slant height, 387
Slope, 413
Slope-intercept form, 417
Solids, 240
  cross section, 396
Space
  coordinates, 431
Spheres, 353
  center, 353
  chord, 353
  diameter, 353
  great circle, 355
  radius, 353
  surface area, 389
  tangent, 353
  volume, 396
Spherical geometry, 315
SQR(X), 514
Square, 226
  area, 364
Square roots, 287
  properties, 288
  radical sign, 287
  radicand, 287
  rationalizing the denominator, 289
SSS, 116
SSS Similarity, 264
Statements
  biconditional, 12
  conditional, 10
  contradictions, 199
Straightedge, 443
Substitution method, 420
Substitution property, 49
Subtraction property
  proportions, 254
Summation property
  proportions, 254
Supplementary angles, 76
Supplement Postulate, 76
Surface area, 381
  right circular cone, 388
  right cylinder, 383
  sphere, 389
  total, right prism, 382
Symmetric property
  equality, 48
Symmetry
  line of, 476
  point of, 476
Systems of equations, 420
  elimination method, 420
  substitution method, 420

T

Tangent, 304
Tangent (line)
  circle, 324, 340
  common, 325
  point of, 324
  segments, 341
  sphere, 353
Terminating decimal, 36
Tests
  parallel lines, 181
  parallelograms, 220
Tetrahedron, 241
Topology, 386
Total probable error, 53
Transformations, 471
  composite, 486
  congruence, 472
  dilation, 492
  isometry, 472
  reflection, 474
  rotation, 482
  similarity, 472
  translation, 479
Transitive property
  equality, 48
  inequality, 59
Translations, 479
Transversal, 172
Trapezoids, 230
  area, 368
  base angles, 230
  bases, 230
  isosceles, 230
  legs, 230
  median, 232
Triangle Inequality Theorem, 156
Triangles
  acute, 104
  altitude, 125
  angle bisector, 126
  Angle Sum Theorem, 107
  area, 368
  congruence, 112
  converse, Hinge Theorem, 160
  equiangular, 104
  equilateral, 104
  exterior angle, 141
    theorem, 142
  exterior and interior, 105
  Hinge Theorem, 160
  Inequality Theorem, 142
  isosceles, 104, 129
  median, 125
  obtuse, 104
  perpendicular bisector, 125
  remote interior angles, 141
  right, 104
    special, 299
  angles, 152–154
  scalene, 104
  sides, 103, 152–154
  similar, 263, 267
  tests for congruence, 116–117, 121–122
  vertices, 103
Trigonometric functions, 375
Trigonometric ratios, 303
  cosine, 303
  sine, 303
  tangent, 304
Trigonometric tables, using, 307
Trigonometry, 303
  using, 311

U

Undefined terms, 5
Unit of measure, 39
Using parallels, 191

V

Vectors, 461
  magnitude, 461
  resultant, 461
Vertical angles, 82
Vertices
  angle, 68
  cone, 388
  polygons, 207
  polyhedrons, 240
  pyramid, 387
  triangle, 103
Vocabulary, 30, 61, 95, 136, 166, 200, 243, 281, 316, 357, 400, 435, 466, 496
Volume
  Cavalieri's Principle, 396
  right circular cone, 395
  right cylinder, 393
  right prism, 392
  right pyramid, 395
  sphere, 396
Volume Addition Postulate, 392
Volume Postulate, 391

W

Whole numbers, 35

X

x-axis, 405
x-coordinate, 405

Y

y-axis, 405
y-coordinate, 405
y-intercept, 417

Selected Answers

CHAPTER 1 POINTS, LINES, AND PLANES

Page 3 Exploratory **1.** point **3.** line **5.** plane **7.** line **9.** plane **11.** point

Page 3 Written **13.** $\overleftrightarrow{AF}$, $\overleftrightarrow{FB}$, n **15.** none **21.** plane AFE, plane ABC, plane DEH **23.** infinitely many **25.** three

Page 7 Exploratory **1.** false **3.** false **5.** true **7.** false **9.** false **11.** true

Page 7 Written **1.** collinear **3.** noncollinear **5.** collinear **11.** noncoplanar **15.** coplanar **19.** good **21.** not good; not reversible **23.** not good; does not identify the set to which term belongs **25.** good **27.** a definition is reversible provided it can be written in "if and only if" form

Page 12 Exploratory **1.** it rains; the grass gets wet **3.** you live in Texas; you are an American **5.** two lines are perpendicular; two lines intersect

Page 12 Written **1.** If lines are parallel, they do not intersect; if lines do not intersect, they are parallel. **3.** If it is a square, it is a rectangle; if it is a rectangle, it is a square. **5.** If $x < 0$, $5x > 6x$; if $5x > 6x$, $x < 0$. **7.** If it rains, it pours; if it pours, it rains. **13.** yes; true **15.** yes; neither **17.** no; neither **19.** yes; true **21.** no; neither **23.** If three points are collinear, they lie on the same line. **25.** If three points are collinear, they are coplanar. **27.** A point has three dimensions. **29.** If points are collinear, they lie on the same line; if points lie on the same line, they are collinear. **31.** If two segments are congruent, they have the same measure; if two segments have the same measure, they are congruent. **33.** If two angles are supplementary, their sum is 180°; if the sum of two angles is 180°, they are supplementary. **35.** Two lines are perpendicular if and only if they intersect at right angles. **37.** Two lines are parallel if and only if alternate interior angles are congruent when the lines are intersected by a transversal.

Page 16 Exploratory **1.** Postulate 1–1 **3.** Postulate 1–4 **5.** Postulate 1–4 **7.** Postulate 1–1 **9.** Postulate 1–6

Page 16 Written **1.** true **3.** false **5.** true **11.** 1 **13.** 3 **15.** 4 **17.** 15 **19.** 1 **21.** infinitely many

Page 20 Exploratory **1.** theorem, given, prove statement, diagram, and proof **3.** conclusion of theorem **5.** yes **7.** yes **9.** statements, reasons **11.** to justify the statements **13.** two lines intersect **15.** a line and plane intersect, and the plane does not contain the line **17.** there is exactly one plane that contains them **19.** their intersection is a line

Page 21 Written **1.** Lines ℓ and m intersect at A; plane $\mathscr{R}$ contains ℓ and m. **3.** Line ℓ and plane $\mathscr{M}$ intersect, and $\mathscr{M}$ does not contain ℓ; ℓ and $\mathscr{M}$ intersect at P. **15.** a point Q not on line m **17.** Planes $\mathscr{A}$ and $\mathscr{B}$ intersect at line ℓ. **19.** $\overleftrightarrow{PQ}$ and $\overleftrightarrow{QR}$ intersect at Q.

Page 24 Exploratory **1.** Theorem 1–2 **3.** Postulate 1–4 **5.** Postulate 1–2 **7.** Theorem 1–2 **9.** none **11.** none

Page 24 Written **1.** Postulate 1–1 **3.** Postulate 1–2 **5.** Postulate 1–5 **7.** Theorem 1–1 **9.** definition of noncollinear points **11.** Exactly one plane contains ℓ and m. **13.** The intersection of $\mathscr{M}$ and $\mathscr{N}$ is a line. **19.** Two planes intersect; the intersection contains two points **21.** Two lines intersect; the lines contain three points **23.** Postulate 1–6; Postulate 1–3

Page 28 Exploratory **1.** A figure is not a triangle. **3.** Three points are noncollinear. **5.** $\mathscr{M}$ and $\mathscr{N}$ do not intersect. **7.** ℓ lies in $\mathscr{M}$.

Page 29 Written **1.** yes **3.** no **5.** yes **7.** no **9.** no **11.** no **13.** yes **15.** no **17.** yes **19.** no **21.** no **23.** no **25.** If it does not rain, the grass does not get wet; if the grass does not get wet, it does not rain. **27.** If you do not live in Texas, you are not an American; if you are not an American, you do not live in Texas. **29.** If two lines are not perpendicular, they do not intersect; if two lines do not intersect, they are not perpendicular. **31.** If n is odd, n^2 is odd; if n^2 is odd, n is odd. **33.** If an animal is not a chimp, it is not a mammal; if it is not a mammal, it is not a chimp. **35.** If lines are not parallel, they intersect; if lines intersect, they are not parallel.

Page 31 Chapter Review

1. **3.**

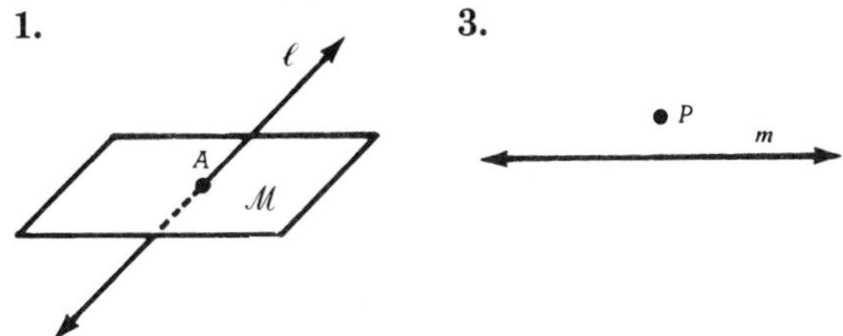

5. Noncoplanar points are points which do not lie in one plane. **7.** If an angle measures 90°, it is right. **9.** If an angle is right, it measures 90°. **11.** Lines are skew if and only if they are not coplanar. **13.** 4 **19.** Postulate 1–2 **21.** If it is not green, then it is yellow; if it is yellow, then it is not green. **23.** If $2x \neq 8$, then $x \neq 4$; if $x \neq 4$, then $2x = 8$. **25.** If it is not May, it is June; if it is not June, it is May; if it is June, it is not May.

CHAPTER 2 MEASURE

Page 37 Exploratory **1.** 1 **3.** $^{-}8$ **5.** 0 **7.** 5 **13.** $\frac{2}{3}$ **15.** $-\frac{4}{3}$ **17.** $^{-}3$ **19.** $\frac{7}{3}$ **21.** $-\frac{1}{3}$ **23.** 0

Page 38 Written **1.** 0.3 **3.** $^{-}0.8$ **5.** $^{-}0.75$ **7.** $0.\overline{6}$ **13.** 1.2 **15.** $^{-}2.7$ **17.** $2.\overline{6}$ **19.** $^{-}7.\overline{142857}$ **25.** $\frac{7}{9}$ **27.** $\frac{5}{9}$ **29.** $\frac{524}{999}$ **31.** $\frac{11}{9}$ **37.** none **39.** $^{-}13, 0$ **41.** $\frac{\pi}{2}, \pi$ **43.** true **45.** false **47.** true **49.** true **51.** false

Page 41 Exploratory **1.** 12 **3.** 30 **5.** 15 **7.** 11 **9.** 3 **11.** 89 **13.** 44 **15.** 52 **17.** 2.3 **25.** true **27.** true **29.** false **31.** true **33.** false **35.** true **37.** true **39.** false

Page 41 Written **1.** 9 **3.** $^{-}12$ **5.** $^{-}69$ **7.** $^{-}153$ **9.** 11 **17.** 3 **19.** 9 **21.** 13.2 **23.** $2\frac{3}{4}$ **29.** $\frac{1}{3}$ **31.** $3\frac{2}{3}$ **33.** $\frac{5}{6}$ **35.** $1\frac{1}{6}$ **43.** 0.3 **45.** 1.1 **47.** 2.3 **49.** 0.7 **51.** 0 **59.** 4 **61.** 19

Page 45 Exploratory **1.** $^{-}1, 0$ **3.** $^{-}8, 9$ **5.** $^{-}4, ^{-}8$ **7.** 6, 3 **9.** $^{-}8, 0$ **11.** $^{-}1, 6$

Page 46 Written **1.** 1 **3.** 17 **5.** 4 **7.** 3 **9.** 8 **11.** 7 **13.** 14 **21.** $RT + TS \neq RS$ **23.** $PN \neq NS$ **25.** $PQ = QS$ **27.** 0 **29.** $2 + 5 = 7$ **31.** $7 - 4 = 2 + 1$ **33.** $^{-}1$ **35.** Distance Postulate; Definition of Between **37.** Definition of Between **41.** Distance Postulate; Definition of Midpoint **43.** $^{-}11; 1$ **45.** $^{-}8; ^{-}2$ **47.** 5

Page 50 Exploratory **1.** Reflexive **3.** Symmetric **5.** Transitive **7.** Reflexive **9.** Substitution **11.** Reflexive **13.** Transitive

Page 51 Written **1–2.** Postulate 2–7 **1–3.** Postulates 2–11, 2–13, 2–9 **1–4.** Postulate 2–12 **1–5.** Postulate 2–8 **1–6.** Postulates 2–13, 2–9 **1–7.** Postulate 2–12 **3–2.** Postulate 2–7 **3–3.** Postulates 2–11, 2–13 **3–4.** Postulate 2–12 **3–5.** Postulate 2–8 **3–6.** Postulate 2–13 **3–7.** Postulates 2–12, 2–9

Page 56 Exploratory **1.** Theorem 2–2 **3.** Theorem 2–3 **5.** Theorem 2–4

Page 56 Written **1.** true **3.** true **5.** true **7.** true **9.** true **11.** M is the midpoint of $\overline{PQ}$. **13.** If $\overline{PM} \cong \overline{MQ}$, then M is the midpoint of $\overline{PQ}$. **15.** $\overline{PQ}$ is bisected at point M. **17.** $\overline{PQ}$ is bisected at point M. **19.** $\overline{PM} \cong \overline{MQ}$ **21.** M is the midpoint of $\overline{PQ}$ if and only if M is between P and Q and $PM = MQ$. **29–2.** Definition of Midpoint **29–3.** Definition of Between **29–4.** Postulate 2–9 **29–5.** Postulates 2–14, 2–9 **29–6.** Postulates 2–8, 2–13, 2–9, 2–12

Page 60 Exploratory **1.** $<$ **3.** $>$ **5.** $>$ **7.** $=$ **9.** $<$ **11.** $<$ **13.** $>$ **15.** $=$

Page 60 Written **1.** $=$ **3.** $>$ **5.** $=$ **7.** $>$ **19.** $PQ > QR$ **21.** $AB < EF$ **23.** b

Page 63 Chapter Review **1.** $^{-}1\frac{3}{4}$ **3.** 0 **5.** 0.7 **7.** $^{-}0.\overline{6}$ **9.** $\frac{1}{3}$ **11.** $\frac{4}{33}$ **13.** $\frac{1}{2}$ **15.** $4\frac{3}{4}$ **17.** $3\frac{1}{2}$ **19.** $\frac{1}{2}$ **21.** $PQ + QR = PR$ **23.** $QS \neq ST$ **25–1.** Given **25–2.** Postulates 2–14, 2–9 **25–3.** Postulate 2–7 **25–4.** Postulates 2–11, 2–13, 2–9

25–5. Postulates 2–11, 2–14, 2–9, 2–12 **25–6.** Postulate 2–7 **25–7.** Postulates 2–11, 2–13, 2–9 **25–8.** Postulate 2–12 **25–9.** Postulate 2–8 **25–10.** Postulates 2–13, 2–9 **25–11.** Postulates 2–12, 2–9

CHAPTER 3 ANGLES AND PERPENDICULARS

Page 69 Exploratory 1. true **3.** false **5.** true **7.** true **9.** false **11.** true **13.** false **15.** true

Page 70 Written 1. one **3.** their endpoint **5.** negative **11.** $\angle PQS$ **13.** Q **15.** $\overrightarrow{QS}, \overrightarrow{QT}$ **17.** $\angle PQV, \angle SQV, \angle 3, \angle 4$ **19.** V **21.** $\angle ABD, \angle ABC, \angle DBC$ **23.** $\angle ABC$

Page 74 Exploratory 1. 170 **3.** 120 **5.** 75 **7.** 25 **9.** 80 **11.** 60 **13.** 65 **15.** 65

Page 74 Written 9. $m\angle TPS$ **11.** $m\angle RPQ + m\angle TPS$ **13.** $m\angle RPQ$, $m\angle SPR$, $m\angle TPS$ **15.** 20 **17.** true **19.** true **21.** true **23.** true **25.** false **31.** 30 **33.** 60 **35.** 90

Page 79 Exploratory
1. two sides of adjacent angles are on one line **3.** $\overrightarrow{BA}, \overrightarrow{BD}$ lie on $\overleftrightarrow{AD}$ **5.** $m\angle 1 + m\angle 2 = 180$ **7.** Postulate 3–4

Page 79 Written 1. 45 **3.** 80 **5.** 45 **7.** 19 **9.** 89 **11.** 108 **13.** 18

Page 83 Exploratory 1. acute **3.** acute **5.** obtuse **7.** right **9.** acute **11.** none of these **13.** An angle with degree measure 90 and a right angle; the angles are congruent.

Page 83 Written 1–1. Given **1–2.** Definition of Linear Pair **1–3.** Postulate 3–4 **1–4.** Theorem 3–2

3.

STATEMENTS	REASONS
1. $\angle 2 \cong 6$	1. Given
2. $\angle 3, \angle 2$ and $\angle 6, \angle 7$ are vertical angles.	2. Definition of Vertical Angles
3. $\angle 3 \cong \angle 2, \angle 6 \cong \angle 7$	3. Theorem 3–10
4. $\angle 3 \cong \angle 7$	4. Theorem 3–1

7. Given: $m\angle A = 90$, $\angle B$ is a right angle.
Prove: $\angle A \cong \angle B$

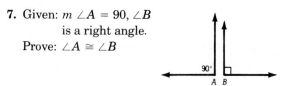

Proof:

STATEMENTS	REASONS
1. $m\angle A = 90$, $\angle B$ is a right angle.	1. Given
2. $m\angle B = 90$	2. Definition of a Right Angle
3. $m\angle A = m\angle B$	3. Postulate 2–9
4. $\angle A \cong \angle B$	4. Definition of Congruent Angles

Page 88 Exploratory 1. false **3.** true **5.** true **7.** true **9.** true **11.** true **13.** false **15.** true **17.** true **19.** false

Page 89 Written 1–1. Definition of Linear Pair **1–2.** Postulate 3–4 **1–3.** Definition of Supplementary Angles **1–4.** Given **1–5.** Definition of Congruent Angles **1–6.** Postulate 2–9 **1–7.** Postulates 2–14, 2–9 **1–8.** Postulates 2–8, 2–9 **1–9.** Definition of Perpendicular Lines

Page 93 Exploratory 1. $\angle R - \overleftrightarrow{PQ} - S$ **3.** $\angle P - \overleftrightarrow{QR} - S$ **5.** $\angle P - \overleftrightarrow{SR} - Q$ **7.** $\angle PQR$ **9.** $\angle PQS$

Page 93 Written 1. $\angle S - \overleftrightarrow{RQ} - Z$ **3.** $\angle QTV$ **5.** yes **7.** no
15. Given: $\mathscr{P} \perp \mathscr{M}$
Prove: $\angle A - \overleftrightarrow{BX} - C$, $\angle C - \overleftrightarrow{BX} - P$, $\angle P - \overleftrightarrow{BX} - M$, and $\angle M - \overleftrightarrow{BX} - A$ are right dihedral angles.

Proof:

STATEMENTS	REASONS
1. $\mathcal{P} \perp \mathcal{M}$	1. Given
2. $\overleftrightarrow{BA} \perp \overleftrightarrow{BX}$	2. Theorem 3–12
3. $\overleftrightarrow{BC} \perp \overleftrightarrow{BX}$	3. Theorem 3–12
4. $\overleftrightarrow{BA} \perp \mathcal{M}$	4. Definition of Perpendicular Planes
5. $\overleftrightarrow{BC} \perp \mathcal{P}$	5. Definition of Perpendicular Planes
6. $\overleftrightarrow{BA} \perp \overleftrightarrow{BC}$	6. Definition of a Line Perpendicular to a Plane
7. $\angle ABC$, $\angle CBP$, $\angle MBP$, and $\angle ABM$ are right angles.	7. Theorem 3–11
8. $\angle A - \overleftrightarrow{BX} - C$, $\angle C - \overleftrightarrow{BX} - P$, $\angle P - \overleftrightarrow{BX} - M$, and $\angle M - \overleftrightarrow{BX} - A$ are right dihedral angles.	8. Definition of Right Dihedral Angles

Page 97 Chapter Review **1.** Q **3.** T **5.** $\overrightarrow{QP}, \overrightarrow{QR}$ **7.** $\overrightarrow{RT}$ **9.** 95 **11.** true **13.** false **15.** 94 **17.** 73

19. STATEMENTS	REASONS
1. $\angle AXB$ is a right angle.	1. Given
2. $m\angle AXB = 90$	2. Definition of a Right Angle
3. $\angle AXD \cong \angle AXB$	3. Given
4. $m\angle AXB = m\angle AXD$	4. Definition of Congruent Angles
5. $m\angle AXD = 90$	5. Postulate 2–6
6. $\angle AXD$ is a right angle.	6. Definition of a Right Angle

23. $\angle C - \overleftrightarrow{BE} - A$, $\angle A - \overleftrightarrow{CB} - E$

CHAPTER 4 CONGRUENT TRIANGLES

Page 105 Exploratory **1.** obtuse **3.** acute **5.** obtuse **7.** isosceles **9.** scalene **11.** scalene **13.** D, E, F **15.** $\angle D, \angle E, \angle F$ **17.** $\overline{DE}, \overline{DF}, \overline{EF}$ **19.** right **21.** scalene

Page 106 Written **9.** S, T, R **11.** $\angle TSR$, $\angle RTS$, $\angle SRT$ **13.** $\overline{QS}, \overline{QR}, \overline{SR}$ **15.** A figure is a triangle if and only if it is formed by three noncollinear segments and each endpoint of a side is also an endpoint of one other side. **17.** A triangle is obtuse if and only if one of its angles is obtuse.
31. $PQ = QR = RP = 34$
33. $PQ = PR = QR = 19$

Page 109 Exploratory **1.** 85 **3.** 81 **5.** 25 **7.** 60 **9.** 56 **11.** 85 **13.** 53 **15.** 66 **17.** 54

Page 109 Written **1.** 150 **3.** $180 - (x + y)$ **5.** $145 - a$ **7.** $2x + 2$ **9.** no

11. STATEMENTS	REASONS
1. $\triangle ABC$ is equiangular.	1. Given
2. $m\angle A = m\angle B = m\angle C$	2. Definition of Equiangular Triangle
3. $m\angle A + m\angle B + m\angle C = 180$	3. Theorem 4–1
4. $m\angle A + m\angle A + m\angle A = 180$	4. Postulate 2–9
5. $3(m\angle A) = 180$	5. Postulate 2–14
6. $m\angle A = 60$	6. Postulate 2–8
7. $m\angle B = 60$, $m\angle C = 60$	7. Postulate 2–9

13. 55 **15.** 55 **17.** 27.5

19. STATEMENTS	REASONS
1. $\angle Q$ and $\angle T$ are right angles.	1. Given
2. $\angle P$ is complementary to $\angle QRP$. $\angle S$ is complementary to $\angle SRT$.	2. Theorem 4–3
3. $\angle QRP \cong \angle SRT$	3. Theorem 3–10
4. $\angle P \cong \angle S$	4. Theorems 3–4, 3–5
5. $m\angle P = m\angle S$	5. Definition of Congruent Angles

Page 114 Exploratory **1.** $\angle S$ **3.** $\angle V$ **5.** $\angle Q$ **7.** $\overline{ST}$ **9.** $\overline{VS}$ **11.** $\overline{QR}$ **13.** $\triangle TSU$ **15.** $\triangle XYZ$

Page 115 Written **1.** no **3.** no **5.** yes **7.** yes **9.** yes **11.** yes **13.** yes **15.** no **17.** yes **19.** $\angle Q$ **21.** $\overline{RP}$ **23.** $\overline{TR}$ **25.** no **27.** no

Page 118 Exploratory **1.** yes; SAS **3.** no **5.** yes; SAS **7.** yes; ASA **9.** yes; ASA **11.** yes; SSS **13.** yes; ASA **15.** no

Page 119 Written

1. STATEMENTS	REASONS
1. $\angle P$ and $\angle T$ are right angles.	1. Given
2. $\angle P \cong \angle T$	2. Theorem 3–6
3. R is the midpoint of $\overline{PT}$.	3. Given
4. $PR = RT$	4. Definition of Midpoint
5. $\overline{PR} \cong \overline{RT}$	5. Definition of Congruent Segments
6. $\angle 1 \cong \angle 2$	6. Given
7. $\triangle QPR \cong \triangle STR$	7. Postulate 4–3
8. $\overline{QP} \cong \overline{ST}$	8. CPCTC

3. STATEMENTS	REASONS
1. $\angle P$ and $\angle T$ are right angles.	1. Given
2. $\triangle QPR$ and $\triangle STR$ are right triangles.	2. Definition of Right Triangles
3. $\angle 1$, $\angle Q$ and $\angle 2$, $\angle S$ are complementary.	3. Theorem 4–3
4. $\angle 1 \cong \angle 2$	4. Given
5. $\angle Q \cong \angle S$	5. Theorem 3–5
6. $\overline{QR} \cong \overline{SR}$	6. Given
7. $\triangle QPR \cong \triangle STR$	7. Postulate 4–3
8. $\overline{PR} \cong \overline{TR}$	8. CPCTC

5. STATEMENTS	REASONS
1. $\angle 1 \cong \angle 6$, $\angle 3 \cong \angle 4$	1. Given
2. $\overline{AC} \cong \overline{CA}$	2. Postulate 2–3, Theorem 2–2
3. $\triangle ADC \cong \triangle CBA$	3. Postulate 4–3
4. $\overline{AD} \cong \overline{CB}$	4. CPCTC

7. STATEMENTS	REASONS
1. $\overline{AC} \cong \overline{EC}$ $\angle A \cong \angle E$	1. Given
2. $\angle 1 \cong \angle 2$	2. Theorem 3–10
3. $\angle 1$ and $\angle 2$ are vertical angles.	3. Definition of Vertical Angles
4. $\triangle ABC \cong \triangle EDC$	4. Postulate 4–3
5. $\overline{AB} \cong \overline{ED}$	5. CPCTC

11. $\angle SVT$ **13.** $\overline{TS}$ **15.** $\overline{SP}$ **17.** $\angle 1$ **19.** $\overline{SR}$ **21.** $\angle 6$ **23.** $\triangle SRP$ **25.** $\angle PVT$ **27.** VS **29.** 120

Page 123 Exploratory **1.** yes; AAS **3.** no **5.** yes; ASA **7.** yes; SSS **9.** yes; SAS **11.** no

Page 123 Written

1. STATEMENTS	REASONS
1. $\overline{BC} \cong \overline{DC}$, $\angle 1 \cong \angle 2$ $\angle A \cong \angle E$	1. Given
2. $\triangle ABC \cong \triangle EDC$	2. Theorem 4–5
3. $\overline{AC} \cong \overline{EC}$	3. CPCTC

3. STATEMENTS	REASONS
1. $\angle A \cong \angle E$ $\angle 1 \cong \angle 2$ $\overline{AC} \cong \overline{EC}$	1. Given
2. $\triangle ABC \cong \triangle ECD$	2. Postulate 4–3
3. $\angle B \cong \angle D$	3. CPCTC

5. STATEMENTS	REASONS
1. $\angle A \cong \angle C$, $\angle 1 \cong \angle 2$	1. Given
2. $\overline{BD} \cong \overline{BD}$	2. Theorem 2–2
3. $\triangle ABD \cong \triangle CBD$	3. Theorem 4–5
4. $\overline{AD} \cong \overline{CD}$	4. CPCTC
5. $AD = CD$	5. Definition of Congruent Segments
6. D is the midpoint of $\overline{AC}$.	6. Definition of Midpoint
7. $\overline{BD}$ bisects $\overline{AC}$.	7. Definition of Segment Bisector

Page 127 Exploratory **1.** 90 **3.** 90 **5.** 45 **7.** 45 **9.** 45 **11.** 90

Page 127 Written

1.

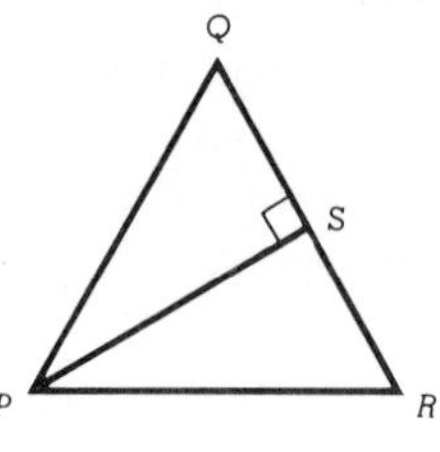

3.

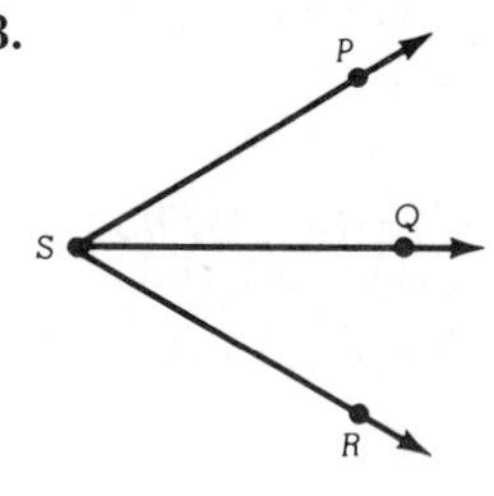

5.

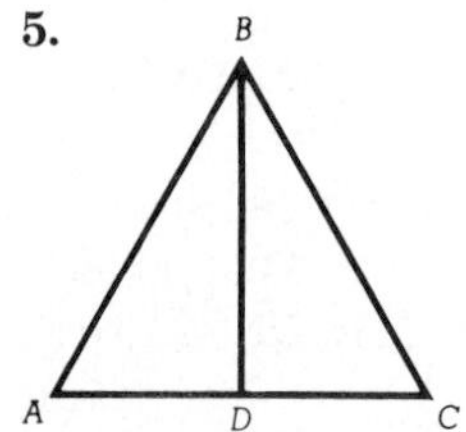

7.

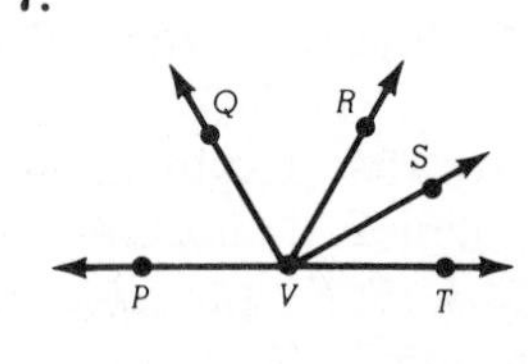

11. STATEMENTS	REASONS
1. $\overline{BC} \cong \overline{AD}$ $\overline{AB} \cong \overline{CD}$ $\overline{CD} \cong \overline{AD}$	1. Given
2. $\overline{DB} \cong \overline{DB}$	2. Theorem 2–2
3. $\triangle DAB \cong \triangle DCB$	3. Postulate 4–1
4. $\angle CBD \cong \angle ABD$	4. CPCTC
5. $m\angle CBD = m\angle ABD$	5. Definition of Congruent Angles
6. $\overline{BD}$ bisects $\angle ABC$.	6. Definition of Bisector of an Angle

13. Given: $\triangle ABC$ is an isosceles triangle. $\overline{BD}$ is a median.
Prove: $\overline{BD}$ bisects $\angle ABC$.

Proof:

STATEMENTS	REASONS
1. $\overline{BD}$ is a median of isosceles triangle ABC.	1. Given
2. $\overline{BD} \cong \overline{BD}$	2. Theorem 2–2
3. D is the midpoint of $\overline{AC}$.	3. Definition of Median of a Triangle
4. $\overline{AD} \cong \overline{DC}$	4. Theorem 2–5
5. $\triangle ABD \cong \triangle CBD$	5. Postulate 4–1
6. $\angle ABD \cong \angle CBD$	6. CPCTC
7. $m\angle ABD = m\angle CBD$	7. Definition of Congruent Angles
8. BD bisects $\angle ABC$.	8. Definition of Bisector of an Angle

Page 131 Exploratory **1.** yes **3.** no **5.** no **7.** yes **9.** no

Page 131 Written **1.**

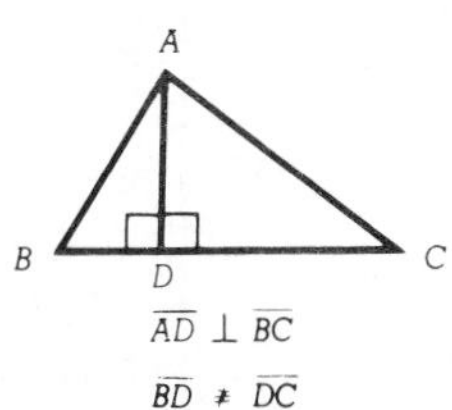

3. isosceles **9.** isosceles **11.** no **13.** yes **15.** no

17. STATEMENTS	REASONS
1. $\overline{AB} \cong \overline{BC}$	1. Given
2. $\angle 1 \cong \angle 2$	2. Theorem 4–6
3. $\angle 1$, $\angle 3$ and $\angle 2$, $\angle 4$ are linear pairs.	3. Definition of Linear Pair
4. $\angle 1$, $\angle 3$ and $\angle 2$, $\angle 4$ are supplementary.	4. Postulate 3–4
5. $\angle 3 \cong \angle 4$	5. Theorem 3–3

Page 135 Exploratory **1.** yes; Postulate 4–4 **3.** yes; Theorem 4–11 **5.** yes; Theorem 4–11

Page 135 Written

1. STATEMENTS	REASONS
1. $\angle Q$ and $\angle S$ are right angles.	1. Given
2. $\triangle QRP$ and $\triangle SPR$ are right triangles.	2. Definition of Right Triangle
3. $\angle 1 \cong \angle 2$	3. Given
4. $\overline{PR} \cong \overline{RP}$	4. Postulate 2–3, Theorem 2–2
5. $\triangle QRP \cong \triangle SPR$	5. Theorem 4–11
6. $\overline{QP} = \overline{SR}$	6. CPCTC

3. STATEMENTS	REASONS
1. $\angle Q$ and $\angle S$ are right angles.	1. Given
2. $\triangle QRP$ and $\triangle SPR$ are right triangles.	2. Definition of Right Triangle
3. $\overline{QP} \cong \overline{SR}$	3. Given
4. $\overline{PR} \cong \overline{RP}$	4. Postulate 2–3, Theorem 2–2
5. $\triangle QRP \cong \triangle SPR$	5. Postulate 4–4
6. $\overline{QR} \cong \overline{SP}$	6. CPCTC

Page 137 Chapter Review **1.** $\triangle TVW$ **3.** $\angle TVW$, $\angle VTW$, $\angle TWV$ **5.** 28 **7.** 62 **9.** $\overline{RQ}$ **11.** $\overline{QS}$ **13.** $\overline{SR}$

15. STATEMENTS	REASONS
1. $\overline{AC}$ and $\overline{BD}$ bisect each other.	1. Given
2. E is the midpoint of $\overline{AC}$ and $\overline{BD}$.	2. Definition of Segment Bisector
3. $\overline{AE} \cong \overline{EC}$ $\overline{BE} \cong \overline{ED}$	3. Theorem 2–5
4. $\angle BEA$ and $\angle CED$ are vertical angles.	4. Definition of Vertical Angles
5. $\angle BEA \cong \angle DEC$	5. Theorem 3–10
6. $\triangle BEA \cong \triangle DEC$	6. Postulate 4–2
7. $\overline{AB} \cong \overline{CD}$	7. CPCTC

17.

STATEMENTS	REASONS
1. $\overline{PR} \perp \overline{QS}$	1. Given
2. $\angle 3 \cong \angle 4$	2. Theorem 3–13
3. $\angle Q \cong \angle S$	3. Given
4. $\overline{PR} \cong \overline{PR}$	4. Theorem 2–2
5. $\triangle PRQ \cong \triangle PRS$	5. Theorem 4–5
6. $\overline{QR} \cong \overline{SR}$	6. CPCTC
7. $QR = SR$	7. Definition of Congruent Segments
8. R is the midpoint of $\overline{QS}$.	8. Definition of Midpoint

21.

STATEMENTS	REASONS
1. $\angle A \cong \angle D$ $\overline{AB} \cong \overline{CD}$, E is the midpoint of $\overline{AD}$.	1. Given
2. $\overline{AE} \cong \overline{DE}$	2. Definition of Midpoint
3. $\triangle ABE \cong \triangle DCE$	3. Postulate 4–2
4. $\overline{BE} \cong \overline{CE}$	4. CPCTC
5. $\angle 3 \cong \angle 4$	5. Theorem 4–6

CHAPTER 5 TRIANGLE INEQUALITIES

Page 143 Exploratory **1.** $x > y$ **3.** $x > y$ **5.** $x < y$ **9.** $m\angle 1 < m\angle 2$ **11.** $m\angle 1 < m\angle 2$ **13.** $m\angle 1 > m\angle 2$ **17.** 33 **19.** 30 **21.** 120

Page 144 Written **1.** 40 **3.** 100 **5.** 20 **7.** 30 **9.** 55 **11.** 70 **13.** 125

15.

STATEMENTS	REASONS
1. $\angle 1 \cong \angle 2$	1. Given
2. $\angle 1, \angle 3$ and $\angle 2, \angle 4$ are linear pairs.	2. Definition of Linear Pair
3. $\angle 1, \angle 3$ and $\angle 2, \angle 4$ are supplementary.	3. Postulate 3–4
4. $\angle 3 \cong \angle 4$	4. Theorem 3–3
5. $\overline{PQ} \cong \overline{RQ}$	5. Theorem 4–9
6. $\triangle PQR$ is isosceles.	6. Definition of Isosceles Triangle

21–1. Given **21–2.** Postulate 2–16 **21–3.** Postulate 2–12 **21–4.** Postulates 2–13, 2–9 **21–5.** Postulate 2–11 **21–6.** Postulate 2–10 **21–7.** Postulate 2–11

Page 149 Exploratory **1.** yes **3.** no **5.** no **7.** yes **9.** yes **17.** no **19.** yes **21.** no **23.** yes

Page 149 Written **1.** sometimes; if angles are marked **3.** yes **5.** yes **7.** yes **9.** sometimes; if angles are marked **13.** $\angle 9, \angle 8$ **15.** $\overline{BE}, \overline{EC}$ **17.** no **19.** no **21.** $\triangle ABC, \triangle ABE, \triangle ADE, \triangle ACE, \triangle DEC$ **27.** $\triangle QRS, \triangle QPS$

Page 154 Exploratory **1.** $\angle B, \angle A, \angle C$ **3.** $\angle I, \angle G, \angle H$ **5.** $\overline{LM}, \overline{LN}, \overline{MN}$ **7.** $\overline{ST}, \overline{TV}, \overline{SV}$

Page 154 Written

1. Given: $\triangle PQR$, $PQ > QR$
Prove: $m\angle 2 > m\angle 1$

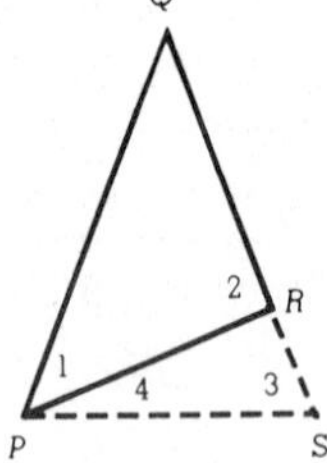

Proof:

STATEMENTS	REASONS
1. $\triangle PQR$, $PQ > QR$	1. Given
2. Extend $\overline{QR}$ to S so that $\overline{QS} \cong \overline{PQ}$.	2. Postulate 2–2
3. $\angle QPS \cong \angle QSP$	3. Theorem 4–6
4. $m\angle QPS = m\angle 1 + m\angle 4$	4. Postulate 3–3
5. $m\angle QPS = m\angle QSP$	5. Definition of Congruent Angles
6. $m\angle QSP = m\angle 1 + m\angle 4$	6. Postulate 2–9
7. $m\angle 2 = m\angle 3 + m\angle 4$	7. Theorem 5–1
8. $m\angle 2 = m\angle 1 + 2(m\angle 4)$	8. Postulate 2–9
9. $m\angle 2 > m\angle 1$	9. Theorem 5–2

3.

STATEMENTS	REASONS
1. $\triangle ABC$, $\angle A$ is a right angle.	1. Given
2. $m\angle A = 90$	2. Definition of a Right Angle
3. $\angle B$ and $\angle C$ are complementary.	3. Theorem 4–3
4. $m\angle B + m\angle C = 90$	4. Definition of Complementary Angles
5. $m\angle A = m\angle B + m\angle C$	5. Postulate 2–9
6. $m\angle A > m\angle C$	6. Theorem 5–2
7. $BC > BA$	7. Theorem 5–5

5. STATEMENTS	REASONS
1. $\triangle PQR, QR > QP$ $\overline{PR} \cong \overline{QP}$	1. Given
2. $PR = QP$	2. Definition of Congruent Segments
3. $QR > PR$	3. Postulate 2–9

Page 157 Exploratory **1.** no **3.** yes **5.** yes **7.** no **13.** 4, 10 **15.** 3, 27 **17.** 5.2 **19.** 0.2

Page 158 Written **1.** yes **3.** yes **5.** no

7. STATEMENTS	REASONS
1. $\angle ABC \cong \angle ACB$	1. Given
2. $AD + AC > CD$	2. Theorem 5–8
3. $\overline{AB} \cong \overline{AC}$	3. Theorem 4–9
4. $AB = AC$	4. Definition of Congruent Segments
5. $AD + AB > CD$	5. Postulate 2–9

9. STATEMENTS	REASONS
1. $\overline{ED}$ bisects $\overline{AC}$. $\overline{ED} \perp \overline{AC}$	1. Given
2. $\angle EDA$ and $\angle EDC$ are right angles.	2. Theorem 3–11
3. D is the midpoint of $\overline{AC}$.	3. Definition of Segment Bisector
4. $\overline{AD} \cong \overline{CD}$	4. Theorem 2–5
5. $\overline{ED} \cong \overline{ED}$	5. Theorem 2–2
6. $\triangle AED \cong \triangle CED$	6. Theorem 4–12
7. $BE + AE > BA$	7. Theorem 5–8
8. $\overline{AE} \cong \overline{CE}$	8. CPCTC
9. $AE = CE$	9. Definition of Congruent Segments
10. $BE + CE > BA$	10. Postulate 2–9
11. $BE + CE = BC$	11. Definition of Between
12. $BC > BA$	12. Postulate 2–9

Page 162 Written

1. STATEMENTS	REASONS
1. $\overline{PQ} \cong \overline{SQ}$	1. Given
2. $\overline{QR} \cong \overline{QR}$	2. Theorem 2–2
3. $m\angle PQR = m\angle PQT + m\angle SQR$	3. Postulate 3–3
4. $m\angle PQR > m\angle SQR$	4. Theorem 5–2
5. $PR > SR$	5. Theorem 5–9

3. STATEMENTS	REASONS
1. $\overline{AB} \cong \overline{BC}$ $m\angle 4 > m\angle 3$	1. Given
2. $\overline{BD} \cong \overline{BD}$	2. Theorem 2–2
3. $AD > CD$	3. Theorem 5–9

5. STATEMENTS	REASONS
1. D is the midpoint of $\overline{AC}$. $AB > CB$	1. Given
2. $\overline{CD} \cong \overline{AD}$	2. Theorem 2–5
3. $\overline{BD} \cong \overline{BD}$	3. Theorem 2–2
4. $m\angle 1 > m\angle 2$	4. Theorem 5–10

11. STATEMENTS	REASONS
1. $\overline{ER} \cong \overline{EC}$ $\overline{GE} \cong \overline{AE}$ $RA > RG$ $m\angle CEA > m\angle REA$	1. Given
2. $\overline{EA} \cong \overline{EA}$	2. Theorem 2–2
3. $CA > RA$	3. Theorem 5–9
4. $CA > RG$	4. Postulate 2–18

Page 167 Chapter Review **1.** $PQ < PR$ **3.** $PQ > PR$ **5.** 120 **7.** 30 **9.** 60 **13.** yes **15.** no **17.** yes **19.** $\triangle CDF, \triangle CDG, \triangle DFG, \triangle DEG, \triangle EFG$ **21.** $\angle A, \angle C, \angle B, \overline{BC}, \overline{AB}, \overline{AC}$

23. STATEMENTS	REASONS
1. $\overline{AK} \cong \overline{AC}$	1. Given
2. $\angle 2 \cong \angle C$	2. Theorem 4–6
3. $m\angle 2 = m\angle C$	3. Definition of Congruent Angles
4. $m\angle 1 > m\angle C$	4. Theorem 5–3
5. $m\angle 1 > m\angle 2$	5. Postulate 2–9

25. no **27.** no **29.** yes **31.** 2; 16

33. STATEMENTS	REASONS
1. $\triangle XYZ$	1. Given
2. $XY < YZ + XZ$	2. Theorem 5–8
3. $XY - YZ < XZ$	3. Postulate 2–16

CHAPTER 6 PARALLELS

Page 173 Exploratory **1.** parallel **3.** skew **5.** parallel or intersecting **7.** parallel **9.** intersecting or skew **15.** false **17.** true **19.** false **21.** true

Page 174 Written **1.** alternate exterior **3.** corresponding **5.** alternate interior **11.** corresponding **13.** alternate exterior **15.** alternate interior **21.** Two rays are parallel if and only if the lines containing them are parallel. **23.** Two angles are corresponding angles if and only if they are formed by two lines and a transversal, they do not have a common vertex, they lie on the same side of the transversal, and one angle is an interior angle and the other is an exterior angle.

Page 178 Exploratory **1.** The leaves of a plant are in groups of three and the plant is not poison ivy. **3.** The radio does not play well and it is not defective. **5.** Two lines interesect and they intersect in less than one point.

Page 179 Written **1.** . . . and the two lines are not parallel. **3.** . . . and they intersect in more than one point. **7.** $\triangle ABC$ is a right triangle with right angle C and $\triangle ABC$ has more than two acute angles; by assumption; Definition of Acute Angle; Given; Definition of Right Angle; Postulate 2–15; the Comparison Property may not be contradicted

9. Given: $\triangle ABC$
Prove: $\triangle ABC$ has at most one obtuse angle.
Assumption: $\triangle ABC$ has more than one obtuse angle.
Proof:

STATEMENTS	REASONS
1. $\angle A$ and $\angle B$ are obtuse.	1. Assumption
2. $m\angle A, m\angle B > 90$	2. Definition of Obtuse Angle
3. $m\angle A + m\angle B > 180$	3. Postulate 2–16
4. $m\angle A + m\angle B + m\angle C = 180$	4. Theorem 4–1
5. $m\angle A + m\angle B < 180$	5. Theorem 5–2

Statement 5 contradicts Statement 3. Hence, $\triangle ABC$ has at most one obtuse angle.

Page 183 Exploratory **1.** Theorems 3–10, 6–6 **3.** Theorem 6–8 **5.** Theorem 6–4

Page 184 Written

1. STATEMENTS	REASONS
1. $\angle R$ and $\angle S$ are supplementary. $\angle Q \cong \angle S$	1. Given
2. $m\angle R + m\angle S = 180$	2. Definition of Supplementary Angles
3. $m\angle Q = m\angle S$	3. Definition of Congruent Angles
4. $m\angle R + m\angle Q = 180$	4. Postulate 2–9
5. $\angle R$ and $\angle Q$ are supplementary.	5. Definition of Supplementary Angles
6. $\overline{QP} \parallel \overline{RS}$	6. Theorem 6–6

3. STATEMENTS	REASONS
1. $\angle 1 \cong \angle 3, \overline{AD} \cong \overline{CB}$	1. Given
2. $\overline{AC} \cong \overline{AC}$	2. Theorem 2–2
3. $\triangle ADC \cong \triangle CBA$	3. Postulate 4–2
4. $\overline{DC} \cong \overline{BA}$	4. CPCTC

5. STATEMENTS	REASONS
1. $\overline{MP} \cong \overline{MQ}$ $\angle 1 \cong \angle N$	1. Given
2. $\angle 2 \cong \angle 1$	2. Theorem 4–6
3. $\angle 2 \cong \angle N$	3. Theorem 3–1
4. $\overline{PQ} \parallel \overline{LN}$	4. Theorem 6–5

7. STATEMENTS	REASONS
1. $\angle 1 \cong \angle 2$	1. Given
2. $\overline{BC} \parallel \overline{FE}$	2. Theorem 6–4

9. STATEMENTS	REASONS
1. $\angle F$ and $\angle 2$, and $\angle C$ and $\angle 1$ are complementary.	1. Given
2. $m\angle F + m\angle 2 = 90$ $m\angle C + m\angle 1 = 90$	2. Definition of Complementary Angles
3. $m\angle F + m\angle 2 + m\angle A = 180$ $m\angle C + m\angle 1 + m\angle D = 180$	3. Theorem 4–1
4. $m\angle A = 90$ $m\angle D = 90$	4. Postulate 2–9, Postulate 2–7

5. $\overline{AF} \perp \overline{AD}$ $\overline{CD} \perp \overline{AD}$	5. Definition of Right Angles, Definition of Perpendicular Lines
6. $\overline{AF} \parallel \overline{CD}$	6. Theorem 6–8

Page 188 Exploratory 1. any four of the following pairs: $\angle 4, \angle 6$, ***t***; $\angle 2, \angle 12$, ℓ; $\angle 3, \angle 5$, ***t***; $\angle 3, \angle 9$, ℓ; $\angle 12, \angle 14$, ***s***; $\angle 6, \angle 16$, ***m***; $\angle 11, \angle 13$, ***s***; $\angle 7, \angle 13$, ***m*** **3.** any four of the following pairs: $\angle 4, \angle 5$, ***t***; $\angle 2, \angle 9$, ℓ; $\angle 3, \angle 6$, ***t***; $\angle 3, \angle 12$, ℓ; $\angle 12$, $\angle 13$, ***s***; $\angle 6, \angle 13$, ***m***; $\angle 11, \angle 14$, ***s***; $\angle 7, \angle 16$, ***m***

Page 189 Written 1. Postulate 6–1 **3.** Postulate 3–2 **5.** Theorem 2–1 **7.** Theorem 2–6 **9.** Postulate 1–1 **11.** 33 **13.** 57 **15.** 123 **17.** 90

Page 193 Exploratory 1. yes **3.** yes **5.** yes **7.** no **9.** no **11.** no **13.** yes **15.** yes **17.** yes **19.** yes **21.** yes

Page 193 Written

1. STATEMENTS	REASONS
1. $\overline{AB} \parallel \overline{CD}, \overline{BC} \perp \overline{CD}$ $\overline{AB} \perp \overline{AD}$	1. Given
2. Draw $\overleftrightarrow{BD}$.	2. Postulate 1–1
3. $\angle A$ and $\angle C$ are right angles.	3. Definition of Perpendicular Lines
4. $\angle A \cong \angle C$	4. Theorem 3–6
5. $\angle ABD \cong \angle CDB$	5. Theorem 6–10
6. $\overline{BD} \cong \overline{BD}$	6. Theorem 2–2
7. $\triangle ABD = \triangle CDB$	7. Theorem 4–5
8. $\angle CBD \cong \angle BDA$	8. CPCTC
9. $\overline{BC} \parallel \overline{AD}$	9. Theorem 6–4

3. STATEMENTS	REASONS
1. $\overline{QS} \parallel \overline{PT}$, $\angle T$ is a right angle.	1. Given
2. $\overline{PT} \perp \overline{RT}$	2. Definition of Perpendicular Lines
3. $\overline{QS} \perp \overline{RT}$	3. Theorem 6–13
4. $\angle 2$ is a right angle.	4. Theorem 3–11
5. $\triangle RQS$ is a right triangle.	5. Definition of Right Triangle

5. STATEMENTS	REASONS
1. $\overline{BA} \parallel \overline{ED}$, $\overline{BA} \cong \overline{DE}$	1. Given
2. $\angle B \cong \angle D$ $\angle A \cong \angle E$	2. Theorem 6–10
3. $\triangle ABC = \triangle EDC$	3. Postulate 4–3
4. $\overline{EC} \cong \overline{AC}$	4. CPCTC

Page 197 Exploratory 1. a line and a point not on the line **7.** In a plane, if two lines are parallel, then they are everywhere equidistant; in a plane, if two lines are everywhere equidistant, then they are parallel.

Page 197 Written 1. yes **3.** no **5.** direct **7.** Theorem 3–12 **9.** indirect **11.** A point is on the bisector of an angle. **13.** Pick any point on the angle bisector and draw lines through the point perpendicular to the sides of the angle. Show that the two triangles thus formed are congruent. Then use CPCTC to show equidistance. **15.** If a point in the interior of an angle is equidistant from the sides of an angle, then the point is on the bisector of the angle.

17. Given: $AD = CD$

Prove: $\overrightarrow{BD}$ is the bisector of $\angle ABC$.

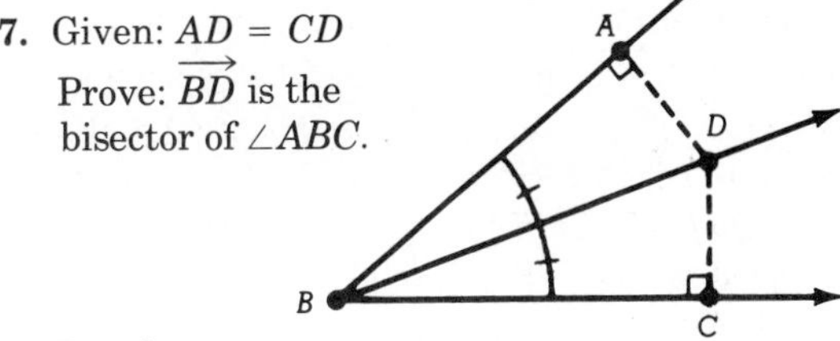

Proof:

STATEMENTS	REASONS
1. $AD = CD$	1. Given
2. $\overline{BD} \cong \overline{BD}$	2. Theorem 2–2
3. $\overline{AD} \perp \overline{AB}$ $\overline{DC} \perp \overline{BC}$	3. Definition of the Distance Between a Point and a Line
4. $\angle BAD$ and $\angle BCD$ are right angles.	4. Theorem 3–11
5. $\triangle BAD$ and $\triangle BCD$ are right triangles.	5. Definition of a Right Triangle
6. $\triangle BAD \cong \triangle BCD$	6. Postulate 4–4
7. $\angle ABD \cong \angle CBD$	7. CPCTC
8. $\overrightarrow{BD}$ bisects $\angle ABC$.	8. Definition of Angle Bisector

Page 201 Chapter Review 1. ***t, n*** **3.** ***t, m*** **5.** ***t, n,*** ℓ

7. Given: $\triangle ABC$ is a right triangle.
Prove: $\triangle ABC$ has only one right angle.
Assumption: $\triangle ABC$ is a right triangle with right angles A and C.

Proof:

STATEMENTS	REASONS
1. $\triangle ABC$ is a right triangle. $\angle A$ and $\angle C$ are right angles.	1. Assumption
2. $m\angle A = 90$ $m\angle C = 90$	2. Definition of Right Angle
3. $m\angle A + m\angle B = 180$	3. Postulate 2–7
4. $m\angle A + m\angle B + m\angle C = 180$	4. Theorem 4–1

Statements 3 and 4 are contradictory.

9. STATEMENTS	REASONS
1. T is the midpoint of $\overline{QS}$ and $\overline{PR}$.	1. Given
2. $\overline{QT} \cong \overline{TS}, \overline{PT} \cong \overline{TR}$	2. Theorem 2–5
3. $\angle 1 \cong \angle 3$	3. Theorem 3–10
4. $\triangle QPT \cong \triangle SRT$	4. Postulate 4–2
5. $\angle QPT = \angle SRT$	5. CPCTC
6. $\overline{QP} \parallel \overline{RS}$	6. Theorem 6–4

11–1. Postulate 6–1 **11–5.** Theorem 6–10

CHAPTER 7 POLYGONS

Page 209 Exploratory **1.** no **3.** no **5.** yes **7.** no **9.** yes

Page 210 Written **1.** triangle **3.** decagon **5.** 24-gon **7.** n-gon **9.** pentagon; convex **11.** hexagon; convex **13.** heptagon; concave **15.** A, B, C, D, E **17.** $\overline{AB}, \overline{BC}, \overline{CD}, \overline{DE}, \overline{EA}$ **19.** convex **21.** any of the following pairs: $\angle A, \angle B$; $\angle B, \angle C$; $\angle C, \angle D$; $\angle D, \angle E$; $\angle E, \angle A$ **23.** A pair of angles of a polygon is consecutive if and only if the two angles share a common side. **25.** regular; it is both equiangular and equilateral **27.** not regular; it is not equiangular

Page 213 Exploratory **1.** 0; 0 **3.** 2; 3 **5.** 4; 5 **7.** 6; 7 **9.** 12; 13 **11.** An angle is an interior angle of a convex polygon if and only if the angle forms a linear pair with one of the interior angles of the polygon.

Page 214 Written **1.** 0 **3.** 5 **5.** 14 **7.** 27 **9.** 90 **11.** 2,700 **13.** 1,800 **15.** 10,260 **17.** $(x - 2)180$ **19.** 12 **21.** 6 **23.** 24 **25.** 10 **27.** 90; 90 **29.** 135; 45 **31.** 128.6; 51.4 **35.** 20 **37.** 12 **43.** 36 **45.** 90

Page 218 Exploratory **1.** yes **3.** yes **5.** yes **7.** no **9.** no **11.** no **13.** yes **15.** yes

Page 218 Written **1.** 16 **3.** 1.2 **5.** 5 **7.** 8 **9.** 60 **11.** 25
13. Given: $\square ABCD$
Prove: $\angle BCD \cong \angle DAB$, $\angle ABC \cong \angle CDA$

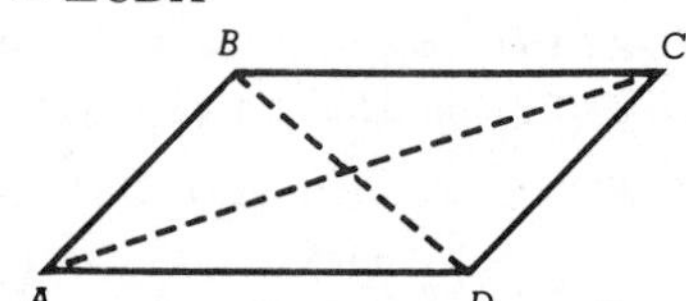

Proof:

STATEMENTS	REASONS
1. $\square ABCD$	1. Given
2. Draw $\overline{AC}$ and $\overline{BD}$.	2. Postulate 1–1
3. $\triangle BCD \cong \triangle DAB$ $\triangle ABC \cong \triangle CDA$	3. Theorem 7–3
4. $\triangle BCD \cong \triangle DAB$ $\triangle ABC \cong \triangle CDA$	4. CPCTC

15. STATEMENTS	REASONS
1. $\square HIJK$	1. Given
2. $\overline{HK} \parallel \overline{IJ}$	2. Definition of Parallelogram
3. $\angle HKJ$ is supplementary to $\angle IJK$.	3. Theorem 6–11

Page 222 Exploratory **1.** yes **3.** yes **5.** no **7.** yes; Theorem 6–4, Theorem 7–8 **9.** no; Theorem 7–6 **11.** yes; Theorem 6–6, Theorem 7–1, Definition of Parallelogram **13.** yes; Theorem 7–9 **15.** yes; CPCTC, Theorem 7–7, Theorem 6–4

Page 222 Written

1. Given: Quadrilateral $ABCD$, $\overline{AB} \cong \overline{CD}$, $\overline{AB} \parallel \overline{CD}$
   Prove: $ABCD$ is a parallelogram.

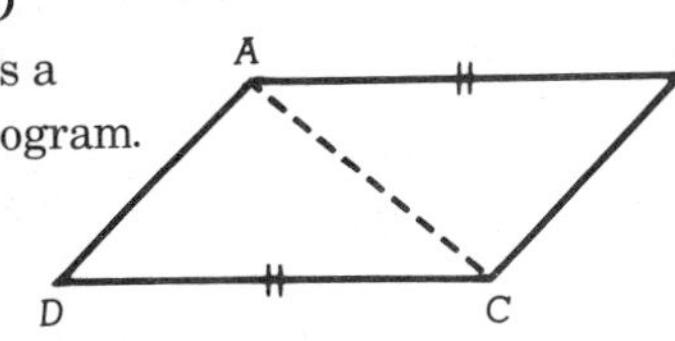

Proof:

STATEMENTS	REASONS
1. $\overline{AB} \cong \overline{CD}$, $\overline{AB} \parallel \overline{CD}$	1. Given
2. Draw $\overline{AC}$.	2. Postulate 1–1
3. $\angle BAC \cong \angle DCA$	3. Theorem 6–10
4. $\overline{AC} \cong \overline{AC}$	4. Theorem 2–2
5. $\triangle ABC \cong \triangle CDA$	5. Postulate 4–2
6. $\overline{BC} \cong \overline{DA}$	6. CPCTC
7. $ABCD$ is a parallelogram.	7. Theorem 7–7

3. Given: Quadrilateral $ABCD$, $\angle A \cong \angle C$, $\overline{AB} \parallel \overline{CD}$
   Prove: $ABCD$ is a parallelogram.

Proof:

STATEMENTS	REASONS
1. $\angle A \cong \angle C$, $\overline{AB} \parallel \overline{CD}$	1. Given
2. Draw $\overline{BD}$.	2. Postulate 1–1
3. $\angle ABD \cong \angle CDB$	3. Theorem 6–10
4. $\overline{BD} \cong \overline{BD}$	4. Theorem 2–2
5. $\triangle ABD \cong \triangle CDB$	5. Theorem 4–5
6. $\overline{AB} \cong \overline{CD}$, $\overline{AD} \cong \overline{CB}$	6. CPCTC
7. $ABCD$ is a parallelogram.	7. Theorem 7–7

5. STATEMENTS	REASONS
1. $\overline{AE} \cong \overline{CE}$ $\angle ECD \cong \angle EAB$	1. Given
2. $\angle AEB \cong \angle CED$	2. Theorem 3–10
3. $\triangle AEB \cong \triangle CED$	3. Postulate 4–3
4. $\overline{AB} \cong \overline{CD}$	4. CPCTC
5. $\overline{AB} \parallel \overline{CD}$	5. Theorem 6–4
6. $ABCD$ is a parallelogram.	6. Theorem 7–8

7. STATEMENTS	REASONS
1. $\triangle PQR \cong \triangle STV$ $\overline{PR} \parallel \overline{VS}$	1. Given
2. $\overline{PR} \cong \overline{SV}$	2. CPCTC
3. $PRSV$ is a parallelogram.	3. Theorem 7–8

11. STATEMENTS	REASONS
1. $\overline{AB} \cong \overline{BC}$, D is the midpoint of $\overline{CF}$ and $\overline{BE}$.	1. Given
2. $\overline{CD} \cong \overline{DF}$, $\overline{BD} \cong \overline{DE}$	2. Theorem 2–5
3. $\angle CDB \cong \angle FDE$	3. Theorem 3–10
4. $\triangle CBD \cong \triangle FED$	4. Postulate 4–2
5. $\overline{BC} \cong \overline{EF}$ $\angle CBD \cong \angle FED$	5. CPCTC
6. $\overline{AB} \cong \overline{EF}$	6. Theorem 2–4
7. $\overline{AB} \parallel \overline{EF}$	7. Theorem 6–4
8. $ABEF$ is a parallelogram.	8. Theorem 7–8

13. STATEMENTS	REASONS
1. $\angle ABF \cong \angle EDF$, $\overline{FD} \parallel \overline{AC}$	1. Given
2. $\angle ABF \cong \angle BFD$	2. Theorem 6–10
3. $\angle BFD \cong \angle EDF$	3. Theorem 3–1
4. $\overline{CD} \parallel \overline{BF}$	4. Theorem 6–4
5. $FBCD$ is a parallelogram.	5. Definition of Parallelogram

15. STATEMENTS	REASONS
1. $\square BCDG$, $\angle E \cong \angle A$ $\overline{CE} \parallel \overline{AF}$	1. Given
2. $\angle A$ is supplementary to $\angle C$.	2. Theorem 6–11
3. $\angle E$ is supplementary to $\angle C$.	3. Postulate 2–9
4. $\overline{AC} \parallel \overline{EF}$	4. Theorem 6–6
5. $ACEF$ is a parallelogram.	5. Definition of Parallelogram

Page 226 Exploratory **1.** rectangle, square **3.** parallelogram, rectangle, rhombus, square **5.** rhombus, square **7.** rhombus, square

Page 226 Written **7.** $10\frac{7}{8}$ **9.** 104.2 **11.** $13\frac{1}{2}$ **13.** 56.3 **15.** 51.8 **17.** 90 **19.** 10

21. Given: $ABCD$ is a square.
Prove: $\overline{AC}$ and $\overline{BD}$ bisect each other.

Proof:

STATEMENTS	REASONS
1. $ABCD$ is a square.	1. Given
2. $ABCD$ is a rectangle.	2. Definition of a Square
3. $ABCD$ is a parallelogram.	3. Definition of a Rectangle
4. $\overline{AC}$ and $\overline{BD}$ bisect each other.	4. Theorem 7–6

23. Given: $\square LMNO$, $\angle O$ is a right angle.
Prove: $LMNO$ is a rectangle.

Proof:

STATEMENTS	REASONS
1. $\square LMNO$, $\angle O$ is a right angle.	1. Given
2. $\overline{LO} \perp \overline{ON}$	2. Definition of Perpendicular Lines
3. $\overline{LM} \parallel \overline{ON}$	3. Definition of Parallelogram
4. $\overline{LO} \perp \overline{LM}$	4. Theorem 6–13
5. $\angle L$ is a right angle.	5. Definition of Perpendicular Lines
6. $\angle O \cong \angle M$ $\angle L \cong \angle N$	6. Theorem 6–4
7. $m\angle O = 90$ $m\angle L = 90$	7. Definition of Right Angle
8. $m\angle M = 90$ $m\angle N = 90$	8. Postulate 2–9
9. $\angle M$ and $\angle N$ are right angles.	9. Definition of Right Angles
10. $LMNO$ is a rectangle.	10. Definition of Rectangle

25. Given: $\square EFGH$, $\overline{EF} \cong \overline{FG}$
Prove: $EFGH$ is a rhombus.

Proof:

STATEMENTS	REASONS
1. $\square EFGH$, $\overline{EF} \cong \overline{FG}$	1. Given
2. $\overline{GH} \cong \overline{EF}$, $\overline{FG} \cong \overline{EH}$	2. Theorem 7–5
3. $\overline{GH} \cong \overline{EH}$	3. Theorem 2–4
4. $EFGH$ is a rhombus.	4. Definition of Rhombus

27. Given: $\square EFGH$
$\overline{EG}$ bisects $\angle E$ and $\angle G$. $\overline{FH}$ bisects $\angle F$ and $\angle H$.
Prove: $EFGH$ is a rhombus

STATEMENTS	REASONS
1. $\square EFGH$, $\overline{EG}$ bisects $\angle E$ and $\angle G$. $\overline{FH}$ bisects $\angle F$ and $\angle H$.	1. Given
2. $\overline{EF} \cong \overline{GH}$ $\overline{FG} \cong \overline{HE}$	2. Theorem 7–5
3. $\angle 1 \cong \angle 2$, $\angle 3 \cong \angle 4$	3. Definition of Angle Bisector
4. $\overline{EG} \cong \overline{EG}$	4. Theorem 2–2
5. $\triangle EFG \cong \triangle EHG$	5. Postulate 4–3
6. $\overline{EF} \cong \overline{EH}$	6. CPCTC
7. $\overline{EF} \cong \overline{FG} \cong \overline{GH} \cong \overline{HE}$	7. Theorem 2–4
8. $EFGH$ is a rhombus.	8. Definition of Rhombus

Page 232 Exploratory **1.** yes **3.** yes **5.** yes **7.** no **9.** yes **11.** no

Page 233 Written **1.** 12 cm **3.** 3 ft **5.** 7 mm **7.** 89.5 cm **9.** $20\frac{3}{4}$ mi **11.** 48.4 m **13.** 8.2 **15.** 13.5 **17.** $DB = AC = 11$ **19.** $AB = CD = 28$ **21.** 115 **23.** 48 **25.** 25 **27.** 27 **29.** 23 **31.** 27

35.

STATEMENTS	REASONS
1. $\overline{LM} \parallel \overline{RN}$ $\overline{LR} \cong \overline{MN}$ $\overline{RP} \perp \overline{LM}$ $\overline{NQ} \perp \overline{LM}$	1. Given
2. $LMNR$ is isosceles.	2. Definition of Isosceles Trapezoid
3. $\angle RLP \cong \angle NMO$	3. Theorem 7–13

41.

STATEMENTS	REASONS
1. $\triangle PQT$ is isosceles. $\overline{TP} \parallel \overline{RS}$	1. Given
2. $\overleftrightarrow{RQ}$ intersects $\overleftrightarrow{SQ}$.	2. Definition of Triangle
3. $\overleftrightarrow{RQ} \nparallel \overleftrightarrow{SQ}$	3. Definition of Parallel Lines
4. $RSPT$ is a trapezoid.	4. Definition of Trapezoid

Page 238 Exploratory **1.** 46 ft **3.** 52 ft **5.** 59 ft **7.** 60 m **9.** 53 ft

Page 238 Written **1.** 9.2 m **3.** $16\frac{2}{3}$ in. **5.** $4\frac{1}{3}$ m **7.** 1.8 cm **9.** 10 m **11.** $8\frac{3}{4}$ in. **13.** 163.6 mi **15.** 55.6 cm **17.** 20 in. **19.** 3.9 mi **21.** $2\frac{1}{2}$ in. **23.** $2\frac{1}{12}$ yd **25.** 72 ft **27.** 99.6 mm **29.** 30 yd **31.** 2.4 m **33.** 3.1 cm **35.** 0.7 km **37.** 214 ft **39.** 1,500 cm

Page 242 Exploratory **1.** Faces: *ABD, BCD, ADC, ABC;* Edges: $\overline{AB}, \overline{BC}, \overline{AC}, \overline{BD}, \overline{CD}, \overline{AD}$; Vertices: *A, B, C, D* **3.** Faces: *ABCD, EFGH, ABFE, DCGH, ADHE, BCGF;* Edges: $\overline{AD}, \overline{DC}, \overline{BC}, \overline{AB}, \overline{EH}, \overline{HG}, \overline{FG}, \overline{EF}, \overline{AE}, \overline{DH}, \overline{CG}, \overline{BF}$; Vertices: *A, B, C, D, E, F, G, H* **5.** 3 **7.** 3 **9.** 240

Page 242 Written **1.** triangle **3.** triangle **5.** 60 **7.** 60 **9.** 240 **11.** 270 **13.** 450 **15.** 360 **17.** 4 faces; 4 vertices; 6 edges **19.** 8 faces; 6 vertices; 12 edges

Page 245 Chapter Review **1.** *Q, R, S, T, U* **3.** $\angle Q, \angle R, \angle S, \angle T, \angle U$ **5.** convex **7.** 720 **9.** 1,800 **11.** 108 **13.** 40 **15.** 7.2 **17.** 3 **19.** 8.2

21. STATEMENTS	REASONS
1. $\square ABCD$, $\overline{AE} \cong \overline{CF}$	1. Given
2. $\overline{BC} \parallel \overline{AD}$, $\overline{AB} \parallel \overline{CD}$	2. Definition of Parallelogram
3. $\angle BAC \cong \angle ACD$, $\angle BCA \cong \angle CAD$	3. Theorem 6–10
4. $\overline{AB} \cong \overline{DC}$, $\overline{BC} \cong \overline{AD}$	4. Theorem 7–5
5. $\triangle AEB \cong \triangle CFD$, $\triangle AED \cong \triangle CFB$	5. Postulate 4–2
6. $\overline{BE} \cong \overline{DF}$, $\overline{DE} \cong \overline{BF}$	6. CPCTC
7. *EBFD* is a parallelogram.	7. Theorem 7–7

23. no **25.** yes **27.** $47\frac{1}{2}$

29. STATEMENTS	REASONS
1. $\overline{BC} \parallel \overline{AD}$, $\overline{AB} \nparallel \overline{CD}$, $\overline{AB} \cong \overline{DC}$	1. Given
2. *ABCD* is isosceles.	2. Definition of Isosceles Trapezoid
3. $\overline{AC} \cong \overline{DB}$	3. Theorem 7–14
4. $\overline{AD} \cong \overline{AD}$	4. Theorem 2–2
5. $\triangle ACD \cong \triangle DBA$	5. Postulate 4–1
6. $\angle CAD \cong \angle BDA$	6. CPCTC
7. $\overline{AE} \cong \overline{DE}$	7. Theorem 4–9
8. $\triangle AED$ is isosceles.	8. Definition of Isosceles Triangle

31. 16 m **33.** 855 cm

CHAPTER 8 SIMILARITY

Page 251 Exploratory **1.** $\frac{14}{26}$ **3.** $\frac{19}{29}$ **5.** $\frac{8}{28}$ **7.** $\frac{14}{27}$ **9.** $\frac{20}{26}$ **11.** 0.538 **13.** 0.50 **15.** 0.25 **17.** 0.33 **19.** 0.40 **21.** 0.32 **23.** 0.57

Page 251 Written **1.** 11 **3.** 15 **5.** 3 **7.** 0.405 **9.** 12 **11.** $\frac{1}{3}$ **13.** 62.5% **15.** $33\frac{1}{3}$% **17.** 37.5% **19.** 41.$\overline{6}$% **21.** 80% **23.** 10% **25.** 75% **27.** 6% **29.** 37.5 g

31. STATEMENTS	REASONS
1. $ad = bc, b \neq 0, a \neq 0$	1. Given
2. $ad \cdot \frac{1}{b} \cdot \frac{1}{d} = bc \cdot \frac{1}{b} \cdot \frac{1}{d}$	2. Theorem 2–8
3. $a \cdot \frac{1}{b} \cdot d \cdot \frac{1}{d} = b \cdot \frac{1}{b} \cdot c \cdot \frac{1}{d}$	3. Postulate 2–11, Postulate 2–10
4. $a \cdot \frac{1}{b} \cdot 1 = 1 \cdot c \cdot \frac{1}{d}$	4. Postulate 2–11, Postulate 2–13
5. $a \cdot \frac{1}{b} = c \cdot \frac{1}{d}$	5. Postulate 2–11, Postulate 2–12
6. $\frac{a}{b} = \frac{c}{d}$	6. Postulate 2–9

Page 256 Exploratory **1.** Theorem 8–5 **3.** Theorem 8–4 **5.** Theorem 8–3 **7.** Theorem 8–6 **9.** Theorem 8–2, Theorem 8–3, Symmetric Property of Equality **11.** Theorem 8–3 **13.** Theorem 8–2, Symmetric Property of Equality **15.** Theorem 8–3

Page 256 Written **1.** 1.2 **3.** 5 **5.** 13

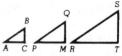

7.

STATEMENTS	REASONS
1. $\frac{a}{b} = \frac{c}{d}$	1. Given
2. $ad = bc$	2. Theorem 8–1
3. $\frac{ad}{cd} = \frac{bc}{cd}$	3. Postulate 2–8
4. $\frac{a}{c} = \frac{b}{d}$	4. Postulate 2–12, Postulate 2–9

9.

STATEMENTS	REASONS
1. $\frac{a}{b} = \frac{c}{d}$	1. Given
2. $\frac{a}{b} - 1 = \frac{c}{d} - 1$	2. Postulate 2–7
3. $b \cdot \frac{1}{b} = 1, d \cdot \frac{1}{d} = 1$	3. Postulate 2–13
4. $\frac{a}{b} - \frac{b}{b} = \frac{c}{d} - \frac{d}{d}$	4. Postulate 2–9
5. $\frac{a-b}{b} = \frac{c-d}{d}$	5. Postulate 2–14

Page 260 Exploratory **1.** $\angle A \cong \angle D$, $\angle B \cong \angle E$, $\angle C \cong \angle F$; $\frac{AB}{DE} = \frac{BC}{EF} = \frac{AC}{DF}$ **5.** yes **7.** yes

Page 261 Written **1.** True; the angles are all 60° and the sides are proportional. **3.** False; the sides may not be proportional. **5.** False; the angles may not be congruent. **7.** False; the angles and the sides may not be congruent. **9.** False; the sides are proportional but may not be congruent. **11.** $1\frac{2}{3}$ ft, $1\frac{1}{3}$ ft **13.** 15 cm, 35 cm

15. Given: $\triangle ABC$
Prove: $\triangle ABC \sim \triangle ABC$

Proof:

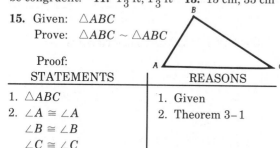

STATEMENTS	REASONS
1. $\triangle ABC$	1. Given
2. $\angle A \cong \angle A$ $\angle B \cong \angle B$ $\angle C \cong \angle C$	2. Theorem 3–1
3. $\overline{AB} \cong \overline{AB}$, $\overline{BC} \cong \overline{BC}$ $\overline{AC} \cong \overline{AC}$	3. Theorem 2–2
4. $AB = AB$ $BC = BC$ $AC = AC$	4. Definition of Congruent Segments
5. $\frac{AB}{AB} = 1$, $\frac{BC}{BC} = 1$ $\frac{AC}{AC} = 1$	5. Postulates 2–8, 2–12, 2–9
6. $\triangle ABC \sim \triangle ABC$	6. Definition of Similar Triangle

17. Given: $\triangle ABC \sim \triangle RST$, $\triangle RST \sim \triangle PQM$
Prove: $\triangle ABC \sim \triangle PQM$

Proof:

STATEMENTS	REASONS
1. $\triangle ABC \sim \triangle RST$ $\triangle RST \sim \triangle PQM$	1. Given
2. $\angle A \cong \angle R$ $\angle B \cong \angle S$ $\angle C \cong \angle T$ $\angle R \cong \angle P$ $\angle S \cong \angle Q$ $\angle T \cong \angle M$	2. Definition of Similar Polygons
3. $\angle A \cong \angle P$ $\angle B \cong \angle Q$ $\angle C \cong \angle M$	3. Theorem 3–1
4. $\frac{AB}{RS} = \frac{BC}{ST} = \frac{CA}{TR}$ $\frac{RS}{PQ} = \frac{ST}{QM} = \frac{TR}{MP}$	4. Definition of Similar Polygons
5. $\frac{\frac{AB}{RS}}{\frac{RS}{PQ}} = \frac{\frac{BC}{ST}}{\frac{ST}{QM}} = \frac{\frac{CA}{TR}}{\frac{TR}{MP}}$	5. Postulate 2–8
6. $\frac{AB}{PQ} = \frac{BC}{QM} = \frac{CA}{MP}$	6. Postulate 2–9
7. $\triangle ABC \sim \triangle PQM$	7. Definition of Similar Polygons

19. 27 in. **21.** 240 m

Page 265 Exploratory **1.** yes **3.** no **5.** yes

Page 266 Written **1.** 11

3.

STATEMENTS	REASONS
1. $\angle D$ is a right angle. $\overline{BE} \perp \overline{AC}$	1. Given
2. $\angle ABE$ is a right angle.	2. Theorem 3–11
3. $\angle D \cong \angle ABE$	3. Theorem 3–6
4. $\angle A \cong \angle A$	4. Theorem 3–1
5. $\triangle ADC \sim \triangle ABE$	5. Postulate 8–1

5.

STATEMENTS	REASONS
1. $\angle Q$ is a right angle. *WSTV* is a square.	1. Given
2. *WSTV* is a rectangle.	2. Definition of Square

3. $\angle SWV$ $\angle WVT$ are right angles.	3. Definition of Rectangle
4. $\angle SWP$ $\angle TVR$ are right angles.	4. Theorem 3–9
5. $\angle SWP \cong \angle TVR$	5. Theorem 3–6
6. $\triangle SWP$ $\triangle PQR$ are right triangles.	6. Definition of Right Triangle
7. $\angle P$, $\angle PSW$ and $\angle P$, $\angle R$ are complementary.	7. Theorem 4–3
8. $\angle PSW \cong \angle R$	8. Theorem 3–4
9. $\triangle PWS \sim \triangle TVR$	9. Postulate 8–1

Page 270 Exploratory **1.** yes **3.** no **5.** no **7.** yes **9.** no **11.** yes **13.** *ER* **15.** *AR* **17.** *AR* **19.** *YO*

Page 270 Written **1.** no **3.** yes **5.** 3 **7.** 6.84 **9.** 3 **11–3.** Definition of Between **11–5.** Postulate 2–7 **11–8.** Theorem 3–1 **11–9.** Theorem 8–8 **11–10.** Definition of Similar Polygons **11–11.** Theorem 6–5 **11–12.** Theorem 8–10 **11–17.** Postulates 2–9, 2–14, 2–8

Page 274 Exploratory **1.** yes **3.** yes **5.** no **7.** yes **9.** no **11.** yes

Page 275 Written **3.** 8 **5.** 5.1 **7.** 11.96 **9.** Suppose $\triangle ABC \sim \triangle PQM$. Then, $\angle A \cong \angle P$ because they are corresponding angles. If $\overline{BD}$ and $\overline{QR}$ are altitudes of the triangles, then $\angle BDA$ and $\angle QPR$ are right angles. By Postulate 8–1, $\triangle ABD \sim \triangle PQR$ which implies that $\frac{BD}{QR} = \frac{BA}{QP}$.

Page 280 Exploratory **1.** 4.5 cm **3.** 12.5 m

Page 280 Written **1.** 48 ft **3.** 2.7 mi **5.** 0.78 cm

Page 283 Chapter Review **1.** 7.5 **3.** 1.25 **5.** 48 **7.** false

9. STATEMENTS	REASONS
1. $\frac{a}{b} = \frac{c}{d}$	1. Given
2. $\frac{a-b}{b} = \frac{c-d}{d}$	2. Theorem 8–5
3. $\frac{a-b}{c-d} = \frac{b}{d}$	3. Theorem 8–2

11. Yes: if two triangles are congruent, then the corresponding angles are congruent. Also, the measures of the corresponding sides are proportional since the measure of each pair of corresponding sides is in the ratio of 1:1.
13. 9 mm, 30 mm

15. STATEMENTS	REASONS
1. $\frac{PR}{QS} = \frac{RS}{QP}$, $\overline{QR} \parallel \overline{PS}$ *PQRS* is an isosceles trapezoid.	1. Given
2. $\angle QRP \cong \angle SPR$ $\angle RQS \cong \angle PSQ$	2. Theorem 6–10
3. $\triangle QRT \sim \triangle SPT$	3. Postulate 8–1
4. $\frac{QT}{ST} = \frac{RT}{PT}$	4. Definition of Similar Polygons
5. $\angle QTP \cong \angle STR$	5. Theorem 3–10
6. $\triangle QTP \sim \triangle STR$	6. Theorem 8–8
7. $\angle QPT \cong \angle RST$	7. Definition of Similar Polygons
8. $\angle RQP \cong \angle QRS$	8. Theorem 7–13
9. $\triangle PQR \sim \triangle SRQ$	9. Postulate 8–1

17. yes **19.** 4 **21.** $5\frac{1}{3}$ **23.** 20.125 ft **25.** 7 ft

CHAPTER 9 RIGHT TRIANGLES

Page 290 Exploratory **1.** 64 **3.** 49 **5.** 0.04 **7.** $\frac{4}{25}$ **9.** 1.69 **11.** 8 **13.** −7 **15.** 0.2 **17.** ±1.3 **19.** $\frac{2}{5}$

Page 290 Written **1.** 1 **3.** 0.5 **5.** 0.3 **7.** $\frac{7}{2}$ **9.** 13 **11.** 16, rational **13.** 30, rational **15.** $4\sqrt{5}$, irrational **17.** $5\sqrt{3}$, irrational **19.** $5\sqrt{3}$, irrational **21.** $\frac{\sqrt{5}}{2}$, irrational **23.** $\frac{\sqrt{2}}{4}$, irrational **25.** $\frac{5\sqrt{3}}{3}$, irrational **27.** $\frac{\sqrt{15}}{3}$, irrational **29.** $\frac{\sqrt{6}}{2}$, irrational **31.** 8.718 **33.** 4.123 **35.** −1.015 **37.** 1.871 **39.** 14.14 **41.** 6.325 **43.** 6.928 **45.** ±5 **47.** ±6 **49.** ±6.708

Page 294 Exploratory **1.** 4 **3.** 6 **5.** 12 **7.** 6 **9.** 4 **11.** 12 **13.** 9 **15.** 8

Page 294 Written **1.** $\sqrt{15}$ **3.** $2\sqrt{10}$ **5.** 12 **7.** $4\sqrt{3}$ **9.** $5\sqrt{3}$ **11.** $3\sqrt{6}$ **13.** $\frac{3}{2}$ **15.** 1 **17.** $\frac{\sqrt{3}}{4}$ **19.** $\frac{\sqrt{2}}{4}$ **21.** 5.477 **23.** 4.899 **25.** 5.292 **27.** $PQ = 9, PR = 13, PV = 3\sqrt{13}, VR = 2\sqrt{13}$

Page 298 Exploratory **1.** no **3.** yes **5.** yes **7.** yes **9.** yes **11.** yes

Page 298 Written **1.** yes **3.** no **5.** yes **7.** no **9.** yes **11.** 20 **13.** 9.4 **15.** 11.9 **17.** 13.6 **19.** 17 ft **21.** 13 units **23.** 19.2 ft

Page 300 Exploratory **1.** $\sqrt{2}$ ft **3.** $2\sqrt{2}$ in. **5.** $45\sqrt{2}$ mm **7.** $1.8\sqrt{2}$ m **9.** $31.2\sqrt{2}$ m **11.** $4\frac{2}{3}\sqrt{2}$ yd **13.** $\frac{\sqrt{3}}{2}$ **15.** $2\sqrt{3}$ cm **17.** $\frac{25\sqrt{3}}{2}$ cm **19.** $1.25\sqrt{3}$ cm **21.** $\frac{\sqrt{3}}{3}$ yd **23.** $\frac{11\sqrt{3}}{8}$ ft

Page 301 Written **1.** 7.1 **3.** 13.0 **5.** 4.9 **7.** 1.0 **9.** 18.0 **11.** 6.0 **13.** 5.3 **15.** 14.8 **17.** 4.2 **19.** 18.0 units **21.** $\sqrt{3}$ **23.** $\sqrt{5}$ **25.** $\sqrt{7}$

Page 305 Exploratory **1.** $\frac{21}{29}$ **3.** $\frac{21}{20}$ **5.** $\frac{21}{29}$ **7.** $\frac{4}{5}$ **9.** $\frac{4}{3}$ **11.** $\frac{4}{5}$ **13.** $\frac{15}{17}$ **15.** $\frac{15}{8}$ **17.** $\frac{15}{17}$

Page 305 Written **1.** $\sin A = 0.882$, $\cos A = 0.471$, $\tan A = 1.875$; $\sin B = 0.471$, $\cos B = 0.882$, $\tan B = 0.533$ **3.** $\sin A = 0.969$, $\cos A = 0.246$, $\tan A = 3.938$; $\sin B = 0.246$, $\cos B = 0.969$, $\tan B = 0.254$ **7.** $\frac{1}{2}$ **9.** $\frac{\sqrt{3}}{3}$ **11.** $\frac{1}{2}$ **13.** They are equal. 15. $\frac{1}{\sin W}$ 17. $\sin T$ **19.** $\frac{1}{\cos W}$ **21.** $\frac{1}{\sin C}$

Page 308 Exploratory **1.** 0 **3.** 1 **5.** 0 **7.** 1 **9.** 0 **11.** 45

Page 309 Written **1.** 0 **3.** 1 **5.** 0.3584 **7.** 0.8480 **9.** 0.7813 **11.** 1 **13.** 0.9272 **15.** 0.8090 **17.** 0.2250 **19.** 1.1918 **21.** 9.5144 **23.** 0.9613 **25.** 1.2349 **27.** 0.9998 **29.** 6° **31.** 26° **33.** 64° **35.** 75° **37.** 88° **39.** 64° **41.** 73° **43.** 39° **45.** 76° **47.** 17° **49.** 49° **51.** 14° **53.** 56° **55.** 87° **57.** 37° **59.** 0.3660 **61.** 1.8660 **63.** 1.000 **65.** 0.500 **67.** $^{-}0.5773$ **69.** 0.4142 **71.** $^{-}0.0670$ **73.** 2.7321 **75.** 0.6830 **77.** 0.0000 **79.** 2.0000 **81.** 0.0000 **83.** 2.5000

Page 313 Exploratory **1.** elevation: $\angle BCA$, depression: $\angle DBC$ **3.** elevation: $\angle YXZ$, depression: $\angle WYX$ **5.** elevation: $\angle JHK$, depression: $\angle IJH$ **7.** $\sin 15° = \frac{QR}{37}$ **9.** $\sin 47° = \frac{10}{PQ}$ **11.** $\cos 16° = \frac{13.4}{PQ}$

Page 313 Written **1.** 39.2126 **3.** 65 **5.** 23 **7.** 10.1175 **9.** 105.6946 **11.** 71.47 m **13.** 132.61 m **15.** 2.8 mi **17.** 19 ft **19.** 4 **21.** 2,572 ft

Page 317 Chapter Review **1.** 5 **3.** $\frac{9}{4}$ **5.** $\frac{\sqrt{15}}{3}$ **7.** 13.23 **9.** 1.528 **11.** 8.5 **13.** 0.4 **15.** yes **17.** yes **19.** yes **21.** 9.8 **23.** 4.2 in. **25.** 10.0 mm **27.** $\sin Q = 0.9, \cos Q = 0.5, \tan Q = 1.9$; $\sin R = 0.5, \cos R = 0.9, \tan R = 0.5$ **29.** 0.8387 **31.** 30 **33.** 44 **35.** 5.91

CHAPTER 10 CIRCLES AND SPHERES

Page 325 Exploratory **1.** P **3.** $\overline{PD}, \overline{PB}, \overline{PC}$ **5.** $\overline{EA}, \overline{DB}$ **7.** $\overleftrightarrow{EA}$ **9.** F, H

Page 326 Written **1.** yes **3.** no **5.** no **7.** two points **9.** two points

11. Given: $\overline{AB}$ is a diameter of $\odot P$. $\overline{PC}$ is a radius of $\odot P$. $PC = r, AB = d$

Prove: $d = 2r$

B
P
A
C

Proof:

STATEMENTS	REASONS
1. $\overline{AB}$ is a diameter of $\odot P$. $\overline{PC}$ is a radius of $\odot P$. $PC = r$ $AB = d$	1. Given

2. $AP = PC$ $PB = PC$	2. Definition of Circle
3. $AP + PB = AB$	3. Definition of Between
4. $AB = PC + PC$	4. Postulate 2–9
5. $d = r + r$	5. Postulate 2–9
6. $d = 2r$	6. Postulate 2–9

Page 329 Exploratory **1.** minor arc **3.** semicircle **5.** major arc **7.** major arc **9.** minor arc **11.** major arc **13.** semicircle **15.** major arc

Page 329 Written **1.** 38 **3.** 28 **5.** 180 **7.** 180 **9.** 114 **11.** 246 **13.** 152 **15.** 218 **17.** 40 **19.** 45 **21.** 135 **23.** 140 **25.** 85 **27.** 320 **29.** no **31.** yes **33.** no **35.** yes

37. Given: $\odot P \cong \odot Q$, $\angle P \cong \angle Q$
Prove: $\widehat{AB} \cong \widehat{CD}$

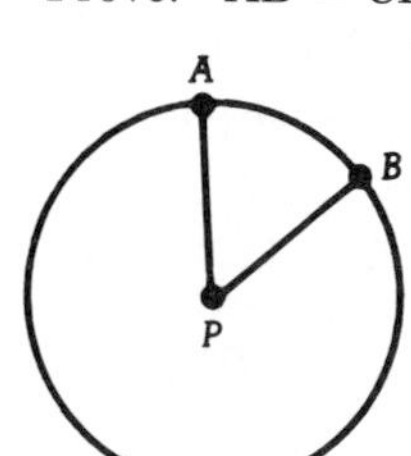

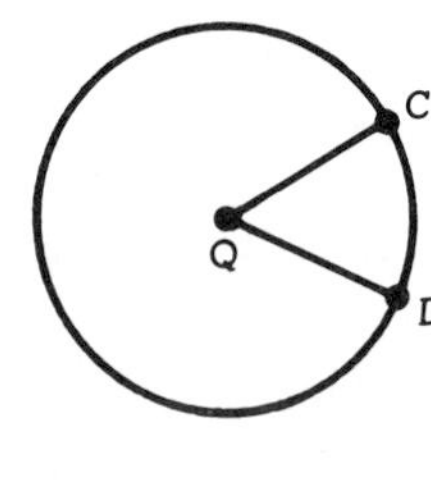

Proof:

STATEMENTS	REASONS
1. $\odot P \cong \odot Q$ $\angle P \cong \angle Q$	1. Given
2. $m\angle P = m\angle Q$	2. Definition of Congruent Angles
3. $m\angle P = m\widehat{AB}$ $m\angle Q = m\widehat{CD}$	3. Definition of Arc Measure
4. $m\widehat{AB} = M\widehat{CD}$	4. Postulate 2–9
5. $\widehat{AB} \cong \widehat{CD}$	5. Definition of Congruent Arcs

39. 32 **41.** 112 **43.** 144 **45.** 216 **47.** yes

Page 333 Exploratory **1.** Theorem 10–3 **3.** Theorem 10–5 **5.** Theorem 10–4 **7.** Theorem 10–4

Page 333 Written **1.** $\overline{QV}$ **3.** V **5.** $\widehat{QS}$ **7.** $\overline{WA}$ **9.** no **11.** 13 in. **13.** 6 cm

15. Given: $\odot P$, $\overline{AB} \cong \overline{CD}$
Prove: $\widehat{AB} \cong \widehat{CD}$

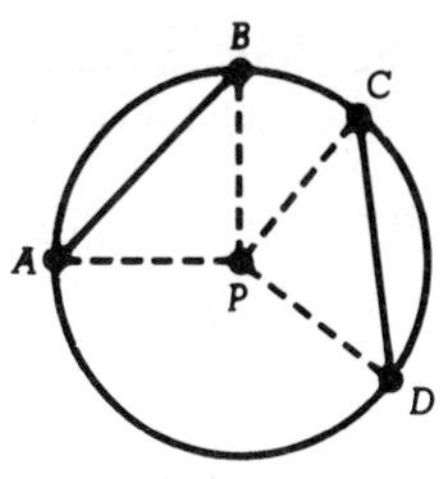

Proof:

STATEMENTS	REASONS
1. $\odot P$, $\overline{AB} \cong \overline{CD}$	1. Given
2. Draw $\overline{AP}$, $\overline{BP}$, $\overline{CP}$, and $\overline{DP}$.	2. Postulate 1–1
3. $AP = DP$, $BP = CP$	3. Definition of Circle
4. $\overline{AP} \cong \overline{DP}$, $\overline{BP} \cong \overline{CP}$	4. Definition of Congruent Segments
5. $\triangle ABP \cong \triangle DCP$	5. Postulate 4–1
6. $\angle APB = \angle DPC$	6. CPCTC
7. $\widehat{AB} \cong \widehat{CD}$	7. Theorem 10–2

17. Given: $\odot P$, $\overline{PX}$ bisects $\widehat{AB}$.
Prove: $\overline{PX}$ bisects $\overline{AB}$.

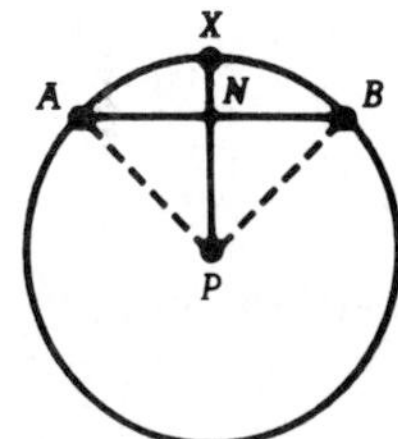

Proof:

STATEMENTS	REASONS
1. $\odot P$, $\overline{PX}$ bisects $\widehat{AB}$.	1. Given
2. $\widehat{AX} \cong \widehat{XB}$	2. Definition of Arc Bisector
3. Draw radii $\overline{AP}$ and $\overline{BP}$.	3. Postulate 1–1
4. $AP = BP$	4. Definition of Circle
5. $\overline{AP} \cong \overline{BP}$	5. Definition of Congruent Segments
6. $\overline{NP} \cong \overline{NP}$	6. Theorem 2–2
7. $\angle APX \cong \angle BPX$	7. Theorem 10–2
8. $\triangle APN \cong \triangle BPN$	8. Postulate 4–2
9. $\overline{AN} \cong \overline{BN}$	9. CPCTC
10. $AN = BN$	10. Definition of Congruent Segments
11. $\overline{PX}$ bisects $\overline{AB}$.	11. Definition of Segment Bisector

23. STATEMENTS	REASONS
1. $\overline{AC}$ is a diameter. $\overline{AC} \perp \overline{BD}$	1. Given
2. $\overline{AC}$ bisects $\widehat{BCD}$.	2. Theorem 10–4
3. $\widehat{BC} \cong \widehat{DC}$	3. Definition of Arc Bisector

25. STATEMENTS	REASONS
1. $\widehat{PTS} \cong \widehat{QST}$ $\overline{RS} \cong \overline{RT}$	1. Given
2. $\overline{PS} \cong \overline{QT}$	2. Theorem 10–3
3. $PS = QT, RS = RT$	3. Definition of Congruent Segments
4. $PS = PR + RS$ $QT = QR + RT$	4. Definition of Between
5. $PR + RS = QR + RT$	5. Postulate 2–9
6. $PR = QR$	6. Postulates 2–7, 2–9
7. $\overline{PR} \cong \overline{QR}$	7. Definition of Congruent Segments
8. $\triangle PQR$ is isosceles.	8. Definition of Isosceles Triangle

Page 338 Exploratory **1.** $\widehat{BC}$, yes **3.** $\widehat{KH}$, $\widehat{IJ}$, no **5.** $\widehat{QT}$, $\widehat{RS}$, no **7.** $\widehat{YZ}$, yes

Page 338 Written **1.** 104 **3.** 47 **5.** 52 **7.** 38 **9.** 47 **11.** 86 **13.** 34 **15.** 81 **17.** 94 **19.** 12 units **21.** $12\sqrt{3}$ units

23. Given: $\odot X$ with diameter $\overline{AB}$ and $\angle CAB$

Prove: $m\angle CAB = \frac{1}{2}(m\widehat{BC})$

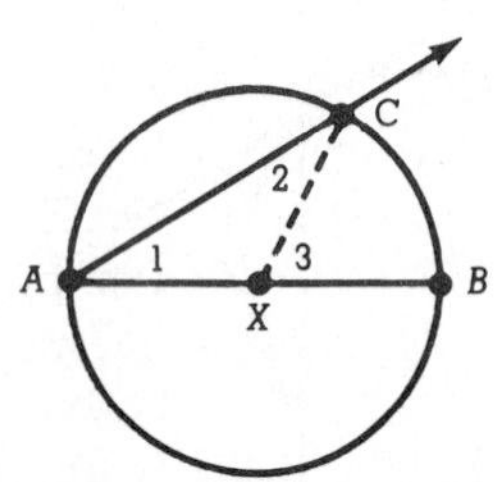

STATEMENTS	REASONS
1. $\odot X$ with diameter $\overline{AB}$, $\angle CAB$ inscribed in $\odot X$.	1. Given
2. Draw radius $\overline{XC}$.	2. Postulate 1–1
3. $AX = XC$	3. Definition of Circle
4. $\overline{AX} \cong \overline{XC}$	4. Definition of Congruent Segments
5. $\angle 1 \cong \angle 2$	5. Theorem 4–6
6. $m\angle 1 = m\angle 2$	6. Definition of Congruent Angles
7. $m\angle 1 + m\angle 2 = m\angle 3$	7. Theorem 5–1
8. $m\angle 1 + m\angle 1 = m\angle 3$	8. Postulate 2–9
9. $2(m\angle 1) = m\angle 3$	9. Postulate 2–9
10. $m\angle 3 = m\widehat{CB}$	10. Definition of Arc Measure
11. $2(m\angle 1) = m\widehat{CB}$	11. Postulate 2–9
12. $m\angle 1 = \frac{1}{2}(m\widehat{CB})$	12. Postulates 2–8, 2–9

27. STATEMENTS	REASONS
1. $\overline{ZY}$ is a diameter of $\odot A$. $\widehat{XY} \cong \widehat{ZW}$	1. Given
2. $\widehat{ZXY}$ and $\widehat{ZWY}$ are semicircles.	2. Definition of Semicircle
3. $m\widehat{ZXY} = 180$ $m\widehat{ZWY} = 180$	3. Definition of Arc Measure
4. $m\widehat{ZXY} = m\widehat{ZWY}$	4. Postulate 2–9
5. $m\widehat{ZXY} = m\widehat{ZX} + m\widehat{XY}$, $m\widehat{ZWY} = m\widehat{WY} + m\widehat{ZW}$	5. Postulate 10–1
6. $m\widehat{ZX} + m\widehat{XY} = m\widehat{WY} + m\widehat{ZW}$	6. Postulate 2–9
7. $m\widehat{XY} = m\widehat{ZW}$	7. Definition of Congruent Arcs
8. $m\widehat{ZX} = m\widehat{WY}$	8. Postulates 2–7, 2–9
9. $\frac{1}{2}(m\widehat{ZX}) = \frac{1}{2}(m\widehat{WY})$	9. Postulate 2–8
10. $m\angle ZXY = \frac{1}{2}(m\widehat{ZX})$ $m\angle WZY = \frac{1}{2}(m\widehat{WY})$	10. Theorem 10–6

11. $m \angle XYZ = m \angle WZY$	11. Postulate 2–9
12. $\angle XYZ \cong \angle WZY$	12. Definition of Congruent Angles

Page 342 Exploratory **1.** 2 **3.** 1 **5.** tangents

Page 342 Written **1.** 12 **3.** 14 **5.** 8 **7.** 45 **9.** 45 **11.** 90 **13.** 45 **15.** 5 **17.** 13 **19.** $5\sqrt{2}$ **21.** $\sqrt{329}$

23. Given: $\odot X$ with radius $\overline{XA}$, $\overline{XA} \perp \overline{CA}$

Prove: $\overleftrightarrow{CA}$ is tangent to $\odot X$.

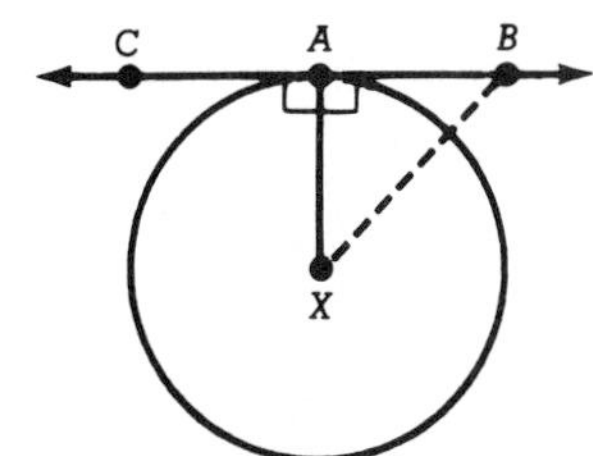

Proof:

STATEMENTS	REASONS
1. $\odot X$ with radius $\overline{XA}$ $\overline{XA} \perp \overline{CA}$	1. Given
2. Choose a point B on $\overleftrightarrow{CA}$ and draw $\overline{XB}$.	2. Postulate 1–1
3. $XA < XB$	3. Theorem 5–6
4. B lies in the exterior of $\odot X$.	4. Definition of Exterior of Circle
5. $\overleftrightarrow{CA}$ is tangent to $\odot X$.	5. Definition of Tangent

25. STATEMENTS	REASONS
1. $\overleftrightarrow{AC}$ is tangent to $\odot P$. $\widehat{DB} = \widehat{BE}$	1. Given
2. $\angle APB \cong \angle CPB$	2. Theorem 10–2
3. $\overline{PB} \cong \overline{PB}$	3. Theorem 2–2
4. $\overline{PB} \perp \overleftrightarrow{AC}$	4. Theorem 10–10
5. $\angle ABP$ and $\angle CBP$ are right angles.	5. Theorem 3–11
6. $\angle ABP \cong \angle CBP$	6. Theorem 3–6
7. $\triangle ABP \cong \triangle CBP$	7. Postulate 4–3
8. $\overline{AB} \cong \overline{CB}$	8. CPCTC

27. STATEMENTS	REASONS
1. $\triangle APC$ is isosceles. $\widehat{DB} \cong \widehat{BE}$	1. Given
2. $\overline{AP} \cong \overline{CP}$	2. Definition of Isosceles Triangle
3. $\angle APB \cong \angle CPB$	3. Theorem 10–2
4. $\overline{PB} \cong \overline{PB}$	4. Theorem 2–2
5. $\triangle APB \cong \triangle CPB$	5. Postulate 4–2
6. $\angle PBA \cong \angle PBC$	6. CPCTC
7. $\overline{PB} \perp \overleftrightarrow{AC}$	7. Theorem 3–14
8. $\overleftrightarrow{AC}$ is tangent to $\odot P$.	8. Theorem 10–11

29. STATEMENTS	REASONS
1. $\overleftrightarrow{AF}$ and $\overleftrightarrow{CF}$ are tangent to $\odot B$.	1. Given
2. $\overline{AF} \cong \overline{CF}$	2. Theorem 10–2
3. $\overline{BF} \cong \overline{BF}$	3. Theorem 2–2
4. $AB = CB$	4. Definition of Circle
5. $\overline{AB} \cong \overline{CB}$	5. Definition of Congruent Segments
6. $\triangle ABF \cong \triangle CBF$	6. Postulate 4–1
7. $\angle AFD \cong \angle CFD$	7. CPCTC
8. $\overline{DF} \cong \overline{DF}$	8. Theorem 2–2
9. $\triangle ADF \cong \triangle CDF$	9. Postulate 4–2
10. $\angle ADF \cong \angle CDF$	10. CPCTC
11. $\overline{BF} \perp \overline{AC}$	11. Theorem 3–14

Page 346 Exploratory **1.** 63 **3.** 35 **5.** 17.5

Page 346 Written **1.** 114 **3.** 66 **5.** 138 **7.** 174 **9.** 49 **11.** 198 **13.** 236 **15.** 38 **17.** 44 **19.** 92 **21.** 46 **23.** 134 **25.** 160 **27.** 100 **29.** 108 **31.** 154 **33.** 144

37. Given: $\overleftrightarrow{AB}$ is tangent to $\odot X$ at A. $\overleftrightarrow{BC}$ is tangent to $\odot X$ at C.

Prove: $m \angle ABC = \frac{1}{2}(m\widehat{ADC} - m\widehat{AC})$

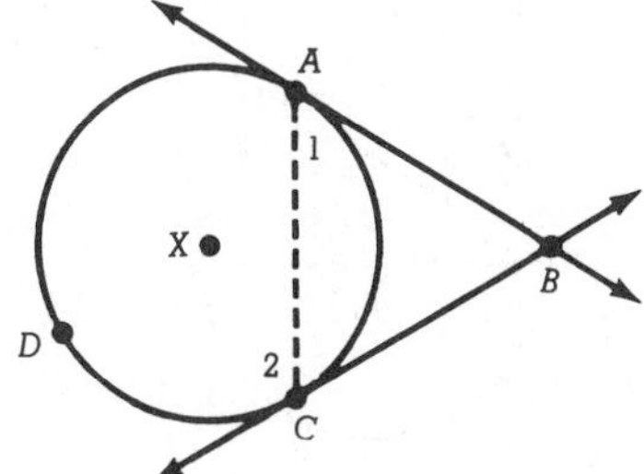

Proof:

STATEMENTS	REASONS
1. $\overleftrightarrow{AB}$ is tangent to $\odot X$ at A. $\overleftrightarrow{BC}$ is tangent to $\odot X$ at C.	1. Given
2. Draw $\overline{AC}$.	2. Postulate 1–1
3. $m\angle 1 = \frac{1}{2}(m\widehat{AC})$ $m\angle 2 = \frac{1}{2}(m\widehat{ADC})$	3. Theorem 10–15
4. $m\angle ABC + m\angle 1 = m\angle 2$	4. Theorem 5–1
5. $m\angle ABC + \frac{1}{2}(m\widehat{AC}) = \frac{1}{2}(m\widehat{ADC})$	5. Postulate 2–9
6. $m\angle ABC = \frac{1}{2}(m\widehat{ADC}) - \frac{1}{2}(m\widehat{AC})$	6. Postulates 2–7, 2–9
7. $m\angle ABC = \frac{1}{2}(m\widehat{ADC} - m\widehat{AC})$	7. Postulate 2–9

Proof:

39.

STATEMENTS	REASONS
1. $\overleftrightarrow{FA}$ is tangent to $\odot P$ and $\odot E$ at A.	1. Given
2. $m\angle CAF = \frac{1}{2}(m\widehat{AC})$	2. Theorem 10–15
3. $2(m\angle CAF) = m\widehat{AC}$	3. Postulates 2–7, 2–9
4. $m\angle CEA = m\widehat{AC}$	4. Definition of Arc Measure
5. $2(m\angle CAF) = m\angle CEA$	5. Postulate 2–9
6. $m\angle CAF = \frac{1}{2}(m\angle CEA)$	6. Postulate 2–9

Page 350 Exploratory **1.** $3x = 4(9)$ **3.** $5(5 + x) = 4(12)$ **5.** $20(20) = 10(x + 10)$ **7.** $3(12) = x(5 + x)$ **9.** $8(8) = x(x + 12)$

Page 351 Written **1.** 12 **3.** 0.3 **5.** 5 **7.** 5 **9.** 5 **11.** 2 **13.** 4 **15.** 6.1 **17.** 19.6

19. Given: $\odot X$, secant segments $\overline{AC}$ and $\overline{CE}$

Prove: $AC \cdot BC = EC \cdot DC$

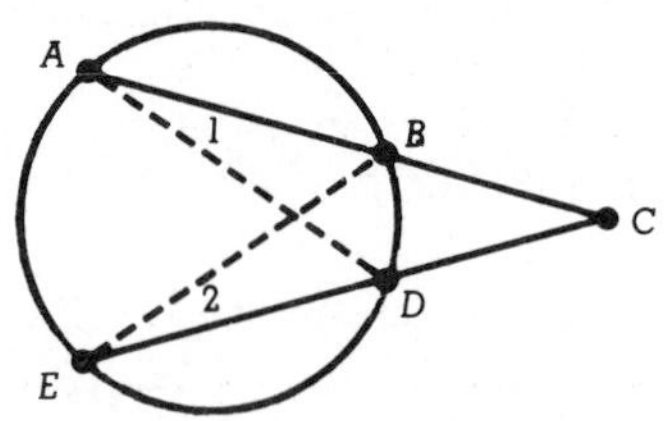

Proof:

STATEMENTS	REASONS
1. $\odot X$, secant segments $\overline{AC}$ and $\overline{CE}$	1. Given
2. Draw $\overline{BE}$ and $\overline{AD}$.	2. Postulate 1–1
3. $\angle C \cong \angle C$	3. Theorem 3–1
4. $m\widehat{BD} = m\widehat{BD}$	4. Postulate 2–4
5. $\widehat{BD} \cong \widehat{BD}$	5. Definition of Congruent Arcs
6. $\angle 1 \cong \angle 2$	6. Theorem 10–7
7. $\triangle ADC \sim \triangle EBC$	7. Postulate 8–1
8. $\frac{AC}{EC} = \frac{DC}{BC}$	8. Definition of Similar Polygons
9. $AC \cdot BC = EC \cdot DC$	9. Theorem 8–1

Page 355 Exploratory **1.** sphere **3.** sphere **5.** circle **7.** circle **9.** circle **11.** neither

Page 355 Written **1.** yes **3.** yes **5.** yes **7.** yes **9.** no **11.** yes **13.** yes **15.** A segment is a radius of a sphere if and only if its endpoints are the center of the sphere and a point on the sphere. **17.** A circle is a great circle of a sphere if and only if the center of the circle and the center of the sphere coincide. **19.** A point lies in the interior of a sphere if and only if the length of the segment joining the point to the center of the sphere is less than the length of the radius of the sphere. **21.** A line is tangent to a sphere if and only if the line intersects the sphere in exactly one point. **23.** A line is a secant of a sphere if and only if it intersects the sphere in exactly two points. **25.** Two spheres are congruent if and only if their radii are congruent. **27.** one **29.** one **31.** one **33.** infinitely many

Page 359 Chapter Review **1.** no **3.** A segment is a diameter of a circle if and only if its endpoints are on the circle and it contains the center of the circle. **5.** 63 **7.** 60 **9.** 117 **11.** 63 **13.** 123 **15.** 10 cm **17.** 36 **19.** 72 **21.** 36 **23.** 72 **25.** $3\sqrt{2}$ **27.** tangents **29.** 55 **31.** 125 **33.** 133 **35.** 0.806 ft **37.** no **39.** two **41.** none

CHAPTER 11 AREA AND VOLUME

Page 365 Exploratory **1.** 1 cm × 24 cm, 2 cm × 12 cm, 3 cm × 8 cm, 4 cm × 6 cm **3.** $A = 36, p = 24$ **5.** $A = 36, p = 30$ **7.** $A = 25, p = 20$ **9.** false **11.** true

Page 365 Written **1.** 20 cm² **3.** 120 ft² **5.** 2269.5 cm² **7.** 667 mi² **9.** $18\frac{1}{3}$ mi² **11.** $23\frac{3}{8}$ in.² **13.** $(x^2 + 3x)$ft² **15.** $(12a^2 + 10a + 2)$in.² **17.** 3.5 in. **19.** 16.3 m **21.** $2\frac{2}{3}$ yd **23.** $2\frac{1}{4}$ ft **25.** 448 square units **27.** 120 square units **29.** 12.5 square units **31.** 240

Page 369 Exploratory **1.** 96 in.² **3.** 18 cm² **5.** 252 mm² **7.** 42 cm² **9.** $4\frac{1}{2}$ in.² **11.** 2.5245 ft² **13.** 38.5 cm² **15.** 850 mi² **17.** 64 in.²

Page 370 Written **1.** 4 ft **3.** 13.16 m² **5.** 1.3 m **7.** $20\frac{1}{4}$ in.² **9.** $(2x^2 + 8x)$m² **11.** 8 ft **13.** 6.58 m² **15.** 2.6 m **17.** $10\frac{1}{8}$ in.² **19.** $(x^2 + 4x)$m² **21.** 4.68 m² **23.** 261 cm² **25.** 31.5 ft²

27. Given: $\triangle ABC$, $\overline{BD} \perp \overleftrightarrow{AC}$
$AC = b, BD = h$

Prove: area of $\triangle ABC = \frac{1}{2}bh$

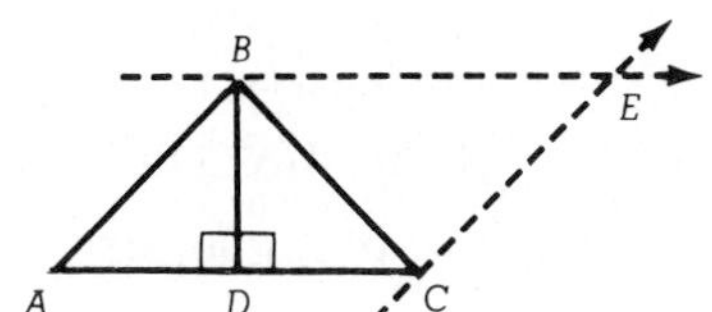

Proof:

STATEMENTS	REASONS
1. $\triangle ABC$, $\overline{BD} \perp \overleftrightarrow{AC}$ $AC = b, BD = h$	1. Given
2. Draw $\overleftrightarrow{BE} \parallel \overline{AC}$ and $\overleftrightarrow{CE} \parallel \overline{AB}$.	2. Postulate 6–1
3. $ABEC$ is a parallelogram.	3. Definition of Parallelogram
4. $\triangle ABC \cong \triangle ECB$	4. Theorem 7–3
5. area of $\triangle ABC$ = area of $\triangle ECB$	5. Postulate 11–2
6. area of $\triangle ABC$ + area of $\triangle ECB$ = area of $ABEC$	6. Postulate 11–3
7. area of $ABEC = bh$	7. Theorem 11–2
8. area of $\triangle ABC$ + area of $\triangle ABC = bh$	8. Postulate 2–9
9. 2(area of $\triangle ABC$) $= bh$	9. Postulate 2–9
10. area of $\triangle ABC = \frac{1}{2}bh$	10. Postulate 2–8

29. 63 square units

Page 373 Exploratory **1.** 120 **3.** 72 **5.** 45 **7.** 36 **9.** $25\frac{5}{7}$

Page 374 Written **1.** $p = 12, a = \frac{2\sqrt{3}}{3}$, $A = 4\sqrt{3}$ **3.** $p = 48, a = 4\sqrt{3}, A = 96\sqrt{3}$ **5.** $s = 3.4, a = 1.7\sqrt{3}, A = 17.34\sqrt{3}$ **7.** 256 in.² **9.** 1,254 mm² **11.** 186 ft² **13.** $27\sqrt{3}$ square units **15.** $216\sqrt{3}$ cm² **17.** 400 ft² **19.** 170.75 m²

21. Given: regular pentagon $ABCDE$, Apothem $\overline{XN}$ has length a.
$AB + BC + CD + DE + EA = p$

Prove: area of $ABCDE = \frac{1}{2}ap$

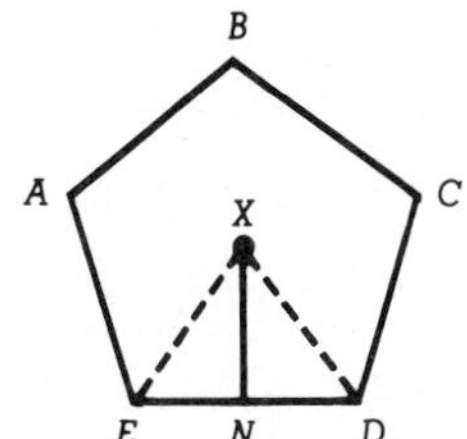

Proof:

STATEMENTS	REASONS
1. Regular pentagon $ABCDE$, Apothem $\overline{XN}$ has length a. $AB + BC + CD + DE + EA = p$	1. Given
2. $\overline{XN} \perp \overline{ED}$	2. Theorem 11–6
3. Draw $\overline{XE}$, $\overline{XA}$, $\overline{XB}$, $\overline{XC}$, and $\overline{XD}$.	3. Postulate 1–1
4. $\overline{XE} \cong \overline{XA} \cong \overline{XB} \cong \overline{XC} \cong \overline{XD}$	4. Definition of Radius
5. $\overline{AB} \cong \overline{BC} \cong \overline{CD} \cong \overline{DE} \cong \overline{EA}$	5. Definition of Regular Pentagon
6. $\triangle AXB \cong \triangle BXC \cong \triangle CXD \cong \triangle DXE \cong \triangle EXA$	6. Postulate 4–2
7. $\overline{XN}$ is an altitude of $\triangle DXE$.	7. Definition of Altitude
8. area of $\triangle DXE = \frac{1}{2}a(ED)$	8. Theorem 11–3
9. area of $\triangle AXB$ + area of $\triangle BXC$ + area of $\triangle CXD$ + area of $\triangle DXE$ + area of $\triangle EXA$ = area of $ABCDE$	9. Postulate 11–2
10. $5\left(\frac{1}{2}a(ED)\right) =$ area of $ABCDE$	10. Postulates 2–9, 2–7
11. $5(ED) = p$	11. Postulate 2–9
12. $\frac{1}{2}ap =$ area of $ABCDE$	12. Postulate 2–9

23. Given: $\triangle ABC$ is equilateral.

Prove: $m\angle 1 = m\angle 2 = m\angle 3 = \frac{360}{3}$

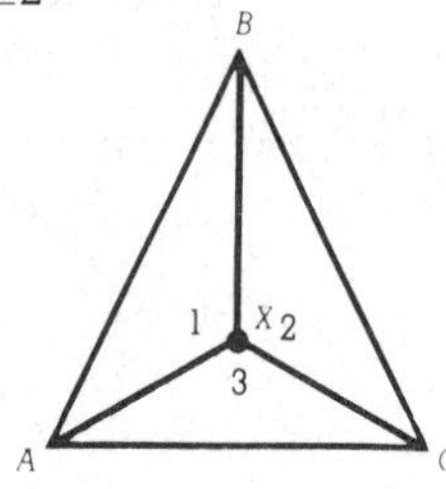

Proof:

STATEMENTS	REASONS
1. $\triangle ABC$ is equilateral.	1. Given
2. Draw $\overline{XA}$, $\overline{XB}$, and $\overline{XC}$.	2. Postulate 1–1
3. $\overline{XA} \cong \overline{XB} \cong \overline{XC}$	3. Definition of Radius
4. $\overline{AB} \cong \overline{BC} \cong \overline{CA}$	4. Definition of Polygon
5. $\triangle AXB \cong \triangle BXC \cong \triangle CXA$	5. Postulate 4–2
6. $\angle 1 \cong \angle 2 \cong \angle 3$	6. CPCTC
7. $m\angle 1 + m\angle 2 + m\angle 3 = 360$	7. Definition of Arc Measure
8. $3(m\angle 1) = 360$	8. Postulates 2–9, 2–7
9. $m\angle 1 = \frac{360}{3}$	9. Postulate 2–8
10. $m\angle 1 = m\angle 2 = m\angle 3 = \frac{360}{3}$	10. Definition of Congruent Angles

25. $\frac{27}{2}\sqrt{3}$ m² **27.** $12 + 4\sqrt{3}$ **29.** $108\sqrt{3}$

Page 379 Exploratory **1.** 14π cm, 49π cm² **3.** 8π in., 16π in.² **5.** 14.8π cm, 54.76π cm² **7.** 4.8π km, 5.76π km² **9.** π ft, $\pi/4$ ft² **11.** $9\frac{1}{3}\pi$ yd, $\frac{196}{9}\pi$ yd² **13.** $10\sqrt{2}\pi$ cm, 50π cm² **15.** $6\sqrt{2}\pi$ in., 18π in.²

Page 379 Written **1.** 44.0 cm **3.** 25.1 in. **5.** 46.5 cm **7.** 15.1 km **9.** 3.1 ft **11.** $68\frac{4}{9}$ yd² **13.** $157\frac{1}{7}$ cm² **15.** $56\frac{4}{7}$ in.² **17.** $\frac{1}{6}$ **19.** $\frac{1}{180}$ **21.** $\frac{1}{24}$ **23.** $\frac{1}{5}$ **25.** 11.1 cm² **27.** 0.4 cm² **29.** 2.8 cm² **31.** 13.3 cm² **33.** 16.6 ft² **35.** 78.48 square units **37.** 34.58 square units **39.** 73.8 square units.

Page 384 Exploratory **1.** *RSTVWPQ*, *CDEFGAB* **3.** 7 **5.** $L = 7sh$

Page 384 Written **1.** 60 cm², 72 cm² **3.** 264 in.², 312 in.² **5.** 40.5 m², 46.6 m² **7.** 175.2 square units, 446.9 square units **9.** 439.6 cm² **11.** 384.3 ft² **13.** 1704.4 m² **15.** 55 m² **17.** $35\frac{4}{9}$ ft² **19.** 10,362 ft² **21.** the hexagonal crystal

Page 389 Exploratory **1.** 27 cm^2 **3.** 36 cm^2 **5.** 45 cm^2 **7.** 54 cm^2 **9.** 72 cm^2

Page 389 Written **1.** 188.4 cm^2 **3.** 132.6 m^2 **5.** 149.5 cm^2 **7.** 77.7 in.^{2} **9.** 376,800 ft^2 **11.** $160\frac{2}{7}$ m^2 **13.** $(44\sqrt{421} + 616)$ ft^2 **15.** 1,256 cm^2 **17.** 50,240,000 ft^2 **19.** 1,738,103 mi^2 **21.** 922,610 ft^2

Page 393 Exploratory **1.** 42 m^3 **3.** 67.2 ft^3 **5.** 14,400 cm^3

Page 394 Written **1.** 48 m^3 **3.** 2580 in.^{3} **5.** 57.4 cm^3 **7.** 100.5 m^3 **9.** 337.6 cm^3 **11.** 28.3 ft^3 **13.** It is eight times as great as the original cube. **15.** It is eight times as great as the original cylinder. **17.** 36 **19.** 19.63 ft^3

Page 397 Exploratory **1.** 35 ft^3 **3.** 10 ft^3 **5.** 120.6 cm^3 **7.** 446.6 cm^3 **9.** 6.3 in.^{3}

Page 397 Written **1.** 418.7 ft^3 **3.** 340.2 m^3 **5.** 928.9 cm^3 **7.** 1,360,666.7 ft^3 **9.** 3140.1 in.^{3} **11.** 0.03768 ft^3 **13.** 1,097,509,500,000 km^3 **15.** 267.9 cm^3 **17.** $\frac{1}{3}\pi r^2 h$

19. $\frac{3s^2\sqrt{3}}{2}\left(h + \frac{\sqrt{l^2 - s^2}}{3}\right)$

Page 401 Chapter Review **1.** 24 ft^2 **3.** 24 m^2 **5.** 130 ft^2 **7.** 1250 cm^2 **9.** 2660.4 cm^2 **11.** 289.4 m^2 **13.** 48 cm^2 **15.** 45 cm^2 **17.** 14,649,984 mi^2 **19.** 2,093.3 cm^3 **21.** 2,786.2 cm^3

CHAPTER 12 COORDINATES

Page 408 Exploratory **1.** $(^-6, 4)$ **3.** $(^-6, ^-5)$ **5.** $(1, 5)$ **7.** $(3, 3)$ **9.** $(^-4, ^-3)$ **11.** $(4, 0)$ **13.** yes **15.** yes **17.** yes

Page 408 Written **13.** $(^-5, 1)$ **15.** $(^-3, ^-3)$ **17.** $(^-2, ^-4)$

Page 412 Exploratory **1.** 7 **3.** 4 **5.** 5 **7.** $(0, 2)$ **9.** $(^-4, 4)$ **11.** $\left(1, \frac{3}{2}\right)$

Page 412 Written **1.** $6\sqrt{2}$ **3.** $7\sqrt{2}$ **5.** $\sqrt{41}$ **7.** $2\sqrt{29}$ **9.** 5 **11.** $|a - c|\sqrt{2}$ **13.** $\sqrt{144 + (a - b)^2}$ **15.** $\frac{1}{5}\sqrt{2}$ **17.** $\left(7\frac{1}{2}, 7\frac{1}{2}\right)$ **19.** $\left(^-8\frac{1}{2}, ^-7\right)$ **21.** $(^-4, ^-4)$ **23.** $(1, ^-4)$ **25.** $\left(\frac{p}{2}, \frac{q}{2}\right)$ **27.** $(0, 0)$ **29.** $\left(\frac{1}{2}, \frac{3}{5}\right)$ **31.** 26 **33.** $\sqrt{97}$ **35.** $(^-21, 2)$

Page 416 Exploratory **1.** The slope is undefined. **3.** The product of the two slopes is $^-1$. **5.** The slope is positive. **7.** The change in y is 2; the change in x is 1; the slope is 2. **9.** The change in y is 4; the change in x is $^-3$; the slope is $-\frac{4}{3}$.

Page 416 Written **1.** 2 **3.** 0 **5.** $\frac{3}{2}$ **7.** $^-3$ **9.** $^-2$ **11.** 2 **13.** 2 **15.** $-\frac{13}{12}$ **17.** slope of $\overline{AB}$ = slope of $\overline{CD} = \frac{4}{3}$; slope of $\overline{BC}$ = slope of $\overline{AD} = -\frac{3}{4}$ **19.** no

Page 419 Exploratory **1.** $-\frac{3}{4}$; 2 **3.** 4; $^-3$ **5.** 3; $^-5$ **7.** 0; 6 **9.** $y = 6x - 5$ **11.** $y = 4x - 1$

Page 419 Written **1.** $y = 2x - 3$ **3.** $y = {^-4}x + 7$ **5.** $y = 8$ **7.** $y + 2 = -\frac{2}{3}(x + 2)$ **9.** $y = 3x - 2$ **11.** $y = {^-6}$ **13.** $y = \frac{1}{2}x - \frac{17}{2}$ **15.** $x = {^-7}$ **17.** 5; $^-3$ **19.** 2; $^-4$ **21.** $\frac{4}{3}$; $-\frac{5}{3}$ **23.** $y = {^-5}x + 4$ **25.** $y = 9x + 37$

Page 422 Exploratory **1.** $(^-10, 6)$ **3.** $(2, 0)$ **5.** $(^-2, 4)$ **7.** $(^-2, 0)$ **9.** b, c

Page 422 Written **1.** $(4, 2)$ **3.** $(2, ^-2)$ **5.** $(^-1, 2)$ **7.** $(10, 15)$ **9.** $(3, 1)$ **11.** $(^-1, ^-1)$ **13.** $(14, 4)$ **15.** $(2, 2)$

Page 424 Exploratory **1.** $(0, 0)$; 4 **3.** $(0, 0)$; 5 **5.** $(4, 6)$; 3 **7.** $(3, 12)$; 6 **9.** $(^-8, 9)$; 9

Page 425 Written **1.** $x^2 + y^2 = 25$ **3.** $(x - 3)^2 + (y - 4)^2 = 36$ **5.** $(x + 1)^2 + (y + 1)^2 = \frac{1}{16}$ **7.** $(x + 2)^2 + (y - 8)^2 = 2$ **9.** $x^2 + y^2 = 14$ **11.** $(x - 6)^2 + y^2 = 144$ **13.** $(x - 3)^2 + \left(y - \frac{1}{2}\right)^2 = \frac{16}{25}$ **15.** $(0, 0)$; 11

17. $(0, 3); 2$ **19.** $(^-3, 4); 2\sqrt{5}$ **21.** $(7, ^-5); 2$ **23.** $(0, 0); 4$ **25.** $(^-7, ^-3); \sqrt{3}$ **27.** $\left(^-4, \frac{1}{2}\right); \sqrt{6}$ **29.** $(^-5, 2); \frac{\sqrt{3}}{2}$ **31.** $(x + 2)^2 + (y - 11)^2 = 32$ **33.** $(x + 5)^2 + (y - 5)^2 = 25$

Page 428 Exploratory **1.** $C(r + s, t)$ **3.** $R(a, b)$ **5.** $C(j + k, h)$

Page 429 Written **1.** $A(^-b, 0), C(b, 2b), D(^-b, 2b)$ **3.** $R(a, b)$ **5.** $A(0, 0), C(a, b + c)$

7. Given: rectangle $ABCD$
Prove: $\overline{BD} \cong \overline{AC}$

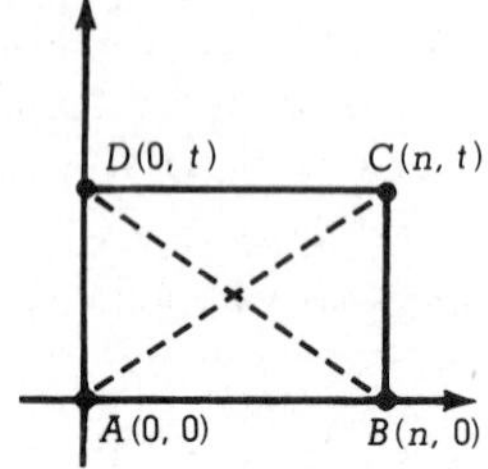

Proof:
By the distance formula,
$BD = \sqrt{(n - 0)^2 + (0 - t)^2} = \sqrt{n^2 + t^2}$
$AC = \sqrt{(n - 0)^2 + (t - 0)^2} = \sqrt{n^2 + t^2}$
By Postulate 2–9, $BD = AC$. By definition of congruent segments, $\overline{BD} \cong \overline{AC}$.

9. Given: isosceles trapezoid $ABCD$
Prove: $\overline{AC} \cong \overline{BD}$

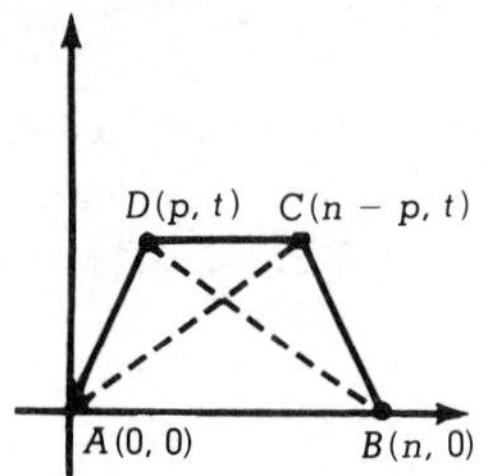

Proof:
$AC = \sqrt{(n - p - 0)^2 + (t - 0)^2}$
$= \sqrt{(n - p)^2 + t^2}$
$BD = \sqrt{(n - p)^2 + (0 - t)^2} = \sqrt{(n - p)^2 + t^2}$
By Postulate 2–9, $AC = BD$. By definition of congruent segments, $\overline{AC} \cong \overline{BD}$.

Page 433 Exploratory **1.** 4 **3.** $\sqrt{6}$ **5.** $(4, 0, 0)$ **7.** $\left(-\frac{1}{2}, 4, 8\right)$ **9.** $(3, 8, 2); 7$ **11.** $(^-4, 2, ^-1); 5$

Page 434 Written **1.** $\sqrt{13}$ **3.** $2\sqrt{5}$ **5.** 6 **7.** $\sqrt{14}$ **9.** $5\sqrt{3}$ **11.** $\left(\frac{3}{2}, ^-2, 2\right)$ **13.** $\left(\frac{5}{2}, -\frac{3}{2}, \frac{5}{2}\right)$ **15.** $\left(-\frac{1}{2}, 4, 5\right)$ **17.** $(6, 5, ^-1); 9$ **19.** $(0, 3, 0); 2$ **21.** $x^2 + y^2 + z^2 = 9$ **23.** $(x + 1)^2 + (y - 2)^2 + (z - 4)^2 = 16$ **25.** $(x - 2)^2 + \left(y - \frac{1}{2}\right)^2 + (z - 1)^2 = \frac{1}{9}$ **27.** $10 + \sqrt{74}$ **29.** $(1, 2, 6)$ **31.** $(x - 1)^2 + (y - 2)^2 + (z - 6)^2 = 26$ **33.** 6

Page 436 Chapter Review **7.** $(^-2, ^-4)$ **9.** $(^-4, 2)$ **11.** 5 **13.** 2 **15.** $|a - b|\sqrt{2}$ **17.** $\left(^-4, \frac{7}{2}\right)$ **19.** $(^-3, ^-5)$ **21.** $\left(\frac{3}{4}, \frac{1}{2}\right)$ **23.** $(^-12, ^-16)$ **25.** $-\frac{2}{3}$ **27.** undefined **29.** 2 **31.** 7 **33.** $\frac{3}{2}$ **35.** 4; 6 **37.** undefined slope; no y-intercept **39.** $y = 3x - 1$ **41.** $x = 4$ **43.** $y = \frac{1}{7}(6x - 30)$ **45.** $(5, 3)$ **47.** $(1, 1)$ **49.** $(6, 1)$ **51.** $(^-2, 0); 2\sqrt{3}$ **53.** $(0, 5); \frac{8}{11}$ **55.** $x^2 + y^2 = 0.09$ **57.** $\left(x + \frac{2}{3}\right)^2 + (y - 5)^2 = \frac{36}{49}$ **59.** $(^-a, 2a); (a, 2a); (^-a, 0)$ **63.** $3\sqrt{11}$ **65.** $\sqrt{74}$ **67.** $\left(\frac{1}{2}, \frac{13}{2}, \frac{1}{2}\right)$ **69.** $(1, 3, 5)$ **71.** $(0, 0, 0); 12$ **73.** $(^-3, ^-4, 1); \sqrt{13}$ **75.** $(x - 9)^2 + (y + 6)^2 + (z - 4)^2 = 64$ **77.** $(x + 2)^2 + (y - 1)^2 + \left(z - \frac{2}{5}\right)^2 = \frac{4}{49}$

CHAPTER 13 LOCI AND CONSTRUCTIONS

Page 449 Exploratory **1.** Postulate 1–1 **3.** Theorem 2–2 **5.** CPCTC **7.** Postulate 4–2 **9.** Definition of Congruent Segments, Definition of Midpoint, Definition of Segment Bisector

Page 453 Exploratory **1.** Definition of Diameter **3.** Definition of Semicircle **5.** Definition of Perpendicular Lines **7.** yes; yes **9.** obtuse

Page 456 Exploratory **1.** Postulate 1–1 **3.** Theorem 10–8 **5.** Theorem 9–2

Page 460 Exploratory **1.** a circle with center C and radius 1 mm; a sphere with center C and radius 1 mm **2.** a circle with center C and radius 2 ft; a sphere with center C and radius 2 ft **9.** a pair of lines each 1 in. from ℓ; a cylinder with ℓ as its axis and radius 1 in. **11.** a pair of lines parallel to and 3 in. from ℓ; a cylinder with ℓ as its axis and radius 3 in.

Page 460 Written **1.** a circle concentric to the given circle and having a radius of 5 cm **3.** a one-inch square having diagonals collinear with the original square **5.** the bisector of the angle **7.** the line that is the perpendicular bisector of the segment having the given endpoints as endpoints **9.** a circle concentric to the given circle and having a radius of 8 cm **11.** a circle in the plane with the given point as its center and having a radius of 7 in. **13.** all points on the bisector of the angle except the vertex of the angle **15.** all points on the line in the plane that is the perpendicular bisector of the given base except the midpoint of the base **17.** a cylinder with the given line as its axis and having the given distance as its radius **19.** two planes parallel to the given plane at a distance of r units from the given plane

Page 463 Exploratory **1.** *c* **3.** *a* **5.** *c*

Page 464 Written **1.** may have no points of intersection; one or both lines may be tangent to the circle; one or both lines may be secants of the circle **3.** may have no points of intersection; one or both lines may be tangent to the outer circle; one or both lines may be tangent to the inner circle; one or both lines may be secants of the outer circle; one or both lines may be secants of both circles **5.** may have no points of intersection; one or both lines may be tangent to the sphere; one or both lines may be secants of the sphere **7.** may have no points of intersection; may be tangent at a point; may intersect in a circle; may coincide **9.** may have no points of intersection; may intersect at one or two points; the circle may lie in the plane **11.** The locus of points 2 cm from the line is a pair of parallel lines; the locus of points 5 cm from a point on the line is a circle having the point as its center; the locus of all points meeting both conditions is the set of four points where the circle and the two parallel lines intersect. **15.** The locus of all the points in a plane that are equidistant from three given points is the center of the circle containing the three points. **17.** The locus of points equidistant from the sides of an angle is the bisector of the angle; the locus of points 4 in. from the vertex of an angle is a circle having the vertex as its center; the locus of all points meeting both conditions is the two points at which the circle and the bisector intersect. **19.** The locus of points equidistant from two given parallel lines is a third line parallel to and midway between the others; the locus of points a given distance from another line is two parallel lines; the locus of all points meeting both conditions may be 0, 1, or an infinite number of points.

Page 467 Chapter Review **19.** The locus of all points in space that are one inch from a given point A is a sphere whose radius is one inch and whose center is point A. **21.** The locus of the points in a plane that are centers of circles with radii measuring 11 cm and which pass through a given point is a circle with the given point as center and a radius of 11 cm. **23.** may have no points of intersection; may be tangent to the sphere; may be secants of the sphere **25.** may have no points of intersection; may be tangent to one or both spheres; may intersect each sphere at two points **27.** The locus is the set of all points which lie at the same distance from both planes.

CHAPTER 14 TRANSFORMATIONS

Page 472 Exploratory **1.** $\overline{DC}$ **3.** $\angle S$ **5.** $\overline{RS}$ **7.** $\angle T$ **9.** $\angle B$

Page 472 Written **1.** E **3.** D **5.** $\angle BDE$ **7.** A **9.** C **11.** $\overline{CA}$ **13.** $\triangle RQS$ **15.** $\triangle NMW$ **17.** $\triangle XYZ$ **19.** $UTSR$ **21.** $\overline{WY}$ **23.** $\triangle XYZ \rightarrow \triangle ZYW$ **25.** A: gray, B: gray

Page 477 Exploratory **1.** A **3.** $\overline{AC}$ **5.** L **7.** $\overline{JL}$ **9.** $\overline{HG}$ **11.** N **13.** both **15.** point

Page 477 Written **7.** no; not all points are at the same distance from 1 **9.** yes **11.** yes **23.** none **29.** none **31.** none **33.** none

Page 480 Exploratory **1.** B **3.** G **5.** H **7.** D **9.** R **11.** Q

Page 480 Written **1.** yes **3.** yes **5.** no **7.** blue to green **9.** blue to green **11.** none **13.** green to red **15.** green to red **17.** none **25.** $\triangle PQR$ **27.** $\triangle LMN$ **29.** $\triangle STU$
31. Plan: A translation is composed of two consecutive reflections. The first reflection with respect to ℓ preserves betweeness of points. The second reflection with respect to m preserves betweeness of points. Therefore, by transitivity, betweeness of points is preserved from preimage to image.

Page 484 Exploratory **1.** yes **3.** $EFCD$ **5.** $HGJK$ **7.** $CDAB$ **9.** 140
11. $m\angle DPJ = m\angle DPK = 140$ **13.** $\overline{GK}$

Page 484 Written **3.** 60° **5.** 120°
7.

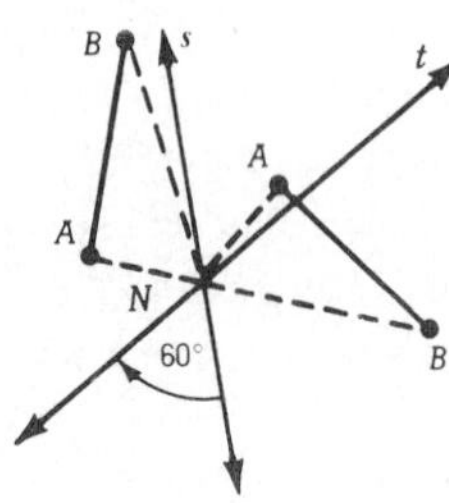

9.

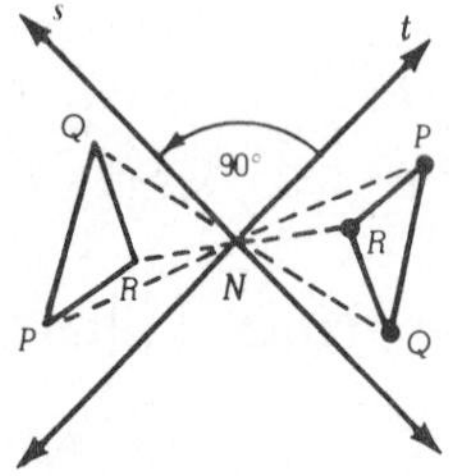

13. yes **15.** yes

Page 489 Exploratory **1.** F **3.** H **5.** p **7.** ℓ, m, p; ℓ, n, q; m, p, q **9.** reflection with respect to r

Page 490 Written **5.** ℓ, p

7.

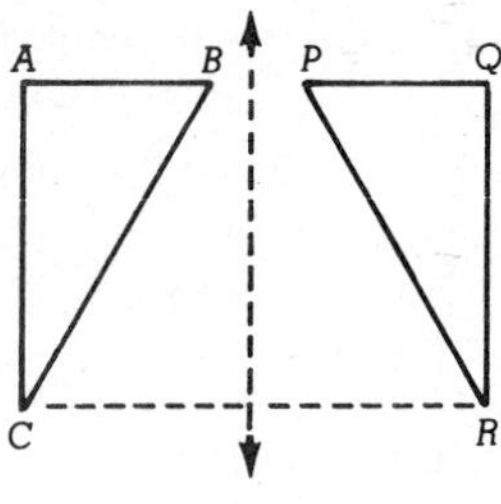

reflection

9.

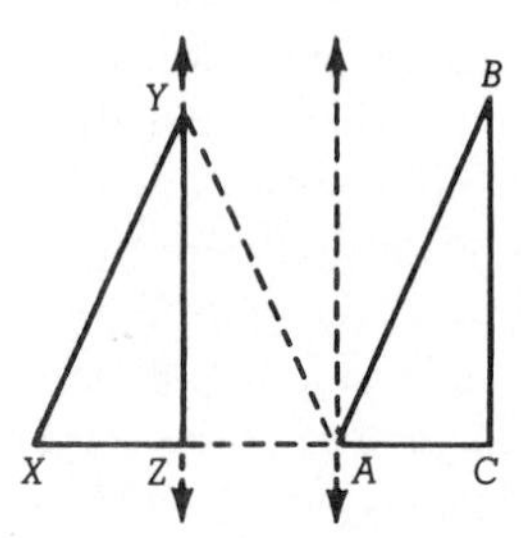

translation

11.

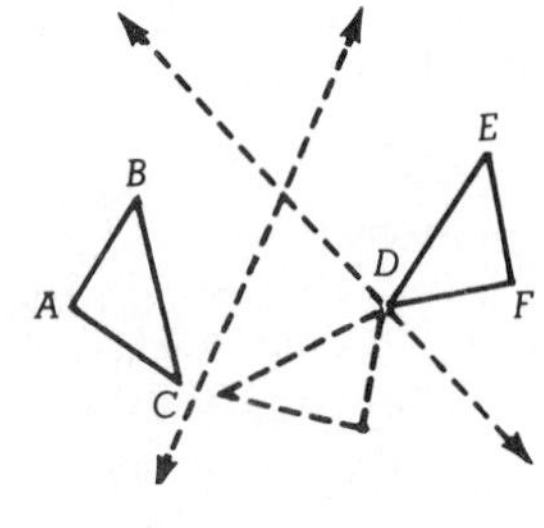

rotation

Page 494 Exploratory **1.** enlargement **3.** reduction **5.** reduction **7.** congruence **9.** no; all figures would have a single point as their dilation images

Page 494 Written **1.** 2 **3.** $\frac{3}{2}$ **5.** $\frac{1}{3}$ **7.** $\frac{1}{2}$ **9.** 3 **11.** enlargement **13.** enlargement **15.** reduction **17.** reduction **19.** enlargement **25.** A **27.** T **29.** S **31.** F **43.** 30 in. **45.** 24 ft **47.** 3 cm

Page 497 Chapter Review **1.** E **3.** B **5.** $\angle C$ **7.** $\overline{CB}$ **17.** reflection with respect to m **19.** reduction **21.** 4